GENERA PALMARUM

A Classification of Palms
Based on the Work of Harold E. Moore, Jr.

Marion Ruff Sheehan

GENERA PALMARUM

A Classification of Palms
Based on the Work of Harold E. Moore, Jr.

NATALIE W. UHL and JOHN DRANSFIELD

L. H. Bailey Hortorium, Cornell University and Royal Botanic Gardens, Kew

With Illustrations by:

MARION RUFF SHEEHAN

THE L. H. BAILEY HORTORIUM and THE INTERNATIONAL PALM SOCIETY

ALLEN PRESS, LAWRENCE, KANSAS

ISBN: 0-935868-30-5

Library of Congress No. 87-81063

© 1987 by Natalie W. Uhl and John Dransfield

Printed by Allen Press, Inc., Lawrence, KS 66044

Legend for Frontispiece

Palm Fruits. By rows from top to bottom, left to right in each row): *Plectocomia elongata, Rhopalostylis sapida, Ammandra decasperma*; *Chamaedorea metallica, Zombia antillarum, Nenga pumila*; *Myrialepis paradoxa, Wodyetia bifurcata, Daemonorops formicaria*; *Pholidocarpus macrocarpus, Kerriodoxa elegans, Hyphaene compressa.*

Legend for Front of Dust Jacket

Palm Habits. Foreground, from left to right: *Chamaerops humilis, Washingtonia filifera, Cyrtostachys renda, Johannesteijsmannia altifrons* (center front), *Pigafetta filaris* (tallest), *Asterogyne martiana, Acoelorraphe wrightii, Laccospadix australasica, Licuala spinosa.*

Legend for Back of Dust Jacket

Some of the Diversity of Palms. Clockwise from upper left: Palmate leaf, *Brahea* sp.; inflorescence in flower and peduncular bract, *Butia capitata*; fruits, *Phoenix reclinata*; bifid leaf, *Asterogyne martiana*; fruits, *Retispatha dumetosa*; fruits, *Coccothrinax* sp.; pinnate leaf, *Chrysalidocarpus lutescens*; fruit, *Gaussia maya*; leaf, *Caryota*; fruit, *Calamus eriocanthus*; fruits, *Synechanthus warscewiczianus*; bifid leaf, *Chamaedorea* sp.; center, fruits, *Nypa fruticans.*

DEDICATION

To Hal whose life's work was "Genera Palmarum"—in appreciation of his patience and enthusiasm, the excellence of his notes and specimens, and his commitment to helping and encouraging young scientists and colleagues.

CONTENTS

FINDING LIST OF GENERIC NAMES

FOREWORD

It is a great privilege to be able to write the foreword to this important book. This survey of the generic classification of palms is based on Professor Harold E. Moore, Jr.'s work on the family, a task which occupied him much of his professional life. Undoubtedly he deserves a place in the history of botany as the foremost student of the palms, worthy to join the ranks of such distinguished predecessors as von Martius, Griffith, Wendland, Spruce, J. D. Hooker, Beccari, and Burret. Harold E. Moore, Jr. was prevented from completing his work by his untimely death, but he left such extensive notes and material that the completion of a Genera Palmarum was possible through the efforts of Natalie Uhl of Cornell and John Dransfield of Kew, both his long-time collaborators. This collaboration in its turn is a monument to Hal Moore's scientific style, characterized by the encouragement and support of younger scientists, particularly those working on the palms, since he saw clearly that systematic conclusions had to be broadly based and that no single expert could cover the fields of specialization which illuminate the central problem of palm classification. The book itself will serve as a foundation and guide because it *is* so broadly based.

The family of palms is an important one. Its members include major tropical crop plants and many species of commercial value in horticulture while some find enormously diversified use in the local economy of all tropical countries. The group is also of major interest scientifically because palms serve as useful models in many disciplines—ecology, demography, anatomy, morphology, biomechanics—and they are likely to become increasingly valuable as study objects in the fields of plant morphogenesis and physiology. Palms also provide good examples for the study of evolutionary processes in the plant kingdom. As an exemplary group, the family needs to be known as precisely as possible at the taxonomic level because systematic biology is the foundation for all other biological disciplines. This book should in turn serve as a model for the type of monographic or systematic compilation which is so much needed for all tropical plant families. It therefore has wide significance because the approaches represented within it have universal application.

I am sure that Natalie Uhl's and John Dransfield's task has not been an easy one, despite the relatively advanced stage at which they may have taken over. Botanists will be ever grateful that they had the courage and ability to take on this responsibility and complete it in such a relatively short time. Scientific progress is best made in a spirit of unselfish collaboration; this is perhaps the testimony which resides most strongly within this book.

June, 1985

P. B. TOMLINSON
E. C. Jeffrey Professor of Biology
Harvard University
Harvard Forest
Petersham, MA 01366

PREFACE

The idea of this "Genera Palmarum" began with Liberty Hyde Bailey, who spent more than 30 years working on palms. His numerous papers are still extremely valuable because he so clearly understood the morphology and diagnostic features of palms. Interviewed in 1951, at the age of 93, Bailey described his project as follows:

"I plan to define what is a palm. I plan to explain what are not palms even though we call them so. I plan to talk about their distribution over the face of the earth and to define what a palm is, so that if a man or woman has a specimen, that plant may be determined. And then I expect to make a classification of all the genera, and to describe every genus. It would be a 'Genera Palmarum' . . ."

Bailey had founded the L. H. Bailey Hortorium in 1935, and in 1948 he brought Dr. Harold E. Moore, Jr. to the Hortorium and interested him in the palms. When Bailey died in 1954, he left the dream of a "Genera Palmarum" to the younger man.

Harold E. Moore, Jr. accepted the challenge enthusiastically. During the late 1950's and early 1960's he studied the historic collections of palms in the great herbaria of Europe and the United States and carried out intensive field work in the American tropics, developing an immense and detailed familiarity with palm genera and species. It soon became evident to him that palms had been very poorly understood and that in many cases the characters which are essential to understanding their relationships and evolution could not be determined from the herbarium specimens available. Thus he was early impressed that it is necessary to obtain first-hand knowledge of palms in the field and to collect adequate material of these cumbersome plants.

In 1956 the International Palm Society was founded, with Dr. Moore deeply involved almost from the beginning as editor of its journal *Principes*. The close association and mutual support that the Society has promoted between basic research on the one hand and the interest and enthusiasm of growers and fanciers of palms on the other has been of immense value.

Moore collected all kinds of palms extensively, but his main objective was to define their genera and to see and collect as many of them as possible in the wild. He pursued this goal energetically, returning again and again to poorly known areas such as Madagascar and New Caledonia, trying to rediscover and collect better material of genera known only from tantalizing scraps and fragments. The great savings in time and money that are afforded by modern air travel allowed him to compare palms throughout the tropics on a scale that was not possible to earlier botanists. In the course of his travels, largely made possible through continuing research support by the National Science Foundation, he visited many remote localities, including such places as the upper Amazon, Mauritius, Rodrigues, and the Seychelles in the Indian Ocean, northern Queensland, New Guinea, the Solomons, and Juan Fernandez Islands. By 1980 he had seen and collected all but 18 of the 200 or so genera of palms in the field, a remarkable achievement that gained his admission to the Explorers' Club. The results of his expeditions in terms of material are unmatched. The L. H. Bailey Hortorium now houses a unique collection of dried and preserved material of palms; nowhere are palm genera better represented.

Early in the 1960's Marion Ruff Sheehan began to prepare diagnostic drawings and plates of palm genera for eventual publication in "Genera Palmarum." To obtain all the necessary stages and parts for these illustrations Moore often had to return to remote areas in different seasons.

In terms of knowledge, Moore's expeditions and collections have been the source of important new ideas concerning the functional significance and relationships of structures. Early in the 1960's he realized that there were questions he could not answer without contributions from specialists in other disciplines. To this end he inspired many others to study palms, and a loosely associated team of collaborators in palm research developed around him. Subjects studied by his close associates during the next two decades, often using material that he had collected from some remote locality, include the nature of the leaf, the vasculature of the stem and flowers, the phloem and xylem, the inflorescence and the nature of the triad, the acervulus and other flower clusters, the development of the gynoecium and fruit, and the chromosomes. This research, also to a large extent supported by the National Science Foundation, contributed a large body of information that Moore used to develop a new generic classification of the family, published in outline form in 1973. It also led to new syntheses of palm geography and evolution.

When the outline of his classification of palms was published in 1973, many questions still remained unanswered, and Moore was not yet ready to publish a formal hierarchy of classification. His major goal had always been a "Genera Palmarum" which, in his words, would "provide in one volume a synopsis of information that would serve as underpinning for the field botanist, the tropical forester, the tropical agriculturalist, the ecologist, the biogeographer, and for a new generation of biologists..." By 1980 he was at long last ready to devote three years to writing the book. In October, 1980, he died suddenly and unexpectedly, leaving still unfulfilled the dream of a "Genera Palmarum."

Professor David M. Bates, then Director of the L. H. Bailey Hortorium, felt it was essential that Moore's great investment in a "Genera Palmarum" should not be lost. A proposal was drafted whereby the present authors would collaborate under the auspices of Cornell University and Kew to write the book. With renewed support from the National Science Foundation, we began the work in the fall of 1981.

During the last four years we have critically reassessed all palm genera; this has resulted in the discovery of new genera, the reduction of some old names to synonymy, and the realization that others are inadequately defined. We have developed a new formal classification of the family that differs in some respects from the informal arrangement of Moore's outline (1973). "Genera Palmarum" as we present it here doubtless also differs somewhat from what Harold E. Moore, Jr. would have written. Nevertheless, many of the major features of the classification are his.

We are aware of certain inadequacies both in the information available to us and in our presentation of it. The geographical area most in need of further exploration is Madagascar. When the palms of this great island are better understood, there may be changes in generic delimitation and the recognition of new genera. We have begun further research on the palms of Madagascar but publication of "Genera Palmarum" would be seriously delayed if we were to wait for the results.

Certain groups of genera are still insufficiently understood. These include *Euterpe* and *Prestoea,* the genera of the Attaleinae, and the complex of genera related to *Gronophyllum* and *Gulubia,* where genera are poorly defined and are determined by characters known to be unreliable elsewhere in the family. Yet to reduce genera to synonymy without

careful research in the field and herbarium seems unjustified. We have maintained these questionable genera but have indicated where problems lie. Not all will agree with our generic concepts, but we have tried to maintain as uniform an approach as possible. It is very evident that many genera require monographic research. The suggestion that palms are well known taxonomically is certainly unfounded at the species level.

Some comments on the keys and nomenclature are necessary. As with other plants, the genera of palms are defined largely on reproductive characters. Keys to the genera on a world scale often depend on characters of flowers and fruits that may be difficult to discern or not available when needed. Wherever possible in keys or notes we have tried to indicate certain vegetative characters that are of diagnostic value. When a genus as a whole is considered, the most obvious vegetative characters that distinguish the majority of species may not apply to a few. We have provided multiaccess keys to several groups and have noted the characters that are useful in identifying most species of a genus. Within limited geographic areas it is often easy to construct keys to the local genera that are based on vegetative characters alone, but obviously this is outside the scope of the book. It should be noted that authorities for scientific names are provided in the "Index to Scientific Names" and are not cited in the text.

Some comments are necessary concerning our sections "Common Names and Uses" in the generic descriptions (Part II). These topics are too diffuse to be completely covered in this book. Several local names may be used for a species in one or in different countries. Often the same name refers to different palms. We have given a few of the most commonly used names within a genus and where possible suggested references to others. The uses of palms are legion. Again we have provided some of the most important for each genus but our listings are not exhaustive.

Dr. Moore intended to include at least some results from a cladistic analysis of higher groups and genera of palms. We have begun such studies; they are in a preliminary state and we cannot apply them to the construction of the hierarchy at present. We also expect to incorporate in the cladistic analyses new information from further research on the androecium, the ovule, and the palms of Madagascar.

The authorship of this book was difficult to determine because of its complex genesis. At first we expected to have Harold E. Moore, Jr. as first author but we have rewritten his materials and added new information as well as interpretations. As time passed it seemed preferable to have his contribution acknowledged in the title. The decision as to first author was then in question. We have shared the writing equally. The book represents a complete amalgam of our separate scientific skills and inputs; the classification, generic formats and concepts, morphology and anatomy, phytogeography, fossils, and evolutionary interpretations have all been discussed back and forth and have ended being neither purely NWU nor JD. The final decision on the authorship reflects the long involvement of Cornell University and Natalie W. Uhl with this project.

We undertook this task in an atmosphere of overwhelming sorrow at the loss of Professor Moore and we were daunted by the amount of work to be done. However, we soon grew to appreciate the great extent of his legacy in terms of notes and materials. The writing of "Genera Palmarum" has been the most exciting project of our lives.

NATALIE W. UHL
JOHN DRANSFIELD

ACKNOWLEDGMENTS

The large scientific data base underlying this work was made possible by continuous support from 1962 to the present by the National Science Foundation. Grants were G-18770, GB-1354, GB-3528, GB-5993, GB-7758, GB-20348X, DEB-7306854 AO3, DEB-77-23374 to H. E. Moore, Jr., DEB-81-09374 to N. W. Uhl and D. M. Bates, and BSR-8407029 to N. W. Uhl.

Many persons and other institutions have contributed to this book. We first extend our appreciation to those who assisted Dr. Harold E. Moore, Jr., during his 32 years toward Genera Palmarum. It has not been our priviledge to become acquainted with all of you, but we realize and appreciate the scope of your efforts.

We thank the directors and staff of several institutions who have provided specimens, information on palms, and the use of their living collections and facilities. These include the Arnold Arboretum, Cambridge, Mass.; the Chinese Academy of Sciences; the Division of Botany, Papua, New Guinea; Fairchild Tropical Garden, Miami; The Forest Department, Sarawak; The Forest Research Institute, Kepong, Malaysia; The Huntington Botanical Gardens, San Marino, Calif.; The Lyon Arboretum, Hawaii; Muséum National d'Histoire Naturelle, Laboratoire de Phanérogamie, Paris; Organisation de Recherche Scientifique et Technique d'Outre Mer, New Caledonia; and others.

During the four and a half years spent in writing the book we have been supported and assisted by a number of individuals. Professor David M. Bates, Director of the L. H. Bailey Hortorium when Dr. Moore died in 1980, the late Professor J. P. M. Brenan, Director of The Royal Botanic Gardens, Kew, and Mr. Peter Green, Keeper of the Herbarium at Kew, were responsible for the original proposal to complete Genera Palmarum. Professor David A. Young, current Director of the Hortorium, Professor E. A. Bell, current Director at Kew, and Mr. Gren Lucas, Keeper of the Herbarium, have continued to support the project.

Our colleagues who work on palms have provided assistance of many sorts. We are grateful to Anthony Anderson, Ray Baker, Michael Balick, Charal Bhoonab, Robin Chazdon, Frederick Essig, Edwino Fernando, Sidney Glassman, Andrew Henderson, De Armand Hull, Anthony Irvine, Dennis Johnson, Johanis Mogea, Robert W. Read, P. B. Tomlinson, and others for their encouragement and input. R. K. Brummitt and William J. Dress have kindly provided expertise on editing and nomenclature, Charles H. Uhl on cytology, and Keith Ferguson and Madeline Harley on palynology. We have consulted Dominick Paolillo and John M. Kingsbury for advice on several important issues.

Marion R. Sheehan, who has spent much of her time since 1963 on the preparation of the illustrations for this book, has served as collaborator as well as artist. The water colors of the dust jacket and frontispiece in addition to the wash drawings accompanying each genus and illustrating Chapter I and the glossary exemplify both her talent and her excellent understanding of the structure of palms.

Members of The International Palm Society have supported us in many ways. The Society has provided a word processor, which proved essential in preparation of the manuscript, as well as salary for photographic and bibliographic assistance. Individual members have contributed greatly. In particular, Paul Drummond, President of The Society when Dr. Moore died, has given us excellent support throughout. Richard Douglas is largely responsible for arranging the joint publication of this work by The Society and The L. H. Bailey Hortorium and also served on the editorial board. Pauleen Sullivan enthusiastically accepted the huge task of fund raising. Mardy Darian, Lynn McKamey, Jim Mintken, Ruth Shatz, and Melvin and Phyllis Sneed, and the current President, Allan Bredeson, have all encouraged and supported us. The opportunity to partake in two Biennial Meetings of The Society and to visit the gardens of many members has been most valuable.

Photocredits are listed separately but certain persons deserve special mention. We are greatly indebted to Walter H. Hodge for contributing his own valuable black and white and color photos as well as those of the late Paul H. Allen. Most of the black and white prints were prepared by former research assistant, A. B. Bednarick, and the color plates by Howard Lyon, photographer at Cornell. Kew photographers, Tudor Harwood and Milan Svanderlik, also contributed pictures. Bente King of the L. H. Bailey Hortorium has assisted with art work of all kinds.

Other staff members at our respective institutions have provided special assistance. We greatly appreciate the dedication and attention to detail of Margaret Vodicka-Asbury who edited descriptions, edited and wrote legends for wash-drawings, and prepared the *Literature Cited.* William Hahn assisted with editing and Sybil Kean with editing, word processing, and plates. Laura Fitt of Kew also helped in many ways.

Throughout the whole project Soejatmi Dransfield and Charles H. Uhl have encouraged and supported us. Without their tolerance and enthusiasm we could not have completed the task.

Lastly but certainly not least, we are grateful to Lucille Herbert, the operator of our word processor, for her enduring patience and excellent work over so many years.

THE FOLLOWING PEOPLE AND INSTITUTIONS HAVE GENEROUSLY CONTRIBUTED TOWARD THE PUBLICATION OF THIS BOOK

Paul and Elizabeth Anderson
William T. and Lynna S. Bailey, Jr.
Iris Bannochie
Mike Bayless
Elwood L. Bear, Jr.
Edith H. Bergstrom
Byron and Libby Besse
Shelly Blank
Josef Bogner
Allan Bredeson
Robert C. Brooks
Sara Calvetto
Donn W. Carlsmith
Ben Ciesla
Marjorie Corbin
Mardy and Cheri Darian
Robert A. DeFilipps
Paul Dewenter
Karl and Helen Dobler
Steven C. Doughty
Richard Douglas
Robert Egge
Elling O. Eide
John C. Elliot
Earl Farris
Joe M. Frauenhofer
Walter R. Frey
Timothy A. Gaskin
Alfred B. Graf
Bill Gunther
Jim L. Harris
Elizabeth Herman
Don Hodel
W. H. Hodge

Vincent and Lois Honc
Louis and Carol Hooper
James K. Ide (in memory of Charles Rauleson)
Dennis V. Johnson
Charles (Hal) Jones
Jose Julia
Stanley G. Kennon
Franklyn and Frankie Ketchum
Jerome P. Keuper
Bernard M. Kitt
Denia Mandt
Virginia Masse
George Massicotte
Stanley Matthews
Edward and Peggy McGehee
Lynn McKamey
Tom Meyer
Harvey E. Millard
Bruce Newgard
Richard W. Palmer
Richard H. Phillips
Valerie Rigby
Anne Rigg
Jane Robinson
Kurt and Lois Rossten
James G. Sharpe
Jim Sherman
Michael J. Shields
Melvin W. and Phyllis Sneed
Dent Smith
Pauleen Sullivan
John D. Tallman
William L. Theobald
Bert Van Der Eijk

Ralph Velez
Gilbert and Nancy Voss
Douglas K. Wadewitz
Lucita H. Wait
Wayne Ward
Maineer and Rouchell Waxman
T. C. Whitmore
Jack W. Wood
U. A. and Ben Young
The Gulf Coast Chapter of the International Palm Society
Hilo Palm Society
Hunt Foundation
The Houston Area Chapter of The International Palm Society
Johnson's Wax Fund, Inc.
The New South Wales Australian Chapter of The International Palm Society
The New Zealand Palm and Cycad Society
The Northern California Chapter of The International Palm Society
The Palm and Cycad Society of Australia
The Palm Society of the Northern Territory of Australia
Rhapis Gardens
The South Florida Chapter of The International Palm Society
The Southern California Chapter of The International Palm Society

COLOR PHOTO CREDITS

P. H. Allen   28C

D. M. Bates   20C

A. Bredeson   17C

M. E. Darian   25D, 27C

J. Dransfield   1A, 3, 4A–D, 5B–D, 7B, 8B–D, 10C, D, 11A, B, D, 12A–D, 13A–D, 14B, D, 15D, 17D, 18A, B, 19B, C, 20D, 21C, 22A, B, 23A, C, 26B, D, 27A, B, 30D

W. H. Hodge   2, 5A, 6A, 8A, 9A, B, D, 10A, B, 18C, 21A, 22D, 28B, 29A, B, 30B

L. H. Bailey Hortorium   17A–B

G. McPherson   25A

H. E. Moore   1B–D, 6B, 7A, 9C, 10C, 11C, 14A, C, 15A, B, C, 16, 19A, D, 20A, B, 21B, D, 23B, 24C, D, 25B, C, 26A, C, 28A, C

R. A. Phillips   24A, B

P. Sullivan   22C

BLACK AND WHITE PHOTO CREDITS

G. Addison   66A

P. H. Allen   31C, 36A, 53A, 54D, 61C, 67C, 75B, 76A, C, 77B, 78D, 79A, B, D, 80C, D, 81C

L. H. Bailey   33A, 35D, 49B, D

L. H. Bailey Hortorium   32C, 41C, 50B, 75A

M. J. Balick   52C, 57B, C, D

A. Braun   78A

M. E. Darian   54A, 73D

T. A. Davis   51A

J. Dransfield   33C, D, 34C, 35A, 37C, 38A, 39A, B, D, 40B, 41D, 43A, D, 44A–D, 45D, 46A–D, 47D, 51A, C, 54B, 64B, C, D, 65A, B, 66B, 68C, 77C, D, 79C, 81D

K. Foster   59A

A. Henderson   38C, 49C, 80A

S. Y. Ho   34D

D. Hodel   67A

W. H. Hodge   32A, D, 33B, 34A, B, 35C, 36A, B, 37A, B, D, 38D, 40A, 42C, 47A, B, 50A, C, D, 51B, D, 52A, B, 55D, 57A, 58A, B, 60C, 62A, 66A, 68A, 74A, D, 75C, 78B

A. K. Irvine   48A, B, 62B

from Louvel (1931)   48D

H. S. MacKee   35B

H. E. Moore   31B, 36C, D, 42A, D, 43B, C, 45A–C, 48C, 49A, 53B, C, D, 54C, 55C, 56A, D, 58C, D, 59B, C, D, 60A, B, D, 62D, 63A, B, C, 64A, 65C, D, 66C, D, 67D, 68B, D, 69A, B, D, 70A–D, 71B–D, 72A–D, 73A–C, 74B, 76B, D, 77A, 78C, 80B, 81A, B

F. Putz   55A

H. Quero   47C

Royal Botanic Gardens, Kew   41A, B, 42B, 62C, 75D

M. Schmid   71A

P. Sullivan   74C

N. W. Uhl   31A, D, 32B, 38B, 39C, 40C, D, 55B, 56B, C, 61A, B, D, 63D, 67B

J. J. Wood   69C

PART I.
THE BASIS FOR THE CLASSIFICATION OF PALMS

CHAPTER I

MORPHOLOGY

Palms represent a microcosm from a structural standpoint. Their morphological diversity is greater than that of any other monocotyledonous family; indeed they may represent one of the most diverse families of seed plants as a whole. Although they appear complex, their structures when carefully studied are often referable to simple patterns. In this chapter we consider the morphology of palms, including, as far as presently known, the different characters and character states expressed and their probable relationships. A few illustrations are provided in this chapter, but many more morphological features are shown in the plates (pp. 75–157) and in the wash drawings accompanying each genus. References to these additional illustrations can be found under the appropriate genus.

HABIT

Solitary or Clustered.—Habits of palms may be considered in regard to ultimate form or to growth patterns. Tree palms, shrub palms, acaulescent palms, and climbing palms (Dransfield 1978b) can be useful terms for field descriptions. In this book we have described palms simply as large to massive, moderate, or small. The vegetative body of a palm is a shoot—a stem that terminates in a crown of leaves (Fig. I.1). Shoots are either solitary or in clusters (Table I.1). Clustering palms exhibit what Holttum (1955) has called a "sympodial habit," which he considered characteristic of monocotyledons. Each new shoot develops from an axillary bud that in palms is usually located near the base of the stem. As each shoot then produces a new axillary shoot in turn, a clustered habit results. Many genera include both species with solitary stems (monopodial) and species that are clustering (sympodial) (Table I.1); the two forms encompass a variety of growth patterns as illustrated in Figure I.1. These include a prostrate stem lying on or beneath the surface of the soil, rooting on the lower side, producing a crown of leaves with axillary inflorescences at the growing end, and at length presumably dying and disintegrating at the older end. *Johannesteijsmannia altifrons, Brahea decumbens* (Coryphoideae), *Elaeis oleifera, Calyptrogyne sarapiquensis* (Arecoideae), *Ammandra,* and *Phytelephas* spp. (Phytelephantoideae) provide examples of this form. A more com-

plex modification is that of *Serenoa repens* (Fig. I.1E, Coryphoideae), in which either inflorescences or vegetative shoots are produced in leaf axils along the usually prostrate stem (Fisher and Tomlinson 1973). Still another form of branching occurs in *Chrysalidocarpus* (Fig. I.1A, Arecoideae), where non-axillary vegetative branches arise from buds initiated on the abaxial surface of the leaf but inflorescences are axillary (Fisher 1973). No palms are truly herbaceous, and none develops bulbs or corms, although enlarged bases of stems such as the saxophone-shaped underground stem in *Sabal* and a few other genera perhaps serve as underground storage organs.

Flowering.—Superimposed on the habits of palms are two modes of flowering (Fisher 1985). In most palms each shoot is potentially of unlimited growth, and the principal stem or stems are not terminated by a flower or an inflorescence, but flowers are produced on specialized axillary branch systems. This "pleonanthic" behavior (Fig. I.4) occurs in palms exhibiting several different habits (Fig. I.1).

A small number of palms have hapaxanthic shoots that are in a sense "determinate" (Table I.2). Their flowering occurs in one of two ways. (1) The shoot undergoes a prolonged vegetative phase and then terminates in a relatively short reproductive phase during which lateral inflorescences are produced in the axils of reduced upper leaves or bracts, after which the shoot dies. In *Corypha* (Fig. I.4), even the main stem appears to end as a flower-bearing rachilla (Tomlinson and Soderholm 1975). (2) There is a prolonged vegetative phase in which lateral inflorescence buds are initiated successively in leaf axils but are suppressed until flowering commences from the uppermost branches with the lower flowering branches following in order basipetally. Such basipetal flowering occurs in all members of Caryoteae (Arecoideae) except a few species of *Arenga* (Moore 1960, Moore and Meijer 1965, Dransfield and Mogea 1984).

The genus *Metroxylon* (Calamoideae) (Fig. I.1) includes species with three forms of growth: *M. amicarum,* a solitary palm with "indeterminate" growth (Moore and Fosberg 1956), is pleonanthic; *M. salomonense, M. upolense, M. vitiense,* and *M. warburgii* are hapaxanthic, having solitary stems with "de-

PLEONANTHIC

HAPAXANTHIC

Table I.1. **PALMS EXHIBITING BOTH MONOPODIAL AND SYMPODIAL HABITS**

I CORYPHOIDEAE	IRIARTEEAE
CORYPHEAE	*Wettinia*
Brahea	ARECEAE
Chelyocarpus	*Areca*
Coccothrinax	*Calyptrocalyx*
Licuala	*Chrysalidocarpus*
Trachycarpus	(non-axillary)
PHOENICEAE	*Cyrtostachys*
Phoenix	*Dypsis*
BORASSEAE	*Euterpe*
Hyphaene	*Gronophyllum*
II CALAMOIDEAE	*Heterospathe*
CALAMEAE	*?Hyospathe*
Calamus	*Iguanura*
Daemonorops	*Leopoldinia*
Metroxylon	*Nenga*
Plectocomia	*Neodypsis*
Raphia	*Neophloga*
IV CEROXYLOIDEAE	*Oenocarpus*
HYOPHORBEAE	*Phloga*
Chamaedorea	*Pinanga*
Synechanthus	*Prestoea*
V ARECOIDEAE	*Ptychosperma*
CARYOTEAE	*Reinhardtia*
Arenga	*Rhopaloblaste*
Caryota	*Vonitra*
Wallichia	COCOEAE
	Aiphanes
	Bactris
	Syagrus
	GEONOMEAE
	Geonoma
	VI PHYTELEPHAN-TOIDEAE
	Phytelephas

Table I.2. **THE HAPAXANTHIC HABIT**

I CORYPHOIDEAE	*Laccosperma*
CORYPHEAE	*Metroxylon* (except
Corypha	*M. amicarum*)
Nannorrhops	*Myrialepis*
II CALAMOIDEAE	*Oncocalamus*
CALAMEAE	*Plectocomia*
Daemonorops	*Plectocomiopsis*
calicarpa	*Raphia*
Eleiodoxa	V ARECOIDEAE
Eugeissona	CARYOTEAE (all genera)
Korthalsia	*Arenga* (not all
	species)
	Caryota
	Wallichia

onizing temporary habitats as discussed by Dransfield (1978b).

Climbing.—The climbing habit has apparently developed independently several times in the family. Among the Calamoideae it occurs in the two genera of the Ancistrophyllinae, in *Korthalsia* (Metroxylinae), in the Plectocomiinae, in the Oncocalaminae, and in six genera of the Calamineae, probably representing three or more different origins in the subfamily. It also occurs in two other subfamilies—in *Chamaedorea elatior* (Ceroxyloideae: Hyophorbeae) and in *Desmoncus* (Arecoideae: Cocoeae).

Dichotomous Branching.—Dichotomous branching (Table I.3) occurs in only distantly related groups in three subfamilies of palms among genera with "indeterminate" monopodial and occasionally sympodial growth (Fisher 1974, Tomlinson and Moore 1966, Tomlinson 1967, 1971b). Dichotomy has also been suggested for *Korthalsia* (Calamoideae), but this needs further study. One genus, *Nannorrhops* (Coryphoideae), has sympodial axillary branching at the bases of the shoots, and apparently dichotomous branching of its erect aerial stems; one half of the dichotomy ends in a "terminal" inflo-

terminate" growth (Moore 1966, Tomlinson 1971a, Hallé et al. 1978); while *M. sagu* produces clusters of hapaxanthic shoots (Moore 1966). In the largely pleonanthic genus, *Daemonorops,* a few species (e.g. *D. calicarpa*) are hapaxanthic (Dransfield 1976a). Many hapaxanthic palms occur in temporary (seral) habitats. Hapaxanthy may be an adaptation to col-

←

I.1—**Diagrammatic Drawings of Habits.** A. Non-axillary growth in *Chrysalidocarpus lutescens.* B. Colonial by rhizome or stolon as in *Bactris coloniata, Chamaedorea stolonifera.* C. Dichotomous branching and basal axillary branching, *Hyphaene coriacea.* D. Prostrate stem, *Brahea decumbens.* E. Prostrate stem, some axillary buds producing inflorescences, others producing vegetative shoots, *Serenoa repens.* F. Stem solitary as in *Trachycarpus fortunei* and many others. G. Stem erect or climbing, caespitose, *Chamaedorea seifrizii.* H. Upright, dichotomously branching stem, *Hyphaene compressa.* I. Dichotomous branching in prostrate stem, *Nypa fruticans.* J. Basipetal hapaxanthic flowering in cluster palm, *Caryota mitis.* K. Basipetal hapaxanthic flowering in solitary stem, *Caryota urens.* L. Solitary upright stem with acropetal hapaxanthic flowering, all species of *Corypha.* M. Acropetal hapaxanthic flowering and basal branching, *Metroxylon sagu.* N. Acropetal hapaxanthic flowering, aerial dichotomous branching, and basal axillary branching, shrub or vine, *Nannorrhops ritchiana* and *Korthalsia.*

Table I.3. **DICHOTOMOUS BRANCHING**

I CORYPHOIDEAE	IV CEROXYLOIDEAE
CORYPHEAE	HYOPHORBEAE
Nannorrhops	*Chamaedorea*
BORASSEAE	*cataractarum*
Hyphaene	V ARECOIDEAE
III NYPOIDEAE	ARECEAE
Nypa	*Vonitra* species
	COCOEAE
	Allagoptera arenaria

rescence and the other half continues as a vegetative axis which may branch again in similar dichotomy.

Architectural Models. —Hallé et al. (1978) proposed about 20 architectural models for trees, of which four are found in palms. Unbranched monocarpic palms such as *Metroxylon salomonense* and the other three species listed above, they called Holttum's model. Unbranched pleonanthic palms, *Metroxylon amicarum* and many other palms, were called Corner's model. Branched palms illustrate Tomlinson's model, and single stems with dichotomous branching Schoute's model. Different individuals of the same species of palms may display Corner's or Tomlinson's models. Whether the stem is determinate or indeterminate (i.e. whether the palm is hapaxanthic or pleonanthic) may be of more fundamental architectural significance (Fig. I.1).

Holttum considers those palms with "sympodial branching" and "determinate" growth, represented by *Metroxylon sagu* (Fig. I.1), to be primitive within the family. Delayed hapaxanthy is suggested as the original growth pattern by Staff and Waterhouse (1981). We consider an erect "indeterminate" stem, with or without sympodial branching (clustering), to be the basic growth form (Fig. I.1, F, G). There may be an axillary bud associated with each leaf axil, and whether or not the basal buds develop into new shoots may be under relatively simple genetic

control. In some cases both solitary and clustered forms occur in the same species.

THE STEM

Palm stems vary greatly in height and diameter. Species of *Chamaedorea* in Costa Rica have stems only 2 cm in diameter and less than 25 cm tall, while trunks 0.5 m in diameter and 60 m or more tall characterize species of *Ceroxylon* in Colombia. Diameters of trunks may reach a meter or more in some genera, such as *Jubaea* and *Borassus.* Stems differ also in the persistence of leaf bases and in the form of the leaf scars which may be narrow or wide, flat or raised, ringlike or oblique (Figs. G.3, G.4). The special characteristics of the "wood" of palms are discussed in Chapter II.

ARMATURE

Armature of various kinds occurs throughout the family (Uhl and Moore 1973, Figs. G.6, G.7, Table I.4). The genus *Phoenix* (Coryphoideae) can be distinguished immediately from all other palms with pinnate leaves by the stout spinelike, induplicate leaflets on the basal portion of the blade. In the Corypheae and Borasseae large teeth are often present along the margins of the petiole and sometimes of the blade. In several coryphoid genera, e.g. *Rhapidophyllum, Zombia,* and in *Trithrinax acanthocoma, Guihaia grossefibrosa,* and *Maxburretia furtadoana,* the leaf sheath disintegrates into long stiff spines derived from its fibers. *Cryosophila* is characterized in part by the presence of usually numerous, sometimes branched spines derived from roots that grow out from the stem. Spines derived from small lateral roots occur on the prop roots of some members of Iriarteeae. Less elaborate root spines also occur on the stems of certain species of *Eugeissona* and *Mauritiella* in the Calamoideae. This subfamily exhibits an immense diversity of spines

Table I.4. **DISTRIBUTION AND DERIVATION OF ARMATURE**

	Pinnae	Sheath	Roots	Teeth	Emergences
I CORYPHOIDEAE					
CORYPHEAE		+	+	+	
PHOENICEAE	+				
BORASSEAE				+	
II CALAMOIDEAE	+		+		+
V ARECOIDEAE					
IRIARTEEAE			+		
ARECEAE					+
COCOEAE	+	+		+	+

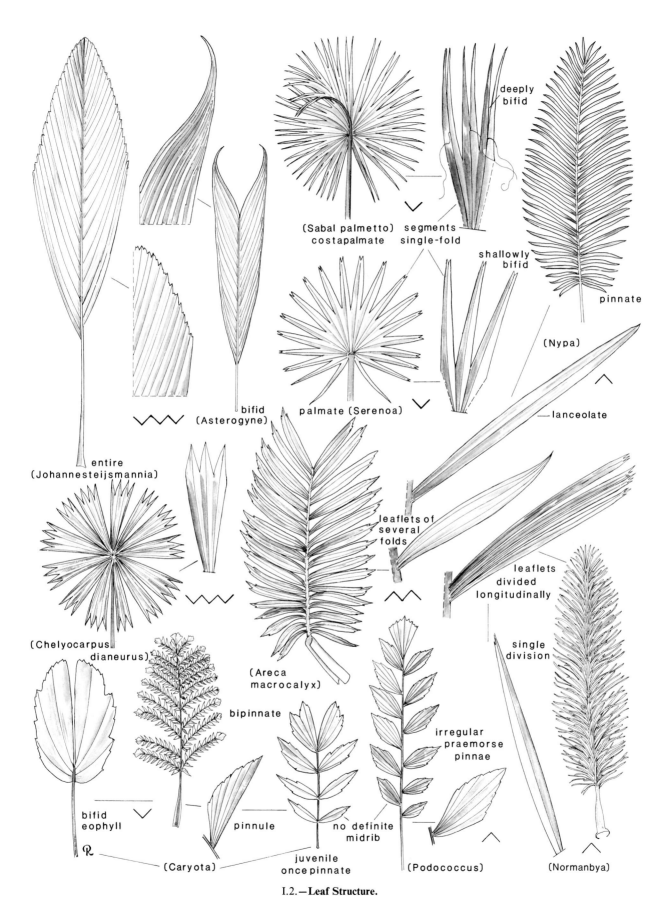

deeply
bifid

(Sabal palmetto)
costapalmate

segments
single-fold

shallowly
bifid

pinnate

(Nypa)

bifid
(Asterogyne)

palmate (Serenoa)

lanceolate

entire
(Johannesteijsmannia)

leaflets of
several
folds

leaflets
divided
longitudinally

single
division

(Chelyocarpus
dianeurus)

(Areca
macrocalyx)

bipinnate

irregular
praemorse
pinnae

bifid
eophyll

pinnule

no definite
midrib

(Podococcus)

(Normanbya)

(Caryota)

juvenile
once pinnate

I.2.—**Leaf Structure.**

7

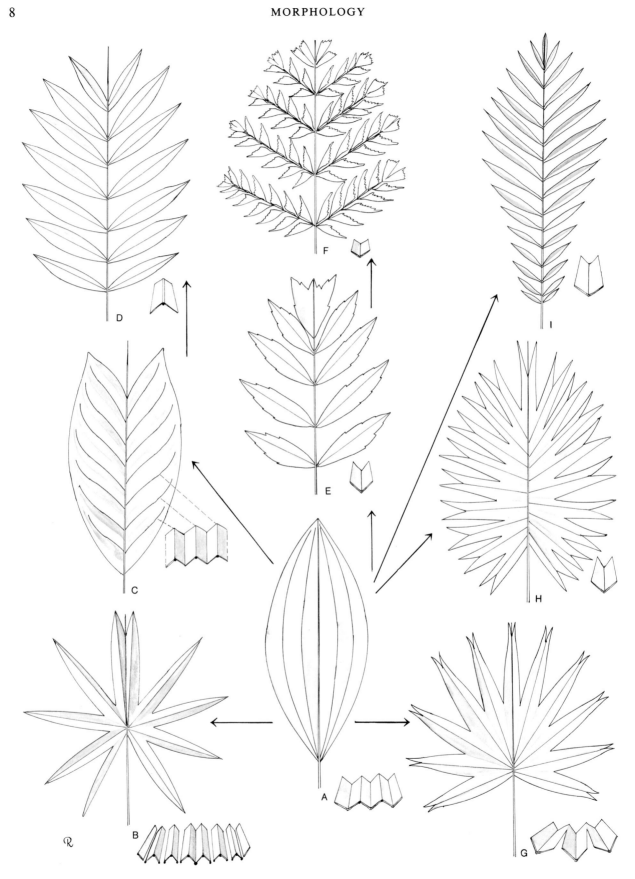

on leaves and inflorescences in several genera, most notably in *Calamus* and *Daemonorops* where spines on the leaf sheaths of some species form elaborate ant galleries. Among the Caryoteae, *Arenga pinnata* is notable for the persistent, spinelike large fibers of the leaf sheath. Sharp fiber bases, marginal teeth on the petiole, and the spinelike bases of the midribs of the leaflets arm certain genera of Cocoeae such as *Elaeis*. The six genera of the Bactridinae (Arecoideae: Cocoeae), and the eight genera of the Oncospermatinae (Arecoideae: Areceae) are distinguished by an abundance of slender to very stout, emergent spines on trunk, leaf, inflorescence, and sometimes even (in Bactridinae) on flowers and fruit.

THE LEAF

The leaf is the most conspicuous and distinctive organ of the Palmae. Its characteristic plication and splitting into segments or leaflets are paralleled only in some members of Cyclanthaceae and in *Curculigo seychellensis* (Hypoxidaceae). The palm leaf is characterized by a sheath that encircles the stem. The sheath may split abaxially at the base in some Coryphoideae or may be a very prominent tubular structure, a crownshaft, in certain Arecoideae (Fig. I.4). The leaf also usually has a distinct petiole, and a blade that has a single stout central axis (the rachis), which is short or absent in truly palmate leaves, better developed in costapalmate leaves, and prominent in the pinnate leaf (Fig. I.2). The leaf or its base may persist on the stem for a long time, as in many Corypheae and in *Phoenix*, but there is a clear trend toward the development of a presumed abscission layer and deciduous nature in some more advanced groups of subfamilies Ceroxyloideae and Arecoideae.

Size. — Leaves of palms differ enormously in size at maturity. Among the smallest are the bifid or undivided blades of *Chamaedorea tenella* and *C. tuerckheimii* with blades sometimes less than 15 cm long; in contrast are the blades of *Raphia* with a length of about 25 m (Hallé 1977), the largest leaves in the plant kingdom. Leaves also differ markedly in size and shape in a progression from eophylls (the first leaves with blades) of seedlings throughout juvenile stages to the mature blade (Tomlinson 1960a).

Plication. — The blade is always folded. Whether the folds or plications originate by splitting or differential growth has been long debated (Kaplan et al. 1982a). Recently detailed studies have shown that differential growth is totally responsible for plication development in the pinnate leaf of *Chrysalidocarpus* (Dengler et al. 1982) and in the palmate leaf of *Rhapis* (Kaplan et al. 1982b).

Division. — The blades of mature palms may be undivided or only bifid at the apex, or much more often regularly or irregularly divided into one-ribbed or several-ribbed units each consisting of a single fold or of several folds (Fig. I.2). These units are called segments in palmate and costapalmate leaves, and leaflets or pinnae in pinnate leaves. One genus, *Caryota*, is characterized by bipinnate leaves in which the pinnae have a prominent midrib but the pinnules lack midribs. In other genera, *Socratea*, *Iriartea*, *Normanbya*, and *Wodyetia*, a bipinnate condition is approached by longitudinally divided primary leaflets. Splitting of the blade into segments or leaflets is a separate event occurring after the origin of the folds.

Induplicate or Reduplicate Form. — Palm leaves differ in another way, as previously noted. Some blades are divided so that the leaflets or segments appear to be V-shaped and the blade is then termed induplicate. Induplicate leaves characterize subfamily Coryphoideae, with a few exceptions, and all genera of tribe Caryoteae of the Arecoideae. All other groups of palms have leaves which are divided so that the leaflets appear to be ∧-shaped and the blade is termed "reduplicate." For illustrations see Figures I.2, I.3, and G.9.

The induplicate or reduplicate nature of the blade is determined by the manner in which the splitting occurs (Tomlinson 1960a) (Fig. G.9). As a rule, the adaxial ribs of palm leaves are stouter than the abaxial. When primary splitting occurs along the adaxial ("upper") ribs, induplicate segments are formed, when along the abaxial ("lower") ribs, reduplicate leaflets are formed. Characteristically the rachis continues through the central segment or leaflet of induplicately folded leaves, while the blade of reduplicately folded leaves is bifid at the apex.

Blade Structure. — In its simplest but not neces-

←

I.3. — **A Suggested Scheme of Evolution for the Leaf.** A. An unspecialized eophyll characteristic of Corypheae, *Phoenix,* many cocosoid palms, *Roystonea,* and some other genera. B–D. "Reduplicate" leaves, (B) palmate, (C) pinnately ribbed, (D) pinnate. E–I. "Induplicate" leaves, (E) the simply pinnate leaf of *Arenga,* (F) the bipinnate leaf of *Caryota,* (G) palmate, (H) costapalmate, (I) the pinnate leaf of *Phoenix.*

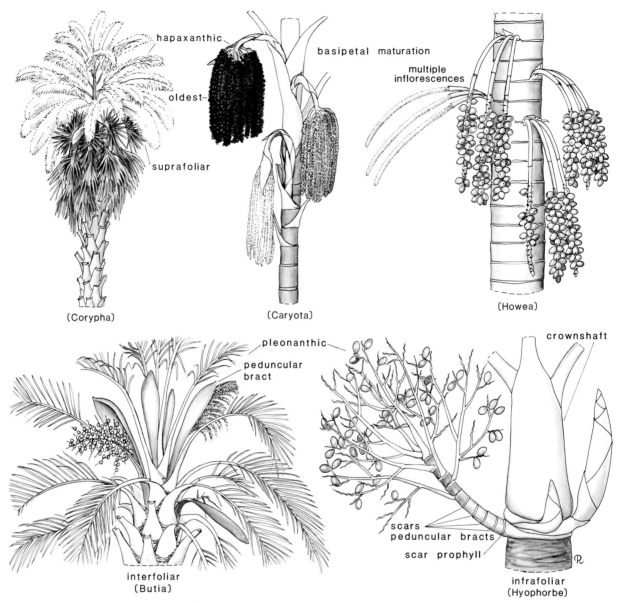

I.4.—**Inflorescence Form.**

sarily most primitive form, the blade is undivided except slightly along the margins, as in such induplicate leaves as *Johannesteijsmannia altifrons* (Fig. I.2) or *Licuala grandis,* and in some reduplicate forms such as *Iguanura sanderiana, Areca dayung,* and *Pinanga tomentella.* It is bifid at the apex in such reduplicate entire leaves as those of *Asterogyne martiana* (Fig. I.2). When the blade is divided the segments or leaflets may each have only a single fold, or in both palmate and pinnate leaves the blade may be unequally divided into segments or leaflets some or all with several folds (Figs. I.2, G.10, G.12).

Segments or leaflets may be regularly arranged as in *Serenoa repens* or *Nypa fruticans* (Fig. I.2), or they may be arranged in separated groups in which the individuals may lie in one plane or in several planes along the rachis. Although the midrib of the leaflet is usually central and most prominent, in a few genera (*Iriartea, Normanbya, Podococcus, Socratea*) the midrib is eccentric and distinguished from other veins or ribs only by its uppermost position at the attachment on the rachis (Fig. I.2). Most leaflets are acute to acuminate or briefly and sometimes unequally bifid at the tip, but expanded, toothed (prae-

Table I.5. **TYPES OF EOPHYLLS**

Group	Undivided	Digitate	Bifid	Pinnate
I CORYPHOIDEAE				
CORYPHEAE	+		+	
PHOENICEAE	+			
BORASSEAE	+	+		
II CALAMOIDEAE	+	+	+	+
III NYPOIDEAE				+
IV CEROXYLOIDEAE				
CYCLOSPATHEAE	+			
CEROXYLEAE	+		+	
HYOPHORBEAE			+	+
V ARECOIDEAE				
CARYOTEAE	+		+	
IRIARTEEAE	+		+	
PODOCOCCEAE	+			
ARECEAE	+		+	+
COCOEAE	+		+	+
GEONOMEAE			+	
VI PHYTELEPHANTOIDEAE				+

morse) tips occur in diverse groups (Fig. G.16, Table I.6).

Eophylls. — The simplest eophyll is linear to elliptic and entire (Table I.5). It occurs in most members of the Coryphoideae and in some Ceroxyloideae, in some genera of Calamoideae, and in some members of four tribes, Caryoteae, Iriarteeae, Areceae, and Cocoeae of the Arecoideae. Undivided eophylls of both induplicate (e.g. *Phoenix*) and reduplicate genera (e.g. *Clinostigma haerestigma, Roystonea*) are basically similar (Fig. G.24). Bifid eophylls are most common in palms with reduplicate leaves, and usually with an obvious rachis. They are divided to the base in *Chelyocarpus* (Corypheae) and *Arenga hastata* and *Caryota* (Caryoteae, Fig. I.2), which represents an apparent advance over the undivided eophyll. Among the palms with reduplicately folded leaves, the bifid eophyll may represent the first step in the division of the leaf. Compound eophylls occur in *Latania* (Coryphoideae: Borasseae) and several spp. of *Chamaedorea*, e.g. *C. elegans* (Ceroxyloideae). These suggest further stages in evolution that may correspond with levels of specialization suggested for major categories, and in *Chamaedorea* they may correspond to levels of specialization within the genus (Moore unpublished). In *Nypa*, the eophyll may sometimes appear imparipinnate.

The eophylls are followed by an often long progression of juvenile leaves, where the size and nature of the mature blade develops through increase in the number of lateral ribs and through the division of the blade into segments or leaflets. The leaf of *Syagrus smithii,* for example, may not divide until it has reached a length of about 3 m (Moore 1963a). The mature leaf of *S. smithii* has numerous leaflets arranged in groups and dispersed in several planes, but during the juvenile interval the blade may easily be mistaken for that of a geonomoid palm such as *Asterogyne martiana.*

The Coryphoid Leaf. — Different patterns of shape and division appear in group after group (Table I.7). The palmate blade varies from flabellate to cuneate in outline, and from nearly lacking a rachis to possessing a long rachis, then approaching a pinnately ribbed form. The great diversity of leaf form in the least specialized subfamily, Coryphoideae, has only recently been appreciated. Within the Coryphoideae there are notable exceptions to the usual induplicate state, and it is particularly interesting that this diversity occurs in the group of palms we regard as being the least specialized. Circumscribed here to include *Phoenix*, the subfamily includes palmate, costapalmate, pinnate, and entire-leaved taxa.

Characteristically leaves of the Coryphoideae are induplicate, and indeed great emphasis was placed on the character of leaf vernation in previous classifications. Leaves are usually regularly divided into single-fold segments by splits along the adaxial ridges; in several palms such as *Trachycarpus fortunei* the adaxial splits are irregular, extending to different depths from the leaf margin. In others, such as *Pholidocarpus*, the blade is divided by a few deep splits into compound (several-fold) segments which are again regularly divided distally by much shorter splits

Table I.6. **DISTRIBUTION OF PRAEMORSE LEAFLETS OR BLADE MARGIN**

II CALAMOIDEAE	ARECEAE
CALAMEAE	
Calamus caryotoides	Oraniinae
Ceratolobus species	*Orania*
Korthalsia	*Halmoorea*
IV CEROXYLOIDEAE	Manicariinae
HYOPHORBEAE	*Manicaria*
Chamaedorea	Malortieinae
tenerrima	*Reinhardtia*
V ARECOIDEAE	Dypsidinae
CARYOTEAE (all)	*Neophloga thiryana*
Arenga	Linospadicinae
Caryota	*Linospadix* (some
Wallichia	spp.)
IRIARTEEAE (all)	Ptychospermatinae
Dictyocaryum	*Balaka*
Iriartella	*Brassiophoenix*
Iriartea	*Carpentaria*
Socratea	*Drymophloeus*
Catoblastus	*Normanbya*
Wettinia	*Ptychococcus*
PODOCOCCEAE (all)	*Ptychosperma*
Podococcus	*Veitchia* (not all)
	Wodyetia
	Arecinae
	Gronophyllum
	Hydriastele
	Loxococcus
	Iguanurinae
	Pelagodoxa
	Iguanura
	Physokentia
	Oncospermatinae
	Verschaffeltia
	Phoenicophorium
	COCOEAE
	Aiphanes
	Bactris caryotifolia

into single-fold induplicate segments. Noteworthy also are the very deep adaxial splits in the strongly costapalmate leaves of *Livistona loriphylla* and *L. decipiens,* in which the distal portion of the blade is divided almost to the rachis into single-fold segments. The apical part of the leaf of these species thus appears remarkably similar to the leaf of *Phoenix.*

The newly recognized *Guihaia* is exceptional in having clearly reduplicate leaves, with rather shallow segments of one or two folds, in marked contrast to its close relative *Maxburretia* which has induplicate leaves (Dransfield et al. 1985b). In several genera another type of abaxial splitting occurs. In *Chelyocarpus, Itaya,* species of *Cryosophila* and *Trithrinax,* and in juvenile states of some species of

Sabal, the otherwise induplicately segmented palmate blade is split along the midline or just to one side of it, by a deep *abaxial* split, effectively dividing the leaf into two halves (Fig. G.10). In *Sabal,* at least, this deep central split occurs earlier in the development of the leaf than the adaxial splits (Uhl, pers. obs.).

Another exceptional form is found in *Licuala,* where in most species the blade is basically induplicate, as can be seen by the lobing of the segment tips. However, superimposed on this are abaxial splits which divide the blade right to its insertion into compound or very rarely (sometimes in *L. bidentata*) single-fold reduplicate segments. As in *Sabal,* these abaxial splits occur very early in the development of the leaf (Dransfield 1970), while the adaxial splits usual in the subfamily occur much later. The abaxial splitting appears to be a specialized development at least in *Licuala.* The abaxial splits are unusual in being the only ones in the subfamily to reach the insertion of the blade, except for the central divisions noted above. Adaxial splits may be very deep but there is always, even in *Phoenix,* a thin flange of lamina tissue between the split and the costa. In Coryphoideae, such as *Johannesteijsmannia* (Fig. I.2), *Licuala grandis* (Fig. G.10), and *L. orbicularis,* the entire or subentire leaves are thought to have evolved from ancestors with compound leaves by loss of splitting (Dransfield 1970). The curious leaf of *Licuala* may have arisen by the reduplicate splitting of such an entire leaf. Further developmental work is needed to understand these apparently anomalous forms.

Another unusual type of splitting occurs in *Rhapis* and *Rhapidophyllum,* where, although the distal margin of the blade may be shallowly and regularly induplicately lobed, the major divisions of the leaf into segments occur between the folds rather than along the adaxial or abaxial ribs (Fig. G.9). As in *Licuala,* these unusual splits occur relatively early in the leaf's development (Dransfield 1970).

The leaf of *Phoenix,* which is clearly pinnate but induplicate, is yet another example of the remarkable diversity of leaf form in the Coryphoideae. It should be noted that leaf development in *Phoenix* is unique and that further study is required. The significance of the haut, an adaxial tissue layer, is not yet understood (Periasamy 1967). In differential elongation of the costa, the leaf of *Phoenix* parallels reduplicate pinnate leaves.

The Pinnate Leaf.—Several different forms of pinnate leaves also occur. The pinnate blade in large

Table I.7. **DISTRIBUTION OF LEAF TYPES**

	Induplicate		Reduplicate	
	Palmate	Pinnate	Palmate	Pinnate
I CORYPHOIDEAE				
CORYPHEAE	+		+	
PHOENICEAE		+		
BORASSEAE	+			
II CALAMOIDEAE				
CALAMEAE				+
LEPIDOCARYEAE			+	
III NYPOIDEAE				+
IV CEROXYLOIDEAE				
CYCLOSPATHEAE				+
CEROXYLEAE				+
HYOPHORBEAE				+
V ARECOIDEAE				
CARYOTEAE		+		
IRIARTEEAE				+
PODOCOCCEAE				+
ARECEAE				+
COCOEAE				+
GEONOMEAE				+
VI PHYTELEPHANTOIDEAE				+

groups, such as the tribes Calameae, Areceae, and Cocoeae, exhibits nearly the full range of dissection from undivided to regularly pinnate. Leaflets may be in groups in one plane, or in groups in several planes (Fig. G.13), sometimes in the same genus as in *Salacca* (Calamoideae), *Chamaedorea* (Ceroxyloideae), and *Bactris* (Arecoideae). Distal leaflets are modified into straight to recurved hooks (acanthophylls) in climbing species of three subfamilies, i.e. in all members of *Laccosperma, Eremospatha,* and *Oncocalamus* (Calamoideae: Calameae), in *Chamaedorea elatior* (Ceroxyloideae: Hyophorbeae), and in the genus *Desmoncus* (Arecoideae: Cocoeae). Other elaborate adaptations for climbing have evolved in many species of the Calamineae, Plectocomiinae, and in *Korthalsia* (Metroxylinae) of Calamoideae, where the rachis extends distally beyond the leaflets as a specialized climbing organ (cirrus), armed with recurved grapnellike spines. A superficially very similar structure, the flagellum, is found in some species of *Calamus* but is derived from an inflorescence (see below).

The Hastula. — Two further structures associated with the leaf are noteworthy. The leaf of many, but not all, members of tribes Corypheae and Borasseae (Coryphoideae) bears an adaxial and sometimes an abaxial crest or hastula at the junction of the petiole and blade (Fig. G.11). The origin and adaptive nature of the hastula are as yet not clear. A small flange occurs on the rachis of some pinnate leaves as *Oraniopsis* (Irvine, pers. comm.), *Ceroxylon* (Plate 14D), and *Cocos,* and may be homologous to the hastula.

Ligules and Ocreas. — Another structure in the position of a ligule at the top of the sheath in front of the petiole, or sometimes lateral to the petiole, is found in the leaves of many palms as in *Livistona,* and some species of Arecoideae including *Arenga,* and some Ptychospermatinae (Fig. G.6). In Calamoideae (where it is termed an ocrea), such a structure occurs in some species of *Calamus,* and *Daemonorops,* and in all species of *Plectocomiopsis, Eremospatha, Oncocalamus, Laccosperma,* and conspicuously in *Korthalsia* where the ocrea is a diagnostic feature at the specific level and often harbors ants (Beccari 1918, Dransfield 1981a). Ants are also present in the ocreas of *Laccosperma* in Africa and in a few species of *Calamus* in the Philippines and New Guinea. *Pogonotium,* unlike any other calamoid genus, has two earlike processes, one on either side of the petiole at its base (Dransfield 1980a).

Evolution. — The evolution of the palm leaf, remains a subject for speculation. We suggest that both palmate and pinnate leaves in palms may be derived by the differential expansion, elongation, and dissection of a primitively simple leaf. This probably resembled the undivided eophyll of most coryphoid palms and of some others such as *Pseudophoenix,*

Roystonea, and several genera of Cocoeae (Fig. I.3). Evidence comes (1) from the work of Dransfield (1970) in which he points out that the conspicuous rachis of the costapalmate leaf in *Johannesteijsmannia* is produced late in development by massive intercalary growth; (2) from the eophylls and stages of elaboration of the blade from juvenile individuals to that of the mature individual (Tomlinson 1960a); (3) from the work of Kaplan et al. (1982b) and of Dengler et al. (1982) who find plication origin and development in the palmate leaf of *Rhapis* virtually identical to that of the pinnate leaf of *Chrysalidocarpus*; and (4) from observation of what appear to be effects of the same processes at a secondary level in the formation of the bipinnate leaf of *Caryota,* and in the longitudinally divided pinnae of some Iriarteeae and of *Normanbya* and *Wodyetia* (Areceae). Most palm leaflets or segments have veins that are fixed in number at maturity and that extend more or less parallel to the midrib from the insertion to the usually acute, acuminate, or bifid tip. Even in leaflets with praemorse apices, the veins diverge from the base, and it is through secondary splitting between thickened veins that the mature leaf of *Socratea exorrhiza* or of *Normanbya normanbyi* arises.

The three genera of Caryoteae are exceptional in that the veins do not all run parallel or diverge from the base of the leaflet; some diverge from the midrib of the leaflet, all tend to terminate along the margin, and there may be increase in the number of veins toward the apex (Fig. I.2). As in caespitose species in Caryoteae, in the Iriarteeae, and in *Normanbya,* and *Wodyetia* (Areceae) the leaflets of juvenile plants are simple, with veins that diverge toward the margin from base and midrib. Secondary splitting between veins of this sort of leaflet is likely to produce leaflets along an extended axis. Although this is presumably the manner in which leaflets of *Caryota* were derived (see Periasamy 1967), further developmental studies are needed to confirm the interpretation.

We suggest that the palmate leaf has arisen by suppression of the central axis and lateral expansion of ribs and tissue from a simple leaf, that the costapalmate leaf has involved both lateral expansion and subsequent elongation of the central axis, and that the pinnately nerved or divided leaf has arisen through elongation of the central axis together with the intercalation of additional ribs and laminar tissue. What appears to have been the development of the pinnate leaf in several lines and the development of the palmate leaf in the Coryphoideae and

Calamoideae may be accounted for by differential development.

The various forms of the palm leaf appear to have arisen more than once (Table I.7). The Coryphoideae seem clearly to constitute a phylogenetic line (Moore 1973a) characterized in large part by the morphology and anatomy of their induplicately folded leaves, even though there is an exception in the reduplicate leaves of *Guihaia.* The palmate leaf appears to have developed separately in the coryphoid and calamoid subfamilies, since it is reduplicate in the latter.

Similarly, the pinnate leaf appears to have evolved three or more times—once in *Phoenix* within the Coryphoideae, once in the Caryoteae, and again in the palms with reduplicately folded leaves, perhaps separately in each of the calamoid, nypoid, ceroxyloid, and arecoid subfamilies. The leaves of Caryoteae although induplicately folded morphologically, are anatomically like reduplicate leaves (Tomlinson 1960b, 1961). Moreover, secondary division of the pinnae has developed in the Caryoteae (*Caryota*) and in the Iriarteeae and Areceae within Arecoideae. A main trend in the evolution of the leaf in palms seems to have been toward greater complexity.

There is a marked disparity between the numbers of genera and species with adaxially split blades and those with abaxially split blades, many more palms having reduplicate blades. If we compare the distribution of palms with the two types of blade it is also clear that palms with adaxially split, induplicate, palmate, and costapalmate blades show a marked association with less tropical or more seasonal climates or more open habitats (as does also *Phoenix*), and that by and large the reduplicately folded or pinnate leaf is associated with palms of wet forests and more even tropical climates. If we assume that protopalms were slow-growing plants adapted to cooler, drier, more seasonal, and more open habitats, as are many of the more primitive genera today, and that the adaptation to the tropical rain forest followed (Moore 1973a), then it may be suggested that the elaboration of the pinnate leaf is an adaptation to the more limited sunlight of the rain forest.

INFLORESCENCE

Pleonanthy, Hapaxanthy.—Inflorescence in palms may be regarded in two ways—in the physiological sense of a reproductive event or flowering, and in the strictly morphological sense of an axillary branch

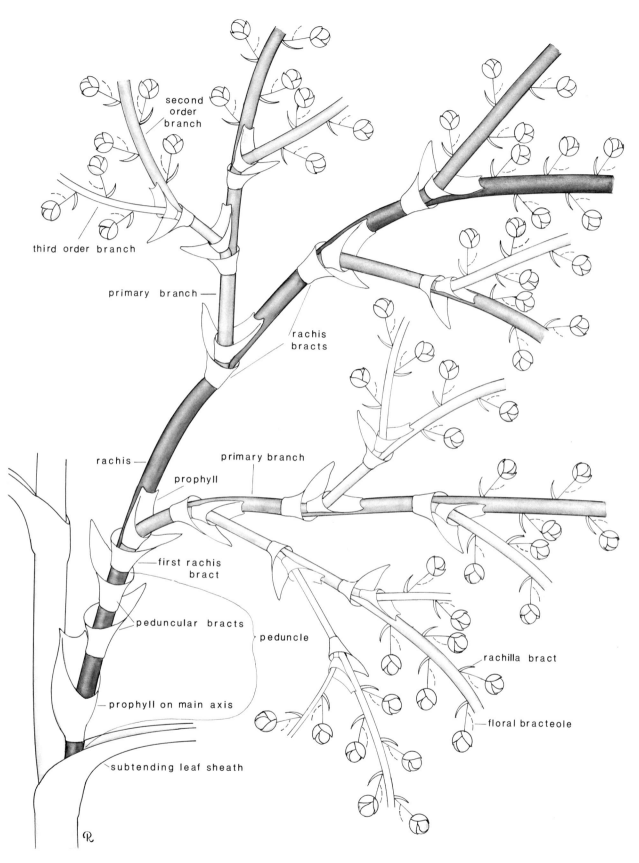

second
order
branch

third order branch

primary branch

rachis
bracts

rachis

primary branch

prophyll

first rachis
bract

peduncular bracts

peduncle

prophyll on main axis

rachilla bract

floral bracteole

subtending leaf sheath

I.5.—A Diagram Showing Basic Inflorescence Structure.

15

Table I.8. **DISTRIBUTION OF SPICATE INFLORES-
CENCE UNITS IN PALMS**

I CORYPHOIDEAE	*Laccospadix*
CORYPHEAE	*Linospadix*
Chuniophoenix nana	*Neonicholsonia*
(not always)	*Neophloga* sp.
Licuala sp.	*Pinanga* sp.
BORASSEAE	*Prestoea* sp.
Borassodendron (♀)	*Reinhardtia*
Borassus (♀, some-	*koschnyana*
times)	*Sclerosperma*
Lodoicea (not	COCOEAE
always)	*Aiphanes* spp.
II CALAMOIDEAE	*Allagoptera*
Korthalsia tenuissima	*Bactris* spp.
Salacca (♀, rarely)	*Cocos nucifera*
IV CEROXYLOIDEAE	(rarely)
Chamaedorea spp.	*Polyandrococos*
VI ARECOIDEAE	*Syagrus* spp.
CARYOTEAE	GEONOMEAE
Arenga spp.	*Asterogyne martiana*
Caryota	*Calptrogyne*
monostachya	*Geonoma* spp.
IRIARTEEAE	*Pholidostachys*
Wettinia spp.	*pulchra*
PODOCOCCEAE	VI PHYTELEPHAN-
Podococcus	TOIDEAE
ARECEAE	*Ammandra* (♀)
Areca chaiana	*Palandra* (♀)
Calyptrocalyx spp.	*Phytelephas* (♀ and ♂)
Dypsis spp.	
Gronophyllum sp.	
Howea belmoreana	
Iguanura spp.	

system. In the first sense, palms appear primitively and predominantly to be of indeterminate growth, i.e. shoots pleonanthic, but determinate growth (hapaxanthy) has developed several times and in different groups (Table I.2). Two genera of Coryphoideae and 11 genera of Calamoideae have shoots that undergo a long to very long vegetative phase (often more than 40 years in *Corypha*) and a relatively short reproductive phase (Dransfield 1976a, 1978b; Tomlinson 1971a; Tomlinson and Moore 1968; Tomlinson and Soderholm 1975; Tuley 1965) that results in a compound inflorescence composed of several to many axillary reproductive branch systems that terminate the shoot (Fig. I.4). The shoot dies after flowering. Most species of the Caryoteae (Arecoideae) also have hapaxanthic shoots, but axillary buds initiated along the stem in acropetal sequence are suppressed until a terminal, or more likely pseudoterminal, inflorescence bud is activated, to be followed by successive basipetal maturation of the other inflorescence buds (Fig. I.1).

Form.—In a morphological sense, a remarkable series of variations is based on an axillary monopodial branch system as characteristic of unspecialized Corypheae (Tomlinson and Moore 1968). This system (Fig. I.5) is composed of a main axis or branch on which is borne an adaxially two-keeled prophyll, and usually one to several empty peduncular bracts, which are followed by rachis bracts, each of which subtends a branch of the first order. These branches, which may sometimes also bear prophylls, may be again branched one to several times, each successive branch subtended by a bract and the ultimate axes or rachillae bearing solitary flowers each subtended in turn by a small bract and sometimes bearing a bracteole. A sympodial or rarely (Phytelephantoideae) monopodial system develops to produce the diverse flower clusters considered below. Except for the prophyll and empty peduncular bracts, there is a 1:1 relationship between bracts and branches including, with a few exceptions (see flowering units), the flowers. A simple system for referring to the orders of branches and of bracts was devised for *Nannorrhops* (Tomlinson and Moore 1968). We have illustrated inflorescence structure in Figures (I.4, I.5, and G.17).

Although it is quite likely that in a few cases there has been increase in the number of orders of branching (in *Sabal mauritiiformis,* for example), the usual tendency seems to be toward reduction in branching. This tendency is apparent in the spicate inflorescence that appears repeatedly within major divisions as well as within genera of palms (Table I.8). Inflorescence form may differ even within a species, as in *Chamaedorea ernesti-augusti* and *C. metallica* where the pistillate inflorescences are normally spicate, the staminate branched with numerous rachillae of the second order.

In *Calamus,* the inflorescence is often modified by sterilization into a specialized climbing organ (flagellum) which is adnate (fused) to the leaf sheath above the sheath which subtends it. In other Calamoideae, adnation between the inflorescence and internode above occurs in *Korthalsia, Myrialepis, Plectocomia,* and *Plectocomiopsis,* and adnation between the inflorescence and both the internode and leaf sheath above occurs in *Calamus, Calospatha, Ceratolobus,* and *Daemonorops* (Fisher and Dransfield 1977), and *Retispatha* and *Pogonotium* (Dransfield 1979c, 1980a). No such adnation is found in inflorescences of *Laccosperma* or *Eremospatha,* genera that usually are considered less specialized than those above, nor in the unusual *Oncocalamus.*

Table I.9. **PALMS WITH MULTIPLE INFLORESCENCES**

IV CEROXYLOIDEAE	IRIARTEEAE
CEROXYLEAE	*Catoblastus*
Ravenea	*Wettinia*
HYOPHORBEAE	ARECEAE
Chamaedorea	*Calyptrocalyx*
V ARECOIDEAE	*Howea forsteriana*
CARYOTEAE	COCOEAE
Arenga spp.	*Aiphanes* spp.

In the Calamoideae the amount of inflorescence adnation usually tends to be greater in presumed specialized species than in unspecialized ones, but in general adnation in the inflorescence occurs in the less specialized subfamilies. Substantial basal adnation of axes to those of the internode above occurs in the Corypheae (Coryphoideae), Nypoideae (Tomlinson and Moore 1968, Tomlinson 1971b, Uhl 1972a), and Calamoideae, but adnation of branches is not found in inflorescences of Ceroxyloideae, Arecoideae, or Phytelephantoideae.

Position.—The most common position of the inflorescence is among the leaves (interfoliar), but in many Arecoideae it is below the crown (infrafoliar), being exposed in bud by the fall of the deciduous subtending leaf which has a long tubular sheath (Fig. I.4). When inflorescences are produced in the axils of bracts above the crown as in *Corypha* (Plate 8A) and *Metroxylon* (Plate 11C), they are suprafoliar.

Multiple Inflorescences.—Most inflorescences are solitary in the leaf axil, but several inflorescences rather than the usual one at each node are produced in two subfamilies. Multiple inflorescences (Table I.9) occur in some members of Caryoteae, Iriarteeae, and Areceae (Arecoideae), and in Ceroxyleae and Hyophorbeae (Ceroxyloideae). In *Arenga,* staminate inflorescences are often multiple, several units occurring at a node, but pistillate inflorescences occur singly. In the Wettiniinae, three or more similar units, each with its own prophyll and peduncular bracts develop in a leaf axil—the central often pistillate, the lateral ones staminate (Moore 1973a, Uhl and Moore 1973).

By studies of development Fisher and Moore (1977) have shown that multiple inflorescence buds develop from an axillary meristem. A central apex on an axillary meristem gives rise to the single inflorescence in most palms. In *Calyptrocalyx* (Arecoideae) two or three separate apices arise nearly simultaneously and develop in unison. Elsewhere multiple inflorescences arise as a centrifugal series

of new apices on either side of the central apex. The new lateral buds are initiated externally to the prophyll of the central bud, and each lateral bud apex develops its own prophyll.

The prophylls remain distinct in species of *Arenga, Catoblastus, Chamaedorea,* and *Wettinia.* In *Calyptrocalyx,* and one species of *Chamaedorea,* the separate prophylls are united laterally during later growth to form a chambered structure that encloses all the bud apices. In these species the collateral inflorescences are interpreted as separate inflorescences superimposed on the single original inflorescence meristem during early development. *Howea forsteriana* and a species of *Aiphanes* probably follow the same pattern, although they have not yet been studied developmentally. In the staminate inflorescence of *Ravenea madagascariensis,* the prophyll of the inflorescence is incompletely sheathing, remaining open abaxially, and somewhat undulate and lobed distally, but the individual axes within are discrete. Developmental study is needed for this genus.

Livistona woodfordii, L. rotundifolia, and species of *Pritchardia* produce inflorescences that appear to be multiple, but the two to three axes are enclosed in a single prophyll indicating that the lateral branches are simply equal in size to the main axis and not separate inflorescences.

The production of multiple inflorescences is interpreted as a developmental shift producing several inflorescences from an originally single and typical axillary bud meristem. They appear to have several adaptive features. Since many of them are staminate, they increase the number of staminate flowers and the amount of pollen produced. They also extend the flowering period for both seasonal and nonseasonal species, and they offer increased protection of reproductive structures against herbivory (Fisher and Moore 1977).

The Prophyll.—Bracts, which are homologous with leaves (Tomlinson and Moore 1968, Tomlinson 1971a, Tomlinson and Soderholm 1975), occur in many different forms. The unvarying presence of an adaxially two-keeled prophyll on the base of the peduncle of the inflorescence is, along with the leaf, a distinctive feature of the Palmae (Figs. I.4, I.5). The prophyll always completely encloses the inflorescence in early stages and in its simplest form is tubular and two-keeled. Maturation of the prophyll occurs at different times in different palms. It may enlarge with the inflorescence and become the largest and sometimes the only bract (Table I.10), com-

Table I.10. **INFLORESCENCES BEARING AN EN-LARGED PROPHYLL BUT NO PEDUNCULAR OR RA-CHIS BRACTS**

I CORYPHOIDEAE	V ARECOIDEAE
CORYPHEAE	ARECEAE
Chamaerops	*Areca*
Licuala species	*Nenga*
PHOENICEAE	*Pinanga*
Phoenix	
BORASSEAE	
Borassus	
II CALAMOIDEAE	
CALAMEAE	
Ceratolobus	
Pogonotium	

Table I.11. **INFLORESCENCES WITH INCOMPLETE PROPHYLL**

IV CEROXYLOIDEAE	V ARECOIDEAE
CEROXYLEAE	ARECEAE
Ceroxylon	*Basselinia*
Louvelia	*Burretiokentia*
Oraniopsis	*Campecarpus*
Ravenea	*Cyphophoenix*
	Cyphosperma
	Physokentia
	Veillonia

pletely enclosing the inflorescence even in late bud and opening when flowers are at anthesis, as in *Chamaerops, Phoenix,* and some genera of Arecoideae in the Arecinae, Iguanurinae, and Oncospermatinae. Sometimes it remains as a permanent shield over the flowering inflorescence as in *Ceratolobus* (Calamoideae) and in two species of *Pinanga* (Arecoideae) (Dransfield 1980b). In other palms, as *Hyophorbe* (Ceroxyloideae) and the genera of the Cocoeae (Arecoideae), the prophyll matures when the inflorescence is in early stages of development and opens apically or otherwise to allow the emergence of the peduncular bracts, each of which in turn encloses the inflorescence as it enlarges. In members of Areceae (Arecoideae), the prophyll may enlarge with the peduncular bract, the two bracts reaching nearly equal size and opening at about the same time. Rarely, in some genera of Ceroxyloideae and Arecoideae, the prophyll is incomplete, only partly encircling the peduncle (Moore 1973a, Table I.11). Developmental study shows that incomplete prophylls result when young stages do not completely close or when an abaxial opening forms at an early stage (Uhl unpublished).

In some Coryphoideae, Calamoideae, and in *Nypa*, prophylls are borne on lateral branches as well as on the main axis. Their occurrence on lateral branches in these less specialized groups, suggests the possibility that a prophyll associated with each branch may represent a basic, primitive condition, although in the Coryphoideae prophylls on lateral branches are associated with such relatively specialized genera as *Brahea, Sabal,* and *Thrinax* and not with genera that are otherwise less specialized. The expanded prophylls on branches of the second and higher orders may in other cases be associated with elaboration of the inflorescence.

Except as noted above, the prophyll completely encloses the inflorescence at its inception and opens at different times in different genera. In early stages of inflorescence development, it often enlarges much more rapidly than other bracts and branches internal to it, as in *Palandra* and *Welfia* (Uhl unpublished). Of rather uniform nature, the prophyll has become the chief protective bract where no peduncular bracts develop and in some Arecoideae where it encloses the peduncular bract or bracts and the inflorescence until maturity.

Peduncular Bracts and Rachis Bracts.—One or a few to many empty bracts, termed peduncular bracts, may be borne on the peduncle above the prophyll. Since even the prophyll may sometimes subtend a first-order branch (Tomlinson and Moore 1968, Tomlinson and Soderholm 1975), it is probable that these peduncular bracts have evolved through suppression of the subtended branch and specialization in various ways. In many coryphoid palms they are small, tubular, sheathing appendages, opening early at the apex. In many palms of the Arecoideae, they are large, closed, exceedingly hard, often beaked structures that enclose the entire inflorescence in bud, splitting abaxially and becoming marcescent or more often deciduous at anthesis.

The number of peduncular bracts is important in delimiting subfamilies and tribes. Three to more than ten empty peduncular bracts characterize most Coryphoideae, Hyophorbeae (Ceroxyloideae), Caryoteae, Iriarteeae, and Podococceae (Arecoideae) and some calamoid genera (e.g. *Mauritia*). They may persist on the inflorescence, as in Caryoteae, Podococceae, most Hyophorbeae, and in *Socratea* (Iriarteeae); or they may be caducous as in *Hyophorbe* (Hyophorbeae) and other Iriarteeae. Bracts that subtend branches of the first or higher orders may also be prominent sheathing structures, especially in tribes Corypheae, Borasseae (Coryphoideae), and in Calamoideae, and Nypoideae, but in the Arecoideae there is a clear trend toward reduction in size or infrequently complete loss (at maturity) of those bracts that subtend branches.

Bracts on the inflorescence in tribes Areceae, Cocoeae, and Geonomeae of Arecoideae and in Phytelephantoideae are usually only two: a sometimes large prophyll and a usually much enlarged single peduncular bract, which is particularly striking in subtribes Butiinae and Attaleinae (Arecoideae: Cocoeae). Here the peduncular bract is woody, often cowllike, markedly plicate in bud, long persistent above the inflorescence, and sometimes brilliant yellow or white internally at anthesis when it may serve as an attractant to pollinators. The plications are especially prominent in bud, less so when the bract has split and spread. Their origin has not been studied. The plications may function in different ways. They may permit expansion for enclosure and protection of the bud during emergence through the heavy bases of leaves in the crown. They may also allow contraction upon splitting to expose the inflorescence branches and flowers at anthesis. In *Beccariophoenix* (Arecoideae: Cocoeae) a most remarkable peduncular bract is borne at the tip of the peduncle; it is immensely thick and woody and is circumscissile (field observations, Dransfield 1986). Other large peduncular bracts occur in many arecoid genera, where they are thinner, fibrous, and deciduous.

Function. — In whatever ways the prophyll, peduncular bracts, and rachis bracts may be modified, they appear to function as protective organs for the developing inflorescence (Uhl and Moore 1977a) and during pollination. In the few cases studied the structure of peduncular bracts has been important in pollination. The timing of bract opening can be correlated with both floral structure and pollination events (Uhl and Moore 1977a, Henderson 1986a). Henderson (1984) has found that the large inflated rachis bracts open distally to provide access for pollinators in *Cryosophila*. In *Socratea*, erect peduncular bracts provide a funnel that guides pollinators into the inflorescence when pistillate flowers are receptive (Henderson 1985).

FLOWER CLUSTERS

Flowers are borne in several kinds of clusters that have a characteristic form in each subfamily (Fig. I.6, Table I.12). The basic flowering unit seems clearly to be a single flower, sessile or borne on a pedicel which is subtended by a bract and bears a

Table I.12. **DISTRIBUTION OF FLOWERING UNITS**

		Solitary	Sympodial	Monopodial
I	CORYPHOIDEAE			
	CORYPHEAE	+	+	
	PHOENICEAE	+		
	BORASSEAE	+	+	
II	CALAMOIDEAE	+	+	
III	NYPOIDEAE	+		
IV	CEROXYLOIDEAE			
	CYCLOSPATHEAE	+		
	CEROXYLEAE	+		
	HYOPHORBEAE	+	+	
V	ARECOIDEAE			
	CARYOTEAE		+	
	IRIARTEEAE		+	
	PODOCOCCEAE		+	
	ARECEAE		+	
	COCOEAE		+	
	GEONOMEAE		+	
VI	PHYTELEPHANTOIDEAE	+ (♀)		+ (♂)

more or less two-keeled bracteole or prophyll. The pedicel, the bract subtending it, or the bracteole may be reduced or absent. Solitary flowers are usually spirally inserted; often they are nearly decussate basally on rachillae, but elsewhere they can be closely crowded and somewhat irregularly arranged. Where single flowers are closely appressed along a thick axis, as in the staminate spikes and the pistillate head of *Nypa fruticans*, the flowers may be in parastichies. In Borasseae (Coryphoideae), Calamoideae, and perhaps elsewhere, some flowers have two bracts which may represent a prophyll and a floral bracteole.

Sympodial. — Clusters of several to many flowers are either sympodial in development and form cincinni, or in phytelephantoid genera they are condensed monopodial branching systems. Cincinni result when a second flower develops in the axil of the floral bracteole, the bracteole below the second flower then subtending a third flower, etc. This type of growth produces flower clusters of various forms, depending on the relative positions of the bracteole and its subtended flower. The form of the cincinnus is characteristic in subfamilies I, II, IV, and V. The trend in Coryphoideae seems to be from short irregular cincinni to longer, regular two-ranked forms. Small irregular cincinni of 2–5 flowers, termed glomerules, occur in several coryphoid genera (*Chamaerops, Trachycarpus, Livistona*) (Fig. I-6). In the cincinnus of *Nannorrhops* bracteoles are tubular and completely sheathing (Uhl 1969a); flowers

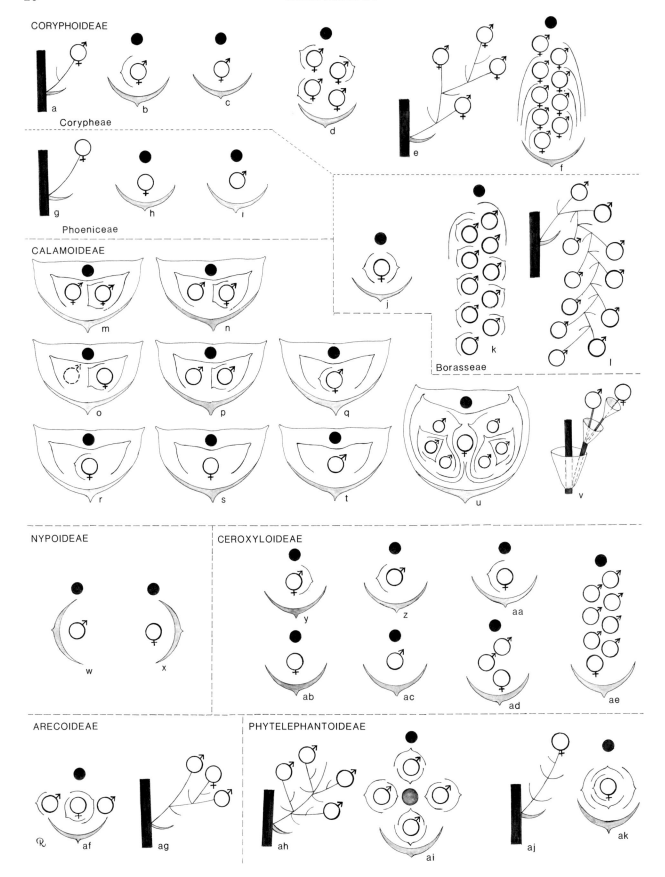

are sessile and bracteoles are adnate to the rachilla in the cincinnus of *Corypha* (Uhl unpublished). The largest and most regular cincinni in the Coryphoideae are the recurved branches borne in pits formed by thick bracts in the staminate inflorescences of *Borassus* and *Lodoicea*.

The Dyad. — A pair of flowers, a dyad, is a basic form and appears to represent a two-flowered sympodial unit (Uhl and Dransfield 1984). A remarkable series of such units occurs in Calamoideae (Dransfield 1970 and unpublished) (Fig. I.6, m–t). Dyads may consist either of two perfect, two staminate, or a pistillate and a neuter (sterile staminate) flower. Evidence from bracteoles suggests that the solitary pistillate flowers in some genera e.g. *Korthalsia* are reduced from dyads (Fig. I.6, q). In *Oncocalamus* (Fig. I.6, u) the flower cluster consists of a central pistillate flower with two lateral cincinni with 0–1 basal pistillate and several distal staminate flowers, an arrangement unlike any other in the family.

The Acervulus. — The monoecious genera of tribe Hyophorbeae (Ceroxyloideae) have unisexual flowers in reversed cincinni adnate to the rachillae, forming distinct lines of closely two-ranked flowers, called acervuli; the proximal flower is usually pistillate, the distal staminate, and the bracteoles are reduced or not evident at anthesis (Uhl and Moore 1978). In *Gaussia maya* (Fig. I.6, ad), the acervulus consists of only three flowers, and thus it superficially resembles the triad (see below), but the position and anatomy of the flowers differ from those of the triad and indicate similarity to the acervulus. *Chamaedorea* is dioecious with pistillate flowers borne singly; in some species staminate flowers also are borne singly, in other species in few-flowered, curved adnate cincinni (e.g. *C. microspadix*). In *Chamaedorea* anatomical evidence suggests that the solitary flower has been derived from an acervulate

unit in which additional flowers fail to develop (Uhl unpublished).

The Triad. — The most common flowering unit in palms, the triad, characterizes all 124 genera of the Arecoideae. It consists of a cincinnus of two lateral staminate and a central pistillate flower (Fig. I.6, af, ag). The bracteoles of the three flowers, which are illustrated in the generic drawings, are sometimes distinctive. The sympodial nature of this unit has been determined by detailed studies in Caryoteae, Iriarteeae, Ptychospermatinae, and Geonomeae (Uhl 1966, 1976a, and unpublished). The triad is basically uniform throughout the Arecoideae except for some variation in the positions of the two staminate flowers relative to the pistillate flower. The pistillate flower is adaxial to the staminate flowers in Geonomeae, abaxial to staminate flowers in Podococceae, and staminate flowers are in various lateral positions relative to the pistillate flower in the other groups. The triad may be modified by the absence of the pistillate and/or one staminate flower to produce paired or solitary staminate flowers distally on the rachilla. Either staminate or pistillate flowers fail to develop or are rudimentary in the unisexual inflorescences of *Wallichia,* some species of *Arenga* (Caryoteae), Wettiniinae (Iriarteeae), *Marojejya* (Areceae), and *Elaeis* and the genera of the Attaleinae (Cocoeae).

Monopodial. — Flower clusters that develop monopodially characterize only the three genera of subfamily Phytelephantoideae. In these palms, splendid series representing reduction in monopodial branching systems are evident (Uhl and Dransfield 1984, Fig. I.6). These clusters appear indeed to demonstrate the kind of condensed branching systems proposed by Bosch (1947) as characteristic for palms in general, but his diagrams do not apply to the triad or to the other sympodial configurations that occur much more frequently in the family.

←

I.6. — **Diagrams of Flower Clusters.** a–l, Coryphoideae. a, b, solitary flower with bracteole; c, same without bracteole; d, e, the glomerule as in species of *Livistona*; f, the adnate cincinnus of *Corypha*; g, h, i, the solitary staminate and pistillate flowers of *Phoenix*; j, the bibracteolate pistillate flower of Borasseae; k, l, the cincinnus of *Borassus*; m–v, Calamoideae, m–t, forms of the dyad; m, two hermaphrodite flowers (Ancistrophyllinae); n, a staminate and hermaphrodite flower (*Eugeissona, Metroxylon*); o, a sterile staminate and hermaphrodite flower (Calaminae); p, two staminate flowers (Calaminae and Pigafettinae); q, a single hermaphrodite flower but note bracteole (*Korthalsia*); r, a single pistillate flower (*Raphia*); s, single pistillate flower (Pigafettinae, Plectocomiinae); t, single staminate flower (*Raphia*); u, the unusual cluster of *Oncocalamus*; v, a dyad showing the tubular bracts. w–x, Nypoideae, w, x, staminate and pistillate flowers of *Nypa*; y–ae, Ceroxyloideae. y, the hermaphroditic flower of *Pseudophoenix*; z, aa, solitary staminate and pistillate flowers with bracteoles (*Ravenea*); ab, ac, lacking bracteoles (*Chamaedorea*); ad, the triad of *Gaussia maya*; ae, an acervulus (*Synechanthus*). af–ag, Arecoideae, the triad. ah–ak, Phytelephantoideae. ah, ai, the monopodial staminate flower cluster (*Palandra*); aj, ak, the solitary pistillate flower, bracts and bracteoles (*Palandra*).

Table I.13. **SEXUAL EXPRESSION IN PALMS**

	Bisexual or Polygamous	Unisexual	
		Monoecious	Dioecious
I CORYPHOIDEAE			
CORYPHEAE	+		+
PHOENICEAE			+
BORASSEAE			+
II CALAMOIDEAE	+	+	+
III NYPOIDEAE		+	
IV CEROXYLOIDEAE			
CYCLOSPATHEAE	+		
CEROXYLEAE			+
HYOPHORBEAE		+	+
V ARECOIDEAE			
CARYOTEAE		+	+ (? *Arenga obtusifolia*)
IRIARTEEAE		+	
PODOCOCCEAE		+	
ARECEAE		+	
COCOEAE		+	
GEONOMEAE		+	
VI PHYTELEPHANTOIDEAE			+

Recent investigations (Uhl and Dransfield 1984) have shown that phytelephantoid palms are conspicuously unlike other palms in certain aspects of the inflorescence and flower structure. Staminate flower clusters in *Palandra* consist of a short axis bearing four flowers in two close subopposite pairs (Fig. I.6, ah–ai). In very young stages each flower is subtended by a bract and bears a bracteole. During ontogeny, pedicels of the flowers elongate and are partially united, and subtending bracts of the flowers also are united into an irregular shallow ring at the base of the pedicels. These monopodial flowering units are arranged in curved rows on the flattened main axis of the inflorescence. Pistillate inflorescences are similar in structure but have only one flower in each unit. The flower is terminal and surrounded by bracts which indicate that it represents one flower of a four-flowered cluster like that in the staminate inflorescence (Fig. I.6, aj, ak). Staminate inflorescences of *Ammandra* are like those of *Palandra* except that the branch bearing the four flowers, and not the united floral pedicels, is developed. Developmental stages of the third genus, *Phytelephas,* show groups of four with sessile flowers in staminate inflorescences. The perianth of the staminate flowers in *Palandra* is clearly four-parted and in two whorls during ontogeny. Some aspects of the inflorescences and flowers in phytelephantoid parts are thus tetramerous, suggesting a parallel with the inflorescence and flower structure of the Cyclanthaceae.

THE FLOWER

Form.—The basic flower structure in palms is trimerous, with three slightly imbricate sepals, three slightly imbricate petals, six stamens in two whorls, and three distinct uniovulate carpels (Fig. G.18). Flowers of all except phytelephantoid palms have an abscission zone betwen the sepals and the bracteole. The flower of *Chelyocarpus chuco,* with similar sepals and petals, represents an unspecialized trimerous flower, while that of *Trithrinax* differs only in having the sepals connate basally. This simple pattern is modified in many ways, even among the least specialized coryphoid palms (see generic drawings), through connation and/or adnation, increase, reduction, or loss of parts, and by differential elongation of the receptacle.

While trimery is the principal pattern, the three species of *Chelyocarpus* demonstrate dimery in *C. ulei,* trimery in *C. chuco,* and tetramery in *C. dianeurus* (Moore 1972). Tetramery occurs regularly in the perianth of staminate flowers of phytelephantoid palms (Uhl and Dransfield 1984), though largely obscured by the time of anthesis. A four- to seven-parted gynoecium may occur in some species of *Orbignya, Attalea,* and perhaps in *Scheelea* among the Cocoeae, but the perianth is trimerous in these genera. Several to ten carpels are present in the pistillate flowers of phytelephantoid palms. Rarely, in Thrinacinae and in the staminate flowers of *Phytelephas,* the entire perianth is reduced to an irregularly lobed whorl with minute segments. In staminate flowers of the phytelephantoid genera these tiny segments contrast sharply in size with the petals of the pistillate flowers, which may reach a length of 10 cm or more.

Reduction from the hermaphrodite flower to the far more common unisexual flower (Table I.13) occurs by abortion or loss of the gynoecium in staminate flowers and the androecium in pistillate flowers. Staminate and pistillate flowers may be very similar and modified only late in ontogeny (Uhl unpublished), as in some Coryphoideae and in most Calamoideae, or they may be markedly dimorphic as in *Nypa*.

The Floral Receptacle.—The receptacle of palm flowers is remarkably variable. It may be elongate below all floral organs or between any two whorls of organs. Elongation of the receptacle is pronounced in some groups where flowers are borne in pits, e.g. in Borasseae, Podococceae, and Geonomeae. Long receptacles also occur where triads are crowded and staminate flowers are elevated above often large pistillate buds, as in *Allagoptera* (Cocoeae), and where staminate flowers are associated with large pistillate buds as in some species of *Areca*. In *Pinanga simplicifrons* and *P. cleistantha,* one staminate flower is sessile and the other has a long receptacular stalk (Dransfield 1982e). In the last instances, the entire base of the flower above the abscission zone is elongate with both whorls of the perianth borne at the apex of a long, slender flattened receptacle. Comparable receptacular elongation occurs in *Schippia* (Coryphoideae) and *Pseudophoenix* (Ceroxyloideae) but without obvious association with crowding. In *Pseudophoenix,* anatomical study has indicated that the sepals are adnate to the receptacular stalk (Read 1968).

In those groups where flowers are borne in pits, the receptacle of the staminate flower elongates between the insertions of the calyx and corolla (*Welfia*), or between the corolla and stamens (*Lodoicea*) by late intercalary growth (Uhl unpublished) to push the stamens out of the pit at anthesis. The pistillate flower of *Podococcus* is similarly exserted, at least after fertilization, but in pistillate flowers of Geonomeae, the style rather than the receptacle elongates to exsert the stigmas, and the fruit develops within the pit and ultimately forces it open. Flowers of *Chuniophoenix* are exserted from tubular bracts by elongation of a receptacular stalk (Dransfield unpublished). Remarkable plasticity of the floral receptacle as well as of the floral organs is evident.

Table I.14. **THE OCCURRENCE OF GAMOPETALY IN SOME GENERA**

		Staminate	Pistillate	Hermaphroditic
I	CORYPHOIDEAE			
	CORYPHEAE	+	+	+
II	CALAMOIDEAE	+	+	+
IV	CEROXYLOIDEAE			
	HYOPHORBEAE	+	+	
V	ARECOIDEAE			
	CARYOTEAE	+	+	
	ARECEAE		+	
	COCOEAE		+	
	GEONOMEAE	+	+	
VI	PHYTELEPHANTOIDEAE	+		

The Perianth.—Except as noted above, the perianth is trimerous with usually distinct alternating whorls of sepals and petals. The size and shape of sepals varies from group to group; connation occurs frequently, especially in the staminate flower. Petals vary similarly, common trends being toward the valvate state at maturity in the hermaphroditic and staminate flower and toward extreme imbrication in the pistillate flower. Gamopetalous, often valvately lobed corollas are present in some genera in all subfamilies except Nypoideae (Table I.14), frequently with connation and/or adnation of stamen filaments or staminodes in the Coryphoideae and Geonomeae. Such adnation occurs more frequently in the pistillate than in the staminate flower. The petals of the pistillate flowers in many palms have short valvate apices, but in Geonomeae the whole free portion is valvate and sometimes circumscissile (see *Calyptrogyne, Calyptronoma*), the last a feature also of *Pritchardia* among the Corypheae.

The Androecium.—The palm stamen typically has a relatively slender, distinct filament and a moderately elongate latrorse anther. The primary vascular supply consists of one or two traces, but several bundles may be present in larger, more specialized filaments. Expansion of filaments and increase in number of traces per stamen appear to be characteristic of advanced groups. Filaments are sometimes fused into a thick-walled cup as in *Chamaerops, Eremospatha, Plectocomiopsis,* and may be adnate to petals as in many Coryphoideae, some Areceae, and Geonomeae. When stamens are reduced in pistillate flowers (Fig. G.20), they may simply have abortive anthers or they may be reduced to filaments, to minute teeth, or to a cupule, some-

Table I.15. **REDUCTION AND ELABORATION IN THE ANDROECIUM**

	Stamens 3	Stamens more than 6
I CORYPHOIDEAE		
CORYPHEAE		
Chelyocarpus		+
Coccothrinax		+
Itaya		+
Thrinax		+
Zombia		+
BORASSEAE		
Borassodendron		+
Latania		+
Lodoicea		+
II CALAMOIDEAE		
Eugeissona		+
Raphia		+
III NYPOIDEAE		
Nypa	+	
IV CEROXYLOIDEAE		
CEROXYLEAE		
Ceroxylon		+
HYOPHORBEAE		
Synechanthus	+	
V ARECOIDEAE		
CARYOTEAE		
Arenga		+
Caryota		+
Wallichia	+	+
IRIARTEEAE		
Catoblastus		+
Iriartea		+
Socratea		+
Wettinia		+
ARECEAE		
Manicariinae		
Manicaria		+
Malortieinae		
Reinhardtia		+
Oraniinae		
Orania	+	+
Halmoorea		+
Euterpeinae		
Jessenia		+
Roystoneinae		
Roystonea		+
Archontophoenicinae		
Actinokentia		+
Archontophoenix		+
Chambeyronia		+
Hedyscepe		+
Kentiopsis		+
Mackeea		+
Cyrtostachydinae		
Cyrtostachys		+
Linospadicinae		
Calyptrocalyx		+
Howea		+

Table I.15. **CONTINUED**

	Stamens 3	Stamens more than 6
Laccospadix		+
Linospadix		+
Ptychospermatinae		
Balaka		+
Brassiophoenix		+
Carpentaria		+
Drymophloeus		+
Normanbya		+
Ptychococcus		+
Ptychosperma		+
Veitchia		+
Arecinae		
Areca	+	+
Gulubia		+
Loxococcus		+
Pinanga		+
Iguanurinae		
Actinorhytis		+
Cyphokentia		+
Heterospathe		+
Oncospermatinae		
Acanthophoenix		+
Deckenia		+
Nephrosperma		+
Oncosperma		+
Phoenicophorium		+
COCOEAE		
Beccariophoenicinae		
Beccariophoenix		+
Butiinae		
Allagoptera		+
Jubaea		+
Jubaeopsis		+
Parajubaea		+
Polyandrococos		+
Attaleinae		
Attalea		+
Orbignya		+
Bactridinae		
Bactris		+
Astrocaryum	+	
GEONOMEAE		
Asterogyne		+
Geonoma	+	
Welfia		+
VI PHYTELEPHANTOIDEAE		
Ammandra		+
Palandra		+
Phytelephas		+

times large and fibrous (*Orbignya,* Cocoeae), at the base of the ovary; sometimes staminodes fail to develop. In some Geonomeae (*Calyptrogyne, Calyptronoma,* see illustrations of genera), staminodes form a unique, distally expanded tube around the stigmas, which in *Calyptrogyne* serves as food for the bat pollinators (Beach, pers. comm.).

The usual number of stamens among the palms is six in two whorls. Reduction to three opposite the sepals occurs in *Nypa*, where the filaments are fused to form a column (Uhl 1972a). Three stamens also characterize one species of *Synechanthus* (Ceroxyloideae), and some species of *Wallichia, Orania, Dypsis, Areca, Astrocaryum,* and *Geonoma* (Arecoideae). More than six stamens occur in some 70 genera, including members of all subfamilies except Nypoideae. Tribes where all taxa have only six stamens are very few: the unigeneric Phoeniceae, Cyclospatheae, and Podococceae, and all five genera of Hyophorbeae (Table I.15). Elsewhere in multistaminate taxa, the number of stamens ranges from seven or eight to mostly nine to many. The largest numbers of stamens within the palms are found in the Phytelephantoideae where samples of 849–954 have been counted in *Palandra,* 419–521 in *Ammandra,* and 120 to over 250 in *Phytelephas.*

Increase in stamen number appears to have occurred in different ways and perhaps in response to different factors in different groups of palms (Uhl and Moore 1980, Table I.15). Androecial development has been studied in all but two of the groups where many stamens occur (Uhl and Moore 1980). After petal inception the floral apex expands in diameter and/or height in a different way in each group to accommodate the larger number of stamens. In Phytelephantoideae stamens arise centrifugally on a circular apex (Uhl and Moore 1977b). Elsewhere stamens develop in different arrangements in antesepalous and antepetalous positions. A larger number of stamens in *Thrinax, Coccothrinax,* and *Zombia* (Thrinacinae) seems associated with wind pollination, but the numerous stamens in *Chelyocarpus* and *Itaya* of the same subtribe must be explained differently. Structurally, androecia of these two palms are similar, with the stamens arranged in an irregular ring that has a larger number of stamens in wider antepetalous positions. In Borasseae, Caryoteae, and Areceae, antesepalous whorls always consist of three stamens, but more stamens develop in wider antepetalous positions. *Eugeissona* (Calameae) has a similar pattern except that the last formed stamens develop in a centrifugal position. Floral apices may also expand in height with stamens in alternating whorls that have one stamen each above each sepal and several above each petal. The only polyandric ceroxyloid genus, *Ceroxylon,* has large primary primordia on which two to three

stamens develop opposite each petal; in species with more than 12 stamens, two to three also develop opposite each sepal. Iriarteeae are characterized by distinctive truncate primordia bearing up to three or more stamens opposite each sepal and petal. Stamens arise in antesepalous and antepetalous arcs of about seven stamens each, on a flat trilobed apex in multistaminate Geonomeae.

All multistaminate taxa except phytelephantoid genera exhibit an underlying trimery. The pattern in Coryphoideae is irregular but involves increase in stamen number in antepetalous positions. As noted above, developmental patterns in Ceroxyloideae and Phytelephantoideae are distinctive. The different patterns of apical expansion and stamen arrangement indicate that polyandry has arisen separately in several tribes, including the Iriarteeae, Geonomeae, and Areceae of Arecoideae. Multistaminate Cocoeae are yet to be studied developmentally. In the development of multistaminate androecia, the mode of the apical expansion and the resulting stamen patterns appears to conform to pressures exerted by bracts and perianth segments. Thus, it seems reasonable to suggest that specialization of the inflorescence bracts and perianth occurred before the advent of multistaminy in the palms as a whole. The presence of a trimerous perianth and gynoecium in the multistaminate taxa (except in Phytelephantoideae) supports this conclusion.

Pollen Morphology. — There is great variation in pollen morphology within the family as demonstrated by Thanikaimoni (1971) and Sowunmi (1972) in their two major surveys of pollen which relied almost exclusively on light microscopy (Tables I.16). I. K. Ferguson and associated workers at Kew have extended these observations by use of scanning and transmission electron microscopy. It is too early to report on all aspects of the Kew palm pollen project, but some results already have implications for the identification of palm pollen, in particular fossil grains. Genera previously thought to show relatively little variation have been shown to be much more diverse, e.g. *Pinanga* (Ferguson et al. 1983, Fig. I.9B–G) and *Daemonorops* (Ferguson et al. unpublished), and even grains superficially very similar with light or scanning electron microscopy show distinctive wall stratification under the transmission electron microscope (Ferguson 1986). Most remarkable has been the discovery of extraordinary parallels in unusual pollen structure in quite unrelated genera (Ferguson in press); for example, pollen of *Arenga borneensis* (Arecoideae: Caryoteae) resembles that of species of the closely related genus *Caryota* but it also resembles species of *Iriartea* and *Dictyocaryum* (Arecoideae: Iriarteeae). Some species of *Pinanga* (Arecoideae: Areceae), *Korthalsia* (Calamoideae: Calameae) and *Daemonorops* (Calamoideae: Calameae) have grains which can be separated from those of *Arenga borneensis* only with careful electron microscope work. Many other examples of convergence are found in pollen form. The most widespread aperture type, monosulcate (e.g. Figs. I.7A, I.8D, G), occurs in all subfamilies except Nypoideae, which has meridionosulcate grains (Fig. I.7G). This latter aperture type is also present in some Borasseae (Coryphoideae), in some Calamoideae, and in the tribe Areceae (Arecoideae) (Fig. 1.9E). Disulcate (Fig. I.7D, E), trichotomosulcate (Fig. I.7K), and tetrachotomosulcate apertures occur scattered through the family. Monoporate grains are present in some Calamoideae (Fig. I.7C), in some Ceroxyleae (Ceroxyloideae) (Fig. I.7), rarely in Areceae (Arecoideae), in *Borassodendron* (Coryphoideae: Borasseae) (Fig. I.7B), and in *Ammandra*

(Phytelephantoideae). Diporate grains occur very rarely in the Calamoideae (Fig. I.8C) and triporate grains are known only in *Sclerosperma* and *Areca klingkangensis* (Arecoideae: Areceae, Fig. I.7K). Pontoperculate grains occur in two, quite unrelated genera, *Chamaerops* and *Iriartella* (Fig. I.8F); the significance of the aperture membrane is not understood. The pollen exine is tectate and the ornamentation can be very varied indeed, though the most frequent and perhaps least specialized type is finely reticulate (e.g. Fig. I.7). Most members of the Corypheae have elliptic monosulcate grains with finely reticulate exines (Fig. I.7). Greater diversity in exine sculpturing is found in certain calamoid genera (e.g. *Korthalsia* (Fig. I.7C) and *Daemonorops*), and arecoid genera (e.g. *Nenga* and the quite extraordinarily varied *Pinanga* (Fig. I.9B–G)). The significance of ornamentation is not understood, but there are some indications of a correlation between diversity of ornamentation within a genus, and the presence of echinate grains (e.g. Figs. I.7G, J, I.8B, E, H, I.9B) with beetle pollination, but there are many exceptions to this generalization. As the pollen project at

→

Fig. I.7.—**Pollen Grains.** A. *Licuala peltata* (*Kerr 1669*), monosulcate grain with coarsely pitted tectate exine. ×ca. 2050. B. *Borassodendron machadonis* (*Nur s.n.*), monoporate grain with reticulate tectate exine. ×ca. 1080. C. *Korthalsia robusta* (*Curran 4185*), monoporate grain with intectate exine bearing large processes. ×ca. 1750. D. *Salacca secunda* (*Prain 391*), disulcate grain with ± smooth tectate exine, perforations very sparse. ×ca. 2850. E. *Calamus javensis* (*Kunstler 6312*), disulcate grain with angulate tectate exine. ×ca. 1650. F. *Mauritiella pacifica* (*Dransfield et al. 4866*), monosulcate grain, exine intectate bearing spinules and deep-seated spines. ×ca. 1650. G. *Nypa fruticans* (*Kerr 6761*), meridionosulcate grain, exine tectate, spiny, finely reticulate between the spines. ×ca. 1360. H. *Louvelia albicans* (*Perrier de la Bâthie 11939*), monoporate grain with reticulate, tectate exine. ×ca. 2550. I. *Wettinia cladospadix* (*Moore and Dransfield 10231*), monosulcate grain with intectate exine bearing spines and nano-pila. ×ca. 2300. J. *Pinanga adangensis* (*Ridley 15885*), trichotomosulcate grain, exine intectate bearing gemmate processes. ×ca. 1800. K. *Areca klingkangensis* (*Dransfield 6103*), triporate grain with punctate tectate exine. ×ca. 2000. L. *Areca chaiana* (*Chai S. 33986*), monosulcate grain with extended sulcus, exine tectate, finely reticulate. ×ca. 1800. Plate courtesy of I. K. Ferguson and M. Harley, Royal Botanic Gardens, Kew.

Fig. I.8.—**Pollen Grains** cont. A. *Hyphaene coriacea* (*Dransfield 4804*), monosulcate grain with verrucate tectate exine, finely reticulate between the warts. ×ca. 2650. B. *Salacca affinis* (*Griffith 6429*), meridionosulcate grain with finely perforate tectate exine bearing supratectal spines. ×ca. 4150. C. *Daemonorops sparsiflora* (*Tiggi S. 3319*) diporate grain with smooth, sparsely perforate tectate exine. ×ca. 2500. D. *Chamaedorea tenella* (*BH69-634*), monosulcate grain with perforate tectate exine. ×ca. 3500. E. *Wallichia densiflora* (*Hooker and Thomson s.n.*), monosulcate grain with intectate exine bearing coarse spines. ×ca. 3800. F. *Iriartella setigera* (*Moore et al. 9501*), pontoperculate grain with finely reticulate exine. ×ca. 4500. G. *Iriartea* sp. (*Moore et al. 10185*), monosulcate grain with intectate exine bearing clavate processes. ×ca. 3000. H. *Catoblastus* sp. (*Steyermark 106837*), monosulcate grain with intectate exine bearing spines, scabrate between the spines. ×ca. 3500. Plate courtesy of I. K. Ferguson and M. Harley, Royal Botanic Gardens, Kew.

Fig. I.9.—**Pollen Grains** cont. A. *Gronophyllum* sp. (*de Vogel 4305*), monosulcate grain with very coarsely reticulate tectate exine. ×ca. 2350. B. *Pinanga cleistantha* (*Dransfield 5179*), monosulcate grain with tectate exine bearing broad-based spines, tectum perforate between the spines. ×ca. 1850. C. *Pinanga maculata* (*Moore and Langlois 7365*), monosulcate grain with coarsely reticulate, tectate exine. ×ca. 2350. D. *Pinanga aristata* (*Dransfield 5341*), monosulcate grain, exine intectate with urnlike structures and sexinous granules. ×ca. 2350. E. *Pinanga celebica* (*Musser 1243*), meridionosulcate grain, exine tectate, coarsely reticulate. ×ca. 2000. F. *Pinanga gracilis* (*Gamble 7881*), monosulcate grain, exine tectate, reticulate, with each lumen surrounded by a separate wall. ×ca. 1850. G. *Pinanga malaiana* (*Furtado 7352*), trichotomosulcate grain with coarsely reticulate tectate exine. ×ca. 2000. H. *Deckenia nobilis* (*Dransfield 6236*), monosulcate grain, exine intectate, clavate with some clavae fused. ×ca. 3000. Plate courtesy I. K. Ferguson and M. Harley, Royal Botanic Garden, Kew.

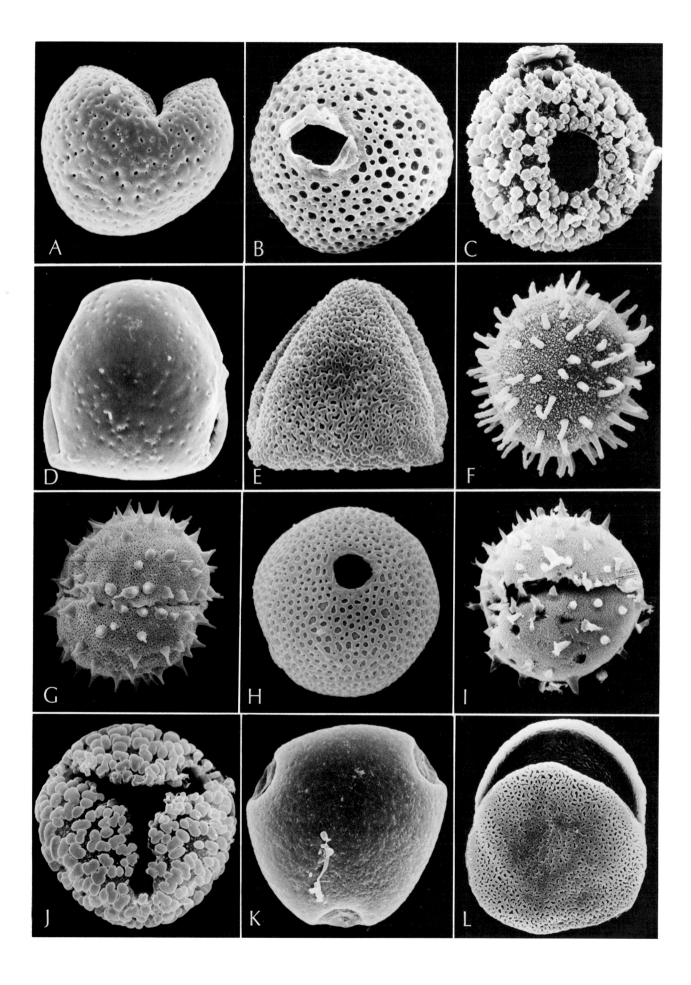

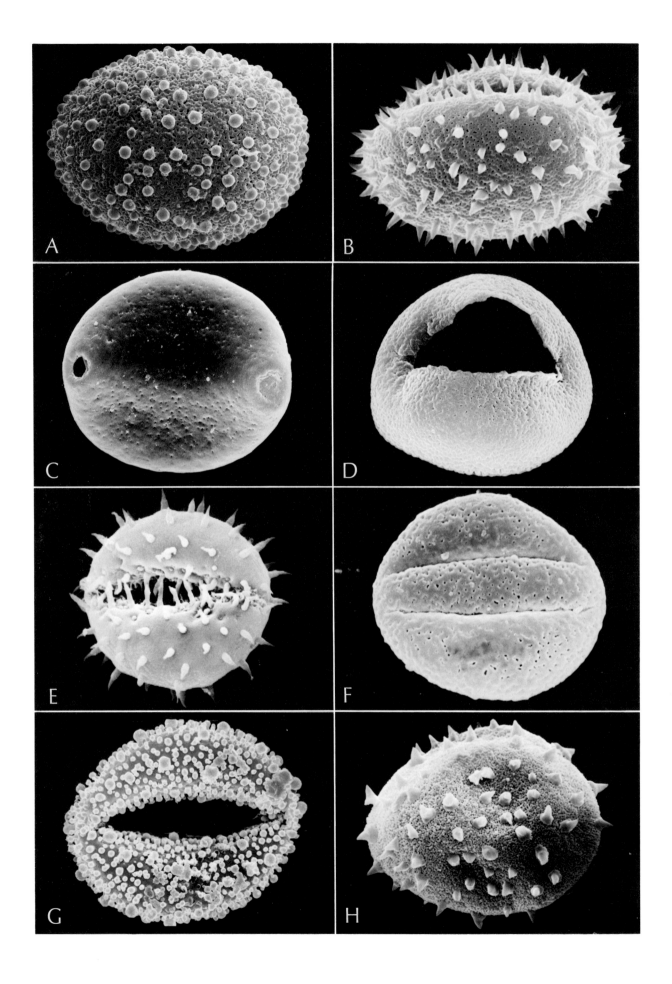

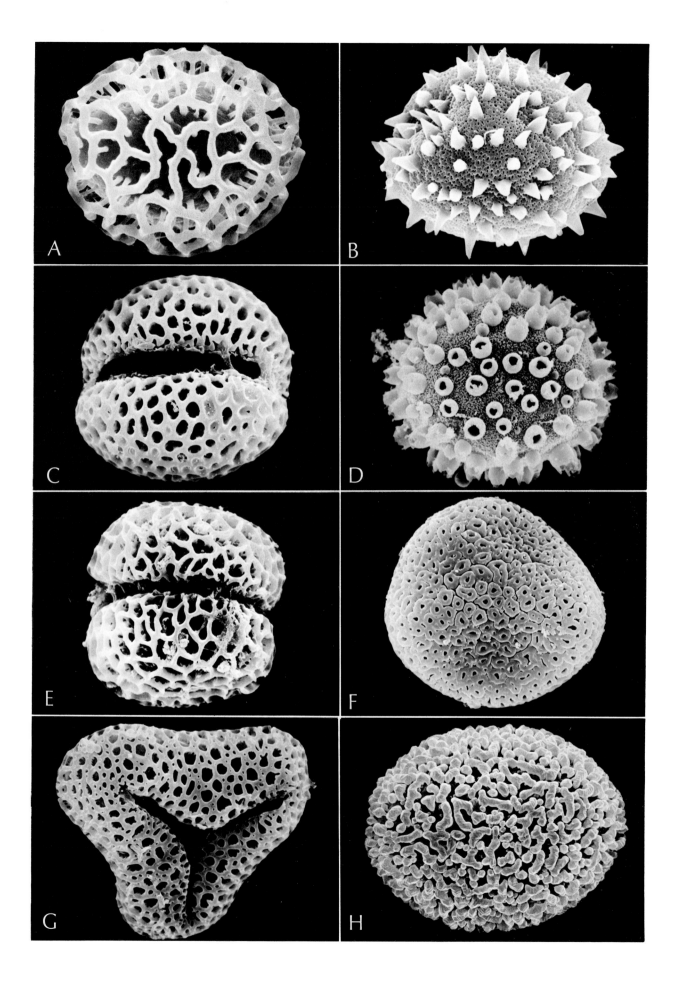

Table I.16. **POLLEN APERTURES**

Group	Mono-sulcate	Trichoto-mosulcate	Meridiono-sulcate	Disulcate	Mono-	Di-	Triporate
I CORYPHOIDEAE							
CORYPHEAE	+	+ rare					
PHOENICEAE	+						
BORASSEAE	+		+ nearly		+		
II CALAMOIDEAE	+		+	+	+	+	
III NYPOIDEAE			+				
IV CEROXYLOIDEAE							
CYCLOSPATHEAE	+	+					
CEROXYLEAE	+				+		
HYOPHORBEAE	+						
V ARECOIDEAE							
CARYOTEAE	+	+ rare					
IRIARTEEAE	+						
PODOCOCCEAE	+						
ARECEAE	+	+	+		+		+
COCOEAE	+	+					
GEONOMEAE	+	+ rare					
VI PHYTELEPHANTOIDAE	+	+ rare			+		

Kew progresses, we may expect an increasingly large data base from which to draw generalizations. The need for more pollination studies is also indicated.

Pollen is described for each genus in the taxonomic section of this book. The descriptions follow Thanikaimoni (1971) but take into account recent studies at Kew; these include descriptions of pollen of some new or obscure genera published here for the first time. For ease of citation "elliptic or circular" refers to the shape of the grain in polar view.

Gynoecium.—Trimery in the gynoecium is basic, as it is also elsewhere in the flower, but there are

Table I.17. **EXCEPTIONS TO TRIMERY IN THE GYNOECIUM**

Carpels	1	2	4–10
I CORYPHOIDEAE			
CORYPHEAE			
Chelyocarpus		+	+
Coccothrinax	+		
Itaya	+		
Schippia	+		
Thrinax	+		
Zombia	+		
V ARECOIDEAE			
COCOEAE			
Attalea			+
Orbignya			+
Scheelea			+
VI PHYTELEPHANTOIDEAE			
Ammandra			+
Palandra			+
Phytelephas			+

exceptions (Table I.17). Among the 16 genera of apocarpous palms (Table I.18), five genera, each specialized in some way, develop only a single carpel. Among the 15 subtribes of the tribe Areceae, all except five triovulate genera in four subtribes exhibit pseudomonomery (where only one carpel develops completely and bears a fertile ovule, but parts of two other carpels are present). More than three carpels occur in only seven genera: *Chely-*

Table I.18. **DISTRIBUTION OF APOCARPY (NUMBER OF CARPELS IN PARENS)**

I CORYPHOIDEAE	
CORYPHEAE	
Thrinacinae (all)	
Trithrinax (3)	
Chelyocarpus (2, 3, 4)	
Cryosophila (3)	
Itaya (1)	
Schippia (1)	
Thrinax (1)	
Coccothrinax (1)	
Zombia (1)	
Trachycarpus (3)	
Rhapidophyllum (3)	
Chamaerops (3)	
Maxburretia (3)	
Guihaia (3)	
Rhapis (3)	
PHOENICEAE	
Phoenix (3)	
III NYPOIDEAE	
Nypa (3)	

Table I.19. **DISTRIBUTION OF OVULE TYPES**

	Anatropous	Hemianatropous	Campylotropous	Orthotropous
I CORYPHOIDEAE				
CORYPHEAE	+	+	+	+?
PHOENICEAE	+			
BORASSEAE				+
II CALAMOIDEAE	+			
III NYPOIDEAE	+			
IV CEROXYLOIDEAE				
CYCLOSPATHEAE			+	
CEROXYLEAE		+		
HYOPHORBEAE			+	
V ARECOIDEAE				
CARYOTEAE		+		
IRIARTEEAE	+			+
PODOCOCCEAE		+		
ARECEAE		+	+	
COCOEAE	+	+		+
GEONOMEAE	+			
VI PHYTELEPHANTOIDAE			+	

ocarpus (Coryphoideae), *Orbignya, Attalea, Scheelea* (Arecoideae: Cocoeae), and all three genera of Phytelephantoideae.

The least specialized carpel among the apocarpous coryphoid (Thrinicinae) and Phoeniceae palms is comparable to that considered primitive in dicotyledons in its follicular shape, conduplicate nature, open ventral suture, and to a large extent in its vascular supply (Uhl and Moore 1971). The highly vascularized carpel of *Nypa*, however, with its conduplicate margins, cupular shape, two-crested distal opening, diffuse internal stigmatic surfaces and laminar to submarginal placentation, may represent a unique type of carpel among the angiosperms (Uhl 1972a). Specialization of the carpel includes modifications of the base or stalk, of the ovarian part, and of the style and stigma (Uhl and Moore 1971). Carpels may have short stalks with a basal nectary between them (*Nannorrhops*). In the ovarian region the locule varies in position from median (Corypheae, Caryoteae), to basal (Borasseae, Cocoeae), and distal (Phytelephantoideae). Increase in thickness of the ovarian wall is correlated with different morphological and anatomical specializations in different groups, e.g. scales in Calamoideae, raphides but few fibers in Ceroxyloideae, and sclerenchyma and other idioblasts in various patterns in Arecoideae (see Uhl and Moore 1973). Differentiation of stylar parts of carpels and the concomitant development of various protective mechanisms has occurred in many groups (Uhl and Moore 1971). In the Corypheae styles are short and tapering (*Trachy-*

carpus), tubular (*Thrinax*), abaxially expanded (*Rhapis*), and elongate (*Sabal*). Stylar regions are extremely wide in Borasseae and Caryoteae, moderate in size in Ceroxyloideae, and either long and wide (*Socratea*) or more slender and elongate (*Wettinia*) in Iriarteeae. The most expanded stylar areas are found in *Nypa* and in Cocoeae, where the basal ovarian portion represents only about $\frac{1}{16}$ the carpel length at anthesis (Attaleinae). The most elongate styles characterize Geonomeae and Phytelephantoideae. Stigmas also vary in form from short, tapering recurved ones (*Trithrinax*), to bilabiate and funnel-shaped (*Thrinax, Nypa*), to sessile (*Sabal*), relatively undeveloped (Borasseae, Caryoteae), large and fibrous (some Cocoeae), and elongate (Phytelephantoideae).

Ovule.—Anatropous, hemianatropus, campylotropous, and orthotropous ovules occur in palms (Fig. G.20, Table I.19). All of these forms are found in the unspecialized Corypheae. In Coryphoideae and in the Cocoeae, anatropous ovules characterize taxa less specialized in other ways suggesting, as might be expected, that anatropous ovules are primitive within the family. Orthotropy occurs within Borasseae, and Cocoeae, and hemianatropy and campylotropy within the Ceroxyloideae and various Arecoideae. The ovule also varies in its position within the locule, in the presence or absence of an aril, in the size and fusion of the two integuments, and in nucellar structure and vascular supply. Since these aspects are not yet known for all genera, a survey is in progress at Cornell University.

Table I.20. **GERMINATION**

Type	Remote-tubular	Remote-ligular	Adjacent
I CORYPHOIDEAE			
CORYPHEAE	+	+	
PHOENICEAE	+		
BORASSEAE	+		
II CALAMOIDEAE		+	+
III NYPOIDEAE			+
IV CEROXYLOIDEAE			
CYCLOSPATHEAE	+		
CEROXYLEAE			+
HYOPHORBEAE			+
V ARECOIDEAE			
CARYOTEAE	+		
IRIARTEEAE			+
PODOCOCCEAE			+
ARECEAE	+ (rare)		+
COCOEAE	+		+
GEONOMEAE			+
VI PHYTELEPHANTOIDAE		+	

THE FRUIT

The most common palm fruit has a fleshy wall and one seed, or much less frequently two to ten seeds. Size varies from fruits about 4.5 mm in diameter in species of *Geonoma* to very large as in *Lodoicea*, where they may be 50 cm long and weigh 18 kg. Although most fruits are smooth, scales cover those of all Calamoideae, hairs appear on those of *Rhapidophyllum* and *Wettinia*, prickles are present on the fruits of some species of *Astrocaryum* and *Bactris*, while warty processes that arise by cracking of the pericarp (Dransfield 1970) characterize fruits of one species of *Chelyocarpus*, and also of *Itaya*, *Johannesteijsmannia*, a few species of *Licuala*, and all but one species of *Pholidocarpus* (Corypheae). *Manicaria, Pelagodoxa, Sommieria* (Areceae), and all three genera of Phytelephantoideae also have warty fruits. Crystals, fibers, fiber-sclereids, sclerenchyma, and tannin are common constituents of the mesocarp, presumably serve a protective function, and may be diagnostic (Essig 1975a, b, 1977b; Essig and Young 1979). Fruits of *Cocos* (Cocoeae) and *Nypa* (Nypoideae) have heavily fibrous walls and are adapted for distribution by water. *Cocos* is usually a strand plant in the Pacific and *Nypa* is a mangrove palm.

A few other genera have exceptional fruits—the Hyphaeneinae have fruits with a rather dry mesocarp; *Lodoicea* has a very large fruit with a heavily fibrous mesocarp which seems to allow it to drop and bounce unharmed from the large rocks so abundant in its habitat; fruits of the Phytelephantoideae have a fibrous mesocarp that eventually disintegrates to free the seeds. Fruits of some palms persist on the tree a long time; on one tree of *Palandra*, 23 fruits ranged from young stages with gelatinous endosperm in the seeds to those which had so disintegrated as to release the seeds (Moore unpublished). An unusual specialization occurs in *Lytocaryum* where fruits have a thin mesocarp that splits into three valves to expose the endocarp, and in some species of *Astrocaryum* and *Socratea* in which the mesocarp splits irregularly at the apex and recurves to expose its colored or white flesh.

The endocarp of primitive palms is not specialized, but a very thick endocarp is developed in the Borasseae, in *Eugeissona* (Calamoideae), *Nypa* (Nypoideae), *Ptychococcus* and the Cocoeae (Arecoideae), and in the Phytelephantoideae. Three types of endocarp have been described (Murray 1973): the coryphoid type differentiates from the inner part of the fruit wall; the chamaedoreoid type forms solely from the locular epidermis; and the cocoid-arecoid type develops from the locular epidermis, bundle sheaths, and intervening parenchyma. Different developmental patterns, described as continuous, discontinuous, and basipetal are correlated with the endocarp types. Recent studies by Essig (1977b) and Essig and Young (1979) confirm the cocoid-arecoid type in the Ptychospermatinae and Arecinae (Arecoideae).

Several other different forms of endocarp occur

in the family. *Eugeissona* is unusual in that two "endocarp" layers are developed, a hard fibrous layer presumably representing the vascularized central part of the carpel is the "false" endocarp, while the inner layer of the pericarp becomes meristematic later to cut off cells in regular files (Dransfield 1970) that form the "true" endocarp. The "false" endocarp is functional and the "true" endocarp disintegrates as the seed enlarges. In a few palms, pyrenes, hard seedlike bodies, are formed when an endocarp develops separately in the wall of each carpel of a syncarpous ovary (see genera of Lataniinae). The pyrene forms a hard, sometimes sculptured outer layer around each seed; in *Latania* the sculpturing of pyrenes is diagnostic. Characteristic features of the heavy endocarps of Cocoeae are the "pores," that are thinner portions in the endocarp. Usually there are three of these but sometimes (*Attalea, Orbignya, Scheelea*) more, with the embryo or embryos opposite them. When only one embryo develops its pore is usually larger than the others. Another specialization is found in the brittle, sometimes highly sculptured endocarps in the Iguanurinae and Oncospermatinae (Areceae) where an operculum (a thin cap) develops opposite the embryo.

THE SEED

The usually ovoid, ellipsoidal, or globose seed, like the fruit, occurs in a wide range of sizes. It is always provided with abundant nuclear endosperm that is most often homogeneous but may be ruminate (Fig. G.23) even in species of the same genus. In a few genera (e.g. *Cocos*) it is hollow. The seed coat is heavily vascularized in Iriarteeae, in some Areceae, and in the Cocoeae, and a sarcotesta, a fleshy outer seed coat (Fig. G.22), is well developed in many Calamoideae. Sometimes the endosperm is invaginated by the seed coat in Corypheae and Phoeniceae, or it may be dissected (*Coccothrinax, Zombia*) or perforate (*Thrinax*). The seed of *Lodoicea,* the largest in the plant kingdom, is bilobed, while seeds of some genera in the Ptychospermatinae, some Borasseae, and the calamoid genus *Eugeissona* are angled or ridged and grooved (see generic drawings). Seeds of some genera of the Iguanurinae are elaborately sculptured in conformity with the endocarp.

The mostly small embryos are cylindrical to conical and late-maturing (Fig. G.23). All three types that are recognized for the monocotyledons by Boyd (1932) occur in the palms, and the embryo of *Nypa* is unusual (Murray 1971). The less specialized palms have remote-tubular germination (Fig. G.24). Remote-ligular germination is largely associated with some genera of advanced groups and appears to represent an adaptation to germination in a moist environment. Germinating palms, for the most part, require considerable moisture and protection from excessive light, and in this respect they are most vulnerable when the tropical forests are cut. Though palms are often left standing in open fields, reproduction is very rarely successful in such a habitat.

CHAPTER II

ANATOMY, DEVELOPMENT, AND CYTOLOGY

Studies of anatomy and development have been important in formulating a classification of palms. Palms are equally as variable in internal structure and developmental pathways as they are in external form. Investigation of their anatomy and development has clarified structure, provided new characters for evaluating relationships, and in some cases indicated how evolutionary changes may have come about. In this chapter we will consider the contributions and current status of anatomical studies of stems, roots, leaves, inflorescences, flowers, fruits, and seeds, as well as research on the conducting tissues, xylem and phloem, and on the chromosomes.

THE STEM-WOOD

Palm "wood" differs from the wood of dicotyledonous trees, which is largely secondary and formed from a ringlike meristem, the cambium. In palms, as in monocotyledons generally, such a cambium is lacking, and the wood consists of primary tissues, which originate from the growing tip. Once fully formed, the stems of many palms do not increase in diameter. Vascular bundles are variously scattered in a parenchymatous ground tissue with fibers of two kinds, vascular fibers, which are associated with the bundles of xylem and phloem, and nonvascular fibers, which occur singly or in bundles but not associated with the conducting tissues.

Most palm stems are divided into a narrow cortex and an inner zone containing scattered vascular bundles. Within the inner zone different palms exhibit different distributions of vascular strands and fibers (Parthasarathy and Klotz 1976). In the Coryphoideae, most climbing palms, and the coconut, the vascular bundles are rather evenly distributed giving a homogenous appearance to the center of the stem in cross-section; in some other palms as *Raphia* (Pyykko 1985) the peripheral vascular bundles are closer together and may be surrounded by more sclerenchyma in the form of larger fibrous bundle sheaths and separate fibrous bundles, forming a stem with a soft center and an extremely tough or hard periphery. The character of the ground tissues also affects the "wood"; the parenchyma cells may be sclerotic or lignified with few intercellular spaces or thin-walled with large intercellular spaces.

In some palms (e.g. *Metroxylon*) they contain abundant starch, which is often exploited by man. Thus, the distribution of the vascular bundles and of the vascular and nonvascular fibers, and the nature of the ground parenchyma give palm wood its character (Rich 1987). Palm stems do not produce lumber comparable to that of dicotyledonous trees, but they show great elasticity in tropical storms. As can be seen in our notes on uses, their toughness and flexibility make some of them valuable as construction materials and others useful for basketry.

THE ROOT

The primary root in palms is very small, developing and functioning for only a short time in the seedling. Subsequent roots are lateral, also described as secondary or adventitious, and usually borne near the base of the stem, sometimes forming large masses near ground level. In *Cryosophila* and some members of Iriarteeae lateral roots develop into spines. Large stilt roots characterize all genera of Iriarteeae and a few other genera (e.g. *Verschaffeltia, Campecarpus*).

The anatomy of palm roots conforms to the usual pattern of alternating bands of xylem and phloem with a central pith (Tomlinson 1961); larger roots may be polystelic. Mahabale and Udwadia (1960), in a study of 37 species, found that several characters—the nature of the cortex, monostely or polystely, lignification of parenchyma, occurrence of bundles in the pith, and distribution of sclerenchyma—may be characteristic and useful in identifications.

SILICA BODIES

The hardness of palm stems and leaves results partly from the presence of silica bodies in specialized cells called stegmata (Tomlinson 1961) which are associated with vascular or nonvascular fibers. The form of the silica bodies, either hat-shaped or spherical, is sometimes of diagnostic value.

XYLEM

The vascular bundles of palm stems and other organs have certain common characteristics. In each bundle there are one, two, or several large xylem elements or vessels (for discussion of terminology

A few subsequent studies have proved diagnostically useful. Read (1975) has found anatomical characters to distinguish all four species of *Thrinax*. The species of *Chelyocarpus* (Uhl 1972c) and of *Hyophorbe* (Uhl 1978c) can also be identified from transections of the lamina. All 17 genera and 32 species of palms in New Caledonia can be separated on anatomical characters of the lamina and midribs (Uhl and Martens in prep.). The study of the New Caledonian palms helped to identify species from both herbarium and fresh material and revealed some remarkable similarities in indigenous members of the Archontophoenicinae. As Tomlinson (1961) suggested, further studies of leaf anatomy of groups of species are needed and seem likely to contribute to both diagnostic and evolutionary studies.

Developmental studies have also been important in understanding the leaf. For a century and a half a debate has been in progress as to how the plications or folds developed in palm leaves. Some scholars thought the folds arose by splitting; others postulated differential growth. By a combination of studies of leaf development with the scanning electron microscope and ultra-thin sections, Kaplan and N. G. and R. E. Dengler established that differential growth is the mode in both a palmate leaf (*Rhapis excelsa*) and a pinnate leaf (*Chrysalidocarpus lutescens*). This study has had broad implications for developmental processes in biology as a whole (Kaplan et al. 1982a, b; Dengler et al. 1982).

INFLORESCENCE

The only anatomical study of a palm inflorescence is the extensive ciné analysis of the inflorescence of *Rhapis excelsa* by Tomlinson and Zimmermann (1968). This study established a direct vascular linkage between the inflorescence and the leaf that subtends it. Inflorescence anatomy resembles that of the stem, but at each branch a part of the vascular supply of the parent axis passes directly into the branch without any connections with the subtending bract. The vascular supply is reduced in the smaller distal branches.

Several developmental studies have provided significant information on inflorescence structure. In *Ptychosperma* (Uhl 1976a) and other genera including *Nannorrhops, Nypa, Caryota, Socratea, Wettinia, Hyophorbe, Welfia* (Uhl unpublished), the rachillae develop first as erect branches in the inflorescence bud; all other branches are intercalated later as the inflorescence enlarges within or is exserted

from its bracts. Study of the development of inflorescence adnation in rattan palms has led to the suggestion that adnation of the inflorescence to the leaf sheath is associated with the evolution of the rattan habit, the most extensive adnation occurring in the most specialized high-climbing species of *Calamus* and *Daemonorops* (Fisher and Dransfield 1977). Adnation between the inflorescence and the internode above occurs in *Korthalsia, Myrialepis, Plectocomia*, and *Plectocomiopsis*, and between the inflorescence and both the internode and the leaf sheath above in *Calamus, Calospatha, Ceratolobus*, and *Daemonorops*. The initially axillary inflorescence bud is displaced to the base of the next younger leaf early in development and later elongation of the internode further separates the inflorescence from its original node. Intrapetiolar inflorescence buds in *Salacca* develop in a chamber in the leaf base and are exserted through an abaxial slit in the leaf base (Fisher and Mogea 1980). Developmental study has also elucidated the structure of multiple inflorescences in palms (Fisher and Moore 1977; see Chapter I).

FLOWER CLUSTERS

The nature of the flower cluster is very important in characterizing the subfamilies of palms. The structure of many of the complex flower clusters can be unraveled only through developmental studies. Flower arrangements in all subfamilies have now been studied. In *Nannorrhops* (Coryphoideae) the flower cluster was found to be a reflexed cincinnus (Uhl 1969a). The dyad of Calamoideae has been shown to be a two-flowered apparently sympodial unit in *Eugeissona* (Uhl and Dransfield 1984) and *Metroxylon* (Uhl unpublished). Spirally arranged single flowers comprise the pistillate head and staminate spikes in Nypoideae. Developmental studies have revealed that the acervulus of several ceroxyloid genera is an adnate cincinnus (Uhl and Moore 1978). The triad of two staminate and a central pistillate flower, which characterizes all members of Arecoideae, was described as a monopodial unit (Bosch 1947), but clearly represents a three-flowered cincinnus on the basis of bract arrangement, anatomy, and development (Uhl 1966, 1976a; Uhl and Moore 1980). Finally, developmental analysis has shown that the flower clusters in Phytelephantoideae are exceptional in the family; they do indeed represent reduced monopodial branches in *Palandra* and *Phytelephas* (Uhl and Dransfield 1984). Similar studies of both staminate and pistillate inflorescences of the third genus of the subfamily, *Ammandra,* are needed.

FLOWERS

Both developmental and anatomical studies of flowers have been exceptionally useful in interpreting structure and function, and in indicating evolutionary patterns. The gynoecium of *Thrinax, Coccothrinax,* and *Zombia* has been identified by vasculature as a single carpel (Uhl and Moore 1971). Certain histological and vascular patterns distinguish genera or groups of related genera. Arrangements of sclerenchyma and tannins may be diagnostic. The presence of similar histology and vasculature in *Chelyocarpus, Cryosophila,* and *Itaya* (Uhl 1972b), of different patterns in the species of *Maxburretia* (Uhl 1978a), and of still other patterns in the ceroxyloid genera *Juania, Ravenea,* and *Ceroxylon* (Uhl 1969b) helped to relate and circumscribe these genera. All species of *Hyophorbe* have been studied anatomically and show rather remarkable variation in the vasculature and histology of perianth parts but consistency in gynoecial and ovule structure (Uhl 1978b).

Floral development has been most useful in interpreting the significance of more than six stamens (polyandry) which characterize 70 genera in all subfamilies except the Nypoideae where only three stamens, apparently representing a reduction from the usual six, are present. Developmental study has shown that the floral apex expands in different ways in different groups of palms (Uhl and Moore 1980, Uhl and Dransfield 1984) to accommodate more than six stamens. The Phytelephantoideae which are unusual in inflorescence and floral morphology, also differ here, stamen development in the subfamily being centrifugal rather than centripetal (Uhl and Moore 1977b). Developmental studies have further indicated that bracts and perianth parts inflict constraints on the apical expansion. The different patterns of apical expansion, characterizing different groups of palms, suggest that polyandry developed after the bracts and perianth parts had attained the form characteristic of each group. Polyandry appears to have arisen several times within the family. The many patterns of polyandry in palms are without parallels in other monocotyledons.

Variation in floral vasculature and histology may be correlated with environmental factors, activities of vectors during pollination, growth sequences, and other factors (Uhl and Moore 1977a). The vasculature of perianth parts varies from none to many bundles, and their histology from parenchymatous to extremely tanniniferous and fibrous, with fibers present in bundle sheaths or as separate strands. Raphides may also occur in specific locations, often in abundance. Stamens and staminodes have one to several vascular bundles and may be fibrous or histologically specialized.

A survey of the palm gynoecium (Uhl and Moore 1971) has shown two unspecialized carpel forms, a follicular form in Thrinacinae, and *Phoenix,* the apocarpous Coryphoideae, and a cupular form in *Nypa* (Uhl 1972a). The palm carpel varies in locular size and position and in shape and size of the style and stigma. Its vasculature usually consists of a dorsal and two ventral bundles, and one to several pairs of lateral bundles. In thick walled carpels accessory bundle systems may also be present. Evolutionary sequences in the gynoecium include reduction or increase in the number of carpels, increase in thickness and histological specialization of carpel walls, differing degrees of closure of ventral sutures and connation of carpels, reduction in locules of two carpels (pseudomonomery), and reduction in locular size often concomitant with increase in size of stylar regions. Gynoecial structure is important in delimiting groups of palms at all levels.

Ovules in palms vary in form, perhaps diagnostic at a generic level as noted above. Some are highly vascularized with numerous bundles entering the large outer integument. The inner integument is usually narrow, frequently two cells wide.

Flowers of many genera have yet to be studied anatomically. Such studies seem certain to have diagnostic, biological, and evolutionary value.

FRUITS

Two recent studies have indicated that the histology of the fruit wall is taxonomically useful. In Ptychospermatinae, Essig (1977b) found that pericarp characters separate small genera, subgenera, and groups of species. The pericarp of Arecinae also (Essig and Young 1979) has been studied and two groups recognized on the basis of the presence or absence of brachysclereids. The anatomical study of fruits is just beginning and promises to contribute significantly to the systematics of palms.

CHROMOSOMES

Chromosome numbers have been published for 111 of the 200 genera of palms (Table II.1). In 59 genera only one species has been studied, but about

Table II.1 **A SUMMARY OF GAMETIC CHROMOSOME NUMBERS IN PALMS**

CORYPHOIDEAE

CORYPHEAE

Thrinacinae

1. *Trithrinax*
   brasiliensis $n = 18$
2. *Chelyocarpus*
   ulei $n = 18$
3. *Cryosophila*
   nana $n = 18$
4. *Itaya*
5. *Schippia*
   concolor $n = 18$
6. *Thrinax*
   excelsa $n = 18$
   morrisii $n = 18$
   radiata $n = 18$
7. *Coccothrinax*
   acuminata $n = 18$
   argentea $n = 18$
   crinita $n = 18$
   inaguensis $n = 18$
   martii $n = 18$
   miraguama $n = 18$
8. *Zombia*
   antillarum $n = 18$
9. *Trachycarpus* $n = 18$
   fortunei $n = 18$
   martianus $n = 18$
10. *Rhapidophyllum*
    hystrix $n = 18$
11. *Chamaerops*
    humilis $n = 18$
12. *Maxburretia*
13. *Guihaia*
14. *Rhapis*
    excelsa $n = 18$
    humilis $n = 18, 36$

Livistoninae

15. *Livistona*
    australis $n = 18$
    chinensis $n = 18$
    rotundifolia $n = 18$
16. *Pholidocarpus*
17. *Johannesteijsmannia*
    altifrons $n = 16$
18. *Licuala*
    grandis $n = 8$
    paludosa $n = 8$
    peltata $n = 14$
    spinosa $n = 14$
19. *Pritchardiopsis*
20. *Pritchardia*
    pacifica $n = 18$
    thurstonii $n = 18$
21. *Colpothrinax*
22. *Acoelorraphe*
    wrightii $n = 18$

23. *Serenoa*
    repens $n = 18$
24. *Brahea*
    aculeata $n = 18$
    armata $n = 18$
25. *Copernicia*
    alba $n = 18$
    prunifera $n = 18$
    yarey $n = 18$
26. *Washingtonia*
    filifera $n = 18$
    robusta $n = 18$

Coryphinae

27. *Corypha*
    umbraculifera $n = 18$
    utan $n = 18$
28. *Nannorrhops*
    ritchiana $n = 18$
29. *Chuniophoenix*
30. *Kerriodoxa*

Sabalinae

31. *Sabal*
    jamaicensis $n = 18$
    mauritiiformis $n = 18$
    minor $n = 18$
    uresana $n = 18$

PHOENICEAE

32. *Phoenix*
    canariensis $n = 18$
    dactylifera $n = 18$
    hanceana $n = 18$
    paludosa $n = 18$
    reclinata $n = 18$
    roebelenii $n = 18$
    rupicola $n = 18$
    sylvestris $n = 18$

BORASSEAE

Lataniinae

33. *Borassodendron*
34. *Latania*
    loddigesii $n = 14$
    lontaroides $n = 14$
    verschaffeltii $n = 14$
35. *Borassus*
    flabellifer $n = 18$
36. *Lodoicea*
    maldivica $n = 17, 18$

Hyphaeninae

27. *Hyphaene*
    coriacea $n = 18$
    crinita $n = 18$
    dichotoma $n = 18$
    thebaica $n = 18$
38. *Medemia*
39. *Bismarckia*
    nobilis $n = 18$

Table II.1.   Continued

CALAMOIDEAE

CALAMEAE

Ancistrophyllinae
   40. *Laccosperma*
   41. *Eremospatha*
Eugeissoninae
   42. *Eugeissona*
Metroxylinae
   43. *Metroxylon*
       sagu $n = 16$
   44. *Korthalsia*
       laciniosa $n = 16$
       rostrata $n = 16$
Calamineae
   45. *Eleiodoxa*
   46. *Salacca*
       zalacca $n = 14$
   47. *Daemonorops*
       calicarpa $n = 14$
       cristata $n = 13$
       formicaria $n = 13$
       grandis $n = 14$
       longipes $n = 14$
   48. *Calamus*
       arborescens $n = 14$
       caryotoides $n = 13, 14$
       khasianus $n = 14$
       leptospadix $n = 14$
       muelleri $n = 13$
       rotang $n = 14$
       scipionum $n = 14$
   49. *Calospatha*
   50. *Pogonotium*
   51. *Ceratolobus*
       concolor $n = 13$
       glaucescens $n = 13$
       pseudoconcolor $n = 13$
   52. *Retispatha*
Plectocomiinae
   53. *Myrialepis*
   54. *Plectocomiopsis*
   55. *Plectocomia*
Pigafettinae
   56. *Pigafetta*
       filaris $n = 14$
Raphiinae
   57. *Raphia*
       farinifera $n = 16$
       longiflora $n = 14$
       taedigera $n = 14$
       vinifera $n = 14$
Oncocalaminae
   58. *Oncocalamus*
Lepidocaryeae
   59. *Mauritia*
       flexuosa $n = 18$

   60. *Mauritiella*
       aculeata $n = 18$
   61. *Lepidocaryum*
NYPOIDEAE
   62. *Nypa*
       fruticans $n = 17$

CEROXYLOIDEAE

CYCLOSPATHEAE
   63. *Pseudophoenix*
       sargentii $n = 17$
       vinifera $n = 17$

CEROXYLEAE
   64. *Ceroxylon*
       alpinum $n = 18$
       parvifrons $n = 18$
   65. *Oraniopsis*
   66. *Juania*
   67. *Louvelia*
   68. *Ravenea*

HYOPHORBEAE
   69. *Gaussia*
       attenuata $n = 14$
       maya $n = 14$
   70. *Hyophorbe*
       amaricaulis $n = 16$
       indica $n = 16$
       lagenicaulis $n = 16$
       verschaffeltii $n = 16$
   71. *Synechanthus*
       fibrosus $n = 16$
   72. *Chamaedorea*
       alternans $n = 16$
       aff. *arenbergiana* $n = 16$
       brachypoda $n = 13$
       cataractarum $n = 13, 16$
       elegans $n = 13$
       ernesti-augusti $n = 13$
       erumpens $n = 13$
       glaucifolia $n = 13$
       graminifolia $n = 13$
       lepidota $n = 16$
       microspadix $n = 13$
       oblongata $n = 13$
       pochutlensis $n = 13$
       pulchra $n = 13$
       pumila $n = 13$
       radicalis $n = 13$
       sartorii $n = 13$
       schiedeana $n = 13$
       seifrizii $n = 13$
       tenella $n = 13$
       aff. *tepejilote* $n = 13, 16$
       tepijilote $n = 13$
   73. *Wendlandiella*

Table II.1. Continued

ARECOIDEAE			
CARYOTEAE			
74. *Arenga*			
caudata	$n = 16, 32$		
engleri	$n = 16$		
obtusifolia	$n = 16$		
pinnata	$n = 16$		
aff. *porphyrocarpa*	$n = 16$		
tremula	$n = 16$		
wightii	$n = 16$		
75. *Caryota*			
cumingii	$n = 17$		
mitis	$n = 14, 16, 17$		
urens	$n = 16$		
76. *Wallichia*			
densiflora	$n = 16$		
disticha	$n = 16$		
IRIARTEEAE			
Iriarteinae			
77. *Dictyocaryum*			
78. *Iriartella*			
79. *Iriartea*			
corneto	$n = 16$		
80. *Socratea*			
Wettiniinae			
81. *Catoblastus*			
82. *Wettinia*			
PODOCOCCEAE			
83. *Podococcus*			
ARECEAE			
Oraniinae			
84. *Halmoorea*			
85. *Orania*			
palindan	$n = 16$		
Manicariinae			
86. *Manicaria*			
Leopoldiniinae			
87. *Leopoldinia*			
Malortieinae			
88. *Reinhardtia*			
Dypsidinae			
89. *Vonitra*			
90. *Chrysalidocarpus*			
lutescens	$n = 14$		
madagascariensis	$n = 14$		
91. *Neophloga*			
92. *Neodypsis*			
decaryi	$n = 16$		
93. *Phloga*			
94. *Dypsis*			

Euterpeinae	
95. *Euterpe*	
oleracea	$n = 18$
96. *Prestoea*	
decurrens	$n = 18$
longipetiolata	$n = 18$
97. *Neonicholsonia*	
watsonii	$n = 18$
98. *Oenocarpus*	
99. *Jessenia*	
100. *Hyospathe*	
Roystoneinae	
101. *Roystonea*	
altissima	$n = 18$
elata	$n = 18$
oleracea	$n = 18$
princeps	$n = 18$
regia	$n = 18, 19$
Archontophoenicinae	
102. *Archontophoenix*	
alexandrae	$n = 14, 16$
cunninghamiana	$n = 14$
103. *Chambeyronia*	
macrocarpa	$n = 16$
104. *Hedyscepe*	
105. *Rhopalostylis*	
106. *Kentiopsis*	
107. *Mackeea*	
108. *Actinokentia*	
Cyrtostachydinae	
109. *Cyrtostachys*	
renda	$n = 16$
Linospadicinae	
110. *Calyptrocalyx*	
spicatus	$n = 16$
sp.	$n = 16$
111. *Linospadix*	
112. *Laccospadix*	
australasica	$n = 16$
113. *Howea*	
belmoreana	$n = 18$
forsteriana	$n = 16$
Ptychospermatinae	
114. *Drymophloeus*	
beguinii	$n = 16$
samoensis	$n = 16$
115. *Carpentaria*	
acuminata	$n = 16$
116. *Veitchia*	
merrillii	$n = 16$
montgomeryana	$n = 16$
sessilifolia	$n = 16$
vitiensis	$n = 16$
117. *Balaka*	
118. *Normanbya*	
119. *Wodyetia*	
bifurcata	$n = 16$

Table II.1. Continued

120. *Ptychosperma*			152. *Basselinia*	
elegans	$n = 16$		153. *Cyphosperma*	
macarthurii	$n = 16$		*trichospadix*	$n = 16$
sanderianum	$n = 16$		154. *Veillonia*	
121. *Ptychococcus*			155. *Burretiokentia*	
lepidotus	$n = 16$		156. *Physokentia*	
122. *Brassiophoenix*			157. *Goniocladus*	
schumannii	$n = 16$		Oncospermatinae	
Arecinae			158. *Deckenia*	
123. *Loxococcus*			159. *Acanthophoenix*	
rupicola	$n = 16$		*rubra*	$n = 16, 18$
124. *Gronophyllum*			160. *Oncosperma*	
125. *Siphokentia*			*tigillarium*	$n = 16$
beguinii	$n = 16$		161. *Tectiphiala*	
126. *Hydriastele* sp.	$n = 16$		162. *Verschaffeltia*	
127. *Gulubia*			*splendida*	$n = 18$
costata	$n = 16$		163. *Roscheria*	
hombronii	$n = 16$		*melanochaetes*	$n = 16$
128. *Nenga*			164. *Phoenicophorium*	
129. *Pinanga*			*borsigianum*	$n = 16$
coronata	$n = 16$		165. *Nephrosperma*	
disticha	$n = 16$		*vanhoutteanum*	$n = 16$
patula	$n = 16$		Sclerospermatinae	
130. *Areca*			166. *Sclerosperma*	
catechu	$n = 16$		167. *Marojejya*	
triandra	$n = 16$		Areceae incertae sedis	
Iguanurinae			168. *Masoala*	
131. *Neoveitchia*			169. *Carpoxylon*	
132. *Pelagodoxa*				
henryana	$n = 16$		COCOEAE	
133. *Iguanura*			Beccariophoenicinae	
wallichiana	$n = 16$		170. *Beccariophoenix*	
134. *Brongniartikentia*			Butiinae	
135. *Lepidorrhachis*			171. *Butia*	
136. *Heterospathe*			*bonnetii*	$n = 16$
elata	$n = 16$		*capitata*	$n = 16$
humilis	$n = 16$		172. *Jubaea*	
137. *Sommieria*			*chilensis*	$n = 16$
affinis	$n = 17$		173. *Jubaeopsis*	
138. *Bentinckia*			*caffra*	$n = 80-100$
condapanna	$n = 16$		174. *Cocos*	
nicobarica	$n = 16$		*nucifera*	$n = 16$
139. *Clinosperma*			175. *Syagrus*	
140. *Cyphokentia*			*comosa*	$n = 16$
141. *Moratia*			*coronata*	$n = 16$
142. *Clinostigma*			*romanzoffiana*	$n = 16$
savoryanum	$n = 16, 18$		*schizophylla*	$n = 15, 16$
143. *Alsmithia*			*vagans*	$n = 15$
144. *Satakentia*			176. *Lytocaryum*	
145. *Rhopaloblaste*			*weddellianum*	$n = 16$
ceramica	$n = 16$		177. *Parajubaea*	
146. *Dictyosperma*			178. *Allagoptera*	
album	$n = 16$		*arenaria*	$n = 16$
147. *Actinorhytis*			179. *Polyandrococos*	
148. *Lavoixia*			*caudescens*	$n = 16$
149. *Alloschmidia*			Attaleinae	
150. *Cyphophoenix*			180. *Attalea*	
151. *Campecarpus*			*allenii*	$n = 16$

Table II.1. Continued

181. *Scheelea* sp.	$n = 16$	190. *Desmoncus*	
182. *Orbignya*		191. *Astrocaryum*	
cohune	$n = 16$	*mexicanum*	$n = 15$
lydiae	$n = 16$	GEONOMEAE	
183. *Maximiliana*		192. *Pholidostachys*	
Elaeidinae		193. *Welfia*	
184. *Barcella*		194. *Calyptronoma*	
185. *Elaeis*		*occidentalis*	$n = 14$
guineensis	$n = 16$	*rivalis*	$n = 14$
oleifera	$n = 16$	195. *Calyptrogyne*	
Bactridinae		196. *Asterogyne*	
186. *Acrocomia*		197. *Geonoma*	
aculeata	$n = 15$	*camana*	$n = 14$
spinosa	$n = 15$	*gracilis*	$n = 16$
187. *Gastrococos*		*vaga*	$n = 16$
crispa	$n = 15$	PHYTELEPHANTOIDEAE	
188. *Aiphanes*		198. *Palandra*	
caryotifolia	$n = 15, 16$	199. *Phytelephas*	
erosa	$n = 15, 18$	sp.	$n = 16$
189. *Bactris*		*macrocarpa*	$n = 18$
gasipaes	$n = 14, 15$	200. *Ammandra*	
caribaea	$n = 14$		
major	$n = 14$		

half of these genera are monotypic. Counts have been reported for nearly 250 species.

These reports of chromosome numbers must be regarded with some caution. On the one hand, problems of fixation and staining may result in cytological preparations that are not clear enough to yield accurate counts; on the other hand, the plants have not always been correctly identified. For these reasons reports (mostly older) of widely deviant (usually much lower) numbers and reports of different numbers in the same genus or species must be viewed with a certain skepticism. Where recent counts are available from well authenticated material, some earlier discrepant counts are not included in Table II.1. Further, since we here reduce some specific names to synonymy and classify a few species under other genera, it must be noted that some counts in the table were originally reported under other names. (See the discussion under each genus for complete listings of names and changes.) In Table II.1 and in the discussion that follows, all chromosome counts are cited as gametic (haploid) numbers regardless of whether the actual counts came from haploid or diploid cells.

With these caveats, all reliable chromosome counts in palms very clearly show a range that includes every gametic number from 13 to 18. Reports of lower chromosome numbers down to $n = 6$, mostly

from the older literature, have never been supported by more recent studies of the same genera and/or species, and we think that all of them probably resulted from mistakes of some kind, or perhaps from study of atypical plants such as monoploids. Until they are confirmed we believe that they cannot be considered valid.

The sequence of consecutive numbers, 13 to 18, is called a dysploid series. It results when chromosomes are broken during evolution and their broken ends are joined together in different ways (translocation). Over time, a series of translocations can transfer all of the vital parts of one original chromosome to other chromosomes, and the non-essential remainder then can be lost. This lowers the gametic number by one, and with enough time a series of consecutive dysploid numbers like that here can result. This scenario of evolutionary change in chromosomes is well known in certain other groups of organisms. Its description is based on classical studies of such groups as *Crepis* (Compositae), *Drosophila* (fruit fly), and mammals. Note that the most primitive or ancestral group is most likely to have the highest basic chromosome number in the dysploid series.

Most palms of the subfamily Coryphoideae, which we consider on other grounds to be the most primitive group, have $n = 18$. This conforms to the foregoing prediction that the highest basic chromosome number in a dysploid series is expected in the oldest group. Eighteen gametic chromosomes may well be the ancestral number in all palms. Rearrangements of chromosome parts and dysploid lowering of the gametic number, one step at a time, has often accompanied evolution in various lines leading to other groups of palms, culminating independently in $n = 13$ in both *Calamus* and *Chamaedorea.*

In other groups of plants gametic chromosome numbers in the range of 13 to 18 are commonly regarded as representing polyploids derived from ancestors with lower numbers. Indeed, Chennaveeraiah (1981) accepted some lower chromosome numbers as authentic, and he speculated that the ancestral chromosome number in palms might be 8 or 9 and that palms having the most common numbers, $n = 16$ and $n = 18$, represent tetraploid derivatives. However, no palm has been reported to have $n = 9$, and reports of $n = 8$ in several genera, as well as some other, mostly older counts of $n = 6$ to $n = 12$ have not been substantiated and we believe that they probably are not correct. There seems no reliable indication of chromosome numbers lower than $n = 13$ in palms. Therefore species of palms having $n = 13$ to $n = 18$ must be regarded as effectively diploid. Conceivably palms might have originated by polyploidy from some unknown, possibly pre-palm, ancestor with fewer chromosomes, but this is only speculation.

Thus we believe that the evidence available points to $n = 18$ as the most likely ancestral chromosome number in palms, with descending series of dysploid numbers as far as $n = 13$ derived from that, probably independently in several different evolutionary lines (Table II.1). As Table II.1 shows there is a remarkable congruence of lower chromosome numbers with higher levels of specialization of groups and genera. We know of only three probably authentic polyploid species in palms: $n = 32$ in *Arenga caudata* (Read 1966), a genus in which several other species have $n = 16$; $n = 36$ in *Rhapis humilis,*

where there are two other counts of $n = 18$ from the same species (Sarkar et al. 1978); and $n = 80-100$ in the monotypic South African *Jubaeopsis* (Robertson 1976).

Within most genera the same chromosome number has been reported in all species that have been studied. However, different numbers have been reported within about 15 genera, sometimes in the same species, usually by different authors. We think it likely that many of these discrepancies are due to errors in cytology or identification and that further study may show that in most genera all species have the same numbers. However, it also seems clear that real dysploid differences in chromosome number are present in several genera. For example, $n = 13$ has been reported in 19 species of *Chamaedorea* and $n = 16$ in 7 species (two of them the same). This is a very substantial difference, especially since intermediate numbers have not been reported, and should be an important consideration in classifying the species of *Chamaedorea.*

Published figures show relatively large chromosomes in some species and smaller ones in other species, sometimes in the same genus (e.g. *Thrinax,* Read 1964). In many species the individual chromosomes differ substantially among themselves in size, the longest often being three times or more as long as the shortest (Satô 1946, Read 1965b). Careful work may allow the comparison of the form of the chromosomes (karyotype) in different taxa for use in studying their relationships.

CHEMISTRY

Very few chemical analyses have been done in palms. These have provided results that are as yet mostly equivocal in taxonomic decisions (Glassman et al. 1981; Harborne et al. 1974; Williams et al. 1973, 1983). Preliminary studies in *Basselinia,* however, seem to support a new treatment of the genus (Knapp, pers. comm.; Moore and Uhl 1984). Much more work is needed before trends can be established.

CHAPTER III

THE ECOLOGY OF PALMS

Because the great morphological diversity of palms is paralleled by a wide range of ecological adaptations and behavior, it is difficult to make broad generalizations about their ecology. In this chapter we attempt to indicate the range and extent of palm ecological studies rather than to produce a complete review. Palms are attractive subjects for ecological research, but many aspects such as nutrient cycling, soil preferences, interspecific competition, and light requirements have yet to be investigated in detail.

PALM DOMINATED COMMUNITIES

Palms are conspicuous and important components of many types of vegetation in the tropics and subtropics. Several species occur in vast natural stands that completely dominate the vegetation. In the eastern tropics *Nypa fruticans* often forms dense colonies on estuarine muds to the exclusion of dicotyledonous mangrove species which mingle with *Nypa* in other situations. Pure stands of *Nypa* may extend for several hundred hectares, especially in parts of Borneo and eastern Sumatra. Such *Nypa* forests are of immense importance to humans, not only in terms of gaseous exchange and mud stabilization but also for the wealth of products *Nypa* can provide. No direct equivalent of this *Nypa* dominated, brackish water vegetation is found in the New World, although Richards (1952) considers *Manicaria* to be analogous to *Nypa*.

On the landward fringe of the mangrove in west Malesia, palms almost completely dominate another type of vegetation. This is the habitat of *Oncosperma tigillarium* and *Calamus erinaceus,* and in Borneo, *Daemonorops longispatha* (Dransfield 1984a). *Raphia taedigera* grows in great abundance on the landward fringe of the mangrove in the Amazon estuary (Bouillenne 1930), and other species of *Raphia* occupy a similar niche in West Africa (Ainslie 1926). In Costa Rica's Pacific and Caribbean coastal plains, *Raphia* forms nearly monospecific zones between marsh and higher diversity dicotyledonous swamp forests (Myers et al. 1985). Further inland *Mauritia flexuosa* occurs in vast numbers, covering the landscape in parts of the Amazon basin. *Copernicia alba* forms huge stands on areas subject to periodic flooding and drought in Paraguay and adjoining parts of Brazil, Argentina, and Bolivia; the

largest populations have been estimated to contain half a billion individuals (Markley 1955). *Copernicia prunifera* in northeastern Brazil occurs in almost equally great concentrations.

In Africa, *Hyphaene compressa* and more locally *Borassus aethiopum* grow in great abundance on riverine flats and coastal plains. The abundance of *Hyphaene* may be partly due to the activity of man, and when left undisturbed, *Hyphaene* woodland may in places revert to closed forest (Dransfield 1978b). In parts of the lowlands of New Guinea, *Metroxylon sagu* dominates freshwater swamplands; like *Hyphaene* the dominance of *Metroxylon* may be due in part to human activity. Elsewhere in Malesia, introduced *M. sagu* dominates some wetland habitats. In the uplands of Borneo, *Eugeissona utilis* grows locally in dense stands to the exclusion of other trees, and in the montane forests of the Caribbean, *Prestoea montana* produces a distinctive type of vegetation. These are a few examples of vegetation where palms are the most conspicuous plants. When the palms are useful, these natural or seminatural stands become immensely significant, either in the local economy or in international commerce.

PALMS WITHIN FOREST COMMUNITIES

Although some palms occur in large stands of single species, most occur as components of mixed tropical and subtropical forests. Of such vegetation, the lowland rain forests of the Sunda Shelf and New Guinea and of Central America and South America are the richest in palm species. The Choco region of Colombia and parts of the island of Borneo may be singled out as being extraordinarily rich in palms. In Sarawak, the Gunung Mulu National Park, a small area of lowland and montane tropical rain forest, a mere 52,864 hectares in extent, carries a palm flora of 111 species in 20 genera; however, nowhere within the park do palms dominate the vegetation (Dransfield 1984b).

Few studies have been made of the diversity of palms within forest communities. Kahn and Castro (1985) provide details of a palm-rich forest in central Amazonia. They recorded 32 species in 12 genera in the 1–2 hectares surveyed and show clear differences between the palm flora of waterlogged soils in seasonal swamps and of well-drained soils on hillslopes. Not only are there differences in the species but also there are physiognomic differences between the palm floras of the two soil types, with tall palms which reach the canopy being confined to the waterlogged soils. It would be of great interest to extend such a study to other types of vegetation and to other geographical areas. De Granville (1978) has discussed the architecture of palms and other monocotyledons in relation to the habitats they occupy in French Guiana.

PALMS OF UNUSUAL SOIL
TYPES AND HABITATS

Unusual soil types often carry distinctive palm floras. Ultrabasic rocks such as serpentine, with their soils rich in the heavy metals, manganese, chromium, iron and copper, usually have a restricted but peculiar palm flora. Thus, in Sabah and on the island of Palawan in the Philippines, ultrabasic soils support a curious assemblage of rattans (Dransfield 1984a) and, more rarely, species of *Pinanga* and *Areca* that are not found on the surrounding non-ultrabasic rocks. In New Caledonia, an island rich in ultrabasics, the palm flora of the serpentine soils is quite different from that of the non-ultrabasic soils. At least ten of the 32 indigenous species are confined to serpentine areas, while 14 are recorded only in non-ultrabasic areas; only three species are found on both rock types (Moore and Uhl 1984). The ecology of these palms has scarcely been investigated beyond the observation that they seem to be confined to soils rich in heavy metals.

Within the humid tropics of Southeast Asia and Malesia, palms are rather rare on limestone, but those which do occur there are often of considerable interest or peculiarity (e.g. *Maxburretia*). The New World has a great diversity of palms that occur on limestone, such as *Brahea, Gaussia,* and *Pseudophoenix,* and species of *Coccothrinax* and *Thrinax.* Drier climates seem to have a greater abundance of calcicolous palms.

Tropical rain forest developed on white sands in Borneo is usually very distinctive physiognomically. Known locally as "kerangas," this forest type occurs on extremely poor soils. Not obviously a prime habitat for palms, "kerangas" nevertheless carries a varied, peculiar, and important palm flora. Many of the palms are restricted to this type of vegetation or to the catena (a closely linked series) between "kerangas" and the neighbouring dipterocarp forests developed on richer soils. *Johannesteijsmannia alti-*

frons is found only in "kerangas" in Sarawak, yet the same species occurs in dipterocarp forest in Malaysia. *Areca insignis* var. *moorei, A. brachypoda, Calamus corrugatus, Licuala bidentata, L. orbicularis,* and *Pogonotium divaricatum* are further examples of palms confined to the "kerangas" habitat. One interesting aspect of "kerangas" is the varied nature of the palm flora from place to place (Dransfield 1982a). Elsewhere in Southeast Asia, white sands seem not to support such an unusual palm flora as in Borneo. Indeed, on white sands in Sumatra and Peninsular Malaysia, palms are very poorly represented.

Rheophytes, plants adapted to the flood zone of fast-flowing, rocky rivers (van Steenis 1981), usually possess narrow leaves or leaflets, presenting a restricted surface area, allowing them to withstand floods. Rheophytes have evolved in many flowering plant families, the few in palms (Dransfield 1978b, van Steenis 1981) include an unnamed species of *Hydriastele* in New Guinea and *Pinanga tenella* var. *tenella, P. tenella* var. *tenuissima, P. rivularis,* and *Areca rheophytica* in Borneo. In the New World, species of *Geonoma* (Dransfield 1978b) occasionally grow as rheophytes, but surely in such a palm rich area more palms may be adapted to this habitat.

MONTANE HABITATS

Tropical montane forests may support a rich, diverse assemblage of palms. In west Malesia (Whitmore 1975), a striking change in the vegetation usually occurs at about 1000 m in altitude, where Hill Dipterocarp Forests (tall forests dominated by dipterocarps) are replaced by Lower Montane Forests (usually shorter, more evenly crowned forest dominated by members of the Lauraceae and Fagaceae). This change occurs more or less at the altitude above which coconuts do not fruit, and the palm flora changes dramatically. Very few species of the lowland and hill dipterocarp forest occur in the montane forests and vice versa. *Plectocomia elongata,* a plant apparently adapted to seral (temporary) forest, is one of these. Above 1000 m the genus *Korthalsia* does not occur. *Johannesteijsmannia, Eugeissona, Plectocomiopsis, Myrialepis,* and many other genera are only very rarely found at higher elevations. Apparently no genus of palms is confined to the montane forest, but a rich assemblage of species of *Pinanga, Areca, Calamus, Daemonorops, Caryota, Livistona,* and others occurs there. The highest elevations recorded for palms in the Malesian region are on G. Kinabalu in Borneo, where *Pinanga cap-*

itata reaches about 2900 m and *Calamus gibbsianus* just over 3000 m.

South America has a greater diversity of palms at high elevations than Southeast Asia and Malesia. Two genera, *Dictyocaryum* and *Ceroxylon*, are confined to the montane forests of the Andes. Two other records for the family are attained by species of *Ceroxylon*. *Ceroxylon quindiuense* is the tallest palm, and *C. utile* occurs at the highest elevation of any palm, over 4000 m in Colombia (Dugand 1974). Many species of *Geonoma, Aiphanes, Prestoea, Euterpe, Chamaedorea, Socratea,* and *Catoblastus* also occur in the Andean forests. In contrast only one species of palm is found in montane forest in Africa, where *Phoenix reclinata* occurs up to 3000 m in altitude in Tanzania (Dransfield 1986).

GROWTH FORMS

The growth forms of palms are discussed in Chapter I and elsewhere by de Granville (1977), Dransfield (1978b), and Hallé et al. (1978). Some major growth forms have not evolved in the family. No parasitic palms are known, nor are there submerged aquatics or deciduous species, and perhaps no true epiphytes, although seedlings or even adults of some palms (e.g. oil palm) are sometimes found as chance-sown individuals in pockets of soil in the crowns of trees. There is also a report of an epiphytic *Chamaedorea* in Costa Rica (S. Knapp, pers. comm.).

Palm Growth Studies. — Growth of the cultivated African oil palm and the coconut has been studied in very great detail; there is an enormous literature pertaining to the agronomy of these important crops (see for example Hartley 1977, Johnson 1977). In contrast, studies of other palms, especially in their natural habitats, are just commencing. Manokaran studied the growth rate of economically important species of rattans (e.g. *Calamus caesius, C. manan, C. scipionum,* and *C. trachycoleus*) under different light and soil moisture regimes in trial plots in Peninsular Malaysia (see Manokaran 1984 for references). His work has indicated that seedlings of these species require light gaps if an aerial stem is to develop, and that rattan plantations will require management of the canopy to let in light. Waterhouse and Quinn (1978) studied the growth of stems of *Archontophoenix cunninghamiana* in the wild. From an analysis of internode thickening and elongation they suggested how patterns of growth were related to survival of individuals and maintenance of the population. Putz (1983) observed that the first stems produced by the seedlings of *Desmoncus isthmius*

are small in diameter and that clumps are built up by the production of aerial stems of successively larger diameter until an adult size is reached. This method of clumping is paralleled in a few species of *Calamus* and probably also in *Eremospatha* (Dransfield 1978b and pers. obs.). De Steven (1986) has found that *Oenocarpus mapora* seems favored in wind-thrown areas of forest on Barro Colorado island. De Steven and Putz (1985), in monitoring mortality rates in undergrowth palms on Barro Colorado Island, Panama, observed that some palms, perhaps because of their single terminal meristems are more susceptible to death from tree falls and herbivory than many dicotyledonous trees. Chazdon (1986) has studied the relationships of leaf size and dissection in three undergrowth palms, *Asterogyne martiana, Geonoma congesta,* and *G. cuneata* in Costa Rica, to aspects of the overall economy of the plant such as the photosynthetic capability, reproductive stress, and susceptibility to leaf damage. *Geonoma cuneata,* which reproduces at small sizes, has the lowest biomass costs of light interception, and can exploit the shadiest habitats. Hogan (1986) has found that *Scheelea* requires large gaps in forest canopy, but *Socratea* grows to maturity in small gaps or closed canopies. Rich (1986), studying growth rates of subcanopy tree palms in Costa Rica, found that increased canopy openness leads to faster growth rates and that faster growing species have structurally weaker stems. In a study of the mechanical architecture of arborescent palms, he further found that palm species differ in their capacity for sustained stem expansion. *Welfia, Prestoea,* and *Cryosophila* begin growth in height with a stem diameter sufficient for future support, but *Iriartea, Socratea,* and *Euterpe* have definite capacity to increase stem diameter by sustained cell expansion. Stem strength and stiffness increased in all six species during growth in height. He concluded that palms have a major capacity for secondary changes within their stems. Many of these studies are the first of their kind with palms.

The Effects of Palms on Soil and Other Plants. — The root systems of some palms have been analyzed in detail by de Granville (1974); in particular he discussed the importance of "breathing" roots to palms growing on waterlogged soils.

Furley (1975) has demonstrated the importance of *Orbignya cohune* in the development of the soil profile. The stems of this palm are initially geotropic and early development (establishment growth) of the stem occurs at depths of up to 1 m. Death of the palm eventually leaves a cavity in the soil which becomes filled in with soil and detritus. Over a large period of time a population of these palms may be responsible for considerable turnover of the soil. Hapaxanthic palms such as *Arenga westerhoutii* in Peninsular Malaysia have a more rapid life cycle, and may cause an even more significant turnover of soil.

Palm leaf litter itself can be an important factor in the ecology of some forest types. In Costa Rica the form of the crown of *Asterogyne martiana* is such that litter and rain falling from the forest canopy are funneled towards the center of the plant (Raich 1983). This undergrowth species may have increased competitiveness because of its enhanced capability to trap nutrients. Many other palms accumulate litter in their crowns; a few good examples are *Eugeissona minor* (Holbrook et al. 1985), all species of *Johannesteijsmannia, Pinanga ridleyana* (Dransfield, pers. obs.), and *Daemonorops verticillaris* (Rickson et al., pers. comm.—see below) and many more. Such nutrient trapping requires further study.

The productivity of palms contributes to forest growth in various ways. Anderson (1985) has measured above-ground dry matter production in *Orbignya phalerata* ("babassu") in Brazil. Productivity was astonishing and recycling contributed to soil fertility under the stands. De Steven and Putz (in press) monitored the leaf, flower, and fruit production of 13 species of palms for three years on Barro Colorado Island. Total leaf production varied little during the years even though a very dry period was included. The month of peak flowering and the month in which reproduction was initiated varied from year to year in different species. Fruiting, however, was generally more synchronized, and flowers produced at some times of the year did not develop into fruit. About 50 of the individuals monitored flowered every year.

In Peninsular Malaysia, *Eugeissona tristis* is locally abundant in hill dipterocarp forest, where its massive leaf litter and deep shade tend to prevent regeneration of dicotyledonous trees. Disturbance of such forest tends to encourage rhizomotous expansion of *E. tristis* with the effect that extensive, almost pure stands of the palm develop to the exclusion of commercially important timber trees. *Oncosperma horridum* also produces a dense leaf litter which prevents regeneration (House 1984).

Mycorrhizae.—Vesicular-arbuscular mycorrhizal associations have been demonstrated in a few palms (see Janos 1977). Their occurrence is likely to be widespread. Barry (1962) suggested that some of the difficulties experienced in raising seedlings of some palm species in nurseries outside the tropics may be due to the absence of particular mycorrhizae.

Palm Demography.—Tomlinson (1979) pointed out that palms are ideal subjects for demographic research, since they are easily recognized as being palms (though great difficulty may be experienced in providing specific names). This usually makes recognizing and charting the individuals of all ages of a given palm in one area much easier than for many dicotyledonous trees. It is also apparently much easier to estimate growth rates of palms than of other plants. The leaf scars are usually easily counted and observations over a relatively short period can indicate the size of the plastochron, the time interval between the production of successive leaves. This in turn can be extrapolated to give an estimate, crude, but probably not too inaccurate, of the age of the individual, given the number of leaves developing in the crown and the time required for establishment growth of the seedling (Corner 1966). Estimates of ages of palms made in this way have given some very surprising results. Kiew (1972) reported that individuals of the Malayan undergrowth palm, *Iguanura wallichiana,* 2 m tall, were approximately 100 years old. Bullock (1980) suggested that the undergrowth palm *Podococcus barteri* in Cameroon lives for 63–74 years. Sarukhán (1978) has estimated that *Astrocaryum mexicanum* can live to 70 years. The last example, being a moderately large palm, is less unexpected than the first two. Hnatiuk (1977), in a study of the population structure of *Livistona eastonii,* estimated that exceptionally tall individuals of this Australian species might be about 720 years old. Studies made by Savage and Ashton (1983) in the Seychelles indicated that *Lodoicea* may reach a maximum age of about 350 years, perhaps less than had been expected for this slow growing, massive species. As a final example of longevity van Valen (1975) suggested that *Prestoea montana* (as *Euterpe globosa*) may reach an age of 150 years. All the studies cited have attempted, to varying degrees, to analyze population structure and to investigate life expectancy and vulnerability of different age classes. The studies of Sarukhán (1978), Sarukhán et al. (1985) and Piñero et al. (1982, 1984, 1986), on the demography of *Astrocaryum mexicanum,* are the most detailed and extensive ecological studies on palms. This research is now considering the duration of individual leaves, as well as the regeneration of the tropical forest as a whole. The wide range of studies of different species indicates the suitability of palms as subjects for demographic research, but it is still too early to suggest major generalizations.

POLLINATION

Henderson (1986) has reviewed pollination in palms. Pollination studies in the family are in their infancy and it is only recently (Uhl and Moore 1977a) that the myth (Delpino 1870) that all palms are wind pollinated has been completed dispelled. On the contrary, it now seems reasonable to predict that most palms will be shown to be insect pollinated, or that both wind and insects are involved. True anemophily does indeed occur (e.g. in *Thrinax,* Read 1975) but even the date palm, *Phoenix dactylifera,* long considered as anemophilous, may be primarily insect pollinated. Production of large quantities of pollen is generally an indicator of wind-pollination, but at least in some palms, it seems to be an adaptation to predation by insects.

Beetle pollination has been observed in *Rhapidophyllum* (Shuey and Wunderlin 1977), *Hydriastele microspadix* (Essig 1973), *Pinanga coronata* (Dransfield and Saeruddin unpublished), *Salacca zalacca* (Mogea 1978), *Bactris gasipaes* and *B. porschiana* (Beach 1984), *B. guineensis* and *B. major* (Essig 1971a), *Cryosophila albida* (Henderson 1984), *Socratea exorrhiza* (Henderson 1985), *Orbignya* (Anderson et al. in press) and it is suggested by casual observations for many species of *Salacca, Daemonorops, Pinanga, Ceratolobus, Manicaria, Johannesteijsmannia,* and *Pogonotium* (Dransfield, pers. obs.).

The beetles involved in palm pollination are often weevils belonging to tribe Derelomini or nitidulids of the genus *Mystrops.* Many of the beetles seem confined to palms, thus implying coevolution (Henderson 1986). Reports by Hartley (1977) that *Elaeis guineensis* is anemophilous have been disproved by Syed (1979), who has shown that the oil palm is pollinated by at least twelve different insects in Cameroon, West Africa, including a weevil, *Elaeiodobius kamerunicus.* Introduction of this insect into oil palm plantations in Peninsular Malaysia has increased fruit set there (Ooi 1982). The thrips, *Thrips hawaiiensis,* had previously been the major pollinator in Malaysia, but hand pollination was necessary to obtain high yields. The similarity in the overall form of the rachillae in *Elaeis* and the quite unrelated *Salacca* and the similar position of

the inflorescences down among the protected leaf bases in both genera is noteworthy, especially as weevils are implicated as pollinators in both.

Nypa, at least in New Guinea, is pollinated by drosophilid flies (Essig 1973), and drosophilid flies have been observed visiting the flowers of *Nypa* in Sumatra (Dransfield unpublished). Syrphid flies are responsible for pollinating *Asterogyne martiana* (Schmid 1970), while bees have been shown to pollinate *Sabal palmetto* (Brown 1976), *Ptychosperma macarthurii* (Essig 1973), and *Iriartea gigantea* (Henderson 1985). Bees appear to be the most likely pollinators of many species of *Calamus, Areca, Actinorhytis,* and many other palms, though in some instances bees may in fact be pollen thieves. Ants may be responsible for pollinating *Iguanura* in Peninsular Malaysia (Kiew 1972). Most recently, bats have been established as pollinators of *Calyptrogyne* in Costa Rica (Beach, pers. comm.).

Some correlations between phenology and pollination syndromes can be suggested. Beetle pollination usually involves protogyny; anthesis occurs in the whole inflorescence over a relatively short period, and the inflorescence is commonly rather condensed or bears crowded flowers. Bee pollination, in contrast, is often associated with protandry; anthesis may occur over an extended period, and the inflorescence is often laxly branched or the flowers are rather distant.

It is probably too soon to make correlations between pollen structure and pollination syndromes; careful extended fieldwork is still required for many species. However, a few general trends do seem to be emerging. Diverse sculpturing of the pollen exine has been recorded in genera such as *Pinanga* and *Daemonorops* which we suggest are beetle pollinated, whereas closely related genera which are apparently bee pollinated have pollen with exine sculpturing that is more uniform and has low relief. *Iriartea,* shown by Henderson (1985) to be bee pollinated, has finely reticulate exine (Ferguson and Dransfield unpublished), whereas beetle-pollinated *Socratea* has spiny pollen grains. The significance of the extraordinary variation in exine ornamentation found among species of *Pinanga* (Ferguson et al. 1983) is not known, but casual observations suggest beetle pollination to be widespread in the genus.

DISPERSAL

Information concerning the methods of dispersal of palms is very scanty, and consists mostly of casual observations. The units of dispersal may be fruits, pyrenes (seed enclosed by endocarp), seeds, or parts of seeds. A few species have fruits dispersed by water; the best known examples are *Nypa fruticans* and the coconut (*Cocos nucifera*), which have very thick, fibrous mesocarps, apparently adapted for floating. We suspect that the very fibrous fruits of *Leopoldinia,* which grows beside black-water rivers in the Amazon basin, also are adapted for dispersal by water. Most palms seem to be dispersed in one way or another by animals, commonly through their digestive systems. All the climbing members of the Calamoideae and most of the non-climbing ones have either a fleshy mesocarp or a well developed sarcotesta surrounding the seed. Fruits of nearly all of the Coryphoideae, Ceroxyloideae, and Arecoideae, have fleshy mesocarps and brightly colored epicarps that are attractive to vertebrates.

Almost all palm fruits or seeds are edible and nutritious, and they form a major part of the diet of many animals. Civet cats in Java are known to feed on and defecate viable seeds of *Caryota maxima, Arenga pinnata,* and *Pinanga coronata* (Dransfield unpublished). Gibbons feed on *Arenga obtusifolia* (Whitten 1980). Hornbills in Malaya are known to ingest whole fruits of *Korthalsia* (Rubeli in Dransfield 1981a); they have also been observed in Borneo feeding on the fruit of *Caryota no* (Dransfield 1974). Ground squirrels, bats, and birds feed on the oil-rich mesocarp of *Raphia hookeri* in Africa (Profizi 1985). Coyotes eat fruits of *Washingtonia* (Henderson 1947) and passage through the gut of a coyote enhances germination (Cornett 1985a). Elephant dung in East Africa is frequently full of pyrenes of *Hyphaene* and *Borassus,* and, although it is not known whether germination is enhanced, clusters of seedlings suggest that, at least, it is not impaired. Agoutis feed on the seeds of *Socratea* (Yeaten 1979). Palm vultures eat the oily fruits of *Elaeis guineensis* and seem to be the most important dispersers of the seeds. These few examples indicate the range of palm fruits eaten by animals. Detailed studies of the fate of fruit are needed to indicate whether seed dispersal is affected or not. In many cases a fine balance exists between predation and dispersal. Scatter hoarding of palm fruits or seeds by animals may be very important in dispersal. The study of dispersal of *Welfia georgii* by Vandermeer et al. (1979) is exceptional in discussing the interplay of dispersal and predation and the demographic consequences. Seed predation has also been studied in detail in *Scheelea rostrata* by Janzen (1971).

Corky warted fruits are found in a few isolated and mostly quite unrelated genera; they are known in some species of *Chelyocarpus* and in *Licuala, Johannesteijsmannia,* and most species of *Pholidocarpus,* and in all species of *Manicaria, Pelagodoxa, Sommieria, Ammandra, Palandra,* and *Phytelephas.* The adaptive significance of the warts, if any, is not understood. The fruits appear dull brown and inconspicuous, with usually no indication of fruit ripeness. *A priori* it might be thought that such palms are unattractive to animals and that they are perhaps not animal dispersed. However, fruits of *Johannesteijsmannia* and *Pelagodoxa* are taken by squirrels and rats long before they are ripe; the warts seem to provide little protection against predation, and in the case of *Johannesteijsmannia,* the warts of the ripe fruit seem often to be chewed. The more substantial, rigid, fibrous warts in the fruits of Phytelephantoideae probably afford much greater protection.

OTHER PALM AND ANIMAL INTERACTIONS

Anyone who has ever collected herbarium specimens of palms in the tropics is familiar with the abundance of arthropods that inhabit different parts of the plants. Lepesme (1947) described in detail the various habitats occupied by insects. Some arthropods feed directly on the palm; such organisms are frequently host specific and of enormous economic importance to cultivated palms. Other arthropods and indeed many other animals inhabit palms without actually feeding on them. In a few instances there are direct, precise relationships between the palm and animal that involve morphological adaptations in the palm. Ants and scale insects live in a very close association with some rattan species. The morphological adaptations related to the associations have been discussed by Dransfield (1979a, 1981a). The most striking are found in some species of *Korthalsia* and a few New Guinea and Philippine species of *Calamus. Laccosperma* in Africa possibly behaves similarly. In these species the ocrea is either swollen and inflated around the sheathed stem or diverges from the sheathed stem at an acute angle, the margins inrolling and forming a chamber. Ants occupy the chambers, using them for nesting and for rearing scale insects on the young tissue toward the apparent tip of the stem (the youngest expanded leaves). Scale insects are milked for honey-dew and, apparently, are moved on by the ants to younger tissue as the ocreas mature.

Another adaptation associated with ant/rattan relationships is found in several species of *Daemonorops* (e.g. *D. formicaria, D. verticillaris, D. macrophylla, D. crinita,* and others) and one species of *Calamus, C. polystachys.* In these species, the leaf sheath bears collars tipped with fine horse-hairlike spines; some collars are reflexed, others upward pointing, and adjacent collars and spines sometimes interlock to form galleries in which ants make their nests. Galleries of successive sheaths are often interconnected by tunnels constructed of "carton," or spicules. It has always been assumed that the close ant/rattan/scale insect association provides protection for the rattan against herbivores and there is indeed some circumstantial evidence to suggest that the presence of ants deters herbivores. A novel interpretation of the relationship has recently been made by Rickson and Rickson (pers. comm.) who have demonstrated the uptake of nutrients from litter accumulating in the crown of *D. verticillaris* and from the detritus of the ant's nests in *D. verticillaris* and *D. macrophylla.* These two rattans obtain enhanced nutrient accumulation from the presence of ants, as well as any protection they may gain against herbivores. Other associations between ants and rattans are discussed in Dransfield (1979a).

Casual observations made by Dransfield (unpublished) in the Kebun Raya Garden, Bogor suggest that *Livistona chinensis* and other species with tardily abscising leaves are favored by bats as roosting sites over species such as *L. rotundifolia.* The daily rain of bat feces at the base of the stem of *L. chinensis* certainly produced noticeably more luxuriant growth of lawn grasses there than under *L. rotundifolia,* and there seemed also to be differences in vigor between the palms themselves. The role of bats in the nutrient economy of palms in the wild has not been investigated but marcescent leaves may indeed be of some adaptive significance.

THE EFFECT OF HUMAN ACTIVITY ON PALMS

As tropical rain forest is cleared for agriculture, larger palms are frequently spared the axe, either because they are useful species or because the stems are too hard for easy felling. Such palms often survive the burning of the felled trees. Unlike dicotyledonous trees, palm stems do not possess a cambium and lacking this superficial, easily damaged, vital zone, can survive even if the stem is partly burned. Residual palms may live for many years giving a false appearance of vigor; they may flower and fruit freely, but they are unable to regenerate in the surrounding cleared land. Some palms seem genuinely adapted to surviving fire. "Cerrado," a major vegetation type of Brazil consisting of open woodland, scrub or savannah, is subject to burning, and although an edaphic rather than a strictly fire climax, seems certainly adapted to fire (Eiten 1972). The palms of the "cerrado" are remarkable for their ability to survive fire. Most of the species are acaulescent with quite deep subterranean stems which grow, at least initially, geotropically rather than upwards. *Allagoptera campestris, Syagrus loefgrenii,* and *Acrocomia* sp. *(Acanthococos emensis)* are examples of such palms (Medeiros-Costa and Panizza 1983). In southeastern U.S.A., *Serenoa repens* seems to be adapted to withstanding fire. In winter, fire will burn off the foliage but do little damage to the growing points, while hot summer burns cause more damage. However, it takes several hot fires to produce noticeable decrease in vigor (Putz, pers. comm.).

Conservation Problems. — Loss of habitat and overexploitation are the major threats to the survival of many species of palms. The prospects for certain species are extremely poor, and it seems likely that some palms are either extinct or dangerously near to becoming so. Yet the arguments for saving palms from extinction are compelling. Clearly the family is of immense economic importance. Recent interest throughout the tropics in the development of sylvicultural or agroforestry systems including previously wild palms such as *Jessenia bataua, Calamus manan,* and *Orbignya phalerata* demonstrates the importance of wild palm populations as the source of genetic material for the agriculture of the future. Also, whole human communities living within rain forest or on the forest boundary depend for much of their livelihood on wild palms. Although rarely included in government statistics, production from these palms is the basis of human survival in such communities. The prospect of palm extinction should thus be of great concern. *Medemia argun* confined to desert oases in southern Egypt and northern Sudan was last seen in 1963 and may well be extinct. The slender rattan, *Ceratolobus glaucescens,* is now known in the wild from only about 30 plants on the south coast of Java, though it does seem likely that it may occur elsewhere. *Beccariophoenix madagascariensis,* known only from two herbarium collections from eastern Madagascar, was rediscovered in 1986 (Dransfield unpubl.). Like so many palms of that island, it is severely threatened by loss of habitat through shifting cultivation and overexploitation. The threats to palms and individual examples of endangered species are discussed in the Plant Red Data Book (Lucas and Synge 1978) and by Moore (1977). Since these two works were published, the situation has certainly deteriorated even further. Cultivation of rare palms may well be the only way to save them from total extinction. The International Palm Society has played a very important role in the popularizing and wide dissemination of rare and unusual species. However, the only way to save viable populations of endangered palms from extinction is by the protection of their habitats. The creation of a Palm Specialist Group within the Species Survival Commission of the International Union for Conservation of Nature and Natural Resources, as well as recent support from the World Wildlife Fund for a project to study palm utilization and conservation, are positive developments. Palm conservation represents a great challenge for all palm enthusiasts in the next decade. The arguments for palm conservation can easily be made, but individuals, companies and governmental agencies need to be educated and persuaded of the present and future value of palms.

CHAPTER IV

THE FOSSIL RECORD

The fossil record of palms is of special interest for several reasons. The first monocotyledons are considered to have been semiaquatic plants that were present in the early Cretaceous, about 100 million years ago (Hickey and Doyle 1977, Muller 1984), but palms are one of the earliest recognizable modern families, appearing as fossils in the Upper Cretaceous, about 65 million years ago (Fig. IV.1). From a consideration of early pollen records Muller (1984) has suggested that palms represent a secondary development of the only large group of woody monocotyledons. However, it is possible that palms may be older than realized. Some Lower Cretaceous pollen grains identified by Walker and Walker (1984) as produced by unspecified early monocotyledons closely resemble pollen grains of some modern palms (Dransfield, Ferguson, and Uhl in press). The early occurrence of their fossils agrees with other evidence that palms are very ancient and that some of them retain characters thought to be primitive among seed plants as a whole (Moore and Uhl 1973). Finally, fossils indicate the presence of a diversity of palms during the Cretaceous at a time when the continents comprising West Gondwana and Laurasia were beginning to rift apart, and this supports the hypothesis that some palms may have reached their present distributions by rafting on appropriate land masses.

Although the long fossil record promises insights into the origin, evolution, and distribution of palms, some limitations must be noted. Detailed studies of palm fossils are few and restricted in extent. A survey of leaves of fossil palms (Read and Hickey 1972) has established five form genera. The authors point out that among all palms only the genus *Phoenix,* which has an induplicately pinnate leaf with the basal pinnae modified into spines, can be definitely identified to genus from leaf remains. They suggest that some or all of the following characters can be used to identify a fossil leaf as a palm: pinnate or palmate form or venation, leaflets with a strong midvein bounded on each side by at least two orders of parallel veins, a hastula at least adaxially, and a well organized primary costa. These distinctions do not apply to all palm leaves. Leaves of some palms are not strongly plicate. In several genera, such as *Podococcus, Iriartea,* and *Iriartella,* the leaflets lack midribs, in others, such as *Rhapidophyllum* and

Rhapis, the ribs are not central in the segments, and still others, *Chuniophoenix, Nannorrhops, Lodoicea,* and *Medemia,* lack hastulae. Nevertheless Read and Hickey's work provides a way to identify many fossil leaves as palms. In another recent study, Daghlian (1978) used epidermal characters to assess costapalmate and palmate fossil leaves from the Eocene of southeastern United States and described five different taxa, only one of them (a new species of *Sabal*) referable to a modern genus. Daghlian's work demonstrates that new techniques may be needed to assess fossil palms. Such detailed work is needed for palm fossils from many localities.

The records of fossil pollen also must be questioned. In a preliminary report of a comprehensive survey, Ferguson (1987) has shown that remarkable variation in exine sculpturing exists within genera and equally remarkable structural parallels exist between genera. His work reinforces similar conclusions by Sowunmi (1972) and Thanikaimoni (1971) and emphasizes the need for careful study, especially at the electron microscope level.

When fossils of all kinds are considered, some have been identified with modern genera, but only rarely has true affinity been firmly established. Although seldom determinable to group or genus (Klotz 1978b), fossil stems are rather easily identified as palms. Fruits and seeds, depending on their preservation, may be easier than leaves or pollen to relate to modern genera. To a large extent, assessments of fossil palms have had to be postponed until the structure and relationships of modern genera are better understood.

Despite the above caveats, fossils show that palms have existed since the Upper Cretaceous or possibly earlier. Some of the fossils can be identified to subfamily or tribe if not always to genus and they do contribute significantly to our understanding of the family.

THE EARLIEST OCCURRENCES

The earliest unequivocal record of palms is from the Upper Cretaceous Magothy Formation of New Jersey which is Santonian (?Coniacian) (Fig. IV.1) in age (Daghlian 1981); leaves of *Sabal magothiensis* (Berry 1911) and stems of *Palmoxylon cliff-*

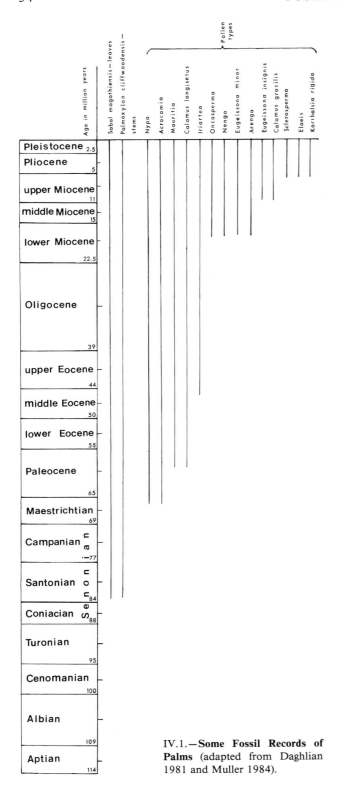

IV.1.—**Some Fossil Records of Palms** (adapted from Daghlian 1981 and Muller 1984).

woodensis (Berry 1916) have been identified in this formation. In North America palm leaves have been found in the Cretaceous Dakota Group of the Rocky Mountains, the Upper Cretaceous Nanaimo Group on Vancouver Island, British Colombia (LaMotte 1952), and a *Sabalites* has been described from the Senonian (Upper Cretaceous) of South Carolina (Read and Hickey 1972). Palms also have been found in the Upper Cretaceous in Japan (Oyama and Matsuo 1964) and possibly in Mexico (see Daghlian 1981).

Pollen records appear at about the same time as those of stems and leaves. Pollen of *Nypa* occurs in the Upper Cretaceous (Maestrichtian) of Borneo (Muller 1984). The identification of a pollen type from Cameroon as an *Areca ipot* (Muller 1981) type seems very questionable. Pollen of an *Acrocomia* type from Germany is also Maestrichtian in age (Muller 1979).

Three pollen groups listed as "pending" by Muller (1981) are of exceptional interest if they do represent palms. The first, listed as Group 1 (Thanikaimoni 1971), has pollen characterized by a single sulcus and a finely reticulate exine and could represent any of a large number of palm species. Such pollen is common today in members of the Coryphoideae such as *Livistona, Sabal,* and *Phoenix.* Most of these records are Paleocene, but Jarzen (1978) has described a *Livistona* from the Maestrichtian, an important report which deserves further study according to Muller (1981).

Two other occurrences of pollen are equally noteworthy. In South America the pollen record indicates a diversification of palms in the Maestrichtian. Palmlike pollen shows a strikingly explosive development in the Lower Senonian of tropical West Africa (Jardiné and Magloire 1965; Muller 1979). If these specimens do represent palms similar to those considered primitive today in South America and Africa, the early and widespread presence of palms in both Laurasia and Gondwanaland is indicated.

It must be noted that all reports of pre-Cretaceous occurrences for palms have been proved incorrect. *Propalmophyllum* O. Lignier, described from the Lower Jurassic of France, is not palmlike and too fragmentary to be assigned to any group of plants (Read and Hickey 1972). *Sanmiguelia lewisii* from the Triassic of southwestern Colorado (Brown 1956a), a "palmlike" plant, has not shown any characters that can be clearly related to palms. *Palmoxylon simperi* and *P. pristina* originally described as

Mid-Jurassic (Tidwell et al. 1970) have been shown to be Tertiary in age (Scott et al. 1972).

TERTIARY PALMS

Palm fossils become more numerous in the Paleocene (early Tertiary) and by the Eocene are abundant in many parts of the world where palms do not occur today. A large number of fruits and seeds has been found in the Eocene London Clay beds. Fruits referable to *Sabal, Serenoa, ?Livistona, ?Trachycarpus,* a seed named as a new species of *Corypha,* fruits of *Nypa, Oncosperma* and *Caryotispermum,* and about 20 species of *Palmospermum,* representing palmlike seeds not corresponding to any modern genus, have been described from the London Clay area (Chandler 1964, 1978).

In Europe from the early Tertiary to the Mid-Miocene, fruits, seeds, stems, and leaves referred to *Phoenix, Sabal, Serenoa, Livistona, Nypa, Oncosperma* and *Trachycarpus* are found. Other fossil genera, such as *Flabellaria, Amesoneuron, Palmacites, Phoenicites, Sabalites, Caryotispermum, Palmospermum,* and *Paleothrinax* are palmlike but not referable to modern genera (Gregor 1980). Well documented coryphoidlike fruits are recorded from the Tertiary of West Greenland (Koch and Friedrich 1972).

Numerous localities in North America have yielded palm remains. The northernmost record is of palmate leaves near the head of Hamilton Bay, Kupreanof Island, Alaska in early Tertiary formations (Read and Hickey 1972). Daghlian (1978) found five well defined genera and species in the Lower and Middle Eocene of the Mississippi Embayment. These include a *Palmacites* (which seems closest to *Chamaerops, Cryosophila,* and *Schippia*), a new genus, *Palustrapalma* (which resembles coryphoid palms but exhibits a different combination of characters), *Sabal dortchii* and *Sabalites grayanus,* both new species, and another new genus, *Costapalma philipii,* also considered related to coryphoid palms. Daghlian's findings emphasize the need for detailed studies of palm fossils from other localities, such as the Raton Flora of northern New Mexico and southern Colorado, the Jackson Flora of Texas, the Eden Valley flora of Wyoming, the Puget Sound flora of Washington and British Columbia, the La Porte flora of California, and the Clarno flora in Northern Oregon, all localities where palm leaves occur, often in abundance. In Oregon and the Denver Basin some fruits also have been found. The geological history in Oregon parallels that elsewhere in North America. Palms appear in the Cretaceous, become relatively abundant during the Eocene, but are limited to relict warm-climate floras of coastal regions in the Oligocene. Post-Oligocene rocks lack palms in Oregon. During cooling in the Miocene and Pliocene there was gradual restriction of palms to their present locations in tropical and subtropical floras in the extreme southern United States and Mexico (Axelrod 1950).

In South America there are fewer records of leaves and fruits but Maury (1930) has recorded *Palmocarpon luisii* from Brazil, Berry (1937) a *Palmocarpon* sp. from the Miocene of Trinidad, and Engelhardt (1891) *Sabal ochseninsii* from Chile and a *Palmacites* from the Miocene of Colombia. Other records include a palm leaf from the Pliocene of Bolivia, a fruit from the Miocene of Trinidad (Menendez 1969), and palm wood from the lower Tertiary of Argentina (Romero 1968). A recent interesting report is of a petrified stem from the Paleocene of Argentina (Arguijo 1979). *Mauritia* pollen is widespread in the tropical South American Tertiary (Muller 1979).

In Africa, pollen of *Sclerosperma* has been described by Medus (1975) from the Miocene of Senegal. Only a few megafossils have been reported from the continent. These include a microslide of a stem presumably from the Tertiary of South Africa (Kaul 1945), and a petiole, *Palmocaulon monodii,* from the Eocene of Senegal (Boureau and Prakash 1968).

Fossils from Asia represent several groups of palms. Five species of *Sabalites* have been found in China in Tertiary (?) formations. The Eocene Deccan Intertrappean beds of India have yielded many palm stems, petioles, and leaves (Lakhanpal 1970, Rao and Achuthan 1973). Recent studies describe a stem showing close affinities with *Livistona* (Prakash and Ambwani 1980), stems that are *Cocos* and *Corypha*like (Lakhanpal, Prakash, and Ambwani 1979), and other stems such as *Palmoxylon arviensis* (Ambwani 1981) that are not identifiable with modern genera.

Pollen representing *Eugeissona* occurs in the earliest Miocene and perhaps in the Oligocene of Borneo (Muller 1979). Pollen of some rattan palms, similar to that of *Calamus gracilis* and species of *Korthalsia,* occurs in the Paleocene of Borneo. Palms of tribe Areceae are represented in Borneo by pollen of *Oncosperma* in the Oligocene and *Nenga* in the

Lower Miocene. Endocarps and pollen of Cocoeae genera have been found in New Zealand (Berry 1926; Couper 1952). The only palm fossil from Australia is pollen of *Nypa* from Eocene deposits in Queensland (Hekel 1972).

Other records and discussion of fossils are included in the generic descriptions.

THE SIGNIFICANCE OF THE FOSSIL RECORD

Although little studied, the fossil record provides some insights into the evolution of palms. The earliest recognizable palms are fossils of certain coryphoid genera and *Nypa.* Morphological, anatomical, and developmental studies have indicated that the apocarpous coryphoid palms (the Thrinacinae) and the genus *Nypa* are today the least specialized living palms. Hermaphroditic flowers, free carpels, and several basic evolutionary trends in the family are evident in the Thrinacinae (Moore and Uhl 1973, 1982). Daghlian has noted that fossils of costapalmate and palmate leaves from southeastern North America are not referable to modern genera but are nevertheless anatomically closest to members of the Thrinacinae. The available fossil record suggests that these palms, long considered primitive in the family, also may be the oldest. Study of such fossils is a most promising area for research on primitive monocotyledons and may provide evidence of the ancestry of recent palms, and the relationships of palms to other monocotyledons.

Current records seem to indicate that palms with costapalmate leaves appeared somewhat earlier than *Nypa.* However, *Nypa,* a palm so different from all others that it is included in a subfamily of its own, is one of the first recognizable modern genera. What is the significance of the early and wide occurrence of this odd genus? In *Nypa,* free and similar perianth parts, apocarpy, and an unusual carpel, possibly representing an ascidiform rather than a follicular primitive type, are considered unspecialized characters. Other characters including habit, inflorescence form, the reduced androecium, and growth sequences of carpels seem to be specializations. The pollen of *Nypa* can be rather easily identified and its mangrove habitat is favorable to the formation of fossils. It thus seems better adapted to fossilization than

palms from upland habitats or those with less distinctive pollen. Nevertheless, the early occurrence of *Nypa,* a genus exhibiting both primitive and advanced characters, suggests that palms diversified very early, perhaps in the Lower Cretaceous. It is of note that the unspecialized characters of *Nypa,* the similar perianth parts and a cupular carpel, seem to be primitive characters within monocotyledons as a whole.

Fossils may also provide some evidence on the evolution of costapalmate, palmate, and pinnate leaves. The earliest unequivocal fossil palm leaves are costapalmate in form. Costapalmate leaves first appear in the Santonian, pinnate leaves in the Maestrichtian, and strictly palmate leaves not until the Paleocene (Daghlian 1981, Read and Hickey 1972). Conclusions from these records are at present tentative as many fossils of leaves await further study.

The fossil record also lends some support for a very early origin of palms, perhaps before the supercontinents of Laurasia and Gondwanaland were widely separated. Beginning from an as yet poorly understood early group, of which Thrinacinae are representative, that was widespread in Gondwana and Laurasia, different groups of palms may have originated in different regions and then followed different distribution patterns as the continents separated. Both pollen and megafossils suggest a diversity of relatively specialized palms by at least the Maestrichtian followed by a rapid and explosive radiation in North America and Asia by the Eocene when climates were warmer in those regions. Chapter V on geography provides further discussion. Although the first palm fossils are from the Upper Cretaceous, it is possible that the family had an earlier origin. Unfortunately, unspecialized palm pollen is of a simple monosulcate form that is found also in several other families of monocotyledons and is difficult to assign with certainty to the family. Indeed, some of the early monocotyledonous monosulcate pollens recorded from the Potomac beds of the early Cretaceous of North America (Walker and Walker 1984, 1986) appear remarkably similar to some extant types of palm pollen. We cannot identify these early fossils as representing palms, but we wish to point out that early palms may well have had pollen of this form.

CHAPTER V

GEOGRAPHY

As stated in Chapter IV fossils that are unequivocally of palms occur in rocks of late Cretaceous age. This occurrence is early enough that the present geographic distribution of the family must have been considerably influenced by the break-up of the ancient continents of Laurasia and Gondwanaland and the subsequent drifting of their fragments. The distribution of living palms supports this hypothesis. There is a high degree of endemism at all taxonomic levels, some subfamilies, tribes, subtribes, or genera showing very restricted distributions. Different genera are present on either side of Wallace's Line (Fig. V.1) where fragments of Laurasia and Gondwanaland (Fig. V.2) have collided, bringing together floras that had long been separated (Dransfield 1981b). Furthermore, the propagules of most palms are large and heavy and, with the exception of *Nypa* and the coconut, seem unsuited for dispersal over long distances. Nevertheless some remarkable disjunctions occur in the distributions of certain taxa. These disjunctions probably reflect past geography and continental movements much more in palms than similar disjunctions do in groups with small, wind-dispersed propagules, such as the much more recent families of Orchidaceae and Compositae.

This chapter must be regarded as an interim account of palm biogeography for several reasons. Although we present a new classification, further research is needed in several areas. Considerable morphological, anatomical, and developmental work remains to be done. These data, and cladistic studies just initiated, should eventually provide a clearer understanding of relationships and biogeographical patterns. We have not explored the congruence of palm distributions with those of other plant and animal taxa; such a study also may contribute to future conclusions.

The fossil record is of primary importance in suggesting how palms may have originated and dispersed. However, all too often fossils are lacking or are of a disputed nature. Recent work on pollen of living palms by Ferguson (1986) has demonstrated numerous parallels in superficial appearance between grains of unrelated taxa, and this shows the need for caution in attributing the names of existing taxa to fossil pollen.

Finally, we know too little about the palm flora of the crucially important island, Madagascar. Separated from Africa about 100 million years ago (Raven and Axelrod 1974), Madagascar carries a rich and diverse fauna and flora. *Beccariophoenix* (Cocoeae), *Louvelia,* and *Ravenea* (Ceroxyleae), all endemic to the island, are probably ancient relics. Most of the other 18 genera and 120 species on the island also are poorly known. The great poverty of the African palm flora may be explained in terms of extinction due to climatic change, but the richness of the Madagascan palm flora seems to indicate that the climate there has remained favorable for palms. Viewed in this light, there are important absences in subfamilial, tribal, and subtribal representation in the flora, perhaps suggesting that some taxa may never have reached the island.

The most important recent consideration of geography is "Palms in the Tropical Forest Ecosystems of Africa and South America" (Moore 1973b), in which the distribution patterns of palms were analyzed and a hypothesis for origin and dispersal of the family proposed. The taxonomic basis for Moore's analysis was his informal classification "The Major Groups of Palms and Their Distribution" (1973a). From the evidence of the fossil record and distributions of modern palms Moore proposed that palms originated during the Cretaceous in what was then West Gondwanaland (modern South America) followed by radiation and dispersal into East Gondwanaland (Africa and Australia) and Laurasia (the continents of the Northern Hemisphere). We present here some insights gained in formulating a new classification and some different suggestions as to how palms may have originated and dispersed.

THE CLIMATIC LIMITS OF PALMS

Palms are found throughout the more humid tropics and subtropics but are absent from deserts and semideserts except where groundwater is near the surface (Map 1). Only a very few occur in temperate regions. At the northern end of their range, *Chamaerops* occurs naturally as far north as 44° in Europe, and *Rhapidophyllum* and *Washingtonia* to almost 33° N in North America; *Trachycarpus* occurs in the wild just outside the tropics in eastern Asia, but will grow outdoors to almost 58° N in Scotland, where greatly benefitting from the warming

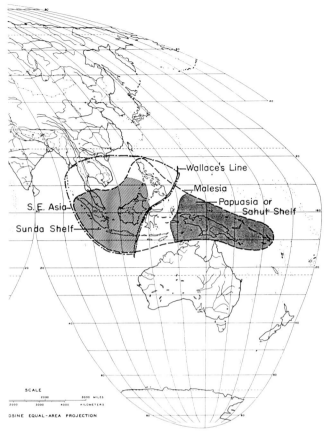

V.1.—Map showing the position of Wallace's Line and the Sunda and Sahul Shelves.

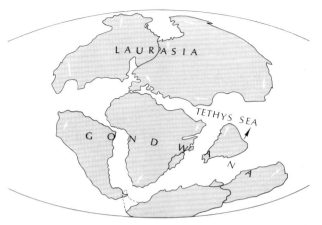

V.2.—The approximate position of the continents in the Mid-Cretaceous (adapted from Dietz and Holden 1970).

THE DISTRIBUTION OF MODERN PALMS

Coryphoideae. The three tribes of the subfamily Coryphoideae display contrasting distribution patterns. Tribe Corypheae is pantropical and subtropical (Map 2), the Phoeniceae is Old World subtropical and tropical (Map 7), and the Borasseae are distributed on the land masses adjoining the Indian Ocean and on its islands (Map 8).

Corypheae. — The distributions of the subtribes of tribe Corypheae differ from each other significantly and suggest very different evolutionary histories.

Subtribe Thrinacinae (Map 3), which contains all the apocarpic members of the tribe, can be divided into two groups of genera; the first, consisting of our genera 1–8, is entirely New World and confined to South and Central America and the Caribbean, while the second group, genera 9–14, is distributed in southern USA, the Mediterranean, Himalayas, Southeast Asia, and China. In the first group, three genera, *Trithrinax, Itaya,* and *Chelyocarpus,* are confined to South America. They appear to be the least specialized members of the subtribe. The other American genera of the first group of Thrinacinae occur in the Caribbean or Central America, with a few species of *Cryosophila* reaching Colombia. The presence of the least specialized members in South America might be seen as supporting a South American (West Gondwanaland) origin of the group. Alternatively, the three genera may be relics of an early colonization by the ancestors of the subtribe which thereafter remained in isolation while other members continued to diversify elsewhere.

effects of the Gulf Stream. In the southern hemisphere, *Rhopalostylis* occurs as far as 44°18′ S in New Zealand (Moore 1970). We may assume that these temperature and moisture constraints are not recent phenomena but have always affected palms. Thus, the finding of palm fossils in areas where palms are not found at present argues for the existence of a warmer and/or wetter climate there in the past. This is supported by associated fossils of other groups of plants; for example, a wide variety of fossils referable to tropical mangrove genera occur together with fossils of *Nypa* in the Eocene London Clay beds of Europe, indicating the presence of a much warmer climate then (Reid and Chandler 1933). Their climatic requirements have made the palms particularly vulnerable to sudden change. The paucity of palms in Africa may in part be due to the sudden shifts in climate, especially in rainfall, which are known to have occurred during the Pleistocene (Moreau 1966).

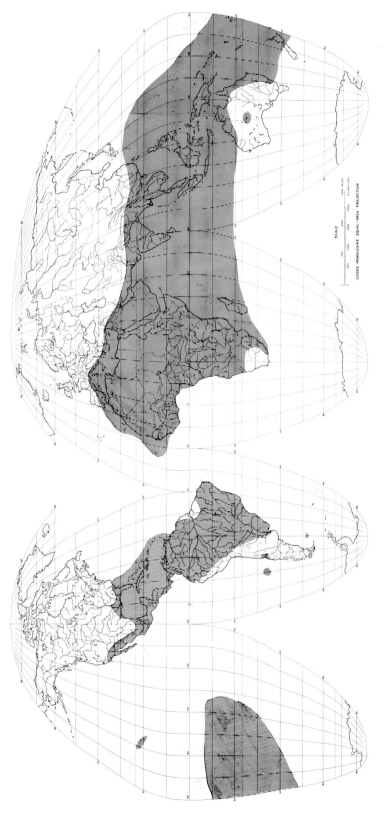

Map 1.—**Distribution of living palms.**

Subtribe Livistoninae (Map 4), the most widespread of all palm subtribes, is represented in South America by three species of *Copernicia* (otherwise a largely Cuban genus) and in Africa (Arabian peninsula and adjoining areas) by only one species of *Livistona*. There is rich representation in the southern part of North America, in Southeast Asia, and in Australia, and two genera are endemic to the Pacific region (*Pritchardiopsis* in New Caledonia and *Pritchardia* in Hawaii, Fiji, Samoa, and the Danger Islands).

The differences between the genera of the Livistoninae are small, and it is certainly difficult to suggest evolutionary pathways within this very natural group. The subtribe includes some of the most drought and cold tolerant of palms and also taxa adapted to the wettest parts of the eastern tropics. In view of this, the extreme paucity of taxa in South America, the presence of only one species in Africa, and their complete absence from Madagascar become very significant. There appears to be a strong northern hemisphere bias in the distribution of the subtribe.

If a northern origin of the subtribe is proposed, there are a few problematic genera. The presence of the three species of *Copernicia* in South America seems best explained as the result of recent dispersal followed by disjunction of the range in relation to Pleistocene climatic change. In the Far East, the northern bias of the subtribe is not so pronounced, *Licuala* and *Livistona* being abundant in Papuasia and Australia. It is now believed that the Malesian region is a composite of Laurasian and Gondwanic fragments which acquired their present approximate configuration in the Miocene, although there may have been island arcs composed of Gondwanic fragments linking the Sunda and Sahul Shelves since the late Cretaceous (Audley-Charles et al. 1981 and in press). Thus *Licuala* and *Livistona* probably dispersed from the northern to the southern hemisphere through the Malesian region. Another problematic distribution pattern is displayed by *Colpothrinax*; this genus is represented by *C. wrightii* in Cuba and *C. cookii* in Guatemala and Panama. The most closely related genus appears to be *Pritchardia* in the Pacific. *Pritchardiopsis,* endemic on a long isolated fragment of land (New Caledonia) on the Australian plate, also needs explanation.

Subtribe Coryphinae (Map 5) contains four genera whose relationships are not yet well understood. *Chuniophoenix* in China and *Kerriodoxa* in Thailand are Asian, but one species of *Corypha* is found throughout the Malay Archipelago and as far south as northern Australia, and *Nannorrhops* occurs in Arabia as well as in northwest India and Afghanistan. Further study of the relationships of these four genera is needed.

The fourth subtribe, Sabalinae (Map 6), the most specialized in terms of gynoecial structure, includes only the genus, *Sabal,* confined to North America, the Caribbean, and the extreme northern part of South America. An extensive fossil record of costapalmate leaves attributed to *Sabal* has been found in North America and Europe, but the affinity of many of the fossils needs reassessment. An origin of the genus in Laurasia is plausible, however.

Phoeniceae. — The Phoeniceae consists of the single genus *Phoenix* which at present ranges from the Atlantic Islands, Africa, the Mediterranean, and Arabia to India, South China, and Southeast Asia (Map 7). Most species are adapted to monsoonal or semiarid climates. The greatest number of species occurs in the Indian subcontinent and in Southeast Asia. One species (*P. reclinata*) is widespread in Africa. A second species, *P. caespitosa,* doubtfully distinct, occurs in the Horn of Africa (Somalia). A wide range of fossils in Europe and North America if correctly attributed, extends the present day distribution to give a strong northern hemisphere or Laurasian bias.

Borasseae. — Tribe Borasseae is divided into two subtribes (Map 8). Members of subtribe Hyphaeninae (Map 10) are present in Madagascar (*Bismarckia* and *Hyphaene*) and Africa (*Medemia* and *Hyphaene*), with a few species of *Hyphaene* reaching Arabia, western India, and probably Sri Lanka. The occurrence of *Hyphaene* east of Arabia may be due to the activities of man. The second subtribe, Lataniinae (Map 9), is represented by *Latania* in the Mascarenes, *Lodoicea* in the Seychelles, *Borassodendron* in Borneo and Peninsular Malaysia, and *Borassus* in Africa, Madagascar, India, Southeast Asia, and the Malay Archipelago to New Guinea and Australia. *Borassus flabellifer* is the most widespread species, but it is important economically and its distribution must have been considerably affected by man. Indeed its presence in Australia may be due to man. On the other hand, the very poorly known *B. heineana* appears to be quite distinct and confined to one small area of New Guinea.

The distribution of this natural, clearly defined tribe suggests early differentiation in Gondwanaland followed by rafting on the Indian Plate, Madagascar, and the Mascarenes with continued differentiation in Africa. *Borassodendron* survives now in the rain forests of Borneo and Peninsular Malaysia. It could have reached its present area of distribution by dispersal from the Indian Plate. However, parts of Borneo and Peninsular Malaysia are thought to be Gondwanic in origin (Ridd 1971; Audley-Charles in press) and if the timing of separation of this Gondwanic fragment were congruent with differentiation of the tribe, *Borassodendron* could have reached Sundaland by rafting. *Borassus heineana* in New Guinea could have had a similar history; because of its large fruits, it does seem improbable that this taxon should have reached New Guinea by long distance dispersal. Further speculation seems unwarranted without a better understanding of the species of *Borassus* and their relationships.

In summary for Coryphoideae, the two least specialized tribes, Corypheae and Phoeniceae may be Laurasian in origin, but the more specialized Borasseae has a Gondwanaland bias.

Calamoideae. The greatest diversity in numbers of genera and species of Calamoideae is found in Southeast Asia (Map 11). The African representation of the subfamily is small, including only five genera, of which three are endemic, a fourth, *Raphia* (Map 18), shared with Central and South America, and a fifth, *Calamus,* shared with Asia. However, two of the endemic genera, *Eremospatha* and *Laccosperma* (Map 12), have dyads of hermaphrodite flowers, and exhibit both sexuality and a flower cluster pattern that seem basic in the subfamily. Two others, *Oncocalamus* and *Raphia,* display divergence from this basic pattern in very different ways. In the Americas there are four calamoid genera. *Raphia,* which is otherwise predominantly African, is represented in tropical America by one species, *R. taedigera,* which also occurs in Africa (Otedoh 1977). Although the species occurs in large stands and to all appearances is indigenous in America, Otedoh thinks it has been introduced there; this viewpoint is not shared by most authors. The other three genera, *Mauritia, Mauritiella,* and *Lepidocaryum,* are closely related to each other and are separated as tribe Lepidocaryeae (Map 20) because of their unusual palmate rather than pinnate leaves. It is not at all clear to which Old World genera the Lepidocaryeae are most closely related, but they may have diverged from the ancestors of the Old World Calameae early in the evolution of the subfamily.

Only one representative of the subfamily, *Raphia farinifera,* is found in Madagascar. This species also occurs in east Africa where it is a very important

multipurpose crop, suggesting that its presence in Madagascar may be the result of introduction by man. Since the climate of east Madagascar supports a rich and varied palm flora, the absence of Calamoideae apart from *Raphia* seems particularly significant. Climatic changes cannot be invoked to account for the absence in terms of extinction, for the unique palm flora suggests a long and ancient presence on the island. Rather it seems more likely that the Calamoideae were prevented from reaching Madagascar, either because they were spatially separated from central southern Gondwanaland or because they evolved after separation of the island.

Two Papuasian genera, *Metroxylon* and *Pigafetta,* have distributions that are difficult to explain. Many calamoid genera and species occur west of Wallace's Line (Dransfield 1981b), but few genera transgress this line and those that do are represented by few species, except for *Calamus* which has a diversity of species in New Guinea and several in Australia. It seems most reasonable that these genera originated to the west of Wallace's Line and that a few have migrated eastwards into Papuasia since the final juxtaposition of the Sunda and Sahul Plates in the Miocene. However, *Metroxylon* is confined to New Guinea and the West Pacific (except for *M. sagu* which has been introduced into west Malesia). We have included *Metroxylon* in the same subtribe with the predominantly west Malesian *Korthalsia* because of the unusual structure of the rachillae (Map 14). In terms of habit, the two genera are very different, *Korthalsia* being a genus of rattans and *Metroxylon* of robust trees. The presence of *Korthalsia* in Papuasia can easily be explained in terms of dispersal eastwards since the Miocene (Dransfield 1981b).

Pigafetta (Map 17) is found in Sulawesi (Celebes), the Moluccas, and New Guinea. It is superficially similar to *Metroxylon,* especially in habit, but the floral morphology is quite different. That *Metroxylon* and *Pigafetta* reached their present position by late Tertiary dispersal eastward across Wallace's Line seems improbable. Perhaps they arrived from the northwest by much earlier dispersal across the island arcs composed of Gondwanic fragments which are now thought to have existed between the Sahul and Sunda Shelves before the Miocene (Audley-Charles in press).

The great diversity of genera in Sundaland and the presence of relatively unspecialized genera in Africa suggests that the shores of the Tethys Ocean may have been an important dispersal route for the subfamily. In the Asian genera there is a strong northern hemisphere bias. However, the subfamily is present on the Gondwanic fragments of South America and Africa but, apart from *Raphia farinifera,* is absent from Madagascar as mentioned earlier. The relationships of the endemic New World genera with the rest of the subfamily are not evident and perhaps will become clearer when the phylogeny is better understood.

The simplest explanation of the present diversity and distribution of the Calamoideae seems to be as follows: an early radiation of calamoid ancestors in North Gondwanaland followed by dispersal to Southeast Asia along the shores of the Tethys, early radiation into South America before complete separation of Africa and South America, and considerable extinction of taxa on the African continent in relatively recent times. The possibility that the Indian Plate might have been important in dispersing the subfamily from Africa to present day Southeast Asia cannot be ruled out. Indeed, fossil pollen types from the Indian Tertiary have been compared with the calamoid genera *Eugeissona* and *Calamus* (Thanikaimoni et al. 1984), but earlier pollen grains referred to the subfamily have been found in Borneo (Muller 1968).

Nypoideae. *Nypa* (Map 21) occurs today in Southeast Asia, the Malay Archipelago, and west Pacific Ocean islands. Its fruit is very well adapted to dispersal by sea, and at present the palm occupies a large area. However, it was much more widespread in the past, having been pantropical in the Eocene as indicated by fossils in Europe, Texas, South America, and Australia. Its earliest record is of pollen in the Maestrichtian of Borneo where it still occurs. *Nypa* seems to have been a very important plant along the shores of the Tethys Ocean and perhaps therefore is Laurasian in origin. Its presence in Australia in the Eocene may be explained by immigration from the Sunda Shelf via the island arcs of Gondwanic fragments mentioned above.

Ceroxyloideae. Of the three tribes of Ceroxyloideae (Map 22), Cyclospatheae is largely Caribbean while the other two, Ceroxyleae and Hyophorbeae, have disjunct austral distribution patterns.

Cyclospatheae. — The tribe Cyclospatheae (Map 23) consists of the single genus *Pseudophoenix,* outstanding because of its hermaphroditic flowers and relatively unspecialized inflorescence. It must surely be regarded as the simplest member of the subfamily and is confined to the islands of the Caribbean and to scattered coastal areas of North and South America.

Ceroxyleae. — The distribution of the Ceroxyleae (Map 24) presents a classic example of disjunction following the break-up of Gondwanaland. *Ceroxylon* radiated in the Andes of South America, *Juania* survives on the Juan Fernandez islands off the coast of Chile, *Ravenea* and the closely related *Louvelia* are confined to Madagascar, and *Oraniopsis* is known only from Queensland, Australia. Rafting on Gondwanic fragments may, however, be too simplistic a story. There seems little doubt that *Oraniopsis* and *Ceroxylon* are more closely related to each other than to the other genera (Dransfield et al. 1985a). The distribution of these two taxa parallels that of several noteworthy genera such as *Araucaria* and *Nothofagus.* Rather than rafting on the Australian Plate, *Oraniopsis* may have reached Australia by dispersal via an austral route along the edge of the Antarctic continent during the late Cretaceous or early Tertiary when land connections are believed to have existed and when the climate there was much warmer. Pollen of palms has been recorded from McMurdo Sound in the Antarctic, dated from some time between the Cretaceous and the Oligocene (Cranwell et al. 1960), at least suggesting that the climate there was suitable for the family. It is noteworthy that *Ceroxylon,* which shows such clear links with Australia, is a genus today adapted to the cool climates of the high Andes. The presence of *Ravenea* and *Louvelia* in Madagascar does indeed seem to be most easily explained by rafting on a Gondwanic fragment.

Hyophorbeae. — Tribe Hyophorbeae (Map 25) has a strikingly disjunct distribution; all genera are confined to Central and northern South America and the Caribbean except for *Hyophorbe,* which occurs in the Mascarene Islands of the Indian Ocean. The Mascarenes are all young volcanic islands; Moore (1978a) suggests that the ancestors of *Hyophorbe* probably arrived on the islands via Africa or Madagascar where they are now extinct. Within the islands the ancestral line differentiated into five species. Of the remaining genera of the tribe, the least specialized, *Gaussia,* is Caribbean in distribution. Greater diversity in *Chamaedorea* in Central America further emphasizes a Central American bias.

Within the whole subfamily austral disjunctions could be most easily explained in terms of the break-up of Gondwanaland, but the least specialized tribe

Cyclospatheae and the least specialized genus within tribe Hyophorbeae show a Caribbean bias.

Arecoideae. — The subfamily (Map 26) is predominantly of the southern hemisphere, with the exception of tribe Caryoteae and a few members of tribe Areceae.

Caryoteae, Iriarteeae. — The wide range of parallels between the first two tribes, the Caryoteae (Map 27) and Iriarteeae (Map 28), perhaps has not been sufficiently appreciated (see taxonomic account, p. 317). The two tribes may have had as a common ancestor one of the earliest precursors of the Arecoideae. At present, Caryoteae have their center in Southeast Asia and Indochina. A few species east of Wallace's Line probably invaded from Sundaland after the Sunda and Sahul Plates became finally juxtaposed in the Miocene. Iriarteeae are entirely New World in distribution, and furthermore only a few taxa are found outside the northern part of South America; thus a South American origin for the tribe seems probable. We speculate that Caryoteae and Iriarteeae may have had a common ancestor in Gondwanaland and that the line of ancestors which eventually became Caryoteae may have rafted northwards on the Indian Plate, while another line diversified into present day Iriarteeae in South America. Fossil seeds referred to as *Caryotispermum* are recorded from the Eocene London Clay in southern Britain (Reid and Chandler 1933); Caryoteae might also have spread along the margin of Tethys, their distribution contracted later by climatic change.

Podococceae. — *Podococcus,* the only genus of the third tribe Podococceae (Map 29), has a single species confined to a small area of humid tropical rain forest in West Africa. The genus seems to be most closely related to Iriarteeae. Until its phylogeny is better understood, we have to assume that *Podococcus* together with *Sclerosperma* are all that remain in tropical Africa of a perhaps more diverse assemblage of arecoid palms most of which became extinct during the climatic vicissitudes affecting Africa in the recent past.

Areceae. — Tribe Areceae is not only the largest in number of genera but also one of the most widespread. The five genera that make up the first four subtribes are triovulate rather than pseudomonomerous, and so are regarded as the least specialized. *Orania* is found throughout Malesia and in eastern Madagascar; closely related *Halmoorea* is confined to eastern Madagascar (Map 30). *Mani-*

caria (Map 31) and *Leopoldinia* (Map 32) are Amazonian, while *Reinhardtia* occurs in northern South America and Central America (Map 33). These genera may represent end points of ancient evolutionary lines separate from the pseudomonomerous Areceae. *Reinhardtia* may be intermediate, since there is a tendency in this genus for only one ovule to develop.

Of the remaining eleven subtribes, only two, Euterpeineae (Map 35) and Roystoneineae (Map 36), are New World. Three others are Madagascan, African, or western Indian Ocean: Dypsidinae are confined to Madagascar (Map 34), the Comores and Pemba; the Sclerospermatineae to Madagascar and West Africa (Map 44); and Oncospermatineae to the Mascarenes, Seychelles, Sri Lanka, and West Malesia, with one species of *Oncosperma* east of Wallace's Line (Map 43).

The remaining six subtribes are most richly represented in or confined to the western Pacific and Papuasia, though with curious bicentricity for some groups. For example, Iguanurinae (Map 42) is overwhelmingly Papuasian and west Pacific in distribution but *Iguanura* (Sundaland), *Bentinckia* (India and Nicobar Islands), and *Dictyosperma* (Mascarene Islands) occur outside the main center of diversity, and *Heterospathe* and *Rhopaloblaste* have species on both sides of Wallace's Line. Ptychospermatinae (Map 40) is entirely Papuasian and West Pacific except for a single species of *Veitchia* on Palawan in the Philippines. Arecinae (Map 41) is almost equally diverse at each end of the Malesian region; *Gronophyllum, Siphokentia, Gulubia,* and *Hydriastele* are confined to the eastern part while *Loxococcus* and *Nenga* occur in the west. *Areca* and *Pinanga* occur on both sides of Wallace's Line but are much more diverse to the west.

Although we do not fully understand the interrelationships of all the subtribes of Areceae and cannot yet suggest how the tribe as a whole has evolved and dispersed, the southern bias is very clear. Dispersal routes eastwards or westwards across the South Pacific via the route envisaged for Ceroxyleae may have been of importance. Also, pre-Miocene links across the Malesian region or rafting on India may account for the presence of endemic genera and the diversity of taxa in the western part of Malesia, the Indian subcontinent, and the Mascarenes. The Dypsidinae perhaps rafted on Madagascar. The absence of members of the tribe in Africa, apart from the poorly understood *Sclerosperma,* seems explicable only in terms of massive extinction. The pollen record of *Areca* from the Maestrichtian of Cameroun in West Africa (Muller 1981) has already been referred to in Chapter IV and doubt cast on its affinities with present day *A. ipot.* It seems improbable that a narrow Philippine endemic should have occurred in the Maestrichtian of Cameroun.

Cocoeae. — Members of the fifth tribe, Cocoeae, at present are almost completely confined to the Americas (Map 45). Exceptions are *Elaeis* (Map 49), which is represented by one species in the Americas and one in equatorial Africa, *Jubaeopsis* endemic to a small area of southern Africa, *Beccariophoenix* endemic to Madagascar (Map 46), and *Cocos* itself. *Cocos* has been shown rather convincingly to be of western Pacific origin with probably native wild populations in the Philippines and Queensland, Australia (Harries 1978, Gruezo and Harries 1984). *Beccariophoenix* has less well defined pores but seems nevertheless to belong to the tribe; perhaps it is a relict of early differentiation. It may not, however, be the only member of the tribe in Madagascar. Dr. M. E. Darian, of Vista, California, has recently shown us endocarps in Madagascar of what appears to be a member of subtribe Butiinae. Fossil members of the tribe seem to be reliably recorded from the Miocene of New Zealand (Berry 1926) and the Eocene of India (Kaul 1951). Empty endocarps of extant members of the tribe can be transported long distances by sea currents, and so records of fossil endocarps referred to Cocoeae from the Eocene of Florida (Berry 1929) and the lower Upper Cretaceous of France (Fliche 1896) without accompanying pollen or vegetative remains may not be valid records for those areas. A member of the subtribe Butiinae (Map 47) related to *Jubaea,* if not actually congeneric, was present until recently on Easter Island but became extinct, probably due to human pressure (Dransfield et al. 1984). An origin of the whole tribe in West Gondwanaland seems most compatible with the present day distribution. *Cocos* itself has probably reached its present natural (as opposed to anthropogenic) distribution by long distance dispersal by floating (to which it is eminently adapted) from the Americas via an austral route (with the fossil in New Zealand as, perhaps, a remnant of this pathway). *Elaeis* in West Africa appears to have a fossil record back to the Miocene, yet the presence of less specialized *Barcella* and *E. oleifera* in the Americas argues for an American origin of the Elaeidinae.

In summary, the Cocoeae probably became differentiated shortly before the breakup of Gondwanaland. They have radiated and become very diverse in the Americas. Members were rafted on the African and Madagascar Plates, where they survive to the present day, and on the Indian Plate, where they are now extinct. The ancestors of modern *Cocos nucifera* probably reached the Western Pacific area by long distance dispersal along a southern route. *Elaeis* may have reached West Africa before the breakup of Gondwanaland, but this hypothesis would require differentiation of the genus before the end of the Cretaceous. *Gastrococos* may have reached the West Indies relatively early in the Tertiary and then become rafted into its present position in Cuba. *Attalea crassispatha* and *Syagrus amara* may have had a similar history. Other central and southern North American members of the tribe probably reached their present position by dispersal along the Isthmus of Panama.

Geonomeae. — The final tribe, Geonomeae, is entirely New World in distribution (Map 51). The largest and most specialized genus, *Geonoma,* is also the most widespread, with species recorded from Mexico southwards to southern Brasil and Paraguay. The other genera display combinations of unspecialized and specialized characters. *Pholidostachys, Welfia, Calyptrogyne,* and *Asterogyne* are found in Central America and in northern South America, while *Calyptronoma* is confined to the Greater Antilles. It is not clear whether the origin of the group is in Central or South America, but in view of the strong austral bias of other tribes, an origin in the southern hemisphere seems more likely.

Phytelephantoideae. This small subfamily of three genera, strictly confined to the lowlands of northern South America (Map 52), is morphologically specialized and without obvious relatives. These genera have extremely heavy fruits and appear to have evolved and radiated in a relatively small area. Their present distribution is disjunct, with some taxa present to the east of the Andes and others to the west. The recent uplift of the Andes seems to have divided a previously continuous distribution into two isolated areas (Prance 1982) that to a large extent also coincide with Pleistocene refugia (Haffer 1969).

THE ORIGIN AND DISPERSAL OF THE PALMS

From the detailed analysis above it seems possible to distinguish in very broad terms two main groups of palms — those with a strong northern hemisphere distribution (i.e. with a Laurasian bias), and those with a strong southern hemisphere distribution (i.e. with a Gondwanic bias). Although we have pointed out exceptions, it is possible to make the following generalizations: Livistoninae, Coryphinae, Sabalinae, Phoeniceae, Calaminae, and Nypoideae are more strongly represented in the northern hemisphere, while the Borasseae, Lepidocaryeae, Ceroxyloideae, Arecoideae (with the exception of Caryoteae), and Phytelephantoideae are most diverse in the southern continents. It is of special note that the least specialized group, the Thrinacinae is present in both northern and southern hemispheres.

The above seems to imply that the palms of Laurasia have evolved somewhat independently from those of Gondwanaland and that mixing of Laurasian and Gondwanic elements has occurred where plates of the respective supercontinents have become juxtaposed, especially at the Isthmus of Panama and in Malesia. Some intermingling seems to have occurred but insufficient to mask the pronounced bicentricity of the family.

Three hypotheses on the origin and dispersal of palms may be considered. Moore (1973b) proposed that the family originated in West Gondwanaland followed by dispersal northwards and eastwards into Laurasia and along the shores of the Tethys to present day Southeast Asia, and rafting on Gondwanic fragments in the southern hemisphere on the breakup of the supercontinent. He based this hypothesis on the diversity of palms in South America and Africa and on the presence of the least specialized Thrinacinae (3 genera) in South America.

However, if the unspecialized apocarpic palms are considered as a whole, then all three major higher taxa (Thrinacinae, Phoeniceae, and Nypoideae) are present in the northern hemisphere or show in the Old World a northern bias, whereas only Thrinacinae are represented in South America. There is then overall a greater representation of the simplest palms in the northern hemisphere than in the southern. If, as Walker and Walker (1986) suggest, the monocotyledons as a whole have an origin in Laurasia rather than in Gondwanaland (as opposed to dicotyledons for which a Gondwanic origin seems more likely), then the presence of all three apocarpic palm groups in the northern hemisphere might lend support to a Laurasian origin for the family.

Wherever the palms originated, the fossil record indicates that by the Eocene they were widespread in North America, South America, Europe, China, and India. Many of the fossils are of costapalmate leaves, indicating, as does present distribution, that a protopalm stock perhaps similar to Thrinacinae was widely distributed early in both Laurasia and Gondwanaland. The first palms may have originated at a time when the separation of Gondwanaland and Laurasia was incomplete and dispersal between the two supercontinents was still possible. Evidence for this is provided both by the fossil record and by the present occurrence of the least specialized Thrinacinae on both supercontinents. This hypothesis differs from the two considered above by suggesting that the first palms quickly became widespread in both Gondwana and Laurasia. Such a hypothesis would better explain the distribution of the least specialized Thrinacinae with equally unspecialized members in South America, North America, Europe, and Asia, but with the closely related subtribes Livistoninae, Coryphinae, and Sabalinae predominantly Laurasian.

The early appearance of palms in the fossil record, the unsuitability of most palms to long distance dispersal, the many endemics, and the obvious Laurasian or Gondawanic bias of some groups make palms ideal organisms to relate to past continental movements. Further studies of fossils, of distributions and relationships of present genera, and of geological data are greatly needed and should be most rewarding.

CHAPTER VI

EVOLUTION AND RELATIONSHIPS

The diversity of palms encompasses many evolutionary trends (Moore and Uhl 1982) that have been used to establish the classification presented in this book. The sequences, as we currently understand them, are listed below:

Habit: from sympodial to monopodial (clustering to solitary)

Size: from moderate toward large and also toward small

Stem: from unbranched to dichotomously branched

from little to much sclerenchyma

from short to elongate internodes

from pleonanthic to hapaxanthic

Leaf: from an undivided eophyll to a palmate, costapalmate, pinnately ribbed or pinnate blade

from undivided and plicate to divided along the adaxial ribs ("induplicate") or along the abaxial ribs ("reduplicate")

from pinnate to bipinnate or to pinnae divided longitudinally

from sheath split opposite the petiole to sheath tubular

from marcescent (dead leaves persistent) to deciduous

from central vascular bundles of the petiole with a single phloem strand to two phloem strands

Inflorescence units: from moderately branched to spicate or less frequently to more diffusely branched

from one unit per leaf axil to more than one per axil

from among the leaves to below them or to above them in a compound terminal inflorescence

Prophyll: from incompletely to completely enclosing the inflorescence

from completely to incompletely encircling the peduncle

Bracts: from conspicuous to small or absent at maturity

first peduncular bract from tubular and open at the apex to completely enclosing the inflorescence in bud, and then from ungrooved to deeply grooved

Flower arrangement: from solitary, pedicellate, bracteolate flowers to a sympodial cincinnus of 2 or 3 or more, or to a short monopodial axis of 2–4 or more

Bracteoles: from sheathing and prophyllate to incompletely developed or absent

Flowers: from bisexual to unisexual, then associated with polygamy, or from monoecism to dioecism

Perianth: from 3-parted to 2-parted or 4-parted to 10-parted or reduced and consisting of only one whorl

Sepals: from distinct and slightly imbricate to connate or separated, or strongly imbricate

Petals: from distinct and slightly imbricate to valvate, or connate, or strongly imbricate

Stamens: from 6 to 3 or to more than 6 (to 950+)

Filaments: from relatively slender and distinct to broad and thick, and often connate or adnate to the perianth, or both

Staminodes: from stamenlike with abortive anthers, to short teeth, or to a cupule at the base of the ovary or completely enclosing the gynoecium, to absent

Pollen: from monosulcate to trichotomosulcate to disulcate to monoporate, diporate, or triporate

Gynoecium: from carpels separate to fused

Carpels or locules: from 3 to 2–1 or to 4–10

Ovules: from moderate to small or to large

from anatropous to hemianatropous or campylotropous or orthotropous

Pistillode: from only slightly modified from the gynoecium to vestigial or lacking or rarely to prominent

Fruit: from fleshy to dry and fibrous

Endocarp: from little differentiated or thin, to thick and hard, and sometimes with a pore or operculum over the embryo

Seed: from moderate to small or to very large

from entire to dissected, bilobed, or perforate

Sarcotesta: from absent to present

Endosperm: from homogeneous to invaginated or ruminate

Germination: from remote-tubular or -ligular to adjacent-ligular

Chromosome complement: from $n = 18$ to $n = 17, 16, 15, 14, 13,$ and 12

SOME COMMENTS ON THE
RELATIONSHIPS OF
THE SUBFAMILIES

The foregoing list identifies a large number of evolutionary sequences in the family. Comments on relationships of genera and higher categories are given throughout the taxonomic treatment after the diagnoses of groups and in notes under each genus. It seems worthwhile to consider somewhat further the relationships of the subfamilies.

Four characters are most useful in circumscribing the subfamilies. These are: 1) the nature of the leaf, in particular its form: palmate, costapalmate, or pinnate, and the splitting: induplicate or reduplicate; 2) the number of peduncular bracts on the inflorescence, i.e. the number of empty bracts between the prophyll and the lowest bract that subtends a primary branch; 3) the arrangement of the flowers: whether solitary, or if in clusters, whether the clusters are monopodial or sympodial, and if sympodial, the form of cincinnus, whether irregular, or symmetrically two-ranked, or with flowers in dyads, triads, or acervuli; 4) the character of the gynoecium: apocarpous, syncarpous in various ways, pseudomonomerous, or multicarpellate.

Subfamily I, the Coryphoideae, is the most diverse, exhibiting many, indeed perhaps most, of the various character states seen elsewhere in the family. The subfamily also has more unspecialized characters than any other. Evolutionary trends include remarkable variation in leaf form, inflorescences with numerous peduncular bracts, or one, or none; flowers predominately solitary, or in irregular, or, in more advanced groups in the subfamily, more regular cincinni; a gynoecium of predominantly three but sometimes one to four carpels, apocarpous, or syncarpous in various ways, but with fruits usually developing from only one carpel. It may also be noteworthy that spines, where present, are petiolar or represent modified organs and are not emergences. The subfamily includes a seemingly related but diverse group of genera which appear to have arisen early from a perhaps widely dispersed protopalm stock. Further study is needed to determine whether the Coryphoideae is polyphyletic.

Subfamily II, the Calamoideae, is distinguished by several shared derived characters, in particular by emergent spines on many organs, predominantly tubular inflorescence bracts and floral bracteoles, the development of special climbing organs (cirrus and flagellum), a dyadic flower cluster, the occurrence of scaly fruits, and a trilocular, triovulate gynoecium in which the ventral sutures of the carpels are not completely closed and the micropyles of the anatropous ovules face the center of the gynoecium. The last three characters are not found elsewhere in the Palmae. Members of the Calamoideae also show great variation in habit and inflorescence form. A few characters, such as several to few or no peduncular bracts, trimerous gynoecia, and the loss of two carpels after fertilization are coryphoidlike, as is the occurrence of adnation in inflorescence branches. Otherwise no clear relationship to other subfamilies is evident. The occurrence of some unspecialized characters such as hermaphroditic flowers suggests that this subfamily also originated early in the evolution of the family.

Subfamily III, the Nypoideae, contains a single genus that is clearly similar to many genera of Calamoideae, Ceroxyloideae, Arecoideae, and Phytelephantoideae in its regularly pinnate leaf. In inflorescence, flower, and fruit structure, *Nypa* is unusual, exhibiting some characters that are unspecialized and other characters that are specialized within both palms and monocotyledons. *Nypa* is also one of the first palms recognizable in the fossil record. It exhibits adnation in the inflorescence, as do members of Coryphoideae and Calamoideae, but no structure except the leaf has yet suggested relationship to any other palms.

Subfamily IV, the Ceroxyloideae, is characterized by leaves of pinnate reduplicate form, by usually several peduncular bracts; by flowers that are solitary and spirally arranged or in special cincinni (acervuli), and by valvate, distinct, or connate sepals and petals, and a triovulate, rounded or somewhat three-lobed, syncarpous gynoecium containing abundant raphides around the locules. The structure of the gynoecium is constant throughout. The genera of the subfamily exhibit variation in habit and in the form of the pinnate leaf. The occurrence in some members of two characters: incomplete prophylls and/or multiple inflorescences, appears to relate the subfamily more closely to certain Arecoideae than to the other subfamilies. The presence of several peduncular bracts, spirally arranged, moderate to small, rather unspecialized flowers, and relatively small fruits, mostly developing from one carpel, suggest affinities with some of the less specialized Coryphoideae.

Subfamily V, the Arecoideae, is characterized by the occurrence in all members of flowers in triads or in clusters derived from triads. This large subfamily includes six extremely diverse tribes. The number of peduncular bracts is characteristic for each tribe; several are present in Caryoteae and Iriarteeae, three in Podococceae, but usually only two in Areceae, Cocoeae, and Geonomeae. The first two tribes, Caryoteae and Iriarteeae, have several characters in common—several peduncular bracts, praemorse leaflets, triovulate gynoecia and in some genera multiple inflorescences, and bipinnate leaves. These tribes seem more closely related to each other than to the other tribes. The third tribe, the Podococceae, consists of a single monotypic genus, which shows some similarities in leaf structure to the Iriarteeae. The tribe Areceae has mostly pseudomonomerous gynoecia and the Cocoeae trimerous gynoecia and endocarps with pores. The two tribes are similar in having one, often specialized, peduncular bract, and in several aspects of flower structure, such as the occurrence of valvate petals in staminate flowers, and extremely imbricate petals in pistillate flowers. The final tribe, the Geonomeae, is distinct in bearing spicate inflorescence branches that bear highly specialized flowers enclosed in pits.

If gynoecial structure is considered in the subfamily as a whole, it appears that pseudomonomery may have arisen three times—in subtribe Wettiniinae of the Iriarteeae, where styles are lateral; in the Areceae, where the least specialized subtribes are triovulate and the much more prevalent pseudomonomerous gynoecia have terminal styles and stigmas; and in the Geonomeae where in the one pseudomonomerous genus, *Geonoma,* styles are lateral but elongate and resemble those of other members of Geonomeae in form.

Other trends within the subfamily are toward specialization of staminate flowers, which usually have distinct sepals and valvate petals but variously differentiated pistillodes, especially in Areceae and Geonomeae. Pistillate flowers have specialized staminodes in Areceae, Cocoeae, and Geonomeae. As with Ceroxyloideae, several trends evident in Coryphoideae are also present here. These include reduction in number of peduncular bracts and reduction or elaboration in inflorescence branching. All tribes of Arecoideae have at least a few genera with trimerous gynoecia, but in Areceae and Geonomeae, pseudomonomery is established at an earlier level, i.e. in the flower rather than during fruit development. Two subtribes, Oncospermatinae (Areceae) and Bactridinae (Cocoeae) have also developed emergent spines, as have many Calamoideae.

Subfamily VI, the Phytelephantoideae, is distinctive in having monopodial flower clusters, multiparted flowers, centrifugal stamen development, and many-seeded fruits. Although the pinnate reduplicate leaves are like those of Ceroxyloideae and Arecoideae, no special similarities other than form can be noted. Only two peduncular bracts are fully developed but many small ones are present (Uhl and Dransfield 1984), suggesting similar reduction series to those in Coryphoideae, Calamoideae, and Arecoideae. Flowers with more than three parts per whorl occur elsewhere in only one genus (*Chelyocarpus*) in Coryphoideae, and multiparted gynoecia and fruits in three genera (*Scheelea, Attalea,* and *Orbignya*) of Arecoideae. The form and histology of the gynoecium bears some resemblance to that of *Manicaria* of the Arecoideae, and some similarities in development to that of Calamoideae, but no definite relationships to other subfamilies can be suggested at this time.

In summary, we point out that no one shared derived feature characterizes all genera of Coryphoideae. Perhaps this subfamily, including as it does a majority of the least specialized characters in the family as a whole, represents in part relicts of an earlier more widespread palm population. Each of the other five subfamilies is characterized by one or several shared derived characters and each appears to represent a natural and monophyletic group of genera. Relationships of some genera, particularly in the large Arecoideae, will certainly be refined as more information accrues.

THE RELATIONSHIP OF PALMS TO OTHER MONOCOTYLEDONS

Palms epitomize the monocotyledons in many ways. Sympodial habits (Holttum 1955), leaves with sheathing bases and parallel venation, and flowers with a trimerous (3 sepals—3 petals—6 stamens—3 carpels) plan are basic characters in palms and in monocotyledons as a whole. In classifications of monocotyledons, palms have been placed separately or united into orders or superorders with three other families: the Araceae, Cyclanthaceae, and Pandanaceae (see Dahlgren and Clifford 1982 for a summary). These families have been thought to share with palms more or less arborescent habits, large, sometimes plicate leaves, and rather small or not colorful flowers. However, as more information has accumulated the families in question have been proved more and more different from each other and from the palms. The taxonomy is now beginning to reflect the differences. Dahlgren and Clifford have noted that Araceae differ from palms in flavonoid chemistry and the lack of silica bodies and have placed the Araceae in a different superorder. Recently Thorne (1983) has placed the Araceae, Pandanaceae, Cyclanthaceae, and Palmae in separate superorders, noting the vast phyletic distances separating these families. Dahlgren, Clifford, and Yeo (1985) also now recognize the isolation of the Palmae. Dahlgren and Clifford (1982) note that the luteolin/apigenin, tricin, flavone sulfates, and silica bodies are similar in palms and grasses but find other major differences between the families. More information on chemistry and inflorescence and floral development is obviously needed if relationships of palms and other monocotyledons are to be understood.

We may conclude that in large part the characters used to relate palms to other monocotyledons are those that distinguish the monocotyledons as a whole. Several characters that we consider unspecialized in palms are also regarded as basic in monocotyledons. Habit, parallel venation in leaves, and trimerous flowers have been noted above. In apocarpous palms, carpels are conduplicate, follicular in shape, and have open ventral sutures; in short, they are like carpels considered primitive in angiosperms as a whole. The unique, perhaps ascidiform carpel of *Nypa* may be a different unspecialized form,

emphasizing further the early and diverse history of the Palmae. We also suppose an entire leaf to be least specialized in palms, as in monocotyledons. Finally the monosulcate pollen found in many palms closely resembles primitive types. As we have noted, some fossil pollen grains considered as belonging to unidentified early monocotyledons could well represent palms.

Some authors (Cronquist 1981; Muller 1984) have suggested that palms represent a secondary radiation of monocotyledonous stock. This does not seem to take into account the large number of character states that palms today reveal. Many evolutionary series occur within the family. On the one hand palms possess characters that appear to represent the earliest forms in monocotyledons; on the other they show many specialized structures and evolutionary trends. When evolutionary sequences are carefully examined, palms appear to retain characters of a very early monocotyledonous stock from which more highly specialized palms and other monocotyledonous families may have evolved. What has not been fully realized is the occurrence within the family of so many characters that may well have distinguished the first monocotyledons or perhaps even the first angiosperms. A better understanding of evolutionary sequences in palms may well reveal clues to the origin of the monocotyledons.

CHAPTER VII

INTRODUCTION TO THE CLASSIFICATION: THE DEVELOPMENT OF PALM TAXONOMY

The preeminence and beauty of palms in tropical landscapes ensured that early European naturalists visiting the tropics would marvel at them as plants and be aware of their many uses. Pre-Linnean studies of natural history such as Rumphius' *Herbarium Amboinense* (1741–1755), van Rheede tot Drakenstein's *Hortus Indicus Malabaricus* (1678–1693) and Kaempfer's *Amoenitatum exoticarum* (1712) introduced European scholars to the details of palms. Some of the early ethnobotanical descriptions of the coconut by Rheede and the sago palm by Rumphius read with a freshness and accuracy which has scarcely been improved upon. Rumphius, furthermore, was aware of a considerable diversity of palms. He described or referred to over fifty different taxa, a number which must include most of the palms to be found in the relatively rich area of the central Moluccas.

Linnaeus knew only *Chamaerops* from living material and had seen herbarium material of *Calamus*. Others he knew of from the writings of these great early naturalists, and on their accounts based the few names of palms that he published, representing nine ethnobotanically important genera (1753). In recognizing these palms as being related to each other but isolated from other flowering plants, Linnaeus laid the basis for future classification. Linnean palm names have now been typified because it has been possible to decide on which elements he probably based his names (Moore and Dransfield 1979). Far more problematical are names published by botanists such as Giseke (1792) just after Linnaeus' time; impressed by the order and convenience of the Linnean binomial system, they published numerous names by putting into binomials names encountered in pre-Linnean works. No types exist for most of these names, and interpretation of their origins is difficult; yet they are validly published and should be respected under the "International Code of Botanical Nomenclature."

In the late eighteenth and early nineteenth centuries exploration by European naturalists, such as Alexander von Humboldt, increased, and through accounts of their travels and their specimens, the palms gradually became better known and described in detail. By 1824 the great diversity among the palms was well appreciated. The first significant attempt at ordering them was published by Martius as "Palmarum Familia" (1824). Martius arranged the genera in six series: Series I Sabalinae, Series II Coryphinae, Series III Lepidocarya, Series IV Borasseae, Series V Arecinae, and Series VI Cocoinae. Although these "series" might be interpreted as subfamilies, they are unfortunately not validly published at that rank. Later, when Martius published the monumental "Historia Naturalis Palmarum" (1823–50) the six "series" were elevated to the rank of family, the order Principes thus comprising six families.

About the same time, two other important botanists, William Griffith and Carl Ludwig Blume, were studying palms. Griffith, working in India and Malaya, published an exemplary account of the palms of British India in the Calcutta Journal of Natural History (1844, 1845). He regarded the palms as a single family and clearly divided the Asiatic palms with which he was familiar into subfamilies. His names are the first published explicitly as subfamilies (although his endings "-inae" do not accord with modern usage). It is to William Griffith that we owe the names Coryphoideae, Calamoideae, and Nypoideae. Blume worked in Java, describing among many other flowering plants the palms of Java, Sumatra, and other islands of the then Dutch East Indies. Although he ordered the palms, he published no acceptable names of higher categories. At the generic and species level, however, his contribution to palm botany is very significant. The nomenclatural problems caused by the almost simultaneous publication of new names by Martius, Griffith, and Blume have been clarified by Dransfield and Moore (1982).

In the New World, Alfred Russel Wallace and Richard Spruce carried out major explorations of the South American tropics in the 1850's and 1860's. Both naturalists were much impressed by the palms and their articles on them are of lasting significance. Wallace (1853) published a popular book on palms of the Amazon and their uses, while Spruce (1871) presented careful detailed descriptions of many South American palms.

The accumulating body of information about palms formed the basis of the most significant system of classification after William Griffith's, that of J. D. Hooker, published in Bentham and Hooker's Genera Plantarum (1883). Hooker arranged all palm genera known to him in six tribes, further divided into subtribes. He saw no reason to recognize a third rank and his tribes are equivalent to Griffith's subfamilies. To Hooker we owe many of the subtribes recognized in the present system. Hooker's system is notable for its thoroughness and conciseness and the accuracy of the descriptions. The alignment of the 132 genera known to him has been followed by many subsequent authors and even the composition of some subtribes has not changed at all in the present work (e.g. Linospadicinae, Iriarteinae, Wettiniinae). Hooker's system of classification synthesizes the work of his predecessors. The importance of his account is not so much the originality of his concepts as the clear, concise order he introduced into the family.

The first phylogenetic classification of the family was that of Drude (1887) in Engler and Prantl's "Die Natürlichen Pflanzenfamilien." Drude recognized the unspecialized nature of the Coryphoideae, Calamoideae, and Nypoideae.

Toward the end of the nineteenth century, Barbosa Rodrigues made a detailed floristic study of the palms of Brazil. His work culminated in two magnificent folio works closely modelled on Martius' "Historia Naturalis Palmarum," published as "Sertum Palmarum Brasiliensium" in 1903.

The greatest palm taxonomist of the latter half of the 19th and the early 20th century, was undoubtedly the Italian botanist Beccari. Beccari's considerable field experience in the Malesian region, in particular in Borneo, is very evident in his writing. He was certainly aware of variation in palm species and when some of his taxa have proved to be conspecific with previously described species, his descriptions are usually so careful and complete that critical realignment is easily accomplished. Beccari concentrated on the palms of Asia, and to a lesser extent on those of Africa and Madagascar. His results were published in a wide range of journals but culminated in a magnificent series of volumes of the Annals of the Royal Botanic Garden, Calcutta, illustrated, for the most part, by natural size photographic plates of types or representative specimens. These monographs of the rattan palms and of the Corypheae remain the most important works on those groups.

Although Beccari published a prodigious number of exceptional works, he left many projects unfinished when he died in 1920. One of these was a monograph of the genera of Old World arecoid palms. Beccari began his work on Old World arecoid palms by continuing the studies that were initiated by Scheffer (1873, 1876) of arecoid genera cultivated in the Botanic Gardens at Bogor. Beccari gradually accumulated an unparalled knowledge of this most complex subfamily. His account was finally edited and published by Pichi-Sermolli (Beccari and Pichi-Sermolli 1955). This extremely important work contains a synopsis of Beccari's classification of the whole family and a very detailed classification of subfamily Arecoideae (sensu Beccari).

Burret, working in Berlin and with relatively very little experience in the field, replaced Beccari in the 1920's and 1930's as the most prolific palm student. He concentrated initially on palms from the New World but soon monographed those of Arabia, China, and the Pacific. His specific and to some extent generic concepts are generally regarded today as being narrow and many a Burret name has been reduced to synonymy. However, his published works on palms are very extensive. He too was working towards a Genera Palmarum. A virtually completed manuscript of the family for *Die Natürlichen Pflanzenfamilien* was destroyed during the second World War. It appears that Burret never recovered from the demoralizing effects of the loss of the manuscript, but an outline of his system was published by Eva Potztal (1964). The classification is certainly of considerable significance.

Saakov (1954) published a system of classification based primarily on the form of the leaf—whether palmate or pinnate—and secondarily on the method of germination. This system results in the wide separation of genera which, based on characters other than germination type, are manifestly closely related (e.g. *Butia* and *Jubaea*). Although Saakov's system seems artificial and less usable, we owe to him the publication of the subtribal names 'Livistoninae' and 'Butiinae.'

Satake (1962) also published a classification of the family based largely on Burret's system, but with rather greater emphasis on leaf vernation. Leaf vernation has proved to be much less reliable as a major

Table VII.1. **A COMPARISON OF MAJOR CLASSIFICATIONS OF THE PALMS***

Dransfield and Uhl 1986 Present classification (subfamilies, tribes)		Moore 1973 Without rank	Potztal 1964 As subfamilies
I Coryphoideae	Corypheae	I Coryphoid palms	5 Coryphoideae
	Phoeniceae	II Phoenicoid palms	6 Phoenicoideae
	Borasseae	III Borassoid palms	3 Borassoideae
II Calamoideae	Calameae	IV Lepidocaryoid palms	4 Lepidocaryoideae
	Lepidocaryeae		
III Nypoideae		V Nypoid palms	2 Nypoideae
IV Ceroxyloideae	Cyclospatheae	VII Pseudophoenicoid palms	Arecoideae tribe Ceroxyleae
	Ceroxyleae	VIII Ceroxyloid palms	Arecoideae tribe Ceroxyleae
	Hyophorbeae	IX Chamaedoreoid palms	Arecoideae tribes Ceroxyleae Chamaedoreae
V Arecoideae	Caryoteae	VI Caryotoid palms	8 Caryotoideae
	Iriarteeae	X Iriarteoid palms	Arecoideae tribe Iriarteeae
	Podococceae	XI Podococcoid palms	Arecoideae tribe Dypsideae
	Areceae	XII Arecoid palms	7 Arecoideae
	Cocoeae	XIII Cocosoid palms	1 Cocosoideae
	Geonomeae	XIV Geonomoid palms	Arecoideae tribe Geonomeae
VI Phytelephantoideae		XV Phytelephantoid palms	9 Phytelephantoideae

* Roman numerals after numbering of original authors; arabic numerals indicate relative position in unnumbered sequences.

taxonomic character than was originally thought, and Satake's system, in relying on this character, also separates some apparently closely related taxa.

Corner (1966) did much to vitalize interest in the palm family with his inspiring book on the natural history of palms, but did not make any direct contribution to the formal taxonomy of palms.

The most important recent classification of the family is that of Moore (1973a), "The Major Groups of Palms and Their Distribution." He arranged the genera as well as his major groups in order of specialization based on an included list of characters. Moore's groupings have been widely followed. For more than a decade they have formed a basis for serious palm students, as they have for this book, and for two other contributions to palm classification (Dahlgren et al. 1985; Imchanitzkaja 1985). The major classifications of the family are compared in Table VII.1.

The present system of classification differs from that of Moore (1973a) in several ways. None of Moore's Major Groups had any formal nomenclatural status. In not indicating ranks for the entities, he left the way open for a decision on whether to divide the whole family into several families or whether to leave it as one and recognize all fifteen Major Groups as subfamilies or tribes. We have veered towards conservatism in recognizing the palms as a single family with clearly defined subfamilies.

Moore recognized five major lines of evolution. We have maintained his first three lines as subfamilies Coryphoideae, Calamoideae, and Nypoideae. His fourth line, the large arecoid group we have split into three subfamilies—Ceroxyloideae, Arecoideae, and Phytelephantoideae. The major difference between Moore's classification and the present system is in the position of the Caryotoid palms. Although

Table VII.1. **EXTENDED**

Satake 1962	Drude 1887	Hooker 1883	Martius 1849–53
As subfamilies	As subfamilies	As tribes	As families
II Coryphoideae	I Coryphinae	III Corypheae	3 Coryphinae
V Phoenicoideae	Coryphinae tribe Phoeniceae	II Phoeniceae	Coryphinae tribe Phoenicinae
I Borassoideae	II Borassinae	V Borasseae	2 Borassinae
IV Calamoideae	III Lepidocaryinae	IV Lepidocaryeae	5 Lepidocaryinae
III Lepidocaryoideae			
X Nypoideae	V Phytelephantinae	Areceae dubiae affinitatis	6 Palmae Heteroclitae
Arecoideae tribe Ceroxyleae	Ceroxylinae-Arecineae subtribe Morenieae		
Arecoideae tribe Ceroxyleae	Ceroxylinae-Arecineae subtribe Iriarteae	Areceae subtribe Ceroxyleae	Arecinae
Arecoideae tribes Ceroxyleae Chamaedoreae	Ceroxylinae-Arecineae subtribe Morenieae	Areceae subtribe Chamaedoreae	Arecinae
VII Caryotoideae	Ceroxylinae-Arecineae subtribe Caryoteae	Areceae subtribe Caryotideae	Arecinae tribe Caryotinae
Arecoideae tribe Iriarteeae	Ceroxylinae-Arecineae subtribe Iriarteae	Areceae subtribe Iriarteeae, Wettinieae	Arecinae
Arecoideae tribe Dypsideae	Ceroxylinae-Arecineae subtribe Geonomeae	Areceae subtribe Geonomeae	
VI Arecoideae	IV Ceroxylinae tribe Arecineae	I Areceae	1 Arecinae
IX Cocosoideae	IV Ceroxylinae tribe Cocoineae	VI Cocoineae	4 Cocoinae
Arecoideae tribe Geonomeae	Ceroxylinae-Arecineae subtribe Geonomeae	Areceae subtribe Geonomeae	Arecinae Alveolares
VIII Phytelephantoideae	V Phytelephantinae	Areceae dubiae affinitatis	6 Palmae Heteroclitae

considered by Moore (1973a) as the fourth separate line of evolution, the group has so many similarities with the Arecoideae that we have included it therein as a tribe. Thus, we recognize six subfamilies in all, viz: Coryphoideae, Calamoideae, Nypoideae, Cer-oxyloideae, Arecoideae, and Phytelephantoideae. The formal taxonomic categories in the present classification were validated in outline form (Dransfield and Uhl 1986). Their relationships are discussed in Chapter VI.

Palm Habits. From left to right: *Chamaerops humilis, Washingtonia filifera, Cyrtostachys renda, Johannesteijsmannia altifrons* (center front), *Pigafetta filaris* (tallest), *Asterogyne martiana, Acoelorraphe wrightii, Laccospadix australasica, Licuala spinosa.*

Some of the Diversity of Palms. Clockwise from upper left: Palmate leaf, *Brahea* sp.; inflorescence in flower and peduncular bract, *Butia capitata*; fruits, *Phoenix reclinata*; bifid leaf, *Asterogyne martiana*; fruits, *Retispatha dumetosa*; fruits, *Coccothrinax* sp.; pinnate leaf, *Chrysalidocarpus lutescens*; fruit, *Gaussia maya*; bipinnate leaf, *Caryota* sp.; fruit, *Calamus eriocanthus*; fruits, *Synechanthus warscewiczianus*; bifid leaf, *Chamaedorea* sp.; center, fruits, *Nypa fruticans*.

Plate 1.—**A.** *Trithrinax acanthocoma,* Huntington Botanical Gardens, California; **B.** *Chelyocarpus ulei,* under surface of leaf, Peru; **C.** *Coccothrinax spissa,* Dominican Republic; **D.** *Coccothrinax spissa,* under surface of leaf, Dominican Republic.

Plate 2.—*Rhapidophyllum hystrix,* in the wild, Florida.

Plate 3.—*Livistona tahanensis,* in montane forest, Gunung Tahan, Malaysia.

Plate 4.—**A.** *Maxburretia furtadoana*, staminate inflorescences and sheath spines, south Thailand; **B.** *Livistona decipiens*, petiole bases and sheaths, cultivated, Florida; **C.** *Pholidocarpus sumatranus*, petiole bases, south Sumatra; **D.** *Johannesteijsmannia altifrons*, inflorescence at anthesis and young fruit, Selangor, Malaysia.

Plate 5.—**A.** *Licuala peltata,* juvenile leaves, cultivated, USA; **B.** *Licuala mattanensis,* ripe fruit, Sarawak; **C.** *Licuala ferruginea,* ants tend scale insects between immature fruit, Malaysia; **D.** *Licuala kunstleri,* open flowers, Malaysia.

Plate 6.—**A.** *Serenoa repens,* glaucous and normal forms, Florida; **B.** *Acoelorraphe wrightii,* showing effects of burning, Mexico; **C.** *Pritchardiopsis jeanneneyi,* immature fruit, New Caledonia.

Plate 7.—**A.** *Brahea edulis,* inflorescence, cultivated, Riverside, California; **B.** *Copernicia rigida,* view into crown of juvenile palm, Fairchild Tropical Garden, Florida.

Plate 8.—**A.** *Corypha umbraculifera*; **B.** *Chuniophoenix hainanensis,* upper surface of blade showing lack of hastula, Guangdong, China; **C.** *Chuniophoenix hainanensis,* young inflorescences, Guangdong, China; **D.** *Chuniophoenix nana,* open flowers and buds, Xishuang-banna, China.

Plate 9.— **A.** *Sabal mexicana,* between Laguna and La Piedra, Vera Cruz, Mexico; **B.** *Sabal palmetto,* Florida; **C.** *Phoenix* sp., Soledad, Cuba; **D.** *Phoenix canariensis,* ripe infructescences, Corfu.

85

Plate 10.—**A.** *Latania loddigesii,* pistillate, cultivated, Florida; **B.** *Latania lontaroides,* cultivated, Florida; **C.** *Borassodendron borneense,* pistillate flower at anthesis, Sarawak; **D.** *Lodoicea maldivica,* staminate inflorescence, cultivated, Jamaica.

Plate 11.—**A.** *Eugeissona utilis,* in flower, Brunei; **B.** *Eugeissona brachystachys,* staminate flower, Pahang, Malaysia; **C.** *Metroxylon solomonense* in flower, Guadalcanal; **D.** *Korthalsia laciniosa,* immature fruit, Thailand.

Plate 12.—**A.** *Salacca zalacca,* pistillate inflorescence, Bali; **B.** *Daemonorops micracantha,* fruit covered in "dragon's blood," Negri Sembilan, Malaysia; **C.** *Daemonorops sabut,* leaf sheath bearing interlocking spines forming ant galleries, Sabah; **D.** *Calamus foxworthyi,* a robust montane rattan, Palawan, Philippines.

Plate 13.—**A.** *Pogonotium divaricatum,* ripe fruit, Sarawak; **B.** *Plectocomiopsis mira,* ripe fruit, Sarawak; **C.** *Pigafetta filaris,* ripe fruit, north Sulawesi; **D.** *Plectocomia dransfieldiana,* open staminate flowers, Perak, Malaysia.

Plate 14.—**A.** *Mauritiella pacifica,* Colombia; **B.** *Nypa fruticans,* inflorescence showing central pistillate head, and lateral staminate rachillae, Sumatra; **C.** *Ceroxylon quindiuense,* in fruit, Colombia; **D.** *Ceroxylon quindiuense,* hastulalike flange of tissue on the rachis, cultivated, California.

Plate 15.—**A.** *Juania australis,* Masatierra, Juan Fernandez; **B.** *Ravenea moorei,* Grande Comore; **C.** *Gaussia attenuata,* Soledad, Cuba; **D.** *Synechanthus warscewiczianus,* cultivated, Ventura, California.

Plate 16.—*Hyophorbe verschaffeltii*, Mauritius.

Plate 17.—**A.** *Chamaedorea metallica,* staminate plant, cultivated, Cornell University, Ithaca, N.Y.; **B.** *Chamaedorea metallica,* fruit, cultivated, Cornell University, Ithaca, N.Y.; **C.** *Wendlandiella polyclada,* with Mrs. A. Bredeson, in tropical rain forest, Peru; **D.** *Caryota cumingii,* details of triads in bud, Palawan, Philippines.

93

Plate 18.—**A.** *Arenga brevipes,* pistillate flowers, Palawan, Philippines; **B.** *Arenga brevipes,* staminate flowers, Palawan, Philippines; **C.** *Wallichia disticha,* staminate inflorescence, Fairchild Tropical Garden, Florida.

Plate 19.—**A.** *Iriartea ventricosa,* Ecuador; **B.** *Catoblastus radiatus,* young fruit showing basal stigmatic remains, Antioquia, Colombia; **C.** *Wettinia cladospadix,* in young bud, Colombia; **D.** *Wettinina quinaria,* infructescence, Buenaventura, Colombia.

Plate 20.—**A.** *Archontophoenix alexandrae,* in flower and fruit, New South Wales, Australia; **B.** *Chambeyronia lepidota,* Mont Panié, New Caledonia; **C.** *Rhopalostylis sapida,* doubleheaded individual, New Zealand; **D.** *Rhopalostylis sapida,* fruit, cultivated, Kew, England.

Plate 21.– **A.** *Cyrtostachys renda,* showing leaf sheaths; **B.** *Veitchia arecina,* in fruit, Fairchild Tropical Garden, Florida; **C.** *Hydriastele microspadix* in flower and immature fruit, cultivated, Sarawak; **D.** *Hydriastele microspadix,* in ripe fruit, Papua New Guinea.

97

Plate 22.—**A.** *Pinanga aristata,* inflorescence at anthesis, the petals of the staminate flowers hairy, the stamens red, Sarawak; **B.** *Pinanga crassipes,* in immature fruit, Sarawak; **C.** *Areca catechu,* in flowers and fruit, Penang, Malaysia; **D.** *Areca catechu,* mature fruit, cultivated, Honduras.

98

Plate 23. — **A.** *Iguanura palmuncula* var. *palmuncula,* immature fruit with subbasal stigmatic remains, Sarawak; **B.** *Pelagodoxa henryana,* view of crown with infructescences, cultivated, Panama; **C.** *Heterospathe elata,* in flower and fruit, cultivated, Florida.

Plate 24.—**A.** *Alsmithia longipes,* crown and unopened inflorescence, Fiji; **B.** *Alsmithia longipes,* fruit, Fiji; **C.** *Campecarpus fulcitus,* stilt roots, New Caledonia; **D.** *Burretiokentia hapala,* New Caledonia.

Plate 25.—**A.** *Basselinia vestita,* in fruit; **B.** *Basselinia pancheri*; **C.** *Basselinia sordida,* with scurfy crownshaft and inflorescence at anthesis; **D.** *Basselinia humboldtiana*; all New Caledonia.

101

Plate 26.—**A.** *Acanthophoenix rubra,* fiercely armed crownshaft, Mauritius; **B.** *Deckenia nobilis,* with one inflorescence in bud, one at pistillate anthesis, and young infructescence, Mahé, Seychelles; **C.** *Tectiphiala ferox,* surviving in cleared land, Mauritius; **D.** *Roscheria melanochaetes,* in montane forest, Mahé, Seychelles.

Plate 27.—**A.** *Nephrosperma vanhoutteanum,* in ripe fruit, Mahé, Seychelles; **B.** *Nephrosperma vanhoutteanum,* with inflorescences, Mahé, Seychelles; **C.** *Marojejya darianii,* with M. E. Darian, northeastern Madagascar.

Plate 28.—**A.** *Jubaea chilensis,* in scrubland, Central Chile; **B.** *Cocos nucifera,* in full fruit, Belize; **C.** *Scheelea rostrata,* in full flower, Costa Rica; **D.** *Scheelea sp.,* pistillate flowers, cultivated, Florida.

Plate 29.—**A.** *Desmoncus isthmius,* in ripe fruit, Colombia; **B.** *Bactris gasipaes,* mature fruit harvested for sale, Costa Rica.

Plate 30.—**A.** *Palandra aequatoralis,* Ecuador; **B.** *Asterogyne martiana,* in undergrowth of rain forest, Costa Rica; **C.** *Phytelephas macrocarpa,* staminate plant in flower, cultivated, Belize; **D.** *Ammandra decasperma,* pistillate inflorescence at anthesis, Colombia.

Plate 31.—**A.** *Trithrinax acanthocoma,* cultivated, Chapman Field, Florida, U.S.A.; **B.** *Chelyocarpus dianeurus,* Colombia; **C.** *Cryosophila guagara,* Costa Rica; **D.** *Schippia concolor,* Fairchild Tropical Garden, Florida.

Plate 32.—**A.** *Thrinax parviflora,* Jamaica; **B.** *Coccothrinax fragrans,* garden of B. Gentry, Florida; **C.** *Zombia antillarum,* stem with spiny sheaths; **D.** *Trachycarpus fortunei,* Madrid.

Plate 33.—**A.** *Rhapidophyllum hystrix,* southern U.S.A.; **B.** *Chamaerops humilis*; **C.** *Maxburretia furtadoana,* on the summit of a limestone hill, Khao Phra Rahu, south Thailand; **D.** *Guihaia argyrata,* upper photo, adaxial surface of blade; lower photo, abaxial surface of blade; note the reduplicate segments; Guilin, Guangxi, China.

110

Plate 34.—**A.** *Rhapis excelsa,* Fairchild Tropical Garden, Florida; **B.** *Livistona australis,* Australia; **C.** *Johannesteijsmannia magnifica,* S. Lalang, Selangor, Malaysia; **D.** *Pholidocarpus sumatranus,* growing with *Pandanus helicopus* in a peat-swamp forest, Sumatra.

Plate 35. — **A.** *Licuala grandis,* cultivated in Kebun Raya, Bogor, Indonesia; **B.** *Pritchardiopsis jeanneneyi,* New Caledonia; **C.** *Pritchardia pacifica,* cultivated, Trinidad; **D.** *Colpothrinax wrightii,* Cuba.

Plate 36.—**A.** *Acoelorraphe wrightii,* Daytona Beach, Florida; **B.** *Serenoa repens, Florida;* **C.** *Brahea salvadorensis,* Belize; **D.** *Copernicia baileyana,* Fairchild Tropical Garden, Florida.

Plate 37.—**A.** *Washingtonia robusta,* California; **B.** *Corypha umbraculifera*; **C.** *Kerriodoxa elegans,* growing with *Caryota mitis,* south Thailand; **D.** *Nannorrhops ritchiana,* cultivated, Coconut Grove, Florida.

114

Plate 38.—**A.** *Chuniophoenix hainanensis,* South China Botanical Garden, Guangzhou, China; **B.** *Sabal palmetto,* Corkscrew Swamp, Florida; **C.** *Sabal causiarum,* Puerto Rico; **D.** *Phoenix reclinata,* Victoria Falls, Africa.

Plate 39.—**A.** *Borassodendron borneense,* in lowland Dipterocarp forest, Sarawak; **B.** *Borassodendron machadonis,* staminate tree bearing several inflorescences, south Thailand; **C.** *Latania* sp., Fairchild Tropical Garden, Florida; **D.** *Borassus flabellifer,* semi-cultivated population, Madura, Indonesia.

116

Plate 40.—**A.** *Lodoicia maldivica,* Sri Lanka; **B.** *Hyphaene compressa,* a many-branched individual, coastal Kenya; **C.** *Bismarckia nobilis,* Chapman Field, Florida; **D.** *Bismarckia nobilis,* Fairchild Tropical Garden, Florida.

Plate 41.—**A.** *Medemia argun,* adaxial view of base of leaf blade showing the lack of hastula, from a herbarium specimen, *d'Albertis, s.n.,* Sudan; **B.** *Laccosperma secundiflorum,* Cameroon; **C.** *Eremospatha cuspidata,* cultivated, Java, *Furtado 31184*; **D.** *Eugeissona utilis,* two stems dying after flowering and fruiting, Brunei.

Plate 42.—**A.** *Metroxylon sagu,* Sabah; **B.** *Korthalsia laciniosa,* stem apex showing inflorescences and reduced leaves, Malaysia; **C.** *Eleiodoxa conferta,* fruiting individual, with headlike masses of fruit, Malaysia; **D.** *Salacca ramosiana,* note the lobed leaflets peculiar to this species, Sabah.

Plate 43.—**A.** *Daemonorops scapigera,* staminate inflorescence, Sarawak; **B.** *Calamus erinaceus,* forming entanglements behind mangrove, with *Oncosperma tigillarium,* Pahang, Malaysia; **C.** *Calospatha scortechinii,* staminate individual in full flower, Negri Sembilan, Malaysia; **D.** *Pogonotium ursinum,* staminate individual; note the paired auricles with the inflorescence held between them, Sarawak.

120

Plate 44.— **A.** *Ceratolobus subangulatus*, infructescence with almost mature fruit, Malaysia; **B.** *Retispatha dumetosa*, details of the staminate inflorescence showing part of a spiny rachis bract and the netlike bracts subtending the catkinlike rachillae, Sabah; **C.** *Myrialepis paradoxa*, leaf sheath of juvenile stem, Negri Sembilan, Malaysia; **D.** *Myrialepis paradoxa*, mature fruit, Negri Sembilan, Malaysia.

Plate 45.—**A.** *Plectocomiopsis mira,* detail of sheath to show ocrea, Sarawak; **B.** *Plectocomia mulleri,* Sabah; **C.** *Plectocomia mulleri,* Sabah; **D.** *Pigafetta filaris,* pistillate tree in full fruit, Sulawesi, Indonesia.

122

Plate 46.—**A.** *Raphia taedigera,* Silico Creek, Nicaragua; **B.** *Oncocalamus mannii,* details of rachillae, Gabon; **C.** *Mauritia flexuosa,* Trinidad; **D.** *Lepidocaryum sp.,* Peru.

Plate 47.—**A.** *Nypa fruticans,* cultivated, Guyana; **B.** *Nypa fruticans,* Fairchild Tropical Garden, Florida; **C.** *Pseudophoenix sargentii* with *Thrinax radiata* below, Mexico; **D.** *Ceroxylon alpinum,* tall individual left after forest clearance, Colombia.

124

Plate 48.—**A.** *Oraniopsis appendiculata,* Queensland, Australia; **B.** *Oraniopsis appendiculata,* close-up of crown, Queensland, Australia; **C.** *Juania australis,* Juan Fernandez Islands; **D.** *Louvelia madagascariensis* from Louvel (1931).

Plate 49.—**A.** *Ravenea moorei,* Grand Comore; **B.** *Gaussia maya,* cultivated, Florida; **C.** *Gaussia attenuata,* roots, Puerto Rico; **D.** *Gaussia attenuata,* Puerto Rico.

Plate 50.— **A.** *Hyophorbe lagenicaulis*; **B.** *Synechanthus warscewiczianus,* Barro Colorado Island, Panama; **C.** *Chamaedorea brachypoda,* cultivated, Florida; **D.** *Chamaedorea sp.,* Costa Rica.

Plate 51.—**A.** *Arenga pinnata,* North Sulawesi, Indonesia; **B.** *Arenga engleri,* cultivated, Costa Rica; **C.** *Caryota no,* note the doubly pinnate leaves, Sabah; **D.** *Caryota urens,* cultivated, Cuba.

Plate 52.—**A.** *Wallichia disticha,* Fairchild Tropical Garden, Florida; **B.** *Dictyocaryum* sp., Colombia; **C.** *Iriartella setigera,* Brazil; **D.** *Socratea durissima,* Costa Rica.

Plate 53.—**A.** *Iriartea gigantea,* Costa Rica; **B.** *Socratea* sp., Colombia; **C.** *Wettinia quinaria,* Colombia; **D.** *Podococcus barteri,* Gabon, Africa.

130

Plate 54.—**A.** *Halmoorea trispatha,* Madagascar; **B.** *Orania sylvicola,* cultivated, Kebun Raya, Bogor, Indonesia; **C.** *Orania sp.,* Papua New Guinea; **D.** *Manicaria saccifera,* Panama.

Plate 55.—**A.** *Leopoldinia piassaba,* Venezuela; **B.** *Reinhardtia simplex,* cultivated, Lyon Arboretum, Hawaii; **C.** *Vonitra utilis,* Madagascar; **D.** *Chrysalidocarpus lutescens,* cultivated, Florida.

132

Plate 56.—**A.** *Neophloga lanceolata,* Madagascar; **B.** *Neodypsis decaryi,* cultivated, F_orida; **C.** *Phloga nodifera,* cultivated, Lyon Arboretum, Hawaii; **D.** *Dypsis louvelli,* Madagascar.

Plate 57.—**A.** *Prestoea montana,* Puerto Rico; **B.** *Oenocarpus mapora* subsp. *mapora*; **C.** *Oenocarpus distichus*; **D.** *Jessenia bataua,* Belem, Brazil.

134

Plate 58.—**A.** *Roystonea regia,* cultivated, Cuba; **B.** *Archontophoenix cunninghamiana,* Australia; **C.** *Chambeyronia macrocarpa,* New Caledonia; **D.** *Hedyscepe canterburyana,* Lord Howe Island.

Plate 59.— **A.** *Kentiopsis oliviformis,* New Caledonia; **B.** *Mackeea magnifica,* New Caledonia; **C.** *Actinokentia divaricata,* New Caledonia; **D.** *Cyrtostachys renda,* Sabah.

136

Plate 60. — **A.** *Calyptrocalyx* sp., Papua New Guinea; **B.** *Calyptrocalyx* sp., Papua New Guinea; **C.** *Linospadix monostachya,* Queensland, Australia; **D.** *Howea belmoreana* right, *H. forsteriana* left, Lord Howe Island.

Plate 61.—**A.** *Drymophloeus beguinii,* cultivated, Drummond Garden; **B.** *Carpentaria acuminata,* Fairchild Tropical Garden; **C.** *Veitchia merrillii,* cultivated; **D.** *Balaka* sp., Fairchild Tropical Garden; all Florida.

Plate 62.—**A.** *Normanbya normanbyi,* Singapore Botanic Gardens; **B.** *Wodyetia bifurcata,* Queensland, Australia; **C.** *Ptychosperma waiteanum* cultivated, Kew, England; **D.** *Ptychococcus lepidotus,* Papua New Guinea.

Plate 63.— **A.** *Brassiophoenix drymophloeoides,* Papua New Guinea; **B.** *Loxococcus rupicola,* Sri Lanka; **C.** *Gronophyllum chaunostachys,* Papua New Guinea; **D.** *Siphokentia beguinii,* cultivated, Drummond Garden, Florida.

Plate 64.—**A.** *Gulubia costata,* Papua New Guinea; **B.** *Nenga pumila* var. *pachystachya,* West Sumatra; **C.** *Nenga pumila* var. *pumila,* details of inflorescence, West Java, Indonesia; **D.** *Pinanga polymorpha,* dense stand developed in mossy upper montane forest, Pahang, Malaysia.

Plate 65.—**A.** *Areca dayung,* note the extraordinary leaf, Sarawak; **B.** *Areca vidaliana* details of inflorescence, Palawan, Philippines; **C.** *Neoveitchia storckii,* Fiji; **D.** *Neoveitchia storckii,* inflorescence, Fiji.

Plate 66.—**A.** *Pelagodoxa henryana,* on left, cultivated, Fiji; **B.** *Iguanura elegans,* note the undivided leaf characteristic of this species, Sarawak; **C.** *Brongniartikentia vaginata,* New Caledonia; **D.** *Lepidorrhachis mooreana,* Lord Howe Island.

Plate 67.—**A.** *Heterospathe elata,* cultivated, Tahiti; **B.** *Sommieria leucophylla,* Fairchild Tropical Garden, Florida; **C.** *Bentinckia nicobarica,* cultivated, Panama; **D.** *Clinosperma bracteale,* New Caledonia.

144

Plate 68.—**A.** *Cyphokentia macrostachya,* New Caledonia; **B.** *Moratia cerifera,* New Caledonia; **C.** *Clinostigma collegarum,* growing in montane forest, New Ireland; **D.** *Satakentia liukiuensis,* Ryuku Islands.

Plate 69.—**A.** *Rhopaloblaste ceramica,* Singapore Botanic Gardens; **B.** *Dictyosperma album,* Mauritius; **C.** *Actinorhytis calapparia* with *Areca catechu* on right, Selangor, Malaysia; **D.** *Lavoixia macrocarpa,* New Caledonia.

146

Plate 70.—**A.** *Alloschmidia glabrata*; **B.** *Cyphophoenix elegans*; **C.** *Campecarpus fulcitus*; **D.** *Basselinia gracilis*; all New Caledonia.

Plate 71.—**A.** *Basselinia sordida*; **B.** *Cyphosperma balansae*; **C.** *Veillonia alba*; **D.** *Burretiokentia hapala*; all New Caledonia.

148

Plate 72.—**A.** *Deckenia nobilis,* Seychelles; **B.** *Acanthophoenix rubra,* Mauritius; **C.** *Oncosperma tigillarium,* Johore, Malaysia; **D.** *Vershaffeltia splendida,* cultivated, Bogor.

Plate 73.—**A.** *Phoenicophorium borsigianum,* Seychelles; **B.** *Sclerosperma mannii,* Ghana; **C.** *Sclerosperma mannii,* Gabon; **D.** *Marojejya darianii,* Madagascar.

150

Plate 74.— **A.** *Butia capitata,* cultivated, Georgia, U.S.A.; **B.** *Jubaea chilensis,* Chile; **C.** *Jubaeopsis caffra,* cultivated, Sullivan collection, California; **D.** *Syagrus romanzoffiana,* Brazil.

Plate 75.—**A.** *Lytocaryum weddellianum,* cultivated, Brazil; **B.** *Parajubaea cocoides,* Ecuador; **C.** *Allagoptera arenaria,* coastal Brazil; **D.** *Polyandrococos pectinata,* cultivated, Kew, England.

152

Plate 76.—**A.** *Orbignya cohune,* cultivated, Cuba; **B.** *Attalea victoriana,* Colombia; **C.** *Scheelea rostrata,* Puerto Cortas, Honduras; **D.** *Orbignya guacuyule,* Mexico.

Plate 77.—**A.** *Maximiliana maripa,* Peru; **B.** *Elaeis oleifera,* Costa Rica; **C.** *Acrocomia antioquiensis,* inflorescence at staminate anthesis, Antioquia, Colombia; **D.** *Gastrococos crispa,* cultivated, Florida.

154

Plate 78.—**A.** *Aiphanes elegans,* cultivated, Venezuela; **B.** *Aiphanes acanthophylla,* cultivated, Florida; **C.** *Bactris gasipaes,* Peru; **D.** *Bactris militaris,* Costa Rica.

Plate 79.—**A.** *Astrocaryum standleyanum,* Palmar Norte, Costa Rica; **B.** *Astrocaryum mexicanum*; **C.** *Pholidostachys pulchra,* Costa Rica; **D.** *Welfia georgii,* Costa Rica.

156

Plate 80.—**A.** *Calyptronoma rivalis,* Puerto Rico; **B.** *Calyptrogyne sarapiquensis,* Costa Rica; **C.** *Asterogyne martiana,* Costa Rica; **D.** *Geonoma congesta,* Costa Rica.

157

Plate 81.—**A.** *Palandra aequatorialis,* Ecuador; **B.** *Ammandra decasperma,* Colombia; **C.** *Phytelephas sp.,* cultivated, Belize; **D.** *Ammandra decasperma,* old staminate inflorescence, near Buenaventura, Colombia.

PART II
CLASSIFICATION

ORDER: **PRINCIPES** Endlicher, Genera Plantarum
244. 1837

FAMILY: **PALMAE** Jussieu, Genera Plantarum 37. 1789 (conserved name). **ARECACEAE** C. H. Schultz-Schultzenstein, Natürliches System des Pflanzenreichs 317. 1832 (conserved alternative name for the family).

Small, medium-sized, or large, solitary or clustered, armed or unarmed, hapaxanthic or pleonanthic, hermaphroditic, polygamous, monoecious, or dioecious plants. Stems "woody," slender to massive, very short to very tall, creeping, subterranean, climbing, or erect, usually unbranched, rarely branching dichotomously, lacking cambium but sometimes increasing in diameter by diffuse growth, sometimes ventricose, internodes very short to elongate, leaf scars conspicuous or not, stilt roots present or absent, roots adventitious, sometimes modified into spines. Leaves alternate, spirally arranged, rarely distichous or tristichous; sheath initially always tubular at the base, later frequently splitting, unarmed or armed with spines or prickles, glabrous or variously scaly or hairy, sometimes with a ligulelike appendage on either side of or in front of the petiole, sheaths sometimes forming a crownshaft; petiole usually present, terete, or variously adaxially channeled or ridged, unarmed or bearing spines or teeth, glabrous or variously scaly or hairy; hastulae present or absent; blade palmate, costapalmate, pinnate, bipinnate, or bifid, or entire and pinnately veined, plicate in bud, splitting along the adaxial folds (induplicate), or abaxial folds (reduplicate), rarely splitting between the folds, or not splitting; segments or leaflets lanceolate or linear to rhomboid or wedge-shaped, V-shaped (induplicate) or ∧-shaped (reduplicate), single-fold or many-fold, a midrib and numerous parallel secondary veins usually present, segments very rarely splitting further between the secondary veins, tips acute, acuminate, truncate, oblique or bifid, praemorse, or irregularly toothed or lobed, sometimes armed with spines or bristles along the margins and/or main veins, variously scaly and hairy, transverse veinlets conspicuous or obscure; proximal leaflets sometimes modified as spines (acanthophylls), rachis prolonged distally into a climbing whip (cirrus) in many climbing palms, sometimes also bearing acanthophylls. Inflorescences axillary, solitary or multiple, infrafoliar, interfoliar, or aggregated into a suprafoliar compound inflorescence, spicate or branched up to 6 orders, usually maturing acropetally, rarely basipetally, in some species of *Calamus* inflorescence modified as a climbing whip (flagellum); peduncle short to long; prophyll usually 2-keeled, very varied in shape and size, rarely subtending a first-order branch; peduncular bracts 0–many, very varied in shape and size; rachis shorter or longer than the peduncle; rachis bracts similar to peduncular bracts, or dissimilar, or much reduced; rachillae (flower-bearing branches) short to long, slender to massive, rachilla bracts conspicuous to minute or apparently lacking, sometimes connate laterally and adnate to the rachilla to form pits containing the flowers.

Flowers hermaphroditic or unisexual, then similar or dimorphic, sessile or stalked, borne singly or in cincinni of various forms including dyads, triads, or acervuli, or rarely in short monopodial clusters; perianth rarely of similar parts, usually clearly differentiated into sepals and petals, rarely uniseriate with a variable number of lobes; sepals (2) 3 (rarely more), distinct or variously connate, usually imbricate or basally connate, rarely valvate or widely separated; petals (2) 3 (rarely more), distinct or variously connate, valvate, imbricate, or imbricate with briefly valvate tips; stamens (3) 6 (or many, to 950 or more), filaments erect or inflexed in bud, free, or variously connate, or adnate to the petals, or both connate and adnate, anthers basifixed or dorsifixed, rarely didymous, or with widely separated anther sacs, straight or rarely twisted, introrse, latrorse, extrorse, or rarely opening by pores; pollen circular or elliptic in polar view, monoporate, diporate, triporate, monosulcate, disulcate, tri- or tetrachotomosulcate, or very rarely pontoperculate, exine intectate or tectate, very varied in ornamentation; staminodes ranging from toothlike to well developed, distinct or connate, sometimes adnate to petals or gynoecium, rarely absent; gynoecium apocarpous with (1–2) 3 (4) carpels, or variously syncarpous with 3 or rarely with more (to 10) locules or pseudomonomerous with 1 fertile locule, carpels follicular or rarely ascidiform, glabrous, variously hairy, or covered with imbricate scales, styles distinct or connate or not clearly differentiated, stigmas erect or recurved, rarely indistinct; ovule solitary in each locule, anatropous, hemianatropous, campylotropous, or orthotropous, basally, laterally, or apically attached, crassinucellate, integuments 2, the outer often wide, the inner narrow, the outer or the inner or both integuments forming the micropyle; pistillode present or absent in the staminate flower, ranging from minute and often trifid to large, bottle-shaped, exceeding the stamens. Fruit usually 1-seeded, sometimes 2–3–10-seeded, ranging from small to very large, stigmatic remains apical, lateral, or basal; epicarp smooth or hairy, prickly, corky-warted, or covered with imbricate scales, mesocarp fleshy, fibrous, or dry, endocarp not differentiated or thin, sometimes with an operculum over the embryo, or thick and then often with 3 or more pores at, below, or above the middle. Seed adhering to the pericarp or free, with thin or sometimes fleshy testa (sarcotesta), endosperm homogeneous or ruminate, sometimes penetrated by the testa; embryo apical, lateral, or basal. Germination adjacent-ligular, remote-ligular, or remote-tubular; eophyll simple and entire, bifid, palmate, or pinnate. Type: **Areca** Linnaeus.

The family is here divided into six subfamilies: **CORYPHOIDEAE** Griffith, **CALAMOIDEAE** Griffith, **NYPOIDEAE** Griffith, **CEROXYLOIDEAE** Drude, **ARECOIDEAE**, **PHYTELEPHANTOIDEAE** Drude.

OUTLINE OF THE GENERIC CLASSIFICATION OF PALMS

CORYPHOIDEAE Griffith, Calcutta Journal of Natural History 5:311. 1844 ('*Coryphinae*').

CORYPHEAE Martius in Endlicher, Genera Plantarum 252. 1837 ('*Coryphinae*').

Thrinacinae Beccari, Webbia 2:9. 1907 ('*Thrinaceae*'). Type: **Thrinax.**
1. Trithrinax (*Diodosperma*)
2. Chelyocarpus (*Tessmanniodoxa, Tessmanniophoenix*)
3. Cryosophila (*Acanthorrhiza*)
4. Itaya
5. Schippia
6. Thrinax (*Hemithrinax*)
7. Coccothrinax (*Haitiella, Thrincoma, Thringis*)
8. Zombia (*Oothrinax*)
9. Trachycarpus
10. Rhapidophyllum
11. Chamaerops (*Chamaeriphe, Chamaeriphes*)
12. Maxburretia (*Liberbaileya, Symphyogyne*)
13. Guihaia
14. Rhapis

Livistoninae Saakov, Palms and their culture in the USSR. 193. 1954. Type: **Livistona.**
15. Livistona (*Saribus, Wissmannia*)
16. Pholidocarpus
17. Johannesteijsmannia (*Teysmannia*)
18. Licuala (*Dammera, Pericycla*)
19. Pritchardiopsis
20. Pritchardia (*Eupritchardia, Styloma*)
21. Colpothrinax
22. Acoelorraphe (*Acanthosabal, Paurotis*)
23. Serenoa (*Diglossophyllum*)
24. Brahea (*Erythea, Glaucothea*)
25. Copernicia (*Arrudaria, Coryphomia*)
26. Washingtonia (*Neowashingtonia*)

Coryphinae Beccari, Webbia 2:4. 1907 ('*Eucorypheae*'). Type: **Corypha.**
27. Corypha (*Codda-Pana, Gembanga, Taliera*)
28. Nannorrhops
29. Chuniophoenix
30. Kerriodoxa

Sabalinae Martius in Endlicher, Genera Plantarum 252. 1837. Type: **Sabal.**
31. Sabal (*Inodes*)

PHOENICEAE Drude in Martius, Flora Brasiliensis 3(2):279. 1881. Type: **Phoenix.**
32. Phoenix (*Dachel, Elate, Palma, Zelonops*)

BORASSEAE Martius in Endlicher, Genera Plantarum 250. 1837 ('*Borassinae*').

Lataniinae Meisner, Plantarum Vascularium Genera 1:357. 1842 ('*Latanieae*'). Type: **Latania.**
33. Borassodendron
34. Latania (*Cleophora*)
35. Borassus (*Lontarus*)
36. Lodoicea

Hyphaeninae Beccari, Palme della Tribú Borasseae, 1. 1924 ('*Hyphaeneae*'). Type: **Hyphaene.**
37. Hyphaene (*Cucifera, Doma, Douma*)
38. Medemia
39. Bismarckia

CALAMOIDEAE Griffith, Calcutta Journal of Natural History 5:4. 1844.

CALAMEAE Drude in Martius, Flora Brasiliensis 3(2):270. 1881.

Ancistrophyllinae Beccari, Annals of the Royal Botanic Garden, Calcutta 12(2):209. 1918 ('*Ancistrophyllae*'). Type: *Ancistrophyllum* = **Laccosperma.**
40. Laccosperma (*Ancistrophyllum, Neoancistrophyllum*)
41. Eremospatha

Eugeissoninae Beccari, Annals of the Royal Botanic Garden, Calcutta 12(2):210. 1918 ('*Eugeissoneae*'). Type: **Eugeissona.**
42. Eugeissona

Metroxylinae Blume, Rumphia 2:157. 1843 ('*Metroxyleae*'). Type: **Metroxylon.**
43. Metroxylon (*Coelococcus, Sagus*)
44. Korthalsia (*Calamosagus*)

Calamineae Meisner, Plantarum Vascularium Genera 1:356. 1842. Type: **Calamus.**
45. Eleiodoxa
46. Salacca (*Lophospatha*)
47. Daemonorops
48. Calamus (*Cornera, Palmijuncus, Rotang, Rotanga, Schizospatha, Zalaccella*)
49. Calospatha
50. Pogonotium
51. Ceratolobus
52. Retispatha

Plectocomiinae J. Dransfield & N. Uhl, Principes 30:3. 1986. Type: **Plectocomia.**

53. Myrialepis (*Bejaudia*)
54. Plectocomiopsis
55. Plectocomia
Pigafettinae J. Dransfield & N. Uhl, Principes 30:3. 1986. Type: **Pigafetta.**
56. Pigafetta
Raphiinae J. D. Hooker in Bentham & J. D. Hooker, Genera Plantarum 3:872, 881. 1883 ('*Raphieae*'). Type: **Raphia.**
57. Raphia (*Sagus*)
Oncocalaminae J. Dransfield & N. Uhl, Principes 30:3. 1986. Type: **Oncocalamus.**
58. Oncocalamus
LEPIDOCARYEAE Martius in Endlicher, Genera Plantarum 248. 1837 ('*Lepidocaryinae*'). Type: **Lepidocaryum.**
59. Mauritia (*Orophoma*)
60. Mauritiella (*Lepidococcus*)
61. Lepidocaryum
NYPOIDEAE Griffith, Palms of British India 7: 1850 ('*Nipinae*'). Type: **Nypa.**
62. Nypa (*Nipa*)
CEROXYLOIDEAE Drude in Martius, Flora Brasiliensis 3(2):271. 1881 (as suborder 'Ceroxylinae').
CYCLOSPATHEAE O. F. Cook, Memoirs of the Torrey Botanical Club 12:24. 1902. Type: *Cyclospathe* = **Pseudophoenix.**
63. Pseudophoenix (*Chamaephoenix, Cyclospathe, Sargentia*)
CEROXYLEAE Satake, Hikobia 3:125. 1962. Type: **Ceroxylon.**
64. Ceroxylon (*Beethovenia, Klopstockia*)
65. Oraniopsis
66. Juania
67. Louvelia
68. Ravenea (*Ranevea*)
HYOPHORBEAE Drude in Martius, Flora Brasiliensis 3(2):275. 1881. Type: **Hyophorbe.**
69. Gaussia (*Aeria, Opsiandra*)
70. Hyophorbe (*Mascarena*)
71. Synechanthus (*Rathea, Reineckea*)
72. Chamaedorea (*Collinia, Dasystachys, Eleutheropetalum, Kinetostigma, Kunthia, Morenia, Nunnezharia, Nunnezia, Spathoscaphe, Stachyophorbe, Stephanostachys*)
73. Wendlandiella
ARECOIDEAE
CARYOTEAE Drude in Martius, Flora Brasiliensis 3(2):278. 1881. Type: **Caryota.**
74. Arenga (*Blancoa, Didymosperma, Gomutus, Saguerus*)

75. Caryota (*Schunda-Pana, Thuessinkia*)
76. Wallichia (*Asraoa, Harina, Wrightea*)
IRIARTEEAE Drude in Martius, Flora Brasiliensis 3(2):278. 1881.
Iriarteinae J. D. Hooker in Bentham & J. D. Hooker, Genera Plantarum 3:872, 875. 1883. ('*Iriarteeae*'). Type: **Iriartea.**
77. Dictyocaryum (*Dahlgrenia*)
78. Iriartella (*Cuatrecasea*)
79. Iriartea (*Deckeria*)
80. Socratea (*Metasocratea*)
Wettiniinae J. D. Hooker in Bentham & J. D. Hooker, Genera Plantarum 3:872, 876. 1883 ('*Wetteniae*'). Type: **Wettinia.**
81. Catoblastus (*Acrostigma, Catostigma*)
82. Wettinia (*Wettinella, Wettiniicarpus*)
PODOCOCCEAE J. Dransfield & N. Uhl, Principes 30:3. 1986. Type: **Podococcus.**
83. Podococcus
ARECEAE
Oraniinae J. Dransfield & N. Uhl, Principes 30: 3. 1986. Type: **Orania.**
84. Halmoorea
85. Orania (*Arausiaca, Macrocladus, Sindroa*)
Manicariinae J. Dransfield & N. Uhl, Principes 30:3. 1986. Type: **Manicaria.**
86. Manicaria (*Pilophora*)
Leopoldiniinae J. Dransfield & N. Uhl, Principes 30:3. 1986. Type: **Leopoldinia.**
87. Leopoldinia
Malortieinae J. D. Hooker in Bentham & J. D. Hooker, Genera Plantarum 3:872, 876. 1883 ('*Malortieae*'). Type: *Malortiea* = **Reinhardtia.**
88. Reinhardtia (*Malortiea*)
Dypsidinae Beccari, Palme del Madagascar 2. 1914. Type: **Dypsis.**
89. Vonitra
90. Chrysalidocarpus (*Macrophloga, Phlogella*)
91. Neophloga (*Dypsidium, Haplodypsis, Haplophloga*)
92. Neodypsis (*Antongilia* tentatively included here)
93. Phloga
94. Dypsis (*Adelodypsis, Trichodypsis*)
Euterpeinae J. Dransfield & N. Uhl, Principes 30:3. 1986. Type: **Euterpe.**
95. Euterpe Martius (*Catis, Plectis, Rooseveltia*)

96. Prestoea (*Acrista, Euterpe* Beccari, *Martinezia* Ruíz & Pavon, *Oreodoxa*)
97. Neonicholsonia (Bisnicholsonia *Woodsonia*)
98. Oenocarpus
99. Jessenia
100. Hyospathe

Roystoneinae J. Dransfield & N. Uhl, Principes 30:3. 1986. Type: **Roystonea.**
101. Roystonea (*Oreodoxa*)

Archontophoenicinae J. Dransfield & N. Uhl, Principes 30:3. 1986. Type: **Archontophoenix.**
102. Archontophoenix (*Loroma*)
103. Chambeyronia
104. Hedyscepe
105. Rhopalostylis (*Eora*)
106. Kentiopsis
107. Mackeea
108. Actinokentia

Cyrtostachydinae J. Dransfield & N. Uhl, Principes 30:3. 1986. Type: **Cyrtostachys.**
109. Cyrtostachys

Linospadicinae J. D. Hooker in Bentham & J. D. Hooker, Genera Plantarum 3:872, 876. 1883 ('*Linospadiceae*'). Type: **Linospadix.**
110. Calyptrocalyx (*Linospadix* Beccari ex J. D. Hooker, *Paralinospadix*)
111. Linospadix H. A. Wendland (*Bacularia*)
112. Laccospadix
113. Howea (*Denea, Grisebachia*)

Ptychospermatinae J. D. Hooker in Bentham & J. D. Hooker, Genera Plantarum 3:872, 874. 1883 ('*Ptychospermeae*'). Type: **Ptychosperma.**
114. Drymophloeus Zippelius (*Coleospadix, Rehderophoenix, Saguaster, Solfia*)
115. Carpentaria
116. Veitchia (*Adonidia, ?Kajewskia, Vitiphoenix*)
117. Balaka
118. Normanbya
119. Wodyetia
120. Ptychosperma (*Actinophloeus, Drymophloeus* Beccari, *Ponapea, Romanowia, Seaforthia, Strongylocaryum*)
121. Ptychococcus
122. Brassiophoenix

Arecinae. Type: **Areca.**
123. Loxococcus

124. Gronophyllum (*Kentia, Leptophoenix, Nengella*)
125. Siphokentia
126. Hydriastele (*Adelonenga*)
127. Gulubia (*Gulubiopsis, Paragulubia*)
128. Nenga
129. Pinanga (*Cladosperma, Ophiria, Pseudopinanga*)
130. Areca (*Gigliolia, Mischophloeus, Pichisermollia*)

Iguanurinae J. D. Hooker in Bentham & J. D. Hooker, Genera Plantarum 3:872, 876. 1883 ('*Iguanureae*'). Type: **Iguanura.**
131. Neoveitchia
132. Pelagodoxa
133. Iguanura (*Slackia*)
134. Brongniartikentia
135. Lepidorrhachis
136. Heterospathe (*Barkerwebbia, Ptychandra*)
137. Sommieria
138. Bentinckia
139. Clinosperma
140. Cyphokentia (*Dolichokentia*)
141. Moratia
142. Clinostigma (*Bentinckiopsis, Clinostigmopsis, Exorrhiza*)
143. Alsmithia
144. Satakentia
145. Rhopaloblaste (*Ptychoraphis*)
146. Dictyosperma (*Dicrosperma, Linoma*)
147. Actinorhytis
148. Lavoixia
149. Alloschmidia
150. Cyphophoenix
151. Campecarpus
152. Basselinia (*Microkentia, Nephrocarpus*)
153. Cyphosperma (*Taveunia*)
154. Veillonia
155. Burretiokentia (*Rhynchocarpa*)
156. Physokentia (*Goniosperma*)
157. Goniocladus

Oncospermatinae J. D. Hooker in Bentham & J. D. Hooker, Genera Plantarum 3:872, 874. 1883 ('Oncospermeae'). Type: **Oncosperma.**
158. Deckenia
159. Acanthophoenix
160. Oncosperma (*Keppleria*)
161. Tectiphiala
162. Verschaffeltia (*Regelia*)

163. Roscheria
164. Phoenicophorium (*Stevensonia*)
165. Nephrosperma

Sclerospermatinae J. Dransfield & N. Uhl, Principes 30:3. 1986. Type: **Sclerosperma**.

166. Sclerosperma
167. Marojejya

Areceae incertae sedis

168. Masoala
169. Carpoxylon

COCOEAE Martius in Endlicher, Genera Plantarum 254. 1837 ('*Cocoineae*').

Beccariophoenicinae J. Dransfield & N. Uhl, Principes 30:3. 1986. Type: **Beccariophoenix**.

170. Beccariophoenix

Butiinae Saakov, Palms and Their Culture in the USSR 193. 1954. Type: **Butia**.

171. Butia
172. Jubaea (*Micrococos, Molinaea*)
173. Jubaeopsis
174. Cocos (*Calappa, Coccus*)
175. Syagrus (*Arecastrum, Arikury, Arikuryroba, Barbosa, Chrysallidosperma, Langsdorffia, Platenia, Rhyticocos*)
176. Lytocaryum (*Glaziova, Microcoelum*)
177. Parajubaea
178. Allagoptera (*Diplothemium*)
179. Polyandrococos

Attaleinae Drude in Engler & Prantl, Natürlichen Pflanzenfamilien 2, 3:27. 78, 1887 ('*Attaleae*'). Type: **Attalea**.

180. Attalea (*Lithocarpos, Pindarea, Sarinia, Ynesa*)
181. Scheelea
182. Orbignya (*Parascheelea*)
183. Maximiliana (*Englerophoenix*) (*Markleya,* an intergeneric hybrid between *Maximiliana* and *Orbignya* included here)

Elaeidinae J. D. Hooker in Bentham & J. D. Hooker, Genera Plantarum 3:873, 882. 1883 ('*Elaeideae*'). Type: **Elaeis**.

184. Barcella
185. Elaeis (*Alfonsia, Corozo*)

Bactridinae J. D. Hooker in Bentham & J. D. Hooker, Genera Plantarum 3:873, 881. 1883 ('*Bactrideae*'). Type: **Bactris**.

186. Acrocomia (*Acanthococos*)
187. Gastrococos
188. Aiphanes (*Curima, Marara, Martine-*

zia of many authors, non Ruiz & Pavon, *Tilmia*)
189. Bactris (*Amylocarpus, Augustinea, Guilielma, Pyrenoglyphis, Yuyba*)
190. Desmoncus (*Atitara*)
191. Astrocaryum (*Avoira, Hexopetion, Toxophoenix*)

GEONOMEAE Drude in Martius, Flora Brasiliensis 3(2):275. 1881. Type: **Geonoma**.

192. Pholidostachys
193. Welfia
194. Calyptronoma (*Cocops*)
195. Calyptrogyne
196. Asterogyne (*Aristeyera*)
197. Geonoma (*Gynestum, Kalbreyera, Taenianthera*)

PHYTELEPHANTOIDEAE Drude in Engler & Prantl, Natürlichen Pflanzenfamilien 2, 3:28, 86. 1887 ('*Phytelephantinae*'). Type: **Phytelephas**.

198. Palandra
199. Phytelephas (*Elephantusia, Yarina*)
200. Ammandra

Key to the Subfamilies

1 Leaves palmate or costapalmate, rarely entire, induplicate, rarely reduplicate (but then apocarpous), or mixed induplicate-reduplicate (*Licuala*), or pinnate but induplicate and the leaflets with entire tips (*Phoenix*); flowers solitary or clustered, never in triads of a central pistillate and 2 lateral staminate . . . . **Coryphoideae**

1 Leaves pinnate, bipinnate, or entire and pinnately ribbed, or rarely palmate but then reduplicate and flowers syncarpous, reduplicate or rarely induplicate but then leaflets with praemorse tips; flowers solitary or clustered, frequently in triads 2

2 Ovary and fruit covered in imbricate scales; flowers hermaphroditic or unisexual but only rarely dimorphic, arranged singly or in dyads or rarely in cincinni . . . .
. . . . **Calamoideae**

2 Ovary and fruit glabrous or with peltate or basifixed scales, hairs, corky warts, or spines but not with imbricate scales; flowers hermaphroditic or unisexual, often dimorphic, borne singly or in triads, or in pairs derived from triads
. . . . 3

3 Pistillate flowers borne in a terminal head, each flower with 3(–4) free, large, asymmetrical carpels and 6 minute perianth segments; staminate flowers crowded on spikes at the tips of inflorescence branches below the pistillate head, each flower with 6 linear distinct perianth segments and 3 anthers borne on a solid stalk . . . . **Nypoideae**

3 Pistillate flowers not borne in a terminal head, or if so then plants dioecious and flowers multiparted; staminate flowers with stamen filaments free or variously connate, very rarely forming a solid stalk 4

4 Pistillate flowers borne in a head on a short peduncle, very large, each with numerous, spirally arranged sepals and petals and an elongate cylindrical style, gynoecium 5–10

locular and ovulate; fruit corky-warted with 5–10 seeds; staminate flowers large, sessile or stalked, receptacle flat or clublike, with reduced uniseriate perianth or perianth scarcely discernible, stamens very numerous . . . . **Phytelephantoideae**

4 Pistillate flowers not borne in a head, both staminate and pistillate flowers with sepals and petals in 2 whorls, style usually short, not long and cylindrical, locules 1–3, rarely more   5

5 Flowers usually unisexual, rarely hermaphroditic, borne singly or in lines (acervuli) very rarely in groups of 3 but then staminate flowers above the pistillate and peduncular bracts numerous . . . . **Ceroxyloideae**

5 Flowers always unisexual, borne in triads or in pairs derived from triads, very rarely the staminate flowers above the pistillate but then peduncular bract 1 . . . . **Arecoideae**

I CORYPHOIDEAE Griffith, Calcutta Journal of Natural History 5:311. 1844 ('*Coryphinae*').

Hermaphroditic, dioecious, polygamodioecious, or polygamomonoecious, never strictly monoecious; leaves usually palmate or costapalmate, only rarely undivided or pinnate, almost always strictly induplicate, but interfold splits occurring in 3 genera and leaves reduplicate in *Guihaia*; flowers solitary or in cincinni, never borne in triads of a central pistillate and 2 lateral staminate flowers; carpels free or variously connate.

The Coryphoideae is a diverse subtropical and pantropical subfamily. In it we include all palms placed in the "Coryphoid Line" by Moore (1973a). The subfamily is divided into three tribes, the Corypheae, the Phoeniceae, and the Borasseae, representing the coryphoid, borassoid, and phoenicoid major groups of Moore. The distinguishing vegetative character is the palmate or costapalmate, induplicately folded leaf. Within the subfamily there are very few differences in leaf form or venation. The only exceptions in form are the undivided leaves of *Johannesteijsmannia* and a few species of *Licuala,* and, of course, the regularly pinnate but induplicate leaf of *Phoenix.* There are a few exceptions to induplicate folding. The leaves of *Guihaia* are palmate and reduplicate; and those of *Rhapis, Rhapidophyllum,* and *Licuala* show anomalous splitting superimposed on a basic induplicate structure. (It is noteworthy that elsewhere in the family the only palmate leaves are reduplicate and belong to three genera of Calamoideae: *Lepidocaryum, Mauritia,* and *Mauritiella.*)

In inflorescence and flower structure the subfamily exhibits evolutionary trends that are basic in palms and to some extent also in monocotyledons. The interfoliar or suprafoliar, often highly branched inflorescences show considerable adnation of branches and reduction to spicate forms. Some of the simplest of all palm flowers belong to the first tribe, the Corypheae. These truly apocarpous flowers, having three sepals, three similar petals, six stamens in two whorls of three, and three follicular carpels, embody a structure considered unspecialized within the monocotyledons as a whole. With the exception of *Nypa,* all apocarpous palms belong to the Coryphoideae; these include the 14 genera of the Thrinacinae and *Phoenix.* Although dioecious, *Phoenix* has flowers which are remarkably similar to those of the Thrinacinae. The other subtribes of the Corypheae and the Borasseae exhibit varying degrees of connation of sepals, petals, stamens, and carpels.

The subfamily is further characterized by gametic chromosome numbers of mostly 18 and by some similarities in vegetative and floral anatomy. Midribs of members of the Corypheae (except for *Itaya,* Uhl 1972c) and Borasseae have vascular bundles with separate fibrous sheaths, but a vascularized midrib is lacking in *Phoenix* (Tomlinson 1961). Variations in floral anatomy appear to be modifications of a basic plan (see Chapter II).

The Borasseae is the most specialized tribe within the subfamily. The staminate (and sometimes pistillate) inflorescences show the development of deep pits formed by the fusion of bracts, and of flowers with elongate floral receptacles which elevate the stamens from the pits at anthesis. Pistillate flowers are characterized by extreme thickness and fibrousness of perianth parts, syncarpy with very thick and histologically specialized carpel walls, and often orthotropous ovules.

Key to the Tribes of the Coryphoideae

1 Leaves palmate, costapalmate or entire; acanthophylls absent   2

1 Leaves pinnate; basal leaflets modified as spines . . . . **Phoeniceae**

2 Hermaphroditic, or polygamodioecious, rarely strictly dioecious; if dioecious, flowers not or only slightly dimorphic; rachillae lacking deep pits; endocarp usually thin, crustaceous or cartilaginous . . . . **Corypheae**

2 Dioecious; flowers usually strongly dimorphic; staminate and sometimes pistillate flowers borne in deep pits formed by connation and adnation of rachilla bracts; endocarp very thick and hard . . . . **Borasseae**

CORYPHEAE Martius in Endlicher, Genera Plantarum 252. 1837 ('*Coryphinae*').

Usually hermaphroditic or polygamodioecious, rarely strictly dioecious, if dioecious, flowers not or only slightly dimorphic; leaves palmate, costapalmate, or undivided and induplicately folded; inflorescence usually with many peduncular and rachis bracts, rarely with prophyll only; rachillae lacking deep pits; fruit usually 1-seeded, if more than 1-seeded, bi- or trilobed; endocarp usually thin, crus-

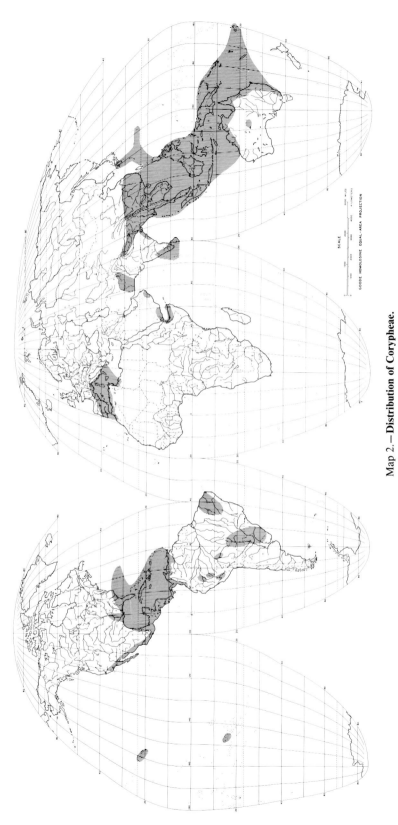

Map 2. — **Distribution of Corypheae.**

taceous or cartilaginous, sometimes not clearly differentiated.

The members of this tribe (Map 2) are distinct from other palms in the combination of induplicately palmate or costapalmate leaves and hermaphroditic or, when unisexual, only slightly dimorphic flowers borne singly or in cincinni. In considerations of the evolution of palms, these 31 genera are of primary importance for two reasons: first, because they include the most primitive palms, and second, because within them one can trace lines of specializations from complex to simple inflorescences, from bisexuality to unisexuality, from trimery to dimery or tetramery, from similar perianth members to clearly differentiated sepals and petals or to a single cupule, from six to many stamens, from apocarpy to various forms of syncarpy or to unicarpy, and from insect to wind pollination. In fact, except for the lack of pinnate leaves, one finds here a majority of the evolutionary trends in the family. Some exceptions are the absence of infrafoliar and multiple inflorescences, of flowers multiparted in all organs, and of adjacent-ligular germination of the seed.

The tribe is divisible into four subtribes based on the nature of the gynoecium. The subtribes are clearly defined and seem to be natural groups. The differences between them are shown by the following key:

Key to the Subtribes of the Corypheae

1 Carpels distinct, usually 3 (1–4) .... **Thrinacinae**
1 Carpels connate, 3 2
2 Carpels basally distinct, united by their styles only ....
.... **Livistoninae**
2 Carpels united basally or throughout 3
3 Carpels united basally, styles free or united, if united then with ± separate stylar canals .... **Coryphinae**
3 Carpels united throughout, with a common stylar canal
.... **Sabalinae**

It is most useful to provide a key to the genera of the whole tribe rather than separate keys for those of each subtribe.

Key to the Genera of the Corypheae

1 Leaves induplicate 2
1 Leaves reduplicate. China, Vietnam .... 13. **Guihaia**
2 Gynoecium of 1–3 free carpels; stamens 5–25 3
2 Gynoecium of 3 carpels, connate by thin erect styles alone, or up to their mid-regions, or completely connate; stamens 6 15
3 Perianth biseriate; carpels 1–3; stamens 5–25 4
3 Perianth uniseriate, usually 6-toothed; carpel 1; stamens 5–15 13

4 Carpel 1 5
4 Carpels 2, 3, or 4 6
5 Flowers with a long stalklike base, proximal flowers on each rachilla hermaphroditic, distal flowers staminate; stamens 6. Belize .... 5. **Schippia**
5 Flowers lacking a long stalklike base, all hermaphroditic; stamens 18–24. Peru, Brazil .... 4. **Itaya**
6 Stamen filaments distinct 7
6 Stamen filaments connate in a tube or upper 3 filaments epipetalous 10
7 Flowers solitary 8
7 Flowers in cincinni of 2–4 9
8 Leaf blade not split centrally to the rachis (but deeply divided in *Trithrinax biflabellata*); sepals united ca. ⅓ their length; stamens with distinct elongate filaments, long exserted. more than twice as long as the corolla; seed with lobed intrusion of the seed coat. Brazil to Argentina .... 1. **Trithrinax**
8 Leaf blade with the central split reaching to the rachis, segments wedge-shaped; sepals imbricate, free nearly to the base; stamens with fleshy wide filaments, only slightly exserted; seed without conspicuous lobed intrusion of the seed coat. Amazonian Bolivia, Peru, Brazil, and western Colombia .... 2. **Chelyocarpus**
9 Leaf sheaths unarmed, fibrous, blade splitting along adaxial ribs to varying lengths; inflorescences exserted from leaf sheaths; seed kidney-shaped or oblong and grooved on the rapheal side, seed coat deeply intruded. Temperate and subtropical East Asia .... 9. **Trachycarpus**
9 Leaf sheaths armed with stout needlelike fibers; leaf blade usually splitting between the folds; inflorescences hidden among the leaf sheaths; seed oblong, the seed coat thickened below the raphe but not conspicuously intruded. Southeastern U.S.A. .... 10. **Rhapidophyllum**
10 Flowers polygamodioecious; stamen filaments connate in a flared cupule; endosperm ruminate. Mediterranean
.... 11. **Chamaerops**
10 Flowers polygamodioecous or hermaphroditic; stamen filaments connate in an erect cupule or epipetalous; endosperm homogeneous 11
11 Stem bearing conspicous root spines at the base; calyx lobes nearly as long as the petals; stamen filaments connate in an elongate erect cupule not attached to the petals, anthers reflexed and radiating at anthesis; carpels with attenuate styles. Central America and Colombia .....
.... 3. **Cryosophila**
11 Stem without root spines; calyx lobes much shorter than the petals; stamen filaments distinct, epipetalous or the antesepalous filaments free, or all filaments connate in an epipetalous cupule but anthers scarcely exserted; carpels without attenuate styles 12
12 Stems slender, reedlike; leaves divided between the folds into many-fold, truncate segments; perianth whorls fleshy, sepals connate; stamen filaments free, epipetalous. South China, Indochina, northern Sumatra .... 14. **Rhapis**
12 Stems scarcely reedlike, stouter; leaves divided along adaxial folds into single-fold, acute or bifid segments; perianth whorls coriaceous; sepals distinct, imbricate; stamen filaments connate in an epipetalous cupule (*M. gracilis, M. furtadoana*), or separate and epipetalous (*M. rupicola*). Thailand and Malay Peninsula .... 12. **Maxburretia**
13 Base of leaf sheath split in petiolar region, inflorescence

emerging through the split; seed umbilicate, excavate, or completely perforate below the raphe, endosperm not furrowed. Caribbean . . . . 6. **Thrinax**

13 Base of leaf sheath not split in petiolar region; seed deeply perforated by furrows 14

14 Leaf sheaths disintegrating into a regular fibrous network, fiber tips reflexed, spinelike; flowers subdistichous on the rachillae; fruit white at maturity; seed deeply bilobed, the lobes again irregularly bilobed. Hispaniola
. . . . 8. **Zombia**

14 Leaf sheath fibers not reflexed or spinelike; flowers borne spirally; fruit tawny yellow, pink, red, or black; seed deeply furrowed, not bilobed. Caribbean . . . . 7. **Coccothrinax**

15 Gynoecium of 3 carpels, free at the base, connate by their styles alone 16

15 Gynoecium of 3 completely fused carpels or carpels connate basally and styles free 27

16 Leaf blades undivided, diamond-shaped, pinnately nerved, the costa prominent; petiole and basal margins of the blade armed with hooked teeth; inflorescences each with several inflated peduncular bracts; fruit warty; endosperm deeply and irregularly intruded by the seed coat. Malay Peninsula, Sumatra, Borneo . . . .
. . . . 17. **Johannesteijsmannia**

16 Leaf blades divided, or if undivided not diamond-shaped and the basal margins of the blade unarmed; fruit smooth or if corky-warted then leaf divided 17

17 Leaf blades divided along abaxial folds to the petiole into single-fold (rarely) to several-fold, usually wedge-shaped, truncate segments, or undivided. China, Southeast Asia, Malesia to Australia . . . . 18. **Licuala**

17 Leaf blades divided along adaxial folds into single-fold or several-fold but not truncate segments 18

18 Inflorescence with long peduncle, branched only at its tip or branched at the very base to produce 2–4 more or less equal long axes, also branched only at their tips, giving the appearance of more than 1 inflorescence per axil; corolla lobes caducous at anthesis exposing the prominent androecial tube; seed coat not intruded. Fiji, Tonga, Danger Islands, Hawaiian Islands . . . 20. **Pritchardia**

18 Inflorescence branching not confined to the tip; corolla lobes not caducous at anthesis, very rarely tardily deciduous 19

19 Rachis bracts split on one side and pendulous, sword-shaped; petals large, flat, chaffy, without grooves on the inner surfaces, becoming strongly reflexed at anthesis; style elongate, about 3 times as long as the ovarian part of the gynoecium; flowers and fruit pedicellate; fruit with persistent chaffy calyx. Southwestern U.S.A. and northwestern Mexico . . . . 26. **Washingtonia**

19 Inflorescence bracts tubular, not splitting into sword-shaped blades at anthesis; petals neither flat nor chaffy and with grooves matching anthers on inner surfaces; styles as long as the ovarian part or rarely 2–2½ times as long (*Serenoa*) 20

20 Fruit large and smooth (ca. 5 cm in diameter at maturity); mesocarp spongy with short fibers near and closely adhering to the endocarp, endocarp with a triangular basal projection, rounded on 1 side, keeled on the other 3 sides; embryo eccentrically apical, endosperm with a conspicuous, lobed intrusion of the seed coat. New Caledonia
. . . . 19. **Pritchardiopsis**

20 Fruit various, if large then usually corky-warted; endocarp smooth, not keeled, without a basal projection; embryo lateral or basal, seed coat intrusion present or not 21

21 Petioles and often margins and/ or veins of leaves with stout teeth; abortive carpels apical in fruit; seeds with ruminate endosperm. West Indies, South America . . .
. . . . 25. **Copernicia**

21 Petioles armed or not, leaves lacking teeth; abortive carpels usually basal in fruit; seeds with homogeneous endosperm, sometimes penetrated by a lobed intrusion of the seed coat 22

22 Endosperm intruded by the seed coat 25

22 Endosperm not intruded by the seed coat 23

23 Trunk solitary, sometimes ventricose at or near the middle; petiole unarmed; androecial tube projecting beyond the corolla lobes. Cuba, Guatemala, Panama . . . .
. . . . 21. **Colpothrinax**

23 Trunks clustered, erect, or creeping and branching; petiole spiny, armed with fine or coarse teeth; androecial tube not projecting beyond the corolla lobes 24

24 Stems erect, densely clustered; flowers in cincinni, but paired or solitary towards the apex of the rachillae; sepals distinct or basally shortly connate, imbricate; stamen filaments united in a basal ring, free portions short, abruptly narrowed; fruit globose; raphe short, scarcely more than half as long as the seed. Southern U.S.A., Central America . . . . 22. **Acoelorrhaphe**

24 Stems prostrate, rarely erect; flowers solitary or occasionally paired; calyx tubular, shortly 3-lobed; stamen filaments shortly united at the base, free portions gradually narrowed; fruit ellipsoidal; raphe extending the length of the seed. Southern U.S.A. . . . . 23. **Serenoa**

25 Sepals distinct, imbricate. Western U.S.A., Mexico, Guatemala . . . . 24. **Brahea**

25 Sepals united basally 26

26 Blade divided by deep splits into compound segments, further divided by shallow splits into single-fold segments; androecial ring conspicuous, thick, almost free at the base, filaments where separate slender not broadly rounded; gynoecium top-shaped; fruit very large (at least 6 cm in diameter at maturity) usually corky-warted (smooth in *P. kingianus*). Malesia . . . . . 16. **Pholidocarpus**

26 Blade regularly divided into single-fold segments, very rarely into compound segments (*L. saribus*); androecial ring broadly scalloped apically, epipetalous; gynoecium widest above the locules, abruptly narrowed to the style; fruit small (rarely exceeding 4 cm at maturity), smooth. Northeast Africa, Arabia, Ryukyu Islands, Southeast Asia to Australia . . . . 15. **Livistona**

27 Dioecious palm; leaf blade dark green on upper surface, grey-white beneath; all inflorescence axes with a thick layer of multicellular hairs; petals inserted on a broad floral stalk well above the calyx; carpels basally connate by ovarian regions only, styles free, widely separated; endosperm shallowly ruminate. Thailand . . 30. **Kerriodoxa**

27 Hermaphroditic palms; leaves not grey-white beneath; rachillae variously tomentose or glabrous; floral stalks present or poorly developed; carpels connate by their ovarian regions and usually through the styles; endosperm homogeneous or ruminate 28

28 Clustering palms; hastulae absent; rachilla bracts tubular
.... 29
28 Solitary palms; adaxial hastula present; rachilla bracts
minute, triangular 30
29 Slender pleonanthic palms; inflorescences spicate or
branching to 2-orders; endosperm homogeneous or ruminate. Indochina and China .... 29. **Chuniophoenix**
29 Moderate hapaxanthic palm, acaulescent or with erect,
often branching stems; inflorescence paniculate, highly
branched; endosperm homogeneous. Western Asia and
Arabia .... 28. **Nannorrhops**
30 Massive hapaxanthic palms; petiole margins armed with
teeth; flowers in adnate cincinni; gynoecium 3-grooved,
abruptly narrowed to the style, stylar canals 3. Southeast
Asia to Australia .... 29. **Corypha**
30 Acaulescent to robust, erect, pleonanthic palms; petioles
unarmed; flowers solitary; gynoecium shallowly 3-lobed,
style elongate, broad, only slightly narrower than the
ovarian part, stylar canal single. Southern U.S.A. to Venezuela .... 31. **Sabal**

Multi-access Key to the Genera of Corypheae

Solitary palms	(1), (2), 3–6, (7), (9), 15–17, (18), 19–21, (24), 25–27, 30, 31.
Clustered palms	(1), (2), (7), 8, (9), 10–14, (18), 22, 23, (24), 28, 29.
Leaf costapalmate	(5), (15), 16, (18), 19–22, 24 (25), 26–28, 31.
Leaf palmate	1–4, (5), 6–14, (15), (18), 23, (25), 29, 30.
Mature leaf entire	17, (18).
Hastula absent in expanded blade	17, 28, 29.
Sheath with a basal triangular cleft	3–6, 26, (27), 28, (29), 31.
Sheath bearing distal fiber spines	1, 8, 10, (12), (13).
Petiole armed with spines or teeth	(9), 11, (15), 16, 17, (18), 22, 23, (24), 25–27.
Blade split along abaxial folds	13, (18).
Blade split along adaxial folds	1–9, 11, 12, 15, 16, 19–31.
Blade split between the folds	10, 14.
Blade with a central deep split	(1), 2–4, (18).
Segments composed of many folds	(2), 3, 4, 10, (13), 14, (15), 16, (18), (29).
Blade adaxially green, abaxially chalky white	3, (6), (7), 8, 10, (11), (13), (17), 21, 22, 30.
Transverse veinlets conspicuous	2–4, 6, 7, (9), (13), 14, (15), 16–19, (20), (21), 22, 23, 27, 29, 30, (31).
Hapaxanthic palms	27, 28.
Inflorescence spicate	(18), (29).
Inflorescence immediately branching to form 2 or more ± equal "inflorescences"	(15), 19, (20).
Rachis bracts split down their length, becoming flattened, woody	26.
Peduncles and rachis bracts scarcely evident	11, (18).
Bracts subtending flower clusters complete, tubular	(25), 28–30.
Dioecious palms	(9), (10), (11), (12), 13, (14), (15), (18), 30.
Polygamous palms	(5), (9), (10), (11), (14), (29).
Flowers solitary	1–8, 11, (12), 13, (14), (15), (16), (17), (18), (19), 20, 21, (22), (23), 24, (25), 26, (29), 31.
Perianth uniseriate	6–8.
Stamens more than 6	(2), 4, (6), (7), 8.
Filaments connate	3, 4, (6), 7, 11, (12), 15–17, (18), 19–22, 24, 25, (30), 31.
Carpel 1	5–8.
Fruit corky-warted	(2), (6-diseased), (16), 17, (18).
Endosperm homogeneous	1–8, (9), 10–24, 26–28, (29), 31.
Endosperm ruminate	(9), 11, 25, (29), 30.
Seed coat penetration conspicuous	1, 3, 6–11, 13–19, 22–24, 31.

Map 3.—**Distribution of Thrinacinae.**

Thrinacinae Beccari, Webbia 2:9. 1907 ('*Thrinaceae*'). Type: **Thrinax**.

Carpels usually 3(1–4), free.

These fourteen genera, largely confined to the subtropics (Map 3), include some of the most drought and cold tolerant palms. Many species grow only on limestone. Within this highly diverse group are genera that exhibit some of the most primitive features in the family. There are two main lines of evolution. One is entirely New World and includes genera 1–8. The main evolutionary trends are in the reduction of the carpels to one and the reduction of the perianth to a single cupule. The second line includes genera 9–14 and with the exception of *Rhapidophyllum* in North America is strictly Old World. Within this line the main trends of specialization are to dioecy and elaboration and fusion of the perianth segments. *Guihaia* is outstanding in having reduplicate leaves, while *Rhapis* and *Rhapidophyllum* have leaves irregularly split in relation to the plications. In some ways the two lines seem to be parallel; the first genus in each, *Trachycarpus* of the Old World and *Trithrinax* of the New World, seem to represent about the same level of specialization.

1. **TRITHRINAX** Martius, Historia Naturalis Palmarum 2:149. 1837. Type: **T. brasiliensis** Martius.
Diodosperma H. A. Wendland, Botanische Zeitung 36:118. 1878. Type: *D. burity* H. A. Wendland (=*Trithrinax schizophylla* Drude).

Moderate, solitary or sometimes clustering, armed, pleonanthic, hermaphroditic palms. Stem erect, clothed with persistent, fibrous, sometimes spiny leaf sheaths, eventually becoming bare, rough, and longitudinally striate. Leaves induplicate, palmate, marcescent; sheath tubular, drying into a fibrous, often ± woody network, the upper fibers becoming stout rigid spines; petiole adaxially shallowly channeled or rounded, abaxially rounded, the margins entire, sharp; adaxial hastula triangular or deltoid usually with a definite point, abaxial hastula similar, often smaller; blade fan-shaped to nearly circular, not or only slightly costapalmate, nearly regularly divided beyond the middle (*T. biflabellata* divided centrally, almost to the base) into numerous single-fold, stiff segments with shallowly to deeply bifid, apiculate to sharp tips, adaxially glabrous, abaxially lightly waxy and tomentose, midribs more prominent abaxially, other veins numerous, small, transverse veinlets not evident. Inflorescences solitary, interfoliar, rather short to moderate, robust, curved, creamy-white when young, branched to 3 orders; peduncle short; prophyll and 2(–3) peduncular bracts similar, inflated, tubular at base, expanded and split along one side, slightly keeled dorsally toward the apex, with short solid

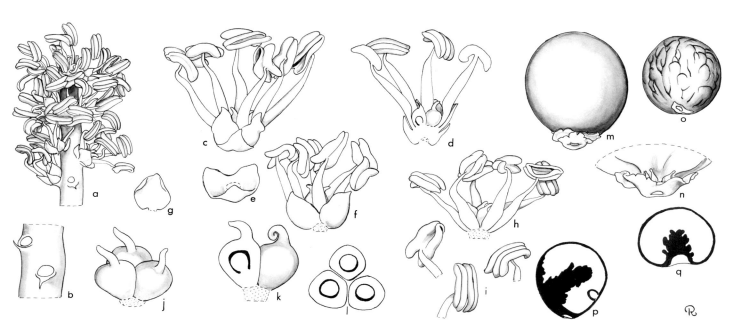

1.—**Trithrinax. a,** portion of rachilla ×3; **b,** portion of rachilla showing floral scars and bracts ×6; **c,** flower ×6; **d,** flower in vertical section ×6; **e,** calyx ×6; **f,** flower, calyx removed ×6; **g,** petal, interior view ×6; **h,** androecium and gynoecium ×6; **i,** stamen in 3 views ×6; **j,** gynoecium ×12; **k,** gynoecium in vertical section ×12; **l,** carpels in cross-section ×12; **m,** fruit ×1½; **n,** base of fruit and abortive carpels ×3; **o,** seed ×1½; **p,** seed in vertical section ×1½; **q,** seed in cross-section ×1½. *Trithrinax acanthocoma*: **a–l,** Read 723; *T. brasiliensis*: **m–q,** Hertrich s.n.

tips, glabrous or densely but irregularly tomentose; rachis longer than the peduncle; rachis bracts like peduncular bracts but becoming smaller, absent distally, each subtending a first-order branch; first-order branches adnate to the rachis and often to the tubular base of next higher bract, stout, curved, bearing chartaceous, small, triangular bracts subtending rachillae; rachillae spirally arranged, ± equal in length, much shorter than first-order branches, bearing small elongate triangular bracts each subtending a flower. Flowers spirally arranged, solitary on short stalks, slightly asymmetrical; sepals 3, very shortly united basally, ovate; petals 3, ± twice as long as the sepals, ovate, imbricate, fleshy, acute; stamens 6, exserted, filaments distinct, twice as long as the petals, slender, tapering, anthers linear oblong, versatile, latrorse; pollen elliptic, monosulcate, with finely reticulate, tectate exine; carpels 3, distinct, ovarian part obovoid, attenuate to a tubular, short to long, erect or recurved style with apical stigma, ovule basal, hemianatropous, with aril. Fruit 1-seeded, white, globose, stigmatic scar apical, abortive carpels basal; epicarp smooth, mesocarp fleshy, endocarp thin, papery. Seed becoming free, globose, hilum circular, basal with ascending branches, endosperm homogeneous with deeply intruded seed coat below the raphe; embryo lateral, opposite the raphe. Germination not recorded; eophyll simple. $n = 18$ (*T. brasiliensis,* Read 1963, 1964, Satô 1946).

Anatomy. — Carpel vasculature, a dorsal bundle and two short ventral bundles, is one of the simplest in palms. The ovule is supplied by three to four bundles from the base of the carpel. See Magnano (1973), Morrow (1965) for floral anatomy, and Tomlinson (1961) for leaf anatomy. There is a single phloem strand in vascular bundles of the petiole.

Distribution. — About five species in Bolivia, western tropical and southern Brazil, Paraguay, Uruguay, and Argentina.

Ecology. — *T. biflabellata* is reported from sandy marshes and along river banks. The other four species occur in dry areas. Several species form dense colonies in saline soils having a pH of 7–8 in the Chaco region of Paraguay.

Common Names and Uses. — Caranday, for other local names see Glassman (1972). Stems are used in construction and leaves as thatch. The leaf sheaths have been used as filters. The fruits are eaten fresh or fermented and the seed can be a source of oil.

Notes. — A small genus, closely related to *Itaya* and *Cryosophila,* differing from the first in the armed leaf sheaths and regularly palmate leaf, and from the second in the free stamen filaments, armed sheaths, and lack of root spines. Species in cultivation are notably resistant to cold and drought. *Trithrinax* is of special interest because it is considered one of the most primitive genera of palms

(Moore 1972), an interpretation supported by floral anatomy.

Taxonomic account. — A new treatment is needed. See Beccari and Martelli (1931).

Plates. — *1A; 31A.*

2. **CHELYOCARPUS** Dammer, Notizblatt des Botanischen Gartens und Museums zu Berlin-Dahlem 7:395. 1920. Type: **C. ulei** Dammer.

Tessmanniophoenix Burret, Notizblatt des Botanischen Gartens und Museums zu Berlin-Dahlem 10:397. 1928. Lectotype: *T. longibracteata* Burret (see Burret 1941) (=[1]*Chelyocarpus ulei* Dammer).

Tessmanniodoxa Burret, Notizblatt des Botanischen Gartens und Museums zu Berlin-Dahlem 15: 336. 1941. Lectotype: *T. chuco* (Martius) Burret (*Thrinax chuco* Martius) (see H. E. Moore, 1963c) (=*Chelyocarpus chuco* (Martius) H. E. Moore).

Moderate, solitary or clustered, unarmed, pleonanthic, hermaphroditic palms. Stem erect, slender, naked except for fibrous remains of leaf sheaths below the crown, closely ringed with narrow leaf scars. Leaves spreading, induplicate, palmate, or shortly costapalmate (*C. chuco*), sheath fibrous, not splitting opposite the petiole, densely velvety-hairy, golden-brown when young, with a prominent fibrous ligule on each side of the petiole at its apex, this disintegrating into loose fibers in age; petiole elongate, unarmed, not splitting basally, adaxially channeled basally, becoming angled distally, abaxially rounded, margins thin; adaxial hastula often large, erect, deltoid, abaxial hastula narrow, ridgelike; blade flat, thin, divided centrally well beyond the middle or nearly to the base, each half further divided into paired or irregularly grouped, rather wide, single-fold segments (*C. chuco*), or divided to the base into elongate, wedge-shaped, many-fold segments, these again divided into several acute or very briefly bifid, single-fold, 1-ribbed segments, midribs raised abaxially, transverse veinlets evident. Inflorescences interfoliar, pendulous, branching to 1 or 2 orders; peduncle flattened, short; prophyll flattened, tubular, with long fibrous beak, shortly 2-keeled laterally, surfaces and margins covered in dense soft tomentum; peduncular bracts 3(–4), like the prophyll but lacking keels; rachis flattened; first-order branches several, recurved, flattened, basally adnate to the rachis, each subtended by a prominent rachis bract similar to those on the peduncle but progressively smaller distally, at least the lower first-order branches bearing a membranous prophyll (*C. chuco*), or the lower rachillae sometimes fasciculate or subfasciculate on short branches but the bracts subtending first-order branches, small and not like those on the peduncle; rachillae usually adnate for some distance above an acute, sometimes elongate subtending bract and bearing spirally arranged, small to prominent, acute bracts each subtending a sessile or shortly pedicellate flower. Flowers (at least in *C. ulei*)

---

[1] Double equal signs (=) are used for both taxonomic and nomenclatural decisions throughout the classification.

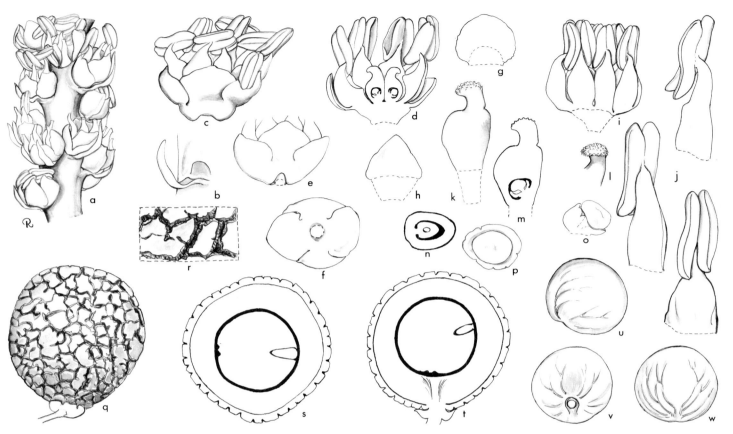

2.—**Chelyocarpus. a,** portion of rachilla ×3; **b,** bracteole and floral scar ×6; **c,** flower ×6; **d,** flower in vertical section ×6; **e, f,** perianth in lateral and bottom views ×6; **g,** sepal ×6; **h,** petal ×6; **i,** flower, perianth removed ×6; **j,** stamen in 3 views ×12; **k,** carpel ×12; **l,** stigma ×12; **m,** carpel in vertical section ×12; **n,** ovary in cross-section ×12; **o, p,** ovule in lateral and top views ×24; **q,** fruit ×1½; **r,** surface of fruit ×3; **s,** fruit in cross-section ×1½; **t,** fruit in vertical section ×1½; **u, v, w,** seed in 3 views ×1½. *Chelyocarpus ulei*: **a-p,** *Moore & Salazar 9494*; **q-w,** *Moore 9548*.

strongly scented; sepals 2 or 3, distinct or briefly connate basally, or 4, distinct, and slightly imbricate; petals like the sepals; stamens 5, 6, 7, 8, or 9, one opposite each sepal, remainder opposite the petals, filaments erect, distinct, fleshy, thick and broad below, ± abruptly narrowed at the tip, anthers exserted at anthesis, dorsifixed at the middle, bifid at apex and base, latrorse; pollen elliptic, monosulcate, with finely reticulate, tectate exine; carpels 3 or 2, rarely 1 or 4, follicular, style short, somewhat recurved, stigma papillose, ovule hemianatropous, attached adaxially at the base, an aril present and basally fused to the locular wall. Fruit usually developing from only 1 carpel, globose with eccentrically apical stigmatic remains; epicarp smooth or coarsely corky-warted, mesocarp thick, dry, endocarp membranous. Seed basally attached, globose, hilum basal, circular, raphe slightly impressed along the length of the seed and with ascending branches, endosperm homogeneous; embryo below or above the middle opposite the raphe. Germination remote-tubular; eophyll bifid. $n = 18$ (*C. ulei,* Read and Moore 1967).

Anatomy.—Leaf anatomy (Uhl 1972c), floral anatomy (Uhl 1972b). Central vascular bundles of petiole with a single phloem strand (Parthasarathy 1968).

Distribution.—Three species in Amazonian Bolivia, Brazil, Peru, and western Colombia.

Ecology.—The species occur at low elevations in areas of high rainfall. It is particularly interesting to note that the distribution of these species corresponds with three of nine refugia—Madeira-Tapajos (7), East Peruvian (6), Chocó (1)—postulated by Haffer (1969) as regions where rain forest persisted during drier epochs of the Pleistocene.

Common Names and Uses.—Not recorded.

Notes.—*Chelyocarpus* has very characteristic distinct carpels and deeply divided palmate leaves. The genus was initially set apart because of the corky-warted surface of the fruit of the type species which so resembled a turtle's carapace as to suggest the generic name. Dammer commented on the dimerous or two-parted perianth of *C. ulei* but lacking flowers thought his material perhaps atypical. More complete collections, however, have shown that the perianth is normally dimerous in the species. Dransfield (1970) has noted the occurrence of corky-warted fruits in three undescribed species of *Licuala,* a genus otherwise with smooth fruits, and similar fruit surfaces have evolved independently in several other genera.

Chelyocarpus must be considered among the most primitive of palm genera, sharing this honor with *Trithrinax,* also South American. *Chelyocarpus chuco,* as also *Trithrinax,* comes close to what might be considered a palm prototype as far as inflorescence, flowers, and fruit are concerned—trimerous perianth whorls, hexamerous androecium, trimerous gynoecium, and continuous growth in the development of fruit (Murray 1971).

Within *Chelyocarpus* there is apparent simplification of the inflorescence and there are modifications of the flower which suggest directions of evolution toward connation and reduction in the perianth, elaboration of the androecium, and reduction of the gynoecium found in the related genus *Itaya* and in the more specialized *Thrinax* alliance.

Taxonomic Account.—Moore (1972).

Plates.—*1B, 31B; Figs. G.10, G.11, G.18, G.20, G.21.*

3. **CRYOSOPHILA** Blume, Rumphia 2:53. 1838 ("1836"). Type: **C. nana** (Kunth) Blume ex Salomon (*Corypha nana* Kunth).

Acanthorrhiza H. A. Wendland, Gartenflora 18:241. 1869. Type: *A. aculeata* (Liebmann ex Martius) H. A. Wendland (*Trithrinax aculeata* Liebmann ex Martius) (=*Cryosophila nana* (Kunth) Blume ex Salomon).

Moderate, solitary, armed, pleonanthic, hermaphroditic palms. Stem slender to rather stout, bearing often-branched root spines, prickly stilt roots sometimes developed. Leaves induplicate, palmate; sheath fibrous, densely floccose-tomentose, becoming split basally and splitting opposite the petiole, margins fibrous; petiole elongate, unarmed, channeled adaxially, rounded abaxially, margins sharp throughout their length; adaxial hastula deltoid, elevated, sometimes grooved, abaxial hastula narrow or lacking; blade divided centrally to or nearly to the base (? except in *C. williamsii*), each half further deeply divided into elongate, wedge-shaped, many-fold segments, these again divided into 2 or more, single-fold, acute or briefly bifid segments, white-tomentose abaxially,

interfold ribs prominent adaxially, midribs prominent abaxially, transverse veinlets evident. Inflorescences interfoliar, curved or pendulous, branching to 2 orders; peduncle short, terete, tomentose; prophyll short, tubular, pointed, 2-keeled, tomentose; peduncular bracts several (to 6 or more), much larger than the prophyll, tubular at base, inflated distally, splitting laterally, densely tomentose; rachis about as long as the peduncle, somewhat angled, bearing several to many, recurved, first-order branches, only the proximal or all (in *C. guagara*) subtended by prominent bracts like those of the peduncle but progressively smaller, or the upper branches with reduced bracts only; first-order branches usually with obvious, not, or only slightly adnate bases but rarely (*C. cookii*) the peduncle and rachis very short and rachillae fastigiately grouped along the rachis; rachillae little or not adnate above an acute subtending bract, spirally arranged, flowers borne on brief pedicels each subtended by a small, acute bract. Flowers small; sepals 3, narrowly ovate to deltoid, briefly connate basally; petals 3, distinct, scarcely longer than sepals, imbricate, rounded at apex; stamens 6, filaments flat, connate basally in a tube ½ their length or more, apically distinct and strap-shaped or terete, anthers exserted and spreading at an angle of 90°, dorsifixed near the base, briefly bifid at base and apex, latrorse; pollen elliptic or subcircular, monosulcate or usually trichotomosulcate, with finely reticulate, tectate exine; carpels 3, distinct, narrowly follicular, styles elongate, exserted, stigma scarcely expanded, ovule campylotropous, inserted adaxially at the base, with a small aril on the funicle. Fruit developing from 1 carpel, white at maturity, stigmatic remains apical; epicarp smooth, mesocarp somewhat fleshy, endocarp membranous. Seed globose, not adherent to the endocarp, with round basal hilum, raphe branches impressed, ascending and anastomosing from the base, endosperm homogeneous with slight intrusion of seed coat adaxially at the base; embryo lateral, at or below the middle. Germination adjacent-ligular; eophyll simple, entire, white abaxially. *n* = 18 (*C. nana,* Read 1965a).

Distribution.—Eight or fewer species from western Mexico to northern Colombia.

Anatomy.—Leaf, root (Tomlinson 1961), leaf (Uhl 1972c), flower (Uhl 1972b).

Ecology.—Species occur at moderate to low elevations in dry woods (*C. nana*) to rain forest.

Common Names and Uses.—Palma de escola, Rootspine palms. Widely cultivated as ornamentals.

Notes.—The species of *Cryosophila* are in need of detailed study in the field. Most herbarium material is completely inadequate for drawing distinctions among species such as have been drawn among those of *Chelyocarpus,* though admittedly the genus is more uniform. Habit, leaf, inflorescence, flowers, and fruit have been illustrated photographically by Allen (1965) and Bartlett (1935). The branched root spines on the trunk are distinctive. In general, *Cryosophila* is unspecialized but seems to be more advanced than *Chelyocarpus,* less so than *Itaya.*

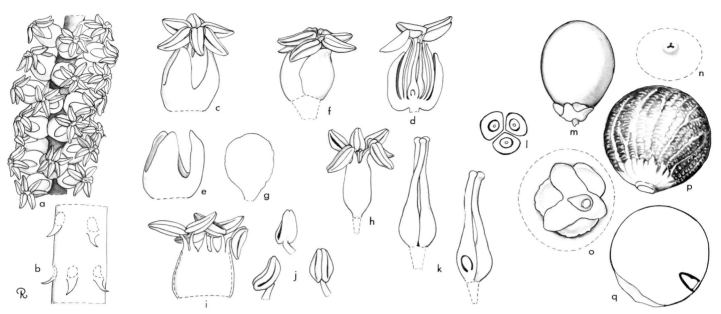

3.—**Cryosophila. a,** portion of rachilla ×3; **b,** portion of rachilla showing floral scars and bracts ×6; **c,** flower ×6; **d,** flower in vertical section ×6; **e,** calyx ×6; **f,** flower, calyx removed ×6; **g,** petal ×6; **h,** androecium ×6; **i,** androecium expanded, interior view ×6; **j,** anther in 3 views ×6; **k,** gynoecium in exterior view and vertical section ×12; **l,** carpels in cross-section ×12; **m,** fruit ×1½; **n,** apex of fruit ×12; **o,** base of fruit ×6; **p,** seed ×3; **q,** seed in vertical section ×3. *Cryosophila argentea*: **a-l,** *Read 689*; *C. nana*: **m-q,** *McVaugh 900.*

Taxonomic Account.—No recent account exists. See Allen (1953) and Moore (1972).

Plate.—31C; Fig. G.4.

4. ITAYA H. E. Moore, Principes 16:85. 1972. Type: **I. amicorum** H. E. Moore.

Moderate, solitary, unarmed, pleonanthic, hermaphroditic palm. Stem smooth (drying roughened), bare except for fibrous remains of sheaths and a lattice of long persistent, split petioles below the crown. Leaves spreading, induplicate, palmate; sheaths short, fibrous, split opposite the petiole, persisting as fibrous margins on the bases of the petioles; petiole elongate, unarmed, the base prominently split, channeled adaxially, rounded abaxially near the base, becoming biconvex and rhomboid in section distally, margins obtuse; adaxial hastula deltoid, often large, basally grooved, abaxial hastula narrow; blade held in one plane, thin, orbicular, divided to ca. ¾ the radius at the middle, each half again deeply divided into several (4–7) elongate, wedge-shaped, 4–7-fold segments, these very shallowly divided apically into briefly, bifid, 1-fold segments, abaxially lighter, midribs very prominent abaxially, transverse veinlets of 2 sizes, very prominent. Inflorescences several, interfoliar, elongate, curved, branched to 3 orders basally, to 1 order distally; peduncle terete; prophyll short, 2-keeled, abaxially split, peduncular bracts ca. 5, bases tubular, apices inflated, acute, coriaceous, persistent, larger than the prophyll, marcescent, lightly tomentose, split on one side; rachis about as long as the peduncle, tapering, ± angled, tomentose; first-order branches each subtended by a persistent, marcescent bract similar to the peduncular bracts but progressively smaller and the uppermost scarcely tubular at the base, the branches ± flattened, adnate to the rachis often nearly to the succeeding bract; rachillae short, rather distant, slightly sinuous, each subtended by a linear acute bract, rachillae bearing spirally arranged, solitary flowers, each on a very short pedicel subtended by a small acute bract. Flowers creamy-white; sepals 3, connate in an acutely 3-lobed cup; petals 3, connate ca. ½ their length, the 3 lobes rounded and erect at anthesis, probably valvate in bud; stamens 18–24, one or two opposite each sepal, the remainder opposite the petals, filaments connate basally in a fleshy tube less than ½ their length, slightly adnate to the corolla basally, fleshy and ± awl-shaped distally, anthers exserted at anthesis, oblong, dorsifixed at the middle, versatile, bifid at apex and base, latrorse; pollen elliptic, monosulcate, with finely reticulate, tectate exine; gynoecium of 1 carpel, eccentrically ovoid, narrowed to a slender curved style and oblique papillose stigma, ovule hemianatropous, attached adaxially at the base, the short funicle bearing a large oblique aril. Fruit oblong-ovoid or subglobose with eccentrically apical stigmatic remains; epicarp minutely granular-roughened and with minute perforations, mesocarp thick, white, dry, with anastomosing fibers and a peripheral layer of sclerosomes, endocarp not differentiated. Seed oblong-ovoid, hilum elliptic, subbasal, raphe branches ascending-spreading, endosperm homogeneous; embryo eccentrically basal. Germination not known; eophyll undivided, elliptic. Cytology unknown.

Anatomy.—Leaf anatomy (Uhl 1972c), floral anatomy (Uhl 1972b).

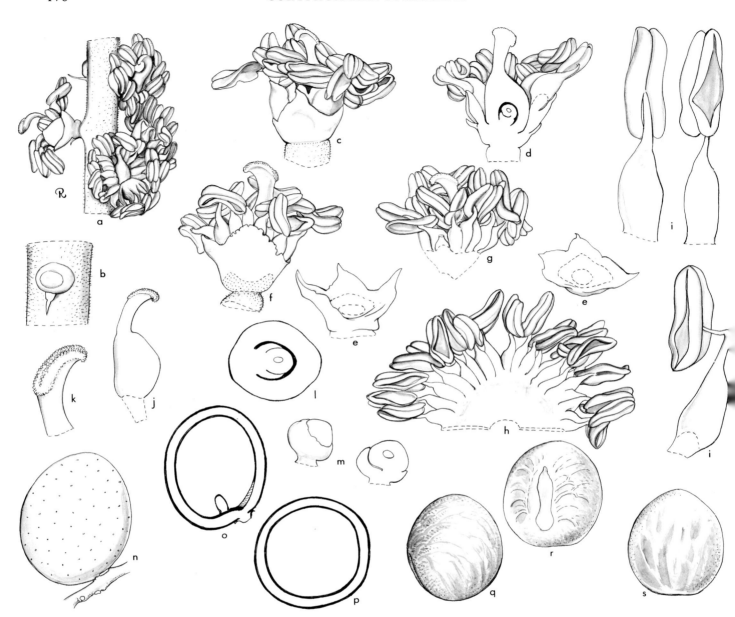

4.—*Itaya*. **a**, portion of rachilla ×3; **b**, pedicel and bract ×6; **c**, flower ×6; **d**, flower in vertical section ×6; **e**, calyx in 2 views ×6; **f**, flower, calyx removed ×6; **g**, flower, perianth removed ×6; **h**, androecium expanded, interior view ×6; **i**, stamen in 3 views ×12; **j**, gynoecium ×6; **k**, stigma ×12; **l**, ovary in cross-section ×12; **m**, ovule in lateral view and vertical section ×12; **n**, fruit ×1½; **o**, fruit in vertical section ×1½; **p**, fruit in cross-section ×1½; **q, r, s**, seed in 3 views ×1½. *Itaya amicorum*: **a-m**, *Moore et al. 9509*; **n-s**, *Gutierrez 1940*.

Distribution.—One species, known from one locality in Amazonian Peru and one in Brazil.

Ecology.—*Itaya amicorum* occurs in seasonal rain forest at low elevations.

Common Names and Uses.—Not recorded. *Itaya* is a promising horticultural subject because of its large and handsome leaves much resembling those of *Licuala* species, its moderate stature, and creamy-white inflorescences and flowers.

Notes.—*Itaya* appears to be most closely related to *Chelyocarpus* and *Cryosophila*. It is, however, more specialized than either in the connation and adnation of sepals and petals, in its numerous stamens, in its unicarpellate gynoecium, and in the

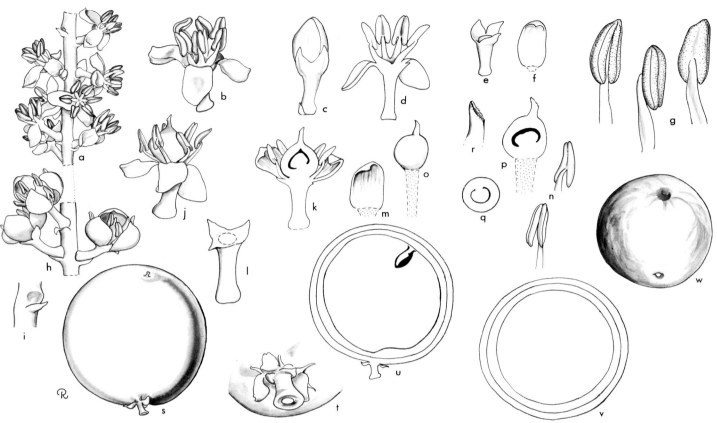

5.—**Schippia. a,** apical portion of rachilla with staminate flowers ×3; **b,** staminate flower, expanded ×6; **c,** staminate bud ×6; **d,** staminate flower in vertical section ×6; **e,** staminate calyx ×6; **f,** staminate petal, interior view ×6; **g,** stamen in 3 views × 12; **h,** lower portion of rachilla with pistillate flowers ×3; **i,** bracteole subtending pistillate flower ×6; **j,** pistillate flower ×6; **k,** pistillate flower in vertical section ×6; **l,** pistillate calyx ×6; **m,** pistillate petal, interior view ×6; **n,** staminodes in 2 views ×12; **o,** gynoecium ×6; **p,** gynoecium in vertical section ×6; **q,** ovary in cross-section ×6; **r,** stigma ×12; **s,** fruit ×1½; **t,** base of fruit ×3; **u,** fruit in vertical section ×1½; **v,** fruit in cross-section ×1½; **w,** seed ×1½. *Schippia concolor*: all from *A. C. & M. Langlois s.n.*

presence of two phloem strands in central vascular bundles of the petiole. The split in the petiole base has been commented on for *Thrinax* by Read (1975). It is an immediately recognizable field character but is not useful with herbarium material which usually lacks leaf bases. In this feature, *Chelyocarpus* and *Cryosophila* are to *Itaya* as *Coccothrinax* and *Zombia* are to *Thrinax*.

Taxonomic Account.— Moore (1972).

Fig. G.20.

5. **SCHIPPIA** Burret, Notizblatt des Botanischen Gartens und Museums zu Berlin-Dahlem 11:867. 1933. Type: **S. concolor** Burret.

Moderate, solitary, unarmed, pleonanthic, hermaphroditic or polygamomonoecious palm. Stem slender, longitudinally striate, rough, with raised, close, oblique leaf scars. Leaves induplicate, palmate to very shortly costapalmate; sheath split basally, densely tomentose, disintegrating to form a thick fibrous network; petiole very long, narrow, adaxially channeled and abaxially keeled basally, biconvex distally, sparsely to densely tomentose, margins acute; adaxial hastula triangular or rounded, rather large, abaxial hastula a low rounded ridge; blade divided to below the middle into narrow, tapering, single-fold segments, with pointed, unequal, very shortly bifid apices, lighter colored beneath, appearing glabrous on both surfaces, midrib conspicuous abaxially, transverse veinlets inconspicuous, very short. Inflorescences solitary, interfoliar, much shorter than the leaves, branched to 2 (rarely 3) orders; peduncle moderate, dorsiventrally flattened; prophyll tubular, elongate, adaxially flattened, abaxially rounded, 2-keeled laterally, pointed, splitting unevenly apically, densely tomentose; peduncular bracts 3, ± like the prophyll but ± keeled dorsally; rachis about as long as the peduncle, glabrous; rachis bracts tubular, pointed, splitting adaxially, densely tomentose; other bracts membranous, pointed, small and inconspicuous; first-order branches adnate above the subtending bracts; rachillae short, narrow, spirally arranged, spreading, becoming smaller distally, bearing small triangular bracts each subtending a solitary flower. Flowers of two kinds, one hermaphroditic, the other lacking a gynoecium; calyx and receptacle forming a long pseudopedicel, calyx tubular basally with 3 triangular-lanceolate lobes; petals 3, distinct, much larger than the calyx, slightly imbricate; stamens 6, filaments distinct, elongate, anthers linear, sagittate basally, dorsifixed, versatile, latrorse; pollen elliptic, monosulcate, with punctate, tectate exine; gynoecium unicarpellate, ovoid, style elongate, tubular, open distally with stigmatic area around the rim, ovule basal, probably hemianatropous. Fruit globose with apical stigmatic scar; epicarp smooth, mesocarp thin, fleshy, endocarp smooth, membranous with anastomosing bundles. Seed globose with indistinct basal raphe, endosperm homogeneous; embryo nearly apical. Germination not recorded; eophyll simple. $n = 18$ (*S. concolor*, Read 1966).

Anatomy.—Leaf anatomy not studied. Evidence from floral anatomy (Morrow 1965) suggests that the long floral stalk is a floral receptacle.

Distribution.—One species in Belize.

Ecology.—Apparently an understory species in tropical rain forest.

Common Names and Uses.—Pimento palm. Occasionally cultivated.

Notes.—An interesting genus which has been little studied. Information on pollination is much desired and may provide further clues as to the significance of the single carpel.

Taxonomic Account.—Burret (1933b).

Plate.—*31D; Fig. G.17.*

6. THRINAX O. Swartz, Prodromus 4:57. 1788. Type: **T. parviflora** O. Swartz.

Hemithrinax J. D. Hooker in Bentham & J. D. Hooker, Genera Plantarum 3:930. 1883. Type: *Trithrinax compacta* Grisebach & H. A. Wendland (*Hemithrinax compacta* (Grisebach & H. A. Wendland) J. D. Hooker ex Salomon, =*Thrinax compacta* (Grisebach & H. A. Wendland) Borhidi & Muñiz).

Small to moderate, solitary, unarmed, pleonanthic, hermaphroditic palms. Stem erect, columnar, smooth or fibrous, tan or gray, obscurely ringed with leaf scars, usually with a basal mass of fibrous roots. Leaves induplicate, palmate, often irregular; sheath becoming split both opposite the petiole and abaxially to emit the inflorescence, disintegrating into irregular fibers, covered in thick, deciduous tomentum, margins fibrous; petiole long, slender, rounded to shallowly ridged both adaxially and abaxially, margins rather sharp; hastula adaxially prominent, long pointed, frequently inrolled, short and blunt at high elevations, abaxially less conspicuous, rounded or triangular, lacking or very small at high elevations; blade fan-shaped, often irregularly folded, segments united basally ½ their length or less, lanceolate, pointed and usually bifid apically, glabrous adaxially, abaxially variously scaly, some-

times white, midrib and marginal ribs conspicuous, transverse veinlets evident. Inflorescences interfoliar, slender, erect to arching, branched to 2 orders, primary branches pendulous; peduncle moderate, rather slender, round in cross section; prophyll short, tubular, 2-keeled, pointed, opening distally, tomentose; peduncular bracts several (ca. 4), like the prophyll but lacking keels, overlapping and very closely sheathing the peduncle; rachis longer than the peduncle, slender, tapering, bearing spirally arranged, long, tubular, pointed distally and obliquely open primary bracts subtending first-order branches; first-order branches each with a short basal bare portion, bearing a 2-keeled, bifid prophyll and spirally arranged, narrow, triangular bracts subtending rachillae; rachillae slender, rather short, stiff, bearing spirally arranged, small triangular bracts subtending solitary flowers, bracteoles apparently lacking. Flowers on very short or conspicuous stalks; perianth a single cupule with 6 lobes or teeth; stamens mostly 6–12 (5–15), filaments very slender, sometimes partly united basally, anthers elongate, dorsifixed near the base, emarginate apically, latrorse; pollen elliptic in polar view, monosulcate with finely reticulate, tectate exine; gynoecium consisting of 1 carpel, unilocular, uniovulate, ovule basally attached, erect, campylotropous but tilted so that the micropyle faces the upper dorsal wall of the locule, and with a basal aril. Fruit very small, white at maturity, stigmatic remains apical, perianth often persistent; epicarp smooth when fresh, sometimes drying pebbled, mesocarp thin, mealy, endocarp very thin, papery. Seed depressed-globose, smooth, hilum round, impressed, forming a basal intrusion, raphe branches deeply impressed forming peripheral ruminations, otherwise endosperm homogeneous; embryo lateral to subapical. Germination remote-tubular; eophyll narrow, lanceolate. $n = 18$ (*T. radiata* as *T. excelsa* and *T. floridana*, Read 1963; *T. microcarpa*, Read 1964; *T. radiata*, Read 1975; *T. morrisii*, Janaki Ammal 1945).

Anatomy.—The species can be identified by characters of leaf anatomy (Read 1975). Correlations of floral anatomy and wind pollination have been suggested (Uhl and Moore 1977a). The vasculature of the carpel consists of a dorsal bundle, 3 pairs of lateral bundles and 2 ventral bundles and confirms that the gynoecium is a single carpel (Uhl and Moore 1971). For floral anatomy see also Morrow (1965).

Distribution.—Seven species; two species, *T. parviflora* and *T. excelsa* are endemic to Jamaica. *T. radiata* also occurs in Jamaica but is widely distributed in littoral habitats of Atlantic Belize, Mexico, and the northern Caribbean. A fourth species, *T. morrisii* has much the same range as *T. radiata* but reaches farther east to the Virgin Islands and Anguilla and is absent from both Hispaniola and Jamaica. The three species formerly of *Hemithrinax* are all very local endemics in Cuba (Muñiz and Borhidi 1982, Borhidi and Muñiz 1985).

Ecology.—Found only on alkaline or ultrabasic

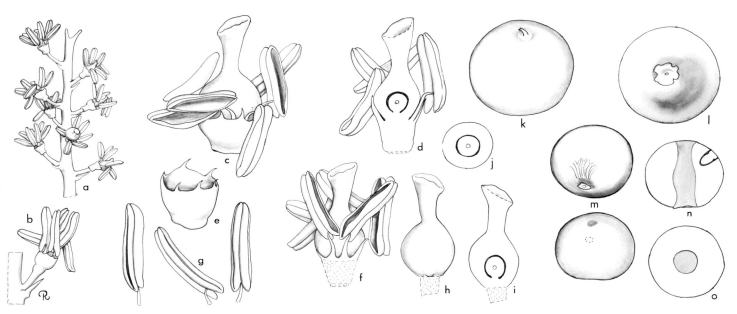

6.—**Thrinax. a,** portion of rachilla ×3; **b,** flower and pedicel with bract ×6; **c,** flower ×12; **d,** flower in vertical section ×12; **e,** perianth ×12; **f,** flower, perianth removed ×12; **g,** anther in 3 views ×12; **h,** carpel ×12; **i,** carpel in vertical section ×12; **j,** carpel in cross-section ×12; **k,** fruit ×3½; **l,** base of fruit ×3½; **m,** seed in 2 views ×3½; **n,** seed in vertical section ×3½; **o,** seed in cross-section ×3½. *Thrinax parviflora*: all from *Read 714*.

soils, specifically on coralline sands or limestone outcrops, from sea level to about 1200 m. Each of the three species in Jamaica is confined to one habitat; *T. parviflora* to dry evergreen woodland or thicket, *T. excelsa,* to lower montane rain forest, and *T. radiata,* which thrives under exposure to salt-laden winds, to littoral woodland or thicket. The species in Cuba are all confined to serpentine soils.

Common Names and Uses.—Thatch palms, Key palms. Leaves are used for thatch, fiber for basketry, and other purposes. The heart of some species is eaten.

Notes.—Most closely related to *Coccothrinax* from which it is distinct in abaxially split leaf bases and white fruits. Forming with *Coccothrinax* and *Zombia* a group of closely related taxa with flowers reduced and apparently adapted for wind pollination. O. F. Cook published the name *Simpsonia* O. F. Cook, Science n.s. 85:332–333. 1937. This name, based on *Thrinax microcarpa,* is invalid as it was published without Latin description.

Taxonomic Account.—Read (1975), Borhidi and Muñiz (1985).

Plates.—32A, and in 47C; Figs. G.19, G.20.

7. COCCOTHRINAX Sargent, Botanical Gazette 27:87. 1899. Type: **C. jucunda** Sargent.

Haitiella L. H. Bailey, Contributions of the Gray Herbarium 165:7. 1947. Type: *H. ekmanii* (Burret) L. H. Bailey (=*Coccothrinax ekmanii* Burret).
Thrincoma O. F. Cook, Bulletin of the Torrey Botanical Club 28:539. 1901. Type: *T. alta* O. F. Cook (=*Coccothrinax alta* (Cook) Beccari).
Thringis O. F. Cook, Bulletin of the Torrey Botanical Club 28:544. 1901. Lectotype: *T. latifrons* O. F. Cook (see H. E. Moore 1963c) (=*Coccothrinax alta* (Cook) Beccari).

Small to moderate, solitary or clustered, unarmed or partly armed, pleonanthic, hermaphroditic palms. Stem slender, at first covered with fibrous leaf sheaths, then with a regular fibrous network or masses of long slender fibers or stout spines, eventually becoming bare, and closely ringed with narrow leaf scars. Leaves induplicate, palmate, ascending to spreading, marcescent; sheath sometimes long persistent and disintegrating into a regular fibrous network or masses of long slender fibers, or becoming ± spiny, covered with dense, deciduous tomentum (? always); petiole long, slender, flat to ridged adaxially, rounded abaxially, densely tomentose or glabrous; hastula prominent adaxially, triangular to ± rounded, absent or a very narrow ridge abaxially; blade fan-shaped, irregularly folded when large, divided to about the middle into long, rather narrow, pointed segments, tips usually bifid, glabrous adaxially, silvery, punctate, with hairs or glabrous abaxially; midribs prominent, lateral ribs sometimes conspicuous, transverse veinlets evident or inconspicuous on one or both surfaces. Inflorescences shorter than the leaves, slender, branched to 2

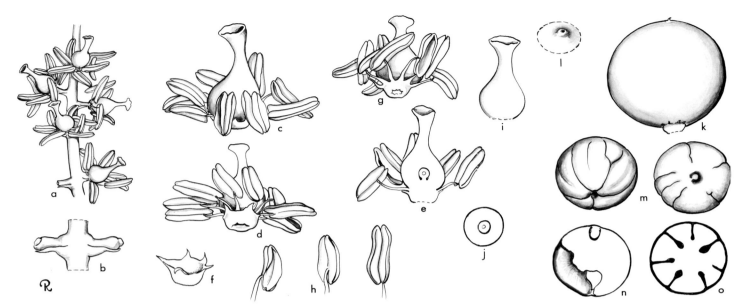

7.—**Coccothrinax. a,** portion of rachilla ×3; **b,** portion of rachilla with floral scars and bracts ×6; **c,** flower ×6; **d,** flower from below ×6; **e,** flower in vertical section ×6; **f,** perianth ×6; **g,** flower, perianth removed ×6; **h,** stamen in 3 views ×6; **i,** gynoecium ×6; **j,** ovary in cross-section ×6; **k,** fruit ×3; **l,** apex of fruit ×6; **m,** seed in 2 views ×3; **n,** seed in vertical section ×3; **o,** seed in cross-section ×3. *Coccothrinax argentata*: **a-j,** *Read 612*; **k-o,** *Dahlberg s.n.*

orders; peduncle rather short, slender; prophyll tubular, 2-keeled, pointed, opening apically; peduncular bracts several, like the prophyll but lacking keels, closely sheathing and overlapping; rachis longer than the peduncle, slender, bearing spirally arranged, tubular, overlapping, pointed bracts subtending rachillae; rachillae rather short, slender, bearing very small, spirally arranged, thin, pointed bracts (?bracts appear to be borne on the floral stalk where seen) each subtending a flower. Flowers solitary, sessile(?) or usually pedicellate; perianth broadly and shallowly cup-shaped with several (5–9) short points; stamens 9 (6–13), filaments slender, flat, shortly connate basally, not inflexed at the apex, anthers oblong or sagittate, dorsifixed near the base, latrorse, apically acute to briefly bifid; pollen elliptic or sometimes almost circular in polar view, monosulcate, with finely reticulate, foveolate, or fossulate, tectate exine; gynoecium of 1 carpel, unilocular, uniovulate, globose basally, attenuate in a long style terminating in a cuplike, ± laterally compressed stigma, ovule basal, erect, nearly orthotropous. Fruit globose, purplish-black at maturity, stigmatic remains apical; epicarp smooth or rough, mesocarp thin or somewhat fleshy with flat, slender, anastomosing fibers next to the membranous endocarp. Seed globose, attached basally, deeply grooved, hilum rounded, basal, endosperm homogeneous except for grooves; embryo apical or subapical. Germination not recorded; eophyll entire, very narrow. *n* = 18 (*C. acuminata, C. crinita, C. inaguensis, C. martii, C. miraguama,* Read 1966; *C. argentea,* Read 1966, Eichhorn 1953, Satô 1946).

Anatomy.—Leaf anatomy (Tomlinson 1961) for *C. barbadensis* and *C. argentea* but identification questioned. Resembles *Thrinax* in floral anatomy (Uhl and Moore 1977a); the vasculature of the gynoecium confirms its interpretation as a single carpel (Uhl unpublished).

Distribution.—About 49 species on islands of the West Indies, with the greatest diversity (about 34 species) in Cuba.

Ecology.—Restricted to limestone or serpentine rocks, usually in dry and often exposed highlands, sometimes in valleys and on coasts.

Common Names and Uses.—Broom, silver, and thatch palms. Have been used for thatch and for making brooms, also grown as ornamentals.

Notes.—Most closely related to *Thrinax;* see notes under that genus. O. F. Cook published the following generic names based on species of *Coccothrinax* in the National Horticultural Magazine Volume 20; as the names appear without Latin descriptions and postdate 1935, they are invalid and lack any botanical standing: *Antia, Beata, Pithodes.*

Taxonomic Accounts.—A new treatment is much needed. See Bailey and Moore (1949), León (1939, 1946), Muñiz and Borhidi (1982), Quero (1980), and Read (1980).

Plates.—*1C, D, 32B; Fig. G.5.*

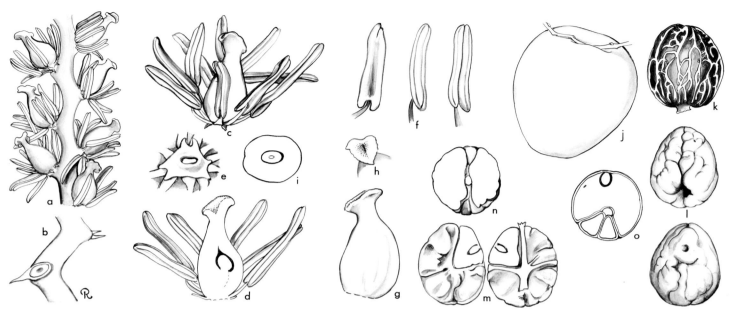

8.—**Zombia. a,** portion of rachilla ×3; **b,** floral scar and bracts ×6; **c,** flower ×6; **d,** flower in vertical section ×6; **e,** perianth ×6; **f,** stamen in 3 views ×6; **g,** gynoecium ×6; **h,** stigma ×6; **i,** ovary in cross-section ×6; **j,** fruit ×1½; **k,** seed with adhering endocarp fibers ×1½; **l,** seed in 2 views ×1½; **m,** seed in vertical section ×1½; **n, o,** seed in cross-section through middle of embryo ×1½. *Zombia antillarum:* all from *Read 721.*

8. **ZOMBIA** L. H. Bailey, Gentes Herbarum 4:240. 1939. Type: **Z. antillarum** (Descourtilz ex Jackson) L. H. Bailey (*Chamaerops antillarum* Descourtilz ex Jackson).

Coccothrinax subgenus *Oothrinax* Beccari, Feddes Repertorium Specierum Novarum Regni Vegetabilis 6:95. 1908 (invalid name). Type: *C. anomala* Beccari (=*Zombia antillarum*).

Oothrinax (Beccari) O. F. Cook, National Horticultural Magazine 20:21. 1941. Illegitimate name.

Moderate, clustering, spiny, pleonanthic, hermaphroditic palm. Stem erect, slender, covered with persistent, overlapping spiny sheaths and bearing erect spinelike pneumatophores at the base. Leaves induplicate, palmate, marcescent; sheath expanding into a regular network of fibers, distal fibers reflexed, forming a partial whorl of spines; petiole very slender, elongate, unarmed, semicircular in cross-section; adaxial hastula 3-lobed, center lobe pointed, lateral lobes rounded becoming irregularly tattered, abaxial hastula also pointed with very shallow lateral ridges; blade irregularly divided along the adaxial folds ½–⅔ to the base into single-fold, lanceolate, rather thin, shortly bifid segments, shiny dark green above, whitish beneath, caducous indumentum along ribs on both surfaces, midrib prominent abaxially, interfold ribs prominent adaxially, transverse veinlets scarcely discernible. Inflorescences interfoliar, shorter than the leaves, branched to 2 orders; peduncle short; prophyll partly included in the subtending leaf sheath, tubular, 2-keeled, opening and ±2-lobed distally, longitudinally striate; peduncular bracts lacking; rachis longer than the peduncle, densely tomentose; rachis bracts tubular, longitudinally striate, sparsely tomentose, each with a short pointed lobe, sometimes with short apical splits; first-order branches distant, each bearing a basal, tubular, 2-keeled, 2-lobed, longitudinally striate, sparsely tomentose prophyll; rachillae (second-order branches) sparse, short, spreading, proximal 2± subopposite, subtended by narrow bracts, distal rachillae subopposite or alternate, subtending bracts minute, inconspicuous, rachillae slender, glabrous, minutely papillose, bearing rather distant, solitary, subdistichous flowers each subtended by a minute triangular bract. Flowers cream-colored; perianth shallow, cup-shaped with 6 short, membranous points; stamens 9–12, the filaments short, variable, slender, anthers basifixed, erect, elongate, latrorse; pollen elliptic, monosulcate, with foveolate, tectate exine; gynoecium obpyriform, unicarpellate, tapered to a large, laterally compressed, cuplike stigma, ovule basal, orthotropous. Fruit falling with the perianth attached and stamen bases often obvious, oblong-globose, white, fleshy, large, with apical stigmatic remains; epicarp smooth except for the stigmatic remains, mesocarp fleshy without obvious fibers, endocarp crustaceous. Seed basally attached, very deeply bilobed, the lobes again divided irregularly in a bilobed fashion, the 2 halves connected by a portion in which the embryo lies centrally, endosperm homogeneous within the lobes. Germination and eophyll not recorded. $n = 18$ (Read 1965b, 1966).

Anatomy.—Leaf (Tomlinson 1961), floral (Morrow 1965, Moore and Uhl 1973).

Distribution.—One species in Hispaniola.

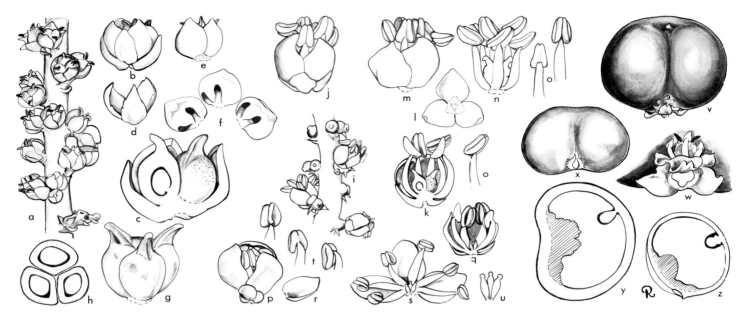

9.—**Trachycarpus. a,** portion of pistillate rachilla ×3; **b,** pistillate flower ×6; **c,** pistillate flower in vertical section ×12; **d,** pistillate calyx ×6; **e,** pistillate flower, calyx removed ×6; **f,** pistillate petals and staminodes, interior view ×6; **g,** gynoecium ×12; **h,** carpels in cross-section ×12; **i,** portion of rachilla with morphologically hermaphroditic flowers ×3; **j,** hermaphroditic flower ×6; **k,** hermaphroditic flower in vertical section ×6; **l,** calyx of hermaphroditic flower, interior view ×6; **m,** hermaphroditic flower, calyx removed ×6; **n,** androecium and gynoecium ×6; **o,** stamen or staminode in 3 views ×6; **p,** staminate flower ×6; **q,** staminate flower in vertical section ×6; **r,** staminate sepal ×6; **s,** staminate flower, expanded, interior view ×6; **t,** stamen in 3 views ×6; **u,** pistillode ×12; **v,** fruit ×3; **w,** base of fruit with abortive carpels ×6; **x,** seed ×3; **y,** fruit in cross-section ×3; **z,** fruit in vertical section ×3. *Trachycarpus fortunei:* **a-h,** *Read 756;* **i-o,** *Bailey & Bailey s.n.;* **p-u** and **w-y,** *Bailey & Bailey s.n.;* **v** and **z,** *Read s.n.*

Ecology.—Open and bushy slopes of very dry hills.
Common Names and Uses.—Zombi palm. A striking ornamental. Fruit are said to be fed to hogs.
Notes.—An unusual palm easily distinguished by the bizarre, persistent, spiny leaf sheaths and differing from *Coccothrinax* by white fruits, from *Thrinax* by the unsplit petioles, and from both by the spiny pneumatophores. See notes under *Thrinax.*
Taxonomic Account.—Bailey (1939b).
Plate.—*32C; Fig. G.5.*

9. TRACHYCARPUS H. A. Wendland in J. Gay, Bulletin de la Société Botanique de France 8:429. 1863(?) ("1861"). Lectotype: *T. fortunei* (W. J. Hooker) H. A. Wendland (*Chamaerops fortunei* W. J. Hooker) (see H. E. Moore 1963c).

Dwarf or moderate, solitary or clustering, acaulescent or erect, unarmed or lightly armed, pleonanthic, dioecious or polygamous palms. Stem decumbent or erect, becoming bare and marked with conspicuous, rather close, oblique leaf scars, or clothed with persistent petiole bases and fibrous sheaths, or obscured by a skirt of dead leaves. Leaves induplicate, palmate, marcescent; sheath disintegrating into a mass of fine and coarse fibers, the upper margin ribbonlike, becoming twisted; petiole elongate, narrow, adaxially flattened or slightly rounded, abaxially rounded or angled, bearing scattered, deciduous indumentum or glabrous, armed along the margins with very fine teeth or unarmed; adaxial hastula well developed, rounded or triangular, abaxial hastula absent; blade fan-shaped to almost circular, equally or unequally divided along adaxial ribs into single-fold segments, shallowly bifid at the tips, longitudinally striate or not, the abaxial surface sometimes glaucous, sometimes dotted with minute brown scales, midrib conspicuous abaxially, transverse veinlets conspicuous or not. Inflorescences solitary, interfoliar, arching or ± erect, copiously branching to 4 orders; peduncle oval in cross-section, bearing sparse indumentum; prophyll complete, conspicuous, with a tubular base, and inflated distally, 2-keeled laterally, splitting apically and along one side, covered with deciduous indumentum; peduncular bracts 1–3, as the prophyll but single-keeled, rachis shorter or longer than the peduncle, bearing spirally arranged bracts similar to the peduncular bracts, but each subtending a first-order branch; bracts of subsequent orders inconspicuous, triangular, not sheathing; rachillae slender, stiff, short, very crowded, bright yellow to greenish, glabrous or sparsely hairy, bearing spirally arranged flowers, solitary or in clusters of 2–3, sessile or borne on low tubercles, each flower bearing a minute, apiculate, membranous bracteole. Flowers similar in both sexes; sepals 3, united at the base, triangular, short or long, glabrous; petals usually considerably exceeding the sepals, 3, distinct, imbricate, ovate, triangular-tipped or rounded, glabrous; stamens 6, filaments distinct, fleshy, ±

parallel-sided, anthers short, oblong, sometimes slightly pointed, latrorse; pollen elliptic, monosulcate, with finely reticulate, tectate exine; staminodes when present, similar to fertile stamens but with flattened filaments and empty anthers, sometimes with filaments connate at the very base; carpels 3, distinct, follicular, hairy, ventral sutures partially open, stylar projections short, ovule basally attached, hemianatropous, surrounded dorsally and ventrally by a fleshy aril; pistillodes when present similar to, but much smaller than the fertile carpels. Fruit usually developing from 1 carpel, purplish-black with a pale bloom, kidney-shaped to oblong, slightly grooved on the adaxial side with lateral or subapical stigmatic remains; epicarp thin, hairy in immature fruit, becoming glabrous in mature fruit, mesocarp thin with scattered layer of tannin cells, endocarp crustaceous; endosperm homogeneous with a shallow to deep lateral intrusion of seed coat, sometimes also with very shallow ruminations; embryo lateral. Germination remote-tubular; eophyll simple, narrow, plicate. *n* = 18 (*T. fortunei,* Eichhorn 1957, and as *T. excelsus,* Sinotô 1929, Satô 1946; *T. martianus,* Sarkar 1970).

Anatomy.—Leaf (Tomlinson 1961), floral (Morrow 1965; Uhl and Moore 1971).

Distribution.—Six species recorded (two of these perhaps only cultivars) ranging from the Himalayas in northern India to northern Thailand and China.

Ecology.—*T. nanus* and *T. martianus* have both been recorded from limestone hills; the latter has been found at altitudes up to 2400 m and appears not to be exclusive to limestone. *T. takil* has been reported from damp oak forests at 2400 m altitude, where the ground is under snow from November to March. *T. fortunei,* the most cold tolerant of all cultivated palms, is hardy in the British Isles.

Fossil Record.—A leaf, *T. raphifolia* and a bilobed fruit referred to a *?Trachycarpus* sp. are reported from Lower Tertiary London Clay by Chandler (1964, 1978).

Common Names and Uses.—Chinese windmill palm, Chusan palm (*T. fortunei*). Stems are used as posts in China, and fibers of leaf sheath and stem for brushes and plaiting; seeds are used medicinally and are believed to have anticancer properties. Grown as ornamentals in cooler climates.

Notes.—The follicular carpels, with open ventral sutures, are among the least specialized in the family.

Taxonomic Accounts.—Beccari (1931), see also Kimnach (1977).

Plate.—*32D.*

10. RHAPIDOPHYLLUM H. A. Wendland & Drude in Drude, Botanische Zeitung 34:803. 1876. Type: **R. hystrix** (Pursh) H. A. Wendland & Drude (*Chamaerops hystrix* Pursh).

Small to moderate, clustering, armed, pleonanthic, dioecious, polygamodioecious or rarely monoecious palm. Stem very short, decumbent or erect, upper ¾ or more covered with needlelike spines and fibers, basally becoming bare, ringed with leaf scars. Leaves induplicate, shortly costapalmate, marcescent; sheath persistent, soft-fibrous with protruding elongate, stout, needlelike spines; petiole adaxially flat, abaxially rounded, the margins entire, sharp, rough; adaxial hastula very short, triangular to truncate, rounded, membranous, abaxial hastula lacking; blade very shortly costapalmate, narrow basally, divided between the folds nearly to the base into linear, mostly 2–4-veined, ± stiff segments, each composed of part of 1 adaxial and 1 abaxial fold and having 2 large ribs, 1 near a margin, tips ± rounded, shortly bifid, adaxial surface with small deciduous scales and wax, abaxial surface with white-waxy small brown scales, sometimes both surfaces glaucous, transverse veinlets inconspicuous. Inflorescences interfoliar, staminate and pistillate similar but pistillate stouter (polygamous not seen), very short, scarcely or not exserted from the leaf sheaths, usually once branched, rarely unbranched; peduncle short; prophyll laterally 2-keeled, inflated, chartaceous, opening distally; peduncular bracts 4–6, short, slightly inflated, tubular at the base, splitting apically, rachis about equalling the peduncle at maturity in pistillate inflorescences, longer in staminate inflorescences, bearing spirally arranged, very small, narrow, elongate bracts subtending rachillae; rachillae short, bearing similar but smaller bracts, each subtending 2–4 small flowers in only slightly elevated cincinni. Staminate flowers globose, predominantly in clusters of 3; sepals 3, distinct to slightly connate at the base, deltoid; petals 3, distinct, fleshy, imbricate, ovate, acute; stamens 6, filaments distinct, slender, slightly exceeding the petals, anthers linear-oblong, dorsifixed near the base, latrorse; pollen elliptic, monosulcate, with finely reticulate, tectate exine; pistillodes 3, minute, resembling the carpels. Pistillate flowers similar to the staminate, predominantly paired; perianth as in the staminate; sterile stamens 6, shorter than the fertile; carpels 3, distinct, follicular, basally tomentose, styles short, recurved, terminating in punctiform stigmas, ovule erect, basal, hemianatropous. Fruit globose to globose-ovoid, covered with deciduous hairs, brownish, slightly flattened on the ventral surface with ventrally eccentric, apical stigmatic scar; epicarp drying in a scalelike pattern, mesocarp thin, fleshy, sweet, endocarp cartilaginous. Seed narrowly ovoid to ellipsoidal, laterally attached, becoming free from the endocarp, hilum basal, raphe ventral, prominent, unbranched, endosperm homogeneous, seed coat somewhat thickened and intruded below the raphe; embryo lateral opposite the raphe. Germination not recorded; eophyll simple, lanceolate, tip truncate. *n* = 18 (Read 1964, 1965a).

Anatomy.—Leaf (Tomlinson 1961), floral (Morrow 1965).

Distribution.—One species in southeastern United States from Beaufort County, South Carolina, south to Highlands and Hardee Counties, Florida, and west to Simpson County in south central Mississippi.

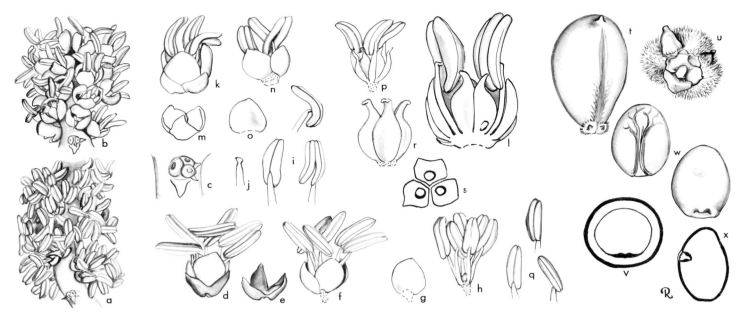

10.—**Rhapidophyllum. a,** portion of rachilla with staminate flowers ×3; **b,** portion of rachilla with hermaphroditic or pistillate flowers ×3; **c,** floral scars and bracts ×6; **d,** staminate flower ×6; **e,** staminate calyx ×6; **f,** staminate flower, calyx removed ×6; **g,** staminate petal ×6; **h,** androecium ×6; **i,** stamen in 3 views ×6; **j,** pistillode ×6; **k,** pistillate flower ×6; **l,** pistillate flower in vertical section ×12; **m,** pistillate calyx ×6; **n,** pistillate flower, calyx removed ×6; **o,** pistillate petal ×6; **p,** pistillate flower, perianth removed ×6; **q,** staminodes in 3 views ×6; **r,** gynoecium ×6; **s,** carpels in cross-section ×6; **t,** fruit ×1½; **u,** base of fruit and abortive carpels ×3; **v,** fruit in cross-section ×1½; **w,** seed in 2 views ×1½; **x,** seed in vertical section ×1. *Rhapidophyllum hystrix:* **a–s,** *Read 773;* **t–x,** *Moore 7822.*

Ecology.—*Rhapidophyllum hystrix* is found in low, moist to wet areas with rich humus, calcareous clay, or sandy soils in woods and swamps. It may occur in grottos, limestone sinks, and shaded pinelands, but usually is associated with limestone. It will thrive in well drained sites in the sun if sufficient moisture is provided.

Rhapidophyllum grows very slowly in the wild presumably due to low light conditions. Growth is accelerated when adequate light is provided but the long time—four to six years—to grow a mature plant from seed has discouraged its cultivation. Reproduction also occurs by suckering. The lower end of the stem decays as the palm grows; the rotting often separates suckers from the main plant but also tends to eliminate anchoring roots causing the trunk to lean. During development flowers and seeds are well protected by the sheath spines. However, it is unclear how seeds are dispersed and they often germinate in situ where seedlings have little chance of survival. The spines are so conspicuous that *Rhapidophyllum* has been called the "vegetable porcupine" (Small 1923).

Pollination appears to be primarily by an undescribed species of *Notolomus* (Curculionidae). Bee-tles are attracted to both staminate and pistillate flowers by a musky odor and feed on pollen and flower parts. The species seems self-compatible although pollinator visits have not been completely worked out (Shuey and Wunderlin 1977).

Common Names and Uses.—Needle palm. Cultivated as a cold tolerant ornamental. Cutting of crowns for decoration during the late 19th and early 20th century decimated many populations and some exploitation by nurseries continues. The species is considered endangered.

Notes.—*Rhapidophyllum hystrix* seems most closely related to *Trachycarpus* of Southeast Asia. It is considered a relict genus (Shuey and Wunderlin 1977) and is of considerable interest as one of the least specialized palms.

Taxonomic Accounts.—Shuey and Wunderlin (1977), Small (1923).

Plates.—2, 33A; Fig. G.9.

11. **CHAMAEROPS** Linnaeus, Species Plantarum 1187. 1753. Type: **C. humilis** Linnaeus.

Chamaeriphe Steck, Dissertatio Inauguralis Medica de Sagu 20. 1757.

Chamaeriphes Pontedera ex J. Gaertner, De Fruc-

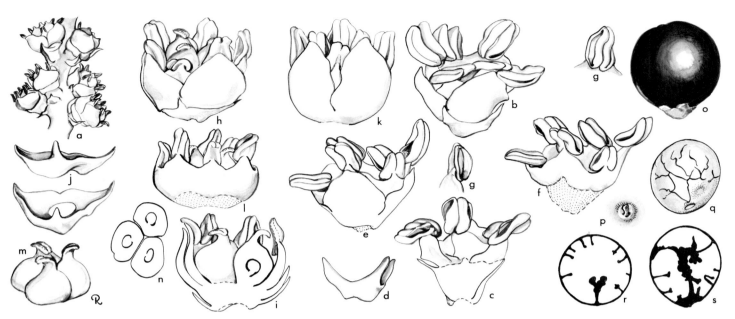

11.—**Chamaerops. a,** portion of pistillate rachilla ×3; **b,** staminate flower ×6; **c,** staminate flower in vertical section ×6; **d,** staminate calyx ×6; **e,** staminate flower, calyx removed ×6; **f,** androecium ×6; **g,** anther in 2 views ×6; **h,** pistillate flower ×6; **i,** pistillate flower in vertical section ×6; **j,** pistillate calyx in 2 views ×6; **k,** pistillate flower, calyx removed ×6; **l,** pistillate flower, perianth removed ×6; **m,** gynoecium ×6; **n,** carpels in cross-section ×6; **o,** fruit ×1½; **p,** apex of fruit ×6; **q,** seed ×1½; **r,** seed in cross-section ×1½; **s,** seed in vertical section ×1½. *Chamaerops humilis*: **a** and **h-s,** *Read 700*; **b-g,** *Read 724*.

tibus et Seminibus Plantarum 1:25. 1788. Type: *C. major* J. Gaertner (illegitimate name) (=*Chamaerops humilis* Linnaeus).

Dwarf, rarely moderate, clustering, acaulescent or shrubby, armed, pleonanthic, polygamous or dioecious palm. Stem clothed with very close, persistent petiole bases and fibrous sheaths, eventually becoming ± bare. Leaves induplicate, palmate, marcescent; sheath disintegrating into a mass of fine fibers; petiole elongate, slender, adaxially flattened or slightly rounded, abaxially rounded or angled, densely covered with caducous white tomentum, armed along the margins with robust, bulbous-based spines pointing towards the leaf tip; adaxial hastula well developed, ± acute, abaxial hastula poorly developed; blade divided to ⅔–¾ the radius into single-fold segments, the segments further divided to ca. ½–⅔ along the abaxial folds, folds longitudinally striate, tips ± rounded or pointed, abaxially sparsely to densely covered with caducous tomentum, midribs prominent abaxially, transverse veinlets obscure. Inflorescences solitary, interfoliar, very short, branching to 2 orders, staminate and pistillate inflorescences similar when present; peduncle very short, oval in cross-section; prophyll conspicuous, tubular, somewhat inflated, laterally 2-keeled, splitting apically into 2 triangular lobes, covered with dense tomentum especially along keels; peduncular bracts absent; rachis short, but longer than the peduncle; rachis bracts inconspicuous, the proximal enclosed within the prophyll, each subtending a first-order branch; first-order branches bearing minute slender bracts subtending short, very crowded, glabrous rachillae. Flowers solitary, spirally arranged, borne on short

tubercles subtended by minute bracts; abnormalities in all floral parts frequent; sepals 3, low, triangular, glabrous, united at the base; petals similar in staminate, pistillate, and hermaphroditic flowers, 3, united at the very base, imbricate, distally triangular; stamens 6, united by their broad triangular filaments to form a conspicuous staminal ring folded in young stages, much expanded at anthesis, anthers yellow, oblong, medifixed, latrorse; pollen broadly elliptical or ± circular, monosulcate, pontoperculate, with finely reticulate, tectate exine; staminodes like the stamens but with empty anthers and less well developed filaments; carpels 3, distinct, follicular, glabrous, with conspicuous recurved apical stigmas, ovule hemianatropous, borne at the base of the locule; pistillodes present as 1–3 minute carpels, or absent. Fruit developing from 1–3 carpels, product of each carpel globose to oblong, ellipsoidal, rich brown, pale-dotted; epicarp smooth, mesocarp thin, ± fleshy, rich in butyric acid, endocarp scarcely developed. Seed globose to ellipsoidal, basally attached, endosperm ruminate, also with a conspicuous lateral intrusion of seed coat; embryo lateral. Germination remote-tubular; eophyll entire, narrow, plicate. $n = 18$ (Eichhorn 1957, Read 1966, Sarkar 1970, Satô 1946).

Anatomy.—Leaf (Tomlinson 1961), flower (Morrow 1965).

Distribution.—One species, *C. humilis,* native to coastal areas of the western Mediterranean, both in Europe and north Africa, becoming rarer eastwards to Malta. Widely cultivated, and very variable, particularly in leaf form and fruit shape.

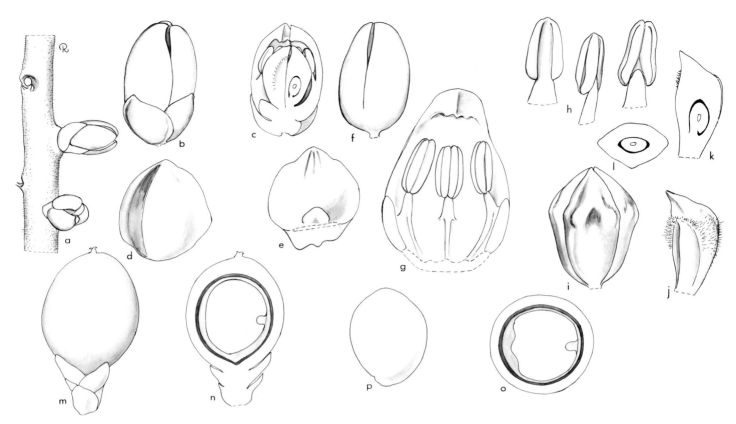

12.—**Maxburretia. a,** portion of rachilla ×6; **b,** flower ×12; **c,** flower in vertical section ×12 **d,** sepal, exterior view ×24; **e,** sepal, interior view ×24; **f,** flower, corolla removed ×12; **g,** petal and stamens, interior view ×24; **h,** stamen in 3 views ×24; **i,** gynoecium ×16; **j,** carpel, ventral view ×24; **k,** carpel in vertical section ×24; **l,** carpel in cross-section ×24; **m,** fruit ×6; **n,** fruit in vertical section ×6; **o,** fruit in cross-section ×6; **p,** seed ×6. *Maxburretia rupicola:* **a-l,** *Whitmore FRI 699;* **m-p,** *Dransfield 910.*

Ecology.—Sandy or rocky ground, usually near the sea but up to 600 m altitude or more on coastal hills, usually acaulescent in the wild but in the absence of burning, producing a well developed trunk as in cultivated specimens.

Common Names and Uses.—European fan palm, windmill palm. Fiber has been used for cordage and woven articles. Forms with abnormal leaves have been selected in cultivation; one such in the garden of R. G. Douglas, California bears leaves with the blade divided between as well as along the folds.

Notes.—Floral abnormalities are of frequent occurrence; for example the following variation may be found within the same inflorescence: petals 2 instead of 3; stamens fewer than 6, and some anthers infertile within same flower; carpels 3, 2, or 1 fertile, with or without fertile stamens, and pistillodes present or absent. Although the androecium is specialized with filaments united forming a shallow cup, and the carpel walls are thick, *Chamaerops* is one

of the least specialized palms; it is closely related to *Trachycarpus* and *Rhapidophyllum.*

Taxonomic Account.—Beccari (1931).

Plate.—*33B; Figs. G.10, G.20.*

12. MAXBURRETIA Furtado, Gardens' Bulletin, Straits Settlements 11:240. 1941. Type: **M. rupicola** (Ridley) Furtado (*Livistona rupicola* Ridley).

Livistona subgenus *Livistonella* Beccari, Webbia 5: 16. 1921. Type: *Livistona rupicola* Ridley.

Symphyogyne Burret, Notizblatt des Botanischen Gartens und Museums zu Berlin-Dahlem 15:316. 1941. Type: *S. gracilis* Burret (=*Maxburretia gracilis* (Burret) Dransfield) (non *Symphyogyna* Nees & Montagne 1836).

Liberbaileya Furtado, Gardens' Bulletin, Straits Settlements 11:238. 1941. Type: *L. lankawiensis* Furtado (=*Maxburretia gracilis* (Burret) Dransfield).

Small, clustering, acaulescent or shrubby, unarmed, pleonanthic, hermaphroditic or dioecious palms. Stem moderate if present, with very close leaf scars, usually completely obscured by persistent leaf sheaths. Leaves induplicate, palmate, marcescent; sheath expanding into a mass of discrete fibers, irregular or neatly joined at the tips opposite the petiole, or developed as rigid spines; petiole well developed, unarmed, ± semicircular in cross-section; adaxial hastula ± triangular or rounded, sometimes hairy, abaxial hastula obscure; blade neatly divided to ca. ⅔ of its radius into slender, single-fold, usually glaucous segments, tips shallowly split along the folds, surfaces often slightly dissimilar, scattered scales sometimes present on abaxial surface, midribs prominent abaxially, transverse veinlets obscure. Inflorescences solitary, interfoliar, arching out of the crown, branching to 1–3 orders; prophyll tubular, 2-keeled, narrow, elongate, usually obscured by the leaf sheaths; peduncular bracts 1–3 or more, similar to the prophyll; rachis bracts closely tubular with triangular limbs, each subtending a first-order branch; subsequent orders of bracts minute, inconspicuous; rachillae slender, bearing distant, spirally arranged, minute, triangular bracts subtending solitary or, rarely, groups of 2–3 flowers. Flowers very small; where plants dioecious, staminate and pistillate flowers superficially similar; sepals 3, distinct, imbricate, ovate or triangular, glabrous; petals 3, joined for ⅓ to ½ their length at the base, somewhat imbricate in midportion, valvate near the tips, elongate, usually with somewhat thickened tips; stamens in staminate and hermaphroditic flowers 6, adnate to the petals, the filaments forming a thin or thick staminal cupule, or distinct, anthers rather short, latrorse; pollen elliptic, monosulcate, with finely reticulate, tectate exine; staminodes in pistillate flower similar to the stamens but with thinner cupule and smaller, empty anthers; carpels 3, distinct, follicular, united for a very short distance at the base, with triangular style, the carpel surface hairy distally in 2 species, glabrous in the third, ovules basally attached, anatropous or intermediate between anatropous and hemianatropous with basal funicular arils; pistillode of staminate flower minute, 3-lobed. Fruit usually developing from only 1 carpel, ellipsoidal (? always), with apical stigmatic remains, perianth whorls persistent; epicarp silky hairy when young, the hairs falling off at maturity (? always), mesocarp thin, fleshy, endocarp scarcely developed. Seed basally attached, endosperm homogeneous, with a thin lateral intrusion of seed coat; embryo lateral opposite the intrusion. Germination not known; eophyll apparently simple, entire, plicate. Cytology not known.

Anatomy. — Leaf anatomy not studied. The three species are very similar in floral anatomy (Uhl 1978a).

Distribution. — Three species in Peninsular Malaysia and Peninsular Thailand; *M. rupicola* at Batu Caves, Bukit Takun and Bukit Anak Takun in Selangor, *M. gracilis* on Pulau Dayang Bunting in the Langkawi Islands, and *M. furtadoana* at Khao Phra Rahu near Surat Thani.

Ecology. — All three species are palms of the low forest on exposed sides and summits of limestone hills.

Common Names and Uses. — Serdang-Batu. Uses not recorded.

Notes. — The three species of *Maxburretia* survive as relics on limestone hills in Southeast Asia. The distinct carpels must be regarded as a primitive feature but the androecium, with stamens adnate to the petals and sometimes also connate, is more specialized. *Maxburretia* is most closely related to *Guihaia* and *Rhapis*.

Taxonomic Account. — Dransfield (1978a).

Plate. — *4A.*

13. **GUIHAIA** J. Dransfield, S. K. Lee & F. N. Wei, Principes 29:7. 1985. Type: **G. argyrata** (S. K. Lee & F. N. Wei) S. K. Lee, F. N. Wei & J. Dransfield (*Trachycarpus argyratus* S. K. Lee & F. N. Wei).

Dwarf, clustering, acaulescent, unarmed, pleonanthic, dioecious palms. Stem decumbent or erect, very short, clothed with persistent petiole bases and sheaths. Leaves reduplicate, palmate, marcescent; sheath disintegrating into an interwoven mass of coarse, erect, black, spinelike fibers or into a tongue-shaped lattice of coarse flat fibers; petiole moderate, unarmed, abaxially rounded, adaxially flattened or slightly rounded, the margins quite sharp, bearing caducous woolly hairs; adaxial hastula rounded, glabrous or bearded with woolly hairs; lamina orbicular or cuneate, rather small, divided to ¾ to ⅘ the radius or nearly to the insertion along the abaxial ribs into several (ca. 20), ± linear, single or rarely 2-fold reduplicate segments, minutely bifid at the tips, the outermost segments consisting of ½ folds only, margins of the segments minutely toothed or smooth, lamina adaxially dark green, glabrous except for scales along the ribs, abaxially covered with a dense felt of silvery woolly hairs or glabrous except for scattered dotlike scales, transverse veinlets obscure or evident. Inflorescences solitary, axillary, interfoliar, branching to 4 orders, staminate and pistillate superficially similar; prophyll elongate, tubular, 2-keeled, thin, somewhat coriaceous, apically splitting along 2 sides, glabrous or bearing caducous hairs; peduncle elongate, ± flattened, caducously scaly; peduncular bracts absent; rachis longer or shorter than the peduncle; rachis bracts ca. 2–5, similar to the prophyll but not 2-keeled, with tattering limbs; first-order branches 4–5, adnate to the rachis to just below the insertion of the following bract; subsequent bracts minute, scarcely evident; rachillae spreading, few to numerous, very slender, ± straight, glabrous, or bearing scattered caducous scales and spirally arranged solitary flowers borne on very low swellings. Staminate flowers extremely small, symmetrical; sepals 3, distinct except at the very base, basally imbricate, ± rounded to ovate, abaxially bearing hairs and fringed with woollike hairs; petals longer than the sepals, basally connate ca. ⅓–½ their length, with rounded lobes, glabrous; stamens 6, the filaments not forming a staminal tube, but completely adnate to the

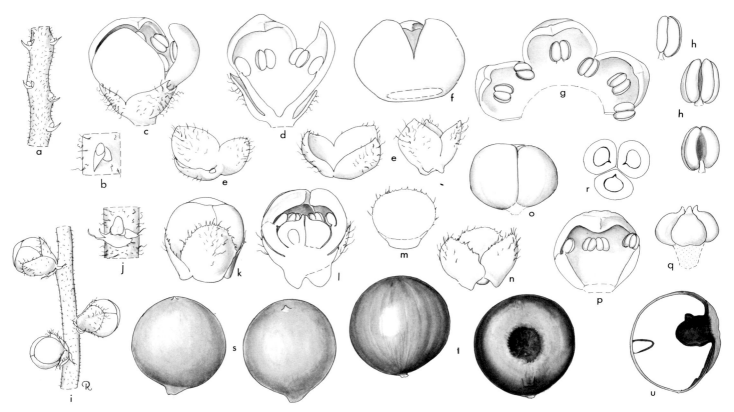

13.—**Guihaia. a,** portion of staminate rachilla ×7½; **b,** scar and bracts of staminate flower ×9; **c,** staminate flower ×15; **d,** staminate flower in vertical section ×15; **e,** staminate calyx in 3 views ×15; **f,** staminate corolla ×15; **g,** staminate corolla with epipetalous stamens, interior view, expanded ×15; **h,** stamen in 3 views ×30; **i,** portion of pistillate rachilla ×7½; **j,** scar, bract, and bracteole of pistillate flower ×9; **k,** pistillate bud ×15; **l,** pistillate bud in vertical section ×18; **m,** pistillate sepal, interior view ×15; **n,** pistillate calyx ×15; **o,** pistillate flower, sepals removed ×15; **p,** pistillate petal with staminodes, interior view ×18; **q,** gynoecium ×18; **r,** carpels in cross-section ×18; **s,** fruit in 2 views ×4½; **t,** seed in 2 views ×6; **u,** seed in vertical section ×6. *Guihaia argyrata*: **a-h,** *Wei 937*; **i-r,** *Wei 1524*: **s-u,** *Wei 1513*.

corolla, anthers ± rounded, didymous, apparently inserted directly on the corolla, latrorse; pollen elliptic, monosulcate, with finely reticulate, tectate exine; pistillode absent. Pistillate flowers similar to the staminate but perhaps more rounded; sepals as in the staminate; petals only slightly longer than to more than twice as long as the sepals, joined in the basal ca. ⅓; staminodes 6, borne directly on the petals; carpels 3, distinct, glabrous, ± abruptly narrowed to a short style, ovule basally attached. Fruit developing from only 1 carpel, rounded to ellipsoidal, blue-black and bearing thin white wax, the stigmatic remains apical, the abortive carpels basal; epicarp glabrous, mesocarp very thin, fleshy, endocarp papery. Seed ± flattened on one side with lateral hilum and a well-defined, rounded intrusion of integument, endosperm homogeneous; embryo lateral. Germination remote tubular; eophyll entire, plicate, very narrow. Cytology not studied.

Anatomy.—Not studied.

Distribution.—Two species, *G. argyrata* endemic to south China (Guangxi and Guangdong) and *G.*

grossefibrosa in northern Vietnam and southwestern Guangxi.

Ecology.—Confined to steep karst limestone hill slopes and crevices in warm temperate to subtropical climates, at low elevations (ca. 200 m above sea level), occurring to about 26° N.

Common Names and Uses.—Common names not recorded. These elegant palms would make fine ornamentals; as far as is known they have no local uses.

Notes.—Closely related to *Maxburretia* and *Rhapis* and in details of the flowers and fruit more or less intermediate between the two genera. The extraordinary reduplicate leaf immediately sets the genus apart from all other coryphoid palms (but see *Licuala*).

Taxonomic Account.—Dransfield et al. (1985b). *Plate.*—*33D; Fig. G.19.*

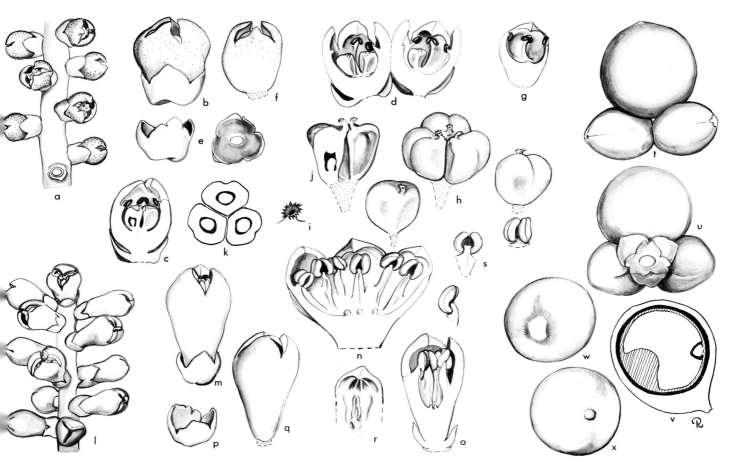

14.—**Rhapis. a,** portion of pistillate rachilla ×3; **b,** pistillate flower ×6; **c,** pistillate flower in vertical section ×6; **d,** pistillate flower, expanded ×6; **e,** pistillate calyx, exterior and interior views ×6; **f,** pistillate flower, calyx removed ×6; **g,** pistillate petal and staminodes, interior view ×6; **h,** single carpel in 2 views and whole gynoecium ×12; **i,** stigma ×24; **j,** gynoecium in vertical section ×12; **k,** carpels in cross-section ×12; **l,** portion of staminate rachilla ×3; **m,** staminate flower ×6; **n,** staminate flower, expanded ×6; **o,** staminate flower in vertical section ×6; **p,** staminate calyx ×6; **q,** staminate flower, calyx removed ×6; **r,** apical portion of staminate petal with base of stamen, interior view ×6; **s,** stamen in 3 views ×6; **t, u,** fruit with 1 mature and 2 partially developed carpels from above and below ×3; **v,** fruit in vertical section ×3; **w, x,** seed in 2 views ×3. *Rhapis excelsa*: all from *Read 774*.

14. **RHAPIS** Linnaeus filius ex W. Aiton, Hortus Kewensis 3:473. 1789. Lectotype: *R. flabelliformis* L'Héritier ex W. Aiton (illegitimate name) (*Chamaerops excelsa* Thunberg = **R. excelsa** (Thunberg) A. Henry ex Rehder).

Small, clustering, unarmed, pleonanthic, dioecious or polygamous palms. Stems slender, reedlike, erect, covered with persistent leaf sheaths, eventually becoming bare, conspicuously ringed with leaf scars. Leaves induplicate, palmate, marcescent, divided to the base or to ca. ¾ the radius between the folds into several-ribbed segments, apices divided along and between the folds to form shallow teeth; sheath composed of numerous, interwoven, black or grey-brown fibers, when young bearing sparse, caducous brown indumentum; petiole elongate, slender, ± elliptic in cross-section, margins smooth; adaxial hastula small, ± triangular, sometimes tomentose, abaxial hastula absent; blade palmate to deeply bifid, segments usually variable in number of ribs, position of splits precise, usually at a position about ⅔ the width of the interfold nearer the abaxial fold, the segment margins minutely toothed, blade glabrous, transverse veinlets conspicuous. Inflorescences interfoliar, usually very short, branching to 1–2 orders in pistillate, up to 3 orders in staminate; peduncle short, frequently entirely enclosed by the leaf sheaths; prophyll tubular, 2-keeled, splitting along the abaxial midline; peduncular bracts absent; rachis longer than the peduncle, bearing 1–2 large, tubular, single-keeled bracts, distal rachis bracts much smaller; rachis bracts each subtending a first-order branch adnate to the axis above the bract node and bearing very inconspicuous, narrow triangular bracts subtending second-order branches; second-order branches adnate to the first-order branches; rachillae glabrous or hairy, lax, spreading in pistillate

and polygamous inflorescences, more crowded in staminate, rachillae bearing spirally arranged, solitary or rarely
paired flowers in the axils of minute apiculate bracts. Staminate flowers symmetrical; calyx cup-shaped, thick,
shallowly 3-lobed distally, the lobes somewhat irregular,
triangular, glabrous or hairy; corolla fleshy, tubular, inserted above calyx and appearing ± stalked basally, the
3 lobes ± triangular, valvate, usually very short, sometimes ciliate at the margins; stamens 6, filaments elongate,
but adnate along ± the entire length of the corolla tube,
free at their very tip, anthers short, rounded, latrorse;
pollen elliptic, monosulcate, with finely reticulate, tectate
exine; pistillode minute, 3-lobed. Pistillate and rare hermaphroditic flowers superficially similar; sepals as in staminate but more fleshy; corolla with a short or long stalklike base, a short tube, and 3 fleshy triangular, basally
imbricate, apically valvate, fleshy lobes; staminodes as
the stamens but smaller and with empty anthers; carpels
3, distinct, wedge-shaped, each with a short apical style,
distally expanded into a conduplicate, fimbriate, tube-
shaped stigma, ovules basally attached, 1 in each carpel,
hemianatropous, with a basal fleshy aril. Fruit usually
developing from 1 carpel with apical stigmatic remains,
more rarely 2 or 3 carpels developing; epicarp becoming
purplish-brown or white, mesocarp fleshy, somewhat fibrous, endocarp thin, brittle. Seed with short lateral raphe,
endosperm homogeneous, laterally penetrated by the seed
coat; embryo sub-basal or lateral. Germination remote-
tubular; eophyll entire, slender, strap-shaped, plicate. $n =$
18 (*R. excelsa*, Read 1966, and *R. excelsa* as *R. flabelliformis*, *R. humilis*, Satô 1946, Sharma and Sarkar 1957).

Anatomy. — Leaf anatomy is described by Tomlinson (1961). *Rhapis excelsa* was chosen because
of its moderate size and availability for analysis of
stem vasculature by cinematography (Zimmermann
and Tomlinson 1965). The technique has been eminently successful and applied to other organs. Floral
anatomy (Uhl et al. 1969) and plication development in the leaf have also been studied (Kaplan et
al. 1982b). *Rhapis* is now the best known palm anatomically. See p. 36 for discussion of these studies.

Distribution. — About 12 species in southern
China, southwards through Indochina to peninsular
Thailand, one undescribed species in northernmost
Sumatra. Despite their horticultural importance,
species of *Rhapis* remain poorly known and little
understood.

Ecology. — Undergrowth palms of dry evergreen
forest; in south Thailand, *Rhapis* (species unknown)
seems to be confined to forest on limestone hills and
the Sumatran species is also found on limestone
(Whitten et al. 1984).

Common Names and Uses. — Lady palms. Widely
grown as ornamentals; many dwarf varieties have

been developed in Japan. See also McKamey (1983).
Stems are used as sticks and canes.

Notes. — *Rhapis* is distinguished by the leaf with
many-fold truncate segments and divisions between
the folds, and by the fleshy flowers with sepals and
petals united basally, and stamens borne on the corolla. Its closest relatives are *Maxburretia* and *Guihaia*. The three genera represent a group of apocarpous taxa more specialized in floral structure than
the other members of the Thrinacinae.

Taxonomic Account. — Beccari (1931).

Plate. — *34A; Figs. G.2, G.9, G.11.*

Livistoninae Saakov, Palms and their culture in the
USSR. 193. 1954. Type: **Livistona.**

Carpels 3, free basally, united by their styles.

The 12 genera of this subtribe are widely distributed throughout the tropics but with so many disjunctions as to suggest a very ancient origin (Map
4). The differences between the genera are mostly
small. Although the leaves are usually palmate or
costapalmate, there are two very distinctive leaf
forms unknown elsewhere in the Corypheae—the
extraordinary diamond-shaped leaf of *Johannesteijsmannia*, and the wedge-shaped segments with
"reduplicate" margins present in almost all species
of *Licuala*. The gynoecium of three carpels connate
by their styles is present throughout; stylar canals
may be separate or shortly united distally. *Washingtonia* stands somewhat apart from the rest of the
members of the subtribe because of its unusual, more
or less woody, swordlike bracts and large, chaffy
perianth segments.

15. **LIVISTONA** R. Brown, Prodromus Florae Novae
Hollandiae 267. 1810. Lectotype: **L. humilis** R.
Brown (see H. E. Moore 1963c).
Saribus Blume, Rumphia 2:48. 1838 ("1836"). Lec-
totype: *S. rotundifolius* (Lamarck) Blume (*Cory-
pha rotundifolia* Lamarck) = *Livistona rotundi-
folia* (Lamarck) Martius (see H. E. Moore 1963c).
Wissmannia Burret, Botanische Jahrbücher für Sys-
tematik 73:184. 1943. Type: *W. carinensis*
(Chiovenda) Burret (*Hyphaene carinensis* Chio-
venda) (=*Livistona carinensis* (Chiovenda) J.
Dransfield & N. Uhl).

Slender (rarely) to robust, solitary, armed or unarmed,
pleonanthic, hermaphroditic (rarely dioecious), shrub or
tree palms. Stem erect, obscured at first by persistent
sheaths, later becoming bare or covered with persistent
petiole bases, conspicuously or obscurely ringed with leaf
scars. Leaves induplicate, palmate or costapalmate, mar-

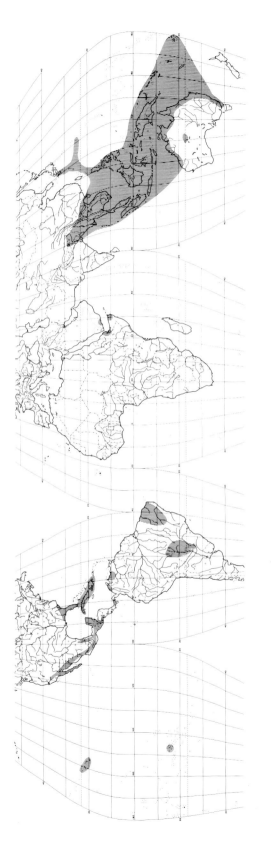

Map 4.—Distribution of Livistoninae.

cescent or deciduous under their own weight, a skirt of dead leaves sometimes developing; sheath disintegrating into a conspicuous interwoven, often clothlike, reddish brown mass of broad and fine fibers; petiole well developed, grooved or flattened adaxially, rounded or angled abaxially, sparsely covered with indumentum or not, expanded and sometimes bulbous at the occasionally persistent base, the margins unarmed or armed with inconspicuous to robust horizontal spines or teeth; adaxial hastula well developed, abaxial hastula poorly developed or absent; blade divided along adaxial ribs to varying depths to form single or, very rarely, multiple-fold segments, these further divided for a short to long distance along abaxial folds near the tip, rarely the adaxial splits almost reaching the hastula and the costa, the segments then all single-fold and very fine; segments stiff or pendulous, interfold filaments sometimes present, scattered caducous indumentum present along ribs, wax sometimes present on the abaxial surface, more rarely waxy on both surfaces, midribs conspicuous, transverse veinlets obscure or conspicuous. Inflorescences interfoliar, solitary, branched to 5 orders, rarely immediately trifurcating to give 3 equal "inflorescences" enclosed within a common prophyll, each branch with its own prophyll (*L. rotundifolia*); peduncle elongate; prophyll 2-keeled, tubular, closely sheathing, variously covered with indumentum or not, frequently tattering at the tip; peduncular bracts 1–few, tubular, like the prophyll; rachis usually longer than the peduncle; rachis bracts variously covered with indumentum, each subtending a first-order branch; bracts of subsequent orders generally inconspicuous; rachillae erect, pendulous or divaricate, glabrous or hairy, usually numerous, bearing spirally arranged flowers, singly or in cincinni of up to 5, sessile or on low tubercles or slender stalks, each group subtended by a minute rachilla bract and each flower bearing a minute bracteole. Flowers small to very small, usually cream-colored; calyx with receptacle often producing a short, broad stalk, tubular above, tipped with 3 triangular lobes, these sometimes imbricate at the very base, glabrous or hairy; corolla shallow, tubular at the base, apically with 3 triangular, valvate lobes; stamens 6, epipetalous, the filaments connate to form a fleshy ring, tipped with short, slender distinct filaments, anthers medifixed, rounded or oblong, latrorse; pollen elliptic, monosulcate, with finely reticulate, tectate exine; gynoecium tricarpellate, the carpels wedge-shaped, distinct in the ovarian region, connate distally to form a common, slender style, with an apical, dotlike or minutely 3-lobed stigma, ovule basally attached, anatropous; where dioecious, anthers or ovules not developing but otherwise as in the hermaphroditic. Fruit usually developing from 1 carpel, globose to ovoid, pyriform, or ellipsoidal, small to medium-sized, variously colored, green, scarlet, blue-green, blue-black, black or dark brown, stigmatic remains apical, sterile carpel remains basal; epicarp smooth, dull or shining, often with a wax bloom, mesocarp thin or thick, fleshy or dry, somewhat fibrous, usually easily separated from the bony or woody endocarp. Seed ellipsoidal or globose, basally attached, hilum circular or ± elongate, raphe branches few or lacking, endosperm homogeneous, penetrated laterally by a variable, frequently convoluted intrusion of seed coat; embryo lateral. Germination re-

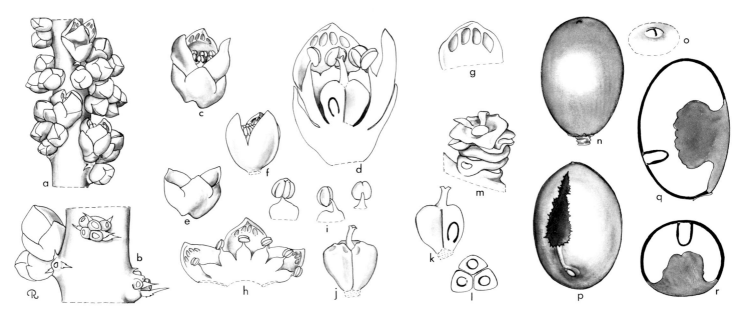

15.—**Livistona. a,** portion of rachilla ×3; **b,** detail of rachilla ×6; **c,** flower ×6; **d,** flower in vertical section ×12; **e,** calyx ×6; **f,** flower, calyx removed ×6; **g,** corolla lobes ×12; **h,** corolla and androecium, expanded ×6; **i,** stamen in 3 views ×12; **j,** gynoecium ×12; **k,** gynoecium in vertical section ×12; **l,** gynoecium in cross-section ×12; **m,** fruiting perianth and scars of flowers ×6; **n,** fruit ×1½; **o,** stigmatic remains, enlarged; **p,** seed ×3; **q,** seed in vertical section ×3; **r,** seed in cross-section ×3. *Livistona chinensis:* all from *Read 712.*

mote-tubular; eophyll lanceolate, plicate, minutely toothed apically. *n* = 18 (*L. australis,* Eichhorn 1953, and as *Corypha australis,* Eichhorn 1957, Sharma and Sarkar 1957; *L. chinensis,* Read 1965b, Sharma and Sarkar 1957, Sarkar et al. 1978, as *L. oliviformis* Eichhorn 1953, and as *L. subglobosa,* Satô, 1946; *L. rotundifolia,* Sharma and Sarkar 1957).

Anatomy.—Leaf (Tomlinson 1961), *L. australis, L. chinensis, L. chinensis* var. *subglobosa,* floral (Morrow 1965).

Distribution.—About 28 species, ranging from the Horn of Africa and Arabia (*L. carinensis*), to the Himalayas and Ryukyu Islands south through Indochina and Malesia to New Guinea, the Solomon Islands and Australia where there is a great diversity of species.

Ecology.—The ecology is very varied. There are species adapted to fresh water and peat swamp forest (*L. saribus*), montane forest (*L. tahanensis, L. speciosa*), undergrowth of tropical rain forest (*L. exigua*), dry savannah woodland (*L. humilis, L. loriphylla*), canyon bottoms with more or less permanent water in desert areas (*L. mariae, L. carinensis*), and subtropical woodland (*L. chinensis, L. australis*). Species are frequently gregarious, the tallest species often occurring in spectacularly beautiful groves (e.g. *L. rotundifolia* in Sulawesi and elsewhere).

Common Names and Uses.—Cabbage palm (*L. australis*), Chinese fan palm (*L. chinensis*), Serdang (W. Malesian species). Many are planted as ornamentals. Leaves of several species are used for thatch, their segments for umbrellas, and fibers for rope and cloth. Trunks have been used for wood. The "cabbage" of *L. australis* is edible.

Notes.—A large and variable genus distinguished by flower structure, in particular by the gynoecium of three carpels connate only by their styles, by united sepals, by petals with internal grooves, by the usually small fruits with apical stigmatic remains and basal carpel remains, by seed with homogeneous endosperm, and a large intrusion of seed coat. Most closely related to *Licuala* and *Pholidocarpus.*

Taxonomic Accounts.—Beccari (1931). See also Dransfield and Uhl (1983b).

Plates.—3, 4B, 34B; Figs. G.4, G.6, G.7, G.11.

16. **PHOLIDOCARPUS** Blume in J. A. & J. H. Schultes, Systema Vegetabilium 7:1308. 1830. Type: *P. rumphii* C. F. Meisner (illegitimate name) (*Borassus ihur* Giseke = **P. ihur** (Giseke) Blume).

Robust, solitary, armed, pleonanthic, hermaphroditic, tree palms. Stem erect, ringed with inconspicuous, close leaf scars. Leaves induplicate, costapalmate, marcescent in immature individuals, abscising under their own weight

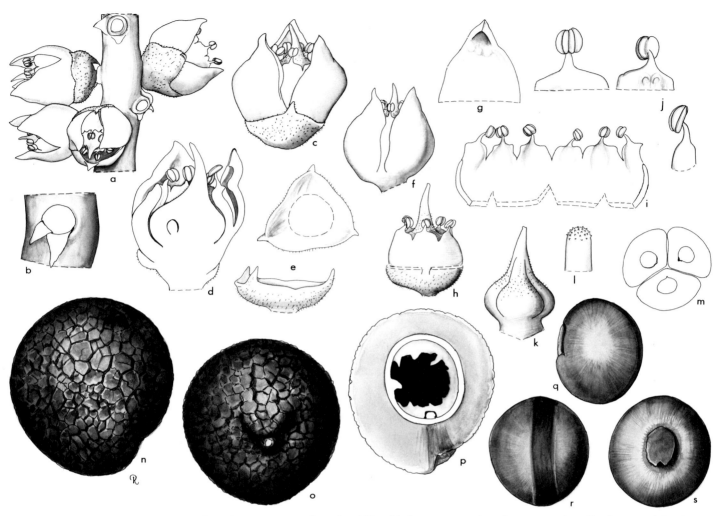

16.—**Pholidocarpus. a,** portion of rachilla ×4½; **b,** portion of rachilla with flower removed to show scar, subtending bract, and floral bracteole ×6; **c,** flower ×6; **d,** flower in vertical section ×7½; **e,** calyx in 2 views ×6; **f,** flower, calyx removed ×6; **g,** petal ×6; **h,** flower, upper portion of perianth removed to show staminal tube and gynoecium ×6; **i,** staminal tube, expanded ×6; **j,** stamen in 3 views ×12; **k,** gynoecium ×6; **l,** stigma, much enlarged; **m,** carpels in cross-section ×7½; **n, o,** fruit in 2 views ×½; **p,** fruit in vertical section ×½; **q, r, s,** seed in 3 views ×½. *Pholidocarpus sumatranus*: **a–m,** *Dransfield 2432*; *P. macrocarpus*: **n–s,** *Corner A1.*

in trunked individuals; sheath disintegrating into a conspicuous interwoven mass of reddish-brown fibers; petiole long, robust, particularly in juveniles, bearing thin caducous indumentum, slightly channeled adaxially, abaxially rounded or angular, frequently with 2 lateral yellowish lines, the margins armed with very robust, bulbous-based, horizontal spines; adaxial hastula well developed, triangular, ringlike, abaxial hastula inconspicuous or lacking; blade divided by splits along adaxial folds almost to the hastula, producing 3–4-fold segments, these further divided along adaxial folds to ⅔ or ½ the radius into single-fold segments, also split very shallowly along abaxial folds, lowermost segments overlapping, interfold filaments not persisting, scattered caducous indumentum present along ribs in young leaves, segments longitudinally striate, midrib prominent, transverse veinlets conspicu-

ous. Inflorescences interfoliar, emerging from the leaf sheath mouths and arching out of the crown, branching to 4 orders, several leaf axils (up to ca. 5) producing inflorescences simultaneously; peduncle robust; prophyll tubular, 2-keeled, somewhat inflated; peduncular bracts 1–ca. 5, conspicuous, robust, tubular, tending to split rather irregularly with age; rachis longer than the peduncle; rachis bracts rather distant, each subtending a first-order branch, adnate to the inflorescence axis; subsequent bracts disintegrating or very inconspicuous; rachillae glabrous or hairy, ± spreading, bearing spirally arranged flowers, solitary or in clusters of 2–3 on low tubercles, subtended by minute triangular bracts and each bearing a minute bracteole. Flowers sessile, golden-yellow; calyx cup-shaped, shallowly 3-lobed, glabrous or sparsely hairy; corolla divided almost to the base into 3 triangular, valvate, gla-

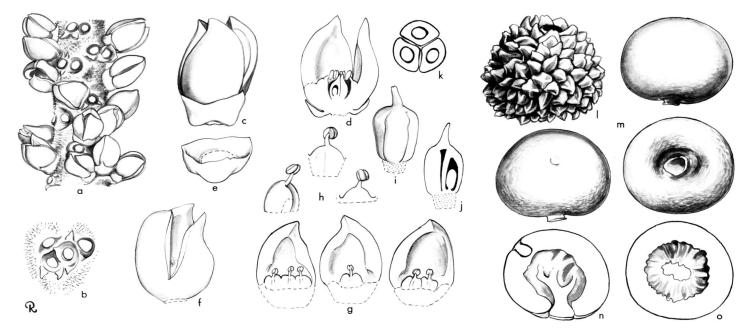

17.—**Johannesteijsmannia. a,** portion of rachilla ×3; **b,** flower cluster with flowers removed ×6; **c,** flower ×6; **d,** flower in vertical section ×6; **e,** calyx ×6; **f,** flower, calyx removed ×6; **g,** corolla and androecium expanded ×6; **h,** stamen in 3 views ×12; **i,** gynoecium ×12; **j,** gynoecium in vertical section ×12; **k,** carpels in cross-section ×12; **l,** fruit ×1½; **m,** seed in 3 views ×1½; **n,** seed in vertical section ×1½; **o,** seed in cross-section ×1½. *Johannesteijsmannia altifrons:* **a-k,** *Moore & Pennington 9051;* **l-o** *Moore 9110.*

brous or sparsely hairy petals; stamens 6, filaments united to form a conspicuous tube, free from the corolla, shallowly 6-lobed, tipped with short, slender, distinct filaments, bearing ± rounded or oblong, dorsifixed, introrse anthers; pollen elliptic, monosulcate, with finely reticulate, tectate exine; gynoecium tricarpellate, distinctly conical, hairy, the carpels distinct from each other basally, united apically in a long slender style, tipped with a dotlike stigma, ovule basally attached, anatropous. Fruit developing from 1 carpel, very large, globose, stigmatic remains scarcely visible but apical; pericarp massive, the epicarp smooth (*P. kingianus*), or cracked into numerous low corky brown warts, mesocarp thick, ± fleshy, frequently traversed by radiating fibers, endocarp crustaceous. Seed attached laterally or near the base, endosperm massive, homogeneous, but penetrated on one side by a large convoluted intrusion of seed coat; embryo subbasal or lateral. Germination remote-tubular; eophyll entire, lanceolate, plicate. Cytology not studied.

Anatomy.—Leaf (Tomlinson 1961), floral anatomy not studied.

Distribution.—Six recognized species, but possibly fewer, from south Thailand, Malaya, Sumatra, Borneo, Sulawesi, and the Moluccas.

Ecology.—In Malaya, Sumatra, and Borneo, species of *Pholidocarpus* are conspicuous palms of the lowlands, usually found in fresh water and peat swamp forest, rarely away from waterlogged soils. They may reach great heights (e.g. 45 m).

Common Names and Uses.—Serdang, Kepau (*P. macrocarpus*). The leaves may be used for thatch.

Notes.—Distinguished by the deeply divided leaves with compound segments and by very large smooth or corky-warted fruits. Most closely related to *Livistona.* Leaf anatomy shows some affinities with *Licuala.*

Taxonomic Accounts.—Beccari (1931). See also Dransfield and Uhl (1983a).

Plates.—4C, 34D.

17. JOHANNESTEIJSMANNIA H. E. Moore, Principes 5:116. 1961. Type: **J. altifrons** (H. G. L. Reichenbach & Zollinger) H. E. Moore (*Teysmannia altifrons* H. G. L. Reichenbach & Zollinger).

Teysmannia H. G. L. Reichenbach & Zollinger in Zollinger, Linnaea 28:657. 1858 ("1856") (Non *Teysmannia* Miquel 1857).

Moderate, solitary, armed, acaulescent or short-trunked, pleonanthic, hermaphroditic palms. Stem very short, decumbent, or erect, ringed with close leaf scars. Leaves large, entire, diamond-shaped, subpinnately ribbed, marcescent; sheath tubular at first, later drying and disintegrating into an interwoven mass of fibers; petiole well developed, ± triangular in cross-section, adaxially flattened, armed along the margins with small, sharp teeth, caducous tomentum present on very young petioles; adaxial hastula present on developing leaves, oblique, disappearing before leaf expansion; costa extending almost to the leaf apex, more prominent abaxially than adaxially; blade subpinnately ribbed, glabrous or the abaxial surface densely covered with white indumentum, lower margins thickened, armed with teeth like the petiole, the upper margins alternately notched, notches short along abaxial ribs, long along adaxial ribs, giving margins an irregularly stepped appearance, and perhaps representing highly reduced induplicate leaflets, midrib raised abaxially, transverse veinlets conspicuous. Inflorescences interfoliar, short, usually partly obscured by leaf litter, branching to 1–5 orders; peduncle well developed, usually curved, tomentose; prophyll tubular, ± inflated, 2-keeled, usually densely tomentose; peduncular bracts conspicuous, up to 7 in number, cream at first, later cinnamon-brown, tubular, ± inflated, distichous in origin but all and the prophyll splitting along the side nearest the ground, allowing the inflorescence to curve; rachis shorter than the peduncle, the branches subtended by minute triangular bracts, the branches tending to form a condensed mass; rachillae 3–6, very thick, or very numerous and slender, glabrous or tomentose, bearing spirally arranged, minute, apiculate bracts subtending flowers, the flowers solitary or in groups of 2–4 arranged in a cincinnus with minute bracteoles, on a short tubercle, or ± sessile. Flowers cream-colored, strongly scented; calyx cup-shaped with 3 low, glabrous, triangular lobes; corolla divided to ⅔ or almost to the base into 3 thin or very thick, fleshy, triangular, glabrous, sometimes densely papillose, valvate lobes; stamens 6, epipetalous, filaments very broad, fleshy, angled, connate basally to form an androecial ring, abruptly narrowed to short, very slender, distinct tips, anthers minute, rounded, introrse; pollen elliptic, monosulcate, with scabrate, tectate exine; gynoecium tricarpellate, the carpels distinct at the base, united by their tips in a common slender elongate style, stigma dotlike, ovule basally attached, anatropous. Fruit rounded, usually developing from 1 carpel, but sometimes from 2 or 3 carpels developing, the fruit then 2 or 3-lobed; epidermis of fruit dying early in development, the mesocarp then cracking to produce thick, corky, pyramidal warts at maturity, chestnut brown in color, endocarp moderately thick, crustaceous. Seed basally attached, endosperm homogeneous, but penetrated by a convoluted mass of seed coat at the base; embryo lateral. Germination remote-tubular; eophyll simple, plicate, minutely dentate at the tip. $n = 16$ (*J. altifrons,* Sarkar 1970).

Anatomy. —Leaf (Tomlinson 1961), floral (Morrow 1965).

Distribution. —Four species, one widespread but very local in south Thailand, Malay Peninsula, Sumatra, and the western part of Borneo, the other three endemic to the Malay Peninsula, where they are also very local.

Ecology. —These magnificent palms are plants of the undergrowth of primary rain forest, and seem very intolerant of disturbance; in Sarawak *J. altifrons* appears confined to some facies of "kerangas" (heath forest); elsewhere it seems less restricted, but avoids wet valley bottom soils. *J. magnifica* and *J.*

lanceolata are plants of hillslopes and *J. perakensis* is a plant of hillslopes and ridgetops. The distribution is remarkably disjunct, species being absent from apparently suitable forest.

Common Names and Uses. —Daun payung. Leaves are used for thatch and shelters.

Notes. —Distinguished by the striking diamond-shaped leaves and the structure of the inflorescence. Most closely related to *Licuala* but differing in inflorescence and leaf shape, and in hooked teeth on the lower margins of the leaf blade. Resembles *Licuala* in leaf anatomy but does not have fiber-sclereids in the blade. At one time the extraordinary leaf was considered to represent the primitive leaf form of the palms, but is now regarded as a specialization of a more typical coryphoid leaf such as that of *Livistona,* and as perhaps an intermediate stage in the evolution of the extraordinary reduplicate leaf of *Licuala* (Dransfield 1970).

Taxonomic Account. —Dransfield (1972b).

Plates. —4D, 34C; Fig. G.8.

18. LICUALA Thunberg, Kongliga Vetenskaps Acadamiens Nya Handlingar 3:286. 1782. Type: **L. spinosa** Thunberg.

Pericycla Blume, Rumphia 2:47. 1838 ("1836"). Type: *P. penduliflora* Blume (=*Licuala penduliflora* (Blume) Miquel).

Dammera Lauterbach & K. M. Schumann in K. M. Schumann & Lauterbach, Die Flora der Deutschen Schützgebiete in der Südsee 201. 1900 ("1901"). Lectotype: *D. ramosa* Lauterbach & K. M. Schumann (see H. E. Moore 1963c) (=*Licuala ramosa* (Lauterbach & K. M. Schumann) Beccari (non Blume 1850) = *L. beccariana* Furtado).

Very small to moderate, solitary or clustered, acaulescent to shrubby, rarely treelike, armed or unarmed, pleonanthic, hermaphroditic (very rarely dioecious) palms. Stem very short and subterranean, creeping or erect, ringed with close leaf scars, partly obscured by remains of leaf sheaths, sometimes bearing short bulbillike shoots at the nodes. Leaves palmate, marcescent; leaf sheath disintegrating into a weft of fibers, the margin sometimes remaining as a broad, ligulelike ribbon or tongue; petiole adaxially channeled near the base, rounded or channeled distally, abaxially rounded or angled, armed along margins with close sharp teeth or triangular spines, or unarmed, caducous indumentum often abundant; adaxial hastula well developed, usually triangular, abaxial hastula absent; blade entire or split variously along the abaxial ribs to the very base to produce single to multiple-fold, wedge-shaped reduplicate segments, these in turn with very short splits along the abaxial folds and slightly longer splits along adaxial folds, the central segment usually entire, sometimes bifid, sometimes borne on a stalklike extension, the

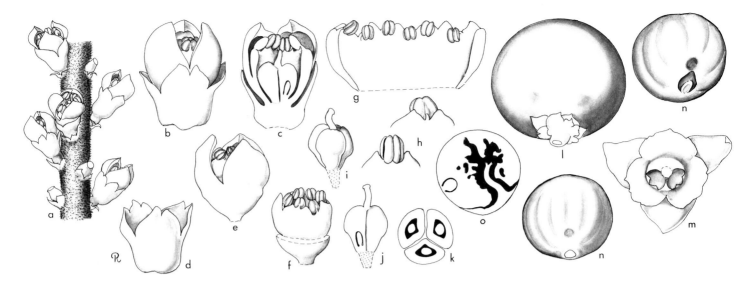

18.—**Licuala. a,** portion of rachilla ×3; **b,** flower ×6; **c,** flower in vertical section ×6; **d,** calyx ×6; **e,** flower, calyx removed ×6; **f,** flower, perianth removed ×6; **g,** androecium expanded ×6; **h,** anther in 2 views ×12; **i,** gynoecium ×6; **j,** gynoecium in vertical section ×6; **k,** carpels in cross-section ×12; **l,** fruit ×3; **m,** fruiting perianth with abortive carpels, interior view ×6; **n,** seed in 2 views ×3; **o,** seed in vertical section ×3. *Licuala grandis*: **a-k,** *Bailey 1640*; **l-o,** *Furtado 36537.*

ribs often with caducous indumentum, transverse veinlets usually conspicuous. Inflorescences interfoliar, much shorter to much longer than the leaves, very varied in aspect and degree of branching, from spicate to branched to 3 orders; peduncle short to very long, bearing a basal, 2-keeled tubular prophyll, and 0–5 or more, similar, tubular, closely sheathing or inflated, glabrous or tomentose, peduncular bracts; rachis bracts subtending usually distant, first-order branches adnate to the inflorescence axis above the bract mouth; subsequent orders of bracts minute; first-order branches spicate or branched further; rachillae few to ca. 30 or more, crowded or spreading, glabrous to variously scaly or hairy, bearing spirally arranged, distant or very crowded flowers. Flowers solitary or in groups of 2–3, sessile or borne on short to long spurs, each subtended by a minute triangular bract; calyx sometimes stalklike at the base, tubular, truncate, irregularly splitting, or with 3 neat triangular lobes, glabrous or variously hairy; corolla usually considerably exceeding the calyx, tubular at the base, divided into 3 rather thick, triangular, valvate lobes, glabrous to variously hairy, usually marked near the tip on the adaxial face with the impressions of the anthers; stamens 6, epipetalous, the filaments distinct, somewhat flattened, or united into a conspicuous tube tipped with 6 equal, short to moderate teeth bearing erect or pendulous anthers, or androecial ring 3-lobed, 3 anthers borne on short distinct filaments, 3 borne at the sinuses between the lobes, anthers rounded or oblong, very small to moderate, latrorse; pollen elliptic, monosulcate, with smooth, rugulate, coarsely pitted, reticulate, or foveate, tectate exine; gynoecium tricarpellate, glabrous or variously hairy, carpels wedge-shaped, distinct in the ovarian region, united distally in a long, slender columnar style tipped with a minute dotlike stigma, ovules basally attached, anatropous. Fruit globose, ovoid, narrow, straight, spindle-shaped or curved, perianth whorls

usually persistent, 1–3 discrete carpels developing, abortive carpels frequently carried with the stigmatic remains at the tip of the fertile carpel, otherwise remaining at the base; epicarp frequently brightly colored, dull or shining, rarely corky-warted, mesocarp fleshy, somewhat fibrous, thin to thick, endocarp thin, crustaceous. Seed basally attached, endosperm homogeneous penetrated by a smooth or greatly lobed intrusion of seed coat, in species with spindle-shaped fruit the intrusion running ± the length of the seed in the middle; embryo lateral. Germination remote-tubular; eophyll strap-shaped, plicate, ± truncate and minutely lobed at the apex. $n = 14$ (*L. spinosa*, Sharma and Sarkar 1957, Sarkar et al. 1978; *L. peltata*, Sharma and Sarkar 1957). $n = 8$ (*L. grandis* as *Pritchardia grandis*, Venkatasubban 1945, *L. paludosa*, Sharma and Sarkar 1957).

Anatomy.—Leaf (Tomlinson 1961), floral (Morrow 1965), two phloem strands in bundles of petiole (Parthasarathy 1968).

Distribution.—About 108 species, ranging from India and southern China through Southeast Asia to Malesia, Queensland, the Solomon Islands and New Hebrides, the greatest diversity being in Malaya, Borneo, and New Guinea.

Ecology.—The species are mostly plants of the forest undergrowth; some are gregarious and lend a distinctive appearance to certain forest types, others are very local and occur as scattered individuals. A few species, e.g. *L. calciphila* are strict calcicoles; *L. spinosa,* the most widespread species, occurs in forest on the landward fringe of mangrove and *L. paludosa* is common in peat swamp forest. A remark-

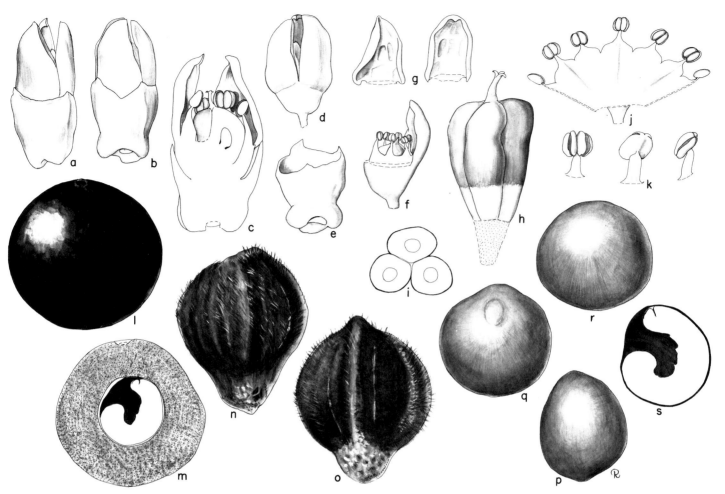

19.—**Pritchardiopsis. a, b,** flowers ×9; **c,** flower in vertical section ×12; **d,** flower, sepals removed ×9; **e,** calyx ×9; **f,** flower, sepals and 2 petals removed ×9; **g,** 2 petals, interior views ×9; **h,** gynoecium ×22½; **i,** gynoecium in cross-section ×22 ½; **j,** androecium ×12; **k,** stamen in 3 views ×22½; **l,** fruit ×1; **m,** fruit in cross-section ×1; **n, o,** endocarp in 2 views ×1½; **p, q, r,** seed in 3 views ×1½, **s,** seed in vertical section ×1½. *Pritchardiopsis jeanneneyi:* **a-k,** *Jeanneney s.n.;* **l-s,** *MacKee 38038.*

able feature of some Bornean forest types is the abundance of *Licuala* spp. which grow sympatrically.

Common Names and Uses. — Licuala palms, palas. Leaves of some species are used for thatching and for making sleeping mats. The sword leaf of some may be used for wrapping food before or after cooking. Smaller stems are used for walking sticks and larger ones as palisades in building. Many species are highly decorative but appear generally to be slow growing. Pith and stem apices are edible.

Notes. — Easily recognizable by the wedge-shaped marginally reduplicate segments of the leaves of most species. Those with undivided leaves (*L. grandis, L. orbicularis*) are unlikely to be confused with other palms. Most closely related to *Johannesteijsmannia*

and *Livistona, Licuala* differs mainly in leaf form as noted. The species examined differ from other coryphoid palms in having large transverse fibersclereids in the mesophyll of the leaf; in some epidermal characters they resemble *Pholidocarpus, Livistona,* and *Johannesteijsmannia.*

Taxonomic Accounts. — Beccari (1931) and Furtado (1940). The latter provides the most recent attempt at a subgeneric and sectional delimitation.

Plates. — *5A–D, 35A; Figs. G.9, G.10, G.19.*

19. PRITCHARDIOPSIS Beccari, Webbia 3:131. 1910.
Type: **P. jeanneneyi** Beccari (see Moore & Uhl 1984).

Moderate, solitary, unarmed, pleonanthic, hermaphroditic, tree palm. Stem erect, smooth, ringed with conspicuous leaf scars. Leaves induplicate, briefly costapalmate, neatly abscising; sheath disintegrating into a network of fine rusty-brown fibers; petiole elongate, adaxially flat to ridged, abaxially rounded, margins smooth, adaxial hastula short, rounded, abaxial hastula lacking; blade stiff, regularly divided to or beyond the middle into single-fold, briefly bifid, lanceolate, spreading segments, glabrous on both surfaces, midribs and intercostal ribs prominent, transverse veinlets conspicuous. Inflorescences interfoliar, branched to 4 orders, branches angled; peduncle very short, flattened; prophyll not seen, inserted above the base; peduncular bracts lacking; rachis very short, deeply divided into 3 elongate first-order branches, each branch bearing 1 peduncular bract below 2 unilateral second-order branches subtended by tubular, chartaceous bracts, bifid and flaring at the apex; proximal two second-order branches flattened, adnate to the first-order branch, subsequent second-order branches not subtended by tubular bracts, not adnate; bracts not evident at bases of rachillae; rachillae short, ± clustered at the ends of second-order branches, bearing rather distant cincinni of 3 flowers basally and solitary flowers distally. Flowers sessile, ebracteolate; calyx tubular, adnate basally to the receptacle, with 3 short free lobes; petals 3, briefly connate basally, valvate and adaxially hollowed distally, persistent; stamens 6, inserted at throat of the corolla, filaments erect, briefly connate and adnate to the petals basally, anthers erect, subglobose, sagittate, introrse; pollen elliptic or circular, monosulcate, with scabrate, tectate exine; gynoecium globose-trilobate, trilocular, triovulate, style slender, short, awl-shaped, stigma dotlike, ovule inserted basally, anatropous. Fruit large, 1-seeded, globose, with apical stigmatic remains; epicarp smooth, mesocarp fleshy to fibrous near endocarp, endocarp woody, rounded on one side, keeled on the opposite side, laterally elongate and attenuate basally. Seed globose, erect, hilum basal, raphe orbicular, adjacent to hilum, endosperm homogeneous, deeply hollowed out basally with a large, erect intrusion of seed coat; embryo eccentrically apical. Germination remote-tubular; eophyll etire, oblanceolate, toothed distally. Cytology not studied.

Anatomy. — Preliminary studies in floral anatomy of herbarium material indicate that the carpels may be connate only through the styles as other members of the *Livistona* alliance (Uhl unpublished). Anatomy of the leaf shows a coryphoid midrib, an irregular 2-layered adaxial hypodermis, and indistinct or lacking palisade layers (Uhl and Martens in manuscript).

Distribution. — A single species in New Caledonia.

Ecology. — Restricted to southeastern New Caledonia on steep slopes with serpentine soils at ca. 200 m in the vicinity of the Bay of Prony, once thought to be extinct but recently relocated in three very small populations.

Common Names and Uses. — Common names not recorded. The apex is edible and destructive exploitation has resulted in near extinction.

Notes. — *Pritchardiopsis* differs from most other Old World members of the Corypheae in lacking any kind of armature on the petioles and, according to Beccari's description, in having a syncarpous gynoecium. The endocarp is unlike that of any other Corypheae. In habit, however, it resembles genera of the *Livistona* alliance, and in the branching of the inflorescence is much like *Livistona woodfordii* Ridley and many species of *Pritchardia,* though it lacks the deciduous petals of the last.

Taxonomic Account. — Moore and Uhl (1984).

Plates. — *6C, 35B; Fig. G.23.*

20. **PRITCHARDIA** B. C. Seemann & H. A. Wendland ex H. A. Wendland, Bonplandia 10:197. 1862 (Conserved name) Type: **P. pacifica** B. C. Seemann & H. A. Wendland ex H. A. Wendland.

Eupritchardia O. Kuntze, Revisio Generum Plantarum 3(3):323. 1898. Type: *E. pacifica* (B. C. Seemann & H. A. Wendland ex H. A. Wendland) O. Kuntze (=*Pritchardia pacifica* B. C. Seemann & H. A. Wendland ex H. A. Wendland).

Styloma O. F. Cook, Journal of the Washington Academy of Sciences 5:241. 1915. Type: *S. pacifica* (B. C. Seemann & H. A. Wendland ex H. A. Wendland) O. F. Cook (=*Pritchardia pacifica* B. C. Seemann & H. A. Wendland ex H. A. Wendland).

Moderate, solitary, unarmed, pleonanthic, hermaphroditic tree palms. Stem erect, sometimes deeply striate, ringed with close leaf scars. Leaves induplicate, costapalmate, marcescent in immature acaulescent individuals, deciduous in trunked individuals; sheath tomentose; soon disintegrating into a mass of fibers; petiole elongate, flattened or channeled adaxially, abaxially rounded or angular, extending into the costa without interruption, usually tomentose; adaxial hastula a ridge with a central point, abaxial hastula absent; blade divided to ca. 1/3 to 1/2 its radius along adaxial folds into single-fold segments, further shallowly divided along abaxial folds, interfold filaments often present, segments stiff, held in 1 plane or variously pendulous, surfaces similar or more distinctly glaucous abaxially, usually copiously tomentose along ribs, frequently with small scales on abaxial surface, transverse veinlets conspicuous or obscure. Inflorescences interfoliar, solitary or 2–4 together in each axil, sheathed by a common prophyll, branched to 3 orders; peduncle conspicuous, stiff, ± erect to pendulous, shorter or longer than the leaves; prophyll tubular, 2-keeled, closely sheathing, densely tomentose, sometimes disintegrating into a weft of fibers; peduncular bracts several, similar to the prophyll, tending to split along one side, irregularly tattering, sometimes inflated, adaxially glabrous, densely tomentose abaxially, rarely becoming glabrous; rachis much shorter than the peduncle; rachillae straight, curved or somewhat zigzag, tending to be crowded forming a head of flowers, glabrous or sparsely to densely hairy, bearing

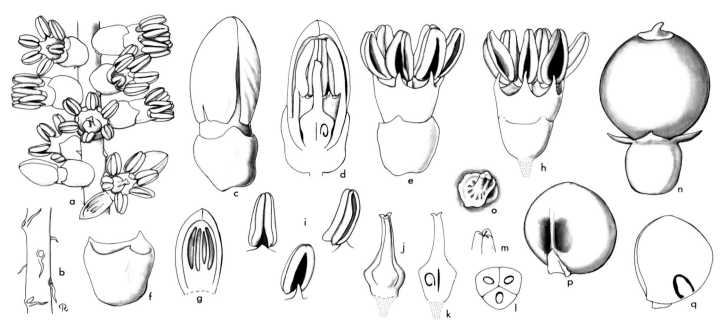

20.—**Pritchardia. a,** portion of rachilla ×3; **b,** portion of rachilla with flowers removed to show bracteoles ×3; **c,** flower with petals already separated ×6; **d,** flower in vertical section ×6; **e,** flower with petals fallen ×6; **f,** calyx ×6; **g,** petal, interior view ×6; **h,** flower with petals fallen and sepals removed ×6; **i,** stamen in 3 views ×6; **j,** gynoecium ×6; **k,** gynoecium in vertical section ×6; **l,** carpels in cross-section ×7½; **m,** stigmas ×12; **n,** fruit ×4½; **o,** stigmatic remains ×6; **p,** seed ×4½; **q,** seed in vertical section ×4½. *Pritchardia thurstonii:* **a–m,** *Read 662;* **n–q,** *Read 690.*

spirally arranged, minute bracts subtending solitary flowers. Flowers sessile or borne on very low tubercles, floral bracteoles apparently absent; calyx tubular, shallowly 3-lobed distally, rather thick and coriaceous; corolla considerably exceeding the calyx, coriaceous, tubular at the base, divided distally into 3 ± elongate valvate lobes, the lobes forming a cap deciduous at anthesis; stamens 6, borne near the mouth of the corolla tube, the filament bases connate to form a conspicuous tube projecting beyond the calyx, with 6 short distinct tips bearing oblong, ± erect, latrorse anthers; pollen elliptic, monosulcate or very rarely trichotomosulcate, with finely reticulate or scabrate, tectate exine; gynoecium tricarpellate, the carpels wedge-shaped, distinct in the ovarian region, connate in a common elongate style bearing a minutely 3-lobed stigma, ovule basally attached, anatropous. Fruit spherical or ovoid, developing from 1 carpel only, bearing apical stigmatic and sterile carpel remains; calyx persistent; epicarp smooth, mesocarp rather thin, fleshy, fibrous, endocarp thin, woody and rather brittle, sometimes thickened at the base. Seed ± spherical, basally or subbasally attached, with rounded hilum, endosperm homogeneous, the seed coat slightly thickened by the hilum but endosperm without conspicuous intrusion of the seed coat; embryo basal. Germination remote-tubular; eophyll entire, lanceolate, plicate. $n = 18$ (*P. pacifica,* Sharma and Sarkar 1957, Venkatasubban 1945; *P. thurstonii,* Read 1965b).

Anatomy.—Leaf (Tomlinson 1961), floral (Morrow 1965), two phloem strands in bundles of petiole (Parthasarathy 1968).

Distribution.—About 37 recognized species from Fiji, Tonga, Danger Islands and Hawaii. All but four species are Hawaiian endemics; many are extremely rare and endangered, or not seen in the wild for several years.

Ecology.—Most of the Hawaiian species are found on the windward slopes of the islands in wet forested areas from sea level to over 1400 m altitude; a few species occur in dry forest on the leeward sides.

Fossil Record.—Stem casts of *Pritchardia* are well known in recent lavas in Hawaii.

Common Names and Uses.—Loulu palms. The large leaves are used as fans and umbrellas.

Notes.—Characterized by the deciduous cap of the corolla lobes and usually distinguishable by the relatively long inflorescence peduncle with flowering branches clustered at the end.

Taxonomic Accounts.—Beccari and Rock (1921). See also Hodel (1980).

Plate.—*35C; Figs. G.3, G.7.*

21. **COLPOTHRINAX** Grisebach & H. A. Wendland, Botanische Zeitung 37:148. 1879. Lectotype: **C. wrightii** Grisebach & H. A. Wendland ex Siebert & Voss (see Vilmorin 1895).

Moderate, solitary, unarmed, pleonanthic, hermaphroditic, tree palms. Stem erect, at first covered with per-

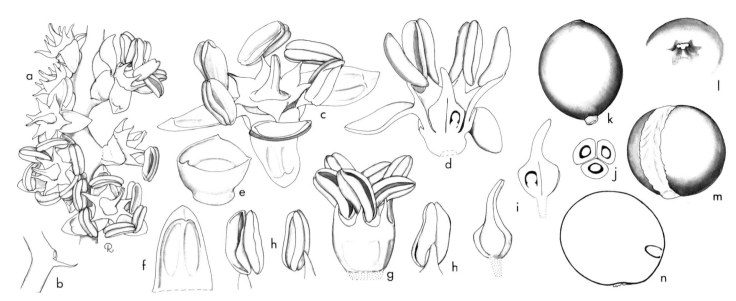

21.—**Colpothrinax. a,** portion of rachilla ×3; **b,** portion of rachilla with floral scar and bract ×3; **c,** flower ×6; **d,** flower in vertical section ×6; **e,** calyx ×6; **f,** free portion of petal, interior view ×6; **g,** androecium, perianth removed ×6; **h,** anther in 3 views ×6; **i,** gynoecium, exterior view and vertical section ×6; **j,** carpels in cross-section ×6; **k,** fruit ×1½; **l,** apex of fruit ×6; **m,** seed ×3; **n,** seed in vertical section ×3. *Colpothrinax wrightii:* **a-l,** *Bailey 12504x;* **k-n,** *Roig s.n.*

sistent fibrous leaf sheaths, later bare, columnar (*C. cookii*) or strongly ventricose (*C. wrightii*), marked with close leaf scars. Leaves induplicate, shortly costapalmate; sheath disintegrating into a coarse fibrous network or into long fine, pendulous fibers, densely tomentose; petiole long, flattened or slightly channeled adaxially, rounded abaxially, margins acute, densely scaly; adaxial hastula conspicuous, triangular or irregularly lobed, abaxial hastula absent; blade orbicular, irregularly divided sometimes beyond the middle into linear, single-fold segments, these shortly bifid at apex, thick, glabrous adaxially except along ribs where caducously scaly, abaxially densely covered with minute scales, midribs prominent, transverse veinlets very short, evident abaxially or invisible. Inflorescences solitary, interfoliar, several present at the same time, shorter than the leaves, branched to 4 orders; peduncle long, rounded in cross-section, enclosed in overlapping bracts, densely tomentose; prophyll short, tubular, 2-keeled laterally, splitting apically, densely scaly; peduncular bracts 4–9, tubular, with single keel, splitting apically to give a long triangular limb, densely tomentose; rachis equalling the peduncle, tomentose; rachis bracts like the peduncular, several (4–7); first-order branches with a conspicuous, somewhat inflated, brown-tomentose, 2-keeled prophyll and a similar empty bract, subsequent bracts, membranous, triangular, very small and inconspicuous; rachillae spreading, densely hairy or glabrous, bearing spirally arranged, minute bracts each subtending a low spur bearing a solitary, sessile flower. Flowers with calyx cuplike, fleshy, not striate, with 3 short points; corolla considerably exceeding the calyx, fleshy, tubular at the base, divided distally into 3, ± elongate, valvate lobes, persistent or tardily deciduous, adaxially grooved; stamens 6, filaments basally connate into an epipetalous cup, adnate to and equalling or only slightly exceeding the corolla tube,

free filaments broad basally, attenuate above, anthers elongate, dorsifixed near the base, connectives very narrow, light in color, latrorse; pollen elliptic, monosulcate, with finely reticulate, tectate exine; carpels 3, follicular, ovarian parts distinct, the styles elongate, connate, stigma dotlike, ovule basal, erect, anatropous. Fruit globose, usually developing from 1 carpel with apical stigmatic and abortive carpel remains, perianth usually persistent; epicarp thin, smooth, mesocarp fleshy with longitudinal anastomosing fibers adjacent to the crustaceous endocarp. Seed subglobose, free from the endocarp except at the small basal hilum, the raphe as long as the seed, rather broad and ± sculptured, lacking noticeable branches, endosperm homogeneous without intruded seed coat below the raphe; embryo lateral towards the base on the antirapheal side. Germination not recorded; eophyll probably simple. Cytology unknown.

Anatomy. — Leaf (Tomlinson 1961), floral (Morrow 1965). Floral anatomy resembles that of *Licuala* according to Morrow. However, the base of the flowers and sepals have scattered tannin and the shallow stamen tube and the carpels have striking peripheral layers of tannin.

Distribution. — Two species, one *C. wrightii* endemic to Cuba, the other *C. cookii* in Guatemala and along the Atlantic slope of mountains in Panama.

Ecology. — *C. wrightii* occurs mostly in open sandy country; *C. cookii* grows on exposed summits and crests of narrow ridges where the forest is somewhat open, at an altitude of ca. 1100 m.

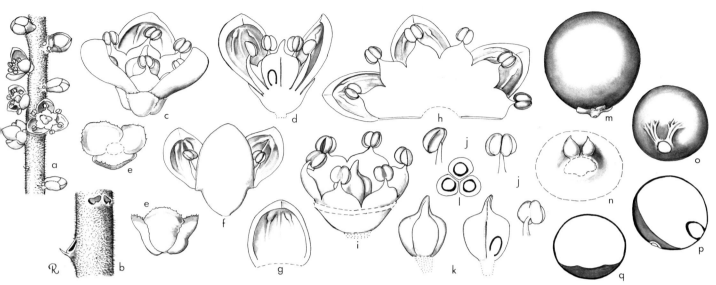

22.—**Acoelorraphe. a,** portion of rachilla ×3; **b,** portion of rachilla showing floral scar and bract ×6; **c,** flower ×12; **d,** flower in vertical section ×12; **e,** sepals, interior and exterior views ×12; **f,** flower, sepals removed ×12; **g,** free portion of petal, interior view ×12; **h,** corolla and androecium expanded, interior view ×12; **i,** flower, sepals and free portions of petals removed ×12; **j,** stamen in 3 views ×12; **k,** gynoecium, exterior view and vertical section ×12; **l,** carpels in cross-section ×12; **m,** fruit ×3; **n,** base of fruit and abortive carpels ×6; **o,** seed ×3; **p,** seed in vertical section ×3; **q,** seed in cross-section ×3. *Acoelorraphe wrightii*: all from *Read 745.*

Common Names and Uses.—Cuban belly palm, barrel palm (*C. wrightii*). The trunks of *C. wrightii* are used for making canoes, its leaves as thatch, and the fruit is eaten by pigs. Both species would make handsome ornamentals.

Notes.—Closely related and similar to *Pritchardia* but differing in similar length of peduncle and rachis in inflorescence, in petals not shed as a cap and in a more shallow stamen tube. The inflorescence seems striking in the length and massiveness of the peduncle and rachis with the branches very small in comparison.

Taxonomic Accounts.—Bailey (1940a) and Read (1969a).

Plate.—35D.

22. **ACOELORRAPHE** H. A. Wendland, Botanische Zeitung 37:148. 1879. Type: **A. wrightii** (Grisebach & H. A. Wendland) H. A. Wendland ex Beccari (*Copernicia wrightii* Grisebach & H. A. Wendland) ('Acoelorhaphe,' 'Acoelorrhaphe').

Paurotis O. F. Cook in Northrop, Memoirs of the Torrey Botanical Club 12:21. 1902. Type: *P. androsana* O. F. Cook.

Acanthosabal Proschowsky, Gardeners' Chronicle, series 3: 77:91. 1925. Type: *A. caespitosa* Proschowsky.

Moderate, armed, clustered, pleonanthic, hermaphroditic palm. Stem slender, erect, clothed with persistent leaf sheaths and petiole bases, older stems naked below, internodes very short. Leaves rather small, induplicate, very briefly costapalmate; sheath disintegrating into an interwoven mass of coarse, rich brown fibers; petiole moderate, slightly channeled or flattened adaxially, rounded abaxially, fiercely armed with robust, triangular, reflexed or inflexed spines, adaxial hastula conspicuous, irregularly lobed, abaxial hastula a low ridge; blade nearly orbicular, relatively flat, regularly divided to below the middle into narrow, single-fold, deeply bifid, stiff segments, usually silvery abaxially due to small scales, midribs prominent abaxially, transverse veinlets conspicuous. Inflorescences slender, solitary, interfoliar, exceeding the leaves, branched to 4 orders; peduncle slender, elongate, elliptical in cross-section, usually erect; prophyll short, partly to completely enclosed by the leaf sheaths, tubular, 2-keeled laterally, splitting apically into short, irregular lobes; peduncular bracts 2, like the prophyll but much longer and more shallowly keeled; rachis about as long as the peduncle, ± glabrous, completely sheathed by tubular bracts, other branches densely tomentose; rachis bracts like the peduncular bract but smaller and decreasing in size distally; first-order branches bearing a 2-keeled membranous prophyll ± included within the primary bract; subsequent bracts very inconspicuous, triangular, membranous; rachillae slender, bearing spirally arranged, minute bracts each subtending a low spur bearing a cluster (cincinnus) of (1)–2–3 flowers, each flower subtended by a small thin bract. Flowers cream-colored; sepals 3, fleshy and slightly connate basally; petals 3, united in a basal tube for ¼ their length; stamens 6, borne at the mouth of corolla tube,

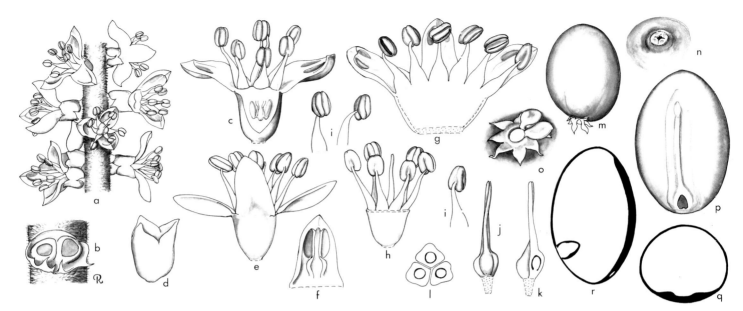

23.—**Serenoa. a,** portion of rachilla ×3; **b,** portion of rachilla showing floral scars and bracts ×6; **c,** flower ×6; **d,** calyx ×6; **e,** flower, calyx removed ×6; **f,** free portion of petal, interior view ×6; **g,** corolla and androecium, expanded, interior view ×6; **h,** stamens and gynoecium, perianth removed ×6; **i,** stamen in 3 views ×6; **j,** gynoecium ×6; **k,** gynoecium in vertical section ×6; **l,** carpels in cross-section ×12; **m,** fruit ×1½; **n,** apex of fruit ×12; **o,** base of fruit and abortive carpels ×6; **p,** seed ×3; **q,** seed in cross-section ×3; **r,** seed in vertical section ×3. *Serenoa repens:* all from *Read s.n.*

filaments connate in a shallow cup at the base, free portions abruptly narrowed to a filiform apex, not inflexed in bud; anthers dorsifixed, short, rounded, versatile at anthesis, latrorse; pollen elliptic, monosulcate, with finely reticulate, tectate exine; gynoecium of 3 glabrous, follicular carpels, connate in stylar regions, ovule basal, erect, anatropous. Fruit small, rounded, developing from 1 carpel, black, stigmatic scar apical, abortive carpels basal; epicarp smooth, mesocarp thinly fleshy with prominent longitudinal fibers, endocarp thin, crustaceous. Seed with basal hilum, endosperm homogeneous penetrated by a thin intrusion of the seed coat at one side; embryo lateral near base on the antirapheal side. Germination not recorded; eophyll simple, narrow, lanceolate. $n = 18$ (Read 1964).

Anatomy.—Leaf (Tomlinson 1961), floral (Morrow 1961), two phloem strands in bundles of petiole (Parthasarathy 1968).

Distribution.—One species in southern Florida, the West Indies, and parts of the Caribbean coast of Central America.

Ecology.—Clump-forming palm occurring naturally in brackish swamps.

Common Names and Uses.—Paurotis palm, saw cabbage palm, silver saw palm, everglades palm. Widely grown as an ornamental.

Notes.—An attractive clustering palm with erect, rather slender, brown trunks and leaves silvery beneath. Suitable for rather moist areas. Most closely related to *Serenoa,* but differing in an erect habit, larger thorns on the petioles, and flowers with free and overlapping sepals. Also related to *Brahea* which usually has a solitary trunk.

Taxonomic Account.—Bailey (1940b).

Plates.—6B, 36A.

23. **SERENOA** J. D. Hooker in Bentham & J. D. Hooker, Genera Plantarum 3:879, 926, 1228. 1883. Type: *S. serrulata* (Michaux) Nicholson (*Chamaerops serrulata* Michaux) = **S. repens** (Bartram) Small (*Corypha repens* Bartram).

Diglossophyllum H. A. Wendland ex Salomon, Die Palmen 155. 1887. Type: *D. serrulatum* (Michaux) H. A. Wendland ex Salomon (*Chamaerops serrulata* Michaux).

Moderate, clustered, shrubby, armed, pleonanthic, hermaphroditic palm. Stem subterranean or prostrate and surface creeping, or rarely erect, covered with persistent leaf sheaths, axillary buds developing as either inflorescences or vegetative suckers. Leaves induplicate, palmate, marcescent; sheath expanding into a tattered mat of brown fibers; petiole flat to slightly rounded adaxially, rounded to angled abaxially, margin armed with numerous small teeth; adaxial hastula conspicuous, ± rounded, membranous, abaxial hastula semicircular, often split, membranous; blade nearly orbicular, regularly divided to below the middle into narrow stiff, shortly bifid, single-fold segments, glabrous except for scattered caducous scales along

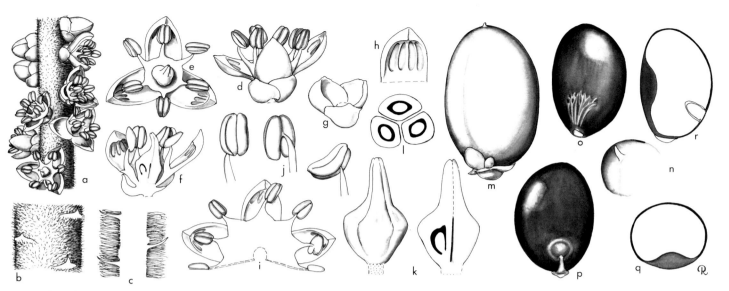

24.—**Brahea. a,** portion of rachilla ×3; **b,** portion of rachilla to show bracts ×6; **c,** portion of rachilla in vertical section to show bracts and floral attachment ×6; **d,** flower ×6; **e,** flower, top view ×6; **f,** flower in vertical section ×6; **g,** calyx ×6; **h,** petal, interior view ×6; **i,** corolla and androecium, expanded, interior view ×6; **j,** stamen in 3 views ×12; **k,** gynoecium, exterior view and vertical section ×12; **l,** carpels in cross-section ×12; **m,** fruit ×3; **n,** apex of fruit ×6; **o, p,** seed in 2 views ×3; **q,** seed in cross-section ×3; **r,** seed in vertical section ×3. *Brahea berlandieri:* **a-l,** *Bailey 727;* B. *prominens:* **m-r,** *Bailey 533.*

the ribs, midribs conspicuous abaxially, transverse veinlets conspicuous, rather distant. Inflorescences interfoliar, erect and about equaling the leaves but often hidden by them, curved, branched to 3(–4) orders; peduncle slender, flattened, rather short; prophyll tubular, 2-keeled, with 2 triangular apical lobes; peduncular bract 1 or lacking, tightly sheathing, caducously tomentose; rachis longer than the peduncle; rachis bracts like the peduncular bract but decreasing in size distally; first-order branches with a short 2-keeled prophyll; subsequent bracts small, membranous; rachillae spreading, densely tomentose, bearing spirally arranged, small, irregularly cleft bracts subtending solitary or paired flowers. Flowers with tubular calyx of 3 triangular, slightly imbricate lobes; corolla tubular, split to ⅔ its length into 3 lobes, valvate, inconspicuously grooved adaxially; stamens 6, filaments borne at the mouth of the corolla tube, gradually tapered, not inflexed, anthers erect in bud, elliptic, dorsifixed, somewhat versatile, latrorse; pollen elliptic, monosulcate, with finely reticulate, tectate exine; carpels 3, basally distinct, united in the attenuate stylar region to a narrow stigma, ovule anatropous. Fruit ellipsoidal to subglobose, dark blue to black at maturity, abortive carpels basal, stigmatic scar apical or subapical; epicarp smooth, mesocarp fleshy without fibers, endocarp thin but somewhat cartilaginous. Seed basally attached with elongate raphe, endosperm homogeneous with a shallow lateral intrusion of seed coat; embryo lateral towards the base opposite the raphe. Germination remote-ligular; eophyll entire, plicate. $n = 18$ (Read 1965b).

Anatomy.—Leaf (Tomlinson 1961), floral anatomy reported by Morrow (1965b) to be similar to that of *Acoelorraphe.*

Distribution.—One species in the southeastern United States.

Ecology.—Common in pinelands, prairies, and coastal sand dunes, often forming dense swards. The unusual habit and its ecological significance have been investigated by Fisher and Tomlinson (1973).

Fossil Record.—Fossil seeds and pollen in Eocene London Clay (Chandler 1961, 1964) have been attributed to *Serenoa* but this determination needs critical reappraisal.

Common Names and Uses.—Saw palmetto. Regarded as a pest in the wild. The glaucous form is much prized as an ornamental.

Notes.—Most closely related to *Acoelorraphe* and *Brahea;* see comments under *Acoelorraphe.*

Taxonomic Account.—Bailey (1934).

Plates.—6A, 36B; Figs. G.2, G.8, G.11, G.17.

24. **Brahea** Martius ex Endlicher, Genera Plantarum 252. 1837. Type: **B. dulcis** (Kunth) Martius (*Corypha dulcis* Kunth).

Erythea S. Watson, Botany of California 2:211. 1880. Lectotype: *E. edulis* (H. A. Wendland ex S. Watson) S. Watson (*Brahea edulis* H. A. Wendland ex S. Watson) (see Cook 1915b).

Glaucothea O. F. Cook, Journal of the Washington Academy of Sciences 5:237. 1915. Type: *G. ar-*

mata (S. Watson) O. F. Cook (*Brahea armata* S. Watson).

Moderate, mostly solitary, rarely clustered, armed or unarmed, pleonanthic, hermaphroditic palms. Stem clothed with persistent leaf sheaths, in age becoming bare. Leaves induplicate, shortly costapalmate, marcescent; sheath becoming fibrous, persistent, eventually splitting basally; petiole short or long, concave, flattened, or channeled adaxially, rounded abaxially, margins unarmed or armed with sparse to dense, small or large teeth, sometimes floccose; adaxial hastula triangular to irregular, thin, membranous, at length fibrous, sometimes large, abaxial hastula a very low ridge or scarcely developed; blade nearly orbicular, regularly divided nearly to the middle or beyond into single-fold, stiff or flexible segments, deeply bifid at the apex, interfold filaments often present, surfaces glabrous, waxy or covered in caducous, floccose indumentum, midribs prominent, other veins fine, ± equal and close together giving a striate appearance, transverse veinlets inconspicuous, sometimes evident abaxially. Inflorescences solitary, interfoliar, nearly equalling or exceeding the leaves, erect or curving, branched to 4 orders; peduncle slender, short to medium; prophyll 2-keeled, closely sheathing, tubular, glabrous (always?), splitting irregularly abaxially; peduncular bracts 0–several, like the prophyll but single-keeled, glabrous or floccose; rachis much longer than peduncle; first-order branches distant, apparently lacking prophylls; subsequent bracts triangular, membranous, very inconspicuous; rachillae crowded, numerous, all branches and rachillae covered in a pale dense felt or deep pile of hairs. Flowers spirally arranged, solitary or in cincinni of 2–3, each subtended by a small bract, buds sometimes obscured by hairs until anthesis; sepals 3, distinct, imbricate, margins minutely toothed (? always); petals 3, united basally in a tube as long as the sepals, briefly imbricate, valvate apically, shallowly to deeply furrowed adaxially; stamens 6, borne at the mouth of the corolla tube, filaments connate in a 6-lobed ring, lobes triangular, abruptly narrowed at tips, anthers broadly elliptic to nearly oblong, dorsifixed, more or less versatile, latrorse; pollen elliptic, monosulcate, with finely reticulate, tectate exine; carpels 3, follicular, united by the styles, ovule basal, erect, anatropous. Fruit usually developing from 1 carpel, globose or ovoid, dark blue to black at maturity, abortive carpels basal, stigmatic remains apical; epicarp smooth, mesocarp fleshy, endocarp crustaceous. Seed basally or subbasally attached, globose or ellipsoidal, endosperm homogeneous, very shallowly to deeply penetrated by a smooth intrusion of seed coat, embryo subbasal to lateral. Germination remote-ligular; eophyll entire. $n = 18$ (*B. aculeata* as *Erythea aculeata*, Read 1964; *B. armata* as *E. glauca*, Eichhorn 1957, and as *E. roezlii*, Sarkar 1970).

Anatomy. — Leaf (Tomlinson 1961), floral (Morrow 1965).

Distribution. — About 16 species in Baja California, Guadalupe Island, Mexico, and Guatemala.

Ecology. — On limestone slopes and other outcrops in dry areas.

Common Names and Uses. — Hesper palms, Guadalupe palms, rock palm, sweet brahea palm (*B. edulis*). The leaves are used for thatch and as a source of fiber. Fruits of some species are edible. Attractive ornamentals for drier areas.

Notes. — A new taxonomic treatment is much needed. For relationships see *Acoelorraphe*.

Taxonomic Account. — Bailey (1937a, b).

Plates. — 7A, 36C; Fig. G.18.

25. **COPERNICIA** Martius ex Endlicher, Genera Plantarum 253. 1837. Type: *C. cerifera* (Arruda da Camara) Martius (*Corypha cerifera* Arruda da Camara) = **C. prunifera** (Miller) H. E. Moore (*Palma prunifera* Miller).

Arrudaria Macedo, Notice sur le Palmier Carnauba 5. 1867. Type: *A. cerifera* (Arruda da Camara) Macedo (illegitimate name).

Coryphomia N. Rojas Acosta, Bulletin de l'Académie Internationale de Géographie Botanique 28: 158. 1918. Type: *C. tectorum* N. Rojas Acosta.

Moderate to tall, solitary, slow-growing, armed, pleonanthic, hermaphroditic palms. Stems covered with persistent leaf sheaths for part or all their length, sometimes becoming bare with age, the naked portion roughened and often with close, rough, ± evident leaf scars, basally expanded or not (*C. berteroana*). Leaves induplicate, palmate to shortly costapalmate; sheath fibrous, petiole lacking or very short to elongate, channeled or flattened adaxially, rounded abaxially, the margins armed with stout teeth; adaxial hastula short to very long, coriaceous, triangular, unarmed or spinose margined or erose, sometimes persisting after the lamina has disintegrated, abaxial hastula absent; blade wedge-shaped or orbicular, divided ¼ to ⅓ to the base into single-fold pointed segments, outermost bifid at the apex, segments often spiny margined, thick, very stiff, major ribs with caducous tomentum, midribs prominent abaxially, transverse veinlets not evident. Inflorescences interfoliar, often exceeding the leaves, frequently densely tomentose, branched to 6 orders; peduncle elongate, narrow, elliptic in cross section; prophyll tubular; peduncular bracts 0–1, apparently 2-winged, irregularly split apically; rachis about as long as or longer than the peduncle; rachis bracts tubular, closely sheathing, first-order branches each bearing a prophyll, subsequent bracts tubular, tightly sheathing, split apically, gradually reduced and lacking on rachillae or present and conspicuous through to the flowers, usually densely tomentose; rachillae of medium length to very short, stout or slender, often recurved, bearing spirally inserted, membranous bracts, each subtending a solitary flower or groups of 2–4 flowers, distant or very crowded, the group and each flower subtended by a membranous bracteole. Flowers with 3 sepals united in a thick-based, 3-lobed cup, lobes usually acute; corolla tubular below with 3 thick-tipped, valvate lobes, prominently pocketed and furrowed within; stamens 6, united by their broad filament bases into a cupule, borne at the mouth of the corolla tube,

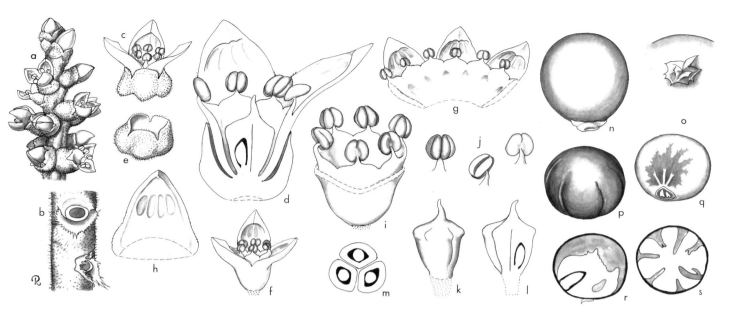

25.—**Copernicia. a,** portion of rachilla ×3; **b,** portion of rachilla, flowers removed to show bracts ×6; **c,** flower ×6; **d,** flower in vertical section ×12; **e,** calyx ×6; **f,** flower, calyx removed ×6; **g,** corolla and androecium, interior view, expanded ×6; **h,** free portion of petal, interior view ×12; **i,** flower, petals removed to show androecium ×12; **j,** stamen in 3 views ×12; **k,** gynoecium ×12; **l,** gynoecium in vertical section ×12; **m,** carpels in cross-section ×12; **n,** fruit ×1½; **o,** apex of fruit and abortive carpels ×3; **p, q,** seed in 2 views ×1½; **r,** seed in vertical section ×1½; **s,** seed in cross-section ×1½. *Copernicia yarey:* all from *Read 606.*

distinct filament lobes abruptly narrowed to short slender tips, these not inflexed in bud, antesepalous lobes sometimes larger than antepetalous ones, anthers usually small, ovate or oblong, dorsifixed near their bases, latrorse; pollen elliptic, monosulcate or rarely trichotomosulcate, with finely reticulate, tectate exine; carpels 3, follicular, distinct basally, styles wide basally, tapering, connate, stigma dotlike, ovule erect, basal, anatropous. Fruit ovoid or spherical, usually developing from 1 carpel, carpellary remains apical, stigmatic remains apical; epicarp smooth, drying minutely roughened, mesocarp slightly fleshy with longitudinally anastomosing fibers, endocarp moderately thick, crustaceous. Seed ovoid or globose, basally attached, with large ovate basal hilum, raphe indistinct, narrow, branching, endosperm deeply ruminate; embryo subbasal. Germination remote tubular; eophyll entire, lanceolate. $n = 18$ (*C. alba,* Eichhorn 1957; *C. prunifera,* Janaki Ammal 1945, Sarkar 1970; *C. yarey,* Read 1965b).

Anatomy.—Leaf (Tomlinson 1961), flower (Morrow 1965).

Distribution.—Twenty-five species, three in South America, two in Hispaniola, the remainder in Cuba.

Ecology.—In savannahs or woodlands in the lowlands in relatively dry situations. The South American species occur in pure natural stands. *C. prunifera* is found in vast natural stands in Brazil and grows in areas liable to seasonal flooding.

Common Names and Uses.—Carnauba (*C. prunifera*), petticoat palm (*C. macroglossa*), Caranda

palms. *C. prunifera* is of great economic importance as the source of high quality Carnauba wax (Johnson 1985). Other parts of all species are also used locally as leaves for thatching, stems for building, and fibers for brushes and rope. Starch from stems and fruits is edible; seedlings are used for fodder.

Notes.—There is considerable diversity in the genus, especially in Cuba. The very large hastulae of some species, e.g. *C. macroglossa,* are most remarkable but their functional significance, if any, has yet to be explained. Another unusual feature is the presence in some species of completely tubular rachilla bracts subtending the flower clusters. Some of the largest species such as *C. baileyana* make most imposing ornamentals but these are notoriously slow growing. The three species in South America are probably relatively recent immigrants from the center of distribution of the genus in the Greater Antilles.

Taxonomic Account.—Dahlgren and Glassman (1961, 1963).

Plates.—7B, 36D; Figs. G.4, G.11.

26. **WASHINGTONIA** H. A. Wendland, Botanische Zeitung 37:1xi, 68, 148. 1879 (conserved name). Type: **W. filifera** (Linden ex André) H. A. Wendland (*Pritchardia filifera* Linden ex André).

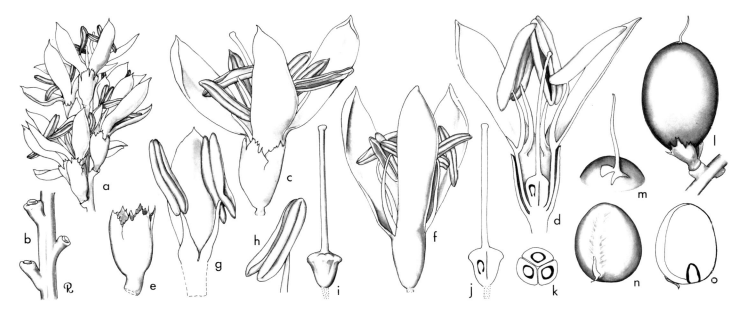

26.—**Washingtonia. a,** portion of rachilla ×3; **b,** portion of rachilla with pedicels ×6; **c,** flower ×6; **d,** flower in vertical section ×6; **e,** calyx ×6; **f,** flower, calyx removed ×6; **g,** petal with 2 stamens, interior view ×6; **h,** anther ×6; **i,** gynoecium ×6; **j,** gynoecium in vertical section ×6; **k,** carpels in cross-section ×6; **l,** fruit ×3; **m,** apex of fruit ×6; **n,** seed ×3; **o,** seed in vertical section ×3. *Washingtonia robusta:* all from *Read 725.*

Neowashingtonia Sudworth, United States Department of Agriculture, Division of Forestry Bulletin 14:105. 1897 (substitute name).

Robust, tall, solitary, armed, pleonanthic, hermaphroditic tree palms. Stem erect, usually partly or wholly covered with persistent dry leaves, ringed with close leaf scars, sometimes enlarged basally. Leaves induplicate, costapalmate, marcescent; sheath with a conspicuous abaxial cleft below the petiole, the margins disintegrating into a dark-brown fibrous network, the sheath densely caducous tomentose, margins becoming fibrous; petiole elongate, adaxially flattened to slightly concave, abaxially rounded, margins strongly armed with curved teeth, teeth becoming smaller and sparser distally; adaxial hastula large, membranous, triangular, irregularly margined and tattering, abaxial hastula a low ridge obscured by a mat of thick tomentum (in *W. robusta*); blade divided irregularly to ca. ⅓ its length into linear single-fold segments, bifid at their apices, pendulous at maturity, filamentous at the tips, interfold filaments conspicuous, midribs prominent abaxially, transverse veinlets obscure. Inflorescence interfoliar, ascending, branched to 3(–4) orders, equalling or generally exceeding the leaves, curved, slender; peduncle short; prophyll tubular, closely sheathing, 2-keeled, irregularly tattered at the tip; peduncular bract 1, like the prophyll but with a single keel; rachis much longer than the peduncle; rachis bracts tubular basally, splitting longitudinally, becoming flattened and swordlike, very coriaceous; subsequent bracts minute or lacking; rachillae numerous, short, very slender, glabrous. Flowers solitary, elongate, spirally inserted, briefly pedicellate; calyx chaffy, tubular proximally with 3 irregularly tattered, imbricate lobes, persistent in fruit; corolla tubular for ca. ¼ its length,

distinct lobes valvate, narrowly ovate, tapering to a point, reflexed at anthesis, thin, almost chaffy; stamens 6, borne at the mouth of corolla tube, filaments elongate, gradually tapering from a fleshy base, anthers elongate, medifixed, versatile, latrorse, connective narrow; pollen elliptic, monosulcate, with reticulate, tectate exine; gynoecium top-shaped, carpels 3, distinct basally, united through the long slender styles, ovule basal, erect, anatropous (?). Fruit small, broadly ellipsoidal to globose, often falling with the pedicel and unilaterally ruptured calyx tube attached, blackish, stigmatic and abortive carpel remains apical; epicarp smooth, thin, mesocarp thin, fleshy with a few flattened longitudinal fibers, endocarp thin, crustaceous, not adherent to the seed, smooth within. Seed ellipsoidal, somewhat compressed, hilum eccentrically basal, raphe extending ⅔ the length of the shining red-brown seed coat, loosely branched laterally, seed coat intrusion very thin, endosperm homogeneous; embryo basal. Germination remote-ligular; eophyll entire, lanceolate. $n = 18$ (*W. filifera,* as *Pritchardia filifera,* Eichhorn 1953, 1957, Sharma and Sarkar 1957, Venkatasubban 1945; *W. filifera,* Read 1966; *W. robusta,* Read 1965b).

Anatomy.—Leaf (Tomlinson 1961), floral (Morrow 1965).

Distribution.—Two closely related species; *W. filifera* southeastern California, western Arizona, and Baja California, *W. robusta,* Baja California and Sonora, Mexico.

Ecology.—Desert palms occurring along streams and canyons and about springs and seepages in more open areas.

Common Names and Uses. — Washington palms, desert fan (*W. filifera*), Mexican washington (*W. robusta*). Excellent ornamentals for the drier subtropics.

Notes. — *Washingtonia* stands apart from other members of the Livistoninae because of its unusual sword-shaped bracts, and curious chaffy perianth, in particular, the large, flat, reflexed petals.

Taxonomic Account. — Bailey (1936).

Plate. — *37A; Figs. G.2, G.16.*

Coryphinae J. Dransfield & N. Uhl, Principes 30:4, 1986. Type: **Corypha.**

Carpels 3, united basally, styles free or united but stylar canals separate.

The genera of this rather heterogeneous subtribe are confined to the Old World (Map 5). Of the four genera, *Nannorrhops* and *Corypha* both have hapaxanthic shoots and somewhat similar flower form; *Chuniophoenix* shares with *Nannorrhops* the completely tubular rachilla bracts and lack of a hastula. *Kerriodoxa* stands apart in dioecism and several floral characters and although having basally connate carpels may be misplaced in the subtribe.

27. **CORYPHA** Linnaeus, Species Plantarum 1187. 1753. Type: **C. umbraculifera** Linnaeus.

Codda-Pana Adanson, Familles des Plantes 2:25, 541. 1763 (type as above).

Taliera Martius, Palmarum Familia 10. 1824. Type: *T. bengalensis* Sprengel (=*Corypha taliera* Roxburgh).

Gembanga Blume in T. F. L. Nees, Flora 8(2):580, 678. 1825. Type: *G. rotundifolia* Blume (=*Corypha utan* Lamarck).

Massive, solitary, armed, hapaxanthic, hermaphroditic, tree palms. Stem erect, closely ringed with leaf scars sometimes in distinct spirals. Leaves induplicate, costapalmate, marcescent in immature individuals, tending to abscise under their own weight in trunked individuals; sheath sometimes with lateral lobes, later sometimes with a conspicuous triangular cleft below the petiole, the margins tending to erode into fibers; petiole massive, long, covered with caducous indumentum, adaxially deeply channeled, abaxially rounded, margins with well defined teeth; adaxial hastula well developed, abaxial hastula rather irregular; blade regularly divided to ca. ½ its radius into single-fold segments, these in turn shallowly divided along the abaxial folds, filaments present at upper folds in young leaves, segments with prominent longitudinal veins, abundant transverse veinlets and caducous floccose indumentum along the folds, indumentum more abundant abaxially. Inflorescences above the leaves, composed of first-order branches equivalent to the axillary inflorescences of pleonanthic palms, the first-order branches subtended by leaves

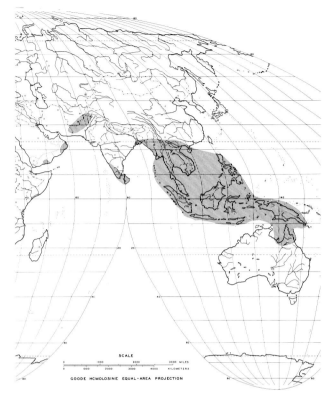

Map 5. — **Distribution of Coryphinae.**

with reduced blades or by tubular bracts, and emerging from their mouths or through an abaxial split, branched to the 4th order, all branches ending as rachillae; prophyll of first-order branches 2-keeled, empty; first-order bracts tubular, the proximal 0–several empty, other bracts inconspicuous, triangular, each subtending a second or higher order branch; rachillae bearing spirally arranged, adnate cincinni of up to 10 flowers; floral bracteoles minute. Flowers borne on short stalks formed by the base of the calyx and the receptacle; calyx tubular basally, with 3 low, triangular lobes; petals ± boatshaped, basally imbricate, the margins usually inrolled, stamens 6, the 3 antesepalous free, the 3 antepetalous adnate basally to the petals, filaments tapering from a fleshy base; anthers short, somewhat sagittate basally, medifixed, latrorse; pollen elliptic, monosulcate or very rarely trichotomosulcate, with finely reticulate, tectate exine; gynoecium tricarpellate, syncarpous, triovulate, ovary globose, distinctly 3-grooved, style elongate, slightly 3-grooved, stigma scarcely differentiated, ovule hemianatropous. Fruit globose, single-seeded with basal abortive carpels and stigmatic remains; epicarp smooth, mesocarp fleshy, endocarp thin, usually remaining attached to the seed. Seed globose, with basal hilum, and shallow grooves corresponding to the rapheal bundles, endosperm homogeneous, with or without a central hollow; embryo apical. Germination remote-tubular; eophyll entire, lanceolate. $n = 18$ (*C. utan* as *C. elata,* and as *C. gebanga,* Eichhorn 1957; *C. umbraculifera,* Sharma and Sarkar 1957).

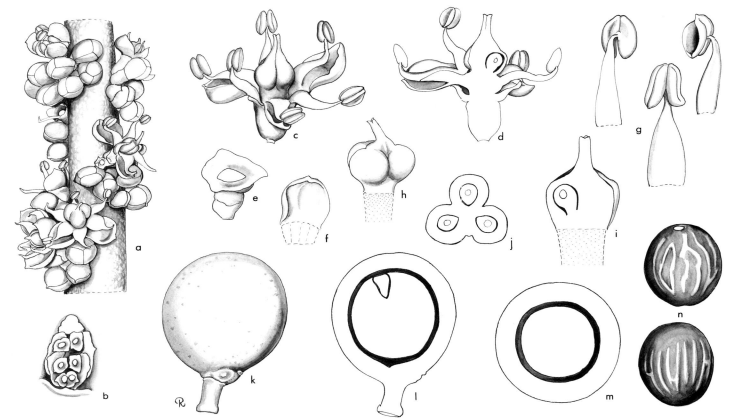

27.—**Corypha. a,** portion of rachilla ×3; **b,** flower cluster, flowers removed to show bracteoles ×3; **c,** flower ×6; **d,** flower in vertical section ×6; **e,** calyx ×6; **f,** petal, interior view ×6; **g,** stamen in 3 views ×12; **h,** gynoecium ×12; **i,** gynoecium in vertical section ×12; **j,** ovary in cross-section ×12; **k,** fruit ×1½; **l,** fruit in vertical section ×1½; **m,** fruit in cross-section ×1½; **n,** seed in 2 views ×1½. *Corypha* sp.: **a-j,** *Read s.n.*; **k-n,** *Moore & Meijer 9223*.

Anatomy.—Leaf (Tomlinson 1961), floral (Uhl and Moore 1971).

Distribution.—Eight recognized species, but probably fewer, ranging from southern India and Sri Lanka, to the Bay of Bengal, and Indochina through Malesia to northern Australia; distribution probably much influenced by man.

Ecology.—*Corypha* species are frequently associated with human settlements, but in the wild are probably a feature of open seral communities such as alluvial plains, or submaritime storm forest; they are not found in climax tropical rain forest.

Fossil Record.—*Corypha wilkinsonii* Chandler, has been described from the Eocene London clay and is said to resemble closely present day Malayan '*C. olivaeformis*' (Chandler 1978). However, as '*C. olivaeformis*' has never been described, the identity of the modern equivalent is not known.

Common Names and Uses.—Gebang (*C. utan*), talipot (*C. umbraculifera*). *Corypha* has a wide range of uses and is intensively exploited. Leaves are used for thatch, writing material, umbrellas, buckets, etc. The stem has been used as a source of starch.

Notes.—Distinguished by toothed petiole margins, flowers in adnate cincinni, and syncarpous ovaries. Species of *Corypha* are most striking palms because of their massiveness. The inflorescence is the largest among seed plants; the number of flowers has been estimated as ten million. See Tomlinson and Soderholm (1975) for a discussion of flowering, fruiting, and inflorescence structure.

Taxonomic Account.—Beccari (1931).

Plates.—*8A, 37B; Figs. G.7, G.18, G.21.*

28. **NANNORRHOPS** H. A. Wendland, Botanische Zeitung 37:148. 1879. Type: **N. ritchiana** (Griffith) Aitchison (*Chamaerops ritchiana* Griffith).

Moderate, shrubby, clustered, unarmed, hapaxanthic, hermaphroditic palm. Stems branched, prostrate or erect, branching in prostrate stems axillary, in erect stems di-

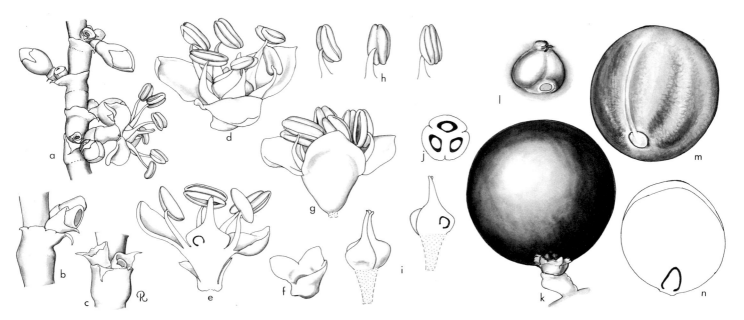

28.—**Nannorrhops. a,** portion of rachilla ×3; **b, c,** portion of cincinnus, flowers removed to show tubular bracts ×6; **d,** flower ×6; **e,** flower in vertical section ×6; **f,** calyx ×6; **g,** flower, calyx removed ×6; **h,** stamen in 3 views ×6; **i,** gynoecium in lateral view and vertical section ×6; **j,** ovary in cross-section ×6; **k,** fruit ×3; **l,** base of fruit with stigmatic remains ×7½; **m,** seed ×3; **n,** seed in vertical section ×3. *Nannorrhops ritchiana*: all from *Read 735.*

chotomous. Leaves induplicate, briefly costapalmate, marcescent; sheath splitting both below and opposite the petiole, brown, woolly tomentose and margins becoming frayed; petiole elongate, shallowly channeled adaxially, rounded abaxially; hastulae absent; blade regularly divided into stiff, glaucous, single-fold segments, further divided by abaxial splits, intersegmental filaments conspicuous, midribs prominent abaxially, transverse veinlets obscure. Inflorescences above the leaves, compound, composed of branches equivalent to the axillary inflorescences of pleonanthic palms, each branch subtended by a leaf with reduced blade or by a tubular bract, and branched to the 4th order; prophyll tubular, 2-keeled; peduncular bracts 0 to several, tubular; bracts subtending first-order branches tubular, tips pointed, each first-order branch with a basal, tubular, 2-keeled, empty prophyll; bracts subtending second-order branches tubular; rachillae bearing conspicuous tubular bracts, variously tomentose, each subtending a flower group. Flowers very short pedicellate, in a condensed cincinnus of 1–3(–7) flowers, each flower bearing a minute tubular bracteole; calyx thin, tubular at the base with 3 triangular lobes; corolla with a short stalklike base, and 3 distinct lobes, imbricate in the proximal ⅔, valvate in the distal ⅓; stamens 6, distinct, the antesepalous with free filaments, and the antepetalous with filaments adnate at the base to the petals, filaments awl-shaped, slightly inflexed at the tip, anthers elongate, versatile, latrorse; pollen elliptic, monosulcate, with finely reticulate, tectate exine; carpels 3, connate except at the very base, ovary distinctly 3-grooved, style single, stigma scarcely differentiated, ovule anatropous, attached ventrally and basally. Fruit subglobose to ellipsoidal, 1-seed-

ed, stigmatic remains basal; epicarp smooth, mesocarp fleshy, endocarp thin. Seed globose to ovoid, with very shallow grooves corresponding to the rapheal bundles, hilum basal, endosperm homogeneous, usually with a small central hollow; embryo basal. Germination not recorded; eophyll undivided. $n = 18$ (Read 1965b, Sarkar 1970).

Anatomy.—Leaf (Tomlinson 1961), floral (Morrow 1965, Uhl 1969a).

Distribution.—One variable species in semi-desert areas of the Middle East (Iran, Afghanistan, Pakistan, and Arabia).

Ecology.—Occurring in semi-desert areas where the water table is not too deep, but tending to avoid subtropical coastal habitats within its range; reaching to 1600 m altitude.

Common Names and Uses.—Mazari palm. The main use of *N. ritchiana* is as a source of fiber for weaving and rope making. Though undoubtedly ornamental and one of the hardiest palms, it is only rarely grown.

Notes.—Distinguished vegetatively by the dichotomously branching stems and large bluish-gray leaves lacking a hastula. *Nannorrhops* is perhaps most closely related to *Corypha*, but has a less reduced cincinnus (Uhl 1969a). Developmental studies of the flowers (Uhl 1969a) have shown that connation of carpels begins in the styles at a relatively

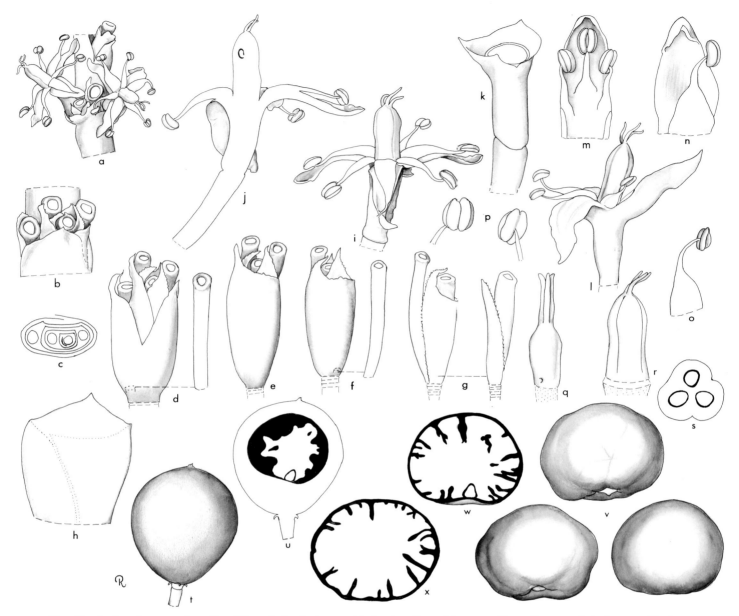

29.—**Chuniophoenix. a,** portion of rachilla ×3; **b,** cincinnus with floral stalks and bracts ×4½; **c,** diagram of cincinnus ×4½; **d-g,** dissections of cincinnus showing positions of flowers and bracteoles ×4½; **h,** bract subtending cincinnus ×6; **i,** flower ×6; **j,** flower with stalk in vertical section ×6; **k,** calyx and stalk ×7½; **l,** flower, calyx removed ×6; **m,** petal with epipetalous stamens ×6; **n,** petal lobe with stamen ×6; **o,** stamen ×6; **p,** anther in 2 views ×9; **q,** young gynoecium ×7½; **r,** mature gynoecium ×7½; **s,** ovary in cross-section ×9; **t,** fruit ×1½; **u,** fruit in vertical section ×1½; **v,** seed in 3 views ×2¼; **w,** seed in vertical section ×2¼; **x,** seed in cross-section ×2¼. *Chuniophoenix hainanensis*: **a-s,** *Wei Chao Fen 123012* and *Whitmore 3152*; **t-x,** *Wei Chao Fen 123194* and *Whitmore 3152.*

late stage in ontogeny, suggesting relationship to members of the Livistoninae where carpels are connate by styles only.

    Taxonomic Account.—Moore (1980a).
    Plate.—*37D; Fig. G.11.*

29. **CHUNIOPHOENIX** Burret, Notizblatt des Botanischen Gartens und Museums zu Berlin-Dahlem 13:583. 1937. Type: **C. hainanensis** Burret.

Small, clustered, unarmed, pleonanthic, hermaphroditic or occasionally polygamodioecious palms. Stem slender, erect, ringed with leaf scars. Leaves induplicate, palmate, apparently marcescent; sheath tubular at first, later splitting opposite the petiole, in *C. hainanensis* with a triangular cleft at the base of the petiole, usually covered with floccose indumentum; petiole well developed, grooved, margins smooth; hastulae absent; blade irregularly divided almost to the base into single- to severalfold segments with entire or shallowly toothed apices, segments thin, with prominent ad- and abaxial ribs, and sparse floccose indumentum, blade margins decurrent on petiole, midribs prominent abaxially, transverse veinlets abundant. Inflorescences among the leaves, spicate or with up to 2 orders of branching; peduncle well developed, adnate at the base to the internode above the subtending node; prophyll short, persistent, tubular, 2-keeled; peduncular bracts several, persistent, tubular, tightly sheathing, distant; rachis where present shorter to much longer than the peduncle; rachis bracts like the peduncular; rachillae erect or spreading, bearing ± imbricate, ± spirally arranged, persistent, tubular bracts with short triangular limbs, each subtending a flower group. Flowers solitary or arranged in a condensed cincinnus of 1–7 flowers, each flower in turn exserted from the rachilla bract on a columnar pedicel, and bearing a 2-keeled tubular (later splitting) bracteole; calyx tubular, somewhat chaffy, shallowly 2–3 lobed, tending to split irregularly in the distal part; corolla with a long stalklike base and 3 triangular, valvate, later reflexed, fleshy lobes; stamens 6, the antesepalous free, the antepetalous adnate to the base of the petals, filaments elongate, fleshy, the antepetalous ones much wider basally than those opposite the sepals, anthers oval to oblong, introrse; pollen elliptic, monosulcate, with finely reticulate, tectate exine; gynoecium tricarpellate, ovary somewhat stalked, elongate, with septal nectaries at the base, style 3-grooved, elongate, trifid at the tip, the stigmas somewhat divergent, ovules anatropous (very rarely 2 present in 1 carpel—? as a monstrosity), attached to the inner carpel wall at the base; ovary or pollen aborting in polygamodioecious individuals. Fruit small, ± rounded, 1-seeded, green when immature, scarlet when ripe, with apical stigmatic remains; epicarp smooth, lustrous, or somewhat pebbled on drying, mesocarp fleshy, endocarp thin. Seed irregularly globose, basally attached with short hilum, grooved along raphe, and with sparse anastomosing grooves corresponding to the raphe branches, endosperm ruminate or homogeneous; embryo basal. Germination unknown; eophyll entire. $n = 5$ (Hsu and Huang 1985).

Anatomy. — Not studied.

Distribution. — Three species occurring in Vietnam, south China, and Hainan Island.

Ecology. — Undergrowth palms in forest.

Common Names and Uses. — Common names unknown. Uses not recorded but certainly desirable ornamentals.

Notes. — *Chuniophoenix,* little known outside China, is a most remarkable genus. The three species obviously comprise one genus even though they display a range of variation in morphology unusual in such a small genus. The rachillae with their completely tubular, conspicuous bracts, have an almost calamoid appearance. The lack of a hastula is also noteworthy. The chromosome count, if confirmed, is unusually low.

Taxonomic Account. — Burret (1937b). See also Tang and Wu (1977).

Plates. — *8B, C, D, 38A; Fig. G.19.*

30. KERRIODOXA J. Dransfield, Principes 27:4. 1983.
Type: **K. elegans** J. Dransfield.

Moderate, solitary, acaulescent or erect, unarmed, pleonanthic, dioecious palm. Stem very short, becoming erect, obscured by marcescent leaf bases, eventually becoming smooth, marked with very close leaf scars. Leaves induplicate, palmate, marcescent; sheath splitting opposite the petiole, not encircling the stem, not fibrous; petiole well developed, channeled adaxially, rounded abaxially, the margins hard and very sharp, surfaces bearing caducous indumentum; adaxial hastula conspicuous, abaxial hastula absent; blade regularly divided along adaxial ribs for ca. ¼–⅓ radius into single-fold segments, thin, narrow, almost herbaceous, adaxially glabrous except for caducous, scurfy indumentum along the ribs, abaxially covered with dense white indumentum, midribs evident abaxially, transverse veinlets conspicuous, interfold filaments present in expanding leaf, soon disintegrating. Inflorescences solitary, interfoliar, staminate and pistillate dissimilar; staminate inflorescence becoming curved, copiously branched to 4 orders, the whole inflorescence very condensed and congested, creamy-white at first, becoming brown with age; peduncle short; prophyll tubular, concealed within leaf sheaths; rachis longer than the peduncle, bearing up to 15 bracts, tubular near the insertion, distally with a ± expanded triangular limb, adaxially glabrous, abaxially densely tomentose; first-order branches adnate to the inflorescence axis to just below the following bract, decreasing in size distally; all axes densely tomentose, each branch above the first-order subtended by a somewhat undulate tubular bract with a triangular apiculate limb; rachillae very slender, somewhat zigzag, bearing spirally arranged, tubular bracts with undulate margins and short, triangular, apiculate limbs, each subtending a low spur bearing 2 flowers and a minute triangular bracteole. Staminate flowers very small, ± symmetrical, creamy-yellow at anthesis; calyx with a basal, 3-angled tube densely covered in pale tomentum, and 3 narrow, triangular, apiculate, keeled, ± glabrous lobes with somewhat undulate margins; corolla stalklike at the base, 3-angled, lobes 3, triangular, the margins and abaxial surfaces papillose, adaxial surface somewhat wrinkled; stamens 6, borne in 2 whorls, the antesepalous filaments free, the antepetalous joined together at the base and partly adnate to the petals, filaments ± equal in size, elongate, gradually tapering, anthers oval, latrorse; pollen elliptic, monosulcate, with coarsely reticulate, tectate exine; pistillode absent. Pistillate inflorescence erect, much more robust than the staminate, and less congested, branching to 2 orders only; peduncular bracts and rachis as in the staminate inflorescence but larger; first- and second-order branches ap-

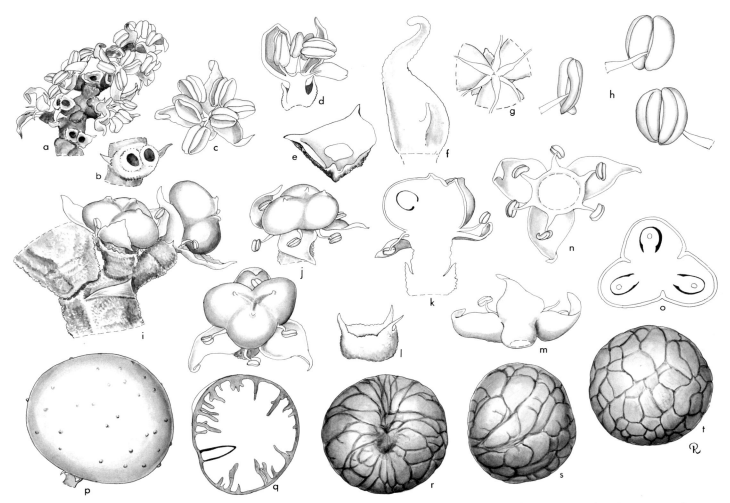

30.—**Kerriodoxa. a,** portion of staminate inflorescence ×4½; **b,** portion of staminate inflorescence, flowers removed to show scars and bracteoles ×9; **c,** staminate flower ×9; **d,** staminate flower in vertical section ×9; **e,** staminate calyx ×15; **f,** staminate petal with adnate stamen filament, interior view ×15; **g,** stamen filaments, sepals, and parts of petals, top view ×15; **h,** stamen in 3 views ×15; **i,** portion of pistillate inflorescence ×6; **j,** pistillate flower in 2 views ×6; **k,** pistillate flower in vertical section ×6; **l,** pistillate calyx ×6; **m,** pistillate corolla ×6; **n,** pistillate corolla and staminodial ring ×6; **o,** ovary in cross-section ×7½; **p,** fruit ×1; **q,** seed in vertical section ×1; **r, s, t,** seed in 3 views ×1. *Kerriodoxa elegans:* **a–o,** *Bhoonab s.n.;* **p–t,** *Dransfield 5421.*

pearing articulated, because of dense tomentum on axes and the truncate, ± glabrous bracts; rachillae somewhat zigzag, bearing low bracts with short triangular tips and glabrous margins, each subtending a short, densely tomentose spur, bearing a pair of flowers; bracteoles, if present, obscured by tomentum. Pistillate flowers larger than the staminate, creamy-yellow at anthesis; calyx forming a densely tomentose tube tipped with 3 short, narrow, triangular, glabrous lobes; corolla base stalklike, densely tomentose, tipped with 3 triangular lobes, spreading at anthesis, glabrous, the margins ± translucent, denticulate or papillose; staminodes 6 with elongate filaments and flattened empty anthers; gynoecium of 3 (rarely 4) carpels, distinct at their tips, connate at the middle, stigmas short, outward curving; ovule laterally attached, anatropous. Corolla base enlarging after fertilization. Fruit 1- or rarely

2-seeded, relatively large, spherical, concave depressed at base, the abortive carpels and stigmatic remains persisting at the fruit base; epicarp orange-yellow, covered in low pustules, mesocarp thick, soft and spongy, endocarp thin. Seed basally attached, endosperm shallowly ruminate; embryo subbasal. Germination remote-ligular; eophyll broadly lanceolate, apically lobed. Cytology not studied.

Anatomy.—Not studied.

Distribution.—One species known from two localities in peninsular Thailand.

Ecology.—*K. elegans* grows gregariously in the undergrowth of rather dry evergreen forest on slopes of hills at altitudes of ca. 100–300 m above sea level. Little is known of the natural history of this palm.

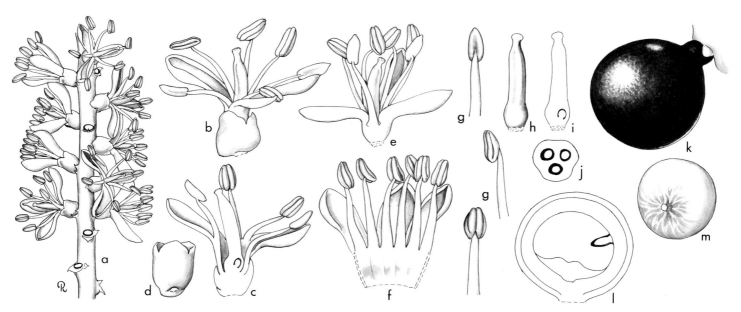

31.—**Sabal. a,** portion of rachilla ×3; **b,** flower ×6; **c,** flower in vertical section ×6; **d,** calyx ×6; **e,** flower, calyx removed ×6; **f,** corolla and androecium, expanded, interior view ×6; **g,** stamen in 3 views ×6; **h,** gynoecium ×6; **i,** gynoecium in vertical section ×6; **j,** ovary in cross-section ×12; **k,** fruit ×3; **l,** fruit in vertical section ×3; **m,** seed ×3. *Sabal palmetto*: all from *Read s.n.*

Common Names and Uses.—Common names unknown. No local uses have been recorded but the ornamental potential is great.

Notes.—*Kerriodoxa* is a very isolated and unusual genus included here, only tentatively, in the Coryphinae. The tubular rachilla bracts, the stalklike base of the corolla, and the basally fused carpels are shared with other members of the subtribe, but dioecy is not.

Taxonomic Account.—Dransfield (1983).

Plate.—*37C.*

Sabalinae Martius in Endlicher, Genera Plantarum 252. 1837. Type: **Sabal.**

Carpels 3, united throughout, with a common stylar canal.

This subtribe consists of the single genus *Sabal* which occurs on the Caribbean islands and adjacent lands (Map 6). The flowers are very similar in form to those of the Livistoninae but fusion of the carpels in *Sabal* is complete and the large canal is single from the locules through the long style.

31. **Sabal** Adanson, Familles des Plantes 2:495, 599. 1763. Lectotype: *S. adansonii* Guersent (illegitimate name), (*Corypha minor* N. J. Jacquin = **S. minor** (N. J. Jacquin) Persoon).
Inodes O. F. Cook, Bulletin of the Torrey Botanical

Club 28:529. 1901. Type: *I. causiarum* O. F. Cook (=*Sabal causiarum* (O. F. Cook) Beccari).

Dwarf, moderate, or tall, usually robust, solitary, acaulescent or erect, unarmed, pleonanthic, hermaphroditic palms. Stem often descending shortly and recurved, covered with leaf bases, rough striate, and obscurely ringed, or becoming ± smooth, grey, and bare with age. Leaves induplicate, marcescent, shortly to prominently costapalmate; sheath later with a conspicuous cleft below the petiole, margins fibrous; petiole often very long, channeled adaxially, rounded abaxially, sometimes bearing caducous

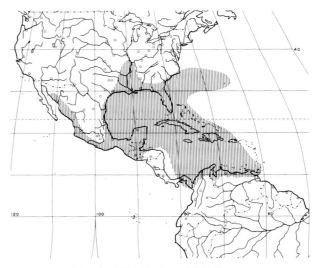

Map 6.—**Distribution of Sabalinae.**

indumentum; adaxial hastula short and truncate or usually elongate and acute or acuminate, margins sharp, abaxial hastula sometimes distinguishable as a low ridge; blade flat to mostly arched, divided to the middle or nearly to the costa into drooping linear, single-fold segments, briefly to rather deeply bifid, sometimes filiferous, segments with midribs prominent abaxially, interfold filaments sometimes present, glaucous or not, sometimes paler beneath, often with caducous indumentum along the major ribs, midribs prominent, transverse veinlets obscure or conspicuous. Inflorescence shorter, as long as, or longer than the leaves, interfoliar, branching to 4 orders; prophyll short, 2-keeled, 2-lobed; peduncular bracts several, tubular below with a conspicuous, short to long and narrow tip, variously caducously tomentose; rachis equalling or longer than the peduncle; rachis bracts like peduncular bracts, decreasing in size distally; bracts of the second and third-order well developed, tubular, decreasing in size distally; prophylls present on most branches; rachillae slender, with spirally arranged bracts, each subtending a low spur branch bearing a solitary flower. Flowers symmetrical; calyx somewhat thickened at the base, tubular, shallowly 3-lobed, often prominently nerved when dried; corolla tubular below, lobes elliptic, slightly imbricate in bud, spreading to suberect with incurved membranous margins at anthesis, becoming strongly inrolled when dry; stamens 6, the filaments rather fleshy, flattened, united in a tube about as high as the calyx, adnate up to the mouth of the corolla tube, then distinct and awl-shaped, not inflexed at the apex, anthers erect in bud, dorsifixed, ± versatile or erect, narrowly elliptic, latrorse; pollen elliptic, monosulcate, with finely reticulate, tectate exine; carpels 3, completely connate, ovarian part trilobed and only slightly broader than the elongate 3-grooved style, stigma capitate, trilobed, papillose, ovule basal, anatropous. Fruit usually developing from 1 carpel, sometimes from 2 or 3, globose to pyriform, stigmatic scar and abortive carpels basal; epicarp smooth, mesocarp fleshy without fibers, endocarp thin, membranous. Seed free from endocarp, shining brown, depressed-globose, usually concave below when dry, raphe and hilum basal, endosperm homogeneous with a shallow intrusion of seed coat; embryo lateral or subdorsal. Germination remote-ligular; eophyll entire, elongate. *n* = 18 (*S. minor* as *S. adansonii, S. mexicana,* Sharma and Sarkar 1957; *S. minor* as *S. adansonii, S. blackburniana,* Satô 1946; *S. minor, S. jamaicensis,* Read 1965b, 1966; *S. palmetto,* Janaki Ammal 1945, Read 1965b; *S. mauritiiformis* as *S. glaucescens, S. uresana,* Eichhorn 1957).

Anatomy. — Floral (Morrow 1965), leaf (Tomlinson 1961).

Distribution. — About fourteen species. One of the larger coryphoid genera confined to the central Western hemisphere from Colombia to northeastern Mexico and the southeastern United States.

Ecology. — Various, some species (*S. minor*) of swampy areas, others from sandy coastal regions and dry open lands.

Fossil Record. — The earliest palm leaves in the fossil record are costapalmate (Daghlian 1981). Much detailed study is required to determine how many of these are referable to *Sabal* or to other modern genera. A careful analysis of epidermal characters by Daghlian (1978) led to the description of a new species, *S. dorchii,* from the Eocene of the Mississippi embayment. *Sabal eocenia* (Leso) Dorf from the Mid to Upper Eocene to the Mid-Upper Oligocene Clarno Formation, Oregon probably cannot be distinguished from *Sabalites* as circumscribed by Read and Hickey (1972). Fruits of *Sabal* are reported from Eocene London Clay (Chandler 1961–1964).

Common Names and Uses. — Palmetto, variously designated as Bush (*S. minor*), Cabbage (*S. palmetto*) etc. Formerly used for making brooms and locally as a source of thatch. Many species are important ornamentals.

Notes. — The occurrence of prophylls on inflorescence branches is useful in delimiting species. *Sabal* is distinguished from other genera with costapalmate leaves by the lack of spines on the petiole and by the split leaf bases.

Taxonomic Account. — Bailey (1944).

Plates. — *9A, B, 38B, C; Figs. G.4, G.5, G.10, G.16, G.24.*

PHOENICEAE Drude in Martius, Flora Brasiliensis 3(2):279. 1881. Type: **Phoenix.**

Dioecious; leaves pinnate, induplicate, leaflets with acute tips, proximal leaflets developed as spines; inflorescence bearing a prophyll only and branching to 1 order; flowers solitary, dimorphic; endocarp membranous; seed with a deep longitudinal furrow.

The tribe consists of the single, wide ranging but strictly Old World genus, *Phoenix* (Map 7). Not only is the pinnate induplicate leaf of *Phoenix* unique in gross morphology but also its development is unlike that of any other palm. The function and homology of a covering layer, the "haut", in the developing leaf are as yet not understood. Floral characters, however, suggest a close relationship with the Corypheae. Staminate and pistillate flowers are alike until late in development (DeMason et al. 1982) and resemble the unspecialized flowers of the Thrinacinae in form. The free carpels are follicular and ovules are anatropous. The apocarpous gynoecium of *Phoenix* represents a primitive character whereas the simplified inflorescence, dioecy, and dimorphic flowers must be regarded as specializations.

32. **PHOENIX** Linnaeus, Species Plantarum 1188. 1753. Type: **P. dactylifera** Linnaeus.

Elate Linnaeus, Species Plantarum 1189. 1753.

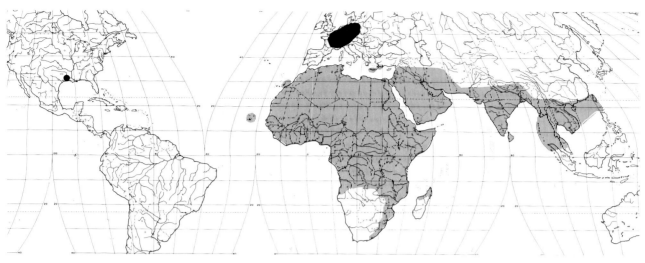

Map 7.—**Distribution of Phoeniceae:** fossils in black.

Type: *E. sylvestris* Linnaeus (=*Phoenix sylvestris* (Linnaeus) Roxburgh).

Palma P. Miller, The Gardener's Dictionary Abridged from the Folio Edition. Edition 4. 1754. Lectotype: *P. dactylifera* (Linnaeus) P. Miller (*Phoenix dactylifera* Linnaeus) (see Moore 1963b).

Phoniphora Necker, Elementa Botanica 3:302. 1790. Type not designated.

Dachel Adanson, Familles des Plantes 2:25, 548. 1763.

Fulchironia Leschenault, in Desfontaines, Catalogus Plantarum Horti Regii Parisiensis (Edition 3) 29. 1829. Type not designated.

Zelonops Rafinesque, Flora Telluriana 2:102. 1837. Type: *Z. pusilla* (J. Gaertner) Rafinesque (*Phoenix pusilla* J. Gaertner).

Dwarf or creeping to large, solitary or clustered, armed, pleonanthic, dioecious palms. Stem, when developed, often clothed with spirally arranged leaf bases. Leaves induplicate, pinnate, usually marcescent; sheath forming a fibrous network; petiole very short to well developed, adaxially channelled to flattened or ridged, abaxially rounded; rachis elongate, tapering, adaxially rounded or flat to angled, abaxially rounded to flat, usually terminating in a leaflet; leaflets single-fold, acute, regularly arranged or variously grouped, the proximal few modified as spines (acanthophylls), parallel-veined, midrib usually evident abaxially, often bearing scales, emergent leaves frequently with brown floccose indumentum and/or wax, transverse veinlets obscure. Inflorescences interfoliar, branching to 1 order, the staminate and pistillate superficially similar; peduncle flattened, short to elongate, in the pistillate frequently elongating after fertilization, bearing an often caducous, sometimes bivalved, 2-keeled, glabrous or floccose-hairy prophyll; other bracts inconspicuous; rachis flattened, usually shorter than the peduncle; rachillae unbranched,

numerous, often in groups in a spiral along the rachis, somewhat adnate above small triangular bracts, the rachillae bearing spirally arranged, low triangular bracts, each subtending a solitary flower. Staminate flowers with 3 sepals connate in a low cupule; petals 3, ± valvate, acute or rounded, much exceeding the calyx; stamens usually 6 (rarely 3 or 9), filaments short, erect, the anthers linear, latrorse; pollen elliptic or circular, monosulcate, with reticulate or finely reticulate, tectate exine; pistillode absent, or of 3 abortive carpels, or a minute trifid vestige. Pistillate flowers globose; sepals connate in a 3-lobed cupule; petals imbricate, strongly-nerved, about twice as long as the calyx or more; staminodes usually 6, scale-like or connate in a low cupule; carpels 3, distinct, follicular, ± ovoid, narrowed into a short, recurved, exserted stigma, ovule attached adaxially at the base, anatropous. Fruit usually developing from 1 carpel, ovoid to oblong with apical stigmatic remains; epicarp smooth, mesocarp fleshy, endocarp membranous. Seed elongate, terete or plano-convex, and deeply grooved with intruded seed coat below the elongate raphe, hilum basal, rounded, endosperm homogeneous; embryo lateral or subbasal. Germination remote-tubular; eophyll undivided, narrowly lanceolate. $n = 18$ (*P. canariensis, P. dactylifera, P. hanceana,* Beal 1937, Sharma and Sarkar 1957; *P. reclinata* as *P. leonensis,* Eichhorn 1957; *P. paludosa,* Aryavand 1977, Sharma and Sarkar 1957; *P. reclinata,* Aryavand 1977, Beal 1937, Read 1966; *P. roebelenii,* Eichhorn 1953, Read 1964; *P. rupicola, P. sylvestris,* Sharma and Sarkar 1957).

Anatomy.—Central vascular bundles of the petioles contain a single phloem strand (Parthasarathy 1968). Leaf (Tomlinson 1961), floral (Uhl and Moore 1971, 1977a), axillary bud, inflorescence, offshoot (Hilgeman 1954).

Distribution.—About 17 species ranging from the Atlantic islands through Africa, Crete, the Middle East and India to Hong Kong, Taiwan, Philippines,

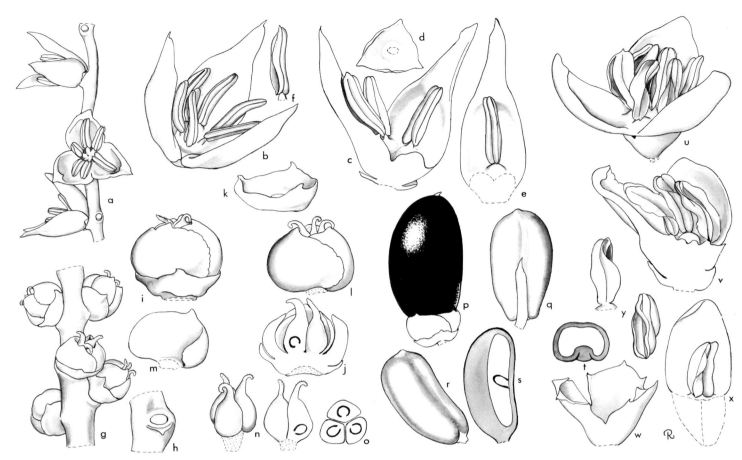

32.—**Phoenix. a,** portion of rachilla with staminate flowers ×3; **b,** staminate flower ×6; **c,** staminate flower in vertical section ×6; **d,** staminate calyx ×6; **e,** staminate petal with adnate stamen, interior view ×6; **f,** stamen ×6; **g,** portion of rachilla with pistillate flower ×3; **h,** bract and scar of pistillate flower ×6; **i,** pistillate flower ×6; **j,** pistillate flower in vertical section ×6; **k,** pistillate calyx ×6; **l,** pistillate flower, calyx removed ×6; **m,** pistillate petal, interior view ×6; **n,** gynoecium, entire and in vertical section ×6; **o,** carpels in cross-section ×6; **p,** fruit ×3; **q, r,** seed in 2 views ×3; **s,** seed in vertical ×3; **t,** seed in cross-section ×3; **u,** staminate flower ×6; **v,** staminate flower in vertical section ×6; **w,** staminate calyx ×6; **x,** staminate petal with adnate stamen, interior view ×6; **y,** stamen in 2 views ×6. *Phoenix roebelenii:* **a-t,** *Read 748* and *749*; *P. canariensis:* **u-y,** *Read 777*.

Sumatra and the Malay Peninsula. Widely cultivated as ornamentals, one species, *P. dactylifera,* the date palm, is a major economic plant, now widespread in semi-arid areas as a fruit tree. For a summary of uses see Johnson (1985).

Ecology.—Most species are plants of semi-arid regions but grow near water courses, oases, or underground water sources; a few species are found in tropical monsoonal areas. *P. paludosa* Roxburgh occurs in the Asian perhumid regions where it is confined to the landward fringe of mangrove forest.

Fossil Record.—The fossil record of *Phoenix* is extensive (Map 7) but in need of review. Berry (1914) noted fossil records for *Phoenicites* from Europe and described and figured a seed from late Eocene or early Oligocene of Texas. Chandler (1961–64) lists

Phoenix pollen from the Eocene London Clay of Britain and Machin (1971) from other British Eocene deposits. Ball (1931) described and figured parts of pinnate leaves from the Eocene of Texas as *Phoenicites*. However, the name *Phoenicites* is now applied to reduplicately pinnate leaves which cannot be related to *Phoenix* (Read and Hickey 1972). In central Europe, Bůžek (1977) described a seed as *P. bohemica* from the Lower Miocene, and Mai and Walther (1978), one as *P. hercynica* from the Upper Eocene of Gerseltal. A record of flowers from Baltic Eocene (Convents 1886) is questionable on the basis of stamen morphology (Daghlian 1981).

Common Names and Uses.—Variously designated as date palms, as wild date (*P. sylvestris*), Roebelin or Miniature date (*P. roebelenii*). The genus

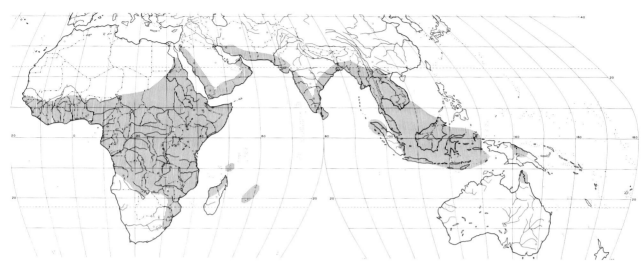

Map 8.—**Distribution of Borasseae.**

is immensely important from an economic point of view. Not only does it include the date palm, the major crop of several Middle Eastern countries and of lesser importance elsewhere, but other species are widely used as a source of fiber for weaving, starch, sugar, and a multiplicity of things such as thatch and fuel. Many species are widely grown as ornamentals. *P. roebelenii* is commercially important as a pot plant. Species are known to hybridize freely. For references on uses see Johnson (1983a, 1984).

Notes. — Easily distinguished from all other palms by the induplicate pinnate leaf with the lower leaflets modified as spines. The distinct carpels and relatively unspecialized perianth and stamens suggest close affinity with the apocarpous genera of the Corypheae. A modern developmental study of the unique leaf is greatly needed.

Taxonomic Account. — Despite the economic importance of *Phoenix* and the great ease of recognition of the genus, the species remain poorly known and in much need of a careful revision. The most useful account of the genus remains that of Beccari (1890).

Plates. — *9C, D, 38D; Figs. G.2, G.3, G.4, G.7, G.12, G.15, G.24.*

BORASSEAE Martius in Endlicher, Genera Plantarum 250. 1837. ('*Borassinae*').

Dioecious; leaves palmate or costapalmate, induplicate; staminate and sometimes pistillate flowers borne in deep pits formed by connation and adnation of the rachilla bracts; staminate flowers rarely solitary, usually in a cincinnus of 2 to many flowers; stamens exserted from the pits by elongation of the floral receptacle between the calyx and corolla; pistillate flowers solitary, bibracteolate; fruit 1–3-seeded with thick, hard endocarp.

The seven genera of the Borasseae are confined to the Old World where they are distributed in the lands bordering the Indian Ocean and on its islands (Map 8). The tribe is divisible into two apparently natural subtribes. Their members are among the most specialized genera of the subfamily. The constant dioecy, the staminate and sometimes also the pistillate flowers borne in pits in catkinlike rachillae, the syncarpous gynoecia with specialized ovules, and fruits with well developed endocarp are characteristic features.

It seems most useful to provide keys to the genera of the whole tribe rather than separate keys to the genera of the two subtribes.

Key to the Subtribes and Genera of the Borasseae (See also Vegetative Key)

1 Staminate and pistillate inflorescences dissimilar; staminate flower clusters concealed in pits; bracteoles subtending staminate flowers not bearing tufts of hairs; pistillate flowers sessile in the axils of large leathery bracts; fruit sessile, symmetrical, 1–3 seeded, endocarp forming pyrenes, stigmatic remains apical (Lataniinae) 2

1 Staminate and pistillate inflorescences similar; flowers of both sexes sunken in pits; bracteoles subtending flowers bearing tufts of hairs; fruit stalked, usually 1-seeded, if 2–3 seeded, lobed, pyrenes not formed, stigmatic and carpellary remains basal (Hyphaeninae) 5

2 Staminate flowers solitary or in cincinni of 2–6 flowers 3

2 Staminate flowers numerous, in cincinni of 30–60 4

3 Bracts of staminate inflorescence imbricate at the margins; pistillode nipplelike; pyrenes densely hairy with thick, internally ridged walls; seed grooved to conform to the ridges. Malay Peninsula, Borneo . . . . 33. **Borassodendron**

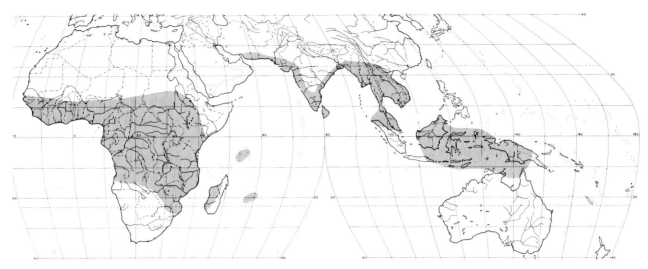

Map 9.—**Distribution of Lataniinae.**

3 Bracts of the staminate inflorescence connate at the margins; pistillode columnar, prominent; pyrenes not hairy, but thin, ridged, sculptured, or apically 3-lobed; seed not grooved. Mascarene Islands . . . . 34. **Latania**

4 Staminate rachillae several, wide; stamens 6; pyrenes not deeply bilobed; seeds usually 3, wider than thick, shallowly to deeply bilobed. Africa, Madagascar, Arabia, India to New Guinea and Australia . . . . 35. **Borassus**

4 Staminate rachillae only 1 or 2, very wide; stamens 15–18; pyrenes deeply bilobed, very thick; seed usually 1(–3), very large, deeply bilobed. Seychelles Islands . . . .
. . . . 36. **Lodoicea**

5 Seed deeply grooved. Madagascar . . . . 39. **Bismarckia**

5 Seed not grooved 6

6 Fruit various in shape, distally expanded, often shouldered, usually asymmetrical, rarely ovoid or spherical; seed irregular with endosperm homogeneous. Africa, Madagascar, Arabia, India . . . . 37. **Hyphaene**

6 Fruit ovoid; seed with endosperm ruminate. Egypt and Sudan . . . . 38. **Medemia**

Vegetative Key to the Genera of Borasseae

1 Hastulae lacking 2

1 Hastulae present 3

2 Blade glaucous, anatomically dorsiventral, split to ⅔ the length of the segments, costa short, transverse veinlets obscure . . . . 38. **Medemia**

2 Blade not glaucous, anatomically isolateral, split ½ to ⅓ the segment length, costa long, almost reaching the leaf tip, transverse veinlets conspicuous . . . . 36. **Lodoicea**

3 Petiole armed 4

3 Petiole unarmed 5

4 Spines on petiole large, regular, mostly upward pointing; transverse veinlets obscure . . . . 37. **Hyphaene**

4 Petiole margins with irregular teeth, transverse veinlets conspicuous . . . . 35. **Borassus**

5 Blade splits varying, some very deep, almost reaching the hastula, blade anatomically isolateral, transverse veinlets conspicuous . . . . 33. **Borassodendron**

5 Blade splits regular, rather shallow, blade anatomically dorsiventral, transverse veinlets obscure 6

6 Hastula conspicuously lopsided, costa long and curved .
. . . . 39. **Bismarckia**

6 Hastula regular; costa short, usually straight . . . 34. **Latania**

Lataniinae Meisner, Plantarum Vascularium Genera 1:357. 1842 ('*Latanieae*'). Type: **Latania.**

Staminate and pistillate rachillae dissimilar; pistillate flowers sessile, not borne in well defined pits; pits in staminate rachillae lacking hairs; fruit unlobed, with 1–3 pyrenes and seeds, stigmatic remains apical.

In this subtribe *Borassus* is the most widespread genus, occurring naturally from Africa to New Guinea (Map 9). *Lodoicea* is confined to the Seychelles, *Latania* to the Mascarene Islands, and *Borassodendron* to the Malay Peninsula and Borneo. Three of the four genera, *Borassodendron, Borassus* and *Lodoicea,* are remarkable in having very large pistillate flowers with thick, leathery sepals and petals. Indeed, those of *Lodoicea* are the largest flowers in the family. The staminate cincinni of these genera consist of three to about 70 flowers enclosed in deep pits formed by thick leathery modified bracts; flowers are exserted one at a time by elongation of a stalklike receptacle. The pistillate flowers of *Latania* are much smaller and the staminate flowers are borne singly in shallower pits. In the fruits of all four genera, the epicarp and mesocarp are common around all carpels, but a separate hard endocarp surrounds the locule of each carpel forming a variously hairy or sculptured "pyrene" which encloses the seed.

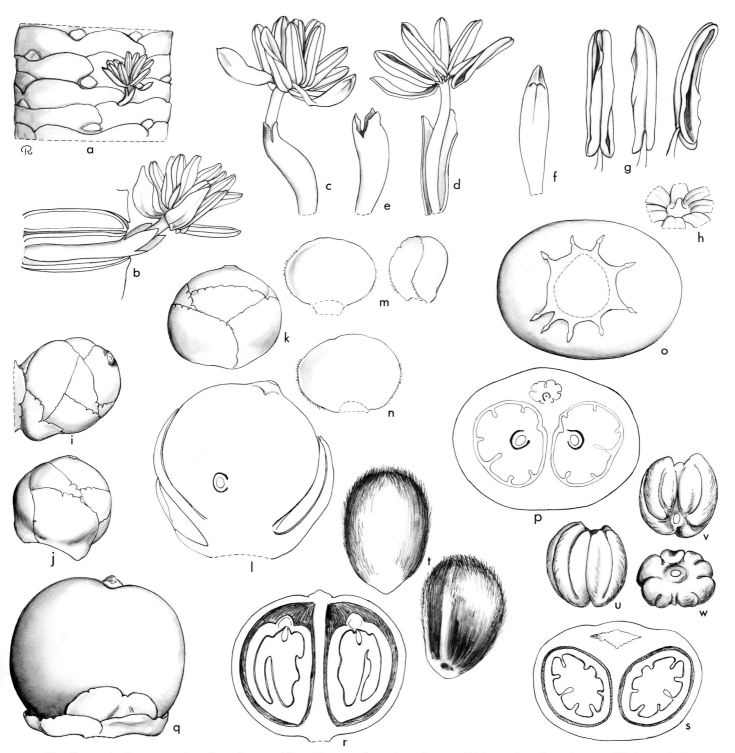

33.—Borassodendron. a, portion of staminate rachilla with exserted staminate flower ×1½; **b,** portion of staminate rachilla in vertical section with flower ×3; **c,** staminate flower ×3; **d,** staminate flower in vertical section ×3; **e,** staminate calyx ×3; **f,** staminate petal, interior view ×3; **g,** stamen in 3 views ×6; **h,** pistillode ×12; **i,** pistillate flower and bracteoles slightly post-anthesis ×3; **j, k,** pistillate flower in 2 views from opposite sides ×3; **l,** pistillate flower in vertical section ×6; **m,** pistillate sepals in 2 views ×3; **n,** pistillate petal, interior view ×3; **o,** gynoecium viewed from below to show staminodes ×6; **p,** very young fruit in cross-section ×6; **q,** fruit ×½; **r,** fruit in vertical section ×½; **s,** fruit in cross-section ×½; **t,** fibrous pyrene (endocarp) in 2 views ×½; **u, v, w,** seed in 3 views ×½. *Borassodendron machadonis*: **a-p,** *Moore 9040*; *B. borneense*: **q-w** *Moore & Meijer 9188*.

33. BORASSODENDRON Beccari, Webbia 4:359. 1914.
Type: **B. machadonis** (Ridley) Beccari (*Borassus machadonis* Ridley).

Robust, solitary, unarmed, pleonanthic, dioecious, tree palms. Stem erect, ringed with close leaf scars. Leaves induplicate, very briefly costapalmate, marcescent in immature individuals, neatly abscising under their own weight in mature trunked individuals; sheath becoming fibrous marginally, narrow, glabrous but tomentose abaxially along the margins, with a conspicuous triangular cleft below the petiole; petiole robust, covered with caducous indumentum, adaxially deeply channeled, abaxially rounded, the margins smooth, very hard and very sharp; adaxial hastula well developed, abaxial hastula absent; blade divided nearly to the insertion into compound segments, these further divided rather irregularly to ¼–⅔ the radius into single-fold segments, in turn shallowly divided along the abaxial folds, interfold filaments persisting, the segment surfaces similar in color or with white indumentum beneath, blade with bands of brown caducous scales, longitudinal veins and transverse veinlets prominent. Inflorescences interfoliar, strongly dimorphic, ± pendulous; staminate inflorescence branched to 2 orders, with a short to long peduncle; prophyll large, 2-keeled, tubular near the base, inflated distally, splitting along much of its length, densely covered in caducous indumentum, tending to disintegrate at the tip and margins into fibers; peduncular bracts 1–few, like the prophyll but with a single keel; rachis shorter or longer than the peduncle; rachis bracts like the peduncular; first-order branches distant or crowded, bare, semicircular in cross-section, with sharp edges, short or long, bearing 1–5 robust catkinlike rachillae crowded at the tip, each subtended by a small triangular bract; rachillae close or diverging, bearing a tight spiral of large scaly or hairy, imbricate bracts, connate to each other laterally and adnate to the axis to form pits, each pit containing a cincinnus of 2–6 flowers, floral bracteoles spathulate. Staminate flowers exserted one at a time from the pit; calyx membranous, tubular, tipped with 3 short triangular lobes, most of the calyx remaining included within the pit; corolla with a long stalklike base, adnate to a long floral receptacle, petals 3, ± imbricate, elongate; stamens 6–15 with very short filaments and elongate latrorse anthers; pollen circular, monoporate or monosulcate with coarsely reticulate, tectate exine; pistillode minute or absent. Pistillate inflorescence unbranched or with up to 4 branches; prophyll, peduncular bracts and rachis bracts as in the staminate inflorescence, inflorescence axis, where unbranched, terminating in a rachilla, where branched, having rachillae borne singly at the tip of bare, flattened first-order branches as in the staminate inflorescence; rachillae short to long, bearing a spiral of large hairy, frequently notched, scaly, imbricate bracts, connate to each other and adnate to the axis to form shallow pits (*B. machadonis*) or almost free but closely overlapping (*B. borneense*), each subtending a solitary pistillate flower (or abortive flower), the rachilla tip frequently bearing sterile bracts, sometimes with an apparently terminal flower, the bract margins frequently erose. Pistillate flowers sessile, ± superficial or partially sunken in pits, each surrounded by 2 large ovate, irregularly margined brac-

teoles; sepals 3, distinct, ovate, imbricate, the margins ± notched; petals 3, distinct, ovate, similar to the sepals; staminodial ring short, with 6–9 teeth bearing minute empty anthers; gynoecium globose, trilocular, triovulate, tipped with 3 fleshy approximate stigmas, ovule form unknown. Fruit large (1–2–)3-seeded, stigmatic remains apical; epicarp smooth, mesocarp fibrous, the interfiber parenchyma becoming sweet, fragrant, and fleshy at maturity, endocarp comprising 3 separate pyrenes, walls thick, stony, with 8 to 12 shallow internal, longitudinal ridges penetrating the seed. Seed grooved longitudinally by the pyrene ridges, endosperm homogeneous, with a slight central hollow; embryo apical. Germination remote-tubular; eophyll palmate with ca. 5 segments. Cytology not studied.

Anatomy. — Leaf (Tomlinson 1961).

Distribution. — Two species, *B. machadonis* in southern Thailand and northern Peninsular Malaysia, *B. borneense* in Borneo.

Ecology. — *B. machadonis* is a rare palm in Peninsular Malaysia, sometimes found in areas of deep soil on limestone hills; little is known of its habitat in southern Thailand. In Borneo, *B. borneense* can be locally abundant but is absent from wide areas of apparently suitable forest. The young leaves of *B. borneense* are eaten by orangutan which can cause considerable damage; the same animals may be responsible for dispersal.

Common Names and Uses. — Bindang. The "cabbage" of *B. borneense* is edible and is sometimes sold in Bornean village markets.

Notes. — Easily recognized by the large palmate but deeply split leaf blade, smooth sharp petiole, and well developed adaxial hastula.

Taxonomic Account. — Dransfield (1972a).

Plates. — *10C, 39A, B.*

34. LATANIA Commerson ex Jussieu, Genera Plantarum 39. 1789. Type: *L. borbonica* Lamarck = **L. lontaroides** (J. Gaertner) H. E. Moore (*Cleophora lontaroides* J. Gaertner).
Cleophora J. Gaertner, De Fructibus et Seminibus Plantarum 2:185. 1791. Type: *C. lontaroides* J. Gaertner.

Moderate, solitary, mostly unarmed, pleonanthic, dioecious, tree palms. Stem erect, rough, marked with spiral, elliptic leaf scars. Leaves induplicate, costapalmate, marcescent in young individuals, abscising cleanly in trunked specimens; sheath narrow, inserted at an angle, asymmetrical, angled, with a flange toward the lower side, split horizontally at the base, smooth or densely tomentose; petiole robust, long, adaxially deeply channeled near the base, distally flattened, abaxially rounded, adaxial surface smooth, abaxial surface densely floccose, margin smooth or with a few shallow teeth; adaxial hastula short but

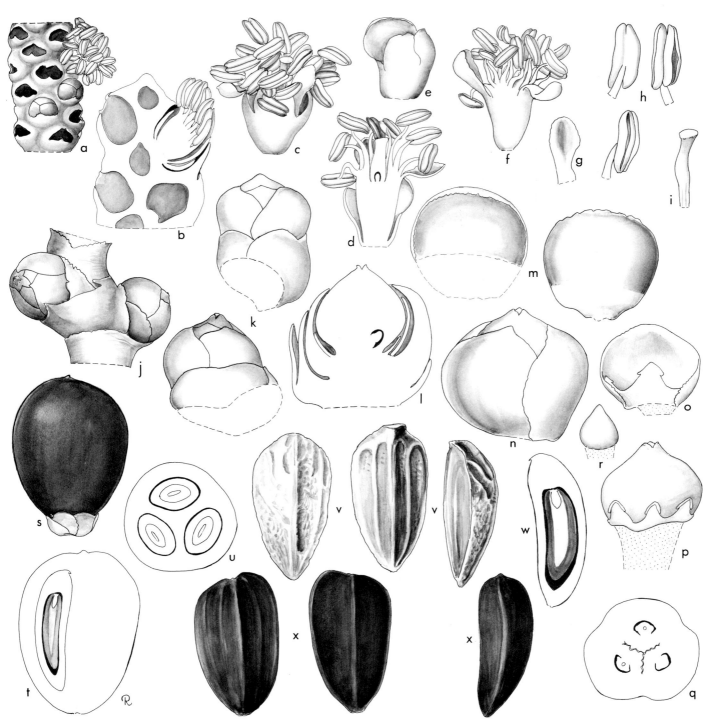

34.—**Latania. a,** portion of staminate rachilla ×1½; **b,** portion of staminate rachilla in vertical section ×3; **c,** staminate flower ×3; **d,** staminate flower in vertical section ×3; **e,** staminate calyx ×3; **f,** staminate flower, calyx removed ×3; **g,** staminate petal ×3; **h,** stamen in 3 views ×6; **i,** pistillode ×6; **j,** portion of pistillate rachilla ×1½; **k,** pistillate flower with bracts in 2 views ×2; **l,** pistillate flower in vertical section ×3; **m,** pistillate sepal in 2 views ×3; **n,** pistillate flower, sepals removed ×3; **o,** pistillate petal, interior view ×3; **p,** gynoecium and staminodes ×3; **q,** ovary in cross-section ×3; **r,** ovule ×12; **s,** fruit ×¾; **t,** fruit in vertical section × ¾; **u,** fruit in cross-section ×¾; **v,** pyrene (endocarp) in 3 views ×1; **w,** pyrene (endocarp) in vertical section ×1; **x,** seed in 3 views ×1½. *Latania verschaffeltii:* **a-i,** *Read 617*; *L. loddigesii:* **j-r,** *Read 678*; **s-x,** *Moore s.n.*

conspicuous, triangular or rounded, abaxial hastula absent; blade divided to ca. ⅓ to ½ its length along adaxial folds into regular, stiff, single-fold segments, these shortly bifid or not, acute to acuminate, abaxial costa and ridges of folds often densely floccose, midribs prominent abaxially, transverse veinlets not evident. Inflorescences interfoliar, staminate and pistillate superficially dissimilar; staminate peduncle elongate, elliptic at base in cross-section, adaxially channeled, thin distally; prophyll short, wide, tubular basally, 2-keeled, with a sharp pointed limb about equal in length to the tubular base, abaxially densely floccose; peduncular bracts 1–2–several, loosely sheathing, resembling the prophyll but with a single keel; rachis longer than the peduncle; rachis bracts like the peduncular; first-order branches short, not exceeding subtending bracts, flat, often wide, crescentic in cross-section, branched digitately at the tip to form several (1–14) rachillae; rachillae short or long, spikelike, terete, bearing short, crowded tubular bracts, each bract connate laterally with proximal and distal bracts to form a pit enclosing a single staminate flower. Staminate flowers each bearing a stiff cupular bracteole; calyx tubular basally, 3 lobed, irregularly rounded, thicker distally; corolla with a stalklike base, adnate to the long receptacle, and 3 spathulate lobes; stamens 15–30 or more, filaments short, slightly tapering, anthers basifixed, latrorse; pollen ± elliptic, monosulcate, with foveolate-fossulate, tectate exine; pistillode columnar, ovarian part slightly expanded. Pistillate inflorescence with prophyll, peduncular, and first-order bracts similar to staminate, but first-order branches fewer, each bearing only 1 or 2 rachillae; rachillae wider, longer, sheathed in fewer, larger tubular bracts, lowermost and distal bracts empty, central bracts, each subtending a pistillate flower, bracts tightly surrounding base of flower but not forming pits. Pistillate flowers fewer, globose, much larger, widely spaced in a ⅖ phyllotaxy, solitary, each bearing 2 stiff, cupular, imbricate, ± connate bracteoles; sepals 3, stiff, imbricate, rounded; petals like the sepals; staminodes 6–9, connate in a low lobed cupule, vestigial anthers sometimes present; gynoecium globose, trilocular, triovulate, style expanded, stigma undeveloped, locules uniovulate but 2 lateral bodies beside the ovule, ovule orthotropous. Fruit usually developing from all 3 carpels, large, oblong or obovoid, stigmatic area apical or subapical, usually 3–(1–2–) seeded, (4 carpels often present); epicarp smooth, mesocarp fleshy, endocarp comprising 3 separate pyrenes, hard, tanniniferous, pyrenes obovoid, variously ridged and sculptured, sculpturing diagnostic for species. Seed almond-shaped, smooth, basally attached, endosperm homogeneous; embryo apical. Germination remote-tubular; eophyll digitate. $n = 14$ (L. lontaroides as L. commersonii, Sharma and Sarkar 1957; L. loddigesii, L. lontaroides, L. verschaffeltii, Read 1966).

Anatomy.—Leaf (Tomlinson 1961), floral (Uhl and Moore 1971, only gynoecium studied).

Distribution.—Three species in the Mascarene Islands.

Ecology.—Once common on coastal cliffs, savannahs, and ravines, the species are now almost extinct in the wild, but are widely cultivated in botanic gardens where they appear to hybridize freely. Some native trees of *L. loddigesii* are present on Round Island. *Latania lontaroides* endemic to Réunion is occasionally left in fields as isolated individuals. *L. verschaffeltii*, endemic and widespread on Rodrigues, is reduced to isolated individuals and a small population at Fond la Bonté above Baie aux Huites. There may be a few native *L. loddigesii* remaining on Mauritius.

Common Names and Uses.—Latan palms, latanier. Leaves have been used as thatch and the trunk as a source of wood; the young seeds are said to be edible. All species are handsome ornamentals.

Notes.—*Latania* is remarkable for the diversity in the sculpturing of the pyrenes; however, the adaptive significance of the pyrene form is not known. Gynoecial structure is similar to that of *Corypha* and *Nannorrhops* but carpel walls are much thicker.

Taxonomic Account.—Moore and Guého (1984).

Plates.—10A, B, 39C; Figs. G.5, G.7.

35. BORASSUS Linnaeus, Species Plantarum 1187. 1753. Type: **B. flabellifer** Linnaeus.

Lontarus Adanson, Familles des Plantes 2:25, 572. 1763 (superfluous name).

Tall, robust, solitary, armed, pleonanthic, dioecious, tree palms. Stem massive, covered in a lattice of leaf bases abscising cleanly in older specimens, then rough, ringed with wide leaf scars. Leaves induplicate, strongly costapalmate; sheath open early in development, later with a wide triangular cleft at the base of the petiole; petiole deeply channeled adaxially, rounded abaxially, surfaces smooth to minutely rough, margins of sheath and petiole armed with coarse irregular teeth; adaxial hastula conspicuous, triangular or scalloped, abaxial hastula a low ridge (? always); blade suborbicular to flabellate, divided along adaxial folds to ca. ½ its length into regular, stiff single-fold segments, these shortly bifid, interfold filaments present or absent, surfaces smooth, ramenta or to-

→

35.—**Borassus. a,** portion of staminate axis in vertical section showing cincinni ×6; **b,** portion of staminate axis showing buds among overlapping bracts ×1½; **c,** staminate flower ×6; **d,** staminate flower in vertical section ×12; **e,** staminate calyx ×6; **f,** staminate receptacle and corolla ×6; **g,** staminate petal, interior view ×12; **h,** stamens in 3 views ×12; **i,** pistillode ×36; **j,** portion of pistillate axis × ½; **k,** pistillate flower and bracts × ½; **l,** pistillate flower × ½; **m,** pistillate flower in vertical section × ½; **n,** pistillate sepal × ½; **o,** pistillate flower, sepals removed × ½; **p,** pistillate petal and staminode, interior view × ½; **q,** gynoecium and staminodes × ½; **r,** ovary in cross-section ×1½; **s,** ovule ×3; **t,** fruit with perianth × ½; **u,** 2-seeded fruit in cross-section × ½; **v,** pyrene (endocarp) × ½; **w, x, y,** seed in 3 views × ½; **z,** seed in vertical section × ½. Borassus aethiopum: **a-i,** Tomlinson s.n.; B. flabellifer: **j-z,** Read 819.

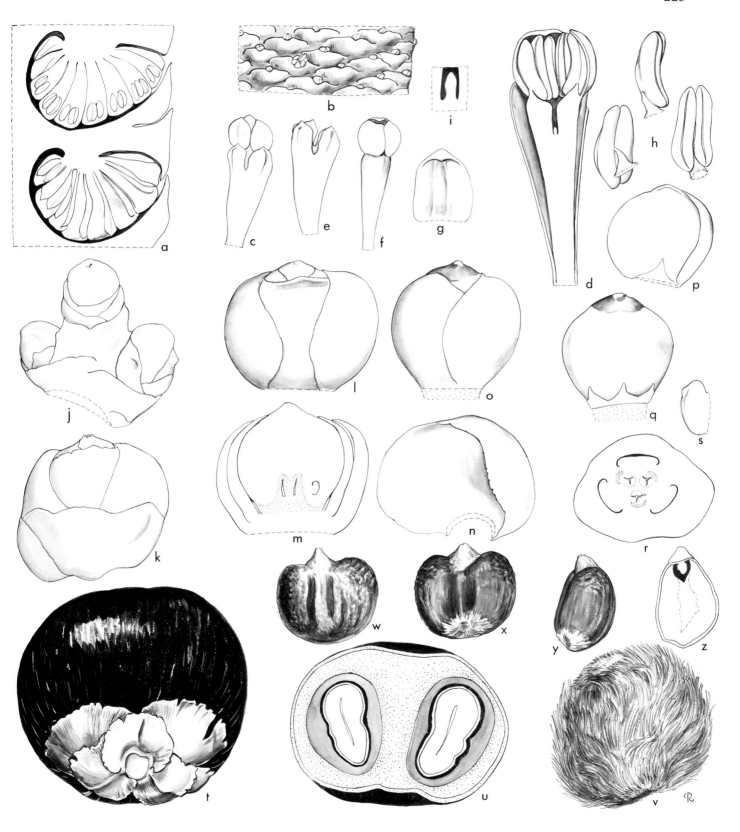

mentum along abaxial costa and ridges of folds, midribs prominent abaxially, transverse veinlets conspicuous, short, numerous. Inflorescences interfoliar, shorter than the leaves, the staminate and pistillate dissimilar; staminate inflorescence branched to 2 orders; peduncle very short; prophyll 2-keeled, with long tubular base, limb short, pointed, variously split apically; peduncular bracts lacking (?); rachis also short, rachis bracts similar to the prophyll; first-order branches long, flattened, each bearing a prophyll and branched digitately into several (1–3) rachillae; rachillae large, catkinlike, elongate, bearing spirally arranged, imbricate bracts, connate laterally and distally to form large pits, each containing a reflexed cincinnus of ca. 30 staminate flowers, exserted singly in succession from the pit mouth. Staminate flowers each subtended by a long membranous bracteole; sepals 3, asymmetrical, connate only basally or to ⅔ their length, distinct lobes keeled, elongate, membranous, stiff; corolla with a long stalklike base and 3 short, rounded lobes, ridged adaxially; stamens 6, filaments short, triangular, anthers medifixed, elongate, latrorse; pollen elliptic, monosulcate, with verrucate, tectate exine, finely reticulate between the warts; pistillode small, conical. Pistillate inflorescence unbranched or with a single first-order branch; peduncle short; prophyll tubular, pointed, 2-keeled, split ventrally about ½ its length; peduncular bracts few (2 or more?), if present as long as or longer than the peduncle; rachilla massive, bearing large cupular bracts, the first few empty, the subsequent each subtending a single pistillate flower, several empty bracts above the flowers. Pistillate flowers large, each bearing 2 lateral cuplike, rounded, leathery, bracteoles; sepals 3 distinct, imbricate, thick, rounded; petals 3, similar to sepals; staminodes triangular, connate basally in a low cupule, sterile anthers present or not; gynoecium rounded, tricarpellate, with a central, basal septal nectary, stylar region hemispherical, stigma a low knob, carpels each with a basal, orthotropous ovule, and 2 lateral bodies, perhaps vestigial ovules. Fruit large, rounded, sometimes wider than long, bearing 1–3 seeds, stigmatic remains apical, perianth enlarged, persistent; epicarp smooth, mesocarp thick, fibrous, often fragrant, endocarp comprising 3 hard bony pyrenes. Seed shallowly to deeply bilobed, pointed, basally attached, endosperm homogeneous with a central hollow; embryo apical. Germination remote-tubular; eophyll undivided, elliptical. $n = 18$ (*B. flabellifer*, Sharma and Sarkar 1957, Rangasamy and Devasahayam 1971, Read 1966).

Anatomy. — Leaf (Tomlinson 1961).

Distribution. — Seven species have been recognized but probably only three or four can be maintained. They occur in Africa, Madagascar, northeastern Arabia, through India and Southeast Asia to New Guinea and Australia.

Ecology. — *Borassus* is one of the most widespread palms. *B. flabellifer* can occur in some mountain districts of India at elevations of 500–800 m, and is also found on banks of rivers. It is most abundant, however, on low sandy plains near sea level where exposed to sun and winds. In Africa, *B. aethiopum* occurs in open secondary forest and savannah.

Fossil Record. — A seed, Upper Senonian (Monteillet and Lappartient 1981), seems very questionable.

Common Names and Uses. — Toddy or wine palm, lontar, palmyra, or siwalan (*B. flabellifer*). *B. flabellifer* is one of the most extensively used palms. Leaves have been used for writing; wood is valuable for building; inflorescences are tapped and the syrup, sugar, or alcohol may be a staple (Fox 1977).

Notes. — Can be recognized by the large stiff costapalmate leaves with both adaxial and abaxial hastulae, and by the large irregular teeth on the petiole.

Taxonomic Account. — Beccari (1924).

Plate. — *39D; Figs. G.7, G.16, G.18, G.20.*

36. **LODOICEA** Commerson ex De Candolle, Bulletin des Sciences, par la Société Philomatique 2(46): 171. 1800. Lectotype *L. callypige* Commerson ex Jaume Saint Hilaire = **L. maldivica** (Gmelin) Persoon (*Cocos maldivica* Gmelin).

Robust, often tall, solitary, unarmed, pleonanthic, dioecious, tree palm. Stem erect, slightly expanded at the base, inconspicuously ringed with leaf scars. Leaves induplicate, costapalmate, marcescent, later abscising under their own weight; sheath soon splitting opposite the petiole and a triangular cleft developing at the petiole base; petiole robust, deeply channeled adaxially, rounded abaxially, abaxial surface with minute black dots, irregularly tomentose, margins fibrous basally, rough to smooth distally; hastulae absent; costa long, tapering, reaching nearly to the end of the blade; blade about as long as the petiole, stiff, basally wedge-shaped, divided ca. ¼ to ⅓ its length into single-fold segments, these shortly bifid, free ends often drooping, adaxial surface shiny, smooth, dull abaxially with thick indumentum along abaxial ridges, midribs

→

36. — **Lodoicea. a,** portion of staminate axis at anthesis × 1½; **b,** portion of staminate axis in vertical section to show arrangement of flowers and bracts × 1½; **c,** staminate flower × 3; **d,** staminate flower in vertical section × 3; **e,** staminate calyx × 3; **f,** staminate flower, calyx removed × 3; **g,** stamen in 3 views × 6; **h,** pistillode × 6; **i,** portion of pistillate axis with flower × ⅓; **j, k,** bracts subtending pistillate flower (removed) in 2 views × ⅜; **l,** pistillate flower × ⅓; **m,** pistillate flower in vertical section × ⅓; **n, o, p,** pistillate sepals, outer, middle, and inner, interior views × ⅓; **q,** pistillate petals and staminodial ring from above, pistil removed × ⅓; **r,** pistillate petal and staminodial ring portion, interior view × ⅓; **s,** gynoecium × ⅓; **t,** ovary in cross-section × ⅔; **u,** portion of ovary with locule and ovule in vertical section × 2; **v,** ovule × 6; **w,** fruit × ⅙; **x,** pyrene in two views × ⅙; **y,** pyrene showing seed in vertical section through groove × ⅙; **z,** pyrene and seed in vertical section × ⅙. *Lodoicea maldivica:* **a–h,** *Read 1488;* **i–z,** *Moore s.n.*

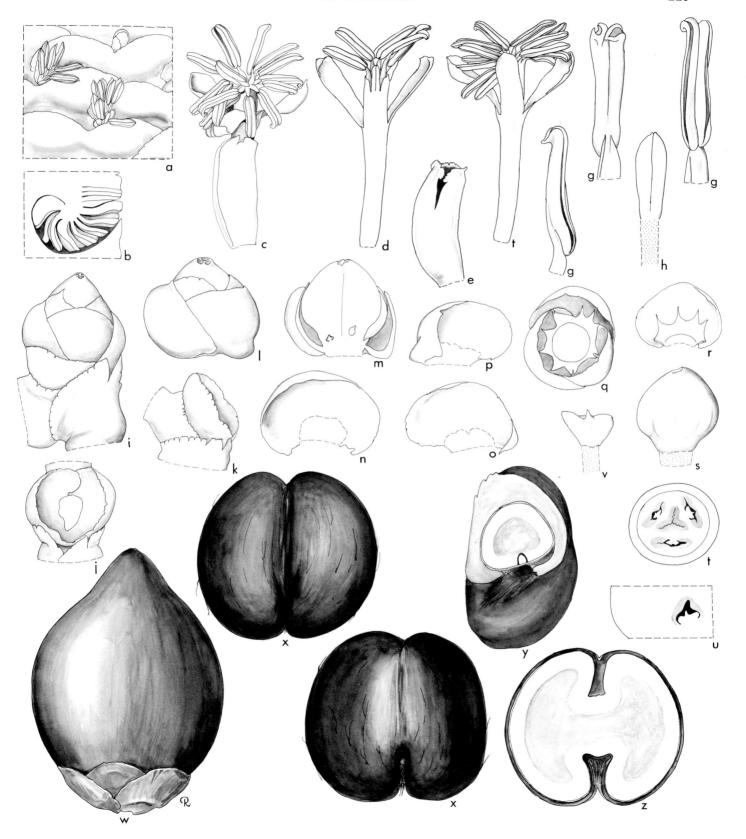

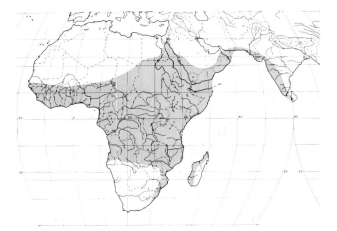

Map 10.—**Distribution of Hyphaeninae.**

prominent abaxially, transverse veinlets long, conspicuous. Inflorescences interfoliar, massive, shorter than the
leaves, pendulous, staminate and pistillate markedly dissimilar; staminate inflorescence with short, narrow peduncle, often unbranched, ridged, terminating in a single
rachilla or 2–3 digitately arranged rachillae; prophyll short,
2-keeled throughout its length, split ventrally but with a
long closed triangular tip; peduncular bracts 1 (or more?),
obscuring the peduncle, completely tubular, split ventrally
above the center leaving a long solid pointed beak; rachillae massive, catkinlike, bearing several large empty,
imbricate cuplike bracts basally, above these bearing spirally inserted, very tough leathery bracts, connate laterally
and distally to form large pits, each containing a recurved
cincinnus of 60–70 staminate flowers. Staminate flowers
each bearing a fibrous bracteole; sepals 3, connate in an
asymmetrical tube, tips distinct, imbricate, irregular; corolla with a long stalklike base and 3 elongate lobes, unequal in width, not closed laterally around the androecium, tips of lobes thick, rounded, imbricate; stamens 17–
22, borne on the surface of an elongate receptacle, filaments short, wide, variously angled, anthers elongate, tips
reflexed, latrorse; pollen elliptic, monosulcate, with foveolate, tectate exine; pistillode columnar, trifid. Pistillate
inflorescence unbranched with prophyll and 2(–3 or several?), tubular peduncular bracts, split ventrally, with long
pointed tips like those of the staminate inflorescence; rachilla a direct extension of and about as long as the peduncle, short, wide, zigzag, tapered distally, bearing several empty incompletely sheathing, cupular bracts,
subsequent bracts completely sheathing, large, each subtending a pistillate flower. Pistillate flowers, the largest
flowers in the palms, each sessile, ovoid, bearing at the
base 2 lateral, large, cupulate bracteoles; sepals 3, distinct,
imbricate, leathery, rounded, thicker basally; petals 3, as
sepals; staminodes triangular, low, briefly connate basally
with several (–11) pointed tips; gynoecium ovoid, tricarpellate, trilocular with a central trilobed septal nectary,
stylar regions wide, triangular, fibrous, stigmas 3, short,
becoming reflexed, ovules beaked, apparently orthotropous, laterally winged and with 2 lateral bodies, perhaps
vestigial ovules. Fruit very large, ovoid and pointed, 1(–3)-

seeded; epicarp smooth, mesocarp fibrous, endocarp comprising one to three 2-lobed, thick, hard pyrenes. Seed,
the largest known, 2-lobed, endosperm thick, relatively
hard, hollow, homogeneous; embryo apical in the sinus
between the 2 lobes. Germination remote-tubular, tube
remarkably long, reported to reach ca. 4 m; eophyll shallowly lobed. $n = 17$ (Read 1966). $n = 18$ (as *L. callipyge*,
Sarkar 1970).

Anatomy.—Leaf (Tomlinson 1961).

Distribution.—One species in the Seychelles Islands.

Ecology.—*Lodoicea* today is restricted to hill
slopes and valleys of Praslin and Curieuse but formerly may have occurred on adjacent islets. It does
not reach coastal plateaus or main ridges.

Common Names and Uses.—Coco-de-Mer or
double coconut. Leaves are used locally as thatch
and plaiting, wood as palisades and water-troughs,
seeds for dishes and vegetable ivory, and down from
young leaves for stuffing pillows. The sale of nuts
to tourists is an important source of revenue.

Notes.—Recognizable by the huge, more or less
diamond-shaped leaf in juvenile stages, by the lack
of hastulae on both surfaces, and when present, by
the huge and bizarre inflorescences, flowers, fruits,
and seeds. Important historically because of the
many legends involving the huge seeds, and as an
oddity.

Taxonomic Account.—Bailey (1942).
Plates.—10D, 40A.

Hyphaeninae Beccari, Palme della Tribù Borasseae
1. 1924 ('*Hyphaeneae*'). Type: **Hyphaene.**

Staminate and pistillate rachillae similar; pistillate flowers pedicellate; pits of both sexes filled with hairs; fruit
1-seeded or 2–3-seeded and then 2–3-lobed; stigmatic remains basal or central between the lobes.

The three genera of this subtribe are closely related (Map 10). *Bismarckia* is endemic to Madagascar, *Hyphaene* is widely distributed in Africa,
Madagascar, and Arabia with one or possibly two
species just reaching the Indian subcontinent; *Medemia*, last seen in 1964 in the Sudan, may well be
extinct. The genera differ largely in details of the
fruits. Pyrenes are not formed; epicarp, mesocarp,
and endocarp develop more or less separately in
each carpel resulting in a lobed fruit if more than
one carpel matures. In *Bismarckia* the endocarp is
irregularly ridged and pitted within and the endosperm is homogeneous; in *Medemia* the endocarp
is thinner and not ridged but the endosperm is ruminate, while in *Hyphaene* the fruits have unridged
endocarps and homogeneous endosperm.

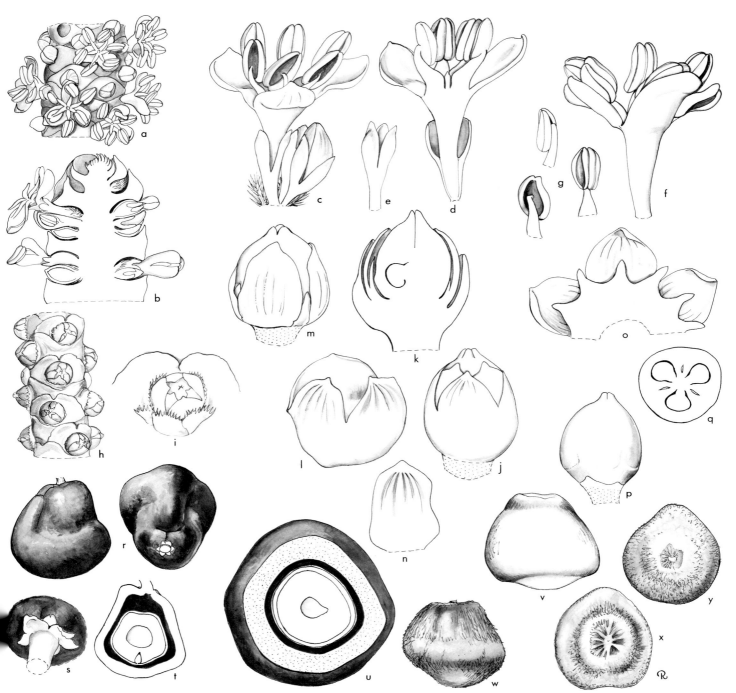

37.—**Hyphaene. a,** portion of staminate rachilla ×1½; **b,** portion of staminate rachilla in vertical section ×3; **c,** staminate flower and buds ×6; **d,** staminate flower in vertical section ×6; **e,** staminate calyx ×6; **f,** staminate flower, calyx removed ×6; **g,** stamen in 3 views ×6; **h,** portion of pistillate rachilla ×1½; **i,** pistillate flower and bracts ×3; **j,** pistillate flower ×3; **k,** pistillate flower in vertical section ×3; **l,** pistillate calyx ×3; **m,** pistillate flower, calyx removed ×3; **n,** pistillate petal ×3; **o,** pistillate corolla and staminodes, interior view, expanded ×3; **p,** gynoecium ×3; **q,** ovary in cross-section ×3; **r,** fruit in 2 views ×½; **s,** base of fruit ×1½; **t,** fruit in vertical section ×½; **u,** fruit in cross-section ×1; **v,** endocarp ×1; **w, x, y,** seed in 3 views ×1. *Hyphaene coriacea*: all from *Read 720.*

37. HYPHAENE J. Gaertner, De Fructibus et Seminibus Plantarum 1:28. 1788. Type: **H. coriacea** J. Gaertner.

Cucifera Delile, Description de l'Égypte. Histoire Naturelle 1:53. 1809. Type: *C. thebaica* Delile (illegitimate names).

Douma Poiret in Duhamel du Monceau, Traite des Arbres et Arbustes (ed. 2) 4:47. 1809. Type: *D. thebaica* Poiret (=*H. thebaica* (Linnaeus) Martius).

Doma Poiret in Lamarck, Tableau Encyclopédique et Methodique. Illustration des Genres 4:t900. 1819 (orthographic variant of *Douma*).

Dwarf to large, solitary or clustered, spiny, pleonanthic, dioecious, acaulescent, creeping, shrubby or tree palms. Stem closely ringed with slightly raised leaf scars, usually branching several times by equal forking (dichotomy), rarely unbranched, and then sometimes the trunk ventricose; trunk surface in juveniles with a lattice of old leaf bases, later becoming bare. Leaves induplicate, costapalmate, marcescent, later abscising under their own weight; sheath soon becoming open, densely tomentose, later with a conspicuous triangular cleft below the petiole, margins fibrous; petiole robust, covered in caducous indumentum, adaxially channeled, abaxially rounded, the margins armed with robust, triangular, reflexed or upward pointing spines; adaxial hastula well developed, often asymmetrical, abaxial hastula absent; blade divided to about ⅓ its length along the adaxial ribs into single-fold segments, these further shallowly divided along the abaxial ribs; interfold filaments often conspicuous; blade surfaces frequently glaucous with abundant wax, and also bearing minute dotlike scales and caducous indumentum, particularly along the ribs, midrib prominent, longitudinal veins close, transverse veinlets inconspicuous. Inflorescences interfoliar, the staminate and pistillate basically similar, though the pistillate more robust and with fewer branches; peduncle bearing a basal, 2-keeled, tubular prophyll and usually 2 empty, tubular peduncular bracts with triangular limbs, bearing abundant caducous indumentum when young; rachis longer than the peduncle; rachis bracts like the peduncular but each subtending a first-order branch; first-order branches basally bare, semicircular in cross-section, ± included in the subtending bract, terminating, in the staminate inflorescence, in a group of 1–6 or rarely more rachillae, each subtended by a low bract, in the pistillate inflorescence terminating in 1–3 rachillae; rachillae catkinlike, bearing a tight spiral of rounded, densely hairy, striate bracts, connate laterally and partially adnate to the axis to produce pits, densely filled with a pile of hairs. Staminate flowers borne in a cincinnus of 3 flowers, embedded in the hairs, one flower emerging at a time, each bearing a small membranous bracteole; calyx tubular at the base with 3 elongate hooded, membranous lobes; corolla with a conspicuous stalklike base almost as large as the calyx lobes, bearing at its tip 3 ovate, hooded, valvate, striate lobes; stamens 6, borne at the base of the lobes, the filaments ± connate at their swollen bases, tapering above, anthers medifixed, versatile, latrorse to introrse; pollen ± elliptic, monosulcate, with verrucate, tectate exine, finely reticulate between the warts; pistillode

minute, 3-lobed. Pistillate flowers borne singly with a bracteole in each pit, on a short densely hairy pedicel, the pedicel sometimes considerably elongating after fertilization; sepals 3, distinct, rounded, imbricate, ± membranous, striate; petals 3, similar to sepals; staminodial ring epipetalous, 6-toothed, the teeth bearing sagittate, flattened, empty anthers; gynoecium globose, tricarpellate, triovulate, stigmas 3, short, septal nectaries present, opening by pores distally, ovules orthotropous, attached adaxially at the base of each carpel. Fruit borne on enlarged pedicel with persistent perianth segments, normally developing from 1 carpel, rarely 2 or 3, the fruit then 2- or 3-lobed, with basal stigmatic remains, the whole fruit very variable in shape, shouldered, distally expanded, usually asymmetrical, rarely ovoid or spherical; epicarp smooth, dull or shining, often pitted with lenticels, colored various shades of brown, mesocarp fibrous, often aromatic, dry but sweet, endocarp well developed, hard, stony. Seed basally attached, endosperm homogeneous with a central hollow; embryo apical opposite a thinner area of the endocarp. Germination remote-tubular; eophyll simple, lanceolate, plicate. n = 18 (*H. crinita*, Eichhorn 1957, Sarkar 1970; *H. dichotoma* as *H. indica*, Sarkar et al. 1978; *H. coriacea* as *H. schatan*, Read 1964, and as *H. wendlandii*, Satô 1946; *H. thebaica*, Sarkar 1970).

Anatomy.—Leaf (Tomlinson 1961).

Distribution.—Numerous names have been published, but there are probably only about ten species distributed in the drier parts of Africa southwards to Natal, Madagascar, Red Sea and Gulf of Eilat coasts, coastal Arabia, and west coast of India. One species recorded for Sri Lanka may be an introduction.

Ecology.—*Hyphaene* species tend to grow in arid or semiarid areas, in habitats where ground water is near the surface, e.g. along seasonal water courses, coastal sand dunes and flats, and oases. In east Africa, *H. compressa* can be found inland at altitudes up to 1400 m above sea level. All species seem to be used by man, thus their distribution has been much influenced by destructive harvesting and accidental or deliberate planting. Elephants and baboons, among other wild animals, are responsible for seed dispersal. Bees have been observed visiting the flowers.

Fossil Record.—Subfossil fruits are found in ancient Egyptian sites. Shete and Kulkarni (1980) describe a petiole, *Palmocaulon hyphaeneoides* from Tertiary, probably Eocene, Deccan Intertrappean beds of India as showing many similarities to petioles of *H. indica* (=*H. dichotoma*).

Common Names and Uses.—Doum palms. The doum palms are locally very important, particularly to subsistence farmers. The leaves are used for thatch and as a source of fiber for plaiting. The apex is often semidestructively tapped to make palm wine. Wood can be used. The fruits provide an edible

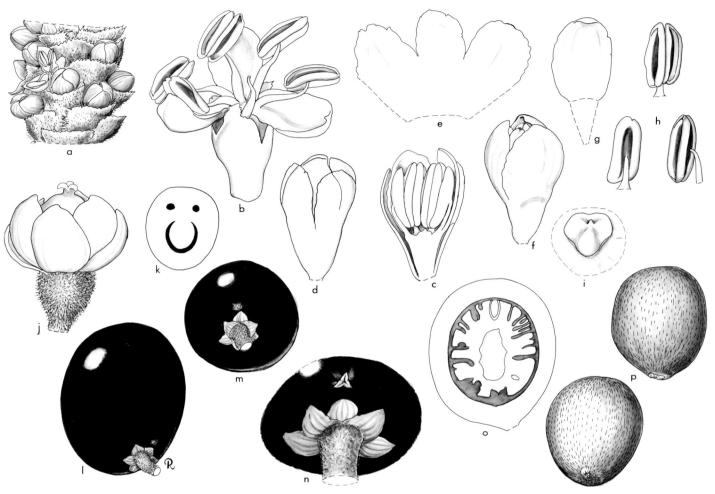

38.—**Medemia. a,** portion of staminate rachilla × 3; **b,** staminate flower × 7½; **c,** staminate flower in vertical section × 7½; **d,** staminate calyx × 7½; **e,** staminate calyx, expanded × 7½; **f,** staminate flower, calyx removed × 7½; **g,** staminate petal × 7½; **h,** stamen in 3 views × 9; **i,** pistillode × 12; **j,** pistillate flower, magnification unknown; **k,** ovary in cross-section, magnification unknown; **l,** fruit × 1; **m,** base of fruit × 1; **n,** base of fruit with stigmatic remains × 2¼; **o,** fruit in vertical section × 1; **p,** seed in 2 views × 1. *Medemia argun:* **a-i** and **l-o,** *Talbot s.n.*; **j** and **k** redrawn from Beccari (1924); **p,** *d'Albertis s.n.*

mesocarp and an endosperm, edible when young, but formerly used when mature as a source of vegetable ivory. All fallen parts of the palms are used as fuel.

Notes.—Distinguished by the elongate costapalmate leaf, often silvery, by the lack of an abaxial hastula, by petiolar spines, and by the frequent presence of dichotomous branching, long, more or less slender inflorescences, and distinctive brown fruits.

Taxonomic Account.—Beccari (1924).

Plate.—40B; *Figs. G.2, G.8, G.21.*

38. **MEDEMIA** Wuerttemberg ex H. A. Wendland, Botanische Zeitung 39:90, 93. 1881. Type: **M. argun** (Martius) Wuerttemberg ex H. A. Wendland (*Hyphaene argun* Martius).

Robust, solitary, unarmed, pleonanthic, dioecious, tree palm. Stem erect, ringed with close leaf scars. Leaves induplicate, costapalmate, marcescent, or falling under their own weight; leaf sheath? (no material available); petiole well developed, flattened adaxially, rounded abaxially, the margins smooth, unarmed; hastulae absent; costa short, more conspicuous abaxially than adaxially; blade divided ± regularly along adaxial folds to ca. ⅔ its length into single-fold segments, these further divided for a very short distance along abaxial folds, interfold filaments persistent at the adaxial sinuses, surfaces ± glaucous, with scattered dotlike scales, particularly along the ribs on the abaxial surface, longitudinal veins crowded, transverse veinlets obscure. Inflorescences interfoliar, becoming pendulous; prophyll and peduncular bracts, if any, not seen; rachis bracts tubular, with scattered caducous scales, and a long triangular limb; first-order branches ± pendulous, devoid of bracts except at the tip, margins sharp, the surfaces bearing scattered caducous scales, staminate inflorescence with first-order branches bearing at their tips 1–7 digitately displayed rachillae, in the pistillate bearing a single rachilla; rachillae catkinlike, bearing a tight spiral of rounded, densely hairy, imbricate bracts, connate laterally and to the axis to produce pits, filled with a dense pile of hairs. Staminate flowers borne in 3's, each bearing a spathulate membranous bracteole included within the pit, the flowers exserted and exposed one by one from the pit; calyx stalklike at the base with 3 narrow, spathulate, membranous, striate lobes with irregular margins; corolla with a conspicuous stalklike base almost as long as the calyx lobes, bearing at its tip 3 oblong, membranous, striate, ± circular lobes; stamens 6, borne at the base of the corolla lobes, filaments elongate, tapering, anthers medifixed, apparently versatile, latrorse; pollen elliptic, monosulcate, with areolate, tectate exine; pistillode 3-lobed, small. Pistillate flowers solitary, borne on a short, densely hairy pedicel, lengthening after fertilization; sepals 3, distinct, imbricate, obtuse, broad, membranous, glabrous, striate; petals 3, similar to the sepals; staminodes(?); gynoecium globose, with 3 eccentric, short, recurved stigmas, ovule probably orthotropous. Fruit ovoid, borne on the elongate pedicel, usually developed from only 1 carpel, rarely from 2 and then bilobed, with basal stigmatic remains, perianth whorls persistent; epicarp smooth, shiny, marked with scattered lenticels, mesocarp moderate, apparently ± dry at maturity, with ± radiating short fibers embedded in soft parenchyma, endocarp rather thin, crustaceous. Seed basally attached, ± broad, ellipsoidal, endosperm with a central hollow, conspicuously ruminate, the ruminations radial; embryo apical. Germination remote-tubular; eophyll entire, lanceolate. Cytology not studied.

Anatomy. — Leaf (Tomlinson 1961).

Distribution. — Apparently monotypic, in Egyptian Nubia and northeastern Sudan. Two species have been described, *M. argun* and *M. abiadensis,* the latter differing in its smaller fruit. Boulos (1968) records variation in fruit size in Egypt and most authors have, since Beccari, accepted one species only, *M. argun.* This palm was well known to the ancient Egyptians. Kunth named subfossil remains as *Areca passalacquae* (Kunth 1826); although it seems almost certain this name refers to fruits of *M. argun* and is an earlier name than *Hyphaene argun,* it may be disregarded as a *nomen nudum,* notes provided by Kunth being insufficient to describe the palm.

Ecology. — In desert oases.

Fossil Record. — Subfossil fruits are present in ancient Egyptian graves.

Common Names and Uses. — Medemia or Argun palm. *Medemia* may have had the same range of uses as *Hyphaene* (Johnson 1985); over-exploitation probably accounts for its extreme rarity.

Notes. — *Medemia argun* has not been recorded in the living state since 1964 (Boulos 1968). It appears to be on the verge of extinction if not already extinct. It would probably thrive as an ornamental in the dry subtropics. The lack of a hastula is particularly noteworthy. Its closest relatives are *Hyphaene* and *Bismarckia.*

Taxonomic Account. — Beccari (1924).

Plate. — *41A.*

39. BISMARCKIA Hildebrandt & H. A. Wendland, Botanische Zeitung 39:90, 93. 1881. Type: **B. nobilis** Hildebrandt & H. A. Wendland.

Robust, solitary, unarmed, pleonanthic, dioecious, tree palm. Stem erect, irregularly ringed with close leaf scars, becoming swollen basally. Leaves induplicate, costapalmate, marcescent in immature individuals, neatly abscising under their own weight in mature trunked individuals; sheath laterally ridged at the base, with a conspicuous triangular cleft below the petiole, with rows of scales in patches, petiole robust, adaxially channeled near the base, distally ± flattened, abaxially rounded, the surfaces grayish white, densely covered in white wax and patches of reddish, fringed caducous scales, the margins smooth; adaxial hastula often very large, distinctly lopsided, abaxial hastula absent; blade divided to ca. ¼–⅓ its length along adaxial folds into regular, stiff, single-fold segments, these further shortly bifid, interfold filaments conspicuous, surfaces obscurely striate, densely covered with wax, and along the folds with caducous scales, transverse veinlets not visible. Inflorescence interfoliar, solitary, shorter than the leaves, the staminate and pistillate similar; peduncle ± rounded in cross-section; prophyll short, 2-keeled, included in subtending sheath; peduncular bracts several, tubular, rather loosely sheathing, with a broad, split triangular limb, sometimes strongly keeled, and covered with caducous scales and wax; rachis longer than the peduncle; rachis bracts like the peduncular, decreasing in size distally; first-order branches crescent-shaped in cross-section, longer than the subtending bract, not bearing a prophyll, branching at the tip to produce a group of 3–7 radiating, catkinlike rachillae, the group sometimes reduced to 1; staminate rachillae usually more numerous than the pistillate, slightly sinuous, bearing a tight spiral of rounded, densely hairy, striate bracts, connate laterally and partially adnate to the axis to produce pits, densely filled with hairs, pistillate rachillae usually more massive than the staminate, each bract subtending a solitary flower. Staminate flowers borne in a cincinnus of 3, embedded in the hairs, one flower emerging at a time, each bearing a membranous bracteole; calyx tubular, membranous, with 3 short, rather irregular lobes distally; corolla with a stalklike base almost as long as the calyx lobes, bearing at its tip 3 ovate, hooded, valvate lobes; stamens 6, borne at the base of the corolla lobes, the filaments elongate, briefly united at the base, gradually tapering, anthers medifixed, versatile, latrorse; pollen elliptic, monosulcate, with areolate, tectate exine; pistillode short, conical. Pistillate flowers solitary, borne on a short hairy pedicel, the pedicel greatly elongating in fruit; sepals 3, imbricate, rounded,

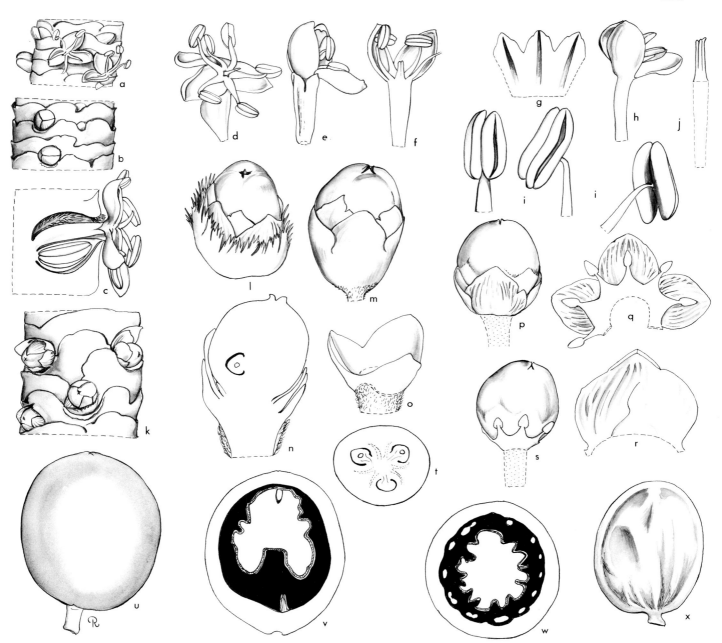

39.—**Bismarckia. a,** portion of staminate rachilla with flowers at anthesis ×3; **b,** portion of staminate rachilla with buds ×3; **c,** portion of staminate rachilla in vertical section with flower and bud ×6; **d, e,** staminate flower in 2 views ×6; **f,** staminate flower in vertical section ×6; **g,** staminate calyx, expanded ×6; **h,** staminate flower, calyx removed ×6; **i,** stamen in 3 views ×12; **j,** pistillode ×12; **k,** portion of pistillate rachilla in flower ×3; **l,** pistillate flower and bracteoles ×6; **m,** pistillate flower ×6; **n,** pistillate flower in vertical section ×6; **o,** pistillate calyx ×6; **p,** pistillate flower, calyx removed ×6; **q,** pistillate corolla and staminodes, interior view, expanded ×6; **r,** pistillate petal, interior view ×12; **s,** gynoecium and staminodes ×6; **t,** ovary in cross-section ×6; **u,** fruit ×1; **v,** fruit in vertical section ×1; **w,** fruit in cross-section ×1; **x,** endocarp ×1. *Bismarckia nobilis*: **a-j,** *Read 808*; **k-t,** *Moore 9597*; **u-x,** *M. R. Sheehan s.n.*

briefly connate basally; petals smaller than the sepals, 3, triangular, briefly connate at the base; staminodes united by their flattened triangular filaments to form a ring with 6 teeth, tipped with flattened empty, sagittate anthers; gynoecium tricarpellate, rounded, tipped with 3 low, slightly reflexed stigmas, septal nectaries present, ovule orthotropous with 2 lateral bodies, attached adaxially at the base. Fruit usually developing from 1 carpel, ± ellipsoidal, ovoid or rounded, the stigmatic remains and abortive carpels basal, the abortive carpels often enlarging to form 2 swellings; epicarp smooth, shiny, rich brown, somewhat speckled with lighter brown, mesocarp fibrous, ± aromatic, endocarp thick, irregularly flanged and pitted, and with a conspicuous central intrusion at the base. Seed basally attached, endosperm homogeneous, but grooved to match the endocarp intrusions; embryo apical. Germination remote-tubular; eophyll simple, strap-shaped. $n = 18$ (Read 1964).

Anatomy.—Leaf (Tomlinson 1961).

Distribution.—One species in the drier parts of Madagascar.

Ecology.—*B. nobilis* occurs as a conspicuous component of savannahs in the western part of Madagascar.

Common Names and Uses.—Bismarck palm. The trunk is used whole or split for house construction and the leaves for thatch. The pith of the trunk produces a rather bitter sago. Outside Madagascar *Bismarckia* is a highly regarded ornamental for the drier tropics and subtropics.

Notes.—Somewhat resembles *Hyphaene* in leaf anatomy but hypodermal layers and fibers are less developed. Distinguished by stiff, whitish, waxy, costapalmate leaves, with large adaxial hastula and petiole with smooth margins. The internal structure of the fruit and seed distinguish it from *Medemia,* in which the genus has sometimes been included.

Taxonomic Account.—Beccari (1924).

Plates.—40C, D; Fig. G.17.

II CALAMOIDEAE

CALAMOIDEAE Griffith, Calcutta Journal of Natural History 5:4. 1844.

Hermaphroditic, monoecious, dioecious, or polygamous; hapaxanthic or pleonanthic; often fiercely armed; leaves pinnate, pinnately ribbed, or rarely palmate, reduplicate; inflorescence often highly branched, frequently displaying adnation, the bracts of all orders usually tubular; flowers almost always borne in dyads or dyad derivatives, unisexual flowers only slightly dimorphic; ovary and fruit covered in reflexed scales, usually arranged in neat vertical rows; ovary incompletely trilocular, ovules basal, anatropous, with the micropyles facing the center of the gynoecium; pericarp usually thin at maturity, endocarp not differentiated (except in *Eugeissona*); seeds 1–3, usually with a thick sarcotesta.

This subfamily is equivalent to the lepidocaryoid major group of Moore (1973a). Unfortunately the name "Lepidocaryoideae," familiar to many, has had to be changed to "Calamoideae," for there is no doubt that Griffith's (1844) use of Calamoideae as a subfamily predates any use of Lepidocaryoideae at the same rank.

The subfamily (Map 11) has 22 genera including the largest genus, *Calamus,* and almost a quarter of all species in the Palmae. Only four genera, *Mauritia, Mauritiella, Lepidocaryum,* and *Raphia,* are found in the New World; the others and also *Raphia* occur in the Old World where they are most abundant in the eastern tropics from Sri Lanka, India, and China to the Fiji Islands and Western Samoa. The Calamoideae occur in areas of high rainfall and are especially frequent in swampy regions where some, such as *Mauritia, Metroxylon,* and *Raphia,* may form extensive pure stands.

Members of the subfamily can be immediately distinguished by the closely overlapping scales which cover the ovaries and fruits. The scales are usually neatly arranged in vertical rows but in a few genera (e.g. *Eugeissona, Myrialepis,* and some species of *Salacca*) are small and rather irregular, and not in definite orthostichies and parastichies. The apparent orthostichies and parastichies are not phyllotactic spirals as once suggested (Eames 1961), but are epidermal appendages rather than foliar organs (Uhl and Moore 1971). The gynoecium, besides being scaly, has several other distinguishing features; the three carpels are connate but their ventral sutures are open and the partitions between the locules thus incomplete. The anatropous ovule in each carpel is unusual in being twisted on its funicle so that the micropyle faces the center of the gynoecium.

The subfamily is further characterized by spines and prickles of several forms. These may be along leaf margins, as for example in *Raphia,* or scattered or in rows on leaf sheaths. Root spines are present on the stems of some genera. Two types of whiplike climbing organ are found among the climbing genera (rattans). The cirrus is an extension of the leaf rachis bearing reflexed spines. In *Eremospatha, Laccosperma,* and *Oncocalamus,* the distalmost leaflets also are modified into reflexed hooks (acanthophylls), a specialization likewise present in the quite unrelated genus *Desmoncus.* In *Calamus* some species bear cirri but others lack cirri and bear flagella, which are modified inflorescences lacking flowers and branches and bearing dense reflexed spines on the tight, tubular peduncular bracts.

Within some characters there is astonishing variation. Stems are creeping, erect, or climbing, and solitary, clustered, or rarely (*Korthalsia*) branched aerially. Leaves are reduplicate but include both pinnate and palmate forms. Inflorescences are extremely variable, interfoliar in pleonanthic forms or aggregated in the axils of reduced leaves or bracts at the end of the stem when hapaxanthic; they may be large and profusely branched, small and with few branches, or catkinlike. Tubular inflorescence bracts are characteristic. The ultimate flower clusters are also distinctive. The basic unit is a dyad, a sympodial pair of flowers. In the simplest state (e.g. *Laccosperma* and *Eremospatha*) the dyad consists of a pair of hermaphrodite flowers. Several structurally different flower pairs in the subfamily appear to be derived from such a dyad (see Fig. I.6). The pair may consist of a staminate and a hermaphrodite flower or the plants may be dioecious with paired or solitary flowers in the staminate plant and a solitary pistillate flower with two bracteoles or a dyad consisting of a pistillate flower and a sterile staminate flower in the pistillate plant. In all genera where pairs of flowers do not occur there is some evidence of a dyadic origin of the floral unit, except in *Oncocalamus* where the flower cluster consists of one to three central pistillate flowers and two lateral cincinni of up to five staminate flowers each; this ar-

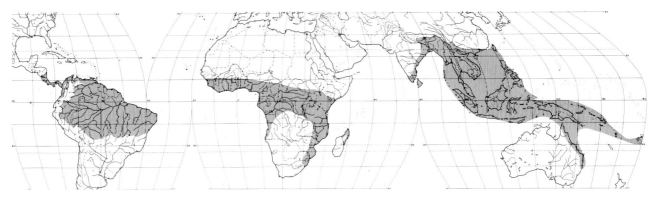

Map 11.—**Distribution of Calamoideae.**

rangement is unique in palms as a whole. The occurrence of a few triads is noteworthy. Triads of hermaphrodite flowers occur scattered through the otherwise dyadic units in the inflorescence of some species of *Laccosperma*. Different triads each consisting of a central sterile staminate flower and two lateral pistillate flowers are found in a few aberrant species of *Calamus*.

Hermaphroditic, staminate, and pistillate flowers are not markedly different. Like the gynoecium the perianth is rather uniform throughout; sepals are usually connate and tubular basally, petals are valvate and sometimes connate at the base. The androecium, however, is variable in both morphology and anatomy of stamen filaments. Polyandry also occurs in two genera, *Eugeissona* and *Raphia* (Uhl and Moore 1980, Uhl and Dransfield 1984). The chromosome complement where known is rather uniform, $n = 13$ or 14. Vegetative anatomy tends to be distinctive (Tomlinson 1961).

The subfamily exhibits a group of uniform characters but also shows considerable diversity. Although the greatest variability and number of species are in the Malesian region, the taxa with the simplest floral characters (*Laccosperma* and *Eremospatha*) occur in Africa. Indeed, the few African genera are very peculiar; *Laccosperma*, *Eremospatha*, and *Oncocalamus* have different inflorescences exhibiting a diversity which seems to suggest a much greater representation in Africa in the past (see Chapter IV). The long fossil record and the occurrence of unspecialized characters suggest that the subfamily diverged early, perhaps in parallel with the Coryphoideae, from a protopalm group. Its relationships with other subfamilies are not evident. Of interest is some similarity in gynoecial development and

structure to Phytelephantoideae (Uhl and Dransfield 1984).

Key to the Tribes of the Calamoideae

1 Leaves pinnate or pinnately ribbed; Old World palms (except for one species of *Raphia*) . . . . **Calameae**
1 Leaves palmate or briefly costapalmate; New World palms . . . . **Lepidocaryeae**

Key to the Subtribes of the Calameae

1 Flower group consisting of a dyad of hermaphroditic flowers . . . . **Ancistrophyllinae**
1 Flower group not consisting of a dyad of hermaphroditic flowers 2
2 Rachillae catkinlike, bearing either dyads of a hermaphroditic and a staminate flower, or single hermaphroditic flowers . . . . **Metroxylinae**
2 Rachillae usually not catkinlike (if so then hermaphroditic flowers lacking) 3
3 Polygamous palms, rachillae bearing single, apparently terminal dyads, each consisting of a hermaphroditic and a staminate flower, but only one flower evident at a time; stamens 20–70; fruit large with very small irregular scales and thick endocarp with 6 or 12 internal ridges . . . .
  . . . . **Eugeissoninae**
3 Monoecious or dioecious palms; rachillae various; stamens 6 except in *Raphia* where 6–30; fruit usually with regular scales and lacking an endocarp 4
4 Monoecious palms 5
4 Dioecious palms 6
5 Climbing palms bearing cirri with acanthophylls; rachilla bracts subtending groups of 3–11 flowers, the central pistillate, with two lateral cincinni bearing 0–1 basal pistillate flowers and several distal staminate flowers . **Oncocalaminae**
5 Massive acaulescent or tree palms; rachilla bracts subtending solitary flowers, the basal pistillate, the distal staminate . . . . **Raphiinae**
6 Pleonanthic, solitary, very tall tree palm; rachillae with minute bracts, in the staminate subtending a dyad of flowers, in the pistillate, solitary flowers . . . . **Pigafettinae**
6 Pleonanthic or hapaxanthic, acaulescent, shrubby or climbing palms; rachillae usually with conspicuous bracts 7

7 Hapaxanthic climbing palms, bracts of staminate rachillae subtending paired or solitary flowers, in pistillate rachillae solitary flowers only .... **Plectocomiinae**

7 Hapaxanthic (very rarely and then sterile staminate flowers present) or pleonanthic, climbing or acaulescent palms; staminate inflorescence with paired or solitary flowers; pistillate inflorescence bearing dyads of sterile staminate and pistillate flowers (except in *Salacca* section *Leiosalacca* and *Retispatha* where sterile staminate flower lacking) .... **Calaminae**

Key to the Genera of the Calamoideae

1 Leaves pinnate or, rarely, simply forked but with pinnate venation 2

1 Leaves palmate with usually numerous reduplicate segments 21

2 Flowers hermaphroditic, borne singly or in dyads or triads (climbing palms) 3

2 Polygamous, monoecious, or dioecious palms (climbing, acaulescent or treelike palms) 5

3 Pleonanthic rattan; rachilla bracts minute, incomplete; floral bracteoles absent; corolla tubular, very thick, with 3 short lobes; filaments united in a fleshy epipetalous ring. Africa .... 41. **Eremospatha**

3 Hapaxanthic rattans; rachilla bracts conspicuous, complete or incomplete; floral bracteoles present (but in *Korthalsia* concealed by hairs); corolla coriaceous, tubular at the base, with 3 boat-shaped lobes; filaments not united in a fleshy ring 4

4 Flowers in dyads, rarely in triads; rachilla bracts distichous, not filled with hairs; leaflets linear-lanceolate, entire. Africa .... 40. **Laccosperma**

4 Flowers solitary; rachilla bracts spiral, forming a tight catkin, usually filled with hairs; leaflets lanceolate to broad, diamond-shaped, praemorse. Southeast Asia and Malesia .... 44. **Korthalsia**

5 Polygamous palms; flowers borne in dyads of 1 hermaphroditic and 1 staminate 6

5 Monoecious or dioecious palms 7

6 Flowers very large, borne in a tight cupule of 7–11 overlapping bracts; petals ± woody, sharply pointed; stamens 20–70. Fruit ovoid, beaked, covered with minute scales; mesocarp fibrous; endocarp thick, woody, with 6 or 12 internal longitudinal flanges penetrating the seed. Malay Peninsula and Borneo .... 42. **Eugeissona**

6 Flowers small, each pair borne in the axil of a rachilla bract filled with hairs; petals neither woody nor spine-tipped; stamens 6. Fruit rounded, with large scales, not beaked; mesocarp thick, sparsely fibrous; endocarp lacking. Papuasia .... 43. **Metroxylon**

7 Monoecious palms 8

7 Dioecious palms 9

8 Climbing palm; flowers borne in clusters of ca. 5–11 in the axils of overlapping distichous bracts, the central 1 or 3 pistillate, the rest staminate in 2 lateral cincinni. Fruit ± rounded, small, covered with small scales. Africa .... 58. **Oncocalamus**

8 Massive acaulescent or tree palms; flowers solitary, each in the axil of a rachilla bract, the proximal on the rachillae pistillate accompanied by 2 bracteoles, the distal staminate accompanied by 1 bracteole, very rarely odd dyads present at the transition from staminate to pistillate. Fruit

very large with few large scales. Africa, Madagascar, Central America, and northern South America .... 57. **Raphia**

9 Pleonanthic, acaulescent palms; inflorescences short, in bud enclosed within the subtending leaf sheath, at anthesis emerging from a vertical groove on the abaxial surface of the sheath; terminal leaflets compound, or the whole leaf flabellate; rachillae of both sexes ± catkinlike. Southeast Asia to West Malesia .... 46. **Salacca**

9 Acaulescent, tree or climbing palms; inflorescences not emerging from a vertical groove on abaxial surface of sheath; terminal leaflets usually single-fold; rachillae catkinlike or not 10

10 Pistillate rachillae bearing dyads of one pistillate flower together with a sterile staminate flower (very rarely 2 pistillate and 1 sterile staminate); staminate rachillae bearing fertile staminate flowers, singly or in pairs ... 11

10 Pistillate rachillae bearing solitary flowers; staminate flowers solitary or paired 17

11 Acaulescent, hapaxanthic palm; rachillae catkinlike in both sexes; staminate flowers borne in pairs; seed with conspicuous wide chalazal pit and adherent sarcotesta. Thailand, Peninsular Malaysia, Sumatra, and Borneo . ... 45. **Eleiodoxa**

11 Acaulescent or climbing, hapaxanthic or pleonanthic palms. Rachillae very rarely catkinlike, if so then not in both sexes; staminate flowers borne singly 12

12 Entire inflorescence enclosed within the prophyll 13

12 Inflorescence not enclosed within the prophyll, or prophyll sheathing only the base of the inflorescence 15

13 Prophyll opening by a pair of pores near the apex, splitting along its length only after anthesis or accidentally. Malay Peninsula, Sumatra, Java, Borneo . 51. **Ceratolobus**

13 Prophyll splitting along its length at anthesis 14

14 Prophyll much larger than any other inflorescence bract; two erect earlike appendages (auricles) present at the mouth of the leaf sheath; climbing whips absent; endosperm homogeneous. Malay Peninsula, Borneo .... 50. **Pogonotium**

14 Prophyll enclosing a series of similar rachis bracts, but with their tips enfolded in the beak of the prophyll; auricles absent; cirrus almost always present; endosperm ruminate. India to New Guinea .... 47. **Daemonorops** (subgenus **Cymbospatha**)

15 Prophyll and rachis bracts splitting along their lengths to the very base, usually neatly falling at anthesis except for the prophyll which may persist long after anthesis; floral bracteoles usually low, often rather inconspicuous; endosperm always ruminate. India to New Guinea ... . 47. **Daemonorops** (subgenus **Piptospatha**)

15 Prophyll and rachis bracts strictly tubular, or, if splitting, then persistent and with a tubular base; floral bracteoles inconspicuous to conspicuous; endosperm ruminate or homogeneous 16

16 Short stout, rattan palm without climbing whips; inflorescence very short with prophyll in normal position, rachis bracts tubular only at the base, expanded, elongate and abruptly narrowed to a spiny beak, inserted distichously at right angles to the prophyll; fruit usually 3-seeded; endosperm homogeneous. Malay Peninsula . ... 49. **Calospatha**

16 Acaulescent to high climbing rattans or thicket-forming shrubs, cirri or flagella usually present; inflorescence short

to very long with strictly tubular bracts, or if bracts expanded, then not abruptly beaked; fruit usually 1-seeded, very rarely 3-seeded; endosperm homogeneous or ruminate. Africa to the Pacific . . . . 48. **Calamus**

17 Very tall, pleonanthic, tree palm; leaf sheaths bearing combs of slender, soft bristlelike spines; rachillae numerous, very slender, well-exserted from conspicuous subtending bracts, densely tomentose, rachilla bracts and bracteoles mostly obscured by hairs; fruit very small, scarcely exceeding 1 cm. Sulawesi to New Guinea . . . .
. . . . 56. **Pigafetta**

17 Pleonanthic or hapaxanthic, rattan palms, usually fiercely armed; rachillae if slender then without tomentum, or enclosed by subtending bracts; fruit at maturity usually at least 1.5 cm wide 18

18 Pleonanthic palm, briefly climbing but lacking climbing whips; inflorescence bracts ± distichous, fibrous, netlike, ± obscuring the rachillae. Borneo . . . . 52. **Retispatha**

18 Hapaxanthic palms, usually high climbing, cirri present; inflorescence bracts not netlike 19

19 First-order inflorescence branches pendulous, bearing strictly distichous, conspicuous, overlapping or not, boat-shaped bracts, often completely enclosing the rachillae; rachilla bracts obscure (except in monstrous forms); staminate flowers borne in pairs. Himalayas to Bali . . . . .
. . . . 55. **Plectocomia**

19 First-order inflorescence branches pendulous or not, bearing bracts scarcely differentiated from other inflorescence bracts, not obscuring rachillae; rachilla bracts conspicuous; staminate flowers borne singly 20

20 Leaf sheath without an ocrea; inflorescences of both sexes diffusely branched, usually to 3 orders; flowers with membranous perianth whorls; anthers borne on long, fine, inflexed filaments, pendulous from the lobes of the androecial ring; fruit covered with innumerable, minute, irregularly arranged scales. Indochina to Malay Peninsula and Sumatra . . . . 53. **Myrialepis**

20 Leaf sheath bearing an ocrea, sometimes disintegrating; inflorescences of both sexes branching to 2 orders only, very rarely diffusely branched to 3 orders; flowers with thick coriaceous perianth whorls; anthers ± sessile, pendulous from the tips of the lobes of the androecial ring; fruit covered in large, regularly arranged scales. Thailand, Burma, Malay Peninsula, Sumatra, Borneo . . . . .
. . . . 54. **Plectocomiopsis**

21 Slender, unarmed, clustered, undergrowth palms; leaf usually irregularly divided into 1–several fold segments; rachillae short and compressed; staminate flowers in dyads borne distichously on the rachillae. South America
. . . . 61. **Lepidocaryum**

21 Moderate to robust, solitary or clustered, armed or unarmed palms; leaf regularly divided into single-fold segments; staminate rachillae and sometimes pistillate rachillae catkinlike, bearing spirally arranged flowers, singly or in pairs 22

22 Moderate, clustered palms with spiny stems; pistillate flowers borne on short catkinlike branches; staminate flowers solitary in the axil of each rachilla bract. South America . . . . 60. **Mauritiella**

22 Massive, solitary palms with unarmed stems; pistillate flowers very few or single, borne on scarcely catkinlike branches; staminate flowers borne in dyads. South America . . . . 59. **Mauritia**

Multi-access Key to Genera of Calamoideae

Stems erect	(42), 43, (47), (48), 56, (57), 59–61.
Stems climbing	40, 41, 44, (47), (48), 49–55, 58.
Acaulescent palms	(42), 45, 46, (47), (48), (57).
Stems clustering	40–42, (43), 44–46, (47), (48), 50–54, (55), (57), 58, 60, 61.
Stems branching aerially	(42), (44), (48).
Stilt roots conspicuous	(42).
Root spines present	(42), 60.
Leaves pinnate or entire and pinnately ribbed	40–58.
Leaves palmate	59–61.
Cirrus present	40, 41, (47), (48), 51, 53–55, 58.
Flagellum present	(48).
Acanthophylls present	40, 41, 58.
Ocrea present	40, 41, 44, (48), 54, 58.
Knee present on leaf sheath	(47), (48), 49, 51.
Auricles present	50.
Terminal leaflets compound	41, 46.
Mid-leaf leaflets sometimes several fold	(41).
Adult blade entire, or entire bifid	(44), (46), (47), (48).
Sheath spines absent	41, (43), (44), (46), (48), (54), (55), 57, 59–61.
Ant galleries present	(47), (48).
Hapaxanthic palms	40, 42, (43), 44, 45, (47), 53–55, 57, 58.
Hermaphroditic palms	40, 41, 44.
Polygamous palms	42, 43.
Monoecious palms	57, 58.
Dioecious palms	45–56, 59–61.
Prophyll absent	41.
Prophyll tubular, but not enclosing inflorescence	40, 42–46, (47), 48, 52, 53–61.
Prophyll splitting, but not enclosing inflorescence	49.
Prophyll enclosing inflorescence, opening by apical pores	51.
Prophyll enclosing inflorescence, opening by splits	(47), 50.
Peduncular and rachis bracts much reduced, very much smaller than the prophyll	50–51.
Primary inflorescence bracts incomplete	41.
Primary inflorescence bracts complete, tubular	40, 42–46, 48, 53–61.
Primary inflorescence bracts complete but splitting	47, 49–50, 52.
Primary bracts deciduous	(47).
Rachilla bracts spiral	42–46, (48), (52), 56, 59, 60.
Rachilla bracts distichous	40, 41, 47, (48), 49–51, (52), 53–55, 57–58, 61.
Rachilla bracts incomplete	41–44, 55, 56.

Flowers borne in pits	43, (44), 45, (46).
Flowers solitary, hermaphroditic	44.
Flowers borne in a dyad, hermaphroditic	40, 41.
Flowers borne in a dyad, one hermaphroditic and one staminate	42, 43.
Flowers borne in a dyad of sterile staminate and pistillate	45, (46), 47–51.
Flowers borne in a dyad of staminate flowers	45, (46), 55, 56, 59, 61.
Flowers solitary, pistillate	(46), 52–57, 59–61.
Flowers solitary, staminate	47–54, 57.
Flowers solitary, but both ♂ & ♀ on rachilla	57.
Flowers borne in a cluster of up to 13, central 1–3 ♀	58.
Stamens 6	40, 41, 43–56, (57), 58–61.
Stamens more than 6	42, (57).
Filaments free from corolla	57, 58.
Filaments connate in a ring	41, 49–58.
Filaments inflexed at tip	42, 45–48, 53, 54.
Anthers rounded	41, 54.
Stigma pyramidal	40–44, 57–61.
Stigma trifid, reflexed	45–56.
Fruit more than 1-seeded	(41), (46), (48), (49).
Pericarp scales irregular, not in neat vertical rows	42, 53.
Mesocarp obsolescent	45–56, 58, 61.
Mesocarp dry fibrous	42, 43.
Mesocarp fleshy	40, 41, 44, 57, 59, 60.
Endocarp present	42.
Sarcotesta present	43, 45–56, 58, 61.
Endosperm homogeneous	40–43, (44), 45, 46, (48), 49, 50, (51), 52–56, (57), 58–61.
Chalazal pit present	43–46, 56, 57, 58, 61.

CALAMEAE Drude in Martius, Flora Brasiliensis 3(2): 270. 1881.

Leaves pinnate, or entire, or bifid with pinnate ribs.

The 19 genera of this tribe represent all the Old World Calamoideae except for one species of *Raphia* (*R. taedigera*), which occurs in the New World. Leaves are pinnate, entire, or bifid with pinnate ribs. Habit and flower arrangement are extremely varied. The division of the tribe into subtribes is based on the progressive modification of a dyad of hermaphroditic flowers like that of *Laccosperma* through several stages, such as dyads of hermaphroditic and staminate flowers (Eugeissoninae), to pistillate and sterile staminate flowers (Calaminae), to solitary staminate or pistillate flowers as in *Plectocomia*.

Map 12.—**Distribution of Ancistrophyllinae.**

The flower cluster of the Oncocalaminae is extraordinary.

Ancistrophyllinae Beccari, Annals of the Royal Botanic Garden, Calcutta 12(2):209. 1918 ('*Ancistrophyllae*'). Type: *Ancistrophyllum* = **Laccosperma.**

Hapaxanthic or pleonanthic climbing palms with cirri bearing acanthophylls; flowers hermaphroditic, borne in dyads.

The dyad of hermaphroditic flowers in *Laccosperma* is an arrangement we believe to be basic in the subfamily. *Eremospatha* has a similar dyad but is unique in the tribe in the almost complete absence of bracts and bracteoles; the very thick androecial ring is also specialized. Although these two genera may have had a common ancestor, they are nevertheless strikingly different (Map 12).

40. **LACCOSPERMA** (G. Mann & H. A. Wendland) Drude, Botanische Zeitung 35:632, 635. 1877. Type: **L. opacum** (G. Mann & H. A. Wendland) Drude (*Calamus opacus* G. Mann & H. A. Wendland).

Calamus subgenus *Laccosperma* G. Mann & H. A. Wendland, Transactions of the Linnean Society of London 24:430. 1864.

Ancistrophyllum (G. Mann & H. A. Wendland) H. A. Wendland (non Göppert 1841) in Kerchove de Denterghem, Les Palmiers 230 (1878). Type:

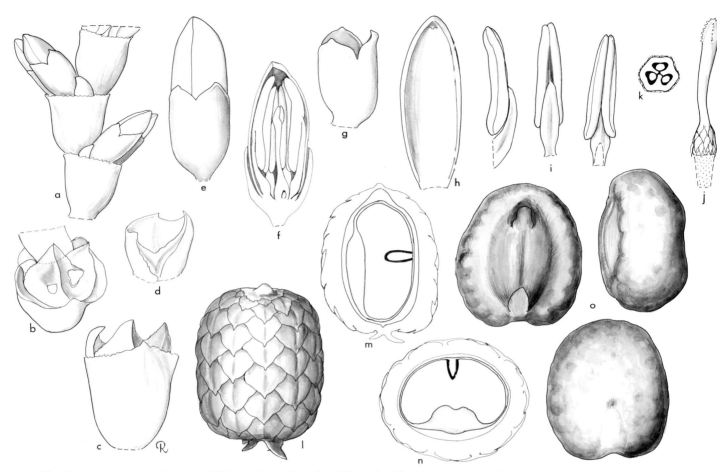

40.—**Laccosperma. a,** portion of rachilla ×3; **b,** portion of rachilla, paired flowers removed to show scars and bracteoles ×6; **c,** bract subtending flower pair ×6; **d,** floral bracteole ×6; **e,** bud ×4½; **f,** bud in vertical section ×4½; **g,** calyx ×4½; **h,** petal ×6; **i,** stamen in 3 views ×6; **j,** gynoecium ×6; **k,** ovary in cross-section ×12; **l,** fruit ×2¼; **m,** fruit in vertical section ×2¼; **n,** fruit in cross-section ×2¼; **o,** seed in 3 views ×3. *Laccosperma acutiflorum:* **j** and **k,** *Soyaux 155; L. secundiflorum:* **a-i** and **l-o,** *Enti s.n.* and *Moore & Enti 9886.*

A. secundiflorum (Palisot de Beauvois) H. A. Wendland (*Calamus secundiflorus* Palisot de Beauvois) (=*Laccosperma secundiflorum* (Palisot de Beauvois) O. Kuntze).

Calamus subgenus *Ancistrophyllum* G. Mann & H. A. Wendland, Transactions of the Linnean Society of London 24:432. 1864.

Ancistrophyllum subgenus *Laccosperma* (G. Mann & H. A. Wendland) J. D. Hooker in Bentham & J. D. Hooker, Genera Plantarum 3:937. 1883.

Ancistrophyllum subgenus *Ancistrophyllum* J. D. Hooker in Bentham & J. D.Hooker, Genera Plantarum 3:937. 1883.

Neoancistrophyllum Rauschert, Taxon 31:557. 1982. Type: *N. secundiflorum* (Palisot de Beauvois) Rauschert (superfluous substitute name).

Clustered, spiny, high-climbing, hapaxanthic, hermaphroditic, rattan palms. Stem eventually becoming bare, with long internodes, circular in cross-section, sucker shoots apparently axillary. Leaf pinnate with a cirrus; sheath strictly tubular, variously armed with scattered spines and abundant caducous indumentum; ocrea conspicuous, split opposite the leaf, scarcely sheathing, sometimes slightly inflated with inrolled edges and ant-infested, unarmed or armed like the sheath; knee absent; petiole present, usually armed with scattered or grouped spines abaxially and along margins, and frequently indumentose, rarely unarmed; rachis armed like the petiole; cirrus armed with reflexed spines and bearing neat pairs of reflexed acanthophylls; leaflets few to very numerous, 1–4-fold, entire, linear to sigmoid, regularly or irregularly arranged, often fiercely armed with short spines along the margins and the main ribs, midribs prominent adaxially, transverse veinlets conspicuous or inconspicuous. Inflorescences produced simultaneously in the axils of the most distal few, frequently reduced leaves, branched to 1-order; peduncle enclosed within the leaf sheath and emerging from its mouth or bursting through the sheath, not adnate to the internode, ± hemispherical in cross-section; prophyll strictly tubular, 2-keeled, enclosed within the leaf sheath; peduncular bracts 1–3; rachis longer than the peduncle; rachis bracts distichous, strictly tubular with a triangular limb, without spines, sparsely indumentose, becoming tattered, each subtending a pendulous or spreading rachilla; rachilla prophyll tubular, 2-keeled, included within the subtending bract, rachilla bracts distichous, tubular with apiculate, triangular limb, striate, sparsely indumentose, the margin sometimes ciliate, each, except sometimes for the basal 1–2, subtending a flower cluster. Flowers very rarely borne in triads, usually in dyads, sometimes solitary towards the tips of the rachillae, the flower cluster bearing a tubular 2-keeled prophyll and 0, 1, or 2, 2-keeled bracteoles (depending on the number of flowers); calyx slightly to strongly stalklike at the base, often bent at right angles, incompletely divided distally into 3 triangular striate lobes; corolla tubular at the very base, divided above into 3 oblong, narrow, triangular, valvate lobes; stamens 6, borne at the very base of the corolla, filaments distinct, much swollen, angular, scarcely narrowed at the connective, anthers medifixed, oblong, latrorse; pollen elliptic, monosulcate, with finely reticulate, tectate exine; gynoecium tricarpellate, triovulate, ovary covered with scales, those at the base of the style minute, spinelike, style elongate, 3-angled, stigma minute, pyramidal, ovules basally attached, anatropous. Fruit 1-seeded (? always), tipped with the base of the style, the rest of the style usually breaking off early in fruit development, the perianth whorls persistent; epicarp covered in vertical rows of reflexed scales with fringed margins, mesocarp fleshy and sweet at maturity, endocarp not differentiated. Seed attached subbasally at one side, ovoid and laterally flattened, or rounded and deeply scalloped, with a very shallow to very deep, lateral pit, seed coat apparently sometimes fleshy, endosperm homogeneous; embryo lateral, opposite the pit. Germination adjacent-ligular; eophyll bifid. Cytology not studied.

Anatomy.—Leaf, stem, root (Tomlinson 1961).

Distribution.—About seven species confined to humid rain forest of west Africa and the Congo Basin.

Ecology.—Apparently most abundant in rain forest on swampy soils.

Common Names and Uses.—Common names unknown. Stems are used as a source of cane.

Notes.—*Laccosperma* and *Eremospatha* are of great interest in possessing dyads of hermaphrodite flowers which, among the calamoid palms, appear to be the unspecialized state of flower arrangement. *Eremospatha*, however, seems to have lost almost all bracts. Very rarely in *Laccosperma* triads of hermaphrodite flowers are present and bract arrangement indicates a sympodial nature for the triad and the dyad.

Taxonomic Accounts.—Beccari (1910b), Dransfield (1982d).

Plate.—41B; Fig. G.19.

41. EREMOSPATHA (G. Mann & H. A. Wendland) H. A. Wendland in Kerchove de Denterghem, Les Palmiers 244. 1878. Lectotype: **E. hookeri** (G. Mann & H. A. Wendland) H. A. Wendland (*Calamus hookeri* G. Mann & H. A. Wendland) (see H. E Moore 1963c).

Calamus subgenus *Eremospatha* G. Mann & H. A. Wendland, Transactions of the Linnean Society of London 24:433. 1864.

Clustered (? always), spiny, high-climbing, pleonanthic, hermaphroditic rattan palms. Stem eventually becoming bare, with long internodes, usually circular in cross-section, sometimes obscurely 3-angled, juvenile stem apparently much more slender than the adult, sucker shoots apparently axillary. Leaves pinnate, bifid in juveniles, with a terminal cirrus; sheath strictly tubular, unarmed, longitudinally striate, sometimes with a thin caducous cover of indumentum; ocrea conspicuous, tightly sheathing, neatly truncate (? always); knee present in mature climbing stems, but rather inconspicuous; petiole present in juvenile stems, absent in mature climbing stems; rachis usually armed with reflexed spines, and sometimes bearing caducous indumentum; cirrus bearing neat pairs (rarely not paired) of reflexed acanthophylls, sometimes also with scattered reflexed spines; leaflets few to numerous, single-fold except, rarely, in juvenile leaves where lamina undivided, praemorse or abruptly narrowed to a pointed tip, or entire, linear to rhomboid, usually somewhat plicate, regularly arranged, variously indumentose, sometimes white tomentose beneath, usually armed along the thickened margins with conspicuous robust, distally pointing or reflexed spines, transverse veinlets moderately conspicuous; proximal few leaflets on each side of the rachis frequently very much smaller than the rest, straplike, heavily armed along margins, and reflexed across the sheathed stem. Inflorescence arching outward, branched to 1 order, branches horizontal, peduncle enclosed within the leaf sheath and emerging from its mouth, flattened, not adnate to the internode, the surface usually minutely papillose; bracts throughout the inflorescence very inconspicuous; prophyll absent?; peduncular bracts absent; rachis much longer than the peduncle; rachis bracts low, triangular, striate, ± opposite or alternate, often united to form an incomplete sheathing collar; rachillae adnate to the inflorescence axis a short distance above the bract, either opposite (in which case subtended by a double bract) or alternate (in which case subtended by a single triangular bract), distal rachillae always alternate, distichous, rachillae minutely papillose, bearing ± distichous, minute, triangular, incomplete bracts, each subtending a pair of equal flowers without bracteoles. Flowers apparently pale in color, very fragrant; calyx thick, coriaceous, very shallowly 3-lobed distally, obscurely veined, minutely papillose; corolla very thick, coriaceous, divided at the apex to ¼ to ⅓ its length into 3, short, triangular, valvate lobes,

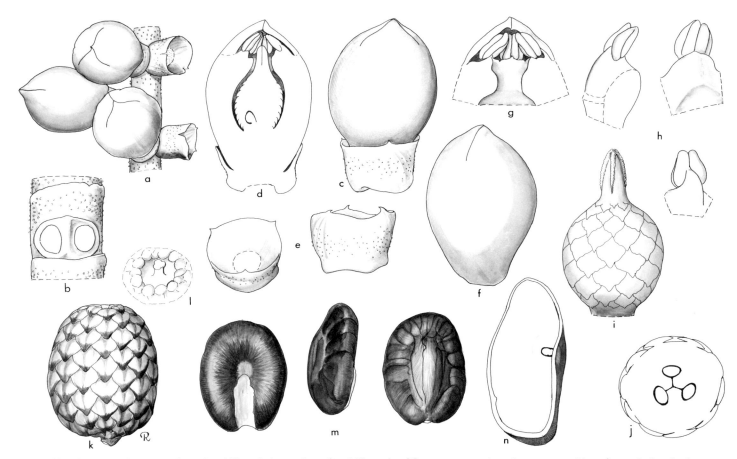

41.—**Eremospatha. a,** portion of rachilla ×3; **b,** portion of rachilla, pair of flowers removed to show scars ×4½; **c,** flower in late bud ×4½; **d,** flower in vertical section ×4½; **e,** calyx in 2 views ×4½; **f,** flower, calyx removed ×4½; **g,** tip of petal with stamens ×7½; **h,** stamen in 3 views ×9; **i,** gynoecium ×9; **j,** ovary in cross-section ×9; **k,** fruit ×1; **l,** tip of fruit with stigmatic remains, enlarged; **m,** seed in 3 views ×1; **n,** seed in vertical section ×1½. *Eremospatha macrocarpa:* all from *Moore 9891.*

remaining approximate even at anthesis, the lobes then separating slightly; stamens 6, united into a massive, fleshy, epipetalous ring, ± occluding the mouth of the flower, clasping the gynoecium, free filaments angled, very short, anthers enclosed within the flower, ± medifixed, very short, somewhat sagittate, latrorse; pollen elliptic, mono-sulcate, the sulcus extended, exine foveolate, tectate; gynoecium tricarpellate, triovulate, rounded, covered in re-flexed scales, tipped by a columnar or tapered, ±3-angled style, apically with 3 stigmatic angles, ovule basally at-tached, anatropous. Fruit 1–3 seeded, stigmatic remains minute, apical, perianth whorls persistent; epicarp cov-ered in vertical rows of reddish-brown reflexed scales with fringed margins, mesocarp apparently fleshy at maturity, endocarp not differentiated. Seed subbasally attached, from the shape of ⅓ of a sphere to hemispherical or ellipsoidal depending on the number of seeds developing, sometimes slightly lobed or grooved, with a conspicuous abaxial ridge opposite the embryo, seed coat thin, scarcely fleshy, en-dosperm homogeneous; embryo lateral. Germination ad-jacent-ligular; eophyll bifid. Cytology not studied.

Anatomy.—Leaf, stem (Tomlinson 1961), floral (Uhl and Moore 1973).

Distribution.—Twelve species (but probably few-er) confined to humid rain forest of west Africa, the Congo Basin, and eastward to Tanzania.

Ecology.—Apparently most abundant in rain for-est on swampy soils.

Common Names and Uses.—Common names unknown. Stems are used as a source of cane.

Notes.—The flowers of *Eremospatha* are remark-able for the thickness of the corolla tube and the small gaps between its short lobes; the androecial tube is also thick, fibrous, and extensively vascu-larized (Uhl and Moore 1973). The flowers are very like those of *Plectocomiopsis,* but this similarity seems a parallel development. Although the dyad of two hermaphrodite flowers in *Eremospatha* is similar to that of *Laccosperma,* the two genera are otherwise rather different. *Eremospatha* has pleonathic shoots and only minute rachilla bracts; shoots of *Laccosperma* are hapaxanthic and rachilla bracts are conspicuous.

Taxonomic Account. — Beccari (1910b).

Plate. — *41C.*

Eugeissoninae Beccari, Annals of the Royal Botanic Garden, Calcutta 12(2):210. 1918 (‘*Eugeissoneae*’). Type: **Eugeissona.**

Hapaxanthic, polygamous, acaulescent or tree palms; rachillae numerous, each comprising a cupule of 7–11 imbricate, leathery bracts enclosing a single dyad of a staminate and a hermaphroditic flower, the staminate flower opening and shed long before exsertion of the hermaphroditic flower; petals very large, woody; stamens 21–70; pericarp scales very small, not clearly ordered; mesocarp fibrous, endocarp woody with 6 or 12 incomplete partitions penetrating the seed; sarcotesta absent.

This subtribe (Map 13) contains a single genus which is exceptional in many respects. The dyad of staminate and hermaphrodite flowers is rather unspecialized within the subfamily, even though many other features, e.g. the "terminal" position of the dyad in the inflorescence, the very large flower size (Uhl and Dransfield 1984), multistaminy, the presence of an endocarp, and remote-ligular germination, all suggest a highly specialized state.

42. EUGEISSONA Griffith, Calcutta Journal of Natural History 5:101. 1844. Type: **E. tristis** Griffith.

Moderate to robust, clustering, spiny, hapaxanthic, polygamous, acaulescent or tree palms. Stem subterranean, erect, or borne on robust stilt roots at heights up to 3 m above the ground, branching sympodially by basal (? axillary) suckers, internodes very short to moderately elongate, usually covered by rotting leaf sheaths, becoming exposed in tree species and sometimes bearing short spinelike adventitious roots; cortex very hard, pith soft with abundant starch deposition before flowering. Leaves pinnate, spirally arranged or markedly 3-ranked; sheath usually splitting opposite the petiole, unarmed at the very base, bearing black, flattened spines distally, sometimes also bearing scales and branched hairs, sheath margin ligulelike distally; petiole well developed, adaxially deeply channeled in proximal portion, distally ± rounded in section, the abaxial surface sparsely to densely armed with black, flattened spines, scattered, paired or in longitudinal rows, scales and hairs usually abundant between spines, sometimes absent; rachis armed as the petiole but more sparsely; leaflets single-fold, numerous, linear to lanceolate, entire, regularly arranged or grouped and fanned within the group to give the leaf a plumose appearance, frequently bearing bristles along the main veins or the margins, and irregular bands of caducous indumentum, midribs prominent, transverse veinlets moderately conspicuous. Inflorescence erect, composed of branches

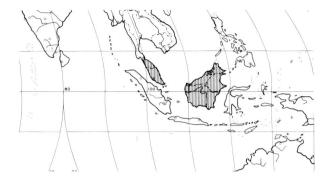

Map 13. — **Distribution of Eugeissoninae.**

equivalent to the axillary inflorescences of pleonanthic palms, each branched to the fourth-order, and subtended by leaves with much reduced blades or by tubular, apiculate, spiny or unarmed, dull brown, longitudinally imbricate bracts; branches of all orders bearing a tubular, 2-keeled prophyll, and terminating in a cupule of dull brown, longitudinally striate, spirally arranged, or more often subdistichous, tightly sheathing bracts enclosing a flower pair; cupule bracts 11–13, rarely 1 or 2 more, the 1–3 most proximal and 1–3 most distal each with an abortive axillary bud, the rest empty, the most proximal up to 5 tubular, the rest open; flower pair consisting of a large staminate and lateral to it a large hermaphroditic flower, the staminate appearing first, then pushed out of the cupule by the developing hermaphroditic flower. Staminate flowers borne on a short flattened pedicel, the flower base compressed on one side by the developing hermaphroditic bud; calyx tubular, coriaceous, striate, dull brown, with 3 short, pointed lobes; corolla tubular in the basal ¼ to ⅓, distally with 3 narrow, elongate, woody, valvate lobes terminating in hard, sharp, spinelike tips; stamens 20–70 borne just above the mouth of the corolla tube, filaments short, erect, anthers narrow, elongate, basifixed, dull yellow to purple, latrorse to introrse, deciduous after anthesis; pollen copious, yellowish or dull purplish, irregularly elliptic or circular, monosulcate, the aperture extended or subcircular, with rugulate, fossulate, or coarsely reticulate, tectate exine; pistillode minute. Hermaphroditic flowers protandrous, sessile, bearing a 2-keeled, coriaceous, tubular prophyll, similar to the cupule bracts, the whole flower very similar in size and shape to the staminate except for the apex, flattened on one side by pressure of the staminate flower in bud; calyx, corolla, and androecium like the staminate; gynoecium tricarpellate, triovulate, ovary columnar, faintly 3-angled, covered in vertical rows of minute reflexed scales, stigma conical to pyramidal with 3 glandular angles, ovules basally attached, anatropous. Fruit ovoid, beaked, stigmatic remains apical, cupule bracts, calyx, and usually the corolla persisting; epicarp covered in irregular vertical rows of very small reflexed, fringed scales, mesocarp somewhat corky at maturity, traversed by longitudinal fiber bundles, endocarp developing from a layer external to the locule wall, dark brown to blackish, very hard and thick, sometimes linked to the fibers of the mesocarp, with 3 + 3, or 3 + 3 + 6 flanges penetrating into the fruit cavity, forming symmetrical, incomplete partitions. Seed basally attached, single, filling the fruit cavity and closely adhering to the endocarp and thus indented by the incomplete partitions, seed coat thin, dry, endosperm homogeneous; embryo basal. Germination remote-ligular; eophyll pinnate. Cytology not studied.

Anatomy. — Leaf (Tomlinson 1961), distinguished from other calamoid genera by short foliar sclereids in some species, perhaps supporting the rather isolated position of the genus. Studies of floral development have shown the apparently terminal flower pair to be lateral and to consist of a typical dyad. The gynoecium consists of three carpels with ventral sutures open, and ovules are initiated directly on the large apex of the floral axis (Uhl and Dransfield 1984).

Distribution. — Six species, two confined to the Malay Peninsula, and four in Borneo, one of which (*E. ambigua*) is still known only from its type.

Ecology. — In Borneo, *E. insignis, E. utilis,* and *E. minor* usually seem to be associated with poor soils with abundant humus; they are particularly conspicuous on scarp faces or sharp ridgetops. *E. minor* and *E. insignis* are also found in low lying kerangas (heath) forest. *E. ambigua,* known only from the type, was collected on a slightly raised heathy area in the Kapuas lake district of West Kalimantan. In Peninsular Malaysia, *E. brachystachys* is associated with richer soils on hillslopes, particularly where some flushing takes place. *E. tristis* is found in a wide range of forest types, from swamp margins to hilltops but grows in greatest abundance on ridgetops up to 1000 m altitude. All but *E. ambigua,* about which very little is known, grow in large colonies.

Fossil Record. — Pollen of a type referable to *E. minor* is known from lower Miocene deposits in Sarawak, while pollen of another type corresponding to the pollen of *E. insignis, E. utilis,* and *E. tristis* is known from the middle Miocene of Sarawak and later (Muller 1981).

Common Names and Uses. — Bertam (*E. tristis*), wild Bornean sago palm (*E. utilis*). All species have a wide range of local uses. Sago from the stems of *E. utilis* forms the staple of the nomadic Punan people of Borneo and *E. insignis* can be used similarly. Leaves of all species may provide thatch. Petioles are used in the manufacture of blinds, blowpipe darts and toys, and the pith of the petioles for the occlusions on blowpipe darts. The young endosperm is edible and even the pollen has been eaten. Stilt roots of *E. minor* make excellent walking sticks. *E. tristis* has become a serious pest of Hill Dipterocarp forest in Malaya where it dominates the undergrowth after logging, thus preventing regeneration of commercially important timber trees.

Notes. — *Eugeissona* is a genus with no obvious close relatives. The dyad of a hermaphrodite and a staminate flower is found elsewhere only in *Metroxylon* but there is almost nothing else to link the two genera. *Eugeissona* is best regarded as a highly evolved palm having arisen probably rather early in the differentiation of the Calameae. The flowers are among the largest in the palms and the development of first the staminate and later the hermaphrodite so that the plant at any one time seems to bear large solitary flowers is also a specialization.

Taxonomic Account. — Dransfield (1970).

Plates. — 11A, B; 41D.

Metroxylinae Blume, Rumphia 2:157. 1843 ('*Metroxyleae*'). Type: **Metroxylon.**

Hapaxanthic or very rarely pleonanthic trees or climbers; flowers solitary, hermaphroditic, or borne in dyads of 1 staminate and 1 hermaphroditic; dyads borne spirally in pits on catkinlike rachillae, the pits usually filled with hairs; mesocarp rather thick and fleshy; sarcotesta rather thin or absent.

Two genera comprise this subtribe (Map 14). Asiatic and west Malesian *Korthalsia,* in its climbing habit, is most unlike the massive Papuasian tree palm *Metroxylon.* The genera share, however, a similar arrangement of flowers; in *Metroxylon* there is a dyad of a staminate and hermaphroditic flower while in *Korthalsia* there is a single hermaphroditic flower borne together with bracteoles suggesting a

→

42. — **Eugeissona.** a, branch bearing three rachillae ×¾; b, single rachilla with bracts and staminate flower ×1; c-d, bracts of single rachilla, expanded ×1; e, staminate flower ×1; f, staminate calyx ×1; g, staminate flower, calyx removed ×1; h, staminate flower, calyx removed, in vertical section ×1; i, pistillode ×3; j, hermaphroditic flower, stamens fallen ×1; k, hermaphroditic flower before anthesis in vertical section ×1; l, hermaphrodite flower, stamens fallen, in vertical section ×1; m, hermaphroditic calyx and remains of stalk of staminate flower ×2; n, hermaphrodite petal in 2 views ×1; o, stamens in 3 views ×3; p, gynoecium ×1½; q, ovary in cross-section ×3; r, ovule in 2 views ×5; s, fruit ×¾; t, fruit in vertical section ×¾; u, fruit in cross-section at 2 levels ×¾; v, portion of epicarp showing imbricate scales, much enlarged; w, seed in 3 views ×¾. *Eugeissona tristis:* a-r, *Moore & Pennington 9059;* E. utilis: s-w, *Moore & Meijer 9219.*

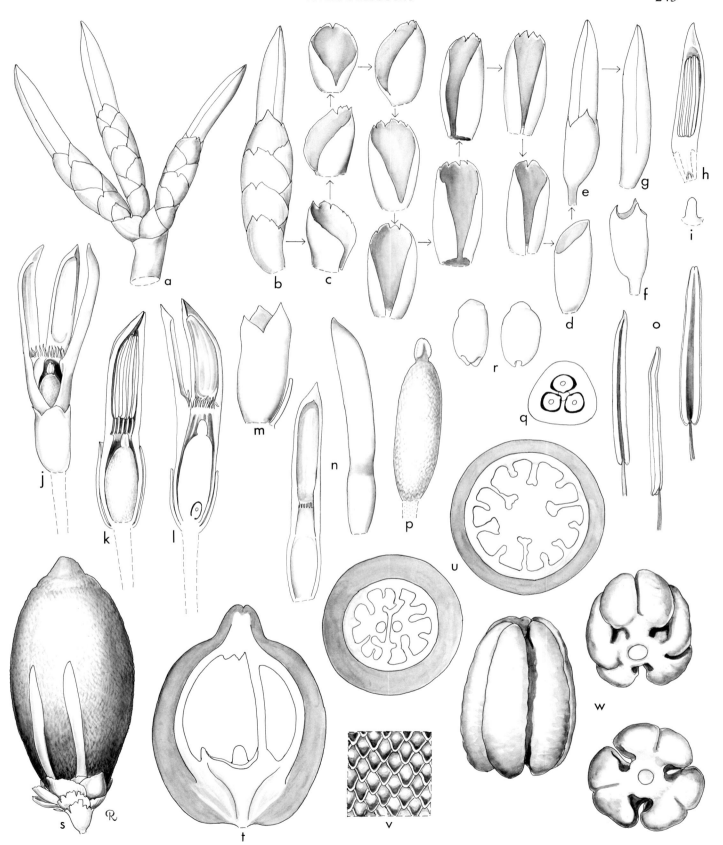

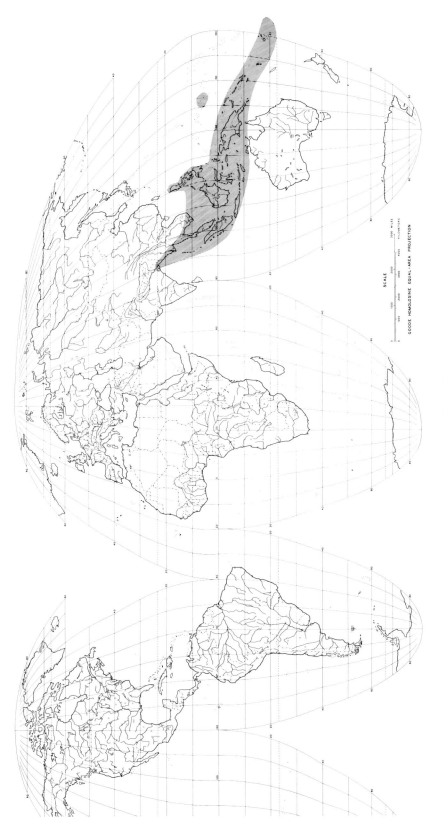

Map 14.—Distribution of Metroxylinae.

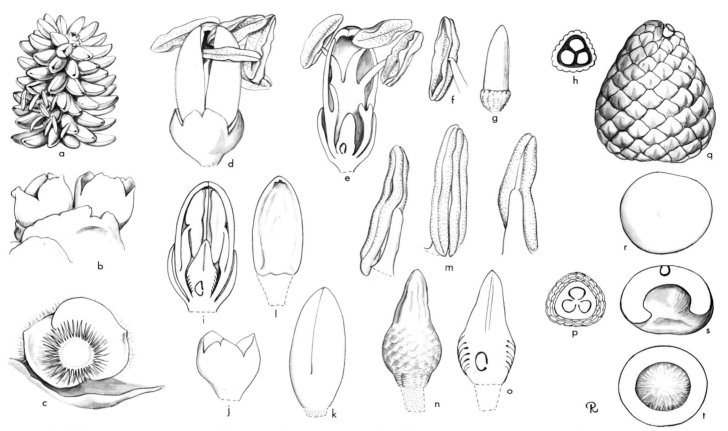

43.—**Metroxylon. a,** portion of rachilla at anthesis ×1; **b,** portion of rachilla to show paired arrangement of flowers with corollas removed ×3; **c,** bracteoles surrounding pistillate flower ×6; **d,** staminate flower ×3; **e,** staminate flower in vertical section ×3; **f,** stamen ×3; **g,** pistillode ×3; **h,** pistillode in cross-section ×12; **i,** hermaphroditic flower in vertical section ×3; **j,** hermaphroditic calyx ×3; **k,** hermaphroditic flower, calyx removed ×3; **l,** hermaphroditic petal ×3; **m,** stamen from hermaphroditic flower in 3 views ×6; **n,** gynoecium ×6; **o,** gynoecium in vertical section ×6; **p,** ovary in cross-section ×6; **q,** fruit ×½; **r,** seed ×½; **s,** seed in vertical section ×½; **t,** seed in cross-section ×½. *Metroxylon warburgii:* all from *Moore 9319.*

dyadic origin. The tight, catkinlike rachillae are superficially very similar.

43. **METROXYLON** Rottboell, Nye Samling af det Kongelige Danske Videnskabers Selskabs Skrifter 2:527. 1783 (Conserved name). Type: **M. sagu** Rottboell.

Sagus Steck, Dissertatio Inauguralis Medica De Sagu 21. 1757. Lectotype: *S. genuina* Giseke (see H. E. Moore 1962b) (non *Sagus* J. Gaertner =*Raphia* Palisot de Beauvois).

Coelococcus H. A. Wendland, Bonplandia 10:199. 1862. Type: *C. vitiensis* H. A. Wendland (*Metroxylon vitiense* (H. A. Wendland) Bentham & J. D. Hooker).

Robust to massive, solitary or clustered, armed or unarmed, hapaxanthic or pleonanthic, polygamous tree palms. Stem erect, usually partly obscured by the marcescent leaf bases, the internodes sometimes bearing ad-

ventitious roots, these usually spinelike; cortex hard, pith soft, rich in starch. Leaves large, pinnate, marcescent or sometimes neatly abscising; sheath splitting opposite the petiole, unarmed, or armed with partial whorls of rather slender spines united by their bases to form low collars, and covered with caducous indumentum; petiole well developed, unarmed or armed as the sheath, channeled adaxially in the proximal part, becoming rounded distally, rounded abaxially throughout; rachis like the petiole, but angled adaxially; leaflets numerous, single-fold, linear, regularly arranged or grouped and fanned within the groups to give the leaf a plumose appearance, rarely bearing white wax on abaxial surface, usually armed with inconspicuous short spines along the margins and main vein, midribs prominent adaxially, transverse veinlets usually conspicuous. Inflorescences branched to 2 orders, either interfoliar in pleonanthic *M. amicarum* or aggregated into a suprafoliar, compound inflorescence, with branches equivalent to axillary inflorescences, each subtended by a reduced leaf or bract and sometimes emerging through a split in its mid-line; peduncle very short; prophyll tubular, tightly sheathing, 2-keeled, 2-lobed; peduncular bract 1–

several, tubular; rachis much longer than peduncle; rachis bracts ± distichous, tubular, tightly sheathing, with a triangular limb, unarmed or rarely with a few scattered spines; first-order branches horizontal or pendulous, each with a basal tubular, 2-keeled, 2-lobed empty prophyll and ± distichous, tightly sheathing, tubular bracts, unarmed or armed with few scattered spines, all but the proximal 1– ca. 3 subtending a catkinlike rachilla (second-order branch of inflorescence); rachillae robust, cylindrical, with a short proximal, bare, stalklike portion, and a dense spiral of imbricate, wide, rounded or apiculate, striate bracts, the proximal and distal few empty, the rest each enclosing a dyad of a small staminate and a similar hermaphroditic flower, in bud partly obscured by a dense pile of hairs, except in *M. amicarum* where hairs sparse, dyad prophyll completely tubular, with 2 keels and 2 triangular lobes, usually bearing dense hairs on the abaxial surface, inner bracteole with 2 keels and dense hairs. Staminate flowers opening before the hermaphroditic; calyx tubular, ± striate, with 3 triangular lobes; corolla usually ± twice the length of the calyx, divided to ±⅔ its length into 3 oblong, valvate, smooth petals with triangular tips; stamens 6, borne on the base of the corolla, filaments fleshy, abruptly contracted and reflexed, anthers medifixed, oblong, latrorse; pollen elliptic, disulcate, with scabrate, foveolate, or coarsely reticulate, tectate exine; pistillode conical. Hermaphroditic flowers superficially similar to the staminate but somewhat fatter; calyx and corolla like the staminate; stamens like the staminate but with filaments united proximally to form an androecial tube surrounding the ovary; gynoecium tricarpellate, triovulate, rounded, covered in vertical rows of minute scales, and bearing a conical style with 3 stigmatic angles, ovule basally attached, anatropous. Fruit rounded, usually large, 1-seeded, with apical stigmatic remains; epicarp covered in neat vertical rows of straw- to chestnut-colored reflexed scales, mesocarp rather corky or spongy, endocarp not differentiated. Seed globose, basally attached, deeply invaginated apically, enveloped in a thin to thick sarcotesta, endosperm homogeneous; embryo basal. Germination adjacent-ligular; eophyll bifid or pinnate. *n* = 16 (*M. sagu*, Sarkar 1970).

Anatomy.—Leaf (Tomlinson 1961). Resembles other erect-stemmed genera, *Lepidocaryum, Mauritia,* and *Raphia,* but is unlike the rattans and shorter stemmed calamoids.

Distribution.—About five species (Rauwerdink 1986) native to east Malesia, the Solomon Islands, New Hebrides, Samoa, Fiji, and the Carolines; one species, *M. sagu,* thought to be native to New Guinea and the Moluccas, is now widespread and naturalized throughout the southeast Asian region as a source of sago and thatching material.

Ecology.—Most species are plants of lowland swamps, where they may grow gregariously in great numbers. *M. amicarum* also grows in deep valleys and high in the mountains in Micronesia (Moore and Fosberg 1956).

Common Names and Uses.—True sago palm, ivory nut palm, sagu, rumbia. The two major uses of *Metroxylon* species are as sources of sago and for materials for house construction such as thatch from leaves and woven walling from split petioles. Sago from *Metroxylon* is of great importance as a staple in parts of the Moluccas, New Guinea, and the western Pacific and the apparatus used in the production of sago is, itself, often made from *Metroxylon.* Seeds of some species furnish a form of vegetable ivory used in the past but of little value now.

Notes.—A report on flowering and inflorescence structure is given by Tomlinson (1971a) for *M. vitiense* and *M. sagu.* The form of the rachillae is very characteristic, and it is this, together with the presence of hermaphrodite flowers, which link *Metroxylon* with *Korthalsia.* The two genera are, however, centered at different ends of Malesia. If indeed they are related then their origin must long predate the final Miocene juxtaposition of the two main tectonic plates of Malesia.

Taxonomic Account.—Beccari (1918), Rauwerdink (1986).

Plates.—*11C; 42A; Fig. G.21.*

44. **KORTHALSIA** Blume, Rumphia 2:166. ("1836") 1843. Lectotype: **K. rigida** Blume (see H. E. Moore 1963c).

Calamosagus Griffith, Calcutta Journal of Natural History 5:22. 1844. Lectotype: *C. laciniosus* Griffith (=*Korthalsia laciniosa* (Griffith) Martius) (see H. E. Moore 1963c).

Slender to moderate, clustered, spiny, high-climbing and aerially branching, hapaxanthic, hermaphroditic rattan palms. Stem eventually becoming partly bare, the inner epidermis of the leaf sheaths tending to adhere to the stem surface, internodes elongate, nodal scars often very uneven, shallowly hollowed, aerial branching possibly due to equal forking (dichotomy), basal suckering leaf-opposed at 130° from the petiole in at least one species. Leaves pinnate, with a cirrus; sheath tubular, sometimes splitting longitudinally opposite the petiole, unarmed, or variously armed with spines, usually with abundant scales and floccose indumentum; knee absent; ocrea always well developed, unarmed or variously spiny, tightly sheathing, or expanded into a loose funnel-shaped net of fibers, or sheathing but distally grossly swollen to form an ant nest-chamber, or diverging from the stem with inrolled margins, also forming an ant chamber; petiole present or absent; rachis and cirrus armed with scattered and grouped, reflexed grapnel spines; leaflets relatively few, single-fold, linear, lanceolate to rhomboid, praemorse, often densely white indumentose beneath, regularly arranged, distant, very rarely a single pair only, frequently borne on short pseudopetiolules ("ansae"), midrib inconspicuous, the main veins radiating from the leaflet base, transverse vein-

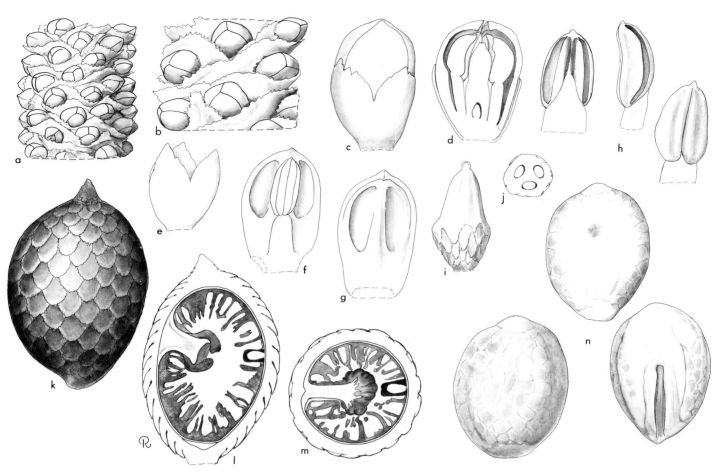

44.—**Korthalsia. a,** portion of rachilla ×3; **b,** portion of rachilla ×6; **c,** bud ×9; **d,** bud in vertical section ×9; **e,** calyx ×9; **f,** petal with stamen ×9; **g,** petal ×9; **h,** stamen in 3 views ×15; **i,** gynoecium ×9; **j,** ovary in cross-section ×9; **k,** fruit ×2¼; **l,** fruit in vertical section ×2¼; **m,** fruit in cross-section ×2¼; **n,** seed in 3 views ×2¼. *Korthalsia brassii:* **a-j,** *Zieck 36204; K. echinometra:* **k-n,** *Corner 30467.*

lets conspicuous or obscure. Inflorescences produced simultaneously in the axils of the most distal few, frequently reduced leaves; sometimes bursting through the leaf sheaths, rarely unbranched, usually branching to 1–2 orders; peduncle adnate to the internode above the subtending leaf; prophyll 2-keeled, tightly sheathing, usually included within the leaf sheath, sometimes subtending a branch; rachis much longer than the peduncle; rachis bracts tubular, tightly sheathing, sparsely armed or unarmed, frequently densely covered with indumentum; bracts on first-order branches similar to rachis bracts; rachillae usually distant, rarely aggregated into a head, cylindrical, and catkinlike, bearing a few empty basal bracts and a tight spiral of imbricate bracts, connate laterally to each other, or, more rarely, distinct, the rachillae then with a looser appearance, each rachilla bract forming a pit, usually densely filled with multicellular hairs, and including a 2-keeled membranous bracteole, densely hairy on the abaxial surface, a minute triangular bracteole, and a single flower. Flowers apparently protandrous; calyx tubular at the base, with 3 valvate lobes distally; corolla tubular

basally with 3 valvate lobes apically, in fruit circumscissile at the level of the ovary equator, carried up on the top of the developing fruit, disintegrating or persisting to mature fruiting; stamens 6–9, borne at the mouth of the corolla tube, filaments fleshy, elongate, anthers short to elongate, introrse or latrorse; pollen elliptic or circular, monosulcate, the sulcus sometimes extended, monoporate, meridionosulcate, disulcate, or diporate, the exine intectate, bearing spines, spinules, and/or smooth grooved or smooth, clavate processes; gynoecium tricarpellate, triovulate, rounded, scaly, style conical or narrow pyramidal with 3 stigmatic lines, ovule anatropous, basally attached. Fruit globose to ovoid, 1-seeded, stigmatic remains apical; epicarp covered with vertical rows of reflexed, imbricate scales, mesocarp thinly fleshy, sweet, endocarp not differentiated. Seed attached basally, raphe elongate, seed coat thin, not fleshy, endosperm homogeneous or ruminate, with a conspicuous pit; embryo lateral. Germination adjacent-ligular; eophyll undivided or bifid, margins praemorse. $n = 16$ (*K. laciniosa* as *K. andamanensis, K. rostrata* as *K. scaphigera,* Sarkar 1970).

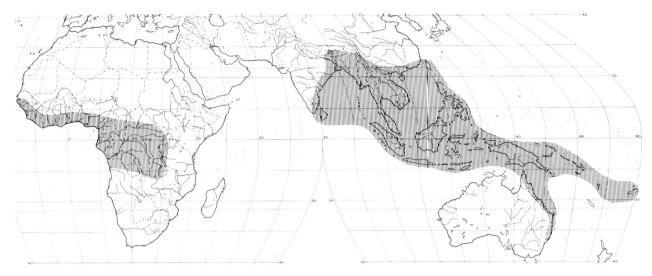

Map 15.—**Distribution of Calaminae.**

Anatomy.—Leaf (Tomlinson 1961).

Distribution.—About 26 species, centered on the perhumid areas of the Sunda Shelf with outliers north as far as Indochina, Burma, and the Andaman Islands, and southeastward to Sulawesi and New Guinea.

Ecology.—All species are confined to lowland and hill tropical rain forest and are absent in montane forest. Most species have, however, a very wide ecological range, and though being abundant in primary forest, seem also to be peculiarly well adapted to withstanding forest disturbance and are a conspicuous feature of old secondary forest or regenerated logged forest. It has been suggested that the hapaxanthic habit may be an adaptation to colonizing secondary habitats (Dransfield 1978b). A few species have very narrow ecological limits, e.g. *K. concolor,* which seems to be confined to forest on ultrabasic rock in Sabah, Borneo. Many species have very close associations with ants. The ants husband scale insects on young tissue within the ocreas of the distal portion of the stem, using the older dry ocreas as brood chambers; in some species (e.g. *K. robusta* and *K. hispida*) the ants produce alarm signals by banging their abdomens on the dry ocreas. The significance of the ant/rattan relationship has not been fully investigated, but there is much to suggest that the relationship provides protection of the rattan against herbivores (Dransfield 1981a). Bees have been observed visiting the flowers of *K. laciniosa* and southern pied hornbills, *Anthracoceros convex-*

us (Temminck), feed on the ripe fruit of the same species (Rubeli in Dransfield 1981a).

Fossil Record.—Pollen referable to present day *K. rigida* or *K. laciniosa* has been recorded from the upper Miocene of northwest Borneo (Muller 1981).

Common Names and Uses.—Ant rattans; for Malay names see Dransfield (1979a). Species of *Korthalsia* produce very hard durable canes much used in local basketware and for binding in house construction. The cane, however, is disfigured by large irregular nodal scars and the inner epidermis of the sheaths closely adheres to the cane surface; these two cane features are responsible for the limited importance of *Korthalsia* in the rattan trade.

Notes.—*Korthalsia* is distinguished by the solitary hermaphroditic flowers borne in catkinlike rachillae and by hapaxanthy. It possesses so many unusual features not found among other Southeast Asian rattan palms that it seems reasonable to suppose that the climbing habit in the Calameae has arisen more than once.

Taxonomic Account.—Dransfield (1981a).

Plates.—*11D; 42B; Figs. G.6, G.15, G.19.*

Calaminae Meisner, Plantarum Vascularium Genera 1:356. 1842. Type: **Calamus.**

Hapaxanthic (rarely) or pleonanthic, dioecious, acaulescent or climbing palms; cirri where present lacking acanthophylls; staminate inflorescence with paired or solitary flowers; pistillate inflorescence bearing dyads of sterile staminate and pistillate flowers (except in *Salacca* sect.

Leiosalacca and *Retispatha* where sterile staminate flowers lacking); sarcotesta well developed.

The eight genera of Calaminae, all dioecious, have their center of diversity in Southeast Asia, though *Calamus* itself is very widely dispersed outside this area (Map 15). In *Eleiodoxa* and *Salacca* (except for section *Leiosalacca*) the staminate rachillae bear dyads of staminate flowers and the dyads of the pistillate rachillae consist of a sterile staminate and a fertile pistillate flower. Modification of this pattern in genera 47–51 results in the presence of a single staminate flower at each rachilla bract in the staminate rachillae, and in *Retispatha* further reduction by the loss of the sterile staminate flower in the pistillate inflorescence. Differences between genera in the group 47–51 are based on the numbers and nature of the inflorescence bracts. *Retispatha* has a highly branched but condensed inflorescence; the absence of a sterile staminate flower suggests it may be more closely related to *Salacca* section *Leiosalacca* than to *Calamus* and its close relatives.

45. ELEIODOXA (Beccari) Burret, Notizblatt des Botanischen Gartens und Museums zu Berlin-Dahlem 15:733. 1942. Lectotype: **E. conferta** (Griffith) Burret (*Salacca conferta* Griffith) (see H. E. Moore 1963c).

Salacca section *Eleiodoxa* Beccari, Annals of the Royal Botanic Garden, Calcutta 12(2):71. 1918.

Moderate, acaulescent, clustering, armed, hapaxanthic, dioecious palm. Stem subterranean with short internodes, bearing strictly axillary sucker shoots. Leaves robust, pinnate, marcescent; sheath splitting opposite the petiole, unarmed at the extreme base, otherwise armed with neat partial whorls of robust spines and abundant caducous scales, the sheath mouth bearing a tattering ligulelike structure; petiole well developed, channeled adaxially in proximal part, rounded abaxially, circular in cross-section distally, armed with neat, somewhat oblique, partial whorls of slender, rigid spines; rachis armed as the petiole, but more sparsely so; leaflets single-fold, linear-lanceolate, regularly arranged, the apical pair slender, very rarely partly united to the penultimate pair, the margins armed with short spines, surfaces similar in color, transverse veinlets distinct. Inflorescences aggregated into a terminal compound inflorescence, held erect at ground level between the leaf bases, the staminate and pistillate superficially similar; first-order branches of the compound inflorescence (i.e. the axillary inflorescences) each subtended by a highly reduced leaf or tattering bract, and bearing an empty, short, tubular, 2-keeled prophyll, quickly tattering, and short, tubular, tattering bracts with triangular limbs, each subtending a robust, erect, cylindrical, catkinlike rachilla; rachilla bearing a basal, 2-keeled, tubular prophyll and a few empty bracts at the base and at the very tip, otherwise bearing a tight spiral of imbricate, laterally

adnate, low triangular-tipped bracts, each enclosing a dyad of flowers, comprising in the staminate inflorescence, 2 staminate flowers, and in the pistillate, 1 sterile staminate and 1 fertile pistillate flower, each flower bearing a prophyllar bracteole and surrounded by a dense pile of hairs. Staminate flowers pinkish-tinged at anthesis; calyx cupular, striate, with 3 triangular lobes; corolla tubular at the base, split to about ⅘ its length into 3 triangular, valvate petals; stamens 6, borne at the mouth of the corolla tube, filaments fleshy, elongate, abruptly contracted and inflexed at the tip, anthers elongate, introrse; pollen elliptic, diporate, exine tectate, smooth with numerous perforations; pistillode absent. Sterile staminate flowers like the fertile but with fleshier filaments, not abruptly contracted, and with empty anthers. Pistillate flowers superficially similar to the staminate but larger, the corolla tubular in the basal ca. ⅓; staminodes 6, borne at the mouth of the corolla tube, filaments closely appressed to the corolla, empty anthers somewhat sagittate; gynoecium tricarpellate, triovulate, globose, covered in reflexed scales, stigmas 3, reflexed, sinuous, in bud compressed into a pyramid, locules incomplete, ovules basally attached, anatropous. Fruit almost always 1-seeded, stylar remains apical; epicarp covered in neat vertical rows of reflexed scales, mesocarp somewhat spongy, endocarp not differentiated. Seed ± rounded, sarcotesta thick, sour, closely adhering to the inner integument and difficult to separate from it due to the presence of short radiating fibers, endosperm homogeneous, ± disklike or very broadly oblate, with a large, wide pit at the apex; embryo basal or lateral due to distortion of the fruit. Germination adjacent-ligular; eophyll bifid with narrow, entire lobes. Cytology not studied.

Anatomy.—Not studied.

Distribution.—Although five names have been published, there appears to be only one widespread species, known from south Thailand, Sumatra, Peninsular Malaysia, and Borneo.

Ecology.—*E. conferta* is a highly characteristic, gregarious, undergrowth palm of lowland fresh water swamps, being particularly abundant in facies of peat swamp forest where a certain amount of water movement occurs.

Common Names and Uses.—Kelubi or asam paya. Leaves are occasionally used for temporary thatching. The extremely sour sarcotesta is used throughout the range of the palm as a substitute for tamarind in cooking and is sometimes made into a sweetmeat.

Notes.—Burret was amply justified in separating *Eleiodoxa* from *Salacca*. In some ways *Eleiodoxa* seems to link the Metroxylinae with the Calaminae; the fruit, hapaxanthy, and leaf are reminiscent of *Metroxylon*, whereas the dioecy and arrangement of flowers are close to *Salacca* section *Salacca*.

Taxonomic Accounts.—Beccari (1918), Burret (1942).

Plate.—*42C.*

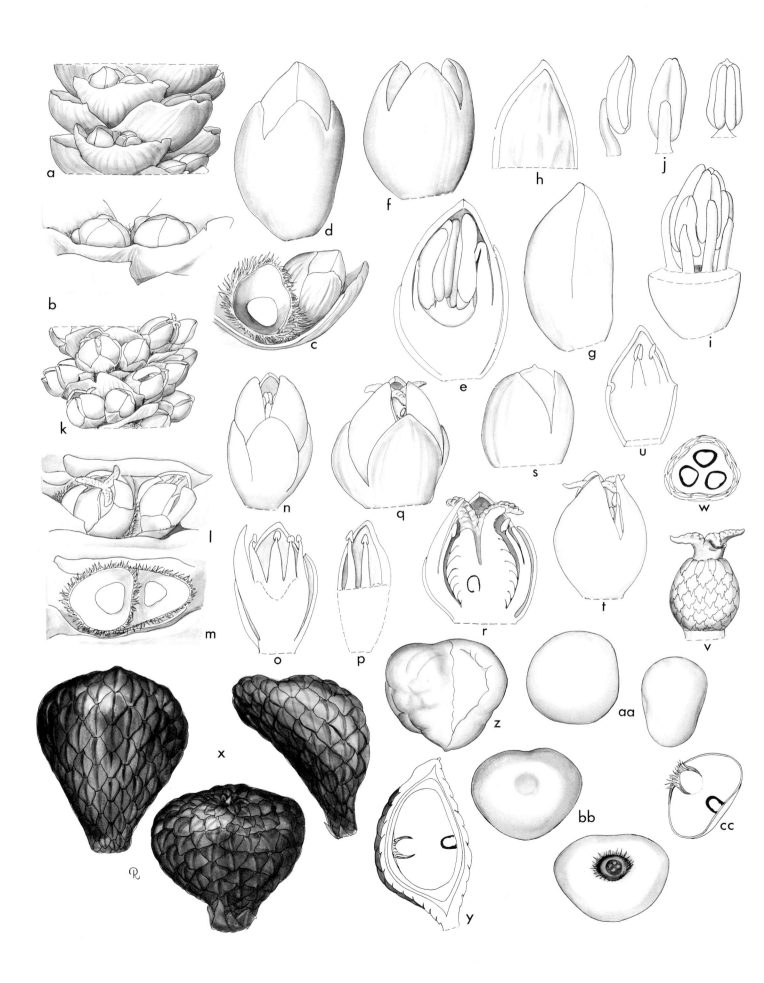

46. SALACCA Reinwardt, Nova Plantarum Indicarum Genera, in Sylloge Plantarum Novarum 2:3. 1826 ("1828"). Type: *S. edulis* Reinwardt = **Salacca zalacca** (J. Gaertner) Voss ex Vilmorin (*Calamus zalacca* J. Gaertner) '*Zalacca*.'

Lophospatha Burret, Notizblatt der Botanischen Gartens und Museums zu Berlin-Dahlem 15:752. 1942. Type: *L. borneensis* Burret (=*Salacca lophospatha* J. Dransfield & Mogea).

Minute to rather robust, usually acaulescent, clustered, spiny, pleonanthic, dioecious palms. Stem subterranean, decumbent or very short and erect, usually obscured by the leaf bases, the internodes short, often with abundant adventitious roots, rarely with short stilt roots, sucker buds leaf opposed at angles of 90–180° from the subtending leaf, very rarely developing as whiplike shoots rooting at their tips. Leaves very small to robust, pinnate, or entire, bifid, with pinnate venation, marcescent; sheath splitting opposite the petiole, unarmed at the extreme base, otherwise very sparsely to very densely armed with robust, scattered or whorled spines and usually with abundant caducous or persistent scales, sheath mouth frequently bearing a tattered ligulelike structure; petiole channeled adaxially near the base, rounded distally and abaxially, variously armed with spines and indumentum, often fiercely so; rachis armed as the petiole, but more sparsely; leaflets single-fold, where pinnate, except for the terminal pair, linear or sigmoid, acuminate or very rarely deeply lobed at the tip, regularly arranged or grouped and fanned within the groups, variously armed with short bristles along the main veins and margins, terminal pair compound, joined along the midline, deeply lobed at the tip, where leaf entire, bifid, the apical margins deeply lobed or almost entire, abaxial blade surface often with a dense covering of powdery indumentum, midribs prominent adaxially, transverse veinlets usually conspicuous. Inflorescences axillary but enclosed within the sheath of the subtending leaf, and emerging through a slit along the midline of the abaxial surface of the sheath, inflorescences usually short, sometimes spicate, more often with 1 or 2 orders of crowded or spreading branches, occasionally hidden by detritus, sometimes arching out of the crown, very rarely whiplike with the tip metamorphosing into a vegetative axis, rooting and becoming established as an independent plant, staminate inflorescences usually branched to at least 1 more order than the pistillate; peduncle usually short; prophyll usually rather inconspicuous, partly enclosed within the leaf sheath slit, tubular, 2-keeled, irregularly tattering; peduncular bracts several, tubular at the base with irregularly tattering, frequently densely scaly limbs; rachis usually longer than the peduncle; rachis bracts like the peduncular bracts; rachillae cylindrical, catkinlike, exposed or hidden by the bracts, bearing a tight spiral of imbricate, triangular or low, rounded bracts, sometimes connate laterally to form a continuous spiral, sometimes very small and scarcely imbricate, each, except for the proximal and most distal few, subtending flowers and sometimes also a dense pile of hairs. Staminate flowers borne in dyads with 2 small prophyllar bracteoles, these sometimes split and variously connate to each other, the flowers exserted from the pit at anthesis; calyx tubular, variously split to give 3 lobes, sometimes distinct almost to the base, chaffy, striate; corolla with a short stalklike base, and a long proximal tube, bearing 3 triangular, ± hooded, valvate lobes; stamens 6, borne at the mouth of the corolla tube, filaments short, wide basally, anthers rounded to elongate, introrse; pollen elliptic, meridionosulcate, with tectate, finely perforate exine and bearing sparse to dense supratectal spines, spinules, or clavate processes (except *S. secunda*, which may be misplaced in *Salacca* and which has elliptic, disulcate pollen with smooth, tectate exine with few perforations); pistillode minute or absent. Pistillate flowers either solitary (Section *Leiosalacca*) or borne in a dyad with a sterile staminate flower (Section *Salacca*) similar to the fertile but with empty anthers; calyx of pistillate flower tubular at the base, distally with 3, triangular, striate lobes; corolla similar with 3, triangular, valvate lobes; staminodes 6, borne at the mouth of the corolla tube, the filaments usually elongate, anthers ± sagittate, empty; gynoecium tricarpellate, triovulate, covered in flattened, smooth, or erect spine-tipped scales, stigmas 3, fleshy, reflexed at anthesis, locules incomplete, ovules basifixed, anatropous. Fruit (1-)(2-) 3-seeded, globose to pear-shaped or ellipsoidal, with apical stigmatic remains; epicarp covered in somewhat irregular vertical rows of reflexed scales, the scale tips smooth (Section *Leiosalacca*) or spinelike and upward pointing (Section *Salacca*), mesocarp very thin at maturity, endocarp not differentiated. Seeds basally attached, conforming to ⅓ or ½ of a sphere (depending on number reaching maturity), sarcotesta very thick, sour or sweet, inner seed coat very thin, endosperm homogeneous, the apex with a pit; embryo basal. Germination adjacent-ligular; eophyll entire bifid. *n* = 14 (*S. zalacca* as *S. edulis*, Sarkar 1970).

←

45.—**Eleiodoxa. a,** portion of staminate rachilla × 3; **b,** dyad of staminate flower × 4½; **c,** dyad of staminate flowers, one flower removed to show bracteole and hairs × 4½; **d,** staminate bud × 7½; **e,** staminate bud in vertical section × 7½; **f,** staminate calyx × 7½; **g,** staminate bud, calyx removed × 7½; **h,** staminate petal × 7½; **i,** androecium × 7½; **j,** stamen in 3 views × 7½; **k,** portion of pistillate rachilla × 2¼; **l,** dyad of a pistillate and sterile staminate flower × 4½; **m,** dyad of a pistillate and sterile staminate flower, flowers removed to show bracteoles and hairs × 4½; **n,** sterile staminate flower × 6; **o,** sterile staminate flower in vertical section × 6; **p,** sterile staminate petal and staminodes × 6; **q,** pistillate flower × 6; **r,** pistillate flower in vertical section × 6; **s,** pistillate calyx × 6; **t,** pistillate flower, calyx removed × 6; **u,** pistillate petal and staminodes, interior view × 6; **v,** gynoecium × 6; **w,** ovary in cross-section × 7½; **x,** fruit in 3 views × 1; **y,** fruit in vertical section × 1; **z,** sarcotesta × 1; **aa,** seed in 2 views × 1; **bb,** seed in 2 views × 1½; **cc,** seed in vertical section × 1. *Eleiodoxa conferta:* **a–j,** *Dransfield 757;* **k–w,** *Dransfield s.n.;* **x–cc,** *Dransfield 724.*

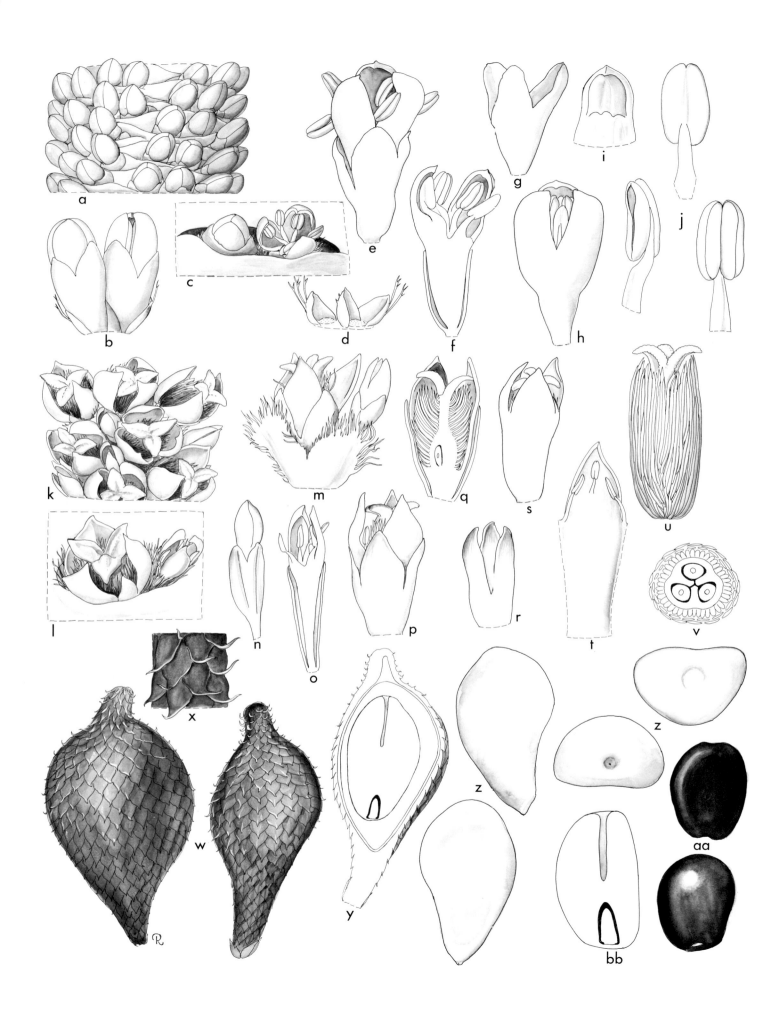

Anatomy.—Leaf, petiole, stem, root (Tomlinson 1961). Differs from other Calamoideae in having very large epidermal cells with sinuous walls.

Distribution.—About 15 recognized species but several more remain to be described; distributed from Burma and Indochina, south and eastwards to Borneo, Java, and the Philippines. *S. zalacca,* wild in Java and Sumatra, has been introduced into Malaya, Borneo, Sulawesi, the Moluccas, and Bali for its excellent fruit. The greatest number of species and morphological diversity is found in Malaya and Borneo.

Ecology.—*Salacca* species are plants of the undergrowth of primary tropical rain forest; however, because of their usefulness as a source of fruit and building materials they may be left after the surrounding forest has been destroyed and persist in the open. Many species favor swampy valley bottoms where they form rather dense spiny thickets. Other species may be found on hillslopes or ridgetops. *S. rupicola* grows in the crevices of limestone cliffs and in the dwarf forest on limestone hilltops.

Common Names and Uses.—Salak. *S. zalacca* is cultivated for its excellent fruit and fruits of other species are eaten although they are sometimes very sour. Petioles of *S. wallichiana* are sometimes used in house construction in Thailand (Dransfield 1981c). The leaves of several species provide temporary thatch. The spiny petioles of *S. zalacca* are occasionally employed in Java to prevent thieves from climbing fruit trees and bats from roosting on roof beams.

Notes.—*Salacca* is neatly divisible into two sections—section *Salacca* with spine-tipped scales and pistillate rachillae bearing dyads of a fertile pistillate and a sterile staminate flower and section *Leiosalacca* with smooth scales and pistillate rachillae bearing solitary pistillate flowers. It is possible that when these interesting plants become better known, it may be necessary to recognize the sections at a generic level. The little known *Salacca secunda* appears to be hapaxanthic (from herbarium material) and is palynologically different from other *Salacca* species; it is possible its affinities lie more with *Eleiodoxa* but until material becomes available, its relationships must remain in doubt.

Taxonomic Accounts.—Beccari (1918), Furtado (1949), Mogea (1980).

Plates.—*12A; 42D.*

47. DAEMONOROPS Blume in J. A. & J. H. Schultes, Systema Vegetabilium 7:1333. 1830. Type: **D. melanochaetes** Blume.

Solitary or clustered, spiny, acaulescent, erect, or high-climbing, hapaxanthic or pleonanthic, dioecious, rattan palms. Stem eventually becoming bare, with short to long internodes, branching at the base from axillary or leaf-opposed buds. Leaves pinnate, very rarely bifid, usually with a terminal cirrus except in a few acaulescent species and in juvenile individuals; sheath splitting in acaulescent species, in the exposed area densely armed with spines, these frequently organized into whorls and in a few species forming interlocking galleries occupied by ants, scaly or floccose indumentum often abundant between the spines and along their margins; ocrea rarely present; knee present in climbing species; flagellum absent; petiole usually well developed, grooved to rounded adaxially, rounded abaxially, variously armed; rachis and cirrus, except in acaulescent species, armed with grouped reflexed grapnel spines and scattered caducous tomentum; leaflets single-fold, entire, linear to broadly lanceolate, regularly arranged or grouped, rarely fanned within the groups, variously armed with bristles along the longitudinal veins and margins, midribs prominent, 1 pair of lateral veins sometimes large, transverse veinlets short, often conspicuous. Inflorescences axillary but adnate to the internode and leaf sheath of the following leaf, very rarely several inflorescences produced simultaneously from the axils of the most distal leaves, the stem then hapaxanthic, branching to 2–3 orders, staminate and pistillate inflorescences superficially similar, but the staminate usually branching to 1 order more than the pistillate; peduncle absent or present, sometimes very long, erect or pendulous, variously armed; prophyll conspicuous, 2-keeled, woody, coriaceous, membranous or papery, variously armed, tubular at first, later splitting along ± its entire length; peduncular bracts usually absent; rachis bracts ± distichous, similar to the pro-

---

←

46.—**Salacca. a,** portion of staminate rachilla ×4½; **b, c,** dyad of staminate flowers in 2 views ×6; **d,** dyad of staminate flowers, flowers removed to show bracteoles ×6; **e,** staminate flower ×7½; **f,** staminate flower in vertical section ×7½; **g,** staminate calyx ×7½; **h,** staminate flower, calyx removed ×7½; **i,** staminate petal, interior view ×7½; **j,** stamen in 3 views ×15; **k,** portion of pistillate rachilla ×3; **l,** dyad of a pistillate and sterile staminate flower ×4½; **m,** dyad of a pistillate and sterile staminate flower with bracteoles ×3; **n,** sterile staminate flower ×3; **o,** sterile staminate flower in vertical section ×4½; **p,** pistillate flower ×3; **q,** pistillate flower in vertical section ×3; **r,** pistillate calyx ×3; **s,** pistillate flower, calyx removed ×3; **t,** pistillate petal with staminodes, interior view ×4½; **u,** gynoecium ×4½; **v,** ovary in cross-section ×7½; **w,** fruit in 2 views ×1; **x,** scales of fruit ×2¼; **y,** fruit in vertical section ×1; **z,** sarcotesta in 4 views ×1; **aa,** seed in 2 views ×1; **bb,** seed in vertical section ×1½. *Salacca glabrescens:* **a-v,** *Dransfield 682; S. zalacca:* **w-bb,** *Dransfield 921.*

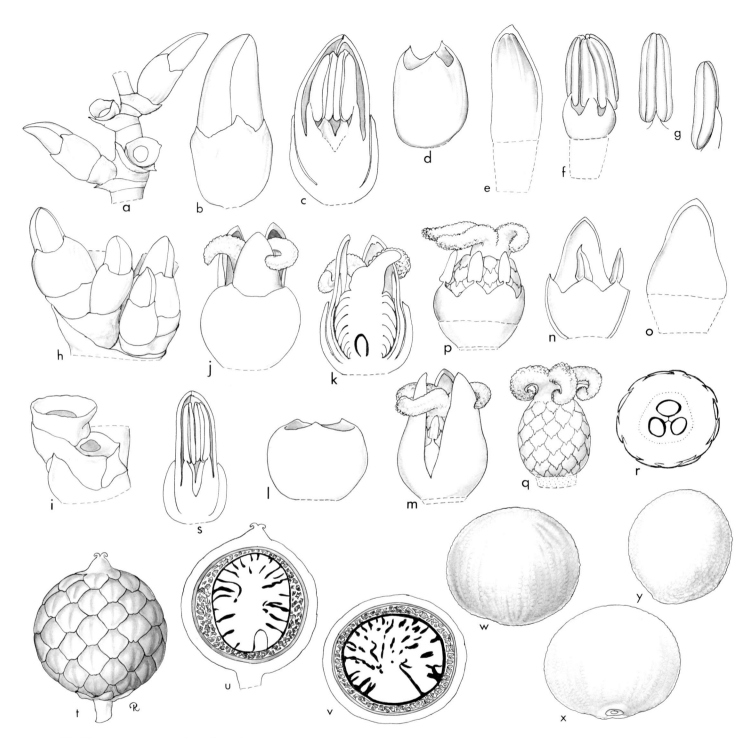

47.—**Daemonorops. a,** portion of staminate rachilla, some flowers removed to show subtending bract and bracteole ×4½; **b,** staminate bud ×9; **c,** staminate bud in vertical section ×9; **d,** staminate calyx ×9; **e,** staminate petal, interior view ×9; **f,** androecium ×9; **g,** stamen in 2 views ×12; **h,** portion of pistillate rachilla with dyads of pistillate and sterile staminate flowers ×4½; **i,** dyad, flowers removed to show bracteoles ×6; **j,** pistillate flower ×6; **k,** pistillate flower in vertical section ×6; **l,** pistillate calyx ×6; **m,** pistillate flower, calyx removed ×6; **n,** pistillate petal and staminodes, interior view ×6; **o,** pistillate petal, interior view ×6; **p,** gynoecium and staminodial ring ×6; **q,** gynoecium ×6; **r,** ovary in cross-section ×6; **s,** sterile staminate flower in vertical section ×6; **t,** fruit ×2¼; **u,** fruit in vertical section ×2¼; **v,** fruit in cross-section ×2¼; **w, x, y,** seed in 3 views ×2¼. *Daemonorops grandis*: **a-g,** *Moore 9044*; *D. angustifolia*: **h-y,** *Moore 9067*.

phyll, also splitting along their entire length, sometimes with the tips remaining enclosed within the tip of the prophyll to form a beak, the flowers at anthesis thus enclosed, or with the tips free, and all bracts but the prophyll normally falling at anthesis, the flowers then exposed or very rarely the bracts persisting; prophyll often empty, sometimes subtending a first-order branch as the other rachis bracts; first-order branches usually covered with abundant floccose indumentum, and bearing very small, truncate, ± distichous bracts, more rarely bracts larger and tattering, each bract subtending a second-order branch adnate to the first-order branch above the node; second-order branches in pistillate inflorescence bearing dyads, in staminate inflorescence branched a further time to give 3 orders of branching, each branch subtended by a bract, staminate inflorescence with flowers sometimes strictly distichous and crowded, or ± distant and subdistichous, sometimes arranged distantly along one side of the rachilla, each flower subtended by a small triangular scale-like bract, more rarely by a short tubular bract, the bracts then ± imbricate. Staminate flowers bearing a short, tubular, 2-keeled prophyll (the involucre of Beccari) sometimes ± stalklike, frequently very inconspicuous; calyx cupular, striate, shallowly 3-lobed; corolla exceeding the calyx, usually at least twice as long, divided almost to the base into 3, narrow triangular petals; stamens 6, borne at the mouth of the tubular corolla base, usually ± equal, rarely of 2 sizes, filaments slender to rather broad, fleshy, terminating in slender to broad connectives, anthers narrow elongate to broad and somewhat sinuous, introrse; pollen mostly elliptic, sometimes slightly curved, disulcate or diporate (with transitional types between the two), the exine intectate and coarsely spiny to densely spinulate, or tectate and smooth, perforate, rugulate, or finely to very coarsely reticulate; pistillode short, trifid to elongate, slender and unlobed, or absent. Pistillate inflorescences like the staminate but with more robust rachillae, pistillate flowers borne in a dyad with a sterile staminate flower; dyad prophyll (involucrophore) usually conspicuously angular, stalklike; prophyll of pistillate flower (involucre) inconspicuous or cuplike, forming a cushion bearing the flower. Sterile staminate flower quickly shed, as the fertile but with empty anthers. Pistillate flowers only slightly larger than the staminate; calyx cupular, striate, shallowly 3-lobed; corolla ± twice as long as the calyx, divided to ±½ into 3, triangular valvate petals; staminodes 6, borne at the mouth of the corolla tube, with empty anthers; gynoecium incompletely trilocular, triovulate, ovary variable in shape, scaly, stigmas 3, recurved, fleshy, ovules basally attached, anatropous. Fruit variously rounded, obpyriform, turbinate, cylindrical or oblate with apical stigmatic remains; epicarp covered in neat vertical rows of reflexed, sometimes resinous scales, mesocarp thin, endocarp not differentiated. Seed, usually only 1 reaching maturity, angular or rounded, covered with thick, sweet or sour and bitter sarcotesta, endosperm deeply ruminate; embryo basal. Germination adjacent-ligular; eophyll usually pinnate, sometimes with congested leaflets and appearing almost palmate. $n = 14$ (*D. grandis*, Eichhorn 1957, Sharma and Sarkar 1957; *D. calicarpa, D. longipes*, Sarkar 1970). $n = 13$ (*D. cristata, D. formicaria*, Johnson 1985).

Anatomy.—Leaf, petiole, stem, and root (Tomlinson 1961). Leaves can often be distinguished from *Calamus* by structure of the guard cells, by more frequent and longer fibers around the transverse veinlets, and by the presence of large tannin cells.

Distribution.—About 115 species; distributed from India and south China through the Malay Archipelago to New Guinea where represented by one species; the greatest morphological diversity and number of species is in the Malay Peninsula, Sumatra, and Borneo.

Ecology.—Species are mostly confined to primary tropical rain forest on a great variety of soils, some species with narrow ecological requirements. A few are of a rather more weedy nature, abundant in forest habitats with high-light intensities such as riverbanks; one species in Borneo, *D. longispatha,* grows on the landward margin of mangrove forest. Some species are strictly montane, occurring at altitudes up to ca. 2500 m above sea level. Several species in Borneo are confined to heath forest, or limestone, or serpentine rock. With so many species, it is difficult to give more precise ecological data.

Fossil Record.—See under *Calamus.*

Common Names and Uses.—Rattan, rotan; for local names see Dransfield 1979a. The canes of many species are of good quality and enter the rattan trade besides being used locally. The apices of several species are sought after for food. In the past, red resin from the fruits of species related to and including *D. draco* and *D. rubra* was collected as "dragon's blood" for medicinal or dyeing purposes and at one time "dragon's blood" was an item of trade between Borneo, Sumatra and the Malay Peninsula, and China.

Notes.—The genus is divisible into two sections based on the arrangement and persistence of the rachis bracts of the inflorescence. Palynologically so-called section "*Cymbospatha*" (correctly section *Daemonorops*) is very uniform whereas section *Piptospatha* shows a truly remarkable diversity in pollen form. The genus is most closely related to *Calamus, Calospatha, Pogonotium,* and *Ceratolobus.*

Taxonomic Accounts.—Beccari (1911), Furtado (1953), and Dransfield (1979a).

Plates.—*12B, C; 43A; Figs. G.20, G.21, G.22.*

48. **Calamus** Linnaeus, Species Plantarum 325. 1753. Type: **C. rotang** Linnaeus.

Rotanga Boehmer in C. G. Ludwig, Definitiones Generum Plantarum Ed. 3. 395. 1760.

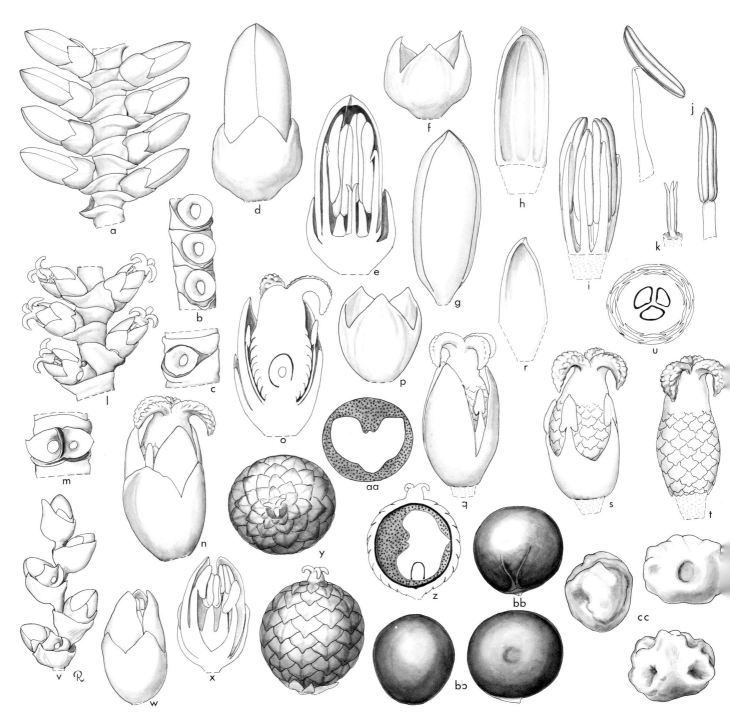

48.—**Calamus. a,** portion of staminate rachilla ×6; **b, c,** portions of staminate rachillae, flowers removed to show subtending bracts and bracteoles ×6; **d,** staminate bud ×12; **e,** staminate bud in vertical section ×12; **f,** staminate calyx ×12; **g,** staminate bud, calyx removed ×12; **h,** staminate petal, interior view ×12; **i,** androecium ×12; **j,** stamen in 2 views ×12; **k,** pistillode ×12; **l,** portion of pistillate rachilla with dyads of pistillate and sterile staminate flowers, sterile staminate flowers removed ×6; **m,** dyad, flowers removed to show subtending bract and bracteoles ×9; **n,** pistillate flower ×15; **o,** pistillate flower in vertical section ×15; **p,** pistillate calyx ×15; **q,** pistillate flower, calyx removed ×15; **r,** pistillate petal ×15; **s,** gynoecium and staminodial ring ×15; **t,** gynoecium ×15; **u,** ovary ×15; **v,** portion of pistillate rachilla with dyads of pistillate and sterile staminate flowers, the latter removed ×6; **w,** sterile staminate flower ×12; **x,** sterile staminate flower in vertical section ×12; **y,** fruit in 2 views ×4½; **z,** fruit in vertical section ×12; **aa,** sarcotesta in cross-section ×4½; **bb,** sarcotesta in 3 views ×4½; **cc,** seed in 3 views ×7½. *Calamus javensis:* **a-k** *Dransfield 4519; C. acuminatus:* **l-u** and **y-cc,** *Moore 9208;* **v-x,** *San 23490.*

Rotang Adanson, Familles des Plantes 2:24, 599. 1763.

Palmijuncus O. Kuntze, Revisio Generum Plantarum 2:731. 1891.

Zalaccella Beccari, Annals of the Royal Botanic Garden, Calcutta 11(1):496. 1908. Type: *Z. harmandii* (Pierre ex Beccari) Beccari (*Calamus harmandii* Pierre ex Beccari).

Schizospatha Furtado, Gardens' Bulletin, Singapore 14:525. 1955. Type: *S. setigera* (Burret) Furtado (*Calamus setiger* Burret).

Cornera Furtado, Gardens' Bulletin, Singapore 14: 518. 1955. Type: *C. pycnocarpa* Furtado (=*Calamus pycnocarpus* (Furtado) J. Dransfield).

Solitary or clustered, spiny, acaulescent, erect, or high-climbing, pleonanthic, dioecious, rattan palms. Stem eventually becoming bare, with short to long internodes, sucker shoots strictly axillary. Leaves pinnate, rarely bifid, sometimes with a terminal cirrus; sheath splitting in acaulescent species, in the exposed area usually densely armed with scattered or whorled spines, in 1 species (*C. polystachys*) the spines interlocking to form galleries occupied by ants, indumentum often abundant on sheath surface; ocrea often present, sometimes greatly elaborated, papery and disintegrating, or coriaceous, rarely greatly swollen or diverging with inrolled margins and occupied by ants; knee present in most climbing species; flagellum (climbing whip derived from a sterile inflorescence) often present in species lacking cirri, very rarely a small vestigial flagellum present in cirrate species; petiole absent or well developed, flattened adaxially, rounded abaxially, variously armed; rachis often armed with distant groups of reflexed grapnel spines; cirrus when present armed with scattered (rarely) or grouped reflexed spines; leaflets few to very numerous, single-fold, entire or very rarely praemorse, linear to lanceolate or rhomboid, sometimes the terminal pair partially fused along their inner margins forming a terminal flabellum to the leaf, regularly arranged or irregular, grouped, sometimes fanned within the groups, concolorous or discolorous, variously bearing hairs, bristles, spines, and scales, midribs conspicuous or not, transverse veinlets conspicuous or obscure. Inflorescences axillary but adnate to the internode and leaf sheath of the following leaf, staminate and pistillate superficially similar, but the staminate usually branching to 3 orders and the pistillate to 2 orders, the inflorescence frequently flagelliform, very rarely rooting at its tip and producing a new vegetative shoot; peduncle absent or present, sometimes very long, erect or pendulous, variously armed; prophyll usually inconspicuous, 2-keeled, tubular, tightly sheathing, variously armed or unarmed, rarely inflated, papery or coriaceous, splitting down one side, usually empty; rachis bracts persistent, like the prophyll, close or sometimes very distant, variously armed, usually strictly tubular, even where splitting remaining tubular at the base, rarely irregularly tattering in the distal part, each subtending a first-order branch or "partial inflorescence," this frequently adnate to the rachis above the bract axil, very

rarely bursting through the bract; first-order branch bearing a 2-keeled, tubular prophyll and ± subdistichous, tubular bracts, unarmed or variously armed, each subtending a second-order branch, usually adnate to the first-order branch above the bract node; rachillae very varied within the genus, spreading to very short and crowded, bearing a basal, 2-keeled prophyll and conspicuous, usually distichous, tubular bracts with triangular tips, variously armed or unarmed, very rarely the bracts highly condensed and spiral, in staminate rachilla, each bract subtending a solitary staminate flower bearing a prophyllar bracteole, in pistillate rachilla each bract subtending a dyad of a sterile staminate and a fertile pistillate flower and 2, usually quite conspicuous, prophyllar bracteoles, very rarely each bract subtending a triad of 2 lateral pistillate flowers and a central sterile staminate flower. Staminate flowers symmetrical; calyx tubular at the base, 3-lobed distally; corolla usually exceeding the calyx, divided into 3, valvate lobes except at the tubular base; stamens 6, borne at the mouth of the corolla tube, filaments often fleshy, elongate, sometimes abruptly narrowed, anthers medifixed, short to elongate, latrorse or introrse; pollen elliptic or circular, disulcate, the exine tectate, finely to coarsely reticulate, verrucate, or sometimes bearing large, rounded excrescences; pistillode minute to quite conspicuous. Sterile staminate flowers like the fertile but with empty anthers. Pistillate flowers usually larger than the staminate; calyx tubular, shallowly 3-lobed; corolla rarely exceeding the calyx, divided more deeply than the calyx into 3 valvate lobes; staminodes 6, epipetalous, the filaments distinct or united into a short ring, anthers empty; gynoecium tricarpellate, triovulate, spherical to ellipsoidal, covered in reflexed scales, stigmas 3, apical, fleshy, reflexed, sometimes borne on a beak, locules incomplete, ovules basal, anatropous. Fruit usually 1-seeded, rarely consistently 2- or 3-seeded, stigmatic remains apical; epicarp covered in neat vertical rows of reflexed scales, mesocarp usually very thin at maturity, endocarp not differentiated. Seed with thick sweet, sour, or astringent sarcotesta, inner part of the seed rounded, grooved, angled, or sharply winged, endosperm homogeneous or ruminate; embryo basal or lateral. Germination adjacent-ligular; eophyll bifid, or pinnate. *n* = 13 (*C. caryotoides, C. muelleri*, Read 1965a). *n* = 14 (*C. caryotoides*, Janaki Ammal 1945; *C. arborescens, C. khasianus, C. leptospadix, C. rotang*, Sharma and Sarkar 1957; *C. scipionum*, Eichhorn 1953).

Anatomy.—Leaf, petiole, stem, root (Tomlinson 1961). Similar in anatomy to *Calospatha, Ceratolobus, Myrialepis*, and *Plectocomiopsis*.

Distribution.—With about 370 species, *Calamus* is the largest palm genus. It has a very wide distribution, occurring in the humid tropics of Africa (1 variable or several closely related species), India, Burma, and south China through the Malay Archipelago to Queensland and Fiji, reaching greatest diversity and number of species in the Sunda Shelf area (especially Borneo), with a second center of diversity in New Guinea.

Ecology.—The ecology is very varied as might be

expected in such a large genus, but, although some species are adapted to seasonally dry habitats such as monsoon forest, there are no species in semi-arid habitats. There are species adapted to submangrove conditions (*C. erinaceus*). Other species have narrow ecological requirements such as limestone or ultrabasic soils. In altitude the genus ranges from sea level to 3000 m (on Mt. Kinabalu—*C. gibbsianus*).

Fossil Record.—Paleocene coal samples in Sarawak contain very large quantities of *Calamus* type pollen (Muller 1979). Fossil pollen is referable to two types. Muller (1981) recorded *C. longisetus* type pollen, from the Paleocene upwards in Borneo and it is also recorded from Upper Paleocene–Upper Eocene of France, the Lower Miocene of Bohemia, and the Eocene of southern U.S. A second type, similar to that of *C. gracilis,* occurs from the middle Miocene upwards in Borneo and is found in several other species of the genus.

Remains of bark, thorns, aerial roots, and leaf bases (*Spinophyllum daemonorops* from the Miocene and Upper Oligocene of numerous European localities have been referred to *Daemonorops, Plectocomia,* and *Calamus* (Czeczott and Juchniewicz 1980) but could represent spiny members of the Cocoeae. Leaves and fruit of *Calamus daemonorops* are reported from Eocene London Clay (Chandler 1961–1964) and other remains from Germany (Gregor 1982).

Common Names and Uses.—Rattans, rotan; for local names see Dransfield (1979a). The finest kinds of rattan are all species of *Calamus*. *C. manan, C. caesius,* and *C. trachycoleus,* in particular, dominate world trade in rattans. Other species are almost as important. For further details of rattans and their exploitation see Dransfield (1979a). Species of *Calamus* have a wide range of uses apart from entering the rattan trade. Leaves are used for thatch, spines in various ways, cirri have been used for constructing fish traps, fruits are eaten and may even be sold in local markets, and some species may be medicinally valuable.

Notes.—This protean genus, the largest in the family, has yet to be treated satisfactorily at the subgeneric level. Beccari's informal groupings remain the most useful subgeneric categories.

Draco Crantz, De Duabus Draconis Arboribus Botanicorum 13. 1768, is occasionally cited as a synonym of *Calamus*. We have been unable to locate a satisfactory lectotypification of the generic name; of the six specific names published by Crantz,

two refer to *Dracaena draco,* two to *Pterocarpus* spp., one (*Draco thaa* Crantz) is without equivalent in Index Kewensis, and one refers to *Calamus rotang* in synonymy. We suggest it more appropriate to select *Draco clusii* Crantz as type of the genus, *Draco* thus becoming a synonym of *Dracaena* (Dracaenaceae). *Calamus rotang* does not produce dragon's blood, nor does any other species of the genus.

Taxonomic Accounts.—Beccari (1908, 1913b), Dransfield (1979a).

Plates.—*12D; 43B; Figs. G.2, G.6, G.7.*

49. CALOSPATHA Beccari, Annals of the Royal Botanic Garden, Calcutta 12(1):232. 1911. Type: **C. scortechinii** Beccari.

Moderately robust, solitary, erect or short-climbing, spiny, pleonanthic, dioecious, rattan palm. Stem eventually becoming bare, relatively robust, nodal scars conspicuous, all parts exuding yellow gum on wounding. Leaves without cirrus, pinnate; sheath tubular, densely armed with robust spines, those around the mouth extremely large and ± erect, caducous indumentum present between spines: ocrea absent; knee very conspicuous, grossly swollen; flagellum absent; petiole well developed, semicircular in cross-section, armed with scattered spines; rachis with reflexed grapnel spines in groups of up to 5 on abaxial surface, scattered spines on both surfaces; leaflets numerous, regularly arranged, single-fold, linear, bearing short teeth along margins and bristles along the main veins, midribs prominent, transverse veinlets conspicuous. Inflorescences axillary but adnate to the internode and sheath of the following leaf, erect at first, becoming pendulous, staminate and pistillate superficially similar, much shorter than the leaves, usually much shorter than the petioles, branching in staminate to 3 orders, in pistillate to 2 orders; peduncle short, very spiny; prophyll persistent, ± horizontal, tubular at first, but splitting along the abaxial face almost to the very base, abruptly contracted to form an apical beak, the beak and the 2 keels with numerous flattened spines, very sparsely armed elsewhere, caducous indumentum abundant; peduncular bracts absent; rachis and rachis bracts scarcely exceeding the prophyll, rachis bracts persistent, tubular at first, soon splitting along the ventral midline, arranged distichously in a plane at right angles to the prophyll, oblong, abruptly narrowed to an apical beak, densely spiny on the abaxial surface of the beak, very sparsely armed or unarmed elsewhere, prophyll and rachis bracts each subtending a first-order branch, ± concealed by the bract; further orders of branches each subtended by small membranous tubular bracts with triangular limbs, and bearing a 2-keeled prophyll. Staminate flowers solitary, each subtended by a minute, short tubular or open, triangular bract and bearing a 2-keeled bracteole; calyx somewhat fleshy, tubular in proximal part with 3, apiculate, valvate lobes, the tube occasionally splitting at anthesis; corolla briefly tubular with 3, fleshy, triangular, valvate lobes; stamens 6, borne at the mouth of the corolla tube, filaments fleshy, adnate laterally and swelling at the base to occlude the corolla

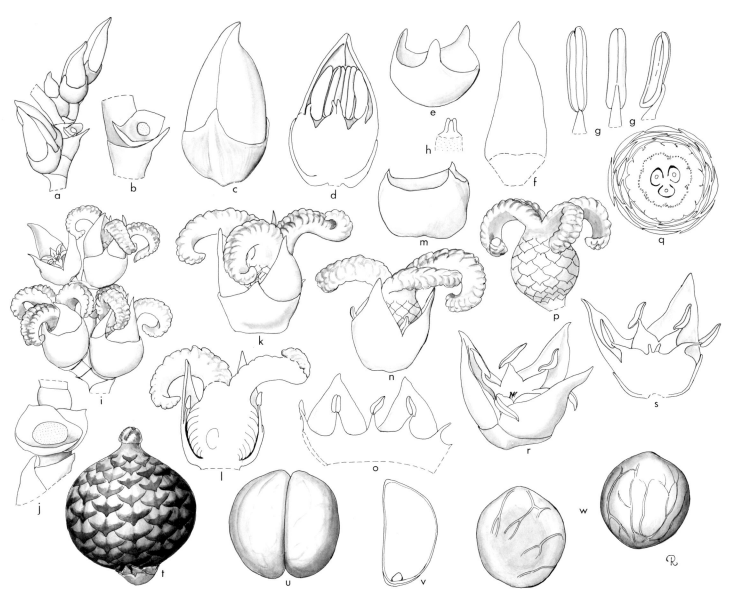

49.—**Calospatha. a,** portion of staminate rachilla ×3; **b,** portion of staminate rachilla, flower removed to show subtending bract and bracteole ×7½; **c,** staminate bud ×7½; **d,** staminate bud in vertical section ×7½; **e,** staminate calyx ×7½; **f,** staminate petal ×7½; **g,** stamen in 3 views ×15; **h,** pistillode ×7½; **i,** pistillate rachilla showing a dyad (top) of a pistillate and sterile staminate flower and two pistillate flowers (bottom) ×3; **j,** portion of pistillate rachilla, flower removed to show subtending bracteoles ×4½; **k,** pistillate flower ×4½; **l,** pistillate flower in vertical section ×4½; **m,** pistillate calyx ×4½; **n,** pistillate flower, calyx removed ×4½; **o,** pistillate corolla and staminodial ring, interior view, expanded ×4½; **p,** gynoecium ×4½; **q,** ovary in cross-section ×7½; **r,** sterile staminate flower ×4½; **s,** sterile staminate flower in vertical section ×4½; **t,** fruit ×1½; **u,** pair of almost mature seeds ×1½; **v,** seed in vertical section ×1½; **w,** seed in 2 views ×1½. *Calospatha scortechinii*: **a-h,** *Dransfield 4995*; **i-s,** *Dransfield 4947*; **t-w,** *Dransfield 5117*.

tube, tapering distally, anthers linear, latrorse; pollen elliptic, diporate, with punctate, tectate exine; pistillode trifid, minute, usually completely obscured by the swollen filament bases. Pistillate flowers in dyads consisting of a pistillate and a sterile staminate flower and 2, 2-keeled bracteoles, the tips of the rachillae sometimes with a few solitary, sterile staminate flowers. Sterile staminate flowers like the fertile but anthers empty and filaments even

fleshier. Pistillate flowers longer than the staminate; calyx tubular, striate, with 3 short triangular, valvate lobes, later tending to split after fertilization; corolla tubular proximally for ½ its length with 3, triangular, valvate lobes; staminodes 6, borne at the mouth of the corolla tube, filament bases united to form a thin membranous ring, the distinct portions of the filaments triangular, empty anthers small, flattened, easily dislodged; gynoecium in-

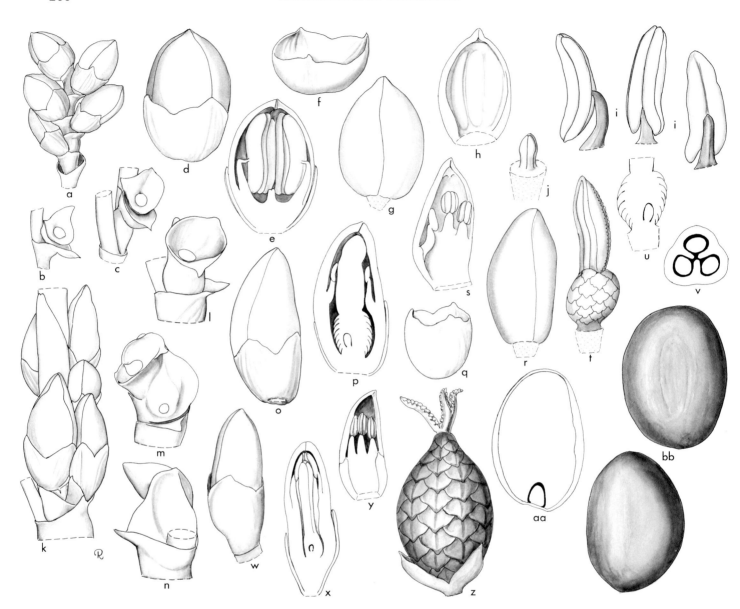

50.—**Pogonotium. a,** portion of staminate rachilla ×4½; **b, c,** portions of staminate rachilla, flowers removed to show subtending bracts and bracteoles ×7½; **d,** staminate bud ×9; **e,** staminate bud in vertical section ×9; **f,** staminate calyx ×9; **g,** staminate bud, calyx removed ×9; **h,** staminate petal, interior view ×9; **i,** stamen in 3 views ×15; **j,** pistillode ×18; **k,** portion of pistillate inflorescence with dyads of pistillate and sterile staminate flowers ×4½; **l,** portion of pistillate inflorescence, pistillate flower removed to show subtending bracteole ×7½; **m,** portion of pistillate inflorescence, pistillate (top) and sterile staminate (bottom) flowers removed to show subtending bracteoles ×7½; **n,** back view of **m** showing portion of axis ×7½; **o,** pistillate bud ×6; **p,** pistillate bud in vertical section ×6; **q,** pistillate calyx ×6; **r,** pistillate bud, calyx removed ×6; **s,** pistillate petal and staminodes, interior view ×6; **t,** gynoecium ×6; **u,** ovary in vertical section ×6; **v,** ovary in cross-section ×9; **w,** sterile staminate flower ×6; **x,** sterile staminate flower in vertical section ×6; **y,** sterile staminate petal with staminodes ×6; **z,** fruit ×3; **aa,** seed in vertical section ×3; **bb,** seed in 2 views ×3. *Pogonotium ursinum*: **a–j,** *Dransfield 5877*; *P. moorei*: **k–bb,** *Dransfield 6102.*

completely trilocular, triovulate, ovoid, scaly, stigmas 3, very large, fleshy, sinuous or reflexed, ovules anatropous, basally attached. Mature fruit usually 3-seeded, globose to ovoid, obscurely 3-angled, beaked, the stigmatic re-

mains apical; epicarp covered in vertical rows of reflexed, shiny, dark brown scales, mesocarp very thin, endocarp not differentiated. Seeds basally attached (shaped as a ⅓ of a sphere where 3 seeds develop or hemispherical where only 2 develop), sarcotesta thick, sweet, endosperm homogeneous; embryo basal. Germination adjacent-ligular; eophyll pinnate. Cytology not studied.

Anatomy. — Leaf (Tomlinson 1961).

Distribution. — Monotypic, endemic to the Malay Peninsula, known from three extant localities in Selangor and Negri Sembilan, previously known from Perak.

Ecology. — *C. scortechinii* seems to be confined to valley bottoms and lower hillslopes in hill Dipterocarp forest at altitudes up to 600 m. Although its habitat is apparently unspecialized and widespread, it is a very rare palm.

Common Names and Uses. — Rotan demuk. The fruits are regarded as a delicacy by the Temuan aborigines of Selangor.

Notes. — The absence of climbing organs, the strange, decorative rachis bracts, and the ± constant presence of three seeds are unusual features that make it easy to identify this striking rattan genus.

Taxonomic Accounts. — Beccari (1918) and Dransfield (1979a).

Plate. — *43C; Fig. G.18.*

50. Pogonotium J. Dransfield, Kew Bulletin 34(4): 763. 1980. Type: **P. ursinum** (Beccari) J. Dransfield (*Daemonorops ursina* Beccari).

Solitary or clustered, spiny, erect or short-climbing, pleonanthic, dioecious, rattan palms. Stem with short internodes. Leaves pinnate, without cirrus; sheath tubular, densely armed with whorled and scattered spines and caducous tomentum, terminating in 2 erect, narrow auricles, 1 on each side of the petiole, the auricles variously armed like the sheath; knee absent or poorly developed; flagellum absent; petiole well developed, flat adaxially, rounded abaxially, armed with reflexed grapnel spines and various papillae and hairs; rachis armed as the petiole; leaflets few to very numerous, linear, single-fold, regularly arranged, very crowded to very distant, the surface covered with a variety of bristles and scales, midribs prominent adaxially, transverse veinlets short, conspicuous. Inflorescences axillary but adnate to the internode and leaf sheath of the following leaf, held erect between the 2 auricles of the subtending leaf, ± sessile, the pistillate branching to 2 orders, the staminate to 3 orders; prophyll enclosing the inflorescence, boat-shaped, with a flattened beak, armed or unarmed, splitting longitudinally along the mid ad- or abaxial line, thus exposing the flowers; peduncular bracts absent; rachis bracts very much smaller than the prophyll, with free tips, each and the prophyll subtending a variously hairy branch; bracts on first-order branches tubular at the base, with triangular limbs. Staminate flowers solitary, borne subdistichously on branches of the second or third order, each subtended by a minute, short, tubular, triangular bract and bearing a 2-keeled bracteole; calyx tubular in proximal part, striate, with 3 triangular lobes;

corolla split almost to the base into 3 triangular valvate lobes; stamens 6, borne at the base of the corolla lobes, filaments fleshy, elongate, inflexed at the tips, anthers oblong, medifixed, sagittate basally, latrorse; pollen elliptic, diporate, with rugulate to reticulate, tectate exine; pistillode minute. Pistillate flowers in dyads, each subtended by a small, triangular bract, and consisting of a pistillate and a sterile staminate flower and 2, 2-keeled cuplike bracteoles. Sterile staminate flower like the fertile but tending to be contorted by close-packing and with empty flattened anthers and a variable pistillode. Pistillate flowers larger than the staminate; calyx cupular, striate, lobes triangular, valvate; corolla split almost to the base into 3 triangular, valvate lobes; staminodes 6, epipetalous; gynoecium incompletely trilocular, triovulate, ovoid, scaly, stigmas 3, fleshy, rugose, divergent, ovule basally attached, anatropous. Fruit 1-seeded, globose or ovoid, beaked, stigmatic remains apical; epicarp covered in neat vertical rows of reflexed magenta to chestnut-colored scales, mesocarp becoming thin and dry at maturity, endocarp not differentiated. Seed basally attached, sarcotesta thick, sweet, endosperm homogeneous; embryo basal. Germination adjacent-ligular; eophyll pinnate or with a single pair of divergent leaflets. Cytology not studied.

Anatomy. — Not studied.

Distribution. — Three species, one in the Malay Peninsula and Sarawak (Borneo), the other two confined to Sarawak.

Ecology. — In Borneo, all three species occur as small populations confined to podsolized soils on ridgetops at about 700–1000 m altitude (at the transition between lowland and montane forest), or to some facies of "kerangas" forest (Bornean heath forest). Nothing is known of the habitat of *P. ursinum* in the Malay Peninsula.

Common Names and Uses. — Common names not recorded. No local uses have been recorded. *P. ursinum* is very decorative, especially when young, but has not been introduced into general cultivation.

Notes. — The highly reduced inflorescence nestling between the two auricles makes this a distinctive and unusual rattan genus. Its closes relatives are *Calamus, Daemonorops,* and *Ceratolobus.*

Taxonomic Accounts. — Dransfield (1980a, 1982f).

Plates. — *13A; 43D.*

51. Ceratolobus Blume in J. A. & J. H. Schultes, Systema Vegetabilium 7:1334. 1830. Type: **C. glaucescens** Blume.

Slender to moderate, clustered, spiny, climbing, pleonanthic, dioecious, rattan palms. Stem eventually becoming bare, with long internodes and conspicuous nodal scars, white latex sometimes exuding from cut surfaces. Leaves of mature climbing stems cirrate, pinnate; leaf sheath tubular, armed with spines and/or spicules, frequently organized into whorls, and often with abundant indumen-

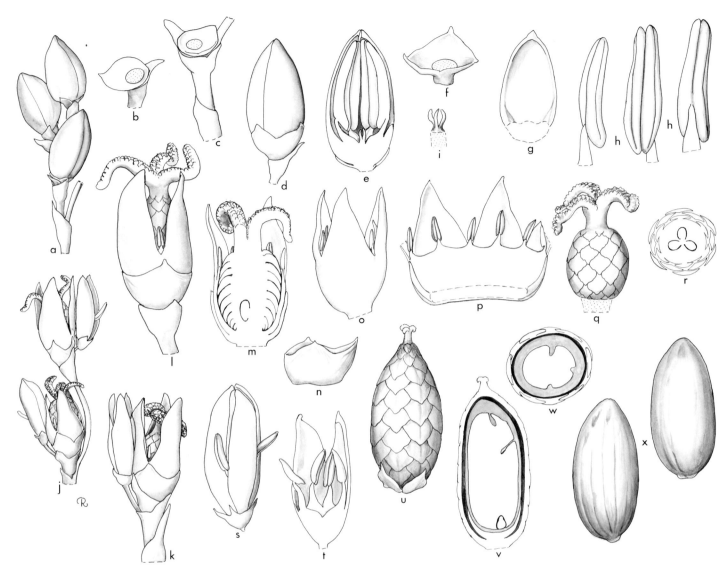

51.—**Ceratolobus. a,** portion of staminate inflorescence ×4½; **b,** bract and bracteole subtending staminate flower ×9; **c,** prophyll, bract, bracteole, and pedicel of staminate flower ×9; **d,** staminate bud ×7½; **e,** staminate bud in vertical section ×9; **f,** staminate calyx ×9; **g,** staminate petal ×7½; **h,** stamen in 3 views ×12; **i,** pistillode ×15; **j,** pistillate inflorescence with dyads of pistillate and sterile staminate flowers ×4½; **k,** portion of pistillate inflorescence with pistillate flower, sterile staminate flower, and subtending bracteoles ×6; **l,** pistillate flower ×7½; **m,** pistillate flower in vertical section ×7½; **n,** pistillate calyx ×7½; **o,** pistillate flower, calyx removed ×7½; **p,** pistillate corolla and staminodial ring, expanded, interior view ×7½; **q,** gynoecium ×7½; **r,** ovary in cross-section ×7½; **s,** sterile staminate flower ×7½; **t,** sterile staminate flower in vertical section ×7½; **u,** fruit ×3; **v,** fruit in vertical section ×3; **w,** fruit in cross-section ×3; **x,** seed in 2 views ×3. *Ceratolobus glaucescens:* all from *Moore 9950.*

tum; knee present, sometimes rather weakly developed; ocrea inconspicuous; flagellum absent; petiole present or absent, if present, flat adaxially, rounded abaxially, armed with spines and sometimes with spicules; cirrus and distal part of rachis armed with regular groups of grapnel spines on the abaxial surface; leaflets relatively few, linear to lanceolate and entire, or rhomboid and praemorse, concolorous or discolorous, regularly arranged or grouped; emerging leaf pink-tinged. Inflorescences axillary but ad-

nate to the internode and sheath of the following leaf, sessile and erect or pendulous on a long slender, unarmed or spiny peduncle, the whole inflorescence much shorter than the leaves; staminate inflorescence branching to 3 orders, pistillate to 2 orders, prophyll persistent, membranous to subwoody, flattened-tubular with lateral wings and a terminal beak, entirely enclosing the inflorescence, opening at anthesis by 2 narrow, lateral slits in the beak, this remaining the only access to the flowers during anthesis and young fruiting stage, prophyll unarmed or rarely armed with scattered spines, frequently bearing caducous indumentum, prophyll often splitting longitudinally in fruit, very rarely falling completely, staminate and pistillate inflorescences indistinguishable without splitting the prophyll; peduncular bracts absent; rachis bracts inconspicuous, tubular, with triangular limbs, each (and the prophyll) subtending a first-order branch, usually adnate to the axis for a short distance above the bract node. Staminate flowers borne singly, subdistichously, rather distant from each other, each subtended by a membranous triangular bract and a 2-keeled, prophyllar bracteole, the latter ± forming a cushion beneath the flower; calyx tubular, with 3, short, triangular lobes; petals 3, boat-shaped, valvate, briefly joined basally; stamens 6, borne at the base of the corolla, filaments short, fleshy, anthers linear, latrorse; pollen elliptic, disulcate, with spiny or finely to coarsely reticulate, tectate exine; pistillode trifid, minute. Pistillate flowers borne with a sterile staminate flower and 2 similar 2-keeled prophyllar bracteoles, in a cup formed by the subtending bract. Sterile staminate flower like the fertile but usually rather distorted by close packing and with empty anthers and borne on a short to long stalk. Pistillate flowers larger than the staminate; calyx tubular, with 3, short, triangular lobes; corolla partially divided into 3, valvate, triangular lobes; staminodes 6, epipetalous, flattened; gynoecium incompletely trilocular, triovulate, globose, or ellipsoidal, covered in scales, stigmas 3, fleshy, recurved, borne on a short style, ovule basally attached, anatropus. Mature fruit 1-seeded, globose to ellipsoidal, stigmatic remains apical, epicarp covered in vertical rows of reflexed scales, mesocarp becoming thin and papery as fruit ripens, endocarp not differentiated. Seed attached basally, globose to ellipsoidal, with thin or thick, sour or sweet sarcotesta and homogeneous or ruminate endosperm; embryo basal. Germination adjacent-ligular; eophyll with 4–6 praemorse or entire, crowded leaflets displayed in a fan. $n = 13$ (*C. concolor, C. glaucescens, C. pseudoconcolor,* Johnson 1979).

Anatomy.—Leaf (Tomlinson 1961).

Distribution.—Six species confined to the perhumid areas of the Sunda Shelf (Malay Peninsula (2), Sumatra (4), Borneo (3), Java (2).

Ecology.—All species are found in lowland and hill tropical rain forest and do not occur above 1000 m altitude; all are usually confined to Dipterocarp forest but *C. subangulatus* also occurs in heath forest in Sarawak where in some facies it is the most conspicuous rattan. The pollination ecology of the extraordinary closed inflorescence deserves further study.

Common Names and Uses.—Rattan, rotan. Species of *Ceratolobus* appear to have weak, not durable canes and for this reason are scarcely ever utilized.

Notes.—*Ceratolobus* has the most reduced inflorescence of all the Calaminae, having only one bract, the prophyll, which remains closed around the inflorescence, but splitting and sometimes falling in fruit. The presence of knees on the leaf sheaths allows those species with rhomboid leaflets to be distinguished in the sterile state from *Korthalsia,* but without inflorescences the remaining species (*C. subangulatus*) cannot be separated from *Calamus* and *Daemonorops.*

Taxonomic Account.—Dransfield (1979b).

Plate.—44A.

52. RETISPATHA J. Dransfield, Kew Bulletin 34(3): 529. 1979. Type: **R. dumetosa** J. Dransfield.

Moderate, clustered, erect or briefly-climbing, spiny, pleonanthic, dioecious, rattan palm. Stem eventually becoming bare, relatively robust, with conspicuous nodal scars and relatively short internodes, short bulblike shoots sometimes present at the nodes in the lower part of the stem, adventitious roots also abundant at lower nodes. Leaves without cirrus, pinnate; sheath tubular, densely armed with slender spines in whorls and partial whorls, and dense indumentum; ocrea absent; knee absent; flagellum absent; petiole well developed, channeled adaxially, armed with abundant lateral and abaxial groups of spines; rachis armed with reflexed grapnel spines in groups of up to 5, and bearing abundant indumentum; leaflets numerous, regularly arranged, single-fold, linear, armed along margins and main veins with bristles, midribs prominent, transverse veinlets conspicuous. Inflorescences axillary, but adnate to the internode and leaf sheath of the following leaf, erect at first, becoming pendulous, staminate and pistillate superficially similar, branched to 3 orders in staminate, to 1 (rarely 2) orders in pistillate; prophyll large, tubular in proximal ½, splitting and tattering distally, densely covered with black spines in partial whorls; peduncular bracts absent; rachis bracts similar to the prophyll; first-order branches becoming pendulous at anthesis, bearing distichous, imbricate, unarmed bracts, tubular in proximal ⅔, with a triangular limb, composed of close crisscross fibers producing a fine network, each netlike bract subtending and partially or wholly enclosing in the staminate inflorescence a catkinlike condensed branching system; each second-order branch subtended by a triangular, membranous, ciliate-margined tubular bract; third-order branchlets (rachillae) bearing membranous ciliate-margined tubular bracts, each subtending a single staminate flower bearing a 2-keeled ciliate-margined, tubular bracteole. Staminate flowers very small, ± symmetrical; calyx tubular with 3 triangular lobes tipped with hairs; corolla about twice as long as the calyx in bud, tubular only at the very base, lobes 3, striate, valvate, at anthesis the receptacle elongating, the corolla then appearing tubular in the basal ⅓; stamens 6, free from the corolla in bud, becoming briefly epipetalous, filaments briefly connate laterally, anthers oblong to ovate, dorsifixed near the base, latrorse; pollen elliptic to circular, monosulcate, with finely reticulate, tectate exine bearing irregularly spaced, broadly based, striate spines; pistillode trifid, very small. Pistillate inflorescences sometimes with

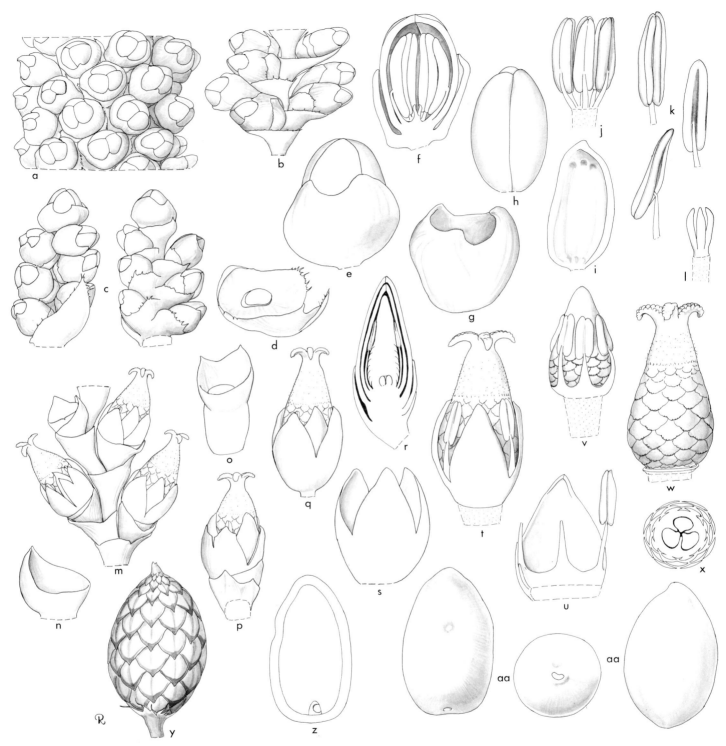

52.—**Retispatha. a, b,** portion of staminate inflorescence, second-order branch, in 2 views ×4½; **c,** portion of staminate inflorescence, third-order branch, in 2 views ×4½; **d,** scar and bracts of staminate flower ×12; **e,** staminate bud ×12; **f,** staminate bud in vertical section ×12; **g,** staminate calyx ×12; **h,** staminate bud, calyx removed ×12; **i,** staminate petal, interior view ×12; **j,** androecium ×12; **k,** stamen in 3 views ×15; **l,** pistillode ×24; **m,** portion of pistillate inflorescence ×2¼; **n,** outer bracteole of pistillate flower ×3; **o,** inner bracteole of pistillate flower ×3; **p,** pistillate flower with bracteoles ×3; **q,** pistillate flower ×3; **r,** pistillate bud in vertical section ×6; **s,** pistillate calyx ×4½; **t,** pistillate flower, calyx removed ×4½; **u,** pistillate petal and portion of staminodial ring, interior view ×6; **v,** young gynoecium and staminodial ring ×7½; **w,** gynoecium ×4½; **x,** ovary in cross-section ×12; **y,** fruit ×1½; **z,** seed in vertical section ×2¼; **aa,** seed in 3 views ×2¼. *Retispatha dumetosa*: **a-l,** *Dransfield 5595*; **m-aa,** *Dransfield 2840*.

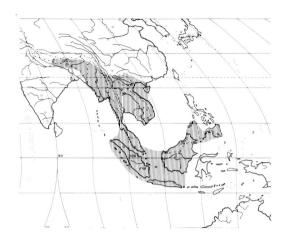

Map 16.—**Distribution of Plectocomiinae.**

1 major branch near the base, the rachillae borne on the axis and on this major branch, or more frequently the rachillae borne on the main axis only; rachillae subtended by distichous, imbricate, netlike bracts as in the staminate inflorescence, rachillae usually concealed by the bracts, bearing up to ca. 20 distichous, tubular, ciliate-margined bracts, each enclosing a 2-keeled prophyllar bracteole, a tubular, second bracteole and 1 pistillate flower; sterile staminate flowers lacking (see notes). Pistillate flowers much larger than the staminate; calyx tubular, with 3, short triangular, valvate lobes, splitting after fertilization; corolla tubular, slightly shorter than the calyx, with 3, short valvate lobes, also splitting further; staminodes 6, briefly epipetalous, filaments connate laterally to form a short tube, empty anthers flattened; gynoecium incompletely trilocular, triovulate, ovoid, scaly, stigmas 3, conspicuous, reflexed, fleshy, borne on a non-scaly style, ovule basally attached, anatropous. Mature fruit 1-seeded, partially concealed by the netlike bracts, ovoid to slightly obpyriform, beaked, stigmatic remains apical; epicarp with neat vertical rows of reflexed scales, mesocarp thin, endocarp not differentiated. Seed basally attached with thin sweet sarcotesta, endosperm obscurely angled, homogeneous; embryo basal. Germination adjacent-ligular; eophyll pinnate with ca. 4 ciliate-hairy leaflets on each side of the rachis. Cytology not studied.

Anatomy.—Not studied.

Distribution.—A single species endemic to Borneo where it has been recorded from scattered localities throughout the island.

Ecology.—*R. dumetosa* forms thickets on hillslopes and valley bottoms in hill Dipterocarp forest; it is absent from montane and heath forest. Although its habitat is widespread, it is a rare palm.

Common Names and Uses.—Wi tebu bruang (Malay, the bear's sugarcane). No local uses have been recorded.

Notes.—*Retispatha* is distinguished by the extraordinary netlike bracts that subtend the flowering

branches and by the lack of both cirrus and flagellum. Although the pistillate rachillae lack the sterile staminate flowers usual in the Calaminae, the affinities of *Retispatha* seem to be with *Calamus* rather than with the Plectocomiinae. Marion Sheehan, in preparing the plate, discovered a single sterile staminate flower borne with an apparently abortive pistillate flower at the very tip of one pistillate rachilla. We have been unable to find any trace of another sterile staminate flower. This single sterile staminate flower can be regarded as an unusual occurrence but perhaps confirming the affinity with the Calaminae.

Taxonomic Account.—Dransfield (1979c).

Plate.—*44B; Fig. G.18.*

Plectocomiinae J. Dransfield & N. Uhl, Principes 30:5. 1986. Type: **Plectocomia.**

Hapaxanthic, dioecious, climbing palms; cirri lacking acanthophylls; bracts subtending rachillae conspicuous or not, rachillae very slender, or highly reduced; staminate flowers paired or solitary; pistillate flowers solitary; sarcotesta thick but rather dry.

This subtribe includes *Plectocomia, Plectocomiopsis,* and *Myrialepis,* which are confined to Southeast Asia and to Malesia west of Wallace's Line (Map 16). The group is distinguished by the solitary pistillate flowers. *Plectocomiopsis* and *Myrialepis* appear more closely related to each other than to *Plectocomia.* Bracts in the first two genera are similar, and flowers differ mainly in degree of thickening of the perianth whorls and in the gynoecium. *Plectocomia* on the other hand has very conspicuous bracts on the first order branches and very obscure rachilla bracts and bracteoles. *Plectocomia* shows some similarity in rachilla and flower structure with *Pigafetta* in the Pigafettinae.

53. **MYRIALEPIS** Beccari in J. D. Hooker, The Flora of British India 6:480. 1893. Type: *M. scortechinii* Beccari (=**M. paradoxa** (Kurz) J. Dransfield (*Calamus paradoxus* Kurz)).

Bejaudia Gagnepain, Notulae Systematicae 6(3):149. 1937. Type: *B. cambodiensis* Gagnepain (=*Myrialepis paradoxa* (Kurz) J. Dransfield).

Robust, clustered, high-climbing, spiny, hapaxanthic, dioecious, rattan palm. Stem eventually becoming bare with long internodes and conspicuous nodal scars, basal vegetative branches borne opposite the leaves. Leaves on mature climbing stems usually massive, pinnate, cirrate; sheath tubular, sparsely armed with neat whorls of large spines in juveniles, with scattered spines in adults, indumentum abundant on sheath surfaces; knee absent; ocrea absent; flagellum absent; petiole very short to well de-

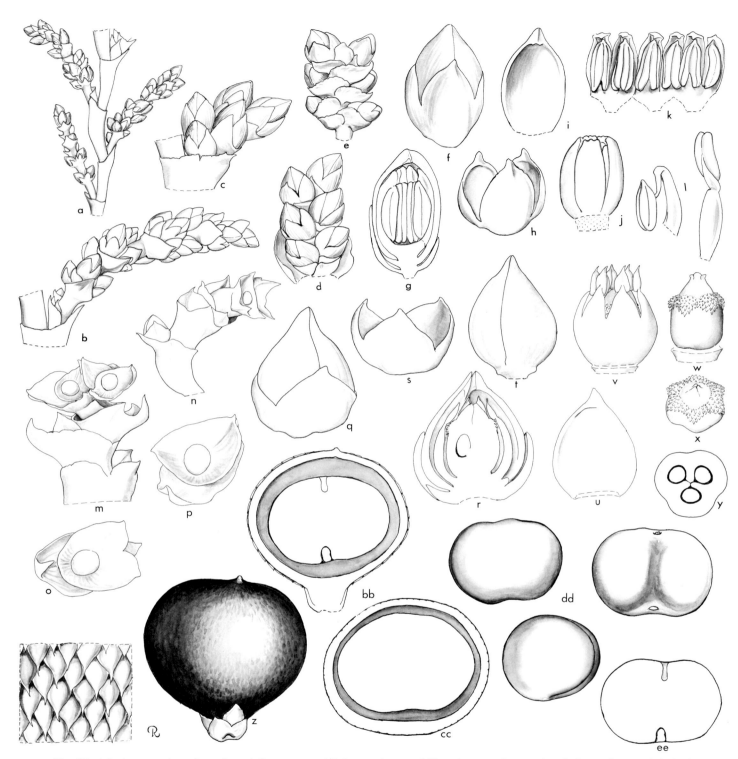

53.—**Myrialepis. a,** portion of staminate inflorescence ×1½; **b,** staminate rachilla ×4; **c,** staminate unit ×6; **d,** staminate unit in bud with subtending bract ×4; **e,** staminate unit, abaxial view ×4; **f,** staminate bud ×12; **g,** staminate bud in vertical section ×12; **h,** staminate calyx ×12; **i,** staminate petal ×12; **j,** androecium in bud ×12; **k,** androecium in bud, expanded, interior view ×12; **l,** stamen in 2 views ×12; **m, n,** portion of pistillate inflorescence in 2 views ×5; **o, p,** scar bract and bracteole of pistillate flower ×9; **q,** pistillate bud ×9; **r,** pistillate bud in vertical section ×9; **s,** pistillate calyx ×9; **t,** pistillate bud, calyx removed ×9; **u,** pistillate petal ×9; **v,** staminodial ring and gynoecium ×9; **w, x,** gynoecium in 2 views ×9; **y,** ovary in cross-section ×12; **z,** fruit ×1½; **aa,** scales of fruit, much enlarged; **bb,** fruit in vertical section ×1½; **cc,** fruit in cross-section ×1½; **dd,** seed in 3 views ×1½; **ee,** seed in vertical section ×1½. *Myrialepis paradoxa*: **a-l,** *Moore 9075*; **m-y,** *Ridley 12500*; **z-ee,** *Rahmat Si Boea 8009*.

veloped, deeply channeled, sparsely armed; rachis sparsely armed proximally, distally armed as the cirrus with regular groups of grapnel spines on the abaxial surface; leaflets numerous, lanceolate, entire, regularly arranged or rather indistinctly grouped, sometimes armed with short marginal spines, adaxial surface bearing bands of caducous indumentum, abaxial surface with scattered minute peltate scales, midribs slightly larger than other veins, transverse veinlets not evident. Inflorescences produced simultaneously in the axils of the most distal few, often reduced leaves, inflorescence axis adnate to the proximal part of the internode above the subtending leaf, emerging from the leaf-sheath mouth, branched to 3 orders; peduncle short; prophyll tubular, 2-keeled, with 2 triangular lobes, included within the leaf sheaths; peduncular bracts absent (? always); rachis much longer than the peduncle; rachis bracts tubular, subdistichous, each subtending a first-order branch; each order of branching with a tubular 2-keeled prophyll and subdistichous tubular bracts, each subtending a branch; rachillae very short, formed from branches of several orders, often somewhat curved, staminate rachillae bearing groups of up to 8 distichous flowers, each subtended by a cuplike rachilla bract and bearing a minute 2-keeled bracteole, pistillate rachillae bearing groups of 2–7 flowers, each subtended by a tubular rachilla bract and bearing a 2-keeled cuplike bracteole. Staminate flowers symmetrical; calyx membranous, tubular, with 3 apical lobes; corolla membranous, divided almost to the base into 3 triangular lobes; stamens 6, borne at the base of the corolla lobes, filaments adnate laterally near the base, free portions gradually narrowing, inflexed at the tip bearing pendulous, medifixed, oblong, somewhat sagittate, introrse anthers; pollen elliptic, disulcate, with finely reticulate, tectate exine; pistillode minute. Pistillate flowers larger than the staminate; calyx membranous, tubular, divided into 3 triangular lobes; corolla membranous, divided almost to the base into 3 triangular lobes; staminodal ring borne at the base of the corolla, bearing 6 triangular lobes, each tipped with a short slender filament bearing empty anthers; gynoecium incompletely trilocular, triovulate, ± spherical, covered with minute hairlike scales, stigmas 3 short, apical, ovule basally attached, anatropous. Fruit 1-seeded, perianth whorls persistent, stigmatic remains very small, apical; epicarp covered in minute, ± irregularly arranged scales, mesocarp thin, fibrous, endocarp not differentiated. Seed rounded, attached near the base, sarcotesta thick but not juicy, endosperm homogeneous; embryo basal. Germination and eophyll not known. Cytology not known.

Anatomy. — Leaf, stem (Tomlinson 1961).

Distribution. — A single species widespread in Indochina, Burma, Thailand, Peninsular Malaysia, and Sumatra.

Ecology. — *M. paradoxa* is found at altitudes from near sea level to about 1000 m in the mountains; it tends to form extensive thickets and, like the other Asiatic hapaxanthic rattan genera, appears to show a preference for disturbed sites in primary forest— such as large light gaps or old landslips. Nothing is known of pollination or dispersal.

Common Names and Uses. — Rattan, rotan kertong. The stems are of poor quality and used only in coarse basketry.

Notes. — *Myrialepis* is very closely related to *Plectocomiopsis* but lacks an ocrea. Other differences are the diffuse branching of the inflorescence, the much thinner androecium, and the minute, irregularly arranged scales on the fruit in contrast to the large, regularly arranged scales of *Plectocomiopsis*.

Taxonomic Account. — Dransfield (1982c).

Plate. — 44C, D.

54. PLECTOCOMIOPSIS Beccari in J. D. Hooker, Flora of British India 6:479. 1893. Lectotype: **P. geminiflora** (Griffith) Beccari (*Calamus geminiflorus* Griffith) (see H. E. Moore 1963c).

Moderate to robust, clustered, high-climbing, spiny, hapaxanthic, dioecious, rattan palms. Stem eventually becoming bare, often 3-angled, with long internodes and conspicuous nodal scars, basal branches borne in an axillary position. Leaves of mature climbing stems pinnate, cirrate; leaf sheath tubular, rather sparsely armed or unarmed, usually bearing caducous indumentum; knee absent; ocrea present, sometimes tattering but usually remaining entire and conspicuous; flagellum absent; petiole present or absent, it and the proximal part of the rachis deeply channeled and sparsely spiny; cirrus and distal part of rachis abaxially armed with regularly arranged groups of reflexed grapnel spines; leaflets few to numerous, singlefold, lanceolate, entire, regularly arranged, sometimes armed along margins and/or midrib with conspicuous bristles and bands of caducous scales, midribs evident, transverse veinlets conspicuous. Inflorescences produced simultaneously from the axils of the most distal, often reduced leaves, branched to 2 (3) orders, inflorescence axis adnate to the proximal part of the internode above the subtending node, emerging from the leaf sheath mouth; peduncle short; prophyll tubular, 2-keeled, included within the leaf sheath; peduncular bracts absent (? always); rachis much longer than the peduncle; rachis bracts tubular, ± distichous, each subtending a horizontal or ± pendulous, first-order branch; first-order branches with basal, 2-keeled prophyll and close, distichous, tubular bracts with triangular limbs, each subtending a flower cluster (except in *P. corneri* where inflorescences diffusely branched to 3 orders, and flowers borne on axes of all 3 orders); flower cluster monopodial, representing a condensed rachilla. Staminate flowers borne ± distichously in clusters of up to 32 flowers, each flower in the axil of a cuplike rachilla bract and bearing a cuplike, 2-keeled bracteole; calyx thick, very leathery, tubular, with 3 short lobes, the abaxial surface often covered in scalelike trichomes; corolla thick, leathery, tubular through most of its length, split distally to form 3 approximately triangular lobes, covered in scalelike trichomes; stamens 6, epipetalous, united laterally to form a tube tipped with 6 short, reflexed, free filaments bearing short, rounded to oblong, medifixed, introrse anthers; pollen elliptic, disulcate, with reticulate or irregular, tectate exine; pistillode minute. Pis

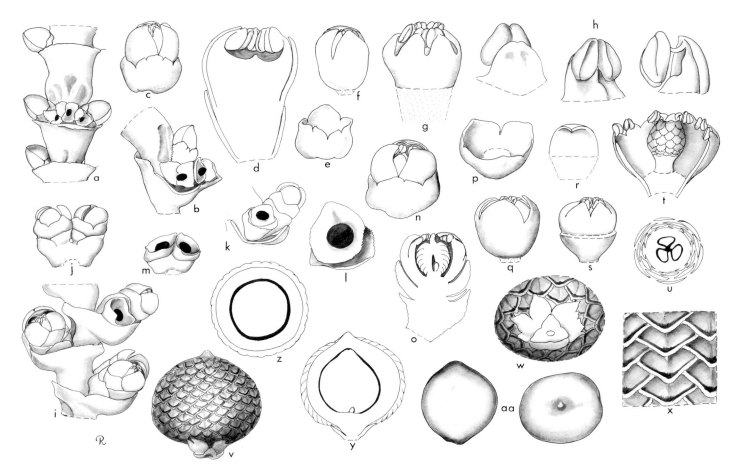

54.—**Plectocomiopsis. a,** portion of staminate inflorescence ×1½; **b,** staminate rachilla, some flowers removed to show scars and bracteoles ×3; **c,** staminate flower ×3; **d,** staminate flower in vertical section ×6; **e,** staminate calyx ×3; **f,** staminate flower, calyx removed ×3; **g,** androecium ×3; **h,** stamen in 3 views ×12; **i,** pistillate inflorescence ×1½; **j,** pair of pistillate flowers ×1½; **k,** pair of pistillate flowers, one flower removed to show bract and bracteole ×1½; **l,** bract and bracteole of pistillate flower ×3; **m,** pair of pistillate flowers, flowers removed to show bracteoles ×1½; **n,** pistillate flower ×3; **o,** pistillate flower in vertical section ×3; **p,** pistillate calyx ×3; **q,** pistillate flower, calyx removed ×3; **r,** pistillate petal ×3; **s,** pistillate flower, perianth removed to show staminodial ring ×3; **t,** pistillate flower, perianth removed and staminodial ring cut open to show gynoecium ×3; **u,** ovary in cross-section ×6; **v,** fruit ×1½; **w,** base of fruit ×3; **x,** scales of fruit ×6; **y,** fruit in vertical section ×1½; **z,** fruit in cross-section ×1½; **aa,** seed in 2 views ×1½. *Plectocomiopsis geminiflora:* **a-h,** *Moore 9602;* **i-u,** *Moore 9203;* **v-aa,** *Moore 9186.*

tillate flowers rarely solitary, usually borne in groups of 2–4 (or more), each in the axil of a cuplike rachilla bract and bearing a 2-keeled, cuplike bracteole and rarely a minute second bracteole; calyx tubular, thick, leathery, divided into 3 low lobes, frequently bearing scalelike trichomes, persisting into fruiting stage, enlarging, splitting and cracking irregularly; corolla thick, leathery, densely scaly, divided into 3 short lobes, later splitting irregularly; staminodial ring epipetalous, bearing 6 very short lobes and pendulous empty anthers; gynoecium ovoid to cylindrical, at anthesis scaly only near the base of the 3 apical stigmas, locules 3, incomplete, each with 1 anatropous, basally-attached ovule. Mature fruit 1- (very rarely 2-) seeded, perianth whorls persistent and enlarging, stigmatic remains apical; epicarp covered in somewhat irregular vertical rows of reflexed scales, mesocarp thin, endocarp

not differentiated. Seed basally attached, usually depressed, globose, sarcotesta thick, but not juicy, endosperm homogeneous; embryo basal. Germination adjacent-ligular; eophyll bifid, lamina composed of several folds. Cytology not studied.

Anatomy.—Leaf, petiole (Tomlinson 1961).

Distribution.—Five species distributed in south Thailand (1 species), Peninsular Malaysia (4), Sumatra (2), Borneo (3).

Ecology.—All species, like *Myrialepis,* seem to be adapted to colonizing seral habitats within primary forest. *P. triquetra* and *P. wrayi* are confined to lowland peat-swamp forest in Borneo and the Malay

Peninsula, respectively; *P. corneri* and *P. mira* are local plants of lowland Dipterocarp forest up to about 700 m altitude, while *P. geminiflora* is found in a wide range of forest types up to about 1200 m altitude.

Common Names and Uses. — Rattan, rotan. The apex of *P. geminiflora,* though bitter, is highly esteemed in Borneo as a vegetable; opinions vary concerning other species with some villagers regarding them as good, others as poisonous. The stems are of little value being prone to split when bent and are used only in coarse basketry.

Notes. — *Plectocomiopsis* is very closely related to *Myrialepis.* See notes under *Myrialepis.*

Taxonomic Account. — Dransfield (1982c).

Plates. — *13B; 45A.*

55. PLECTOCOMIA Martius ex Blume in J. A. & J. H. Schultes, Systema Vegetabilium 7:1333. 1830. Type: **P. elongata** Martius ex Blume.

Robust (very rarely slender), solitary or clustered, high-climbing, spiny, hapaxanthic, dioecious, rattan palms. Stem eventually becoming bare, with long internodes and conspicuous nodal scars, sometimes bearing multiple, bulblike shoots in the proximal part of the lower internodes, clear gum frequently exuding from cut surfaces. Leaves of mature climbing stems usually massive, cirrate, pinnate; sheath tubular, unarmed or sparsely to very densely armed with spines, usually borne in partial whorls, and also bearing abundant, caducous, floccose hairs on and between spines; knee absent; ocrea absent; flagellum absent; petiole present or absent, it and the proximal portion of the rachis deeply channeled and sparsely to densely armed; cirrus and distal part of rachis armed abaxially with regular groups of massive reflexed grapnel spines; leaflets numerous, single-fold, entire, usually lanceolate, regularly arranged or grouped and fanned within the groups, adaxial surface often with scattered bands of caducous indumentum, the abaxial often bearing white tomentum, midribs and submarginal ribs slightly larger than other veins, transverse veinlets not evident. Inflorescences produced simultaneously in the axils of the most distal 2–20, frequently reduced leaves, axis of inflorescence adnate to the proximal part of the internode above the subtending leaf, emerging from the leaf-sheath mouth, branching to (1) 2 (very rarely 3) orders; peduncle short; prophyll empty, tightly sheathing, 2-keeled, usually included within the leaf sheaths; peduncular bracts few, tubular, tightly sheathing; rachis much longer than the peduncle; rachis bracts similar to the peduncular, ± distichous, each subtending a pendulous first-order branch; first-order branches 3–20 or more, each with a basal tubular 2-keeled prophyll and 1–several empty tubular bracts, distal bracts very conspicuous, distichous, tubular at first, before anthesis splitting longitudinally almost to the base opposite the insertion, spreading or usually remaining imbricate and partially or completely enclosing the rachillae, or very rarely subtending second-order branches bearing similar bracts subtending the rachillae (? teratological), bract

texture thin to very thick, coriaceous or subwoody, glabrous or with scattered hairs or scales; rachillae slender, frequently densely covered in trichomes, in the pistillate inflorescence bearing from (1) 2–10 flowers, in the staminate from 2–ca. 100 flowers; staminate flowers sometimes borne in distinct dyads, otherwise basic dyad arrangement obscured by overcrowding and elongation of pedicels, rachilla bracts minute; floral bracteoles minute or obscure. Staminate flower sessile or with a stalklike base; calyx tubular, much shorter than the corolla, with 3 short lobes; corolla tubular at the very base with 3 triangular to lanceolate lobes; stamens usually 6, rarely to 12, filaments sometimes connate basally, borne near the mouth of the corolla tube, anthers usually elongate, latrorse or introrse; pollen elliptic, disulcate or rarely meridionosulcate, with reticulate, foveolate, or scabrate, tectate exine; pistillode minute or absent. Pistillate flowers solitary, often pedicellate with the rachilla bract carried by adnation and subsequent growth on to the pedicel, each flower also bearing a 2-keeled bracteole; calyx tubular at the base, with 3, very short to very long, triangular lobes, usually splitting further after anthesis; corolla tubular at the base with 3, narrow to broad, triangular lobes, slightly to greatly exceeding the calyx, becoming flattened out in fruit; staminodes 6 with flattened filaments and empty anthers; gynoecium rounded, scaly, stigmas 3, usually very long, flexuous, sometimes with a well developed style, locules 3, incomplete, ovules 3, basally attached, anatropous. Mature fruit 1- (rarely 2–3-) seeded, with apical stigmatic remains; epicarp covered in numerous vertical rows of reflexed scales, the scale tips frequently fringed and upward pointing, mesocarp thin, fibrous, endocarp not differentiated. Seed globose, attached near the base, sarcotesta thick but not juicy, endosperm homogeneous; embryo basal. Germination adjacent-ligular; eophyll where known, simple, lanceolate, plicate, not split. Cytology not studied.

Anatomy. — Leaf, petiole, stem, root (Tomlinson 1961). Similar to *Myrialepis* in having large epidermal cells.

Distribution. — About 16 species distributed from the Himalayas, south China and Hainan, south through Burma and Indochina to the Sunda Shelf and the Philippines; not known east of Wallace's Line.

Ecology. — *P. elongata* and *P. mulleri* are the two most widespread species and also appear to have the widest altitudinal range, being found from sea level up to ca. 2000 m in the mountains; the former is characteristic of disturbed sites on poor soils and the latter is found in similar habitats but also as a conspicuous component of some facies of peat-swamp forest and heath forest ("kerangas"). Other species are less well known and seem to be more restricted in distribution; however, many do appear to be characteristic of seral forest on poor soils. In the Himalayas, *P. himalayana* has been recorded at altitudes of about 2000 m. There are indications

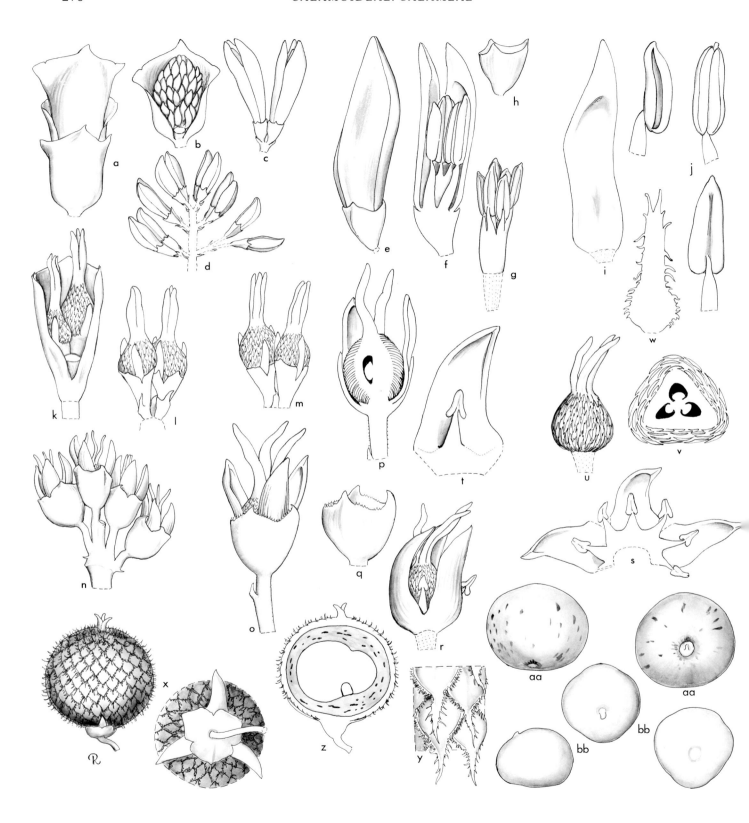

that the hapaxanthic habit may be an adaptation to the colonization of temporary habitats such as landslips.

There are suggestions that in some localities *P. elongata* may flower gregariously (see Dransfield 1979a). Trigonid bees and nitidulid and staphylinid beetles have been observed visiting the intensely fragrant staminate flowers of *P. dransfieldiana*. Nothing is known of fruit dispersal. Neither is anything known of the time taken to reach flowering size.

Common Names and Uses.—Rattan, rotan. The stems of *Plectocomia* species have a soft pith which renders them unsuitable for fine furniture construction. They are used only for coarse or temporary basketry. The dried inflorescences are sometimes used as ornaments.

Notes.—The inflorescence of *Plectocomia* is striking and beautiful; the long pendulous first-order branches with large distichous boat-shaped bracts are unlike those of any other palm. Of particular note are the much reduced rachillae with scarcely evident bracts. The distinctive first-order branches and paired staminate flowers separate *Plectocomia* from the other hapaxanthic, high-climbing rattans, *Myrialepis* and *Plectocomiopsis*.

Taxonomic Account.—Madulid (1981).

Plates.—*13D; 45B, C; Fig. G.17.*

Pigafettinae J. Dransfield & N. Uhl, Principes 30: 5. 1986. Type: **Pigafetta.**

Pleonanthic, dioecious, tree palm; rachillae slender bearing highly reduced bracts; staminate flowers paired; pistillate flowers solitary; sarcotesta well developed.

This monotypic subtribe is confined to Sulawesi, Moluccas, and New Guinea (Map 17). Although there is a superficial resemblance to *Metroxylon* in habit and leaf, the structure of the rachillae, the dioecism, the flower structure, and the much smaller fruit are very different. The rachilla structure with large tubular bracts approaches that of *Plectocomia*.

Map 17.—**Distribution of Pigafettinae.**

56. Pigafetta (Blume) Beccari, Malesia 1:89. 1877. (Conserved name). ('*Pigafetta*'). Lectotype: **P. filaris** (Giseke) Beccari (*Sagus filaris* Giseke).

Sagus section *Pigafetta* Blume, Rumphia 2:154. 1843.

Metroxylon section *Pigafetta* (Blume) Martius, Historia Naturalis Palmarum 3:213 (edit. 2). 1845.

Massive, solitary, armed, pleonanthic, dioecious, tree palm. Stem erect, becoming very tall, with conspicuous nodal scars, internodes glossy, green in distal areas, becoming brown with age, usually bearing abundant, somewhat spinelike, adventitious roots near the base, the cortex very hard, pith soft. Leaves pinnate, strongly curved, abscising neatly in trunked individuals; sheath splitting opposite the petiole, bearing a tattered ligule around the mouth, unarmed at the very base, distally armed with low collars bearing abundant soft flexible spines, both sheath surface and spines with a dense caducous felt of tomentum; petiole massive, channeled adaxially, rounded and armed like the sheath abaxially; rachis angled adaxially, rounded and armed with sparse collars and spines abaxially; leaflets single-fold, numerous, regularly arranged, curving, slender, elongate, acuminate, armed with short marginal bristles and long bristles on the main veins, midribs large, one other pair of large veins evident, transverse veinlets sinuous, moderately conspicuous. Inflorescences axillary, interfoliar at anthesis, sometimes becoming infrafoliar after abscission of the subtending leaf, ± horizontal, tending to diverge obliquely from the plane of the leaf, branched to 2 orders; prophyll tightly sheathing, with 2 triangular limbs and dense caducous indumentum; peduncular bracts ca. 8, tubular, in the staminate inflores-

---

←

55.—**Plectocomia. a,** portion of staminate inflorescence ×1½; **b,** staminate axis and bract ×1½; **c,** paired staminate flowers ×6; **d,** portion of staminate axis, extended to show arrangement of paired units ×3; **e,** staminate bud ×12; **f,** staminate bud in vertical section ×12; **g,** androecium ×12; **h,** staminate calyx ×12; **i,** staminate petal, interior view ×12; **j,** stamen in 3 views ×12; **k,** paired pistillate flowers in bract ×1½; **l, m,** paired pistillate flowers, bract removed, in 2 views ×1½; **n,** pistillate flowers, bract removed ×1½; **o,** pistillate flower ×3; **p,** pistillate flower in vertical section ×3; **q,** pistillate calyx ×3; **r,** pistillate flower, calyx removed ×3; **s,** pistillate corolla and staminodes, expanded, interior view ×3; **t,** pistillate petal and staminode, interior view ×6; **u,** gynoecium ×3; **v,** ovary in cross-section ×6; **w,** scale ×12; **x,** fruit in 2 views ×1½; **y,** scales of fruit, much enlarged; **z,** fruit in vertical section ×1½; **aa,** sarcotesta in 2 views ×1½; **bb,** seed in 3 views ×1½. *Plectocomia mulleri*: **a–m** and **x–bb,** *Moore et al. 9158*; *P. elongata*: **n–w,** *Rahmat Si Boea 7417* (MICH).

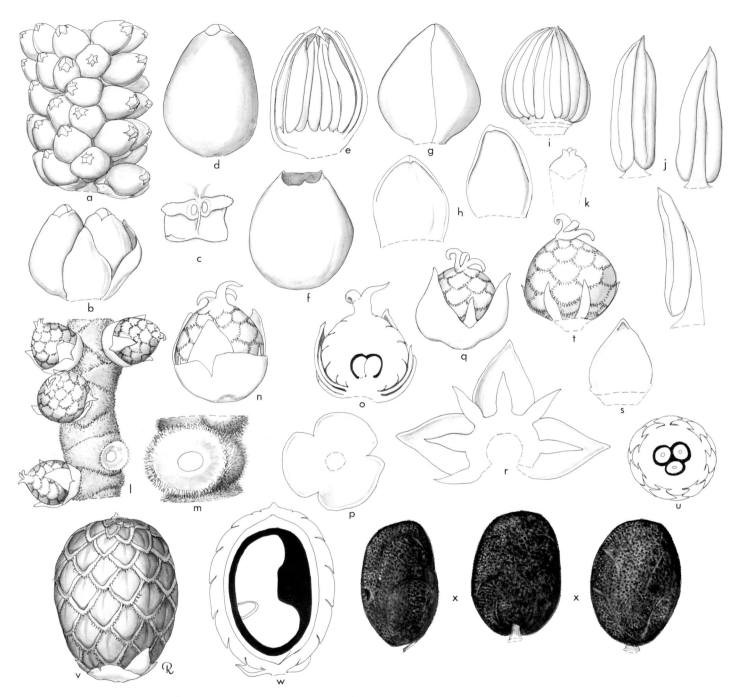

56.—**Pigafetta. a,** portion of staminate rachilla ×4½; **b,** dyad of staminate flowers ×9; **c,** dyad, flowers removed to show bract and bracteoles ×6; **d,** staminate bud ×12; **e,** staminate bud in vertical section ×12; **f,** staminate calyx ×12; **g,** staminate bud, calyx removed ×12; **h,** staminate petal in 2 views ×12; **i,** androecium ×12; **j,** stamen in 3 views ×18; **k,** pistillode ×30; **l,** portion of pistillate rachilla ×4; **m,** scar of pistillate flower ×8; **n,** pistillate flower ×8; **o,** pistillate flower in vertical section ×8; **p,** pistillate calyx ×8; **q,** pistillate flower, calyx removed ×8; **r,** pistillate corolla and staminodial ring, expanded, interior view ×8; **s,** pistillate petal ×8; **t,** gynoecium and staminodes ×8; **u,** ovary in cross-section ×8; **v,** fruit ×4; **w,** fruit in vertical section ×4; **x,** seed covered with sarcotesta in 3 views ×4. *Pigafetta filaris:* **a-k,** *Dransfield 3867;* **l-u,** *Mogea 5353;* **v-x,** *Essig 55078.*

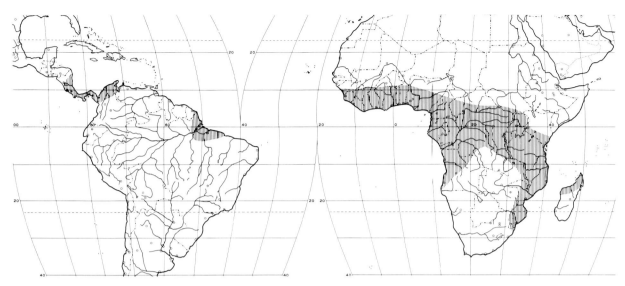

Map 18.—Distribution of Raphiinae.

cence somewhat inflated, with short triangular limbs and dense caducous indumentum; rachis much longer than the peduncle; rachis bracts subtending pendulous first-order branches, partly adnate to the primary axis above the bract; first-order branches with a tightly sheathing prophyll and numerous tubular bracts each subtending a ± pendulous rachilla; flower-bearing part of the rachilla exserted from the bracts on a bare flattened basal stalk; rachilla prophyll minute, 2-keeled, empty, borne at the distal end of the rachilla stalk; rachilla bracts minute, membranous, striate, triangular, in the staminate inflorescence subtending a dyad of fertile staminate flowers, and in the pistillate subtending a single fertile pistillate flower; bracteoles in both sexes minute. obscured by a deep pile of crowded hairs. Staminate flowers symmetrical; calyx striate, cupular, with 3 very shallow lobes; corolla exceeding the calyx, tubular at the base, divided distally into 3 striate, narrow, triangular, valvate lobes; stamens 6, borne at the mouth of the corolla tube, the filaments connate laterally in a low ring, the anthers elongate, somewhat sagittate, apparently latrorse; pollen elliptic, monosulcate, with finely reticulate, tectate exine; pistillode minute. Pistillate flowers ± globose; calyx cupular with 3 very short lobes, later splitting; corolla divided ± to the base into 3 broad triangular lobes; staminodes 6, united by their filaments into a short ring with 6 narrow lobes bearing flattened empty sagittate anthers; gynoecium incompletely trilocular, triovulate, globose, covered in reflexed scales, stigmas 3, short, reflexed, ovules anatropous, basally attached. Fruit relatively very small, ovoid, single-seeded; epicarp covered in neat vertical rows of reflexed scales, mesocarp thin, endocarp thin, not differentiated. Seed basally attached, laterally somewhat flattened, covered in thick sweet sarcotesta, endosperm homogeneous with very shallow depressions and laterally with a shallow pit; embryo lateral, opposite the pit. Germination adjacent-ligular; eophyll bifid, with very narrow leaflets and softly spiny petiole. $n = 14$ (Johnson 1985).

Anatomy.—Not studied.

Distribution.—The single species, *P. filaris,* is confined to Sulawesi, Moluccas, and New Guinea.

Ecology.—*P. filaris* seems to behave as a pioneer palm of seral habitats in the mountains, where it is most abundant between 300 and 1500 m. It grows on old landslips, old lava flows, and river banks, and also seems to colonize cultivated land reverting to secondary forest. Seedlings appear to require high light intensities. The seed, which is very small for the size of the palm, shows staggered germination. This is the tallest recorded palm species in the Asian Tropics, individuals sometimes reaching 50 m in height; it is also very fast growing (see Dransfield 1976b).

Common Names and Uses.—Pigafetta palm, Wanga. The trunks are used for the piles of houses in parts of Sulawesi. This beautiful palm is much sought after by collectors but has proved difficult to cultivate outside the tropics.

Notes.—There is a remarkable and perhaps unexpected similarity between the rachillae of *Pigafetta* and those of *Plectocomia*. Otherwise the two genera are extremely different, *Pigafetta* a tall solitary pleonanthic tree and *Plectocomia* a hapaxanthic rattan. Habit and leaves are similar between *Metroxylon* and *Pigafetta* but the structure of the inflorescences, flowers, and fruit is very different. The genus is isolated and its relationships are not obvious.

Taxonomic Account.—Beccari (1918).

Plates.—*13C; 45D.*

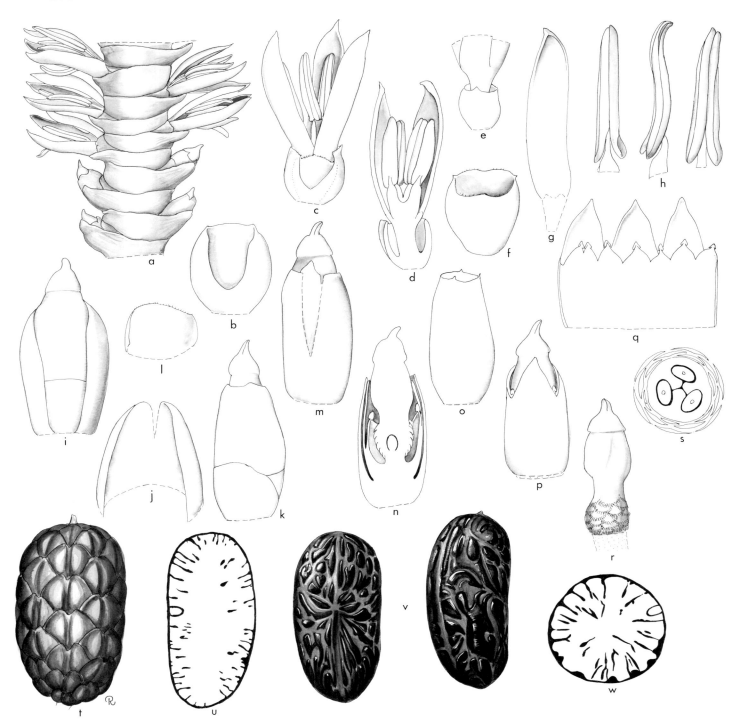

57. — **Raphia. a,** portion of rachilla, staminate flowers above, pistillate flowers below ×3; **b,** bracteole of staminate flower ×6; **c,** staminate flower with bracteole ×4½; **d,** staminate flower in vertical section ×4½; **e,** staminate calyx and portion of corolla ×4½; **f,** staminate calyx ×6; **g,** staminate petal ×6; **h,** stamen ×9; **i,** pistillate flower with two bracteoles ×6; **j,** outer bracteole of pistillate flower ×6; **k,** pistillate flower with inner bract ×6; **l,** inner bracteole of pistillate flower ×6; **m,** pistillate flower, calyx split to show corolla ×6; **n,** pistillate flower in vertical section ×6; **o,** pistillate calyx ×6; **p,** pistillate flower, calyx removed ×6; **q,** pistillate corolla and staminodial ring, expanded, interior view ×6; **r,** gynoecium ×6; **s,** ovary in cross-section ×12; **t,** fruit ×¾; **u,** seed in vertical section ×¾; **v,** seed in 2 views ×¾; **w,** seed in cross-section ×¾. *Raphia farinifera:* **a-s,** from Fairchild Tropical Garden; *R. palmapinus:* **t-w,** *Moore 9889.*

Raphiinae J. D. Hooker in Bentham & J. D. Hooker, Genera Plantarum 3:872, 881. 1883 ('*Raphieae*'), Type: **Raphia.**

Massive, hapaxanthic, monoecious, acaulescent or tree palms; flowers solitary, dimorphic; staminate flowers distal on the rachillae, unibracteolate, petals much longer than the sepals, conspicuously exserted; pistillate flowers proximal, bibracteolate, petals and sepals subequal, scarcely longer than the bracts and bracteoles, usually only the stigmas exserted; fruit generally large, with large scales; testa dry.

Raphia, the only member of the subtribe, is confined to Africa except for one species, *R. taedigera,* which occurs in both Africa and the Americas (Map 18). *Raphia* is unusual in many respects. It is monoecious with highly organized rachillae bearing pistillate flowers basally and staminate flowers distally. Flowers of the two sexes are rather strongly dimorphic. Although *Oncocalamus* shares monoecy with *Raphia,* the structure of the flower groups is totally different. There are no obvious close relatives.

57. **Raphia** Palisot de Beauvois, Flore d'Oware et de Bénin, en Afrique 1:75 t. 44–46. 1806. Lectotype: **R. vinifera** Palisot de Beauvois.

Sagus J. Gaertner, De Fructibus et Seminibus Plantarum 1:27. 1788. Type: *S. palmapinus* J. Gaertner (=*R. palmapinus* (J. Gaertner) J. Hutchinson) (non *Sagus* Steck, 1757 =*Metroxylon* Rottboell).

Massive, solitary or clustered, armed, hapaxanthic, monoecious, acaulescent or tree palms. Stem subterranean to erect, usually partly obscured by the marcescent leaf bases, the internodes sometimes bearing short, negatively geotropic, ± spinelike roots, cortex hard, pith soft. Leaves massive, pinnate, marcescent; sheath unarmed, splitting opposite the petiole, with or without a conspicuous ligule, disintegrating into thin sheets or sometimes partly into black fiber bundles ("piassava"); petiole short to very long, unarmed, usually deeply channeled adaxially only at the base, rounded distally; rachis unarmed, angled adaxially, rounded abaxially; leaflets single-fold, linear, numerous, regularly arranged or grouped and fanned within the groups to give the leaf a plumose appearance, often whitish beneath, armed with short spines along the margins and the midrib, the margins frequently greatly thickened, midribs very large, transverse veinlets conspicuous or inconspicuous. Inflorescences branched to 2 orders, produced simultaneously in the axils of the most distal few leaves, either interfoliar and pendulous, or aggregated into a massive, erect, suprafoliar, compound inflorescence; peduncle short; prophyll tubular, 2-keeled, closely sheathing to inflated, sometimes splitting opposite the keels, with 1 or 2 short triangular lobes; peduncular bracts several, ca. 6, and inflated basally with triangular limbs; rachis much longer than the peduncle; rachis bracts distichous or in 4 ranks, tubular, closely sheathing to somewhat inflated, usually each subtending a first-order branch, rarely empty; first-order branches reflexed or variously spreading, sometimes scarcely exserted from the bract, bearing a basal, 2-keeled, tubular prophyll, and distichous or 4 ranked, tubular bracts with triangular limbs, each, except for the prophyll and 1–few basalmost, subtending a rachilla; rachillae very crowded to distant and sometimes not exserted; rachilla prophyll tightly sheathing, 2-keeled; subsequent rachilla bracts tending to be distichous or in 4 ranks, tubular, tightly sheathing, with short, striate triangular limbs; distal 1–3 bracts empty, of the remaining, the proximal bracts from ¼–⅔ the rachilla length, each subtending a pistillate flower and 2 prophyllar bracteoles, the distal, each subtending a staminate flower with a single prophyllar bracteole, very rarely at the junction between staminate and pistillate parts of the rachilla, the bract subtending a dyad of 1 staminate and 1 pistillate flower; rarely in apical portions of the inflorescence, rachillae bearing staminate flowers only. Staminate flowers conspicuously exserted; calyx tubular, shallowly 3-lobed; corolla greatly exceeding the calyx, sometimes glossy, tubular at the base, with 3, elongate, triangular, sometimes spinelike, valvate lobes; stamens 6–30, filaments narrowly spindle-shaped, joined to the corolla near the base, variously distinct or connate into a fleshy tube, abruptly contracted at the connective, anthers elongate, sagittate basally, uneven distally, introrse or latrorse; pollen elliptic, monosulcate, with scabrate, tectate exine; pistillode absent or minute. Pistillate flowers sometimes only partly exserted from the rachilla bracts; calyx tubular, ± truncate or shallowly 3-lobed, later splitting; corolla exceeding or scarcely longer than the calyx, tubular in proximal ca. ½, distally with 3 valvate triangular lobes; staminodes united into an epipetalous ring, with 6–16 irregular teeth of varying lengths bearing the flattened, sagittate, short, empty anthers; gynoecium tricarpellate, triovulate, ovoid to somewhat conical, with a short style and conical 3-lobed stigma, locule partitions incomplete, ovule basally attached, anatropous. Fruit frequently large, elliptical, 1-seeded, with apical stigmatic remains; epicarp covered in neat vertical rows of large reflexed scales, mesocarp thick, mealy, oil-rich, endocarp not differentiated. Seed elongate, subbasally attached with dry seed coat, variously coarsely furrowed, endosperm with a few large ruminations; embryo lateral. Germination adjacent-ligular; eophyll usually pinnate, more rarely bifid. $n = 14$ (*R. longiflora, R. vinifera,* Sarkar 1970; *R. taedigera,* Read 1966). $n = 16$ (*R. farinifera* as *R. ruffia,* Satô 1946).

Anatomy.—Leaf, petiole, stem, root (Tomlinson 1961).

Distribution.—About 28 species recognized, but probably actually fewer, throughout the more humid areas of Africa; one species in Madagascar possibly introduced; one species, *R. taedigera,* in tropical America, but stated by Otedoh (1977) also to occur in West Africa and to be introduced in tropical America (this, however, seems unlikely).

Map 19.—**Distribution of Oncocalaminae.**

Ecology.—Most species of *Raphia* seem to be plants of swamplands, but *R. regalis* occurs on hill-slopes in humid tropical rainforest.

Common Names and Uses.—Raphia palms. Species of *Raphia* are ethnobotanically extremely important. Raphia fiber is obtained by stripping off the cuticle and hypodermis from the emerging leaflets; locally it is used for a wide range of purposes such as basketware and twine, and is exported for garden twine and weaving. Piassava is obtainable from the leaf sheaths of *R. hookeri.* Petioles of many species are used as a substitute for bamboo in house and furniture construction and leaflets are used for thatch. Palm wine can be obtained by tapping the stem apex. The mesocarp of some species provides

a source of cooking oil. The kernels and stem apex are sometimes eaten. The fruit of some species is used as a fish poison.

Notes.—*Raphia* is an isolated genus with no obvious close relatives within the Calameae. The only other monoecious genus, *Oncocalamus,* has such unusual flower clusters that it is unlikely to be related to *Raphia.* The leaves reaching 25 m in *R. regalis* (Hallé 1977) are considered to be the longest in the plant kingdom.

Taxonomic Accounts.—Beccari (1910a), Russell (1965), and Otedoh (1982).

Plate.—*46A.*

Oncocalaminae J. Dransfield & N. Uhl, Principes 30:5. 1986. Type: **Oncocalamus.**

Hapaxanthic, monoecious climbers; cirri bearing acanthophylls; rachilla bracts subtending groups of 3–11 flowers, the central flower pistillate with 2 lateral cincinni bearing 0–1 basal pistillate flowers and several distal staminate flowers.

The single genus of the subtribe is confined to humid tropical Africa (Map 19). The structure of the flower group is unique (see comments under genus).

58. ONCOCALAMUS (G. Mann & H. A. Wendland) G. Mann & H. A. Wendland ex J. D. Hooker in Bentham & J. D. Hooker, Genera Plantarum 3: 881, 936. 1883. Type: **O. mannii** (H. A. Wendland) H. A. Wendland ex Drude (*Calamus mannii* H. A. Wendland).

Calamus subgenus *Oncocalamus* G. Mann & H. A. Wendland, Transactions of the Linnean Society of London 24:436. 1864.

Clustered, spiny, high-climbing, hapaxanthic, monoecious, rattan palms. Stem eventually becoming bare, circular in cross-section, with long internodes. Leaves pinnate, bifid in juveniles, with a terminal cirrus; sheath strictly

→

58.—**Oncocalamus. a,** portion of rachilla with one entire flower cluster ×6; **b,** flower cluster, schematic to show bract and flower arrangement, bracts drawn separately ×6; **c,** flower cluster in bud, outer bract removed ×6; **d,** flower cluster in adaxial view, pistillate flower central, staminate flowers lateral, outer bract removed ×6; **e,** flower cluster in abaxial view, pistillate flower central, staminate flowers lateral, outer bract removed ×6; **f,** flower cluster in lateral view, pistillate flower right, staminate flowers left, outer bract removed ×6; **g,** flower cluster in tangential view, pistillate flower center back, staminate flowers front, outer bract removed ×6; **h,** flower cluster in median view, pistillate flower left (note lack of bracts), staminate flowers right, outer bract removed ×6; **i,** staminate bud ×9; **j,** staminate bud, outer portion of calyx removed ×9; **k,** staminate bud in vertical section ×9; **l,** staminate sepal in 2 views ×9; **m,** staminate bud, calyx removed ×9; **n,** staminate petal ×9; **o,** androecium ×9; **p,** androecium, expanded ×15; **q,** stamen in 3 views ×18; **r,** pistillode ×15; **s,** pistillate bud ×9; **t,** pistillate bud in vertical section ×9; **u,** pistillate sepal ×9; **v,** pistillate petal in 2 views ×9; **w,** staminodial ring ×9; **x,** staminodial ring, expanded ×9; **y,** gynoecium ×15; **z,** gynoecium in vertical section ×15; **aa,** ovary in cross-section × 15; **bb,** fruit ×2¼; **cc,** stigmatic remains ×6; **dd,** scales of fruit ×3; **ee,** fruit in vertical section ×2¼; **ff,** seed in 2 views ×2¼. *Oncocalamus mannii:* all from *Letouzey 11889.*

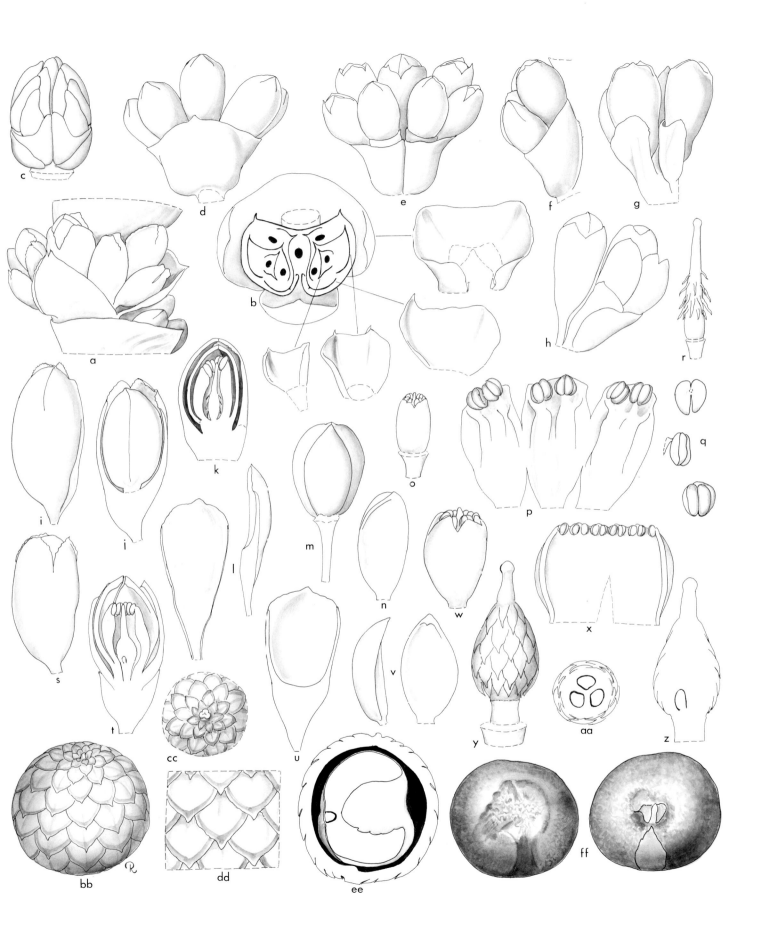

tubular, bearing scattered, black, bulbous-based, triangular, brittle spines and scattered, thin, caducous indumentum; ocrea conspicuous, tightly sheathing, neatly truncate, armed as the sheath; knee absent; petiole present but usually very short, absent in mature flowering stems; rachis armed with scattered spines as the leaf sheath; cirrus bearing neat pairs of reflexed acanthophylls; leaflets few to numerous, usually single-fold, sometimes with 2 or more folds, entire, acute, linear, lanceolate or somewhat sigmoid, regularly arranged, usually armed along the thickened margins with robust spines, midribs evident, other large veins rather distant, transverse veinlets conspicuous; proximal few leaflets sometimes smaller than the rest, heavily armed and reflexed across the sheathed stem. Inflorescences produced simultaneously in the axils of the uppermost, often reduced leaves; peduncle enclosed within the leaf sheath and emerging from its mouth, ± hemispherical in cross-section; prophyll tubular, tightly sheathing, 2-keeled, 2-lobed at its tip, much shorter than the sheath; peduncular bracts ca. 4, ± distichous, tightly sheathing at first, later splitting longitudinally, each with a short triangular lobe; rachis longer than the peduncle; rachis bracts like the peduncular, rather close; first-order branches pendulous or spreading with a basal 2-keeled tubular prophyll and numerous distichous, short, tubular, somewhat inflated, striate bracts, each enclosing a flower cluster, after anthesis eventually irregularly splitting and tattering; flower cluster partially covered by a tubular 2-keeled prophyll and consisting of up to 11 flowers arranged in a group with a central 1 or 3 pistillate flowers and 2 lateral cincinni of 2–4 staminate flowers, each flower, apart from the central pistillate, bearing an open, spathulate, 2-keeled, prophyllar bracteole (the precise arrangement of the flowers not yet understood). Staminate flowers symmetrical; calyx membranous, striate basally, stalked, tubular, with 3, short, triangular, apiculate lobes; corolla apparently only slightly exceeding the calyx, divided almost to the base into 3, elongate, striate, valvate petals; stamens 6, filaments united to form a thick, fleshy androecial tube, free from the corolla, tipped with 6 shallow lobes, bearing pendulous, rounded, latrorse anthers on the inside; pollen elliptic, monosulcate, with scabrate, tectate exine; pistillode very narrow, conical, slightly exceeding the androecial tube. Pistillate flowers superficially very similar to the staminate except slightly broader; the calyx and corolla similar; staminodial tube bearing minute empty anthers; gynoecium tricarpellate, triovulate, ± ellipsoidal, covered in reflexed scales, style long, narrow, 3-angled, ovule form unknown. Fruit ± spherical, stigmatic remains minute, conical, apical; epicarp covered in vertical rows of rather thin reflexed scales, mesocarp very thin, almost obsolescent at maturity, endocarp not differentiated. Seed single, ± rounded basally attached with an oval hilum, covered with a ?thick sarcotesta, endosperm homogeneous, laterally deeply penetrated by a smooth-margined mass of inner seed coat; embryo lateral opposite the intrusion. Germination and eophyll unknown. Cytology not known.

Anatomy.—Not studied.

Distribution.—Five taxa described from equatorial west Africa and the Congo Basin, but probably only two or three are good species.

Ecology.—Little is known of the ecology of *Oncocalamus* species apart from their being confined to low-lying tropical rain forest.

Common Names and Uses.—Common names unknown. No local uses have been specifically recorded but the stems are probably used as a source of cane.

Notes.—The strange flower cluster of *Oncocalamus* is unique, not only in the subfamily, but indeed within the whole family. Vegetatively *Oncocalamus* is certainly very similar to *Eremospatha* and *Laccosperma* of the Ancistrophyllinae. We have removed *Oncocalamus* from this group which includes other endemic African rattan genera because of the very different flower clusters and unisexual flowers. The apparently isolated position of *Oncocalamus* perhaps argues for a long and complex evolutionary history of the Calamoideae in Africa, with much extinction.

Taxonomic Account.—There is no recent reassessment of the genus; herbarium material is scanty and generally very incomplete.

Plate.—46B.

LEPIDOCARYEAE Martius in Endlicher, Genera Plantarum 248. 1837 ('*Lepidocaryinae*').

Leaves palmate or briefly costapalmate.

This tribe of three New World genera (Map 20) of the Calamoideae is immediately distinguished from the Calameae by the palmate or costapalmate leaf. Reduplicate palmate leaves are found nowhere else in the palms except in *Guihaia* (Coryphoideae). Although so distinctive in the leaf, the genera nevertheless clearly belong to the Calamoideae, possessing a whole suite of characters common in the subfamily. Relationships of the Lepidocaryeae to the subtribes of the Calameae are not clear.

59. **MAURITIA** Linnaeus filius, Supplementum Plantarum 70, 454. 1782. Type: **M. flexuosa** Linnaeus filius.

Orophoma Spruce, Journal of the Linnean Society, Botany 11:93. 1860 ("1871"). Type: *Mauritia carana* Wallace.

Massive, solitary, unarmed, pleonanthic, dioecious, tree palms. Stem erect, partly obscured by marcescent leaf sheaths above, becoming bare basally, cortex hard, pith soft. Leaves large, reduplicate, briefly costapalmate; sheath tubular at first, splitting opposite the petiole, the margins sometimes bearing coarse fibers; petiole conspicuous, adaxially channeled near the base, otherwise circular in

Map 20.—**Distribution of Lepidocaryeae.**

cross-section, smooth, unarmed; blade bearing a low has-tulalike crest adaxially at the base, abaxially with a low ridge; blade orbicular, divided along abaxial folds almost to the insertion into numerous crowded single-fold segments, very shortly bifid at their tips, midribs prominent, transverse veinlets not conspicuous. Inflorescences solitary, interfoliar, the staminate and pistillate superficially similar; prophyll short, tubular, 2-keeled, with 2 short triangular lobes, striate; peduncle shorter than the rachis, elliptical in cross-section, bearing numerous overlapping distichous, tubular, striate, peduncular bracts, each with a short, triangular, dorsal limb and a shallow point on the opposite side; rachis bracts numerous, completely sheathing the branches, distichous, as the peduncular, each subtending a ± pendulous or spreading first-order branch; the first-order branch bearing a short, 2-keeled, striate, tubular prophyll, and 1–few empty distichous bracts, subsequent bracts tubular, flaring, short, each subtending a very short or moderate, straight or recurved rachilla; staminate rachilla catkinlike, bearing a basal, tubular, 2-keeled prophyll and crowded, spirally inserted bracts, each subtending a pair of staminate flowers, each flower bearing a basal 2-keeled bracteole; pistillate rachilla very short, not catkinlike, bearing a basal, tubular, 2-keeled prophyll, and subdistichous, ± explanate bracts, each subtending a solitary pistillate flower with a flattened, 2-keeled bracteole, and often also bearing a minute spathulate, second bracteole, with 2 minute flanges on its abaxial surface. Staminate flowers with calyx tubular, shortly 3-lobed, often densely scaly; petals 3, elongate, much exceeding the calyx, valvate, coriaceous, joined briefly at the base; stamens 6, the filaments ± free, thick, ± angled, elongate, anthers elongate, basifixed, latrorse; pollen elliptic to circular, monosulcate or monoporate, exine intectate with spinules and deep-seated spines; pistillode minute. Pistillate flow-

ers larger than the staminate; calyx tubular, striate, shortly 3-lobed, often densely scaly; corolla tubular in the basal $\frac{1}{3}$–$\frac{1}{2}$, with 3 valvate, elongate lobes distally; staminodes 6, connate laterally by their flattened broad filaments and adnate to the corolla at the mouth of the tube; gynoecium trilocular, triovulate, ± rounded, covered in vertical rows of reflexed scales, style short, conical, stigmas 3, ovules anatropous, basally attached. Fruit ± rounded, very large, usually 1-seeded, with apical stigmatic remains; epicarp covered in many neat vertical rows of reddish-brown, reflexed scales, mesocarp rather thick, fleshy, endocarp not differentiated. Seed rounded, attached near the base, apically with a blunt beak, seed coat thin, raphe elongate, branches anastomosing, endosperm homogeneous; embryo basal. Germination adjacent-ligular; eophyll with a pair of divergent leaflets (? always). $n = 18$ (*M. flexuosa* as *M. setigera*, Sarkar 1970).

Anatomy.—Leaf, petiole, stem (Tomlinson 1961). Despite difference in leaf form, *Mauritia* and *Lepidocaryum* are not significantly different in leaf anatomy.

Distribution.—About three species distributed in wetter parts of Trinidad, Colombia, Ecuador, Peru, Venezuela, Guyana, Surinam, French Guiana, and Brazil.

Ecology.—Occurring often in vast natural stands in periodically inundated areas in the lowlands.

Fossil Record.—Pollen referable to *Mauritia* has been recorded from the Paleocene of South America. The type may also include *Lepidocaryum* and *Mauritiella* (Muller 1981). Herngreen (1975) considers *Echimonocolpites* sp. from the Senonian of Brazil as a possible forerunner of this type, but Muller lists this record as "pending." Pollen of *Mauritiidites crassibaculatus* (Van Hoeken-Klinkenberg 1964) from Paleocene of Nigeria cannot certainly be included as baculate forms are unknown in the included genera.

Common Names and Uses.—Mauritia palms, moriche palms, buriti. The buriti palms are immensely useful. They may be a source of oil and starch, wine, timber, cork, fiber for weaving and tying, and palm hearts. The palms are so important locally that they are referred to as the tree of life.

Notes.—*Mauritia* and *Mauritiella* have been combined (Balick 1981) but there are consistent differences in flower clusters and habits. In *Mauritiella*, pistillate flowers are borne on short branches and staminate flowers are solitary while in *Mauritia*, pistillate flowers are borne singly or on very short branches and staminate flowers are in pairs. Species of *Mauritia* are solitary with unarmed stems and species of *Mauritiella* clustering with spiny stems. These differences seem to warrant maintaining the two genera.

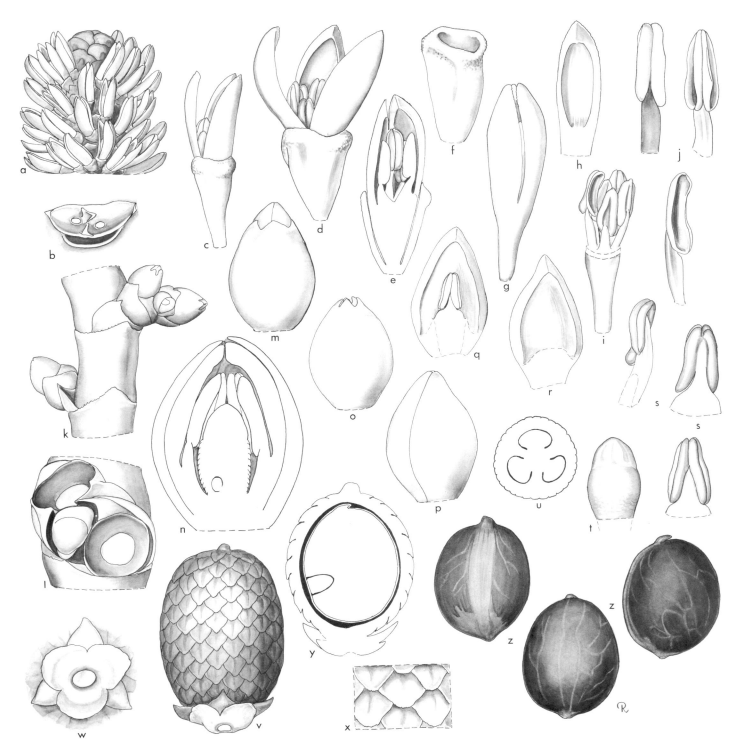

59.—**Mauritia. a,** portion of staminate rachilla ×2; **b,** staminate dyad, flowers removed to show bract and bracteoles ×6; **c, d,** two staminate flowers ×6; **e,** staminate flower in vertical section ×6; **f,** staminate calyx ×6; **g,** staminate flower, calyx removed ×6; **h,** staminate petal, interior view ×6; **i,** androecium ×6; **j,** stamen in 3 views ×9; **k,** portion of pistillate rachilla ×1½; **l,** portion of pistillate rachilla, two buds removed to show bracts and bracteoles ×6; **m,** pistillate bud ×4½; **n,** pistillate bud in vertical section ×6; **o,** pistillate calyx ×4½; **p,** pistillate bud, calyx removed ×4½; **q,** pistillate petal and staminode, interior view ×4½; **r,** pistillate petal, interior view ×4½; **s,** staminode in 3 views ×6; **t,** gynoecium ×6; **u,** ovary in cross-section ×9; **v,** fruit ×1; **w,** base of fruit with perianth ×1; **x,** scales of fruit ×2¼; **y,** fruit in vertical section ×1; **z,** seed in 3 views ×1. *Mauritia carana: a-j, Schultes & Cabrera 18315; M. flexuosa:* **k-z,** *G. P. Lewis s.n.*

Taxonomic Account. — There is no recent assessment of variation in *Mauritia*.

Plate. — *46C.*

60. MAURITIELLA Burret, Notizblatt des Botanischen Gartens und Museums zu Berlin-Dahlem 12: 609. 1935. Type: **M. aculeata** (Kunth) Burret (*Mauritia aculeata* Kunth).

Lepidococcus H. A. Wendland & Drude ex A. D. Hawkes, Arquivos de Botânica do Estado de São Paulo ser. 2, 2:173. 1952. (Non *Lepidococca* Turczaninow 1848). Type: *L. aculeatus* (Kunth) H. A. Wendland & Drude ex A. D. Hawkes (*Mauritia aculeata* Kunth) (superfluous name).

Moderate clustered, armed, pleonanthic, dioecious, tree palms. Stem erect, partly obscured by marcescent leaf sheaths above, becoming bare at the base, the internodes frequently bearing spinelike adventitious roots. Leaves moderate, reduplicate, briefly costapalmate; sheath splitting opposite the petiole; petiole conspicuous, adaxially channeled near the base, otherwise circular in cross-section, smooth, unarmed, frequently waxy; a hastulalike crest present adaxially at the base of the blade; blade ± orbicular in outline, divided along abaxial folds almost to the insertion into numerous crowded single-fold segments, very briefly bifid at their tips, adaxial surface glabrous, abaxial surface usually covered with white wax and short bifid scales, midribs prominent, transverse veinlets inconspicuous. Inflorescences solitary, interfoliar, the staminate and pistillate superficially similar; peduncle short, ± elliptical in cross-section; prophyll short, tubular, 2-keeled, with 2 short, striate, triangular lobes; peduncular bracts numerous, overlapping, distichous, striate, each with a triangular limb; rachis much longer than the peduncle; rachis bracts similar to the peduncular, each subtending a ± pendulous or spreading first-order branch; the first-order branch bearing a short 2-keeled, striate, tubular prophyll and 1–few empty distichous bracts; subsequent bracts tubular, short, ± flaring, each subtending a very short, straight or recurved rachilla; staminate rachilla catkinlike, bearing a basal, tubular, 2-keeled prophyll and crowded, ± rounded, spirally arranged rachilla bracts, connate shortly at the base, each subtending a single staminate flower bearing a tubular, 2-keeled bracteole; pistillate rachilla very short, ± catkinlike, bearing a basal, 2-keeled prophyll and spiral to subdistichous rachilla bracts, each subtending a solitary pistillate flower bearing a flattened 2-keeled bracteole. Staminate flower symmetrical; calyx tubular, briefly 3-lobed, often scaly; corolla tubular at the very base with 3 elongate, valvate, leathery lobes much exceeding the calyx; stamens 6, the filaments distinct, thick, ± angled, elongate, anthers elongate, basifixed, latrorse; pollen elliptic to circular, monosulcate, exine intectate with spinules and deep-seated spines; pistillode minute. Pistillate flowers larger than the staminate; calyx tubular, striate, briefly 3-lobed, often scaly; corolla tubular in the basal 1/3–1/2 with 3 elongate, valvate lobes; staminodes 6, connate laterally by their flattened broad filaments and adnate to the corolla at the mouth of the tube;

gynoecium trilocular, triovulate, ± rounded, covered in vertical rows of reflexed scales, style short, conical, stigmas 3, ovules anatropous, basally attached. Fruit ± rounded, usually 1-seeded, with apical stigmatic remains, perianth persistent; epicarp covered in many neat vertical rows of reddish-brown reflexed scales, mesocarp rather thick, fleshy, endocarp scarcely differentiated. Seed ± rounded to ellipsoidal, attached basally, apically with an elongate knob, and thin seed coat, raphe branches curved, endosperm homogeneous; embryo basal. Germination adjacent-ligular; eophyll with a pair of divergent leaflets (? always). $n = 18$ (*M. aculeata* as *Mauritia aculeata*, Sarkar 1970).

Anatomy. — Not studied.

Distribution. — About 14 species have been described from northern South America but there are probably far fewer.

Ecology. — Species of *Mauritiella* are predominantly lowland palms. Several species are characteristic of the banks of black-water rivers.

Fossil Record. — Not differentiated from *Mauritia*.

Common Names and Uses. — Buriti. Leaves are used for thatching and the fruit eaten.

Notes. — See under *Mauritia*.

Taxonomic Account. — There is no recent reassessment of the genus, but see Balick (1981).

Plate. — *14A.*

61. LEPIDOCARYUM Martius, Historia Naturalis Palmarum 2:49. 1824. Lectotype: **L. gracile** Martius (see H. E. Moore 1963c).

Slender, clustered, unarmed, pleonanthic, dioecious, undergrowth palms. Stem erect, colonial by slender rhizomes, partly obscured by marcescent leaf sheaths above, becoming bare basally, with rather short internodes and inconspicuous nodal scars. Leaves small, reduplicately palmate; sheath splitting opposite the petiole, frequently covered with very dense, caducous tomentum; petiole conspicuous, ± rounded in cross-section except at the base where channeled adaxially; hastulae mostly absent, a low crest sometimes present adaxially; blade flabellate or ± orbicular with a very short costa, divided along a few abaxial folds to the insertion into few broad or narrow single-fold or compound, spathulate, acuminate segments, tips sometimes bristly, blade surfaces similar in color, midribs more prominent abaxially, transverse veinlets conspicuous, rather distant and somewhat sinuous; young leaves sometimes reddish-tinged. Inflorescences solitary, interfoliar, the staminate and pistillate superficially similar, branched to 2 orders; prophyll tubular, closely sheathing, 2-keeled, with 2 short triangular lobes; peduncle elongate, bearing several (ca. 6) closely sheathing, tubular bracts with short triangular limbs; rachis longer than the peduncle; rachis bracts like the peduncular, but tending to split at the tip, each subtending a first-order branch; first-order branches few, rather short, bearing a basal, tubular, 2-keeled prophyll and sometimes 1 empty tubular bract,

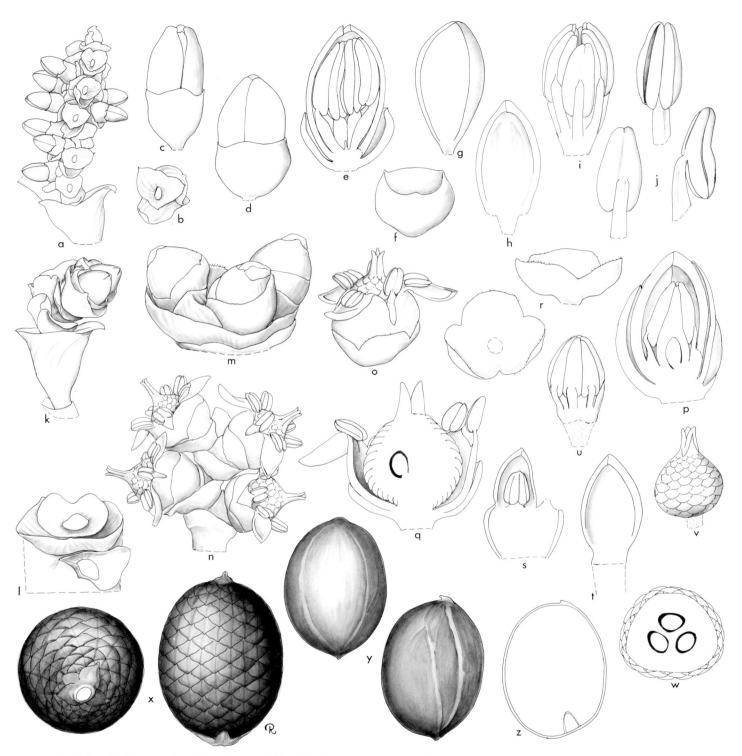

60.—**Mauritiella. a,** portion of staminate rachilla ×3; **b,** bract and bracteole of staminate flower ×6; **c, d,** two staminate flowers ×7½; **e,** staminate bud in vertical section ×9; **f,** staminate calyx ×9; **g,** staminate bud, calyx removed ×9; **h,** staminate petal, interior view ×9; **i,** androecium ×9; **j,** stamen in 3 views ×9; **k,** rachilla of pistillate inflorescence with prophyll ×3; **l,** portion of pistillate rachilla, flowers removed to show bracts and bracteoles ×3; **m,** portion of pistillate rachilla in bud ×3; **n,** portion of pistillate rachilla in flower ×2¼; **o,** pistillate flower ×3; **p,** pistillate bud in vertical section ×4½; **q,** pistillate flower in vertical section × 4½; **r,** pistillate calyx in 2 views ×3; **s,** pistillate petal with staminode, interior view ×4½; **t,** pistillate petal, interior view ×7½; **u,** staminodes ×4½; **v,** gynoecium ×3; **w,** ovary in cross-section ×4½; **x,** fruit in 2 views ×1½; **y,** seed in 2 views ×1½; **z,** seed in vertical section ×1½. *Mauritiella armata*: **a-w,** *Balick et al. 913*; **x-z,** *Moore et al. 9537.*

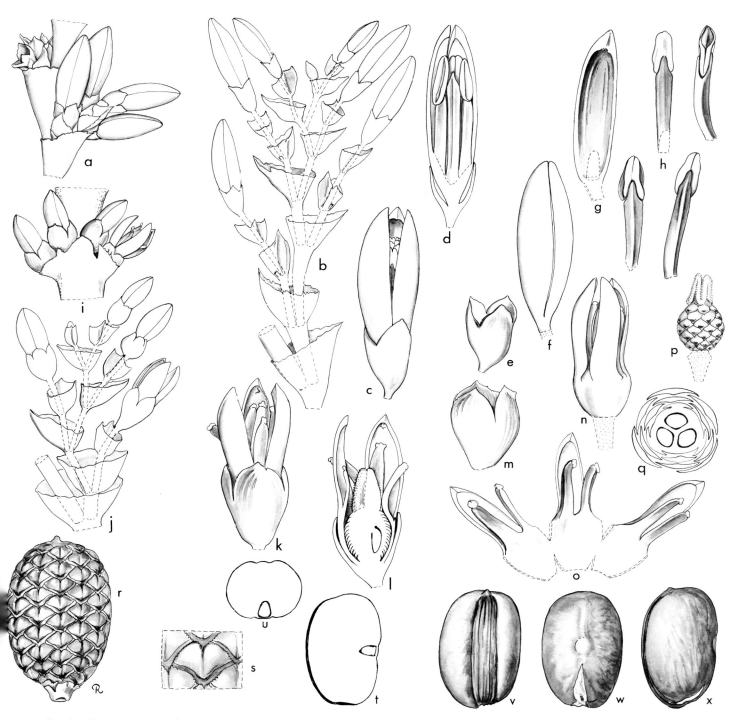

61.—**Lepidocaryum. a,** portion of staminate inflorescence ×3; **b,** portion of staminate inflorescence, lateral axis expanded to show arrangement of bracts with flowers ×3; **c,** staminate bud ×6; **d,** staminate bud in vertical section ×6; **e,** staminate calyx ×6; **f,** staminate bud, calyx removed ×6; **g,** staminate petal, interior view ×6; **h,** stamen in 4 views ×6; **i,** portion of pistillate inflorescence ×3; **j,** portion of pistillate inflorescence, lateral axis expanded to show arrangement of bracts and flowers ×3; **k,** pistillate flower ×6; **l,** pistillate flower in vertical section ×6; **m,** pistillate calyx ×6; **n,** pistillate flower, calyx removed ×6; **o,** pistillate corolla with staminodes, interior view, expanded ×6; **p,** gynoecium ×6; **q,** ovary in cross-section ×12; **r,** fruit ×1½; **s,** scales ×3; **t,** seed in vertical section ×1½; **u,** seed in cross-section ×1½; **v, w, x,** seed in 3 views ×1½. *Lepidocaryum gracile*: **a-h,** *Schultes & Cabrera 15198*; **r-x,** *Schultes & Cabrera 15756*; *L. tenue*: **i-q,** *Schultes & Cordeiro 6511*.

and distichously arranged, tubular, triangular tipped bracts, each subtending a rachilla; staminate rachilla short, becoming recurved, with a basal, membranous, striate, 2-keeled prophyll and few (up to 12) distichous, membranous, apiculate, cup-shaped bracts, each, including sometimes the prophyll, subtending a solitary staminate flower bearing a 2-keeled bracteole, or a pair of staminate flowers enclosed within a 2-keeled, explanate bracteole, one of the pair bearing a second bracteole; pistillate rachilla usually very short, sometimes scarcely exserted from the subtending bract, bearing a basal, membranous, 2-keeled, striate prophyll and few (up to ca. 8) distichous, membranous, cuplike, apiculate bracts, each, including sometimes the prophyll, subtending a solitary pistillate flower, bearing a 2-keeled bracteole and a minute, ovate, flattened second bracteole. Staminate flowers symmetrical; calyx tubular, briefly 3-lobed, ± striate; petals much exceeding the calyx, basally connate, the tips valvate; stamens 6, borne at the very base of the petals, filaments thick, fleshy, ± angled, the anthers small, basifixed, latrorse; pollen elliptic to circular, monosulcate or monoporate, exine intectate with spinules and deep-seated spines; pistillode minute or short, columnar. Pistillate flowers larger than the staminate; calyx tubular, 3-lobed, splitting somewhat irregularly after fertilization; corolla much exceeding the calyx, tubular in basal ca. ⅓, with 3 elongate, valvate lobes; staminodes 6, adnate to the base of the corolla lobes, the filaments somewhat angled, the empty anthers minute; gynoecium incompletely trilocular, triovulate, ± rounded, covered in vertical rows of reflexed scales, style conical, briefly 3-lobed, ovule anatropous, basally attached(?). Fruit rounded or oblong, usually 1-seeded, with apical stigmatic remains; epicarp covered in vertical rows of reflexed reddish-brown scales, mesocarp thin, endocarp not differentiated. Seed attached near the base at one side, with a shallow furrow along the raphe, testa fleshy(?), endosperm homogeneous; embryo lateral. Germination adjacent-ligular; eophyll bifid. Cytology not studied.

Anatomy.—Leaf (Tomlinson 1961). See *Mauritia*.

Distribution.—About nine species, distributed in the wetter parts of Colombia, Peru, Venezuela, Guyana, and Brazil.

Ecology.—Species of *Lepidocaryum* are palms of the undergrowth of lowland tropical rain forest.

Common Names and Uses.—Poktamui. Leaves are used as thatch.

Notes.—*Lepidocaryum* is the most reduced member of the tribe in terms of habit and inflorescence, but the three genera, *Mauritia, Mauritiella,* and *Lepidocaryum,* are clearly very closely related.

Taxonomic Account.—There is no modern reassessment of the genus.

Plate.—*46D.*

III NYPOIDEAE

NYPOIDEAE Griffith, Palms of British India 7. 1850 ('*Nipinae*'). Type: **Nypa.**

Monoecious, pleonanthic; stem prostrate, branching dichotomously; unarmed; leaves pinnate, reduplicate; inflorescence terminated by a pistillate head with lateral branches ending in short spikes of staminate flowers; flowers extremely dimorphic; perianth parts 6, distinct, linear, similar in both sexes; stamens 3, filaments united in a column, pistillode absent; carpels 3, free, irregularly polyhedric, curved and angled, with a funnel-shaped stylar opening; fruiting head large, globose, composed of irregularly compressed, enlarged carpels, with or without seeds.

This subfamily contains a single monotypic genus *Nypa,* a mangrove palm of Asia and the west Pacific (Map 21). The large reduplicate pinnate leaf is similar to leaves of the other subfamilies except Coryphoideae. The presence of only two bracts, a prophyll and a single peduncular bract on the inflorescence resembles inflorescences in some Arecoideae, although the tubular bracts in *Nypa* differ markedly in shape from bracts in other subfamilies. Otherwise in both vegetative and reproductive characters *Nypa* is unlike other palms. The prostrate, dichotomously branched stem (Tomlinson 1971b) and the erect inflorescence (Uhl 1972a) bearing a terminal head of pistillate flowers and lateral spikes of staminate flowers are unique in the family. Similar sepals and petals in both staminate and pistillate flowers, lack of staminodes and pistillodes, an androecium of only three stamens with united filaments, and three separate carpels of unusual form are exceptional floral characters. The adaptation of the fruit for floating is also noteworthy.

Certain characters of the genus—solitary flowers, distinct and similar sepals and petals, distinct carpels of cupular form—appear primitive within palms and to some extent within monocotyledons, but these are combined with specialization in the form of the rachillae, in the lack of staminodes and pistillodes, in the reduced stamen number and fusion of the filaments, and in adaptation of the fruit for floating.

The pistillate head was once thought similar to those of phytelephantoid palms causing early scholars (Drude 1887, Martius 1823–1850) to classify *Nypa* with the phytelephantoid palms, but both the arrangement and the structure of the flowers are markedly different.

The genus is of special interest because of its long fossil record. Its occurrence in the Senonian makes it not only one of the first palms, but also one of the earliest recognizable modern genera of monocotyledons. Further developmental studies of flowers and chemical and DNA analyses may assist in understanding the relationships of this remarkable palm.

62. NYPA Steck, Dissertatio Inauguralis Medica de Sagu, 15. 1757. Type: **N. fruticans** Wurmb.
Nipa Thunberg, Kongliga Vetenskaps Acadamiens Nya Handlingar 3:234. 1782. Type: *N. fruticans* Thunberg (=*Nypa fruticans* Wurmb).

Large, creeping, unarmed, pleonanthic, monoecious palm. Stem stout, prostrate or subterranean, branching dichotomously, curved leaf scars evident above, roots borne along the lower side. Leaves few, erect, reduplicately pinnate; sheath soon splitting, glabrous; petiole stout, elongate, wide basally, channeled adaxially, terete distally, the base often persistent as a conical stub after the blade has disintegrated; rachis terete basally, becoming angled distally; leaflets numerous, single-fold, regularly arranged, acute, coriaceous, midrib prominent bearing distinctive, shining, chestnut-colored, membranous ramenta abaxially, transverse veinlets not evident. Inflorescences solitary, interfoliar, erect, branching to 5(–6) orders, protogynous; peduncle terete; prophyll 2-keeled, tubular; peduncular bract tubular, somewhat inflated, pointed, rubbery, splitting longitudinally; rachis usually shorter than the peduncle, terete, terminating in a head of pistillate flowers and below this bearing 7–9 spirally arranged, closed, ± inflated, tubular bracts each subtending a first-order branch; first-order branches adnate ca. ½ their length above the subtending bracts, each bearing and enclosed by a tubular prophyll in bud; subsequent branches all bearing a complete, tubular, closed prophyll and ending in a short catkinlike rachilla, bearing densely crowded, spirally arranged, solitary staminate flowers, each subtended by a small bract. Staminate flowers sessile; sepals 3, distinct, narrow, oblanceolate; petals 3, distinct, slightly imbricate, similar to the sepals but slightly smaller, both loosely closed over the stamens in bud; stamens 3, filaments and connectives connate in a solid stalk, anthers elongate, extrorse; pollen elliptic or ± circular, meridionosulcate, exine tectate, spiny and finely reticulate between the spines; pistillode lacking. Pistillate flowers very different from the staminate; sepals 3, distinct, irregularly oblanceolate, petals 3, similar to those of the staminate flower; staminodes lacking; carpels 3(–4), distinct, much longer than and obscuring the perianth at maturity, ± obovoid, asymmetrical, angled by mutual pressure, ± acute distally, and with a ± lateral, funnel-shaped stigmatic opening, ovule anatropous, attached dorsally or submarginally near the base of the locule. Fruiting head ± glo-

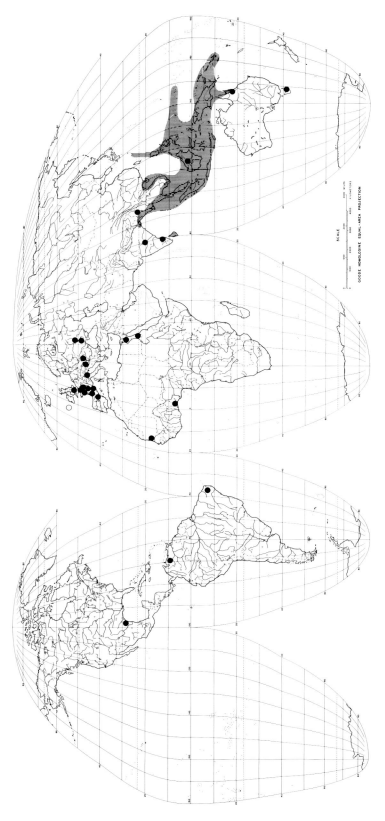

Map 21.— **Distribution of Nypoideae:** fossils in black.

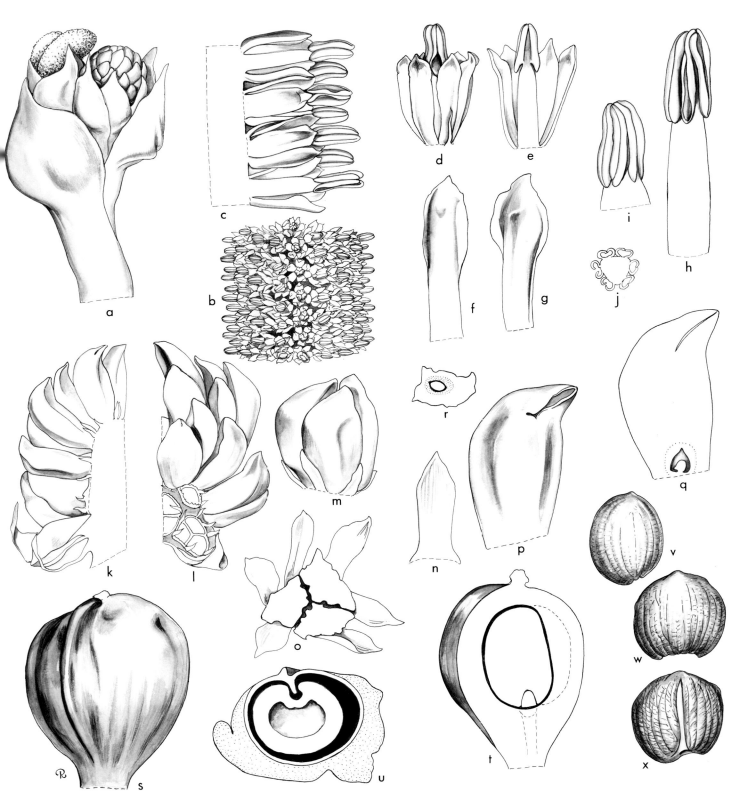

62.—**Nypa. a,** portion of inflorescence showing terminal pistillate head and lateral staminate branches ×½; **b,** portion of staminate axis ×3; **c,** portion of staminate axis in vertical section ×6; **d,** staminate flower ×6; **e,** staminate flower in vertical section ×6; **f,** staminate sepal ×12; **g,** staminate petal ×12; **h,** androecium ×12; **i,** anthers ×12; **j,** anthers in cross-section ×6; **k,** portion of pistillate head in vertical section ×1½; **l,** portion of pistillate head, some flowers removed ×1½; **m,** pistillate flower ×3; **n,** pistillate perianth segment ×6; **o,** pistillate flower, carpels removed ×6; **p,** carpel ×6; **q,** carpel in vertical section ×6; **r,** ovary in cross-section ×3; **s,** fruit ×½; **t,** fruit in vertical section ×½; **u,** fruit in cross-section ×½; **v, w, x,** seed in 3 views ×½. *Nypa fruticans: **a-r,** Moore 5846; **s-x,** L. H. Bailey 520.*

bose, fertile and partially developed fruits intermixed, 1–3 carpels per flower maturing a seed; fruit developing from 1 carpel, compressed and irregularly angled, stigmatic remains terminal, pyramidal; epicarp smooth, mesocarp fibrous, endocarp thick, composed of interwoven fibrous strands, with an adaxial internal longitudinal ridge intruded into the seed. Seed broadly ovoid, grooved adaxially, hilum basal, raphe branches ascending from the base, endosperm homogeneous; embryo basal. Germination on the head with the plumule exserted and pushing the fruit away; eophyll bifid or with several leaflets. $n = 17$ (Read 1966). $n = 8$ (Radermacher 1925, Sarkar 1970, probably from Radermacher, both seem incorrect in view of the later count).

Anatomy. — Leaf (Tomlinson 1961). Silica bodies hat-shaped, central vascular bundles of petioles with a single phloem strand. Floral (Uhl 1972a, Uhl and Moore 1977a). The pistillate flowers appear to be structurally and developmentally unique within the family. Although the perianth encloses the carpels in early stages, by anthesis the carpels much exceed the perianth, members of which are displaced and obscured. The carpel is basally tubular with a mouthlike stigmatic opening and appears to represent a different, non-follicular, unspecialized form.

Distribution. — A single species, *Nypa fruticans,* occurring from Sri Lanka and the Ganges Delta to Australia, the Solomon Islands, and the Ryukyu Islands.

Ecology. — *Nypa* is strictly a mangrove palm, occurring in a variety of estuarine situations; it usually grows in soft mud, often in vast natural stands. Pollination appears to be by drosophilid flies (Essig 1973); correlations of pollination with floral anatomy and development have been noted (Uhl and Moore 1977a).

Fossil Record. — Known from the Paleocene of Brazil, the Eocene and Miocene of Europe, probably Africa, India, and parts of Borneo (Tralau 1964, Muller 1981). Pollen of *Nypa* was among the first seven earliest angiospermous pollens precisely identified, dating from the Senonian (Upper Cretaceous) of Borneo where the genus may have been present continuously since (see Muller 1979). Characteristic *Nypa* pollen in the Senonian of tropical West Africa and Borneo represents some of the earliest records of palms. *Nypa* fossils are pantropical in distribution including southern U.S., South America, and Europe, a remarkably expanded record compared with its present distribution (Muller 1979).

Common Names and Uses. — Nipah, mangrove palm. *Nypa fruticans* is ethnobotanically very important. The leaves are one of the most important sources for the production of palm shingles ("atap") for thatching, and are also used in minor ways as for cigarette papers and fishing floats. The inflorescences are tapped for sap for sugar and alcohol production. The large natural stands of *Nypa* remain a greatly underexploited resource for fuel alcohol. The young endosperm is eaten, usually boiled in syrup, as a sweetmeat. The great but passive potential of *Nypa* as a stabilizer of estuarine mud in preventing coastal erosion should not be underestimated. For details of the utilization of *Nypa* see Burkill (1966) and Brown and Merrill (1919).

Notes. — See commentary under Nypoideae.

Taxonomic Account. — Tralau (1964).

Plates. — *14B; 47A, B, Fig. G.17.*

IV CEROXYLOIDEAE

CEROXYLOIDEAE Drude in Martius, Flora Brasiliensis 3(2):271. 1881 (as suborder 'Ceroxylinae'). Type: **Ceroxylon.**

Tall, moderate, or small, solitary or clustered, unarmed; hermaphroditic, monoecious, or dioecious; leaves regularly or irregularly pinnate, bifid, or entire and pinnately ribbed, reduplicate, crownshafts present or absent, inflorescence with prophyll and usually several peduncular bracts, very rarely with 1 (*Wendlandiella*); flowers when unisexual, only slightly dimorphic, solitary, or in acervuli, very rarely the acervulus of only 3 flowers; gynoecium syncarpous, triovulate.

The Ceroxyloideae (Map 22) includes only 11 genera which make up three tribes, the Cyclospatheae, Ceroxyleae, and Hyophorbeae, representing the pseudophoenicoid, ceroxyloid, and chamaedoreoid major groups of Moore (1973a). The subfamily is best represented in the New World but two genera occur in Madagascar, one in the Mascarene Islands, and one in Australia. The distinguishing characteristics are numerous peduncular bracts in the inflorescence (except for *Wendlandiella* with only one), flowers borne singly or in rows (acervuli) but not (or only very rarely) in triads, and a syncarpous, triovulate gynoecium. Of the tribes, the Cyclospatheae, possessing spirally arranged, solitary, hermaphroditic flowers, seems the least specialized. Members of the Ceroxyleae, although dioecious, bear solitary flowers and appear less specialized than the genera of the Hyophorbeae, which are monoecious but have small flowers usually borne in acervuli and exhibiting more connation of perianth parts. Chromosome complements support this interpretation. They are: Cyclospatheae $n = 17$, Ceroxyleae $n = 18$, and Hyophorbeae 16, 14, 13. The occurrence of several similar characters, as multiple inflorescences and incomplete prophylls, suggest that the Ceroxyloideae are more closely related to the Arecoideae than to the other subfamilies.

Key to the Tribes of the Ceroxyloideae

1 Proximal flowers on the rachillae bisexual, the distal usually smaller and staminate, all borne on long stalks . . . . **Cyclospatheae**
1 All flowers unisexual, if stalked, then briefly so 2
2 Dioecious palms; crownshafts not formed; flowers borne singly on short, usually bracteolate pedicels; flowers open from early in development, the stamens equalling or exceeding the petals . . . . **Ceroxyleae**

2 Monoecious or dioecious palms; crownshafts present or absent; flowers sessile, usually ebracteolate at anthesis, borne singly or in acervuli of a pistillate and 2 to several staminate, or in lines of staminate flowers, or rarely pistillate flowers (*Wendlandiella*); stamens included within the staminate flower until or sometimes at anthesis . . . . **Hyophorbeae**

CYCLOSPATHEAE O. F. Cook, Memoirs of the Torrey Botanical Club 12:24. 1902. Type: *Cyclospathe* = **Pseudophoenix.**

Stems moderate, erect; leaves pinnate, sheaths tubular forming a short crownshaft; flowers hermaphroditic, solitary, spirally arranged, pseudopedicellate, borne in the axils of small bracts; filaments apically embedded in connectives.

The tribe (Map 23) contains the single genus, *Pseudophoenix.*

63. PSEUDOPHOENIX H. A. Wendland ex Sargent, Botanical Gazette 11:314. 1886. Type: **P. sargentii** H. A. Wendland ex Sargent.
Chamaephoenix H. A. Wendland ex A. H. Curtis, Florida Farmer and Fruit Grower 1(8):57: 1887. Type: *C. sargentii* H. A. Wendland ex A. H. Curtiss (illegitimate name) (=*Pseudophoenix sargentii* H. A. Wendland ex Sargent).
Sargentia H. A. Wendland & Drude ex Salomon, Die Palmen. 160. 1887 (rejected name). Type: *S. aricocca* H. A. Wendland & Drude ex Salomon (illegitimate name) (=*Pseudophoenix sargentii* H. A. Wendland ex Sargent).
Cyclospathe O. F. Cook in Northrop, Memoirs of the Torrey Botanical Club 12:25. 1902. Type: *C. northropii* O. F. Cook (=*Pseudophoenix sargentii* H. A. Wendland ex Sargent subsp. *saonae* (O. F. Cook) R. W. Read var. *saonae*).

Moderate, solitary, pleonanthic, polygamous or hermaphroditic palms. Stem erect, often swollen, prominently ringed with rather wide leaf scars, smooth to finely striate, gray or green, waxy. Leaves few, mostly ca. 10, reduplicately pinnate, deciduous by a basal abscission zone; sheath forming a short, somewhat swollen crownshaft, splitting distally opposite the petiole, waxy; petiole channelled adaxially, rounded abaxially; rachis flat to angled adaxially, rounded abaxially, ± glabrous; leaflets numerous, irregularly arranged, grouped and fanned within the groups, stiff, acute, single-fold, waxy on both surfaces, midribs evident, other veins small, transverse veinlets not evident. Inflorescences interfoliar, pendulous or arched,

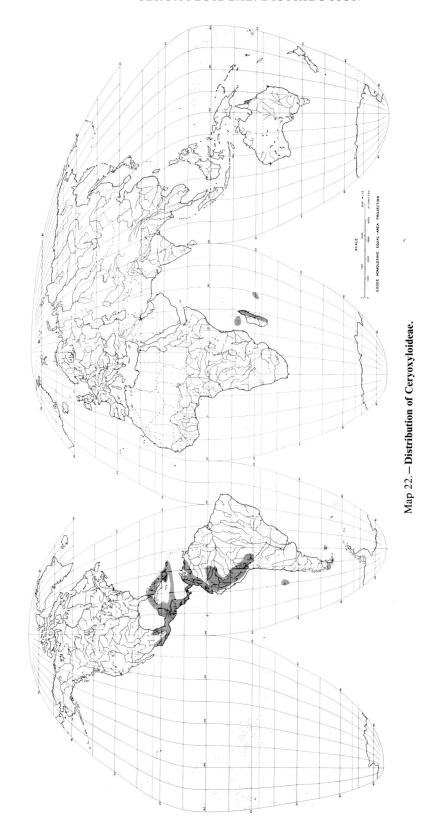

Map 22.—Distribution of Ceroxyloideae.

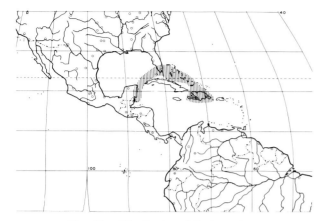

Map 23.—**Distribution of Cyclospatheae.**

branched to the fifth-order; peduncle elongate, dorsiventrally flattened; prophyll tubular, 2-keeled, flattened, leathery, persistent, opening at the apex; peduncular bracts 2, the first similar to the prophyll, the second usually collarlike; rachis longer than or about as long as the peduncle; rachillae stiffly spreading or pendulous, each subtended by a small open bract. Flowers borne singly, spirally arranged, each subtended by an acuminate bract, hermaphroditic proximally but the distal few staminate with a much reduced pistil, base of the flower extended in a pseudopedicel formed by fusion and elongation of the receptacle and the base of the calyx; calyx 3-lobed with rounded, apiculate tips; petals 3, valvate, thick, much longer than the calyx, basally connate in a very short tube; stamens 6, filaments thin, dilated and briefly connate in a ring basally, the apex lying in a groove in the abaxial surface of the anther to about the midpoint of the connective, then bent sharply inward, anthers large, elongate, ± pointed apically and basally, dorsifixed, latrorse; pollen elliptic, monosulcate or very rarely trichotomosulcate, with coarsely reticulate, tectate exine; gynoecium conical, trilocular, triovulate, with 3 glands at the base opposite the petals, stigmas sessile, very short, becoming recurved after fertilization, ovules campylotropous, inserted on the adaxial side of the locule. Fruit 1–3-seeded, waxy red, globose or 2–3-lobed, stigmatic remains near the base or in a central depression in 3-seeded fruits; epicarp smooth,

63.—**Pseudophoenix. a,** portion of rachilla with staminate flowers ×3; **b,** staminate flower ×6; **c,** staminate calyx ×6; **d,** staminate petal, interior view ×6; **e,** androecium ×6; **f,** stamen in 2 views ×6; **g,** pistillode ×6; **h,** pistillate flower ×6; **i,** pistillate flower in vertical section ×3; **j,** gynoecium, exterior view and in vertical section ×6; **k,** ovary in cross-section ×6; **l,** fruit with 2 seeds ×1½; **m,** base of fruit and stigmatic remains ×3; **n,** endocarp ×1½; **o,** seed ×3; **p,** seed in vertical section ×3. *Pseudophoenix sargentii:* all from *Read 759.*

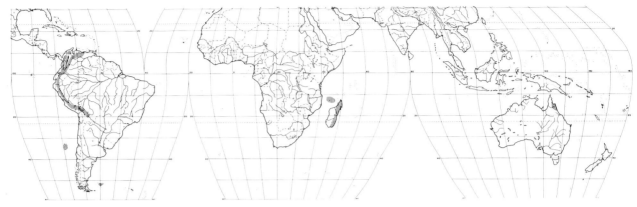

Map 24.—Distribution of Ceroxyleae.

mesocarp fleshy, with raphides, lacking fibers, endocarp hard, brown, smooth. Seed not adherent to endocarp at maturity, hilum basal, raphe branches ascending and spreading in shallow grooves, endosperm homogeneous; embryo subbasal. Germination remote-tubular; eophyll narrow lanceolate. $n = 17$ (*P. sargentii, P. vinifera,* Read 1966).

Anatomy.—Leaf and floral (Read 1968). The vascular system of the carpel—three major bundles with ventral bundles in "lateral" positions and an ovular supply associated with ventral bundles only—resembles that of members of Ceroxyleae and Hyophorbeae. Ground tissue of the gynoecium, which lacks tannins but has abundant raphides, is like that of *Chamaedorea* (Read 1968, Uhl and Moore 1971).

Distribution.—Four species from Florida, the Bahama Islands, Cuba, Hispaniola, and Dominica, to Mexico and Belize.

Ecology.—*Pseudophoenix* occurs on well drained sand or porous limestone near the coast or inland on dry hills. The seeds are long-lived for palms, germinating after as much as two years in storage. Fruits become buoyant when dry and in *P. sargentii* may be adapted for dispersal by sea (Read 1968).

Common Names and Uses.—Cherry palm, Buccaneer palm. Leaves may be used for thatch, and the fruit of some species for animal food. In the past, juice from the trunk of *P. vinifera* and *P. ekmanii* was used in making a fermented drink. All species are striking ornamentals.

Notes.—*Pseudophoenix* stands apart as the only genus of the Ceroxyloideae having hermaphroditic flowers. It has unique anatomical features of the leaf and mode of attachment of the anther as well as an unusually elongate base or pseudopedicel on the flower.

The spirally arranged single flowers on a highly branched interfoliar inflorescence, certain anatomical features, and the presence of but a single phloem strand in central vascular bundles of the petiole ally *Pseudophoenix* with the Ceroxyleae and Hyophorbeae. There is no known fossil record, but the genus suggests an ancient stock specialized in some respects but having retained several primitive features.

Taxonomic Accounts.—Quero (1981), Read (1968, 1969b).

Plate.—47C; Figs. G.1, G.5, G.19.

CEROXYLEAE Satake, Hikobia 3:125. 1962. Type: Ceroxylon.

Stems often very tall, very rarely slender; dioecious; sheaths not forming crownshafts; flowers open from early in development, solitary, spirally or subdistichously arranged in the axils of small bracts, usually pedicellate.

The five genera in this tribe are widely distributed, occurring in the Juan Fernandez Islands (*Juania*), Andean South America (*Ceroxylon*), Madagascar (*Ravenea, Louvelia*), and Australia (*Oraniopsis*) (Map 24). All are dioecious trees lacking crownshafts, with large pinnate leaves, and with flowers of medium size, borne on short to long pedicels, subtended by small bracts, and often bearing a small bracteole. All genera except *Juania* have incomplete prophylls. Staminate and pistillate flowers are similar but easily distinguished from each other; staminodes are large and usually bear vestigial anthers. Stamens are prominent, often exceeding the petals in bud. *Juania, Ravenea,* and *Ceroxylon* (Uhl 1969b) are remarkably similar in floral anatomy. The flowers are open from early in development, an unusual feature, the significance of which is not yet understood. Such "congenitally" open flowers are found elsewhere scattered through the family in unrelated

64.—**Ceroxylon. a,** portion of pistillate rachilla ×3; **b,** portion of staminate rachilla ×3; **c,** staminate flower ×12; **d,** staminate flower in vertical section ×12; **e,** staminate calyx ×6; **f,** staminate flower, calyx removed ×6; **g,** stamen in 3 views ×6; **h,** pistillate flower ×6; **i,** pistillate calyx ×6; **j,** pistillate petal ×6; **k,** gynoecium ×6; **l,** ovary in vertical section ×6; **m,** ovary in cross-section ×6; **n,** seed ×3; **o,** seed in vertical section ×3. *Ceroxylon* sp.: all from *Cuatrecasas 19322.*

taxa. The geographical distribution suggests great antiquity (see Chapter V).

Key to the Genera of the Ceroxyleae

1 Stigmatic remains basal in fruit 2
1 Stigmatic remains lateral to subapical in fruit 3
2 Peduncular bracts 5–7, petals basally united; stamens 6–15 or more. Andes of South America ...... 64. **Ceroxylon**
2 Peduncular bracts 3–5, petals free; stamens 6. Queensland .... 65. **Oraniopsis**
3 Androecium with united filaments; seeds usually 3. Madagascar .... 67. **Louvelia**
3 Androecium with free filaments; seeds usually 1 4
4 Pistillate flower with staminodes bearing rudimentary anthers; staminate inflorescences often multiple; prophyll incomplete. Madagascar .... 68. **Ravenea**
4 Pistillate flower with staminodes lacking rudimentary anthers; staminate inflorescence solitary; prophyll complete. Juan Fernandez Islands .... 66. **Juania**

64. **CEROXYLON** Bonpland ex DeCandolle, Bulletin des Sciences, par la Société Philomatique 3:239. 1804. Type: **C. alpinum** Bonpland ex DeCandolle.
Klopstockia Karsten, Linnaea 28:251. 1856. Lectotype: *K. cerifera* Karsten (see H. E. Moore 1963c) (=*Ceroxylon ceriferum* (Karsten) Burret).
Beethovenia Engel, Linnaea 33:677. 1865. Type: *B. cerifera* Engel (=*Ceroxylon beethovenia* Burret).

Tall to very tall, solitary, unarmed, pleonanthic, dioecious palms. Stems smooth, usually waxy, with prominent leaf scars. Leaves moderate to large, reduplicately pinnate, neatly abscising; sheath splitting opposite the petiole at maturity, usually not forming a crownshaft, leathery; petiole channeled adaxially, rounded abaxially; rachis adaxially flat to angled, glabrous, abaxially rounded, silvery-gray tomentose; leaflets acute, single-fold, evenly spaced or clustered, usually glossy adaxially, often waxy or tomentose-scaly abaxially, midrib conspicuous, larger adaxially, no other veins evident. Inflorescences interfoliar, solitary in the leaf axil, branched to 3–4 orders; peduncle elongate; prophyll tubular, 2-keeled, flattened, open apically, incompletely encircling the peduncle abaxially; peduncular bracts several (ca. 5–7), inserted near the base of the peduncle, the lower ones open apically, the upper 3–4 terete, beaked, completely enclosing the inflorescence in bud, splitting abaxially at anthesis, the uppermost sometimes reduced and inserted higher than the others, prophyll and peduncular bracts with indumentum or scales; rachis bracts small, open; rachillae usually flexuous or zigzag, often short, the pistillate usually shorter than the staminate, glabrous or with indumentum, bearing small, pointed bracts subtending the flowers. Flowers ebracteolate, open from early in development, borne singly along the rachillae, pedicellate. Staminate flowers with 3 sepals connate in a low, acutely or acuminately lobed cupule; petals 3, fleshy, acute or acuminate, briefly connate basally with each other and with the bases of antesepalous stamen filaments, separate above at anthesis; stamens 6–15(–17), filaments awl-shaped, not inflexed at the apex in bud, anthers basifixed, bifid basally, bifid to acute or pointed apically; pollen elliptic, monosulcate, with coarsely reticulate, tectate exine; pistillode minute, conic, usually minutely trifid. Pistillate flowers similar to the staminate but staminodes usually smaller with halberd-shaped or sagittate abortive anthers; gynoecium ovoid, trilocular, triovulate, but 2 ovules usually aborting, stigmas 3, recurved at anthesis, ovules pendulous, hemianatropous. Fruit red, orange-red, or orange to purplish-black at maturity, globose, normally 1-seeded, stigmatic remains lateral near the base; epicarp smooth or minutely roughened, mesocarp fleshy with few fibers, endocarp thin, not adherent to seed. Seed globose, hilum basal, round, raphe branches obscure, ascending from the hilum, endosperm homogeneous; embryo lateral near the base. Germination adjacent-ligular; eophyll elliptic or narrowly lanceolate. $n =$ 18 (*C. alpinum* as *C. andicolum*, *C. parvifrons*, Sarkar 1970).

Anatomy.—Leaf (Tomlinson 1961), floral (Uhl 1969b), stamen development (Uhl and Moore 1980).

Distribution.—About 20 or fewer species occurring at high elevations in the Andes from Venezuela through Colombia, Ecuador, and Peru to Bolivia.

Ecology.—Species of *Ceroxylon* are some of the tallest palms. They occur in premontane to low and high montane forest often among clouds for most of the time. Today trees are frequently left standing in fields where the forest has been cleared. All species are endangered (Moore 1977). *C. utile* grows between Colombia and Ecuador, near Volcan Chiles, at an elevation of just over 4000 m, perhaps a record altitude for palms.

Common Names and Uses.—Andean wax palms. Provide wax for candles and matches and fruit for cattle food.

Notes.—Species of *Ceroxylon* are certainly among the most beautiful palms. They are closely related to *Oraniopsis* of Australia, to *Juania* of the Juan Fernandez Islands, and to *Ravenea* and *Louvelia* of Madagascar. Morphology and anatomy (Uhl 1969b) of the flowers of the widely disjunct *Juania, Ravenea,* and *Ceroxylon* are very similar. The development of polyandry in *Ceroxylon* is different from that in other subfamilies (Uhl and Moore 1980).

Taxonomic Accounts.—Burret (1929a), Moore and Anderson (1976), Galeano-Garces and Bernal-Gonzalez (1982), Bomhard (1937).

Plates.—14C, D; 47D; Fig. G.20.

65. ORANIOPSIS (Beccari) J. Dransfield, A. K. Irvine & N. Uhl. Principes 29(2):57. 1985. Type: **O. appendiculata** (F. M. Bailey) J. Dransfield, A. K. Irvine & N. Uhl (*Areca appendiculata* F. M. Bailey).

Orania Zippelius subgenus *Oraniopsis* Beccari in Beccari & Pichi-Sermolli, Webbia 11:172. 1955.

Medium, solitary, unarmed, pleonanthic, dioecious palm. Stem erect, sometimes quite tall, becoming bare,

leaf scars apparently not very conspicuous. Leaves numerous, reduplicately pinnate, ± upward-pointing, marcescent, several dead leaves hanging vertically for some time, forming a skirt below the crown before falling completely; sheath apparently tubular at first, soon splitting opposite the petiole, the leaf base then open; petiole short, adaxially channeled, ± glabrous, abaxially rounded, densely covered with scales and tomentum, the margins smooth and rather sharp; rachis ± stiffly held, adaxially flattened or channeled near the base, abaxially rounded, distally angled adaxially, a minute flange present at the junction between the flattened and angled areas of the rachis, both surfaces of the rachis bearing scattered scales; leaflets very numerous, single-fold, regularly arranged, ± stiff, ± linear, unevenly acute or acuminate, the basalmost few on each side short, narrow and crowded, adaxial surface ± glabrous or with scattered scales along the midrib, abaxial surface covered with dot-like scales and a dense felt of indumentum; transverse veinlets not evident. Inflorescences solitary, axillary, interfoliar, shorter than the leaves, staminate and pistillate superficially similar, branching to 4 orders; prophyll short, obscured by the leaf bases, incompletely tubular, 2-keeled, ± leathery, becoming fibrous and disintegrating distally, sparsely tomentose, the basal margins decurrent; peduncle elongate, ± flattened and winged at the base, distally ± elliptic in cross-section, sparsely to densely tomentose; peduncular bracts 3–5, elongate, the first inserted near the prophyll, the rest ± evenly spaced along the peduncle, the distal 2–3 ± enclosing the inflorescence in bud, ± beaked, leathery, tubular at first, then splitting longitudinally and becoming flattened, sparsely to densely tomentose, eventually caducous, leaving circular or crescentic scars; rachis slightly shorter than the peduncle; rachis bracts numerous, inconspicuous, short, triangular, acute or acuminate, membranous, incomplete, each subtending a first-order branch; first-order branches with a basal bare portion, distally bearing spirally arranged second-order branches each subtended by a minute incomplete bract; rachillae crowded, ± twisted or zigzag at anthesis, the pistillate spreading but remaining rather zigzag in fruit, bearing rather distant, spirally arranged or subdistichous, minute triangular bracts, each subtending a short stalk bearing a minute, membranous, incomplete, triangular bracteole and terminating in a solitary flower. Staminate flowers symmetrical, or somewhat misshapen from close packing, open from early in development; sepals 3, very small, triangular, membranous, connate basally and forming a cup; petals 3, distinct, fleshy, much longer than the sepals, narrow, triangular; stamens 6, almost as long as or longer than the petals, the antesepalous inserted between the petals in, apparently, the same whorl, the antepetalous epipetalous, filaments very fleshy with ± conical, swollen bases, tapering to the connective, anthers oblong, versatile, basally sagittate, latrorse; pollen elliptic, monosulcate, exine tectate, the distal face perforate, the proximal face reticulate; pistillode usually very much shorter than the filaments, 3-angled, apically trifid. Pistillate flowers like the staminate but with slightly broader sepals and petals; staminodes like the stamens, the empty anthers large; gynoecium tricarpellate, triovulate, conspicuously 3-lobed, stigmas apical, short, becoming recurved; ovules laterally attached, hemianatropous(?). Mature fruit developing from 1 carpel, round-

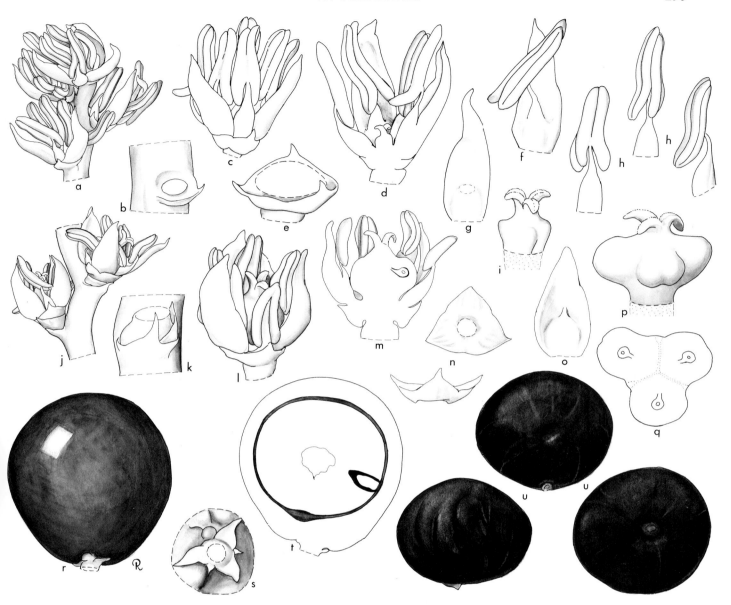

65.—**Oraniopsis. a,** portion of staminate rachilla ×3; **b,** scar and bract of staminate flower ×6; **c,** staminate flower ×4½; **d,** staminate flower in vertical section ×6; **e,** staminate calyx ×9; **f,** staminate petal and stamen ×6; **g,** staminate petal, interior view ×6; **h,** stamen in 3 views ×6; **i,** pistillode ×18; **j,** portion of pistillate rachilla ×3; **k,** portion of stalk, subtending bract, and bracteole of pistillate flower ×6; **l,** pistillate flower ×6; **m,** pistillate flower in vertical section ×6; **n,** pistillate calyx in 2 views ×6; **o,** pistillate petal, interior view ×6; **p,** gynoecium ×9; **q,** ovary in cross-section ×9; **r,** fruit ×1½; **s,** base of fruit ×2¼; **t,** fruit in vertical section ×1½; **u,** seed in 3 views ×1½. *Oraniopsis appendiculata*: **a-q,** *Irvine s.n.*; **r-u,** *Moore 9237.*

ed, the stigmatic and carpel remains basal; epicarp smooth, yellow at maturity; mesocarp ± fleshy, with horizontal fibers and stone cells; endocarp obsolescent. Seed, rounded, the integuments thick, ± woody, with a basal short spur, and few sparsely branched, impressed vascular strands; endosperm homogeneous with a narrow central hollow; embryo lateral to subbasal. Germination adjacent-ligular; seedling leaf bifid with entire tips. Cytology not studied.

Anatomy.—Not studied.

Distribution.—Queensland, Australia; the single species *Oraniopsis appendiculata* occurs in rain forests of mountain ranges between the upper Tully River area (15°40′S), southwards to the Big Tableland (17°50′S) about 25 km south of Cooktown with the most inland occurrence being on the Great Di-

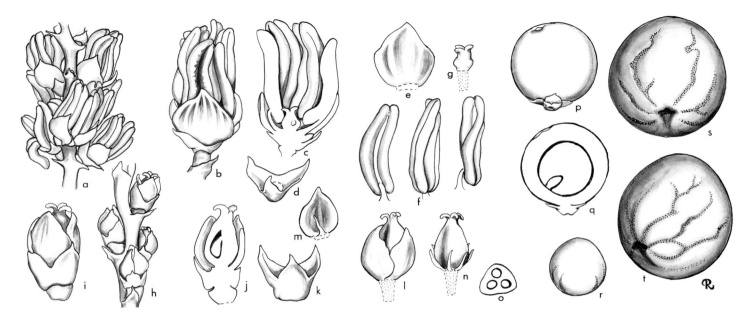

66.—**Juania. a,** portion of staminate rachilla in bud ×3; **b,** staminate bud ×6; **c,** staminate bud in vertical section ×6; **d,** staminate calyx ×6; **e,** staminate petal, interior view ×6; **f,** stamen in 3 views ×6; **g,** pistillode ×6; **h,** portion of pistillate rachilla in bud ×3; **i,** pistillate bud ×6; **j,** pistillate bud in vertical section ×6; **k,** pistillate calyx ×6; **l,** pistillate flower, calyx removed ×6; **m,** pistillate petal and staminode, interior view ×6; **n,** gynoecium and staminodes ×6; **o,** ovary in cross-section ×6; **p,** fruit ×1½; **q,** fruit in vertical section ×1½; **r,** seed ×1½; **s, t,** seed in 2 views ×3. *Juania australis:* **a–g,** *Moore et al. 9369;* **h–t,** *Moore et al. 9368.*

viding Range, southwest of Atherton, some 75 km inland, above 1100 m altitude.

Ecology.—The species occurs mostly above 300 m up to ca. 1500 m altitude, and also in narrow gorges and gullies at the foot of abruptly descending coastal ranges, but does not extend on to the broader coastal plains. Rainfall is mostly above 1800 mm per annum, with frequent cloud mist compensating rainfall in the 1800 mm regions. Soil types are mostly of granitic and metamorphic origin; the palm also occurs on shallow basaltic soils with impeded drainage, but is usually absent from deep, well-drained basalt soils. It occurs in the following rain forest types (Tracey & Webb 1975): Simple Microphyll Vine Fern Thicket, Simple Notophyll Vine Forest, Upland Mesophyll Vine Forest, and Complex Mesophyll Vine Forest.

Common Names and Uses.—Not recorded. The palm should be a handsome ornamental.

Notes.—Seeds begin to germinate after 200–400 days, but some may continue to germinate 3–4 years after sowing. The palm is very slow growing and seems to stay in the rosette stage for at least 20–30 years. In dense rain forest, rosettes may even be twice this age with erect leaves 3–8 m long. Unless growth rates accelerate markedly when a trunk is produced, tall stemmed individuals must be several hundred years old.

Taxonomic Account.—Dransfield et al. (1985a). Most closely related to *Ceroxylon* from which it differs in 3–5 rather than 5–7 peduncular bracts, in bracteolate flowers, and in petals free rather than united basally (See Chapter V).

Plate.—48A, B; Fig. G.19.

66. **Juania** Drude, Nachrichten von der Königlichen Gesellschaft der Wissenschaften und von der Georg-Augusts-Universität 1878(1):40. 1878. Type: **J. australis** (Martius) Drude ex J. D. Hooker (*Ceroxylon australe* Martius).

Solitary, moderate, unarmed, pleonanthic, dioecious palm. Stem stout, leaf scars oblique, internodes shorter above middle and very short at the crown, green, very smooth, with slight bloom. Leaves reduplicately pinnate, erect at first, then spreading; sheath fibrous, splitting opposite the petiole, not forming a crownshaft, covered with scaly tomentum when young; petiole much shorter than the rachis, channeled adaxially, rounded abaxially, with small brown scales; rachis triangular in cross-section, ridged adaxially, slightly rounded abaxially; leaflets narrow, single-fold, relatively short, bifid at tips, stiff, smooth, midribs more prominent adaxially, transverse veinlets not evident. Inflorescences interfoliar, solitary, usually 2 developed each year, the remainder aborting, branched to 2 orders at least proximally; peduncle elongate; prophyll short, tubular, laterally keeled, flat, open apically; peduncular bracts 3, similar to the prophyll, the second the largest and enclosing the third in bud, both the second and third larger than and inserted at some distance above the prophyll and first bract, all tubular and ± dorsiventrally compressed in bud, splitting abaxially at anthesis, becoming pendulous, persistent in fruit and at length marcescent; rachis elongate, longer than the peduncle, bearing numerous, spirally arranged branches, those at the base once-branched into short stiff rachillae, distal branches less divided or undivided, each branch and rachilla subtended by a small, sometimes adnate bract, bracts often lacking distally. Flowers white, solitary, open from early in development, briefly pedicellate, the pedicel subtended by an acute bract, the individual flowers usually with a bracteole on the pedicel. Staminate flowers with 3 sepals, united in a 3-lobed cupule, the lobes acute, about as long as to longer than the tube; petals 3, distinct, ± asymmetrical, ovate-acute, imbricate basally, separated above and shorter than the stamens in bud and at anthesis; stamens 6, the filaments distinct, anthers basifixed, versatile, emarginate to bifid apically, sagittate but the locules not divergent basally, latrorse; pollen elliptic, monosulcate, with finely reticulate, tectate exine; pistillode minute, ovoid, with trifid apex. Pistillate flowers with 3 sepals, united in a 3-lobed cupule, the lobes, or some of them, as long as the tube; petals 3, distinct, imbricate basally and separated above in bud and in flower; staminodes 6, awl-shaped, distinct, lacking abortive anthers; gynoecium ovoid-attenuate, trilocular with 3 ovules, only 1 normally maturing, stigmas 3, short, recurved, ovules pendulous, hemianatropous. Fruit globose or nearly so, orange-red at maturity with eccentrically subapical stigmatic remains; epicarp smooth, mesocarp succulent and ± orange, with a few, flat, longitudinal, unbranched, whitish fibers adjacent to the very thin, cartilaginous endocarp, this adherent to the seed. Seed globose with mostly simple or forked vascular strands ascending from the base, endosperm homogeneous; embryo lateral in lower ⅓ or near the base. Germination adjacent-ligular; eophyll lanceolate, entire. Cytology not studied.

Anatomy. — Leaf, stem (Tomlinson 1961), flowers (Uhl 1969b). Single phloem strands in large vascular bundles of the petiole. Patterns of floral vasculature are similar to those of *Ravenea* and *Ceroxylon* and also to those of the genera of the Hyophorbeae (Uhl 1969b).

Distribution. — One species on the Juan Fernandez Islands.

Ecology. — On steep slopes and ridges in lower and upper montane forest at altitudes of 200–800 m above sea level, most abundant above 500 m.

Common Names and Uses. — Juania palm, Chonta palm. The apex is edible. In the past the wood was used for walking sticks, cabinet work, and carvings.

Notes: — Closely related to *Ceroxylon* (see *Ceroxylon*).

Taxonomic Account. — Moore (1969f).
Plates. — 15A; 48C.

67. LOUVELIA H. Jumelle & H. Perrier de la Bâthie, Comptes Rendus Hebdomadaires des Séances de l'Académie des Sciences 155:411. 1912. Type: L. madagascariensis H. Jumelle & H. Perrier de la Bâthie.

Robust, solitary, unarmed, pleonanthic, dioecious palms. Stem short to tall, covered with persistent leaf bases, or becoming bare and marked with leaf scars. Leaves very robust, reduplicately pinnate, marcescent or deciduous under their own weight, a crownshaft not present; sheath apparently tubular at first, sometimes with a ligulelike projection opposite the petiole, densely covered in dark scales or bearing a uniform or horizontally striped covering of light or dark tomentum, the sheath apparently later disintegrating, and becoming fibrous; petiole very short to long, with smooth, almost sharp margins, bearing indumentum or scales as the sheath, adaxially flattened or channeled, abaxially rounded or angled; rachis robust, adaxially angled or with 2 keels, bearing indumentum as the sheath; leaflets very numerous, regularly arranged, single fold, linear, ± acute, concolorous or bearing dense white indumentum on the abaxial surface, sometimes with scattered scales along the main vein on adaxial and/or abaxial surfaces, marginal veins sometimes very distinct, transverse veinlets indistinct or very distinct, short. Inflorescences solitary, axillary, interfoliar, ± erect, short and rather condensed, scarcely exserted from the sheaths, or ± lax, branching to 1 order; peduncle relatively short, ± elliptic in cross-section, variously tomentose or scaly; prophyll incomplete, short, 2-keeled, apparently disintegrating at anthesis (Jumelle and Perrier 1945) or remaining hidden within sheaths; peduncular bracts 3–4, the proximal shorter than the distal, ± thinly coriaceous, tubular, somewhat inflated, splitting distally, variously tomentose or scaly; rachis not differing much in length from the peduncle, bearing spirally arranged, rather crowded or lax, short to elongate rachillae; rachillae each subtended by a very short triangular bract, the staminate rachillae more slender than the pistillate, bearing spirally arranged, solitary, congenitally open flowers. Staminate flowers somewhat asymmetrical, ± fleshy; calyx very short, deeply trilobed or comprising 3, distinct sepals; petals much longer than calyx, narrow, striate, basally connate (? always); stamens 6, the antesepalous filaments free, the antepetalous adnate to the petals (according to Jumelle and Perrier) or connate into an androecial ring (in *L. madagascariensis*, Perrier 12021 (P)), anthers apparently basifixed, latrorse; pollen circular, monoporate, with neatly reticulate or spiny, tectate exine; pistillode minute. Pistillate flowers with short, 3-lobed calyx; petals much longer than the calyx, distinct (according to Beccari and Pichi-Sermolli 1955); staminodes 6 with conspicuous rudimentary anthers; gynoecium trilocular, triovulate, with short apical stigma, ovule form unknown. Fruit globose, sometimes irregularly so, with apical stigmatic remains and 1–3 seeds; epicarp smooth, in *L. madagascariensis* brown and dotted with lenticels, mesocarp fleshy, endocarp very thin. Seed

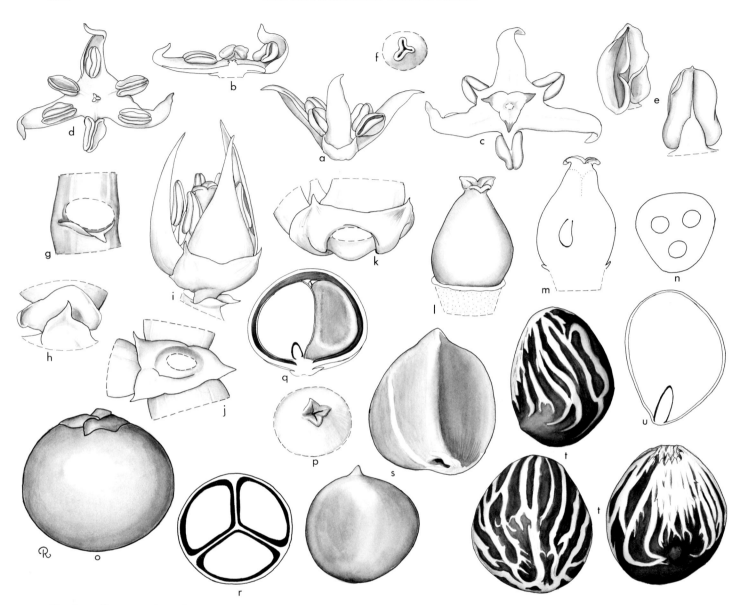

67.—**Louvelia. a,** staminate flower ×4½; **b,** staminate flower in vertical section ×4½; **c,** staminate flower, bottom view to show calyx and corolla ×6; **d,** staminate flower, top view to show corolla, androecium, and pistillode ×4½; **e,** anther in 2 views ×12; **f,** pistillode, much enlarged; **g,** scar, subtending bract, and bracteole of pistillate flower ×6; **h,** subtending bract of pistillate flower ×4½; **i,** pistillate flower and subtending bract ×6; **j,** calyx and base of petals, bottom view ×6; **k,** calyx and base of petals, lateral view ×8; **l,** gynoecium ×6; **m,** gynoecium in vertical section ×6; **n,** ovary in cross-section ×9; **o,** fruit ×2; **p,** stigmatic remains ×7¾; **q,** fruit in vertical section ×1½; **r,** diagram of fruit in cross-section to show 3 seeds ×1½; **s,** seed in 2 views ×3; **t,** seed (coat removed) in 3 views ×3; **u,** seed in vertical section ×3. *Louvelia madagascariensis:* all from *Perrier de la Bâthie 12021.*

black, basally attached, globose, hemispherical, or in shape like ⅓ of a sphere, raphe branches very coarse, sparsely anastomosing, endosperm homogeneous; embryo basal. Germination remote-ligular; eophyll pinnate. Cytology unknown.

Anatomy.—Not studied.

Distribution.—Three species confined to humid areas of the east coast of Madagascar.

Ecology.—Little is known of the ecology of these palms but they appear to grow in lowland rain forest.

Uses.—The apex of *L. albicans* is said to be edible.

Notes.—*Louvelia* remains very poorly known, and

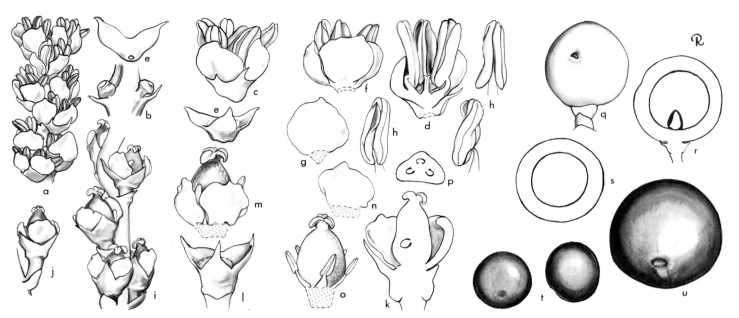

68.—**Ravenea. a,** portion of staminate rachilla ×3; **b,** pedicels and bracteoles of staminate flowers ×6; **c,** staminate flower ×6; **d,** staminate flower in vertical section ×6; **e,** staminate calyx in 2 views ×6; **f,** staminate flower, sepals removed ×6; **g,** staminate petal ×6; **h,** stamen in 3 views ×6; **i,** portion of pistillate rachilla ×3; **j,** pistillate flower, pedicel, and bracteole ×3; **k,** pistillate flower in vertical section ×6; **l,** pistillate calyx ×6; **m,** pistillate flower, calyx removed ×6; **n,** pistillate petal ×6; **o,** gynoecium and staminodes ×6; **p,** ovary in cross-section ×6; **q,** fruit ×1½; **r,** fruit in vertical section ×1½; **s,** fruit in cross-section ×1½; **t,** seed in 2 views ×1½; **u,** seed ×3. *Ravenea madagascariensis*: **a-h,** *Moore 9010*; **i-p,** *Moore 9019*; *R. moorei*: **q-u,** *Moore 9028*.

few comments can be made on its relationships with *Ravenea.*

Taxonomic Account.—Jumelle and Perrier de la Bâthie (1945).

Plate.—48D.

68. **Ravenea** Bouché ex H. A. Wendland in J. D. Hooker, Botanical Magazine 110:t6776. 1884. Type: **R. hildebrandtii** Bouché ex H. A. Wendland.

Ranevea L. H. Bailey, Cyclopedia of American Horticulture 1497. 1902. Type: as above (proposed as a substitute name for *Ravenea,* because of the close similarity in spelling to *Ravenia* Vellozo (1825) (Rutaceae); however, *Ravenea* Bouché is generally accepted as legitimate).

Solitary, slender to robust, unarmed, dioecious, pleonanthic palms. Stem erect, rarely very short, often tall, becoming bare, sometimes swollen at the base, conspicuously ringed with leaf scars or not. Leaves few to numerous, reduplicately pinnate, often upward pointing, abscising neatly; sheaths soon disintegrating opposite the petiole into fine or coarse fibers, densely tomentose; petiole very short to moderately long, adaxially flattened or channeled, abaxially rounded, usually densely tomentose; rachis flattened adaxially, triangular abaxially, sometimes channeled laterally; leaflets numerous, single-fold, usually stiff, elongate, acute or acuminate, the proximal few sometimes very short and slender, abaxially frequently with small narrowly elliptic ramenta, midribs more prominent adaxially, transverse veinlets not evident. Inflorescences interfoliar, 1 or several within a single prophyll in a leaf axil, usually large, the staminate and pistillate superficially similar but the staminate more slender, branched to 1–2 orders; peduncle slender to robust, elongate, ± circular in cross-section distally, usually scaly or tomentose; prophyll short, 2-keeled, incomplete; peduncular bracts tubular, 3–5, 2 usually short, apically open and tattered, the 2 or more distal bracts narrow lanceolate, as long as and enclosing the inflorescence in bud, splitting longitudinally, all bracts persistent, always densely scaly or tomentose abaxially, membranous, coriaceous, or almost woody; rachis usually shorter than the peduncle, bearing spirally arranged, usually numerous, first-order branches, the first-order bracts very small, acute or long acuminate, usually adnate to the subtended branch; proximal first-order branches subdigitately branched or unbranched, the distal unbranched; rachillae elongate, usually stiff, slender, eventually pendulous, the staminate shorter and more slender than the pistillate, slightly zigzag, sparsely to densely scaly, bearing spirally arranged, rather lax peglike floral stalks, each subtended by a minute, narrow triangular rachilla bract, usually adnate to the stalk. Flowers more crowded and somewhat grouped distally, congenitally open. Staminate flowers ± symmetrical; sepals 3, triangular, connate in the basal ⅓, adnate to the floral stalk, to the base of the stamen filaments and to the petal

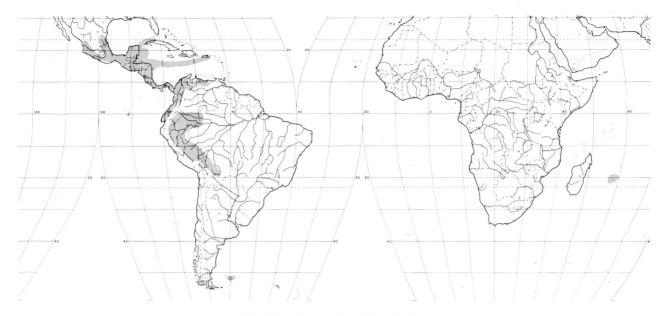

Map 25.—**Distribution of Hyophorbeae.**

bases; petals 3, broadly ovate, distinct, fleshy; stamens 6, filaments slender, short, basally expanded, shortly adnate to sepals and petals; anthers somewhat twisted, ± sagittate, latrorse; pollen ± circular, monoporate, exine tectate with supratectal spines; pistillode short, trifid, with 3 vestigial locules and ovules. Pistillate flowers with sepals and petals similar to staminate; staminodes 6, broadly triangular with sterile anthers; gynoecium ovoid, tricarpellate, carpels connate, trilocular, triovulate, stigmas 3, fleshy, recurved, ovules pendulous, hemianatropous. Fruit globose, usually brightly colored, stigmatic remains subbasal, lateral, or subapical; epicarp minutely pebbled, mesocarp fleshy, endocarp thin. Seed globose, hilum basal, raphe branches indistinct, endosperm homogeneous; embryo basal. Germination adjacent-ligular; eophyll bifid. Cytology not studied.

Anatomy.—Vegetative (Tomlinson 1969), floral (Uhl 1969b).

Distribution.—Ten species, eight endemic to Madagascar, two in the Comores Islands.

Ecology.—Tropical rain forest from sea level to 2000 m, including mossy montane forest, one species in Didiereaceous and Euphorbiaceous forest in the driest area of the island. Often gregarious, the rain forest species sometimes growing in full light.

Common Names and Uses.—For Malagasy local names see Jumelle and Perrier de la Bâthie (1945). Trunk of *R. madagascariensis* is very hard and flexible and is used in various ways; that of *R. robustior* has abundant pith, rich in starch, and is used as a source of sago. The "cabbage" of most species is edible, but may be bitter.

Notes.—As noted under *Louvelia,* the relationships of the two Madagascan genera in the Ceroxyleae remain poorly understood.

Taxonomic Account.—Jumelle and Perrier de la Bâthie (1945). The genus is much in need of revision.

Plates.—*15B; 49A; Fig. G.18.*

HYOPHORBEAE Drude in Martius, Flora Brasiliensis 3(2):275. 1881. Type: **Hyophorbe.**

Moderately robust to very slender, rarely climbing, acaulescent or stems erect; monoecious or dioecious, flowers solitary or in acervuli, bracts scarcely evident, flowers tightly closed in bud.

The Hyophorbeae include five genera, three ranging from Mexico south to Peru with one (*Gaussia*) in Mexico, Puerto Rico, and Cuba, and the fifth (*Hyophorbe*) in the Mascarene Islands (Map 25). There is greater diversity in habit in this tribe than elsewhere in the subfamily. Crownshafts are conspicuous in *Hyophorbe,* present only in some species of *Chamaedorea,* and not formed elsewhere. Leaves are pinnate but may be divided, bifid, or entire. The globose flowers, smaller and more compact than those of the other tribes, and arranged in an acervulus (a cincinnus of linear form) are diagnostic (Uhl 1978b, Uhl and Moore 1978). Although *Chamaedorea* usually has solitary flowers, flower clusters when present are in curved or straight rows (acervuli). The least specialized genus is *Gaussia* which

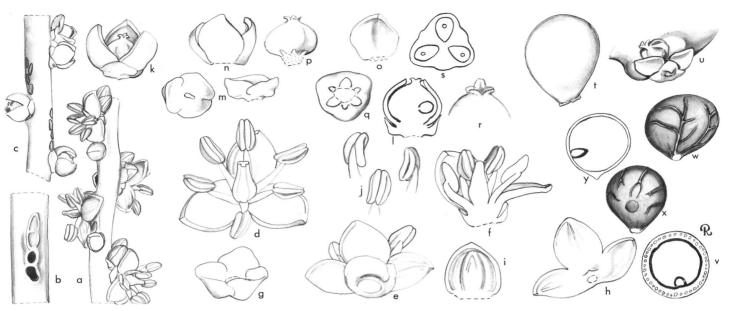

69.—**Gaussia. a,** portion of rachilla showing acervuli with staminate flowers and pistillate buds ×3; **b,** portion of rachilla with floral scars ×3; **c,** portion of rachilla at pistillate anthesis ×3; **d,** staminate flower ×6; **e,** staminate flower from below ×6; **f,** staminate flower in vertical section ×6; **g,** staminate calyx ×6; **h,** staminate corolla, exterior view ×6; **i,** staminate petal, interior view ×6; **j,** stamen in 3 views ×6; **k,** pistillate flower ×6; **l,** pistillate flower in vertical section ×6; **m,** pistillate calyx in 2 views ×6; **n,** pistillate corolla ×6; **o,** pistillate petal ×6; **p,** gynoecium and staminodes ×6; **q,** gynoecium and staminodes from below ×6; **r,** stigmas ×12; **s,** ovary in cross-section ×6; **t,** fruit ×1½; **u,** base of fruit and abortive carpels ×3; **v,** fruit in cross-section ×1½; **w, x,** seed in 2 views ×1½; **y,** seed in vertical section ×1. *Gaussia attenuata*: all from *Read 757.*

closely resembles *Pseudophoenix* when sterile, but the much larger flowers of *Pseudophoenix* are hermaphrodite rather than unisexual and spirally arranged rather than in acervuli. The distribution of the tribe is of much interest (see Chapter V).

Key to the Genera of the Hyophorbeae

69. GAUSSIA H. A. Wendland, Nachrichten von der Königlichen Gesellschaft der Wissenschaften und von der Georg-Augusts-Universität. 327. 1865. Type: **G. princeps** H. A. Wendland.

Aeria O. F. Cook, Bulletin of the Torrey Botanical Club 28:547. 1901. Type: *A. attenuata* O. F. Cook (=*Gaussia attenuata* (O. F. Cook) Beccari).

Opsiandra O. F. Cook, Journal of the Washington Academy of Sciences 13:182. 1923. Type: *O. maya* O. F. Cook (=*Gaussia maya* (O. F. Cook) H. Quero & R. W. Read).

Solitary, moderate or tall, unarmed, monoecious, pleonanthic palms. Stem occasionally leaning, brown or gray to whitish, straight or somewhat ventricose basally or near the middle, leaf scars prominent and broad, or inconspicuous, roots bearing small prickly lateral roots in a prominent mass at the base of the trunk. Leaves pinnate; sheath wide basally, narrowing distally into the petiole, split opposite the petiole at maturity, not forming a distinct crownshaft, upper edges reflexed, edges sometimes shredded; petiole short, subterete, only narrowly and shallowly channeled adaxially; rachis prominently ridged adaxially, ± rounded abaxially; leaflets acute, single-fold, broadly reduplicate at insertion, obscurely or prominently pulvinate above, lightly waxy, midribs prominent with 2 or more conspicuous secondary pairs of ribs, transverse veinlets not evident. Inflorescences interfoliar, not long-persistent, falling with or soon after the subtending leaves, branching to 2–3 orders; peduncle elongate, ascending; prophyll very short, tubular, flat, ± 2-keeled, pointed, open at apex; peduncular bracts 4–7, each progressively longer, tubular with obliquely open apices, the distal usually reaching or exceeding the base of the first flowering branches; rachis about as long as the peduncle; first-order branches numerous, crowded, spirally inserted; rachillae glabrous, slender, lacking bracts, bearing spirally arranged rows of flowers (acervuli) of a proximal pistillate and (2–) 3–7, distal staminate, the distal flower opening first, the pistillate maturing and expanding normally when all the staminate have been shed, all flowers caducous after anthesis unless fertilized. Flowers small, green in bud, yellow or yellow-green at anthesis. Staminate flowers ovoid to ellipsoidal in bud; sepals 3, rounded, imbricate basally; petals 3, valvate, strongly nerved in bud (when dry), fleshy or thin and not prominently nerved when expanded; stamens 6, filaments subulate, very short or well developed, not inflexed at the apex in bud, emarginate or deeply divided apically, anthers dorsifixed above the middle, deeply sagittate or bifid at the base, shallowly bifid at the apex; pollen elliptic, monosulcate, with scabrate, tectate exine; pistillode angled-columnar, as long as the stamens in bud. Pistillate flowers ovoid; sepals 3, distinct, rounded, imbricate basally; petals 3, narrowly imbricate basally and subvalvate to valvate distally, the tips spreading at anthesis; staminodes 6, minute, toothlike; gynoecium angled-ovoid, with 3 recurved stigmas, trilocular, triovulate, ovules laterally attached, with funicular aril, campylotropous. Fruit ellipsoidal or globose to kidney-shaped, red or deep orange, fleshy, with basal stigmatic remains; epicarp smooth, mesocarp lacking anastomosing fibers against the membranous endocarp. Seed ellipsoidal to kidney-shaped or subglobose, not adherent to the endocarp, with stalked or indistinct, round basal hilum, raphe not evident, raphe branches few, sparsely branched, ascending adaxially, curved laterally, descending abaxially toward the embryo, endosperm homogeneous; embryo lateral. Germination and eophyll not recorded. $n = 14$ (*G. attenuata, G. maya* as *Opsiandra maya,* Read 1966).

Anatomy. — Leaf (Tomlinson 1961).

Distribution. — Four species, two in Mexico and one each in Guatemala, Belize, Cuba, and Puerto Rico.

Ecology. — On limestone hills (mogotes), sometimes growing from crevices in very steep rocks and at low elevations on limestone escarpments or low hills, often on pyramids in the archeological region of Guatemala, less frequently on the forest floor in high forest over limestone.

Common Names and Uses. — Llume palm (*G. attenuata*), maya palm (*G. maya*). Local uses are not recorded. Species are rarely grown as ornamentals.

Notes. — The recent discovery in Mexico of a new species intermediate between *Gaussia* and *Opsiandra* (Quero and Read 1986) has led to the placement of *Opsiandra* in synonymy.

Taxonomic Accounts. — Quero and Read (1986) and Beccari (1912).

Plates. — 15C; 49B, C, D; Fig. G.5.

70. **HYOPHORBE** J. Gaertner, De Fructibus et Seminibus Plantarum 2:186. 1791. Type: **H. indica** J. Gaertner.

Sublimia Commerson ex Martius, Historia Naturalis Palmarum 3:164. 1838. Type: *S. vilicaulis* Commerson ex Martius (=*Hyophorbe indica* J. Gaertner).

Mascarena L. H. Bailey, Gentes Herbarum 6:71. 1942. Lectotype: *M. revaughanii* L. H. Bailey (see Pichi-Sermolli 1955) (=*Hyophorbe lagenicaulis* (L. H. Bailey) H. E. Moore).

Solitary, moderate, unarmed, pleonanthic, monoecious palms. Stem in some species variously swollen, of ± uniform diameter in others, ringed with narrow leaf scars, ± striate, gray. Leaves pinnate, neatly abscising; sheaths forming a prominent crownshaft; petiole short, robust, channeled adaxially, rounded abaxially; rachis flat adaxially, rounded abaxially; leaflets acute to acuminate, single-fold, stiff, midrib prominent with 0–2(–3) evident veins on each side, ramenta prominent on the midrib beneath. Inflorescences infrafoliar, solitary, branched to 3–4 orders, hornshaped and erect in bud, becoming ± horizontal, protandrous; peduncle stout, elongate; prophyll very short, tubular, caducous, opening at the apex; peduncular bracts 5(4–9), caducous, progressively opening apically, rachis prominent, slightly longer than the peduncle, first-order branches spirally arranged, divaricate, each with a short basal bare part; rachillae slender, elongate, pendulous at first, becoming divaricate; bracts subtending branches and rachillae not evident at anthesis. Flowers orange, yellowish, or white at anthesis, sometimes fragrant, borne in acervuli of a basal pistillate and 3–7 distal staminate, bracts subtending the acervuli and bracteoles subtending the flowers not evident at anthesis. Staminate flowers symmetrical or somewhat asymmetrical in bud; sepals 3, distinct, imbricate or basally connate; petals 3, valvate, briefly connate basally; stamens 6, filaments connate basally and adnate to the corolla or extending beyond the adnation in a tube, distally free, subulate, erect, anthers dorsifixed at or above the middle, bifid basally for ½ their length or more, emarginate or briefly bifid apically, latrorse; pollen elliptic, monosulcate, with scabrate, tectate exine; pistillode conic-ovoid and shorter than the stamens or sometimes minute, 3-lobed. Pistillate flowers symmetrical, ovoid; sepals 3, distinct and imbricate, or connate basally in a cupule, the lobes then slightly imbricate; petals 3, valvate or slightly imbricate, briefly connate basally; staminodes connate basally in a 6-lobed cupule, sometimes with minute abortive anthers; gynoecium trilocular, triovulate, with 3 recurved, minutely papillate stigmas at anthesis, ovary with septal nectary, ovules laterally attached, hemianatropous, arillate in *H. verschaffeltii.* Fruit ellipsoidal to globose or obpyriform, orange to black, red, or brown, normally 1-seeded, with basal stigmatic remains, perianth persistent, thickened; epicarp

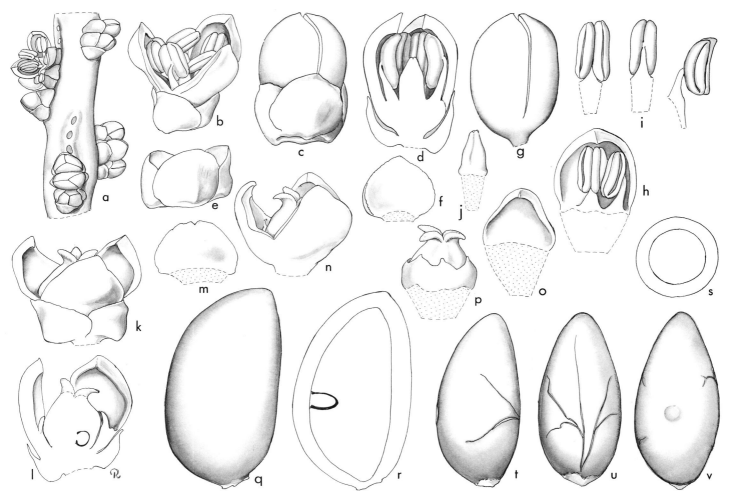

70.—**Hyophorbe. a,** portion of rachilla ×4½; **b,** staminate flower ×12; **c,** staminate bud ×12; **d,** staminate bud in vertical section ×12; **e,** staminate calyx ×12; **f,** staminate sepal, interior view ×12; **g,** staminate corolla ×12; **h,** staminate petal with stamens attached, interior view ×12; **i,** stamen in 3 views ×12; **j,** pistillode ×12; **k,** pistillate flower ×12; **l,** pistillate flower in vertical section ×12; **m,** pistillate sepal ×12; **n,** pistillate flower, sepals removed ×12; **o,** pistillate petal, interior view ×12; **p,** staminodes and gynoecium ×12; **q,** fruit ×3; **r,** fruit in vertical section ×3; **s,** fruit in cross-section ×3; **t, u, v,** seed in 3 views ×3. *Hyophorbe verschaffeltii*: **a-p,** *Read 1387*; **q-v,** *Moore s.n.*

smooth or drying somewhat roughened or minutely warty, mesocarp thin, fleshy, with numerous reddish tannin cells and flat fibers of various widths in more than one layer, endocarp thin. Seed ovoid to ellipsoidal or globose, the hilum small, basal, vasculature of few simple or little-branched strands radiating distally and laterally from the hilum, endosperm homogeneous; embryo lateral to apical. Germination adjacent-ligular; eophyll bifid or rarely pinnate. $n = 16$ (*H. lagenicaulis* as *Mascarena lagenicaulis, H. verschaffeltii* as *M. verschaffeltii,* Read 1966, Eichhorn 1957, Satô 1946; *H. amaricaulis* as *M. amaricaulis, H. indica* as *M. indica, H. verschaffeltii* as *M. verschaffeltii,* Sarkar 1970).

Anatomy.—The anatomy of leaves and flowers has been studied and comparison made among the species (Uhl 1978b, c). Developmental studies have shown that the acervulus is an adnate cincinnus (Uhl and Moore 1978).

Distribution.—Five species endemic to the Mascarene Islands, one each on Rodriguez and Réunion, three on Mauritius and Round Island.

Ecology.—These handsome palms once covered the mountains and valleys of the Mascarene Islands. All species are now nearly extinct in the wild state but formerly were apparently palms of the forest to ca. 700 m altitude or perhaps of the coastal savanna (*H. lagenicaulis*). The last is now restricted to a few individuals on the exposed rock of Round Island;

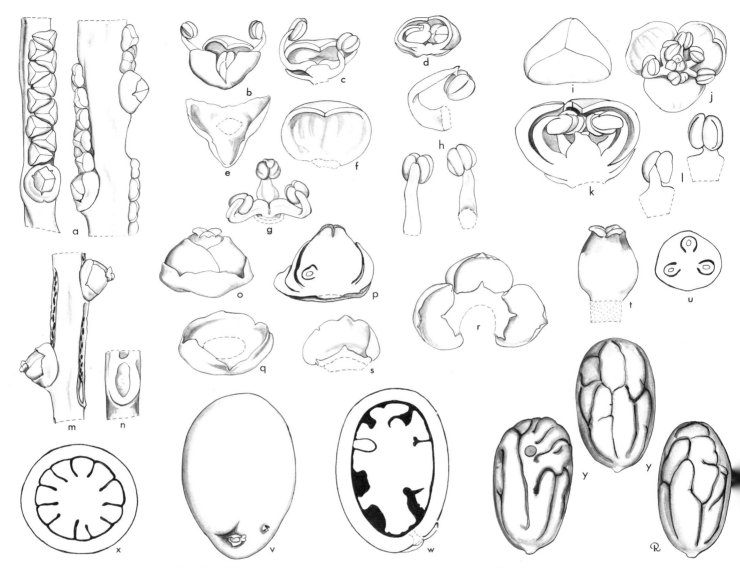

71.—**Synechanthus. a,** portion of rachilla with acervuli in 2 views ×6; **b,** staminate flower ×12; **c,** staminate flower in vertical section ×12; **d,** staminate bud in vertical section ×12; **e,** staminate calyx, interior view ×24; **f,** staminate petal, interior view ×24; **g,** androecium, note 3 stamens ×12; **h,** stamen in 3 views ×24; **i,** staminate bud ×12; **j,** staminate flower with 6 stamens ×12; **k,** staminate bud in vertical section ×24; **l,** stamen in 2 views ×24; **m,** portion of rachilla at pistillate anthesis ×6; **n,** portion of rachilla with scar of pistillate flower ×6; **o,** pistillate flower ×12; **p,** pistillate flower in vertical section ×12; **q,** pistillate calyx ×12; **r,** pistillate petals and staminodes, interior view, expanded ×12; **s,** pistillate petal and staminodes, interior view ×12; **t,** gynoecium ×12; **u,** ovary in cross-section ×12; **v,** fruit ×1½; **w,** fruit in vertical section ×1½; **x,** fruit in cross-section ×1½; **y,** seed in 3 views ×1½. *Synechanthus warscewiczianus:* **a–h,** *Moore & Parthasarathy 9486;* **m–u** and **w,** *Moore et al. 9466;* **v, x,** and **y,** *Moore & Parthasarathy 9409; S. fibrosus;* **i–l,** *Hernandez X. & Sharp x-1287.*

the others occur on volcanic soils or on both volcanic soils and calcarenite limestones (*H. verschaffeltii*). Only a single tree of *H. amaricaulis* now remains, growing in the botanic garden at Curepipe, Mauritius, and relatively few individuals of the other four species can be found (Moore 1978a).

Common Names and Uses. — Bottle palms, spin-

dle palm (*H. verschaffeltii*). These are important ornamentals, often commanding high prices in the horticultural trade. Some species apparently have poisonous cabbage while others, e.g. that of *H. amaricaulis,* despite being very bitter, was eaten in the past.

Notes. — The combination of a prominent crownshaft, a hornlike inflorescence bud borne below the leaves, briefly connate but valvate petals, adnation and some connation of stamen filaments, connate staminodes, and large fruits distinguishes *Hyophorbe* from the other genera of the Hyophorbeae. It seems most closely related to *Gaussia* and *Synechanthus*.

Taxonomic Account.—Moore (1978a).

Plates.—16; 50A; Figs. G.3, G.7.

71. SYNECHANTHUS H. A. Wendland, Botanische Zeitung 16:145. 1858. Lectotype: **S. fibrosus** (H. A. Wendland) H. A. Wendland (see Moore 1963c).

Reineckea Karsten, Wochenschrift für Gärtnerei und Pflanzenkunde 1:349. 1858. ("*Reineckia*"). (Non *Reineckea* Kunth, 1844, conserved name). Type: *R. triandra* Karsten (=*Synechanthus warscewiczianus* H. A. Wendland).

Rathea Karsten, Wochenschrift für Gärtnerei und Pflanzenkunde 1:377. 1858. Type. *R. fibrosa* (H. A. Wendland) Karsten (*Chamaedorea fibrosa* H. A. Wendland) (=*Synechanthus fibrosus* (H. A. Wendland) H. A. Wendland).

Moderate, solitary or clustered, unarmed, pleonanthic, monoecious palms, sometimes flowering when still acaulescent. Stem slender, usually erect, rarely decumbent, smooth, yellowish or glossy deep or dark olive-green, ringed with prominent widely spaced leaf scars. Leaves reduplicately pinnate; sheath elongate on new leaves but soon splitting opposite the petiole and differentiated from it only by a narrow, usually fibrous, dry strip along each margin; petiole circular in cross-section; rachis angled adaxially, rounded abaxially; leaflets broadly reduplicate at insertion, acute to acuminate, slightly to markedly sigmoid or, when broad-based, the apex sickle-shaped, with 1 to several principal nerves, these elevated above, or the blade sometimes undivided except at the bifid apex. Inflorescences interfoliar or becoming infrafoliar, branched to 1 or 2 orders basally, erect at anthesis, curved or pendulous in fruit, solitary; peduncle long; prophyll short, tubular, sheathing, ultimately disintegrating into fibers, open apically; peduncular bracts 4–5, similar to but longer than the prophyll and inserted at increasingly greater distances, the distalmost usually somewhat exceeding the peduncle; rachis usually elongate; rachillae slender, nearly equal in length, 4-angled to markedly flattened and ± flexuous, the tips usually slender and almost spinelike. Flowers borne in distichously arranged lines (acervuli) of a proximal pistillate and 5–13 distal, biseriate, staminate flowers, the distal flower of the acervulus opening first and subsequent flower-opening basipetal. Staminate flowers green in bud, golden-yellow at anthesis, depressed-triangular in bud; sepals 3, connate in a low, acutely 3-lobed cupule; petals 3, valvate, very prominently nerved in bud when dry, spreading at anthesis; stamens 6, filaments short, incurved in bud, erect at anthesis, or 3, with long filaments markedly incurved and inflexed at the apex in bud, horizontally exserted at anthesis, anthers basifixed, shallowly

bifid at apex and base, latrorse; pollen elliptic, monosulcate, with scabrate, tectate exine; pistillode small, deltoid-ovoid, apically 3-lobed or absent. Pistillate flowers yellowish at anthesis; sepals 3, connate in a 3-lobed cupule; petals 3, distinct, imbricate, twice as long as the sepals or more; staminodes apparently lacking or 3, minute, or connate in a 6-lobed ring and partially adnate to the petals; gynoecium, ovoid, drying 3-angled, trilocular, triovulate, stigmas 3, short, recurved, ovules laterally attached, campylotropous but laterally elongate. Fruit rather large, round or elongate, yellow, becoming red at maturity, with basal stigmatic remains; epicarp smooth, mesocarp fleshy with few slender, loosely anastomosing, flat fibers against the membranous endocarp. Seed not adherent to endocarp, with inconspicuous basal hilum, raphe branches distinctive, large, ascending adaxially from the base, little anastomosed, curving laterally and descending abaxially; endosperm homogeneous or minutely ruminate marginally to markedly ruminate; embryo lateral above the middle to subapical. Germination adjacent-ligular; eophyll bifid. $n = 16$ (*S. fibrosus* as *S. mexicanus*, Read 1966).

Anatomy.—Leaf (Tomlinson 1961), distinguished from other palms by guard cells with only one outer cutinized edge.

Distribution.—Two species or possibly three in southern Mexico, Central America, and northwestern South America.

Ecology.—Fairly frequent in wet forests at sea level and low elevations but up to 1200 m in the mountains.

Common Names and Uses.—Bolá, palmilla, jelly bean palm. Widely cultivated as an ornamental.

Notes.—Seven species were described in the genus which is very variable in leaf form ranging from undivided to irregularly and regularly pinnate, and in fruit form which may be ellipsoidal or globose in the same population. These taxa are now regarded as variants of the two species. The inflorescence is distinctive because of the long peduncle with erect rachillae near its end. The yellow to bright orange fruits are very attractive.

Taxonomic Account.—Moore (1971a).

Plates.—15D; 50B; Figs. G.13, G.15, G.18.

72. CHAMAEDOREA Willdenow, Species Plantarum 4(2) 638, 800. 1806 (conserved name). Type: *C. gracilis* Willdenow (illegitimate name) **C. pinnatifrons** (N. J. Jacquin) Oersted) (*Borassus pinnatifrons* N. J. Jacquin).

Morenia Ruiz & Pavon, Florae Peruvianae et Chilensis Prodromus 150. 1794 (rejected name). Type: *M. fragrans* Ruiz & Pavon. (=*Chamaedorea poeppigiana* (Martius) A. Gentry (*Morenia poeppigiana* Martius)).

Nunnezharia Ruiz & Pavon, Florae Peruvianae et

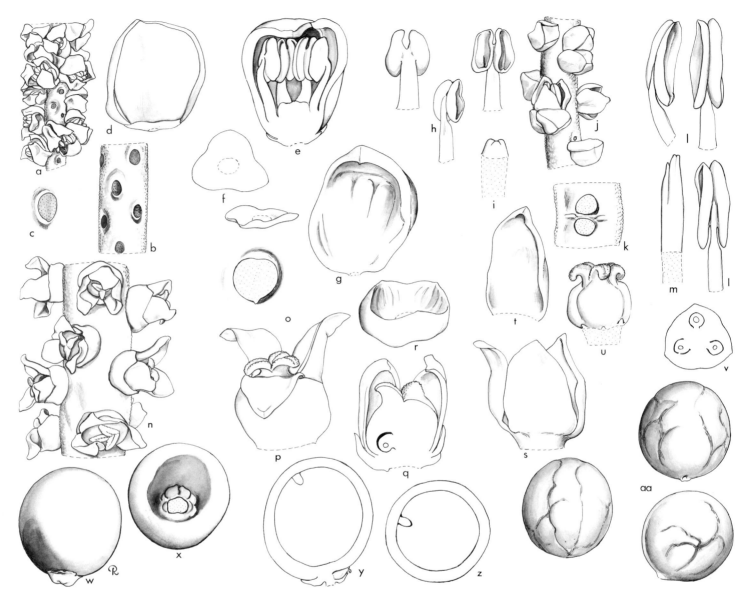

72.—**Chamaedorea. a,** portion of staminate rachilla ×3; **b,** portion of staminate rachilla, flowers removed ×6; **c,** scar of staminate flower ×12; **d,** staminate bud ×12; **e,** staminate bud in vertical section ×12; **f,** staminate calyx in 2 views ×12; **g,** staminate petal, interior view ×12; **h,** stamen in 3 views ×12; **i,** pistillode ×12; **j,** portion of staminate rachilla with paired flowers ×3; **k,** scars of paired staminate flowers ×12; **l,** stamen in 3 views ×12; **m,** pistillode ×12; **n,** portion of pistillate rachilla ×3; **o,** scar of pistillate flower ×6; **p,** pistillate flower ×6; **q,** pistillate flower in vertical section ×6; **r,** pistillate calyx ×6; **s,** pistillate corolla ×6; **t,** pistillate petal, interior view ×6; **u,** gynoecium and staminodes ×6; **t,** pistillate petal, interior view ×6; **u,** gynoecium and staminodes ×6; **v,** ovary in cross-section ×6; **w,** fruit ×1½; **x,** base of fruit showing stigmatic remains and abortive carpels ×1½; **y,** fruit in vertical section ×1½; **z,** fruit in cross-section ×1½; **aa,** seed in 3 views ×1½. *Chamaedorea* sp.: **a–i** and **n–aa,** *Moore & Parthasarathy 9488*; *C. poeppigiana*: **j–m,** *Moore et al. 8354.*

Chilensis Prodromus 147. 1794 (rejected name). Type: *N. fragrans* Ruiz & Pavon (=*Chamaedorea fragrans* (Ruiz & Pavon) Martius).

Nunnezia Willdenow, Species Plantarum 4:890, 1154. 1806. (=*Nunnezharia*).

Kunthia Humboldt & Bonpland, Plantae Aequinoctiales 2:127. 1813. Type: *K. montana* Humboldt & Bonpland (=?).

Stachyophorbe (Liebmann ex Martius) Liebmann ex Klotzsch, Allgemeine Gartenzeitung 20:363.

1852. Lectotype: *S. cataractarum* (Martius) Liebmann ex Klotzsch (=*Chamaedorea cataractarum* Martius) (see H. E. Moore 1963c).

Chamaedorea sect. *Stachyophorbe* Liebmann ex Martius, Historia Naturalis Palmarum 3:309. 1849.

Collinia (Liebmann) Liebmann ex Oersted, Videnskabelige Meddelelser fra Dansk Naturhistorisk Forening 1858:5. 1859. Non Rafinesque 1819. Lectotype: *C. elegans* (Martius) Liebmann ex Oersted (*Chamaedorea elegans* Martius) (see Burret 1933a).

Chamaedorea sect. *Collinia* Liebmann in Martius, Historia Naturalis Palmarum 3:308. 1849.

Dasystachys Oersted, Videnskabelige Meddelelser fra Dansk Naturhistorisk Forening 1858:25. 1859. Type: *D. deckeriana* (Klotzsch) Oersted (*Stachyophorbe deckeriana* Klotzsch) (=*Chamaedorea deckeriana* (Klotzsch) Hemsley).

Eleutheropetalum H. W. Wendland ex Oersted, Videnskabelige Meddelelser fra Dansk Naturhistorisk Forening 1858:6. 1859. Type: *E. ernesti-augusti* (H. A. Wendland) H. A. Wendland ex Oersted (*Chamaedorea ernesti-augusti* H. A. Wendland).

Spathoscaphe Oersted, Videnskabelige Meddelelser fra Dansk Naturhistorisk Forening 1858:29. 1859. Type: *S. arenbergiana* (H. A. Wendland) Oersted (*Chamaedorea arenbergiana* H. A. Wendland).

Stephanostachys (Klotzsch) Klotzsch ex Oersted, Videnskabelige Meddelelser fra Dansk Naturhistorisk Forening 1858:26. 1859. Type: *S. casperiana* (Klotzsch) Oersted (*Chamaedorea casperiana* Klotzsch).

Chamaedorea subgenus *Stephanostachys* Klotzsch, Allgemeine Gartenzeitung 20:363. 1852.

Kinetostigma Dammer, Notizblatt des Königlichen Botanischen Gartens and Museums zu Berlin 4: 171. 1905. Type: *K. adscendens* Dammer (=*Chamaedorea adscendens* (Dammer) Burret).

Small, sometimes moderate, erect or procumbent, rarely climbing, acaulescent or trunked, solitary or clustered, unarmed, pleonanthic, dioecious palms. Stem usually slender, covered wholly or partially in fibrous leaf bases or smooth, green, prominently ringed with leaf scars. Leaves bifid or variously pinnate, very rarely entire, reduplicate; sheath closed or becoming split, short or elongate, sometimes with a marcescent lobe opposite the petiole; petiole short to elongate, flattened adaxially, rounded abaxially, sometimes with a prominent pale green or yellow, abaxial stripe; rachis rounded, angled, or flattened adaxially, rounded abaxially; blade entire, bifid and pinnately ribbed, or regularly or irregularly pinnately divided, leaflets few or many, of 1 or several folds, narrow or broad, often oblique or sigmoid, acuminate, surfaces glabrous. Inflorescences among or below the leaves, solitary or several per leaf axil, unbranched or branched to 1(–2) orders, sometimes forked; staminate often more branched than pistillate; peduncle short to elongate; prophyll tubular with tapering bifid tip; peduncular bracts 2–several, elongate, tubular, sheathing the peduncle, coriaceous or membranous, persistent, tips short, bifid; rachillae long or short, slender or fleshy, sometimes ridged, lacking bracts at maturity, bearing closely appressed or rather widely spaced, spirally arranged staminate or pistillate flowers, rarely bearing curved acervuli of staminate flowers. Flowers sessile or partly enclosed in a cavity in the fleshy rachilla, small or minute. Staminate flowers symmetrical; sepals 3, entire, united basally or distinct; petals 3, distinct or variously connate, lobes valvate; stamens 6, filaments short, broad or awl-shaped; anthers dorsifixed, included, oblong or didymous; pollen elliptic, circular, or elliptic and dilated at one extremity, monosulcate, with scabrate, finely reticulate, fossulate, or areolate, tectate exine; pistillode various, cylindric or expanded basally, sometimes trilobed. Pistillate flowers with sepals 3, as in the staminate; petals 3, usually connate, distinct lobes valvate or imbricate; staminodes present and toothlike or absent, gynoecium ovoid, trilocular, triovulate, stigmas small, recurved, ovule campylotropous, laterally inserted. Fruit small, globose or oblong, stigmatic remains basal; epicarp smooth, mesocarp fleshy, endocarp thin. Seed erect, globose, or ellipsoidal, hilum small, basal, branches of raphe obscure, endosperm cartilaginous; embryo basal or dorsal. Germination adjacent-ligular; eophyll bifid or pinnate. $n = 12$ (*C. ernesti-augusti*, Eichhorn 1957). $n = 13$ (*C. elegans*, Janaki Ammal 1945, Read 1966; *C. ernesti-augusti*, Read 1963; *C. cataractarum*, *C. graminifolia*, *C. oblongata*, *C. pumila*, *C. tepejilote*, Eichhorn 1957; *C. pochutlensis*, *C. pulchra*, *C. tenella*, Essig 1970; *C. ernesti-augusti*, *C. erumpens*, *C. microspadix*, *C. oblongata*, *C. radicalis*, *C. sartorii*, *C. schiedeana*, *C. seifrizii*, *C.* aff. *tepejilote*, Read 1966). $n = 16$ (*C. alternans*, *C.* aff. *arenbergiana*, *C. cataractarum*, *C.* aff. *tepejilote*, Read 1966; *C. glaucifolia*, *C. lepidota*, Sarkar 1970).

Anatomy. —Leaf lacking hairs, characterized by a cutinized epidermis, lack of hypodermis, stomata diffuse in intercostal bands, much more numerous adaxially. Species studied are rather uniform in leaf anatomy but differ in arrangement of nonvascular fibers (see Tomlinson 1961). Some features of floral anatomy including vascularization of the ovule by a strand from each ventral bundle and abundant raphides in styles and stigmas are characteristic of other genera in Hyophorbeae and Ceroxyleae (Uhl and Moore 1971).

Distribution. —About 100 species ranging from central Mexico to Brazil and Bolivia.

Ecology. —All species are plants of the understory. They occur in moist, wet, or mixed forest in low-

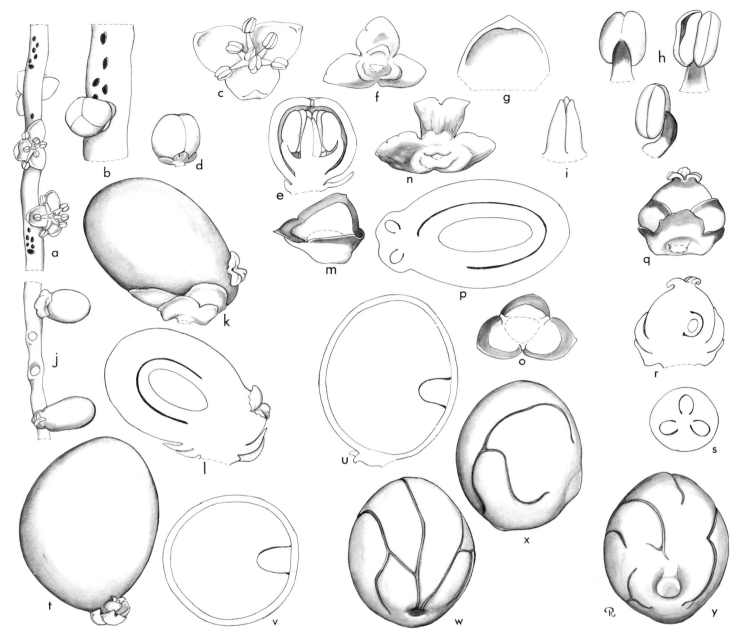

73.—**Wendlandiella. a,** portion of staminate rachilla ×6; **b,** portion of staminate rachilla with single staminate bud and scars of others ×12; **c,** staminate flower at anthesis ×12; **d,** staminate bud ×12; **e,** staminate bud in vertical section ×24; **f,** staminate calyx, exterior view ×24; **g,** staminate petal, interior view ×24; **h,** stamen in 3 views ×24; **i,** pistillode ×24; **j,** portion of pistillate rachilla with young fruit ×3; **k,** young fruit ×12; **l,** young fruit in vertical section ×12; **m,** pistillate calyx in young fruit ×12; **n,** pistillate calyx from below ×12; **o,** pistillate corolla, interior view to show staminodes ×12; **p,** young fruit in cross-section to show abortive locules ×12; **q,** pistillate flower, reconstructed from perianth in young fruit ×12; **r,** pistillate flower in vertical section, reconstructed from young fruit ×12; **s,** ovary in cross-section, reconstructed from young fruit ×12; **t,** fruit ×6; **u,** fruit in vertical section ×6; **v,** fruit in cross-section ×6; **w, x, y,** seed in 3 views ×6. *Wendlandiella polyclada:* **a-s,** *Moore 9511; W. gracilis;* **t-y,** *Killip & Smith 27775* (US).

lands or mountain forest. Some species occur on limestone.

Fossil Record. — Fossil leaves from the Eocene of southeastern United States have been described as *C. danai* by Berry (1916), but correspondence with the modern genus is not certain.

Common Names and Uses. — Parlor palm, Neanthe Bella (*C. elegans*), bamboo palm (*C. seifrizii*). Inflorescences of a few species (e.g. *C. tepejilote*) are eaten as vegetables and leaves of some species are used for thatch. Some are used medicinally (Plotkin and Balick 1984). Commercially, several species are extremely important as pot plants, produced in vast quantities in Europe and North America.

Notes. — There is great diversity in leaf, inflorescence, and flower form in the genus which is divided into sections on the basis of floral structure. Because there are so many species, and considerable variation in leaf form within some species, identification of species is often difficult.

O. F. Cook published the following generic names for species of *Chamaedorea* in the *National Horticultural Magazine* and *Science;* as the names appear without Latin description and postdate 1935, they are invalid and without any botanical standing: — *Anothea, Cladandra, Discoma, Docanthe, Ercheila, Legnea, Lobia, Lophothele, Mauranthe, Meiota, Migandra, Neanthe, Paranthe, Platythea.*

Taxonomic Accounts. — Burret (1933a), Standley and Steyermark (1958). The latter treatment was provided by H. E. Moore, Jr., and includes a key to the 32 species that occur in Guatemala. Dr. Moore was working toward a much needed monograph of the genus. His work is being prepared for publication by R. W. Read and N. W. Uhl. See also Galeano-Garces (1986).

Plates. — *17A, B; 50C, D; Figs. G.1, G.4, G.8, G.13, G.15, G.16.*

73. **WENDLANDIELLA** Dammer, Botanische Jahrbücher für Systematik 36 (Beiblatt 80):31. 1905. Type: **W. gracilis** Dammer.

Dwarf, clustering, unarmed, pleonanthic, dioecious palms. Stem very slender, internodes long, ringed with leaf scars. Leaves pinnate or entire, bifid and pinnately nerved; sheaths slender, tubular, not splitting opposite the petiole; petiole slender; rachis ± triangular in cross-section; leaflets when present only 2–4 per side, with broad insertions, thin, smooth, lanceolate, midrib and sometimes another pair of veins larger, transverse veinlets not apparent. Inflorescences interfoliar, staminate and pistillate inflorescences superficially similar, branching to 1(–2) orders; peduncle elongate; prophyll tubular; peduncular bract 1, tubular, it and the prophyll included within the sheath or exserted and exceeding the peduncle; rachis shorter than the peduncle; rachillae slender, few and subdigitate to numerous, bearing low membranous bracts, floral bracteoles not evident. Staminate flowers in acervuli of 2–6; sepals 3, briefly connate and markedly gibbous basally, distinct distally and the lobes ± hooded at least in bud, the margins usually thin; petals 3, thin, nerveless when dry, valvate, spreading to recurved at anthesis; stamens 6, the filaments erect in bud, distinct, anthers with rounded ends, connectives fleshy, very short; pollen elliptic, monosulcate, with finely reticulate, tectate exine; pistillodes 3, distinct or somewhat connate. Pistillate flowers solitary or in vertical pairs; sepals 3, connate in a low, 3-lobed cupule, gibbous basally; petals 3, imbricate, gibbous, about twice as long as the sepals; staminodes 3, minute; gynoecium subglobose, trilocular, triovulate, stigmas 3, reflexed, ovule pendulous, form unknown. Fruit ellipsoidal, with basal stigmatic remains and remnants of abortive carpels, orange-red at maturity; epicarp smooth, mesocarp thin, lacking fibers, endocarp membranous, not adherent to the seed. Seed with a single raphe branch ventrally curving over the top and a side branch curving around each lateral surface, endosperm homogeneous; embryo lateral slightly below the middle. Germination and eophyll unrecorded. Cytology not studied.

Anatomy. — Not studied.

Distribution. — Three species in Amazonian Peru.

Ecology. — Not known.

Common Names and Uses. — Common names unknown. Grown as ornamentals by a few enthusiasts.

Notes. — *Wendlandiella* is closely related to *Chamaedorea* but differs in having only two bracts on the inflorescence, the staminate and sometimes pistillate flowers borne in rows (acervuli), sepals of both staminate and pistillate flowers connate in a low ring, and endocarp membranous, not hard. Further study of both genera is needed and will determine whether *Wendlandiella* can be maintained.

Taxonomic Account. — Dammer (1905).

Plate. — *17C.*

V ARECOIDEAE

ARECOIDEAE

Monoecious, leaves pinnate, pinnately ribbed, or bipinnate, reduplicate or rarely (Caryoteae) induplicate, flowers borne in triads of a central pistillate and 2 staminate or with some evidence of triads in the inflorescence.

The Arecoideae as defined here includes six diverse tribes (Map 26). These are the Caryoteae, Iriarteeae, Podococceae, Areceae, Cocoeae, and Geonomeae. Our greatest departure from the classification of Moore (1973a) lies in the inclusion of the Caryoteae which has previously been regarded as a subfamily of its own (Moore 1960, Satake 1962, Potztal 1964) and was considered as an independent intermediate line between the induplicate coryphoid and reduplicate arecoid palms by Moore. The Caryoteae have induplicate leaves but the plication of the leaf seems less significant now that both induplicate and reduplicate (*Guihaia*) leaves are known in the Coryphoideae. The leaf anatomy of Caryoteae is known to resemble that of reduplicate leaves (Tomlinson 1960b). There are also several structural parallels between the Caryoteae and the second tribe Iriarteeae.

In circumscribing the Arecoideae we have added the caryotoid major group to five other major groups, the iriarteoid, podococcoid, arecoid, cocosoid, and geonomoid palms, which together made up the largest subunit of Moore's arecoid line of evolution. The distinguishing character uniting the tribes is the presence of triads of two staminate and a central pistillate flower or of flower clusters derived from triads in the inflorescence. Other characters are inflorescences bearing a prophyll and one or several peduncular bracts but without any adnation of branches, and with reduction of bracts throughout the inflorescences (branches of all orders are subtended by open, small or minute bracts). Leaves are uniformly pinnate or pinnately ribbed and with a few exceptions reduplicate. The three genera of the Caryoteae have induplicate leaves. *Caryota* has a bipinnate leaf and in certain genera of the Iriarteeae and Areceae the pinnae split longitudinally approaching a bipinnate form. A discussion of relationships is provided under each tribe.

Key to the Tribes of the Arecoideae

1 Palms frequently hapaxanthic with basipetal production of inflorescences; leaves pinnate, or doubly pinnate, induplicate, leaflets praemorse; inflorescences bisexual or unisexual by reduction of triads . . . . **Caryoteae**
1 Palms never hapaxanthic; leaves pinnate or pinnately ribbed, reduplicate, the leaflets various, sometimes praemorse; inflorescences rarely unisexual 2
2 Leaflets praemorse at the tips and with several principal ribs divergent from the base, or leaflets sometimes divided longitudinally into 1–several ribbed parts; inflorescence with a prophyll and more than 2 large peduncular bracts 3
2 Leaflets usually acute, or if praemorse or longitudinally divided, the inflorescence with a prophyll and (0) 1 (2) large peduncular bracts 4
3 Inflorescence rarely spicate, usually branched to 1–2 orders; flowers sessile, not sunken in pits . . . . **Iriarteeae**
3 Inflorescence spicate; flowers sunken in pits and exserted at anthesis on elongate receptacles . . . . **Podococceae**
4 Flowers usually superficial, rarely enclosed in pits; petals of staminate flowers free and valvate; pistillate petals imbricate with minutely to conspicuously valvate apices, rarely basally connate or valvate, styles not elongate . . . 5
4 Flowers always sunken in pits in the rachillae; petals of both staminate and pistillate flowers connate basally in a soft tube, the lobes valvate, styles elongate, conspicuous . . . . **Geonomeae**
5 Gynoecium usually pseudomonomerous, only very rarely triovulate, when triovulate, the fruit rarely more than 1–seeded, if so then fruit lobed; fruit with a thin or rarely thick endocarp, sometimes with a basal operculum but lacking 3 or more pores . . . . **Areceae**
5 Gynoecium trilocular, triovulate, the fruit never lobed; fruit almost always with a thick bony endocarp enclosing 1–3, rarely more, seeds and with 3, or rarely more, clearly defined pores . . . . **Cocoeae**

CARYOTEAE Drude in Martius, Flora Brasiliensis 3(2):278. 1881. Type: **Caryota.**

Slender to robust, acaulescent or stems erect; leaves pinnate or bipinnate, induplicate; leaflets praemorse; hapaxanthic (usually flowering basipetally) or pleonanthic, monoecious, very rarely dioecious(?); inflorescences bisexual or unisexual, sometimes dimorphic, sometimes multiple, bearing a prophyll and several, usually large peduncular bracts, branched to 1(–2) orders, rarely spicate; flowers superficial; pistillate flowers with valvate petals; gynoecium triovulate; fruit 1–3 seeded, if more than 1-seeded, not lobed.

This Old World tribe (Map 27), immediately recognizable by the induplicate nature of the leaf, includes three closely related but easily distinguished genera. The bipinnate leaf of *Caryota* is unique in the family although bipinnate forms are also found in Iriarteeae and Areceae. Basipetal hapaxanthy, characteristic of the tribe, is not found in every species. *Caryota* and *Wallichia* are completely hapaxanthic, but several species of *Arenga* are pleon-

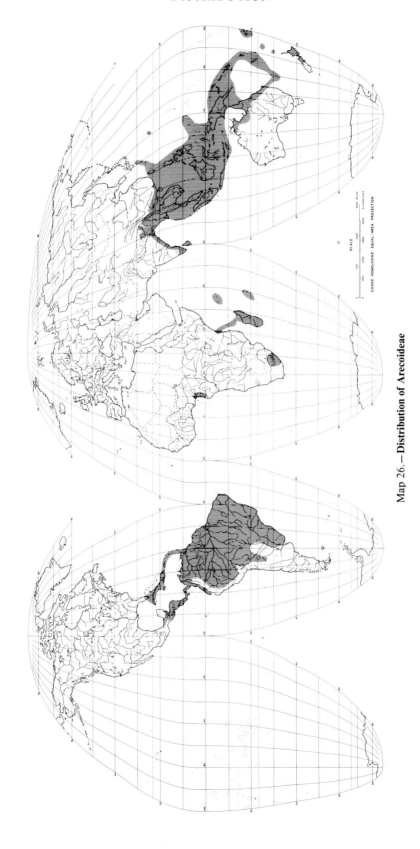

Map 26. — **Distribution of Arecoideae**

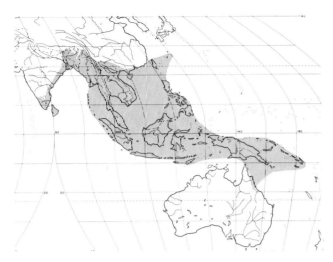

Map 27.—**Distribution of Caryoteae.**

anthic (Dransfield and Mogea 1984). The doubly pinnate leaf appears to be a specialized feature. However, the Caryoteae, and in particular *Caryota* itself, retain several features, that are rather unspecialized in the subfamily, such as numerous peduncular bracts, triads throughout the inflorescence, and triovulate flowers.

Key to the Genera of the Caryoteae

1 Leaves doubly pinnate; inflorescences always bearing flowers of both sexes; endosperm ruminate. China, Indochina, India, Sri Lanka, Southeast Asia, Malesia, Solomons, Australia . . . . 75. **Caryota**

1 Leaves simply pinnate; inflorescences rarely bisexual, usually unisexual; endosperm homogeneous 2

2 Hapaxanthic, flowering basipetally; inflorescences always unisexual; sepals of staminate flowers connate in a tube; stamens (3) 6 (9–15). India, China, Indochina southwards to south Thailand . . . . 76. **Wallichia**

2 Pleonanthic or hapaxanthic, flowering basipetally or rarely acropetally; inflorescences sometimes bisexual; sepals of staminate flower free, imbricate; stamens (6)–numerous. China, Ryukyus, Southeast Asia, Malesia, Christmas Island (Indian Ocean), Australia . . . . 74. **Arenga**

74. ARENGA Labillardière in De Candolle, Bulletin des Sciences, par la Société Philomatique 2:162. 1800 (Conserved name). Type: *A. saccharifera* Labillardière = **A. pinnata** (Wurmb) Merrill.

Saguerus Steck, Dissertatio Inauguralis Medica de Sagu 15.1757. Type: *S. pinnatus* Wurmb (rejected name—see ICBN 237. 1961).

Gomutus Correa, Annales du Muséum National d'Histoire Naturelle 9:288. 1807. Type: *G. rumphii* Corrêa (=*A. pinnata* (Wurmb) Merrill).

Blancoa Blume, Rumphia 2:128. 1843 ("1848").

(Non J. Lindley 1840). Type: *Caryota tremula* Blanco (=*Arenga tremula* (Blanco) Beccari).

Didymosperma H. A. Wendland & Drude ex J. D. Hooker in Bentham & J. D. Hooker, Genera Plantarum 3:917. 1883. Lectotype: *D. porphyrocarpum* (Blume ex Martius) H. A. Wendland & Drude ex J. D. Hooker (*Wallichia porphyrocarpa* Blume ex Martius) (=*A. porphyrocarpa* (Martius) H. E. Moore) (see Beccari and Pichi-Sermolli 1955).

Dwarf to large, solitary or clustered, unarmed or lightly armed, pleonanthic or hapaxanthic, monoecious or very rarely apparently dioecious, acaulescent, shrubby or tree palms. Stem with congested or elongate internodes, usually obscured by persistent fibrous leaf bases and sheaths, more rarely becoming bare, conspicuously ringed with scars. Leaves flabellate and induplicately ribbed (rarely) or induplicate, imparipinnate, marcescent, or rarely abscising under their own weight; sheath covered in a great variety of tomentum, scales and hairs, often extended beyond the petiole to form a ligule, eventually disintegrating into a mass of black fibers, some of which are very robust and almost spinelike; petiole usually well developed, slender to very robust, channeled or ridged (*A. undulatifolia*) at base adaxially, rounded abaxially, usually covered with a variety of indumentum; rachis rounded to angled adaxially, rounded to flat abaxially; leaflets singlefold (except for the terminal flabellum), regularly arranged or grouped and held in several planes, or deeply lobed and wavy, often with 1 or 2 basal auricles, the distal margins praemorse, with small sharp teeth, sometimes with a short to long, laterally compressed, basal stalk, the veins parallel to the fold, or diverging from the base, or ± pinnately arranged along the fold, adaxial surface of blade glabrescent, margins sometimes toothed, abaxial surface usually densely covered in pale indumentum with or without scattered bands of dark brown scales, midribs prominent abaxially, transverse veinlets scarcely visible. Inflorescences interfoliar, sometimes infrafoliar, often bursting through the leaf sheaths, produced in an acropetal sequence in pleonanthic species, in a basipetal sequence in hapaxanthic species, the distalmost inflorescences usually subtended by greatly reduced leaves, bisexual, or unisexual by sterilization of triad components, where unisexual the pistillate tending to be distal to the staminate, the pistillate sometimes very much larger than the staminate, the staminate or bisexual inflorescences sometimes multiple, otherwise solitary, rarely spicate (*A. retroflorescens*), usually branched to 1–2 orders; peduncle very short to well developed, slender to massive, bearing a generally rather inconspicuous, basal, 2-keeled prophyll and several conspicuous, spirally arranged, peduncular bracts, soon splitting adaxially, the bract limb ± triangular, the abaxial surface usually densely covered with indumentum; rachis shorter or longer than the peduncle; rachis bracts inconspicuous, triangular; rachillae erect or pendulous, distant or crowded, very slender to extremely massive, frequently tomentose, bearing a loose to dense spiral of triads, subtended by inconspicuous low bracts. Staminate flowers in bisexual inflorescences opening before the pistillate; sta-

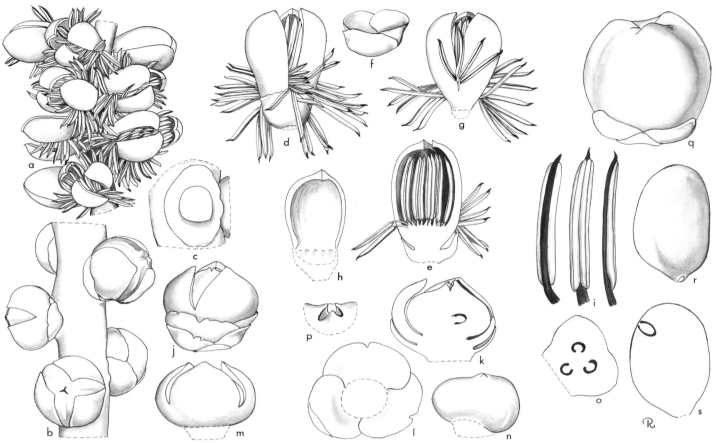

74.—**Arenga. a,** portion of staminate rachilla ×1; **b,** portion of pistillate rachilla ×1; **c,** bracteole subtending pistillate flower ×3; **d,** staminate flower ×1½; **e,** staminate flower in vertical section ×1½; **f,** staminate calyx ×1½; **g,** staminate flower, calyx removed ×1½; **h,** staminate petal ×1½; **i,** stamen in 3 views ×3; **j,** pistillate flower ×1½; **k,** pistillate flower in vertical section ×1½; **l,** pistillate calyx ×1½; **m,** pistillate flower, calyx removed ×1½; **n,** gynoecium ×1½; **o,** ovary in cross-section ×1½; **p,** stigmas ×9; **q,** fruit ×1; **r,** seed ×1; **s,** seed in vertical section ×1. *Arenga pinnata*: all from *Read 618.*

minate flowers with sepals 3, rounded, imbricate, coriaceous, distinct, or joined very briefly at the base; corolla tubular at the very base, with 3 ovate to oblong triangular-tipped, coriaceous, valvate lobes; stamens rarely as few as 6–9, usually many more than 15, filaments short, anthers elongate, latrorse, connective sometimes prolonged into a point; pollen elliptic or circular, monosulcate, with intectate exine bearing scattered spines, sometimes with dense spinules in between; pistillode absent. Pistillate flowers usually globose, sometimes massive; sepals 3, distinct, rounded, coriaceous, imbricate; petals 3, connate in the basal ca. ½, valvate, triangular distally; staminodes 3–0 (? sometimes more, also reported as fertile, then flower pseudohermaphrodite); ovary globose, trilocular, stigmas 2–3, low, fertile locules 2–3, septal glands present basally and opening at the ovary surface, ovules inserted adaxially at the base, hemianatropous. Fruit globose to ellipsoidal, often somewhat angled, 1–3 seeded with apical stigmatic remains; epicarp smooth, dull to brightly colored, mesocarp fleshy, filled with abundant, irritant needle crystals, endocarp not differentiated. Seeds basally attached, smooth, endosperm homogeneous; embryo lateral. Ger-

mination remote-tubular; eophyll ovate to elliptic with erose margin or bifid with rhombic, divergent segments. $n = 16$ (*A. caudata*, Read 1966; *A. engleri*, Satô 1946; *A. obtusifolia*, Sharma and Sarkar 1957; *A. pinnata*, Read 1966; *A. aff. porphyrocarpa*, Read 1966; *A. tremula*, Read 1966; *A. wightii*, Read 1966). Two other counts ($n = 13$ *A. pinnata*, Janaki Ammal 1945; $n = 14$ *A. porphyrocarpa* as *Didymosperma porphyrocarpum*, Gassner 1941) seem incorrect in view of later work.

Anatomy.—Leaf (Tomlinson 1961). Two characters are distinctive in leaf anatomy: hairs with a basal cylinder of sclerotic cells surrounding 1–3 thin-walled cells and guard cells with transverse ridges on the cutinized ledges. The gynoecium has a basal septal nectary opening by pores on its upper surface. A vascular cylinder for each carpel is evident in the gynoecial base and raphides and tannin are abundant around the locules (Uhl and Moore 1971).

Distribution.—About 17 species ranging from India, South China, Ryukyus and Taiwan, through Southeast Asia, Malesia including Christmas Island (Indian Ocean) to north Australia, the greatest diversity occurring on the Sunda Shelf.

Ecology. — Most species are plants of primary forest in the lowlands and hills of the perhumid tropics; a few species are tall tree palms which grow gregariously, and with their massive leaf litter, must have a pronounced effect on forest dynamics. The smaller species, formerly included in the genus *Didymosperma,* are forest undergrowth palmlets.

Fossil Record. — Fossil pollen attributed to *Arenga* has been recorded from Miocene deposits in Borneo (Muller 1970); a record from the Lower Eocene of India (Lakhanpal 1970) has been rejected by Muller (1981).

Common Names and Uses. — Sugar Palm (*A. pinnata,* and several other species), Black Fiber, Gomute, aren, enau, kabang (*A. pinnata*). The more slender forest undergrowth species are scarcely used but the larger species are among the most important economic plants of Southeast Asia and Malesia. The uses of *Arenga pinnata* are legion; it is widely cultivated as a source of sugar, wine, fiber, thatch, sago, and many other products (Miller 1964). Other large species are often used in similar ways. Special mention may be made of *A. microcarpa,* as a source of sago in Sangihe and Talaud Islands, Indonesia; this seems to be a palm with considerable potential.

Notes. — Within this relatively small genus there is an astonishing range of form and flowering behavior. In reproductive features *Arenga* occupies a position intermediate between unspecialized *Caryota* and specialized *Wallichia.*

Taxonomic Account. — There is no useful account of this extraordinary, diverse genus, but monographic research is being done by J. P. Mogea in Bogor. See Dransfield and Mogea (1984).

Plates. — *18A, B; 51A, B; Figs. G.15, G.16, G.19, G.21.*

75. CARYOTA Linnaeus, Species Plantarum 1189. 1753. Type: **C. urens** Linnaeus.

Schunda-Pana Adanson, Familles des Plantes 2:24, 602. 1763.

Thuessinkia Korthals ex Miquel, Flora Indiae Batavae 3:41. 1855. (Illegitimate name.) Type: *T. speciosa* Korthals ex Miquel (*Caryota furfuracea* Blume ex Martius = *C. mitis* Loureiro)

Moderate to large, solitary or clustered, hapaxanthic, monoecious palms. Stems with ± elongate internodes, obscured at first by persistent fibrous leaf bases and sheaths,

usually becoming bare, conspicuously ringed with narrow leaf scars, striate. Leaves induplicately bipinnate (except in juveniles where pinnate), marcescent or abscising under their own weight; sheath triangular, eroding opposite the petiole into a mass of strong black fibers, a ligulelike extension frequently present, disintegrating into strong black fibers, the sheath surface covered in a dense felt of indumentum and caducous chocolate-brown scales; petiole scarcely to well developed, channeled adaxially, rounded abaxially, bearing indumentum like the sheath; secondary rachises similar in form to the primary rachis, arranged ± regularly except rarely in 1 or 2 species where the most proximal few crowded; leaflets very numerous, borne ± regularly along the secondary rachises, obliquely wedge-shaped with no distinct midrib but several major veins diverging from the swollen, sometimes stalklike base, upper margins deeply praemorse, blade concolorous, with broad bands of caducous chocolate-brown scales abaxially, transverse veinlets obscure. Inflorescences bisexual, solitary, produced in a basipetal sequence, interfoliar and sometimes infrafoliar (the proximal few), usually branched to 1 order or rarely spicate (*C. monostachya*), usually pendulous; peduncle ± circular in cross-section, densely scaly; prophyll tubular at first, soon splitting, 2-keeled, relatively small, densely tomentose and/or scaly; peduncular bracts to ca. 8, conspicuous, large, enclosing the inflorescence in bud, coriaceous, tubular at first, tending to split irregularly, usually densely tomentose and/or scaly; rachis shorter or longer than the peduncle; rachillae spirally arranged, densely crowded, usually scaly, each subtended by a small, low, triangular bract; the rachilla base usually somewhat swollen, with a short to moderately long bare section above this, distal portion of rachilla bearing close or rather distant, spirally arranged, protandrous triads, each subtended by an inconspicuous rachilla bract; floral bracteoles shallow, rounded. Staminate flowers usually ± elongate, symmetrical; sepals 3, ± distinct, coriaceous, ± rounded, imbricate; petals 3, valvate, coriaceous, connate at the very base, considerably exceeding the sepals; stamens 6–ca. 100, the filaments short, basally sometimes connate, anthers ± linear, latrorse, the connective sometimes prolonged into a point; pollen elliptic, circular, or monosulcate, rarely trichotomosulcate, with intectate exine bearing spines or clublike processes; pistillode absent. Pistillate flower ± globular; sepals 3, coriaceous, rounded, imbricate, connate at the very base; petals 3, coriaceous, valvate, connate into a tube in the basal ca. ⅓–½; staminodes 0–6; ovary rounded or somewhat 3-angled, trilocular with 1–2 locules fertile, septal glands present basally, stigma trilobed, apical, ovule hemianatropous, inserted adaxially at the base. Fruit globose, 1–2-seeded, with apical stigmatic remains; epicarp smooth, becoming dull, bright or dark colored at maturity, mesocarp fleshy, filled with abundant, irritant, needlelike crystals, endocarp not differentiated. Seeds basally attached, irregularly spherical or hemispherical, somewhat grooved or smooth, endosperm ruminate; embryo lateral. Germination remote-tubular; eophyll bifid with rhombic, divergent, praemorse segments. $n = 17$ (*C. cumingii; C. ?mitis,* Read 1966). $n = 16$ (*C. mitis,* Sarkar et al. 1978, Sharma and Sarkar 1957; *C. urens,* Read 1966); $n = 14$ (*C. mitis,* Eichhorn 1957).

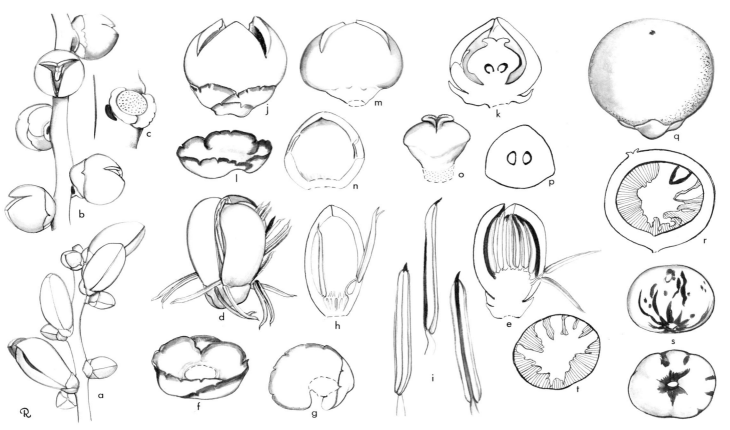

75.—**Caryota. a,** portion of rachilla with triads ×1; **b,** portion of rachilla in pistillate flower ×1½; **c,** triad, flowers removed ×3; **d,** staminate flower ×1½; **e,** staminate flower in vertical section ×1½; **f,** staminate calyx ×1½; **g,** staminate sepal ×1½; **h,** staminate petal 1½; **i,** stamen in 3 views ×3; **j,** pistillate flower ×3; **k,** pistillate flower in vertical section ×3; **l,** pistillate calyx ×3; **m,** pistillate flower, calyx removed ×3; **n,** pistillate corolla in section showing 1 petal and 2 staminodes ×3; **o,** gynoecium ×3; **p,** ovary in cross-section ×3; **q,** fruit ×1½; **r,** fruit in vertical section ×1½; **s,** seed in 2 views ×1½; **t,** seed in cross-section ×1½. *Caryota maxima*: all from *Read 760*.

Anatomy. — Leaf, petiole, stem, root (Tomlinson 1961). Developmental study of the numerous stamens has shown a pattern somewhat similar to that of *Lodoicea* (Borasseae) and *Ptychosperma* (Areceae) (Uhl and Moore 1980).

Distribution. — About 12 species occurring from Sri Lanka, India, southern China, southwards through Southeast Asia, Malesia to northern Australia and the Solomon Islands.

Ecology. — Ranging from monsoon climates to perhumid areas, from sea level to ca. 2000 m in the mountains, in secondary forest (especially *C. mitis*) and in primary forest.

Fossil Record. — Fossil pollen from the Oligocene of the Isle of Wight, England, has been referred to *Caryota* (Machin 1971) but Muller (1981) does not comment on this record. Seeds probably corresponding to *Caryota* were described from the Lon-don Clay as *Caryotispermum* by Reid and Chandler (1933).

Common Names and Uses. — Fishtail palms. All species appear to be utilized in some way. The apex is edible and good. Stems provide sago, the larger species being especially favored. Timber of *C. urens* is used for construction purposes. Leaf sheath fibers are extremely durable and harvested for thatch, cordage, and other purposes. The woolly indumentum on leaf sheaths, petioles, and rachis is used variously as tinder or wadding. Inflorescences, especially of *C. urens,* are tapped for palm wine or sugar. There are several other minor local uses. Many species are cultivated as ornamentals.

Notes. — The leaf is unique, being the most conspicuous bipinnate leaf in the palms. A problematic stemless plant from southern Sumatra has features of *Caryota* in inflorescence and texture but has a simply pinnate leaf; unfortunately fruits have not yet been found (Dransfield, unpublished).

Taxonomic Account.—There is no useful recent account of this important genus; a revision is much needed.

Plates.—*17D; 51C, D; Figs. G.5, G.8, G.14, G.15.*

76. **WALLICHIA** Roxburgh, Plants of the Coast of Coromandel 3:91. 1820. Type: **W. caryotoides** Roxburgh.

Harina F. Buchanan-Hamilton, Memoirs of the Wernerian Natural History Society 5:317. 1826. Type: *H. caryotoides* F. Buchanan-Hamilton.

Wrightea Roxburgh, Flora Indica (edit. 2) 3:621. 1832. Non *Wrightia* R. Brown 1810. Type: *W. caryotoides* Roxburgh.

Asraoa J. Joseph, Bulletin of the Botanical Survey of India 14:144. 1975 ("1972"). Type: *A. triandra* J. Joseph (=*Wallichia triandra* (J. Joseph) S. K. Basu).

Dwarf to large, solitary or clustered, hapaxanthic, monoecious or ?dioecious, acaulescent, shrubby or tree palms. Stem with congested or elongate internodes, usually obscured by persistent fibrous leaf bases and sheaths. Leaves spirally or distichously arranged, induplicate, imparipinnate, marcescent; sheath covered in a great variety of tomentum, scales and hairs, often extended beyond the petiole to form a ligule, eventually disintegrating into a mass of black fibers; petiole well developed, slender to robust, ± circular in cross-section or channeled adaxially, rounded abaxially, covered in a variety of scales and tomentum; rachis angled adaxially, rounded abaxially, variously tomentose, leaflets single-fold except for the terminal flabellum, regularly arranged or grouped and fanned within the groups, linear-lanceolate, irregularly rhomboid or deeply lobed, sometimes auriculate at base, the distal margins praemorse, the veins parallel to the fold or radiating from the base, or ± pinnately arranged along the fold, adaxial blade surface glabrous, abaxial surface usually densely covered in pale indumentum and scattered bands of brown scales, transverse veinlets obscure. Inflorescences axillary, interfoliar, solitary, bursting through leaf sheaths, produced in a basipetal sequence, branching to 1 order only, unisexual, usually dimorphic, the pistillate usually the most distal or "terminal," with inconspicuous bracts, the staminate proximal (lateral), often hidden by very conspicuous bracts; peduncle ± circular in cross-section, usually densely covered with indumentum; prophyll small, 2-keeled, tubular only at the very base; peduncular bracts several, ± spirally arranged, much larger than the prophyll, tubular at the very base, splitting, usually densely covered in brown scales and tomentum; rachis usually longer than the peduncle; rachis bracts minute; rachillae numerous, rather slender, ± spirally arranged, usually densely covered with indumentum, bearing spirally arranged, minute bracts, subtending flowers. Staminate flowers paired or solitary, sometimes accompanied

by the rudiments of a central pistillate flower; calyx tubular, truncate, usually with 3 lobes or teeth; floral receptacle elongate and stalklike between calyx and corolla; corolla much exceeding the calyx, tubular near the base, with 3, elongate, valvate lobes distally; stamens 3–15, the filaments united basally in a short to long column, adnate partially or completely to the corolla tube, sometimes partly adnate to the lobes, anthers linear, apically obtuse or acute; pollen elliptic, monosulcate, with intectate, spiny exine; pistillode absent. Pistillate inflorescence usually erect, with fewer, more robust rachillae; pistillate flowers, solitary, spirally arranged, each subtended by a low bract and surrounded by 3 bracteoles; sepals 3, low, rounded, imbricate, ± distinct or joined briefly at base; petals 3 united basally to about middle, valvate distally; staminodes 0–3; gynoecium ± globose, 2–3 locular, 2–3 ovulate with a conical apical stigma, ovules inserted adaxially at the base, hemianatropous. Fruit ellipsoidal, small, reddish or purplish, 1–2, rarely 3-seeded, stigmatic remains apical; epicarp smooth, mesocarp fleshy, filled with irritant needlelike crystals, endocarp not differentiated. Seeds basally attached, ellipsoidal or hemispherical, endosperm homogeneous; embryo lateral. Germination remote-tubular; eophyll ovate to elliptic with erose margins. $n = 16$ (*W. densiflora*, Read 1965a, Sarkar et al. 1978; *W. disticha*, Sarkar 1970).

Anatomy.—Leaf (Tomlinson 1961).

Distribution.—Seven species, from the Indian Himalayas and upper Burma to China and southwards to peninsular Thailand.

Ecology.—Found in humid tropical forest from near sea level to 2000 m altitude; the genus peters out southwards in Thailand suggesting that it is adapted to cooler or more seasonal climates than those found in Peninsular Malaysia. Most species are undergrowth palms, but *W. disticha* is a moderate tree, recorded as growing gregariously on steep sandstone declivities in deep valleys in east Sikkim (Anderson 1869).

Common Names and Uses.—Wallich palms. Leaves of *W. densiflora* have been used as thatch and the stem of *W. disticha* as a source of sago. All species are ornamental.

Notes.—In floral characters, specifically in the connate sepals and elongate receptacles of the staminate flowers, *Wallichia* is the most specialized of the Caryoteae.

Taxonomic Account.—There is no recent revision.

Plates.—*18C; 52A.*

IRIARTEEAE Drude in Martius, Flora Brasiliensis 3(2): 278. 1881.

Slender to robust, erect, stilt-rooted, pleonanthic, monoecious; leaves pinnate, reduplicate, leaflets praemorse, the ribs and major veins radiating from the base, fre-

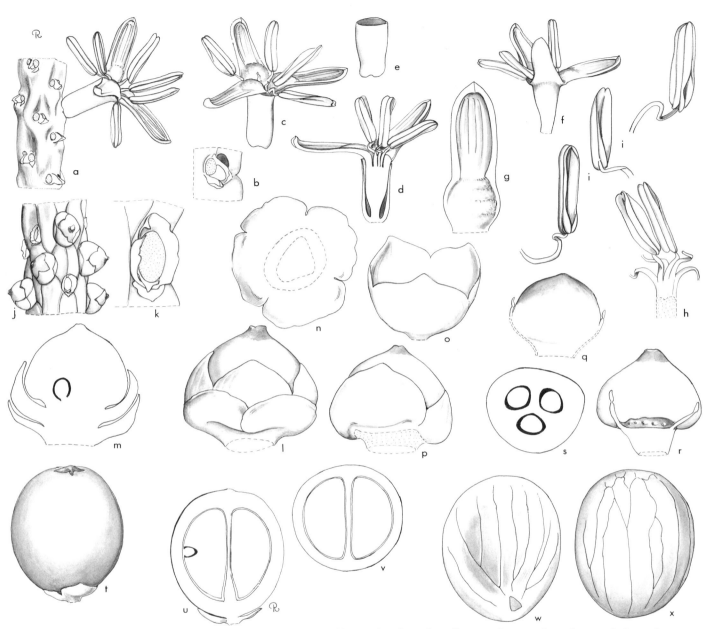

76.—**Wallichia. a**, portion of staminate rachilla ×3; **b**, scars and bracteoles of staminate flowers ×3; **c**, staminate flower ×3; **d**, staminate flower in vertical section ×3; **e**, staminate calyx ×3; **f**, staminate flower, calyx removed ×3; **g**, staminate petal ×6; **h**, androecium ×6; **i**, stamen in 3 views ×6; **j**, portion of pistillate rachilla ×1½; **k**, scar and bracteoles of pistillate flower ×6; **l**, pistillate flower ×6; **m**, pistillate flower in vertical section ×6; **n, o**, pistillate calyx in 2 views ×6; **p**, pistillate flower, calyx removed ×6; **q**, pistillate petal and staminodes ×6; **r**, gynoecium and staminodes ×6; **s**, ovary in cross-section ×6; **t**, fruit ×3; **u**, fruit in vertical section ×3; **v**, fruit in cross-section ×3; **w, x**, seed in 2 views ×4½. *Wallichia densiflora*: **a-s**, *Moore 9256*; **t-x**, *Fairchild Tropical Garden FG-58-475-B*.

quently longitudinally divided into many segments; inflorescences sometimes multiple, bisexual or unisexual, spicate or branched to 1 order only, bearing a prophyll and several usually large peduncular bracts; flowers superficial, pistillate flowers with imbricate petals and valvate tips, or petals open from early in development; gynoecium 1–3 ovulate; fruit 1-seeded, or if more than 1-seeded, lobed.

This New World tribe of six genera (Map 28), characterized by the almost constant presence of stilt roots is divided into two subtribes, the Iriarteinae and the Wettiniinae. The tribe exhibits many parallels to the Caryoteae of the Old World. The reduplicate leaflets are strongly praemorse and

Map 28.—Distribution of Iriarteeae.

sometimes deeply split between the folds (thus being almost bipinnate). Both unisexual and multiple inflorescences occur in the tribe; the inflorescences in bud often bear a strong resemblance to those of the Caryoteae. There are also striking similarities in pollen morphology. We suggest that the Iriarteeae diverged early in the evolution of the subfamily.

Key to the Subtribes of the Iriarteeae

1 Inflorescences solitary, bisexual; gynoecium with apical styles and stigmas .... **Iriarteinae**
1 Inflorescences multiple, rarely solitary by abortion, usually unisexual; gynoecium with basal styles and stigmas
.... **Wettiniinae**

Key to the Genera of the Iriarteeae

1 Inflorescences always solitary at a node; staminate and pistillate flowers borne on the same inflorescence in triads or, toward the tips of the rachillae, the staminate paired or solitary. (*Iriarteinae*) 2
1 Inflorescences usual several at a node, the central pistillate or rarely staminate, the lateral always staminate; staminate and pistillate flowers usually borne on separate inflorescences, pistillate flowers sometimes (*Catoblastus*) accompanied by abortive lateral staminate flowers. (*Wettiniinae*) 5
2 Stigmatic residue apical or subapical in fruit; staminate flowers with 9–100 or more stamens 3

2 Stigmatic residue near or at the base in fruit; staminate flowers with 6 stamens 4
3 Stilt roots mostly slender, sparsely prickly, forming a dense cone obscuring the stem; inflorescences terete and cornutely decurved in bud, the numerous (10 or more) bracts falling from the peduncle as the inflorescence expands, the rachillae long, slender, laxly pendulous; staminate flowers ± symmetrical, closed in bud, with imbricate sepals and 9–20 stamens; seed with lateral embryo. Costa Rica to Bolivia .... 79. **Iriartea**
3 Stilt roots stout, mostly densely prickly forming an open supporting cone; inflorescences dorsiventrally compressed and erect in bud, the 4–7 bracts splitting abaxially, subpersistent and erect on the dorsiventrally compressed peduncle which becomes reflexed at anthesis; rachillae shorter, stouter, rather stiffly spreading at anthesis, pendulous in fruit; staminate flowers ± asymmetrical, or at least angled by close packing, open in bud; stamens 20–100 or more; seed with apical or eccentrically apical embryo. Nicaragua to Bolivia .... 80. **Socratea**
4 Slender undergrowth palmlets of lowland forest; leaflets borne in one plane, undivided; inflorescences interfoliar, or becoming infrafoliar in fruit, erect, branching to 1 order only, long pedunculate, the bracts ± persistent; fruit small, ellipsoidal or obovoid; seed with apical or eccentrically apical embryo. Peru to Guyana, western Amazon Basin
.... 78. **Iriartella**
4 Robust canopy palms of upland or montane forest; leaflets divided into several segments displayed in different planes; inflorescences infrafoliar, erect or cornutely decurved in bud, branching to 2 orders; the bracts deciduous; fruit mostly globose; seed with basal embryo. Panama, Colombia, Ecuador, Peru, Bolivia, Venezuela (Guyana highlands) .... 77. **Dictyocaryum**
5 Inflorescence with several lax branches; flowers separated on slender rachillae, styles very short or absent; fruits globose to ellipsoidal, epicarp glabrous or very sparsely hairy; endosperm homogeneous or ruminate. Panama, Colombia, Ecuador, Peru, Venezuela and west Brazil ..
.... 81. **Catoblastus**
5 Inflorescence with a few large branches; flowers densely crowded on thick, branched or unbranched rachillae; styles lateral, short or elongate; fruits borne in dense masses, prismatic through close packing; epicarp densely hairy, warty or spiny; endosperm homogeneous. Panama, Colombia, Peru, Ecuador, west Brazil .... 82. **Wettinia**

Iriarteinae J. D. Hooker in Bentham & J. D. Hooker, Genera Plantarum 3:872, 875. 1883. ('*Iriarteeae*'). Type: **Iriartea.**

Inflorescences solitary, bisexual; gynoecium with apical styles and stigmas.

The four genera in this subtribe, confined to Central and South America, are distinguished by solitary inflorescences and apical stigmas. There is considerable variation in size from the undergrowth palmlet *Iriartella* to the very tall *Iriartea* and *Dictyocaryum*. The morphology of the staminate flowers also differs, those of *Socratea* being open from

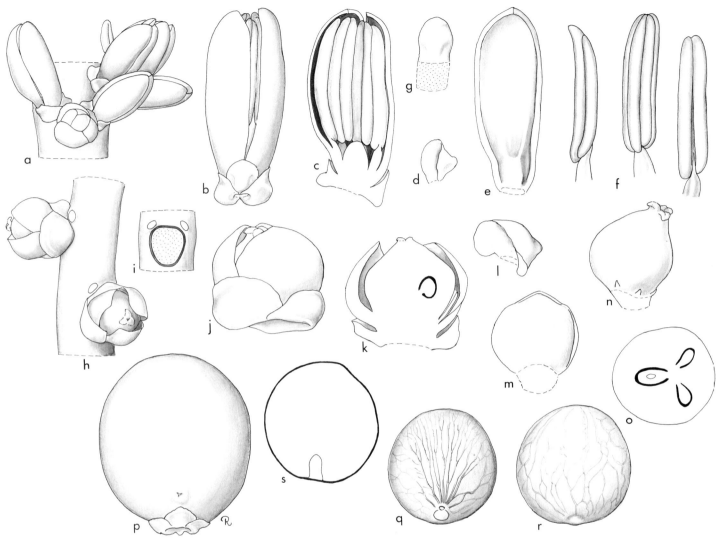

77.—**Dictyocaryum. a,** portion of rachilla with triad at staminate anthesis ×3; **b,** staminate flower ×6; **c,** staminate flower in vertical section ×6; **d,** staminate sepal ×6; **e,** staminate petal ×6; **f,** stamen in 3 views ×6; **g,** pistillode ×9; **h,** portion of rachilla at pistillate anthesis ×4½; **i,** triad with scars of staminate and pistillate flowers ×4½; **j,** pistillate flower ×7½; **k,** pistillate flower in vertical section ×7½; **l,** pistillate sepal ×7½; **m,** pistillate petal, interior view ×7½; **n,** gynoecium and staminodes ×7½; **o,** ovary in cross-section ×9; **p,** fruit ×1½; **q, r,** seed in 2 views ×1½; **s,** seed in vertical section ×1½. *Dictyocaryum* sp.: **a–g,** *Moore et al. 9846*; *D. fuscum*: **h–s,** *Steyermark 91502.*

early in development, while those of the other three genera are closed until anthesis. In terms of sexuality, inflorescence, and flower structure the subtribe is less specialized than the Wettiniinae.

77. DICTYOCARYUM H. A. Wendland, Bonplandia 8:106. 1860. Lectotype: **D. lamarckianum** (Martius) H. A. Wendland (*Iriartea lamarckiana* Martius) (see H. E. Moore 1963c).

Dahlgrenia Steyermark, Fieldiana: Botany 28:82. 1951. Type: *D. ptariana* Steyermark (=*Dictyo-caryum fuscum* (Karsten) H. A. Wendland (*Socratea fusca* Karsten)).

Solitary, robust, unarmed, pleonanthic, monoecious tree palms. Trunk erect, slightly or rarely markedly ventricose, conspicuously ringed with leaf scars, with stilt roots bearing short somewhat sharp or cylindrical, lateral roots. Leaves few, pinnate, neatly abscising; sheath forming a conspicuous crownshaft, bearing scattered small scales (?always); petiole short or very short, adaxially channeled at the base, rounded or angled distally, rounded abaxially, sometimes densely tomentose; rachis angled to convex adaxially, rounded abaxially; leaflets massive with numerous ribs, longitudinally divided between the ribs to the base into narrow segments displayed in many planes giving the whole leaf a dense plumose appearance, each segment praemorse at the apex, blade strongly discolorous, abaxially green or densely covered in white indumentum and abundant unbranched hairs and/or dotlike scales, usually 1 large rib per segment, transverse veinlets not evident. Inflorescences solitary, infrafoliar, erect or pendulous and curved, branched to 2 orders, in bud sometimes horn-shaped, protandrous; peduncle winged or not at the base, elongate, rounded in cross-section, massive; prophyll short, 2-keeled, tubular, soon opening at the tip, eventually shed, tomentose; peduncular bracts up to 9, tubular with pointed tips, completely sheathing at first, then splitting apically to allow elongation of the peduncle, proximal few rather short, middle to distal much longer, conspicuously beaked, all shed at anthesis, prophyll and peduncular bracts coriaceous to woody; rachis ± equalling to much longer than the peduncle; rachis bracts spirally arranged, triangular, proximally conspicuous; first-order branches spreading, swollen at the base with a long bare portion, the proximal bearing about 3–4 rachillae, distal unbranched; rachillae slender, elongate, flexuous, very numerous, bearing rather distant, spirally arranged triads proximally, paired and solitary staminate flowers distally. Staminate flowers fleshy, sessile, ± symmetrical; sepals 3, distinct, imbricate, rounded, strongly gibbous basally; petals much longer than the sepals, 3, slightly connate at the base, ± lanceolate, valvate; stamens 6, filaments short, broad, fleshy, anthers elongate, basifixed, latrorse; pollen elliptic, monosulcate, with smooth, rugulate, coarsely pitted, reticulate, or foveolate, tectate exine; pistillode short, broad, columnar, rounded or minutely trifid at the apex. Pistillate flowers smaller than the staminate, sessile; sepals 3, distinct, rounded, imbricate, thick; petals ca. 3 times as long as the sepals, ± triangular, imbricate; staminodes 6, minute, straplike or toothlike; gynoecium tricarpellate, triovulate, rounded, tipped with 3 low stigmas, ovule probably anatropous; Fruit developing from 1 carpel, globose or ellipsoidal, with basal carpel and stigmatic remains; epicarp smooth, usually yellow at maturity, dark brown when dry, mesocarp thick with outer layer of sclereids and inner layer of tannin and fibers, endocarp very thin, scarcely differentiated. Seed spherical, basally attached, seed coat thick with a conspicuous network of raphe fibers, hilum rounded, endosperm homogeneous; embryo basal. Germination adjacent-ligular; eophyll bifid. Cytology not studied.

Anatomy. — Not studied.

Distribution. — Nine species described in Colombia, Ecuador, Peru, Bolivia, Venezuela, Guyana, and Panama, but probably only one or two (A. Henderson, pers. comm.).

Ecology. — Montane rain forest at medium elevations, usually on very steep slopes, often occurring in great numbers, and forming a conspicuous component of the forest canopy.

Common Names and Uses. — Araque, palma real. Specific uses have not been recorded.

Notes. — The genus remains very poorly known. There appear to be two apparently very different inflorescence habits within the genus; the inflorescence may be more or less erect with wide spreading rachillae, or pendulous and curved in bud with pendulous rachillae. These differences merit further investigation.

Taxonomic Account. — There is no recent synopsis of the genus, but one is being prepared by A. Henderson.

Plate. — 52B; *Fig. G.20.*

78. IRIARTELLA H. A. Wendland, Bonplandia 8:103, 106. 1860. Type: **I. setigera** (Martius) H. A. Wendland (*Iriartea setigera* Martius).

Cuatrecasea Dugand, Revista de la Academia Colombiana de Ciencias Exactas, Físicas y Naturales 3(12):392. 1940. Type: *C. vaupesana* Dugand (=*Iriartella setigera* (Martius) H. A. Wendland).

Usually clustered, slender, lightly armed, pleonanthic, monoecious palms. Stem erect, conspicuously ringed with leaf scars, stilt roots well developed at the base, internodes densely covered in scales, hairs, and sometimes sharp black bristles, becoming smooth in age. Leaves few, pinnate, neatly abscising; sheaths forming a crownshaft, sparsely to densely armed with solitary or clustered black bristles and abundant scales and hairs, sometimes with a short ligule; petiole well developed, ± rounded in cross-section; armed like the sheath; rachis adaxially angled, abaxially flattened, densely hairy; leaflets regularly arranged, distant, rhombic to trapezoidal, upper margins irregularly lobed and praemorse, distal pair of leaflets truncate, joined along the rachis, ribs numerous, conspicuous abaxially, ± parallel, scaly or rough hairy abaxially, sometimes also adaxially, transverse veinlets not evident. Inflorescences solitary, interfoliar at first, becoming infrafoliar in fruit, branching to 1 order, protandrous; peduncle elongate, flattened, elliptic in cross-section; prophyll inserted near the base, tubular, 2-keeled, membranous, included in the leaf sheath, eventually disintegrating; peduncular bracts 3–4, exceeding the prophyll, similar but not 2-keeled, the proximal included within the leaf sheath, the distal exposed; rachis shorter than the peduncle, bearing minute triangular, incomplete, spirally arranged bracts each subtending a rachilla; rachillae slender, 3 to ca. 30, short to moderately long, bearing spirally arranged, close, slightly sunken triads throughout except at the very tip where bearing paired or solitary staminate flowers, rachilla bracts not evident. Staminate flowers borne in a close pair distal to the pistillate, symmetrical; sepals 3, rounded, keeled, distinct, imbricate or basally connate, both connate and distinct sepals found in different collections of *I. setigera*; petals 3, distinct, oblong, valvate, about 3 times the length of the sepals; stamens

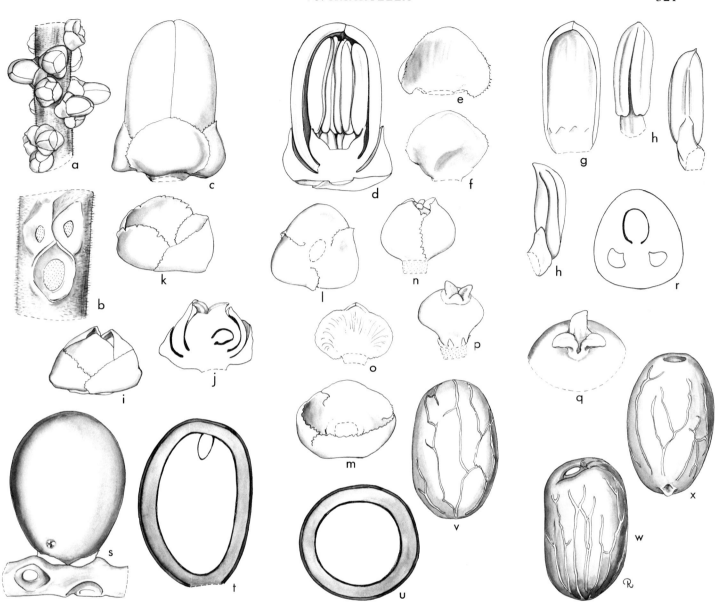

78.—**Iriartella. a,** portion of rachilla with staminate and pistillate flowers ×3; **b,** triad with flowers removed ×6; **c,** staminate bud ×12; **d,** staminate bud in vertical section ×12; **e, f,** staminate sepal, interior (**e**) and exterior (**f**) views ×12; **g,** staminate petal, interior view ×12; **h,** stamen in 3 views ×12; **i,** pistillate flower ×12; **j,** pistillate flower in vertical section ×12; **k, l, m,** pistillate calyx in 3 views ×12; **n,** pistillate flower, calyx removed ×12; **o,** pistillate petal, interior view ×12; **p,** gynoecium and staminodes ×12; **q,** stigmas ×18; **r,** ovary in cross-section ×24; **s,** fruit ×3; **t,** fruit in vertical section ×3; **u,** fruit in cross-section ×3; **v, w, x,** seed in 3 views ×3. *Iriartella setigera:* **a-h,** *Moore et al. 9501;* **i-r,** *Schultes & Cabrera 13729;* **s-x,** *Moore et al. 9533.*

6, filaments very short, broad, fleshy, anthers oblong, basifixed, latrorse; pollen elliptic, monosulcate, pontoperculate, with reticulate, tectate exine; pistillode absent. Pistillate flowers smaller than the staminate; sepals 3, distinct or basally connate, broad, imbricate, splitting into 3 in fruit; petals 3, imbricate basally with short triangular, valvate tips; staminodes 6, minute, toothlike; ovary globular, trilocular, triovulate, tipped with 3 short, recurved stigmas, ovule form unknown. Fruit usually developing from 1 carpel, scarlet, orange, or brownish, ellipsoidal, stigmatic and carpellary remains basal; epicarp smooth, mesocarp slightly fleshy with few longitudinal fibers, endocarp thin. Seed ellipsoidal, attached basally, with loosely branched raphe and tannin network, endosperm ho-

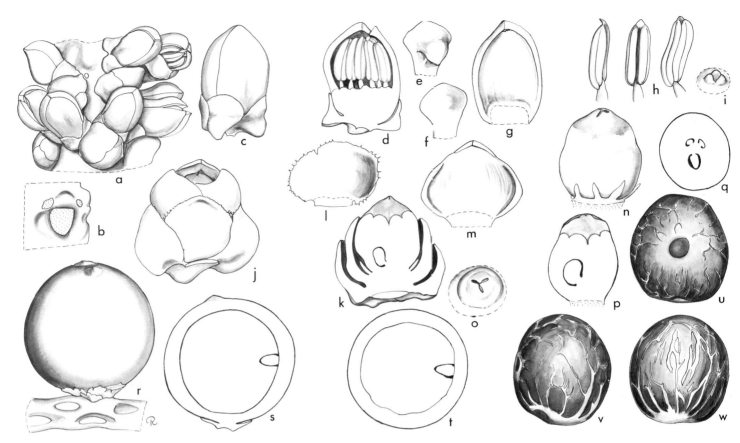

79.—**Iriartea. a,** portion of rachilla at staminate anthesis ×3; **b,** triad, flowers removed ×6; **c,** staminate bud ×6; **d,** staminate bud in vertical section ×6; **e,** staminate sepal, exterior view from below ×6; **f,** staminate sepal, interior view ×6; **g,** staminate petal, interior view ×6; **h,** stamen in 3 views ×6; **i,** pistillode ×6; **j,** pistillate flower ×6; **k,** pistillate flower in vertical section ×6; **l,** pistillate sepal ×6; **m,** pistillate petal, interior view ×6; **n,** gynoecium and staminodes ×6; **o,** stigmas ×6; **p,** gynoecium in vertical section ×6; **q,** ovary in cross-section ×6; **r,** fruit ×1½; **s,** fruit in vertical section ×1½; **t,** fruit in cross-section ×1½; **u, v, w,** seed in 3 views ×1½. *Iriartea* sp.: **a–i** and **r–w,** *Moore & Parthasarathy 9491; I. gigantea:* **j–q,** *Moore 6524.*

mogeneous; embryo apical. Germination not recorded; eophyll shallowly bifid. Cytology unknown.

Anatomy.—Not studied.

Distribution.—Two species limited to the Amazonian drainage of Peru, Ecuador, Colombia, Brazil, Venezuela, and Guyana.

Ecology.—Undergrowth palms of lowland tropical rain forests.

Common Names and Uses.—Palma de cerpatana (*I. setigera*). An infusion of leaf bases is used medicinally. Stems are hollowed out and used for the exterior tube of blow guns.

Notes.—Although slender and so different in habit from other members of the Iriarteeae, *Iriartella* undoubtedly belongs to this tribe. Flower and fruit characters are like those of other Iriarteeae. Similarities to *Podococcus* are of a superficial nature only.

The pontoperculate pollen grain is a very unusual feature, but its significance is not yet understood.

Taxonomic Account.—Moore (1963d).

Plate —52C; *Fig. G.23.*

79. **IRIARTEA** Ruiz & Pavon, Florae Peruvianae et Chilensis Prodromus 149. 1794. Type: **I. deltoidea** Ruiz & Pavon.

Deckeria Karsten, Linnaea 28:258. 1857 (non *Deckera* C. H. Schultz (1834)). Lectotype: *D. corneto* Karsten (=*Iriartea corneto* (Karsten) H. A. Wendland) (see H. E. Moore 1963c).

Solitary, robust, often very tall, unarmed, pleonanthic, monoecious tree palms. Stem erect, ± bellied, conspicuously ringed with leaf scars, bearing slender, sparsely prickly stilt roots forming a dense cone obscuring the stem base. Leaves rather few in number, pinnate, neatly abcising; sheaths forming a well defined crownshaft; petiole rather short, adaxially channeled, abaxially rounded; rachis adaxially angled, abaxially rounded; leaflets large, asymmetrically deltoid to elliptic, the proximal margin entire for ca. ⅓ its length then praemorsely toothed, the distal margin entire for a shorter distance, then praemorsely toothed, ribs conspicuous sometimes with scaly margins, the main ribs diverging from the base to the margin, the whole leaflet usually irregularly split into linear segments displayed in different planes giving the leaf a plumose appearance, transverse veinlets not evident. Inflorescences solitary, infrafoliar, pendulous, strongly curved in bud, branching to 1 order distally to 2 orders proximally, protandrous; peduncle massive, ± circular in cross-section; prophyll short, tubular, 2-keeled, apically open; peduncular bracts 8–12, spirally arranged, tubular, the proximal several short, soon splitting, the distal very long, tubular, enclosing the inflorescence, all bracts variously hairy, eventually deciduous, leaving conspicuous, close annular scars; rachis equalling or slightly longer than the peduncle, bearing spirally arranged, minute, collarlike bracts; first-order branches digitately branched proximally, unbranched distally, bases of branches swollen; rachillae very long, moderately robust, bearing spirally arranged, slightly sunken, close triads throughout their length except at tips where bearing solitary or paired staminate flowers; rachilla bracts and floral bracteoles not evident. Staminate flowers ± symmetrical; sepals 3, distinct, gibbous, rounded, imbricate, bearing deciduous, bristlelike hairs; petals 3, 3–4 times longer than the sepals, valvate, ± boat shaped and curved, the tips rounded to acute; stamens 9–20, filaments very short, slender, anthers elongate, acute to mucronate apically, latrorse; pollen elliptic or ± circular, monosulcate, with intectate, clavate exine; pistillode minute or lacking. Pistillate flowers smaller than the staminate; sepals 3, distinct, broadly imbricate; petals 3, distinct, broad, rounded, imbricate except at the triangular valvate tips; staminodes to 12, very small, toothlike; gynoecium globose, trilocular, triovulate, stigmas 3, low, only 1 ovule normally maturing, basally attached, form unknown. Fruit mostly globose, yellow when ripe, stigmatic remains apical; epicarp smooth, mesocarp granular and fibrous, endocarp very thin. Seed globose, basally attached, hilum circular, raphe branches coarse, anastomosing, endosperm homogeneous; embryo lateral. Germination adjacent-ligular; eophyll praemorse, undivided. $n = 16$ (*I. corneto, I. costata*, Sarkar 1970).

Anatomy. — Leaf similar to *Socratea* (Tomlinson 1961), stamen development (Uhl and Moore 1980).

Distribution. — Seven species described but perhaps only one or two (Henderson, pers. comm.), distributed from Costa Rica southwards to Colombia, Ecuador, Peru, Bolivia, Venezuela, and Brazil.

Ecology. — Frequently gregarious in lowland tropical rain forest but reaching 1200 m, often as a distinct component of the forest canopy. Where known, pollination is by bees (Henderson 1985).

Fossil Record. — *Iriartea* type pollen reported from the Eocene of Colombia, Mid and Upper Eocene of Venezuela, Pliocene of Colombia, and Quarternary

of Guyana (Muller 1981). Berry has described fossil material as *Iriartites*; material described as *Sabalites* from Venezuela (Berry 1921b) somewhat resembles a leaflet of *Iriartea*, but these fossils need to be restudied.

Common Names and Uses. — Stilt palms, horn palm (*I. ventricosa*). The outer part of the trunk is extremely hard and durable and is used in construction of dwellings and in making spears. Wallace (1853) records the use of swollen sections of the trunk of *I. ventricosa* as canoes. For medicinal uses see Plotkin and Balick (1984).

Notes. — *Iriartea* is distinguished from *Socratea* by the dense rather than open cone of stilt roots, the closed staminate flowers with fewer stamens, the clavate rather than spinose pollen grains, and the very different pollination syndrome described by Henderson (1985).

Taxonomic Accounts. — The only synopsis is Burret (1930b); see also Henderson (1985). A new treatment is being prepared by A. Henderson.

Plate. — *19A.*

80. **SOCRATEA** Karsten, Linnaea 28:263. 1857. ("1856"). Lectotype: **S. orbigniana** (Martius) Karsten (*Iriartea orbigniana* Martius) (see H. E. Moore 1963c).

Metasocratea Dugand, Revista de la Academia Colombiana de Ciencias Exactas, Físicas y Naturales 8:389. 1951. Type: *M. hecatonandra* Dugand (=*Socratea hecatonandra* (Dugand) Bernal).

Solitary, moderate, pleonanthic, monoecious tree palms. Stems erect, conspicuously ringed with leaf scars, bearing an open cone of stout, usually densely prickly, stilt roots. Leaves rather few, pinnate, neatly abcising; sheaths tubular forming a well defined crownshaft; petiole short, adaxially channeled or flattened, abaxially rounded, bearing a variety of indumentum types; rachis adaxially angled, abaxially rounded; leaflets regularly arranged, asymmetrically deltoid to elliptic, proximal margin entire for much of its length, distal margin entire ca. ⅓ its length, otherwise praemorse, main ribs numerous, radiating from the base, leaflets remaining entire or splitting longitudinally between the ribs into narrow segments displayed in different planes giving the leaf a plumose appearance. Inflorescences solitary, infrafoliar, somewhat dorsiventrally compressed and erect in bud, branching to 1-order, branches pendulous when exposed, protogynous; peduncle well developed, elliptic in cross-section, winged at base; prophyll inserted near the base, short, tubular, 2-keeled, apically open, thinly coriaceous; peduncular bracts ca. 5, tubular, tips pointed, central ones larger than proximal or distal, ± flattened, eventually deciduous after anthesis; rachis ± flattened, shorter or longer than the peduncle, bearing spirally arranged, pendulous rachillae, each subtended by a minute collarlike bract; rachillae rather ro-

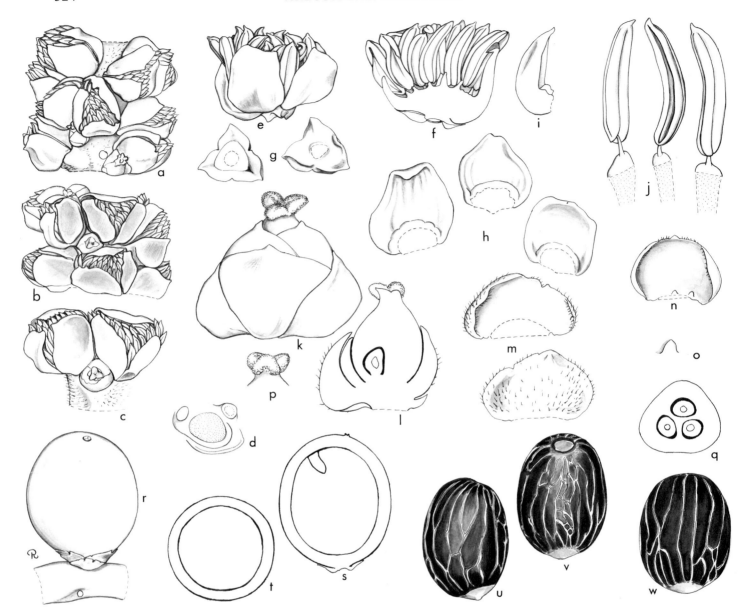

80.—**Socratea. a, b,** portions of rachilla at anthesis ×1½; **c,** triad at anthesis ×2¼; **d,** triad, flowers removed ×2¼; **e,** staminate flower ×3; **f,** staminate flower in vertical section ×3; **g,** staminate calyx, interior and exterior views ×3; **h,** staminate petals, interior views ×3; **i,** staminate petal, lateral view ×3; **j,** stamen in 3 views ×6; **k,** pistillate flower ×6; **l,** pistillate flower in vertical section ×6; **m,** pistillate sepal, interior and exterior views ×6; **n,** pistillate petal, interior view with staminodes ×6; **o,** staminode ×24; **p,** stigmas ×6; **q,** ovary in cross-section ×6; **r,** fruit ×1½; **s,** fruit in vertical section ×1½; **t,** fruit in cross-section ×1½; **u, v, w,** seed in 3 views ×3. *Socratea exorrhiza*: **a-q,** *Moore et al. 9550*; **r-w,** *Moore et al. 9538*.

bust, often somewhat flattened, elongate, bearing spirally arranged, crowded triads; rachilla bracts and bracteoles scarcely evident; staminate and pistillate flowers maturing at the same time. Staminate flowers open in bud, sepals 3, triangular, united basally in a low, complete or partially interrupted ring; petals 3, distinct, fleshy, markedly asymmetrical, lightly imbricate basally, much longer than the sepals; stamens 20–100 or more, filaments very short, awl-

shaped above expanded bases, anthers erect, basifixed, linear, acute or apiculate, latrorse; pollen elliptic, monosulcate, exine intectate, spinose, often with nano-pila between spines; pistillode much shorter than the stamens, conical, briefly trifid. Pistillate flowers symmetrical, much smaller than the staminate, ± 3-angled; sepals 3, rounded, strongly imbricate, dorsally thickened; petals 3, distinct, strongly imbricate, ± rounded with a minute, triangular valvate apex; staminodes 6, minute, toothlike; gynoecium ovoid, tricarpellate, triovulate, stigmas 3, apical, fleshy, reflexed, ovules basally attached, orthotropous, one usually larger than the others. Fruit separated at maturity, ellipsoidal to subglobose with eccentrically apical stigmatic remains; epicarp minutely roughened when dry, at maturity splitting into ± distinct valves at apex, exposing the rather dry white mesocarp with included reddish sclerosomes and slender fibers, endocarp thin. Seed ± ovoid, basally attached, hilum circular, raphe branches conspicuous, numerous, sparsely anastomosing, endosperm homogeneous; embryo eccentrically apical. Germination adjacent-ligular; eophyll bifid with praemorse tips. Cytology not known.

Anatomy.—Leaf, root (Tomlinson 1961), gynoecium (Uhl and Moore 1971). Floral development has shown an expansion of the floral apex into a large truncate area opposite each sepal during stamen initiation. This pattern appears characteristic of the tribe (Uhl and Moore 1980).

Distribution.—Twelve species described but possibly only five (Henderson, pers. comm.), distributed from Nicaragua and Costa Rica southward to Colombia, Ecuador, Peru, Venezuela, Guyana, Surinam, Brazil and Bolivia.

Ecology.—Lowland and montane tropical rain forest; pollination where known, is by beetles (Henderson 1985).

Common Names and Uses.—Stilt palms. The outer layers of the trunk are extremely hard and durable and are used, split, in construction of houses and corrals. Wallace (1853) records the use of the spiny roots as cassava graters. Older palms may be cut to make bows (Balick 1985).

Notes.—Wessels Boer (1965) and MacBride (1960) included *Socratea* in *Iriartea*; however there is a whole suite of characters separating the two (see *Iriartea*). Furthermore, floral biology is significantly different in the two genera (as confirmed by Henderson 1985). The separation of *Metasocratea* was based on a misinterpretation of the position of the embryo.

Taxonomic Account.—A new reassessment is being prepared by Henderson. The last account is that of Burret (1930b). See also Henderson (1985), Bernal-Gonzalez and Henderson (1986).

Plate.—*52D.*

Wettiniinae J. D. Hooker in Bentham & J. D. Hooker, Genera Plantarum 3:872, 876. 1883. ('*Wetteniae*'). Type: **Wettinia.**

Inflorescences multiple, rarely solitary by abortion, usually unisexual; gynoecium with basal styles and stigmas.

The distribution of this subtribe is more restricted than that of the Iriarteinae, the two genera being confined to northwestern South America. The genera exhibit several rather unusual features. Inflorescences are often multiple at each node, the central usually pistillate and the lateral staminate; abortion of inflorescences of one sex results in staminate and pistillate phases. The stigmas are always basal and the ovary shape and indumentum, especially in some species of *Wettinia,* may be quite bizarre.

81. **CATOBLASTUS** H. A. Wendland, Bonplandia 8:104, 106. 1860. Lectotype: **C. praemorsus** (Willdenow) H. A. Wendland (*Oreodoxa praemorsa* Willdenow) (see O. F. Cook & Doyle 1913).

Acrostigma O. F. Cook & Doyle, Contributions from the United States National Herbarium 16:228. 1913. Type: *A. equale* O. F. Cook & Doyle (=*Catoblastus equalis* (O. F. Cook & Doyle) Burret).

Catostigma O. F. Cook & Doyle, Contributions from the United States National Herbarium 16:230. 1913. Type: *C. radiatum* O. F. Cook & Doyle (=*Catoblastus radiatus* (O. F. Cook & Doyle) Burret).

Solitary or clustered, slender to moderate, unarmed, pleonanthic, monoecious tree palms. Stem erect, conspicuously ringed with leaf scars, with short to long prickly stilt roots at the base. Leaves rather few, pinnate, neatly abscising; sheaths forming a well defined crownshaft, bearing a variety of indumentum; petiole relatively short, convex or slightly channeled adaxially, rounded abaxially; rachis angled adaxially, rounded abaxially, indumentum various on rachis and petiole; leaflets broad-deltoid to narrow-elliptic, proximal and distal margins entire for ⅔ their length, tips praemorse, conspicuously ribbed, the main ribs diverging from the base, unsplit or splitting between the ribs into broad or narrow segments displayed in several planes, bands of tomentum or scales frequent on abaxial surface; transverse veinlets not evident. Inflorescences unisexual, infrafoliar, branching to 1 order, 3 to several in an axil, the central pistillate or staminate, the lateral staminate; peduncle short, curved, circular in cross-section, variously hairy; prophyll short, tubular, 2-keeled, open at the apex; peduncular bracts 4–5, proximal 2 rather short, tubular, rounded, not flattened, open apically, distal bracts much longer, tubular, ± beaked, enclosing the inflorescence, splitting longitudinally, prophyll and all peduncular bracts very coriaceous, persisting long into the fruiting stage; rachis bearing few, spirally arranged, pendulous rachillae of nearly equal length; bracts subtending rachillae very small; rachillae straight or coiled in bud, bearing spirally arranged flowers. Staminate flowers paired, apparently ebracteolate, densely crowded; sepals 3, distinct, very small, triangular; petals 3(–4), distinct, narrow, acute or acuminate, open in bud, long, much exceeding the sepals; stamens 6 to many, filaments slender, short, anthers elongate, linear, basifixed, apiculate,

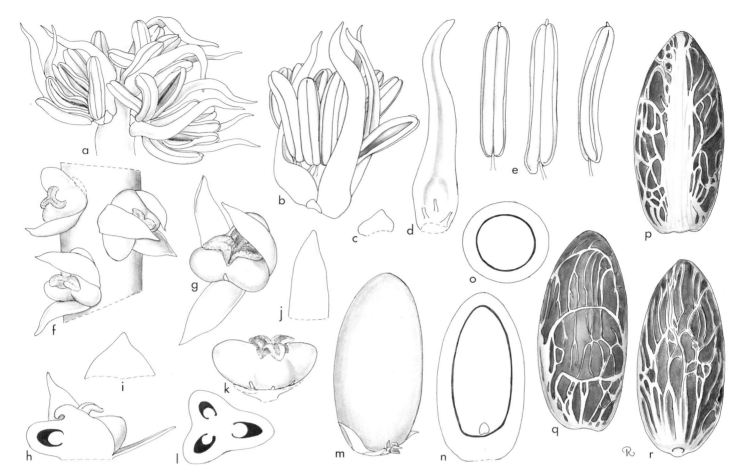

81.—**Catoblastus. a,** portion of staminate rachilla ×3; **b,** staminate flower ×4½; **c,** staminate sepal ×9; **d,** staminate petal with stamen bases, interior view ×6; **e,** stamen in 3 views ×6; **f,** portion of pistillate rachilla ×4½; **g,** pistillate flower ×6; **h,** pistillate flower in vertical section ×6; **i,** pistillate sepal ×9; **j,** pistillate petal ×6; **k,** gynoecium and staminodes ×6; **l,** ovary in cross-section ×6; **m,** fruit ×2; **n,** fruit in vertical section ×2; **o,** fruit in cross-section ×2; **p, q, r,** seed in 3 views ×2¼. *Catoblastus* sp.: **a-e,** *Steyermark 106290; C. radiatus:* **f-r,** *Moore et al. 9452.*

latrorse; pollen elliptic, monosulcate, exine intectate, spinose, often with nano-pila between spines; pistillode minute and trifid or absent. Pistillate flowers open in bud, solitary or at the base of the rachilla accompanied by 2 vestigial staminate flowers; sepals 3, distinct, small, triangular; petals 3(–4), rather narrow or broad-triangular, acute, about 3 times as long as the sepals; staminodes 6, minute, toothlike; gynoecium tricarpellate, carpels minutely roughened or hairy, gynoecium evenly 3-lobed or with 1 (or 2) carpels horizontally elongate, projecting between 2 petals, stigmas 3, terminal, short, borne at the base of fertile carpel, sessile or on a short style, fleshy, recurved, ovule basally attached, form unknown. Fruit developing from 1 carpel, rarely from 2, ellipsoidal to globose, usually dull brown, stigmatic remains basal; epicarp minutely roughened or with short brown hairs, mesocarp with a layer of sclereids external to a parenchymatous layer with included tannin cells and elongate fibers, endocarp thin. Seed basally attached, hilum circular, raphe branches reticulately anastomosing from the base, endo-

sperm homogeneous or ruminate; embryo basal. Germination adjacent-ligular; eophyll entire, praemorse. Cytology not known.

Anatomy.—Leaf (Tomlinson 1961 under *Catostigma*).

Distribution.—Seventeen species described in Panama, Colombia, Ecuador, Brazil, Venezuela, and Peru.

Ecology.—Palms of humid lowland and montane tropical rain forest.

Common Names and Uses.—Palma prapa (*C. praemorsus*). Outer parts of the trunk are used in construction.

Notes.—Three segregate genera have been recognized: *Catoblastus* with a single fertile carpel, a short style, and ruminate endosperm, *Catostigma* with a single fertile carpel, sessile stigmas, and homogeneous endosperm, and *Acrostigma* with three equal carpels at anthesis and homogeneous endosperm. The plants of these three genera all look very similar. Inflorescence structure is virtually identical and, except for the ruminate endosperm, other differences are only of degree. Thus, the separation of genera seems unjustified.

Taxonomic Account. — Burret (1930b).

Plate. — *19B.*

82. WETTINIA Poeppig in Endlicher, Genera Plantarum 243. 1837. Type: **W. augusta** Poeppig & Endlicher.

Wettinella O. F. Cook & Doyle, Contributions from the United States National Herbarium 16:235. 1913. Type: *W. quinaria* O. F. Cook & Doyle (=*Wettinia quinaria* (O. F. Cook & Doyle) Burret).

Wettiniicarpus Burret, Notizblatt des Botanischen Gartens und Museums zu Berlin-Dahlem 10:937. 1930. Type: *W. fascicularis* Burret (=*Wettinia fascicularis* (Burret) H. E. Moore & J. Dransfield).

Solitary or clustered, moderate to robust, unarmed, pleonanthic, monoecious tree palms. Stem erect, conspicuously ringed with leaf scars, bearing at the base a cone of stilt roots, covered in small sharp lateral roots. Leaves few in number, pinnate, neatly abscising or rarely marcescent; sheaths forming a well defined crownshaft, covered with a variety of indumentum types; petiole rather short, adaxially channeled, abaxially rounded, rachis adaxially angled, abaxially rounded, bearing hairs of various types; leaflets of two sorts, one undivided, elongate, asymmetrically and narrowly elliptic in outline, the proximal margin entire for ca. ⅔ its length, then praemorsely toothed, the distal margin entire for ca. ¼ its length, then praemorsely toothed, conspicuously ribbed, the main ribs diverging from the base to the praemorse margin, the other leaflet type similar but with stouter ribs, and split between the ribs to the base into narrow segments displayed in several planes giving the whole leaf a plumose appearance, leaflets densely hairy abaxially, transverse veinlets not evident. Inflorescences unisexual, infrafoliar, 3–8 (–15) at a node, maturing centrifugally, the central pistillate or staminate, the lateral staminate, or sometimes the inflorescence single by abortion of accessory buds at the node, either staminate or pistillate, spicate or branched to 1 order; peduncle prominent, ± as long as rachis; prophyll short, tubular, 2-keeled, open at the apex; peduncular bracts several (4–5), variously hairy or bristly, the proximal 2 short, tubular, open at the apex, the distal 2–3 tubular in bud, acute, enclosing the inflorescence, splitting longitudinally abaxially, at length deciduous or marcescent; rachis where inflorescence branched, bearing small, collarlike or scarcely evident, spirally arranged bracts; the rachis and branches often coiled in bud. Flowers white or cream-colored at anthesis, densely crowded. Staminate flowers crowded in ebracteolate pairs or solitary, open within the inflorescence bud; sepals 3(–4), briefly connate or distinct, ± narrow-triangular, small; petals much longer than the sepals, 3(–4), narrow triangular, straight or hooked at the apex, briefly valvate at the base; stamens 8–19, filaments short, slender, anthers basifixed, erect, elongate, latrorse; pollen elliptic, monosulcate, exine intectate, spinose, with nano-pila between spines; pistillode absent (or minute according to J. D. Hooker 1883). Pistillate flowers asymmetrical due to close packing, usually borne with 2 vestigial staminate flowers; sepals 3 (–4), imbricate, or separated, or briefly connate basally, deltoid to elongate triangular; petals 3 (–4), similar to but usually longer and broader than the sepals; staminodes absent; gynoecium of 1 (–2) hairy or bristly fertile carpels and (1–) 2 abortive carpels, with basal, short to elongate, glabrous or hairy style, and 3 elongate, large stigmas, persistent or deciduous in fruit, ovule laterally attached at the base, anatropous. Fruits densely crowded, 1-seeded prismatic, irregular, stigmatic remains basal; epicarp softly hairy, or hairy and warty, or prickly with shining straight or twisted spines, mesocarp granular, endocarp very thin. Seed ellipsoidal or subglobose, sometimes enclosed in a gelatinous mass when fresh, basally attached with rounded hilum, raphe elongate with reticulate branches, endosperm homogeneous; embryo basal. Germination adjacent-ligular; eophyll praemorse, undivided or with a brief apical split. Cytology not studied.

Anatomy. — Leaf (Tomlinson 1961), gynoecium (Uhl and Moore 1971), stamen development (see *Socratea*).

Distribution. — About nine species in Panama, Colombia, Peru, west Brazil, and Ecuador, with greatest diversity in Colombia, west of the Andes in the Chocó refugium, but also found east of the Andes.

Ecology. — Confined to everwet tropical rain forest at low to medium elevations, often occurring in abundance.

Common Names and Uses. — Stilt palms. Leaves are used for thatching and the trunk split and used for flooring and walling.

Notes. — In a pseudomonomerous gynoecium with basal styles and in warty, bristly, or prickly, angled fruits, *Wettinia* is the most specialized member of the Iarteeae.

Taxonomic Accounts. — Moore and Dransfield (1978), see also Moore (1982) and Galeano-Garces and Bernal-Gonzalez 1983).

Plates. — *19C, D; 53C.*

PODOCOCCEAE J. Dransfield & N. Uhl, Principes 30: 6. 1986. Type: **Podococcus**.

Slender, erect, unarmed; pleonanthic; leaves reduplicate, pinnate, leaflets praemorse, ribs radiating from the base; inflorescence bisexual, spicate, bearing a prophyll

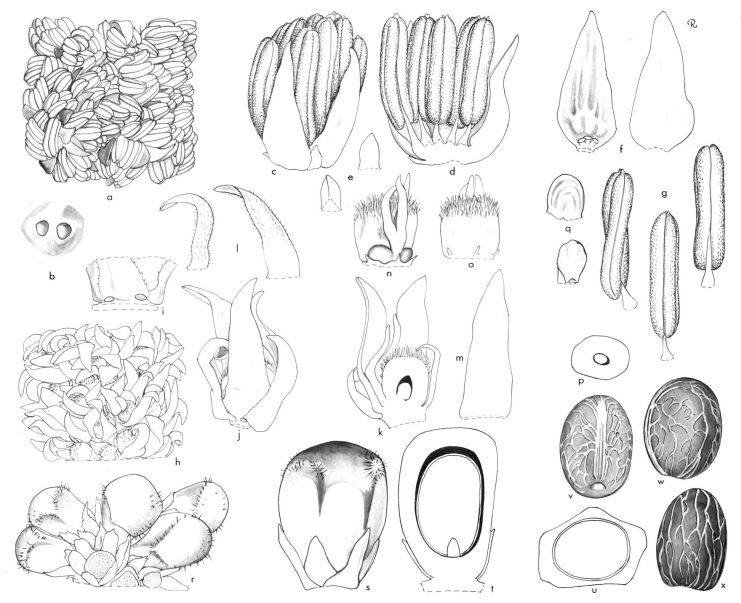

82.—**Wettinia. a,** portion of staminate rachilla ×3; **b,** scars of staminate flowers ×6; **c,** staminate flower ×6; **d,** staminate flower in vertical section ×6; **e,** staminate sepals in exterior (upper) and interior (lower) views ×6; **f,** staminate petal in interior (left) and exterior (right) views ×6; **g,** stamen in 3 views ×6; **h,** portion of pistillate rachilla ×1½; **i,** base of pistillate flower and scars of abortive staminate flowers ×3; **j,** pistillate flower ×3; **k,** pistillate flower in vertical section ×3; **l,** pistillate sepals in 2 views ×3; **m,** pistillate petal ×3; **n, o,** gynoecium in 2 views with staminodes ×3; **p,** ovary in cross-section ×3; **q,** ovule in 2 views ×12; **r,** portion of fruiting axis ×1; **s,** fruit ×1½; **t,** fruit in vertical section ×1½; **u,** fruit in cross-section ×1½; **v, w, x,** seed in 3 views ×1½. *Wettinia quinaria*: all from *Moore & Parthasarathy 9485*.

and 2–3 peduncular bracts; triads of flowers borne in deep pits, both staminate and pistillate flowers exserted by receptacular elongation between calyx and corolla; petals of pistillate flower imbricate; gynoecium trilocular, triovulate, fruit 1–3 lobed, lobes horizontal, stigmatic remains basal; seeds 1–3 (1 per lobe).

The Podococceae includes only the genus *Podococcus* confined to the equatorial rain forests on the west coast of Africa (Map 29). *Podococcus* bears a spicate inflorescence with triads of flowers in pits which led Hooker (1883) to include the genus in his subtribe Geonomeae. However, the flowers in the triad are arranged with the pistillate flower adaxial to the staminate flowers in all genera of the Geonomeae but abaxial to the staminate flowers in *Podococcus*. Pit-closing bracts are well developed in Geonomeae and reduced in *Podococcus*. Flower and fruit structure also differ. Sepals and petals are connate in the Geonomeae and free in *Podococcus*, and the long styles characteristic of Geonomeae are not present in *Podococcus*. There are also major differences in fruits and seeds.

The affinities of *Podococcus* seem instead to be with members of the Iarteeae. Similarities include stiltlike roots with lateral spiny projections, the rhombic, praemorse leaflets which lack midribs and are like those of some species of *Iriartella*, an eophyll resembling those of *Wettinia*, pistillate flowers with imbricate petals, and gynoecia with basal styles. Differences in *Podococcus* are the enclosure of the flowers in pits, the elongation at maturity of both pistillate and staminate floral receptacles between the sepals and petals, two phloem strands rather than one in bundles of the petioles, and a stalklike base on the fruit. Moore (1973a) has noted that the embryo may be basal in development. This unusual genus is considered further in Chapter V.

83. PODOCOCCUS G. Mann & H. A. Wendland, Transactions of the Linnean Society of London 24:426. 1864. Type: **P. barteri** G. Mann & H. A. Wendland.

Small, colonial, unarmed, pleonanthic, monoecious palmlet. Stem erect, slender, reedlike, covered in reddish-brown fibrous leaf bases, eventually bare and ringed with leaf scars, axillary stolons present basally and extending horizontally and eventually vertically, developing roots, and becoming new shoots; prop roots with pneumatophores developed basally. Leaves few, marcescent, pinnate, the first leaves on new shoots undivided, elliptical, pinnately ribbed, margins toothed, apex very shallowly bifid; sheath tubular, becoming split opposite the petiole, margins fibrous; petiole very slender, narrowly channeled adaxially, rounded abaxially, with dotlike scales and deciduous tomentum; rachis like the petiole but longer, tapering, extending through the terminal, often minutely bifid leaflet; leaflets rhombic, single-fold, basal half of each leaflet wedge-shaped with smooth margins, the upper half triangular, margins doubly toothed, 5 large ribs divergent from the base, midrib not evident, blade glabrous adaxially, densely covered with slender, bulbous-based, tanniniferous hairs abaxially. Inflorescences solitary, interfoliar, spicate, erect at first, pendulous in fruit, protandrous; peduncle very slender, with deciduous tomentum; prophyll basal, tubular, 2-keeled, disintegrating into long fi-

Map 29.—**Distribution of Podococceae.**

bers; peduncular bracts 2–3, inserted at wide intervals above the prophyll, tubular, disintegrating as the prophyll; rachis about as long as or longer than the peduncle, bearing spirally arranged triads of flowers basally, paired or solitary staminate flowers distally, flowers enclosed in pits; rachis bracts subtending the triads evident only as raised, curved lower margins of the pits, densely covered in stellate hairs between and inside the pits; floral bracteoles membranous, irregular, mostly pointed. Staminate flowers ± adaxial to the pistillate; staminate sepals 3, distinct, somewhat keeled dorsally, tips irregular or rounded, imbricate basally; petals 3, valvate, about twice as long as the sepals, at anthesis adnate about ⅔ their length to a solid receptacle, nearly equalling the depth of the pit, distinct lobes exserted, spreading; stamens 6, in 2 whorls, the outer opposite the sepals and shorter than the inner antepetalous whorl, filaments awl-shaped, rather short, incurved distally, anthers short, dorsifixed near the base, latrorse, connective tanniniferous; pollen elliptic, monosulcate, with finely reticulate, tectate exine; pistillode short, briefly 3-lobed. Pistillate flower symmetrical; sepals 3, distinct, irregular, variously notched distally, about half as long as the petals, imbricate; petals connate and adnate basally ⅓ to ½ their length to a solid receptacle, nearly equalling the depth of the pit, apices imbricate in bud, spreading at anthesis; staminodes 6 (according to Mann and Wendland 1864), minute; gynoecium ovoid, trilocular, triovulate or 2 locules abortive, style not evident, stigmas 3, short, recurved at anthesis, ovule pendulous. Fruit long, ellipsoidal or with ellipsoidal lobes, often slightly curved, bright orange, 1–3-seeded, stigmatic remains central in 3-seeded fruits, lateral in 1–2-seeded fruits, the base

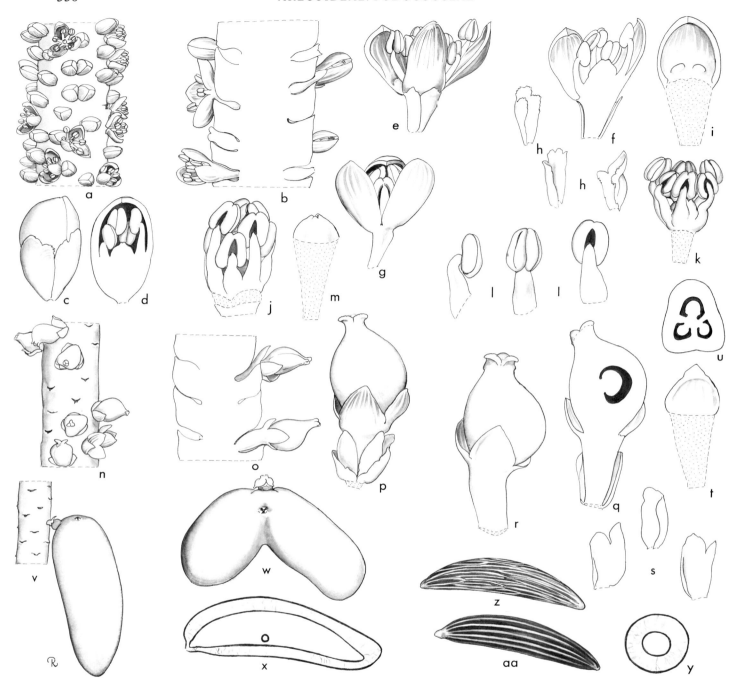

83.—**Podococcus. a,** portion of inflorescence at staminate anthesis ×3; **b,** portion of inflorescence at staminate anthesis in vertical section ×3; **c,** staminate bud ×10; **d,** staminate bud in vertical section ×10; **e,** staminate flower at anthesis ×10; **f,** staminate flower at anthesis in vertical section ×10; **g,** staminate flower, sepals removed to show elongate base ×10; **h,** staminate sepals ×10; **i,** staminate petal, interior view ×10; **j,** androecium in bud ×10; **k,** androecium at anthesis ×10; **l,** stamen in 3 views ×10; **m,** pistillode ×10; **n,** portion of inflorescence with very young fruit ×3; **o,** portion of inflorescence with very young fruit in vertical section ×3; **p,** pistillate flower in very young fruit ×10; **q,** pistillate flower in very young fruit in vertical section ×10; **r,** pistillate flower, sepals removed to show elongate base ×10; **s,** pistillate sepals ×10; **t,** pistillate petal, interior view ×10; **u,** ovary in cross-section ×10; **v,** portion of inflorescence with 1-seeded fruit ×1½; **w,** 2-seeded fruit ×1½; **x,** 1-seeded fruit in vertical section ×1½; **y,** 1-seeded fruit in cross-section ×1½; **z,** seed with adherent fibers ×1½; **aa,** seed with fibers removed ×1½. *Podococcus barteri*: all from *Moore 9900*.

briefly stalked, lobes developing horizontally to the floral axis; epicarp thin, smooth, rather leathery, mesocarp gelatinous with an internal layer of fibers ± adherent to the seed, endocarp crustaceous. Seed ellipsoidal, basally attached, hilum basal, raphe branches anastomosing from the base, endosperm homogeneous; embryo lateral near the middle, ± basal (?) relative to the plane of the seed. Germination adjacent-ligular; eophyll rhombic, undivided, minutely bifid, toothed above the middle. Cytology not known.

Anatomy. — Vegetative, silica bodies of stegmata spherical, central vascular bundles of the petiole with two phloem strands (Parthasarathy, pers. comm.). Floral, sepals of both staminate and pistillate flowers usually lack a vascular supply. Rarely the second sepal in the pistillate flower may have one or two small fibrous bundles. Petals have about four to five parallel bundles in pistillate and about nine parallel bundles in staminate flowers. Stamens each have a single trace. In the young gynoecium, carpels are connate with a distal septal nectary and the pistillode also appears to be secretory. Each carpel has a dorsal and two ventral bundles and a pendulous ovule with two integuments. (Uhl, unpublished).

Distribution. — One species of western Africa from Nigeria to Gabon, ranging from the Niger delta almost to the Congo River.

Ecology. — Found in rain forest at low elevations. The genus apparently never occurs more than 200 km inland. Its distribution conforms roughly to the limits of the Biafran forest and closely related associations and it is not found in post-cultivation or roadside habitats. Mostly it occurs on soils of the feralitic latosol type but is not confined to one soil type (Bullock 1980).

Common Names and Uses. — Not recorded.

Notes. — *Podococcus* is similar in leaf and gynoecial structure to some members of Iriarteeae but several characters set it apart. See comments under Podococceae.

Taxonomic Account. — Moore (1973a).

Plate. — *53D; Figs. G.21, G.23.*

Areceae

Slender to robust; acaulescent, creeping, or erect; pleonanthic; leaves pinnate or pinnately ribbed, reduplicate, leaflets acute or praemorse; inflorescence bisexual (usually unisexual in *Marojeya*), never multiple, bearing a prophyll and a single peduncular bract except peduncular bracts 2 in *Halmoorea,* and none in *Areca, Pinanga, Nenga;* peduncular bracts usually enclosed by or not much exceeding the prophyll; inflorescence spicate or branched to 4 orders; flowers superficial or occasionally in pits,

pistillate flowers almost always with imbricate sepals and petals; staminodes usually toothlike or absent (connate in a ring in *Roystonea*); gynoecium rarely trilocular, triovulate, usually pseudomonomerous; fruit 1-seeded (rarely 2–3-seeded in triovulate genera); endocarp thin to moderately thick, sometimes operculate but lacking 3 well defined pores.

The Areceae comprise fifteen subtribes which are arranged here according to their degree of specialization. The first four subtribes contain palms with trilocular, triovulate gynoecia; in all the rest of the subtribes the gynoecia are pseudomonomerous. The four trilocular, triovulate subtribes include only five genera which are remarkable in many respects; so diverse are they that only the gynoecium links them together. We have recognized them as representing four quite distinct, unrelated relics of the early evolution of the Areceae, and eschewed the convenience of including them in a single subtribe, in order to emphasize their diversity. After a more refined phylogenetic analysis, these four subtribes may require realignment.

The interrelationships of the eleven pseudomonomerous subtribes are complex and by no means fully understood. The Dypsidinae of Madagascar shows most clearly the origin of the pseudomonomerous gynoecium from a trilocular state; rather large abortive carpels are present in several taxa. Only two of the subtribes, the Euterpeinae and the Roystoneinae, are present in the New World, and Africa has but one representative, *Sclerosperma,* in the Sclerospermatinae. Although they possess several features in common with other members of the tribe, the two genera, *Sclerosperma* and *Marojeya,* are extraordinary palms. The largest subtribe, the Iguanurinae, is particularly well represented in the western Pacific; this subtribe includes unarmed palms with a well defined operculum in the endocarp. The Oncospermatinae are very closely related but its members are spiny at least in the juvenile stage.

We have indicated levels of specialization; a phylogeny will have to wait until further morphological, anatomical, and developmental studies are completed and cladistic analysis of the whole tribe can be undertaken.

Key to the Subtribes of the Areceae

1 Gynoecium triovulate   2
1 Gynoecium pseudomonomerous, rarely 2 abortive carpels present   5
2 Leaf very large, undivided, or irregularly divided; inflo-

rescence at anthesis entirely enclosed by a netlike prophyll and peduncular bract; fruit corky-warted ....
.... **Manicariinae**

2 Leaf pinnate or if entire rather small; inflorescence not
enclosed by prophyll and peduncular bract at anthesis;
fruit smooth 3

3 Prophyll very much smaller than peduncular bract(s),
usually obscured by the leaf sheaths; peduncular bracts
large, woody, usually beaked .... **Oraniinae**

3 Prophyll and peduncular bract similar; peduncular bract
membranous or coriaceous but scarcely woody, not conspicuously beaked 4

4 Moderate palms with stems obscured by sheath fibers;
inflorescence with numerous spreading branches of up
to the 4th order; staminate flowers rounded with 6 stamens; fruit lenticular or ovoid, stigmatic remains basal
.... **Leopoldiniinae**

4 Diminutive to moderate palms with slender stems not
obscured by sheath fibers; inflorescence spicate, or with
few ± approximate branches of 1, rarely 2 orders; staminate flowers pointed with 8–40 stamens; fruit ovoid
to ellipsoidal, stigmatic remains apical ...... **Malortieinae**

5 Endocarp with a well defined operculum covering the
embryo 6

5 Endocarp lacking a well defined operculum 7

6 Spines present, at least in juvenile stages ....
.... **Oncospermatinae**

6 Spines absent .... **Iguanurinae**

7 Petals of pistillate flower connate; staminodes connate
in a cupule adnate to the petals .... **Roystoneinae**

7 Petals of pistillate flower free, imbricate, very rarely connate (*Siphokentia*); staminodes toothlike, not forming a
cupule 8

8 Leaf large, bifid or irregularly divided; inflorescence spicate or branched to 1 order, congested, bearing 1 large
complete and 2–several small, incomplete peduncular
bracts; staminate sepals narrow, separated in bud ....
.... **Sclerospermatinae**

8 Leaves various; inflorescence usually not bearing incomplete peduncular bracts, variously branched, congested
or not; staminate sepals imbricate, valvate, or connate,
not widely separate 9

9 Flowers borne in pits or depressions in long peduculate,
interfoliar spikes, spikes solitary or several together in a
leaf axil; staminate flowers symmetrical or nearly so;
sepals rounded, broadly imbricate; stigmatic remains
apical .... **Linospadicinae**

9 Flowers superficial or if in pits, inflorescence branched,
infrafoliar; flowers symmetrical or asymmetrical; sepals
various; stigmatic remains various 10

10 Flowers borne in pits with prominent, rounded lips; inflorescence infrafoliar, branched to 3 orders; peduncle
very short; basal branches sharply divaricate; crownshaft
well developed; staminate flowers symmetrical, rounded
in bud; sepals broad, rounded, imbricate; stamens 6–15;
stigmatic remains apical .... **Cyrtostachydinae**

10 Flowers not borne in pits or if so, then staminate flower
with acute sepals and/or fruit with lateral stigmatic remains and the inflorescence branching to 1 order only
.... 11

11 Staminate flowers strictly symmetrical, rounded or bullet-shaped 12

11 Staminate flowers usually asymmetrical, if symmetrical

then inflorescence bracts 1 only, or staminate flower not
rounded or bullet-shaped 13

12 Leaflet tips almost always entire; inflorescences usually
interfoliar, spicate or branched up to 4 orders; staminate
flowers often very small, ± rounded apically in bud with
sepals nearly half as long as the petals in bud; stamens
6 or 3; gynoecium often trilocular but uniovulate; stigmatic remains basal .... **Dypsidinae**

12 Leaflet tips praemorse; inflorescence infrafoliar, branched
to 4 orders; staminate flowers moderate, bullet-shaped
in bud with sepals less than half as long as the petals;
stamens numerous; gynoecium unilocular; stigmatic remains apical .... **Ptychospermatinae**

13 Inflorescence branched to 1 order, sometimes hippuriform, rarely spicate, peduncular bract slightly to markedly exserted from the prophyll, if not exserted, then
stigmatic remains lateral; staminate flower usually with
filaments markedly inflexed; stigmatic remains apical,
basal or lateral. New World .... **Euterpeinae**

13 Inflorescence spicate or branched to 3 orders, peduncular
bract if present not exserted from the prophyll; staminate
flowers with filaments inflexed or not; stigmatic remains
always apical. Old World 14

14 Inflorescence branches bearing a prophyll only or if also
bearing a peduncular bract, triads usually borne along
the entire length of the rachilla (except *Loxococcus*),
branches usually not widely spreading, rachillae straight,
scarcely zigzag, not irregularly angled; flowers borne spirally, distichously, or in whorls, or on one side of the
rachilla only; staminate flowers usually more or less 3
times as long as the pistillate or more when inflorescence
bract(s) open, if not then peduncular bract lacking ....
.... **Arecinae**

14 Inflorescence always bearing a prophyll and a peduncular
bract, branches spreading widely, sometimes pendulous,
rachillae usually distinctly zigzag, irregularly angled,
flowers spirally inserted; staminate flowers only slightly
larger than the pistillate when bracts open ....
.... **Archontophoenicinae**

Multi-access Key to Genera of Tribe Areceae (parens indicate character not always present in genus)

Stilt roots present	(96), (108), (109), (114), (128), (129), (130), (133), (137), (142), (144), (147), (149), (151), (154), (155), 156, (158), 162, (163).
Crownshaft present	(90), (91), (92), (94), (95), (96), 100–109, 114–127, (128), (129), (130), (133), 138, 140–142, 144, (145), 146, 147, 149–152, 154, (155), 156–161, 163.
Spines present	158–165 (but N.B., spines some-times inconspicuous or almost absent in some of these gen-era).
Entire adult leaves present	(86), (88), (91), (94), (96), (100), (110), (111), (129), (130), 132, (133), (136), (137), (152), (153), 162, 164, (166), (167).

Middle leaflets of adult leaves composed of more than one fold — (86), (88), (91), (94), (96), (100), (111), (124), (126), (128), (129), (130), (133), (136), (137), (152), (153), (156), 163, 165, (166), (167).

Leaflets longitudinally split to the base — 118, 119.

Blade with windows — (88).

Terminal leaflets in adult compound, leaf composed of several folds — 86, (88), (91), (94), (96), (97), (100), (110), (111), (114), 123–130, (133), (136), (137), 149, (152), (153), (156), 163, 165, 166, 167.

Leaflets or blade margin praemorse — 84–86, 88, (91), (111), 114, 115, (116), 117–123, (124), 125, 126, 132, 133, (156), 162, 166.

Peduncular bract absent — 128–130.

Prophyll incomplete — 150–156.

Peduncular bract exceeding prophyll — 84, 85, 89–94, 96–101, 110–114, 117, 122, 131–137, 143, 148, 150–157, 163, 166.

Two large peduncular bracts present — 84.

Inflorescence spicate — (88), (91), (94), (96), 97, 110–113, (124), (128), (129), (130), (133), (137), 166.

Inflorescence hippuriform — 98, 99, (124), (125).

Inflorescence entirely enclosed in netlike bracts — 86.

Flowers borne in pits or flowers somewhat sunken — 86, (92), 93, (94), 95, 98, 99, (103), 109–113, 131, 132, (133), 137, 138, (147), (148), (149), 153, 161, 166, 168.

Triads present ± throughout the length of the rachillae — (91), (92), (93), (102), (104), (106), (107), 109, (110), (111), (112), (113), (116), (117), (121), (122), 124–127, 129, (133), (135), (136), 137, (138), (142), (145), (149), 158, 159, 161, (165).

Flowers spirally arranged — 84, (85), 86–89, (90), 91–115, (116), 118–123, 128, (129), (130), 132–160, 162–165, 167.

Flowers distichous, or opposite and decussate, or whorled — (85), (90), (116), 117, 124–127, (129), (130).

Flowers borne in more than 5 clear vertical rows — 131, 161, 166.

Sepals of staminate flowers connate — (84), 85, 86, (96), 97, (98), 99, 100, 124–129, (130), (131), 158, 159, (160), 167.

Stamens conspicuously biseriate — 89, 93, 100, 137, 138, (142).

Stamens 3 — (85), 94, (130).

Stamens 6 — (85), 87, 89–93. 95–100, (101), 105, (110), (111), (124), 126, (127), 128, (129), (130), 131–135, (136), 137–139, 141–144, (145), 146, 148–157, (158), (159), (160), (161), 162, 163, 167.

Stamens more than 6 — 84, (85), 86, 88, 99, (101), 102–104, 106–109, (110), (111), 112–123, (124), 125, (127), (129), (130), (136), 140, (145), 147, (158), (159), (160), (161), 164–166.

Pistillode present — (85), 87, 89–102, 104–108, (109), 111, 112, 114–122, 123, 124, (125), (127), (130), 131–163, 165, 167.

Sepals of pistillate flowers connate — (84), 85, (88), (96), 100, 125, (129), 137, (166).

Petals of pistillate flowers connate — 101, 125.

Staminodes basally connate to form a clear ring — 88, 101, (113), (122), 123, (145), 163.

Ovules 3 — 84–88.

Ovules 1 only — 89–167.

Fruit corky-warted — 86, 132, 137.

Stigmatic remains basal — 84(?), 85–87, 89–94, 100, 101, 132–134, 137, 138, 140, (142), 158, 162–164.

Stigmatic remains lateral — (95), (96), 135, (136), 139, 141, (142), 148, 153, 154, (159), (160), 165, 167.

Stigmatic remains apical — 88, (95), (96), 97–99, 102–131, (136), (142), 143–147, 149–152, 155–157, (159), (160), 161, 166.

Endocarp ridged, sculptured, angled or misshapen — 117, (120), 121, 122, (133), 143, 148, 153–156, 162, 165.

Operculum present — 131–165.

Hilum basal — 85, 86, (88), 89–95, 97–100, 102, (110), 111, 125, 129, 130, 132–134, 137–141, (142), 148, 152, 158, 159, 162–164.

Hilum lateral — 87, (88), 96, 101, 103–108, (110), 112, 113, 117–120, 123, 124, 126–128, 131, 136, (142), 143–147, 149, 151, 153–156, 160, 161, 165, 166.

Hilum apical — 109, 114–116, 121, 122, 135, 150, 167.

Endosperm homogeneous — 85–87, (88), 90, 91, 94, (95), (96), 98, 100, 101, 103–109, (110), 111, 113, (114), 115, (116), 117, 118, (120), 122, (124), (126), (127), (129), 131, 132, (133), 134, 135, 137–144, 148, 149, 151–155, (156), 158, 159, 161, 166, 167.

Endosperm ruminate — (88), 89, 92, 93, (95), (96), 97, 99, 102, (110), 112, (114), (116), 118, (120), 121, 123, (124), 125, (126), (127), 128, (129), 130, (133), 136, 145–147, (156), 160, 162–165.

Embryo basal — 86–88, (90), (91), 95–148, 150–156, 158–163, 165–167.

Embryo lateral — (85), 89, (90), (91), 92–94, 149.

Embryo apical — (85).

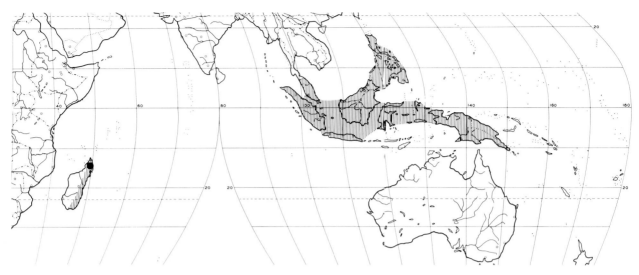

Map 30.—**Distribution of Oraniinae:** cross hatching = *Orania*; black circle = *Halmoorea.*

Oraniinae J. Dransfield & N. Uhl, Principes 30:9. 1986. Type: **Orania.**

Moderate to robust, unarmed; leaves pinnate, leaflets praemorse; prophyll much shorter than the peduncular bract, usually hidden by the leaf sheath; petals of pistillate flower valvate; gynoecium triovulate; fruit 1–3 seeded, rounded or lobed, stigmatic remains basal, epicarp smooth; embryo lateral or subapical.

The subtribe includes two genera, *Orania* in the Malesian region and Madagascar, and *Halmoorea* in Madagascar (Map 30). Several characters exhibited by these two genera seem unspecialized in the Areceae. These are the lack of a crownshaft, the presence of two peduncular bracts in *Halmoorea,* pistillate flowers with valvate rather than imbricate petals and, of course, the triovulate gynoecium. In many ways the subtribe embodies features that we might expect in the ancestors of the tribe Areceae. The distribution also suggests that the subtribe is an ancient one.

Key to the Genera of the Oraniinae

1 Inflorescence bearing 2 sheathing, beaked, woody peduncular bracts; sepals of staminate flower truncate, free, or rarely 2 united; stamens 27–32; sepals of pistillate flower free or rarely united; staminodes 12. Madagascar . . . . . .
. . . . 84. **Halmoorea**
1 Inflorescence bearing 1 sheathing, beaked, woody peduncular bract; sepals of both flowers connate with acute lobes; stamens 3–14; staminodes 3–6. Madagascar, Southeast Asia, Malesia . . . . 85. **Orania**

84. HALMOOREA J. Dransfield & N. Uhl, Principes 28(4) 164. 1984. Type: **H. trispatha** J. Dransfield & N. Uhl.

Solitary, moderate, unarmed, pleonanthic, monoecious palm. Stem erect, bare, internodes short, irregular, nodes prominent. Leaves distichous, reduplicate, pinnate, neatly abscising, sheath splitting, somewhat swollen basally, short, thick, woody, densely covered with brown scales, fibrous along the margins; petiole elongate, stout, adaxially channeled, abaxially rounded, with pale indumentum abaxially; rachis much longer than the petiole, curved, abaxially rounded, adaxially angled except at the base where grooved, with indumentum as on the petiole; leaflets single-fold, numerous, regularly arranged in 1 plane, rather stiff, linear-lanceolate, obliquely praemorse, green above with prominent midnerve, 2 marginal nerves, and numerous tertiary nerves, adaxially ± glabrous, abaxially with thin gray indumentum, small dot-like scales, and irregular large gray-brown ramenta along the main veins especially near the base, transverse veinlets obscure. Inflorescences interfoliar, about as long as the petiole, branching to 3 orders; peduncle stout, covered in caducous brown scales; prophyll ± ovate, 2-winged, persistent, margins irregular, irregularly splitting and becoming fibrous at the tip; peduncular bracts 2, tubular, inflated, beaked, both entirely enclosing the inflorescence, ± woody, deciduous at anthesis, densely covered with irregularly margined, brown scales; rachis longer than the peduncle, brown-tomentose, bearing spirally arranged, low, glabrous, coriaceous, collarlike bracts subtending first-order branches; first-order branches bearing few, spirally arranged, similar bracts, each subtending a second-order branch; second-order branches with a basal bare portion and a few small, spirally arranged bracts subtending rachillae, all branches finely roughened; rachillae moderate, irregular, bearing up to 10 spirally arranged triads basally, paired or solitary flowers distally; rachilla bracts and floral bracteoles low, rounded,

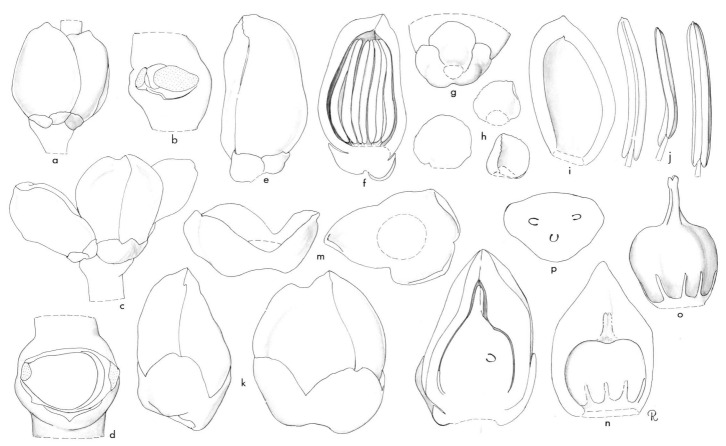

84.—**Halmoorea. a,** portion of rachilla with dyad of staminate flowers ×3; **b,** dyad, flowers removed to show scars and bracteoles ×9; **c,** portion of rachilla with triad ×3; **d,** triad, flowers removed to show scars and bracteoles ×4½; **e,** staminate flower ×4½; **f,** staminate flower in vertical section ×4½; **g,** staminate calyx ×6; **h,** staminate sepals ×6; **i,** staminate petal ×4½; **j,** stamen in 3 views ×6; **k,** pistillate bud in 2 views ×4½; **l,** pistillate bud in vertical section ×4½; **m,** pistillate calyx in 2 views ×4½; **n,** pistillate petal, interior view ×4½; **o,** gynoecium and staminodes ×4½; **p,** ovary in cross-section ×4½. *Halmoorea trispatha*: all from *Moore 9921.*

inconspicuous. Staminate flowers asymmetrical, fleshy, angled; sepals 3, distinct imbricate or rarely 2 united, rounded, margins somewhat irregular; petals 3, distinct, valvate, ovate-triangular, blunt or subacute, thickened at the tip; stamens 27–30, filaments short, slender, erect, anthers linear-oblong, briefly bifid at the base, basifixed, latrorse, connective broad, pointed at the tip; pollen ± circular, monosulcate, with finely rugulate, tectate exine; pistillode absent. Pistillate flowers in bud only slightly larger than the staminate, at anthesis much larger; sepals 3, rather large, distinct except basally where briefly united, irregular, apically truncate, centrally thickened, laterally striate; petals 3, distinct, irregular, broadly triangular, valvate, abaxially smooth, adaxially irregularly roughened at the thickened tips; staminodes 11–12, distinct, threadlike, pointed; gynoecium trilocular, triovulate, irregularly obovoid, with 3 round bulges, one larger, stigmas 3, terete, ovule laterally attached, pendulous, probably hemianatropous. Fruit developing from 1, 2, or 3 carpels, rounded, bi- or trilobed, relatively large, further details not known. Cytology not studied.

Anatomy.—Leaf not studied. The 32 stamens are arranged in a pattern similar to that of *Ptychosperma* (Uhl 1976b) where there are alternating whorls of three antesepalous and several antepetalous stamens (Uhl, unpublished).

Distribution.—One species in Madagascar.

Ecology.—Found in low elevation rain forest.

Common Names and Uses.—Unknown.

Notes.—*Halmoorea* is known only from the type collection, but Dr. M. E. Darian reports that there may be another species in Madagascar. The genus seems closely related to *Orania*. The two genera are alike in habit, leaf form, and in having a triovulate gynoecium. *Halmoorea,* however, has two large peduncular bracts rather than a single one and the staminate flowers have large, blunt or subacute, imbricate sepals and 27–32 stamens, while staminate

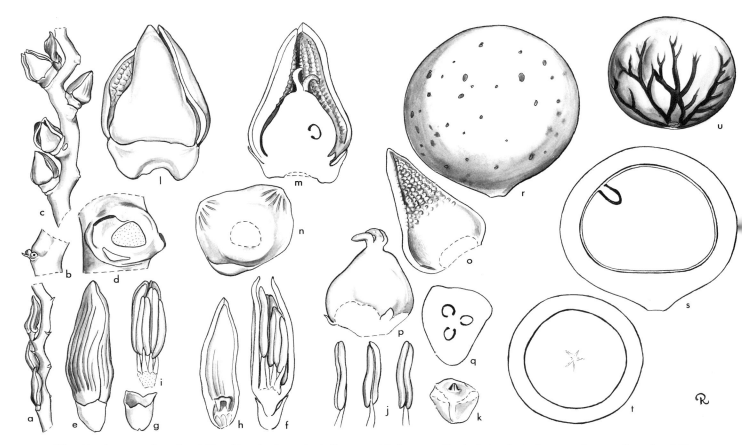

85.—**Orania. a,** portion of rachilla with paired staminate flowers ×1½; **b,** scars of paired staminate flowers ×3; **c,** portion of rachilla with triads in pistillate flower ×1½; **d,** triad, flowers removed ×6; **e,** staminate bud ×6; **f,** staminate bud in vertical section ×6; **g,** staminate calyx ×6; **h,** staminate petal, interior view ×6; **i,** androecium ×6; **j,** stamen in 3 views ×6; **k,** pistillode ×12; **l,** pistillate flower ×6; **m,** pistillate flower in vertical section ×6; **n,** pistillate calyx ×6; **o,** pistillate petal, interior view ×6; **p,** gynoecium ×6; **q,** ovary in cross-section ×6; **r,** fruit ×1; **s,** fruit in vertical section ×1; **t,** fruit in cross-section ×1; **u,** seed ×1. *Orania paraguanensis*: all from *Moore & Meijer 9222.*

flowers in *Orania* have connate, acute sepals, and only 9–15 stamens.

    Taxonomic Account.—Dransfield and Uhl (1984b).

    Plate.—54A; Figs. G.18, G.20.

85. **ORANIA** Zippelius in Blume, Algemene Konsten-Letter-bode 1:297. 1829. Type: **O. regalis** Zippelius.

Arausiaca Blume, Rumphia 2:viii, t. 122. 1838–39. Type: *A. excelsa* Blume (=*O. regalis* Zippelius).

Macrocladus Griffith, Calcutta Journal of Natural History 5:489. 1845. Type: *M. sylvicola* Griffith (=*O. sylvicola* (Griffith) H. E. Moore).

Sindroa H. Jumelle, Annales de l'Institut Botanico-Géologique Colonial de Marseille sér. 5. 1(1):11. 1933. Type: *S. longisquama* H. Jumelle (=*O. longisquama* (H. Jumelle) J. Dransfield & N. Uhl).

Small to large, solitary, unarmed, pleonanthic, monoecious palms. Stem erect, short to tall, becoming bare, conspicuously ringed with leaf scars, and sometimes bearing corky, warty protuberances. Leaves distichous (*O. disticha* and sometimes *O. lauterbachiana*) or spirally arranged, large, pinnate, deciduous under their own weight; crownshaft not present; sheath well developed, splitting longitudinally opposite the petiole, usually densely tomentose. distally narrowing into the petiole; petiole usually relatively short, channeled adaxially, rounded abaxially, bearing abundant persistent or caducous tomentum; rachis much longer than the petiole; leaflets single-fold, regularly arranged and held ± in one plane, or rarely (*O. archboldiana*) grouped and held in several planes giving the leaf a plumose appearance, linear-lanceolate, often narrow, frequently somewhat plicate, apices praemorse, adaxial surface glabrous, dark green, abaxial surface covered with dense white indumentum and very rarely with brown ramenta along the mainvein (*O. longisquama*), midrib very prominent adaxially, transverse veinlets obscure. Inflorescences axillary, interfoliar, solitary, often massive, branching to 1–3 orders, apparently protandrous; prophyll short, tubular, 2-keeled, included within the subtending leaf, usually becoming frayed distally; peduncular bract borne just above the prophyll, very large and conspicuous, almost woody, tubular, completely enclosing the inflorescence in bud, before anthesis splitting along its length to expose the inflorescence, eventually deciduous with a solid flattened, lanceolate beak, and bearing sparse to abundant tomentum, often grooved on drying; peduncle ± circular in cross-section, short to very long, variously tomentose; subsequent first-order bracts very inconspicuous except rarely in *O. oreophila* where well developed in one collection; rachis shorter or longer than the peduncle; first-order branches often with a basal pulvinus; further branches, where present, each subtended by an inconspicuous triangular bract; rachillae usually spreading, flexuous (in *O. regalis* and *O. aruensis* congested), glabrous or variously tomentose, bearing rather distant triads proximally and solitary or paired staminate flowers distally, more rarely with triads almost throughout, or with staminate flowers throughout; triads subdistichous or spirally arranged, ± superficial, subtended by a minute triangular rachilla bract; floral bracteoles minute or not visible. Staminate and pistillate flowers superficially rather similar, cream-colored. Staminate flowers narrower and longer than the pistillate; calyx very short, flattened, with 3, low triangular lobes; petals 3, distinct, valvate, broad to narrow-lanceolate, ± striate in dried state; stamens 3, 6, or 9–14, filaments distinct, short to moderate, rather fleshy, anthers elongate, basifixed, erect, with large connective, extrorse, or latrorse; pollen elliptic, monosulcate, with finely reticulate, tectate exine; pistillode usually lacking, minute and trilobed in *O. moluccana* and *O. paraguanensis,* sometimes present in *O. sylvicola* (minute, conical). Pistillate flowers ± conical or pyramidal; calyx flattened, very short, with 3 low, triangular lobes; petals 3, distinct, valvate, triangular; staminodes 3–6, very short, awl-shaped, or well developed, possibly rarely producing pollen (some collections of *O. sylvicola*); gynoecium trilocular, triovulate, ± pyramidal, stigmas 3, short, recurved at anthesis, ovule form unknown. Fruit developing from 1, 2, or rarely 3 carpels, orange, green, or dull orange to yellowish-brown at maturity, spherical or very slightly pear-shaped, where more than 1 carpel developing, each lobe spherical, stigmatic remains subbasal; epicarp smooth, mesocarp thin or thick, fleshy, traversed by numerous short radial fibers, endocarp rather thin. Seed spherical, basally attached with a ± circular hilum, the surface of the seed somewhat grooved by a sparse network of fibers, endosperm homogeneous, sometimes with a very small central hollow; embryo subapical or lateral. Germination remote-tubular; eophyll bifid with praemorse apices, or rarely pinnate (*O. paraguanensis*). n = 16 (*O. sylvicola* as *O. macrocladus, O. palindan* as *O. philippinensis,* Eichhorn 1957).

Anatomy.—Leaf (Tomlinson 1961) does not show obvious affinities with any group of palms.

Distribution.—About 17 species, distributed in south Thailand, Peninsular Malaysia, Sumatra, Java, Borneo, Phillippines, Sulawesi, Moluccas, New Guinea, and one species in Madagascar, the greatest diversity occurring in New Guinea, with a minor radiation in the Philippines.

Ecology.—Most species are large tree palms of the canopy or subcanopy of humid tropical rain forest in the lowlands or hills up to ca. 1700 m; *O. parva* and *O. oreophila* are smaller palms of the forest undergrowth. There is some evidence that *O. sylvicola* avoids the highest rainfall areas within its range of distribution. Nothing is known of pollination or dispersal of the species.

Common Names and Uses.—Orania palms, ibul. Outer part of the trunk is reputed to be strong and has been used for spears. The "cabbage" of all species seems to be poisonous and avoided by local people; *O. sylvicola* is reputed to be very poisonous in all its parts.

Notes.—*Orania* is of considerable interest. Not only does it have an astonishingly disjunct distribution but the inflorescence and flowers are very unspecialized within the Areceae. Indeed the ancestors of the Areceae and Cocoeae may well have been similar in form to *Orania,* but we know relatively little about the morphology of the genus.

Taxonomic Account.—The only recent synopsis of the genus is Essig (1980). However, extra New Guinean species receive scant attention. The genus is in need of a critical revision.

Plate.—54B, C.

Manicariinae J. Dransfield & N. Uhl, Principes 30: 7. 1986. Type: **Manicaria.**

Moderate to short stemmed, unarmed; leaves large, entire or irregularly pinnate, margins praemorse; prophyll and peduncular bracts beaked, netlike, both enclosing the inflorescence; petals of pistillate flower valvate; gynoecium triovulate; fruit 1–3 seeded, rounded or lobed, corkywarted, stigmatic remains subbasal; embryo basal.

The subtribe contains the unusual single genus *Manicaria,* confined to northern South America (Map 31). See notes under the genus.

86. MANICARIA J. Gaertner, De Fructibus et Seminibus Plantarum 2(3):468. 1791. Type: **M. saccifera** J. Gaertner.

Pilophora N. J. Jacquin, Fragmenta Botanica 32: t. 35, 36. 1802 ("1809"). Type: *P. testicularis* N. J. Jacquin (=*Manicaria saccifera* J. Gaertner).

Robust, solitary, or clustered, unarmed, pleonanthic, monoecious palms. Stem rather short, erect or leaning, conspicuously ringed with leaf scars, enlarged and with a mass of roots evident basally. Leaves very large, marcescent, pinnate, undivided or variously divided to or part way to the rachis, sometimes with separated leaflets; sheath

Map 31.—**Distribution of Manicariinae.**

Map 32.—**Distribution of Leopoldiniinae.**

splitting opposite the petiole, becoming narrow and deeply channeled distally, margins with many fibers; petiole long, deeply channeled adaxially, keeled abaxially, covered with small, rough scales abaxially; leaflets where blade divided single-fold, narrow, elongate, tips pointed, shortly bifid, midribs very prominent adaxially, intercostal ribs also prominent, hairs present or absent, scales usually present along ribs abaxially, transverse veinlets not evident. Inflorescences solitary, interfoliar, protandrous, branched to 1–4 orders; peduncle short, rounded in section, rather slender, covered in dense dark red tomentum; prophyll long, tubular, somewhat bulbous basally, tapering to a solid tip, completely enclosing the inflorescence, flexible, netlike, composed of thin, interwoven fibers; peduncular bract (? always present) like the prophyll but inserted near the middle of the peduncle, a few long, fibrous, incomplete peduncular bracts present above the first; rachis longer than the peduncle bearing spirally arranged, rather long, narrow, pointed bracts each subtending a rachilla; rachillae short to moderate, rather crowded, glabrous or with deciduous, dark red tomentum; rachilla bracts stiff, pointed, subtending basally a few (1–3) triads followed by closely appressed staminate flowers, each with a prominent stiff, pointed bracteole, flowers somewhat sunken, rachilla bracts

and floral bracteoles persistent, surrounding rounded, shallow floral insertions giving a characteristic pattern to the rachillae after flowers are shed. Staminate flowers slightly asymmetrical, obovoid in bud; sepals 3, broadly rounded, united basally for nearly ⅓ their length, imbricate where distinct, thick basally, margins thin and variously notched; petals 3, more than twice as long as the sepals, united with the receptacle to form a solid base, adnate to stamen filaments basally, lobes distinct, thick, valvate, grooved adaxially; stamens 30–35 (*M. saccifera*), filaments terete, moderate in length, variously coiled in bud, anthers elongate, dorsifixed above the base, introrse, connective tanniniferous; pollen elliptic, often with one extremity broader, monosulcate, with reticulate or fossulate, tectate exine; pistillode lacking. Pistillate flowers shortly ovoid in bud; sepals 3, distinct, imbricate, truncate, margins variously notched; petals 3, unequal, thick, valvate; staminodes ca. 15, linear, flat, thin; gynoecium triangular in cross-section, obovoid, truncate, trilocular, triovulate, bearing 3 central, linear, connate styles ending in 3 linear stigmas, ovules basally attached, anatropous. Fruit large, rounded, 1–3 lobed, 1–3 seeded, stigmatic remains subbasal; epicarp obsolescent at maturity, outer mesocarp woody, covered in wartlike projections, inner mesocarp spongy, tanniniferous, endocarp thin, smooth. Seed rounded, basally attached, raphe branches sunken,

→

86.—**Manicaria. a,** portion of rachilla with staminate buds × 1½; **b,** scar of staminate flower with bract and bracteole × 3; **c,** staminate bud × 6; **d,** staminate bud in vertical section × 6; **e,** staminate calyx × 6; **f,** staminate flower, sepals removed × 6; **g,** staminate petal, interior view × 6; **h,** stamen in 3 views × 12; **i,** portion of rachilla with triads × 1½; **j,** triad, flowers removed to show scars and bracteoles × 3; **k,** pistillate bud × 6; **l,** pistillate bud in vertical section × 6; **m,** pistillate sepal, exterior view × 6; **n,** pistillate flower, sepals removed × 6; **o,** pistillate petal, interior view × 6; **p,** gynoecium and staminodes × 6; **q,** ovary in cross-section × 6; **r, s, t,** 1-, 2-, and 3-seeded fruits × ½; **u,** fruit in vertical section × 1; **v,** fruit in cross-section × 1; **w,** endocarp × 1; **x, y, z,** seed in 3 views × 1. *Manicaria saccifera:* **a–q,** *Bailey 214*; **r–z,** *Moore & Parthasarathy 9453*.

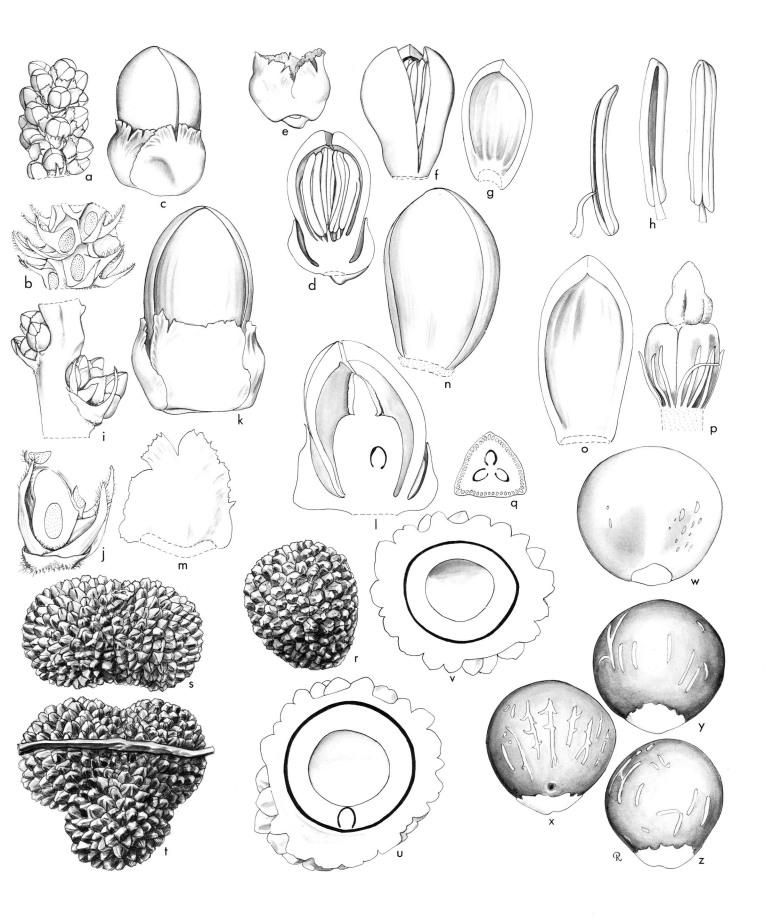

parallel, sparsely branched, endosperm homogeneous, hollow; embryo basal. Germination adjacent-ligular; eophyll bifid. Cytology not studied.

Anatomy.—Leaf (Tomlinson 1961). Histology of the gynoecium resembles that in phytelephantoid palms (Uhl, unpublished). Silica bodies are spherical.

Distribution.—Probably about four species occurring from Central America, across Trinidad, the Orinoco delta, and the Guianas to the lower Amazon River; or there may be only one species which varies in inflorescence branching and in the development of scales on leaves.

Ecology.—Inhabits freshwater swamps near the coast, sometimes occurring as large dense stands.

Common Names and Uses.—Sleeve palm, monkey cap palm, temiche. Makes excellent thatch. Intensively used as food, raw material, and medicine by South American Indians (Plotkin and Balick 1984). The inflorescence bracts have been used as caps (Wilbert 1980a) and the leaves as sails (Wilbert 1980b).

Notes.—Very striking and remarkable palms especially with regard to the huge, ± entire leaves, the trilocular, triovulate gynoecium, and the warty fruits. The resemblance of the gynoecium to that of phytelephantoid palms needs further study.

Taxonomic Accounts.—No recent treatment exists. See Burret (1928b) and Bailey (1933).

Plate.—*54D; Figs. G.19, G.21.*

Leopoldiniinae J. Dransfield & N. Uhl, Principes 30:7. 1986. Type: **Leopoldinia.**

Moderate, short-stemmed, unarmed; leaves pinnate, leaflets entire; prophyll and peduncular bract more or less similar; pistillate flower with valvate petals; gynoecium triovulate; fruit 1-seeded, rounded or lenticular, epicarp smooth, mesocarp with conspicuous fibers, stigmatic remains basal; embryo basal.

The Leopoldiniinae contains the single genus *Leopoldinia* confined to Amazonia in South America (Map 32). See notes under genus.

87. **LEOPOLDINIA** Martius, Historia Naturalis Palmarum 2:58. 1824. Lectotype: **L. pulchra** Martius (see H. E. Moore 1963c).

Moderate, solitary or clustered, unarmed, pleonanthic, monoecious (*L. pulchra* rarely dioecious according to Spruce 1869) palms. Stems erect, covered with marcescent leaf sheath fibers, eventually becoming bare, internodes short, at the base of the stem with abundant adventitious roots. Leaves pinnate, marcescent; sheath with a triangular ligulelike projection opposite the petiole,

densely tomentose, the whole expanding and drying into an elegant interwoven mesh of broad flattened fibers, the margins remaining entire, or the whole disintegrating into extremely long black fiber bundles ("piassava") which hang down and obscure the stem; petiole well developed, adaxially flattened or convex, abaxially rounded or ± angled, bearing abundant, caducous scales; rachis longer than the petiole, adaxially angled, abaxially rounded or flattened, scaly as the petiole; leaflets single-fold, linear, acuminate or minutely bifid, numerous, regularly arranged, somewhat plicate, concolorous or discolorous, adaxially glabrous, abaxially bearing ramenta along the midrib, particularly near the base, transverse veinlets conspicuous. Inflorescences interfoliar, solitary, much shorter than the leaves, branching to 4 orders, the whole densely brown-tomentose, staminate inflorescences alternating with pistillate, or proximal rachillae pistillate and the distal staminate, or each rachilla pistillate at base, staminate at the tip or, rarely, plants apparently dioecious; peduncle elongate, partially obscured by subtending leaf sheaths, narrow-crescentic in cross-section; prophyll borne considerably above the base, tubular, narrowly elliptical in outline, 2-winged, ± membranous, splitting down its entire length early in development, circumscissile near the base, leaving a low membranous collar; peduncular bract 1, like the prophyll, also early caducous; rachis usually much shorter than the peduncle; first-order branches rather slender, each subtended by a very small, low, membranous, triangular bract; second, third, and fourth-order branches slender, tending to be somewhat divaricate or sinuous; rachillae rather slender, very densely tomentose, the flowers partially immersed in tomentum, where pistillate flowers borne on separate rachillae, the rachillae more robust than the staminate, pistillate flowers apparently solitary or in triads, staminate flowers usually paired or solitary. Staminate flowers very small, ± globular, bearing a striate chaffy bracteole; sepals 3, distinct, rounded, imbricate, ± striate; petals 3, distinct, valvate, ± triangular-ovate, marked on adaxial face by impressions of anthers; stamens 6, very small, filaments very short, connate only at the very base, rather broad, ± inflexed at the tip, anthers ± oval in outline, latrorse; pollen elliptic, monosulcate, with finely reticulate, tectate exine; pistillode barrel-shaped. Pistillate flowers larger than the staminate; sepals 3, distinct, imbricate, rounded, ± hooded, the margins ± toothed; petals 3, distinct, valvate; staminodes 6, distinct, very small, short, flat and ± truncate; gynoecium trilocular, triovulate before anthesis, pseudomonomerous by anthesis, ± pyramidal, stigmas 3, linear, spreading at anthesis, ovule form unknown. Fruit dull red at maturity, ovoid, slightly flattened laterally, or strongly lenticular or disciform, 1-seeded, developing from 1 carpel, perianth whorls persisting, stigmatic and sterile carpellary remains basal; epicarp smooth, mesocarp composed of several complex reticulate systems of thick anastomosing fibers, embedded in fleshy parenchyma, the fibers becoming more numerous and closer towards the center of the fruit, endocarp thin, smooth internally, with thin fibers, transverse and adherent to seed. Seed rounded or lenticular, attached opposite the stigmatic remains, with a vertical hilum running across one of the lateral faces, endosperm homogeneous; embryo subbasal. Germination

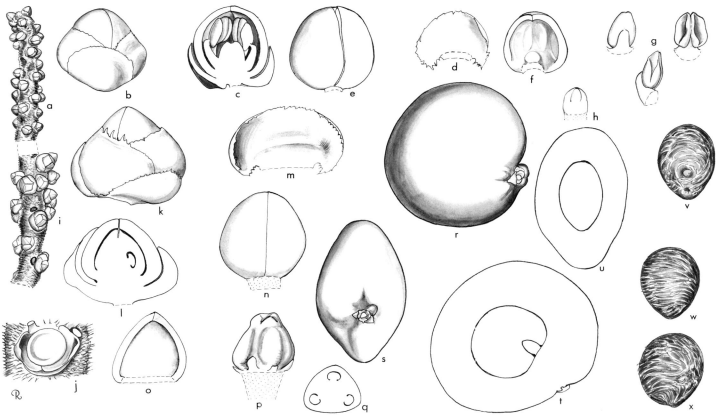

87.—**Leopoldinia. a,** apical portion of rachilla with paired staminate buds ×3; **b,** staminate bud ×24; **c,** staminate bud in vertical section ×24; **d,** staminate sepal, interior view ×24; **e,** staminate flower, sepals removed ×24; **f,** staminate petal, interior view ×24; **g,** stamen in 3 views ×24; **h,** pistillode ×24; **i,** lower portion of rachilla with triads ×3; **j,** triad, flowers removed ×12; **k,** pistillate bud ×24; **l,** pistillate bud in vertical section ×24; **m,** pistillate sepal, interior view ×24; **n,** pistillate flower, sepals removed ×24; **o,** pistillate petal, interior view ×24; **p,** gynoecium and staminodes before anthesis ×24; **q,** ovary in cross-section ×24; **r, s,** fruit in 2 views × 1½; **t,** fruit in vertical section ×1½; **u,** fruit in cross-section ×1½, **v, w, x,** seed with adherent endocarp fibers in 3 views ×1½. *Leopoldinia pulchra*: all from *Moore et al. 9525.*

adjacent-ligular; eophyll bifid, the segments very slender. Cytology not studied.

Anatomy.—Leaf (Tomlinson 1961). Silica bodies ± spherical.

Distribution.—Four species, confined to west Brazil, Amazonian Colombia, and southern Venezuela.

Ecology.—All species are recorded from low lying, periodically flooded, tropical rain forest; Spruce (1871) records *L. pulchra* and *L. major* from the banks of blackwater rivers and on stony islands and *L. piassaba* from low sandy flats. *L. insignis* is a poorly known taxon.

Common Names and Uses.—Jará palms, piassava palm (*L. piassaba*). The stems of *L. pulchra* are used as fence posts and the fruits of *L. major* burned to produce a salt substitute. However, the most useful species is undoubtedly *L. piassaba*; its leaves are used as thatch and the mesocarp crushed with water makes a creamy drink. Commercially it is important as a source of piassava used for a variety of purposes from rope making to brooms (Putz 1979). See also Plotkin and Balick (1984) for medicinal uses.

Notes.—This is a remarkable genus in many respects, combining as it does a triovulate ovary with some unusual vegetative features. Most striking is the presence of two quite different leaf sheath types in the same genus; in one the sheath is composed of a broad network of fibers, while in the other there is conspicuous development of long free black fibers (piassava). The fruit shape is also variable. Further study of flower and fruit morphology may suggest whether the genus is related to the other triovulate members of the Areceae.

Taxonomic Account.—There has been no recent

Map 33.—**Distribution of Malortieinae.**

reassessment of the genus. Drude (1882) provides the most complete account.
Plate.—55A.

Malortieinae J. D. Hooker in Bentham & J. D. Hooker, Genera Plantarum 3:872, 876. 1883 ('*Malortieae*'). Type: *Malortiea* = **Reinhardtia.**

Very small to moderate, unarmed; stems slender or moderate; leaves regularly or irregularly pinnate or pinnately ribbed, subpraemorse; prophyll and peduncular bract ± similar; petals of pistillate flower valvate; gynoecium triovulate; fruit 1-seeded with apical stigmatic remains, epicarp smooth; embryo basal.

Reinhardtia, the only genus in the subtribe, is restricted to the New World (Map 33). Two ovules may abort, the gynoecium thus showing, to some degree, reduction towards pseudomonomery.

88. **REINHARDTIA** Liebmann in Martius, Historia Naturalis Palmarum 3:311. 1849. Type: **R. elegans** Liebmann in Martius.
Malortiea H. A. Wendland, Allgemeine Gartenzeitung 21:25. 1853. Type: *M. gracilis* H. A. Wendland (=*Reinhardtia gracilis* (H. A. Wendland) Drude ex Dammer).

Very small to moderate, solitary or clustered, unarmed, pleonanthic, monoecious palms. Stem erect, rarely exceeding 8 m tall, usually very much less, sometimes stilt-rooted at the base, with very short to moderately long internodes and conspicuous leaf scars. Leaves undivided and pinnately ribbed, with a very short or conspicuous apical notch, or pinnate, sometimes "windowed," marcescent or abscising under their own weight; sheaths tubular but not forming a crownshaft, expanding and drying into an interwoven mass opposite the petiole, brown-scaly, produced beyond the level of the petiole into a membranous or fibrous ligule, in age the fibers often disintegrating;

petiole well developed, adaxially concave or flattened, abaxially rounded or angled, or narrowed and almost winged along margins, bearing caducous brown scales; leaflets 1–several-fold, where single-fold the tips bifid, where compound, the tips appearing obliquely and sharply toothed, subpraemorse, veins conpicuous in the expanding leaf, in some species short splits ("windows") occurring next to the rachis along the abaxial folds in the otherwise unsplit compound leaflets, caducous brown scales present along the ribs in expanding leaves, transverse veinlets obscure. Inflorescences solitary, interfoliar, apparently protandrous, spicate or branching to 1 or 2 orders, shorter than or as long as the leaves; peduncle very slender to moderate, continuing to elongate after anthesis; prophyll tubular, membranous, 2-keeled, distally with 2 triangular lobes, usually ± included within the subtending leaf sheath (except perhaps *R. elegans*); peduncular bract single, tubular or not, elongate, papery, at first included within the prophyll, eventually carried out by peduncular elongation and distintegrating, rarely a second peduncular bract also present; peduncle extending into a simple spike (*R. koschnyana*) or bearing a few crowded unbranched rachillae at its tip, the rachillae long, exceeding the rachis, each subtended by a narrow triangular bract, or the proximal branches once branched, all axes greenish at first, covered in caducous brown scales, after fertilization becoming orange-red to bright red; rachilla bracts spirally, subdistichously, or distichously arranged, short, triangular, each subtending a triad borne in a shallow depression, except distally subtending solitary or paired staminate flowers. Staminate flowers bearing a 2-keeled, irregularly lobed and split bracteole; sepals 3, distinct, imbricate, obtuse, concave, striate on drying; petals 3, to 2–3-times as long as the sepals, valvate, connate at the very base, striate when dry; stamens 8–40, filaments short, slender, briefly connate at the base and adnate to the base of the petals, anthers basifixed or medifixed, elongate, the apices acute or bifid, latrorse; pollen elliptic, monosulcate, with finely reticulate, tectate exine; pistillode lacking. Pistillate flowers bearing a prophyllar bracteole; sepals 3, distinct, subglobose, imbricate, becoming striate when dry; petals 3, exceeding the sepals, slightly imbricate and partially connate at the base, valvate distally, or valvate throughout, distally grooved on the adaxial surface, the upper ca. ½ of the petals spreading at anthesis; staminodes connate at the base, adnate to the petals very shortly or to ½ the petal length, distally each portion of the staminodial ring bearing 2–5 teeth, the teeth usually erect, projecting, conspicuous at anthesis; gynoecium ovoid or ellipsoidal, trilocular at the base, triovulate, style robust, stigmas recurved at anthesis, ovules attached slightly above the base, form uknown. Fruit 1-seeded, black, borne on the enlarged reddish-tinged rachillae, usually ovoid or ellipsoidal, stigmatic remains apical; epicarp smooth, mesocarp fleshy with 2 layers of flattish longitudinal fibers, endocarp thin, fragile. Seed ovoid or ellipsoidal, basally or laterally attached, usually furrowed by sparse vascular strands, raphe superficial or impressed, endosperm homogeneous or ruminate; embryo basal. Germination adjacent-ligular; eophyll simple or bifid. Cytology not studied.

Anatomy.—Tomlinson (1961). Silica bodies hat-shaped.

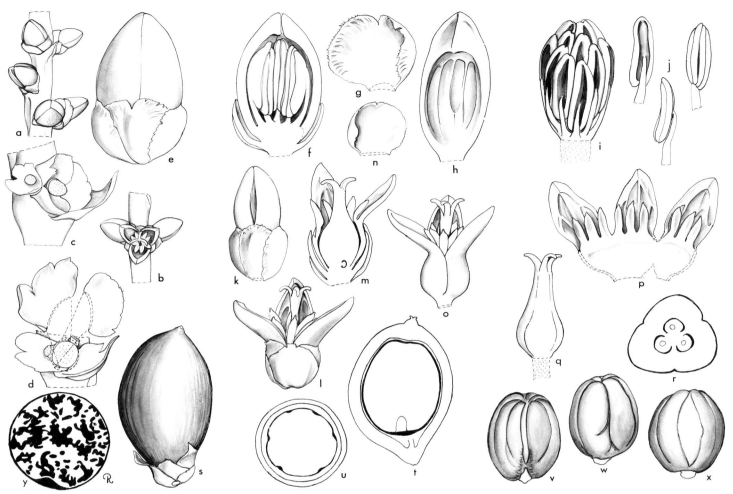

88.—**Reinhardtia. a,** portion of rachilla with triads ×3; **b,** protogynous triad with staminate buds and expanded pistillate flower ×3; **c,** triad, flowers removed to show bracteoles ×6; **d,** triad, flowers and bracteoles around pistillate flower removed to show arrangement of flowers and the bracteole of a staminate flower ×6; **e,** staminate bud ×12; **f,** staminate bud in vertical section ×12; **g,** staminate sepal, interior view ×12; **h,** staminate petal, interior view ×12; **i,** androecium ×12; **j,** stamen in 3 views ×12; **k,** pistillate bud ×6; **l,** pistillate flower, expanded ×6; **m,** pistillate flower in vertical section ×6; **n,** pistillate sepal, interior view ×6; **o,** pistillate flower, sepals removed ×6; **p,** pistillate corolla with staminodes, expanded ×6; **q,** gynoecium ×6; **r,** ovary in cross-section ×12; **s,** fruit ×3; **t,** fruit in vertical section ×3; **u,** fruit in cross-section ×3; **v, w, x,** seed in 3 views ×3; **y,** seed in cross-section ×3. *Reinhardtia simplex*: **a-r,** *BH 61-868*; **s-x,** *Moore 6529*; *R. elegans*: **y,** *Hernandez & Sharp X-1245*.

Distribution.—Six species, distributed from Mexico to Panama, one species reaching northwest Colombia, and one in Dominican Republic.

Ecology.—Undergrowth palms, usually found in lowland tropical rain forest. *R. elegans* and *R. gracilis* var. *tenuissima* are found at altitudes of 1000–1500 m.

Common Names and Uses.—Window palm, reinhardtia. No local uses appear to have been recorded; all species are ornamental and have been rather widely cultivated by enthusiasts.

Notes.—Small habit, sometimes praemorse leaf-lets, and numerous stamens combine with a triovulate condition to make this a very interesting genus, but its relationships are not evident.

Taxonomic Accounts.—Moore (1957c), (Read, Zanoni, and Mejia 1987).

Plate.—55B; Figs. G.13, G.16.

Dypsidinae Beccari, Palme del Madagascar 2. 1914.
Type: **Dypsis.**

Very small to large, unarmed, sometimes dichotomously branched; leaves pinnate or pinnately ribbed; leaflets usually entire, very rarely praemorse; inflorescences mostly interfoliar, spicate, or branched to 4 orders; peduncle ± elongate, basal branches not sharply divaricate;

Map 34.—Distribution of Dypsidinae.

flowers with anthers scarcely sagittate and conical; pistillode trifid or acute. Madagascar .... 91. **Neophloga**

3 Moderate to rather large palms; leaves pinnate with single-fold leaflets; staminate flowers with anthers usually sagittate; pistillode conical or columnar and trifid. Madagascar, Comoro Islands, Pemba Island .. 90. **Chrysalidocarpus**

4 Staminate flowers with stamens ± equal, filaments inflexed in bud, anthers versatile, ± sagittate basally; triads usually ± sunken in shallow depressions in the rachillae. Madagascar .... 92. **Neodypsis**

4 Staminate flowers with stamens in 2 series, one series shorter than the other, the filaments not inflexed, anthers basifixed; triads usually ± superficial 5

5 Moderate to robust palms with stems usually aerially branching by apparently equal forking; leaf sheaths usually disintegrating into a mass of fibers in the crown; fruit ± rounded to obovoid with abundant fibers in the mesocarp. Madagascar .... 89. **Vonitra**

5 Slender undergrowth palms with unbranched canelike stems; leaf sheaths not disintegrating into fibers; fruit ± ellipsoidal with sparse mesocarp fibers. Madagascar ...

.... 93. **Phloga**

89. **VONITRA** Beccari, Botanische Jahrbücher für Systematik 38 (Beiblatt 87):18. 1906. Type: *V. thouarsiana* (Baillon) Beccari (*Dypsis thouarsiana* Baillon) = **V. fibrosa** (C. H. Wright) Beccari (*Dictyosperma fibrosum* C. H. Wright) (see H. E. Moore 1971b).

Solitary or clustered, moderate, unarmed, pleonanthic, monoecious palms. Stem erect at maturity, unbranched or forked once or repeatedly, eventually bare, conspicuously ringed with leaf scars. Leaves numerous, pinnate; sheaths not forming a well defined crownshaft, bearing opposite the petiole a well defined ligule, usually disintegrating into a pendulous interwoven mass of fibers obscuring the sheaths and clothing at least the upper part of the stem; petiole elongate, adaxially channeled, abaxially rounded, the margins sharp; rachis adaxially angled except proximally where sometimes flattened, abaxially rounded, angled, or flattened; leaflets regularly arranged, numerous, single-fold, acuminate or minutely bifid, with 3–6 major nerves including the midrib, transverse veinlets not evident, emerging leaves sometimes reddish-brown. Inflorescences solitary, interfoliar, branching to 3 orders basally, to 2–1 orders distally, ?protandrous; peduncle elongate; prophyll basally inserted, included within the leaf sheaths, persistent, tubular, 2-keeled, open at the apex; peduncular bract 1, inserted at some distance above the prophyll, longer than the prophyll, tubular, conspicuously beaked, enclosing the inflorescence in bud, splitting abaxially, deciduous as the inflorescence elongates; rachis elongate but shorter than the peduncle, bearing small triangular, spirally arranged bracts each subtending a first-order branch; proximal first-order branches with a long bare portion, all branches swollen at the base; rachillae numerous, ± pendulous, slender, spreading, bearing spirally arranged triads proximally, paired or solitary staminate flowers distally, each flower group subtended by a spreading, rounded, liplike bract; floral bracteoles minute. Staminate flowers very small, symmetrical; sepals 3, distinct,

peduncular bract usually conspicuous, exserted and caducous, prophyll often adnate to the peduncle basally; staminate flowers symmetrical, ± rounded, sometimes very small; petals of pistillate flowers imbricate; gynoecium often trilocular but uniovulate; fruit with basal stigmatic remains; seed with basal hilum.

The Dypsidinae contains six genera confined to Madagascar, the Comoro Islands, and Pemba Island off the coast of Tanzania (Map 34). This subtribe is in great need of a critical reassessment, which, for lack of material and time for field work, we have been unable to carry out during the present study. Although very diverse, the genera are based on characters shown often to be unreliable elsewhere in the family. The subtribe is of particular interest in that several of its members show, to varying degrees, the presence of abortive locules in the gynoecium, suggesting close affinity to a presumed ancestral triovulate condition.

Key to the Genera of the Dypsidinae

1 Endosperm homogeneous 2
1 Endosperm ruminate 4
2 Diminutive palms with extremely small flowers; fertile stamens 3, often alternating with 3 lobes or staminodes; anthers globular with broad short connectives. Madagascar .... 94. **Dypsis**
2 Slender palmlets to tall trees; fertile stamens 6, anthers elongate with narrow connectives 3
3 Slender undergrowth palmlets; leaves bifid or if pinnate with at least the apical leaflets many-ribbed; staminate

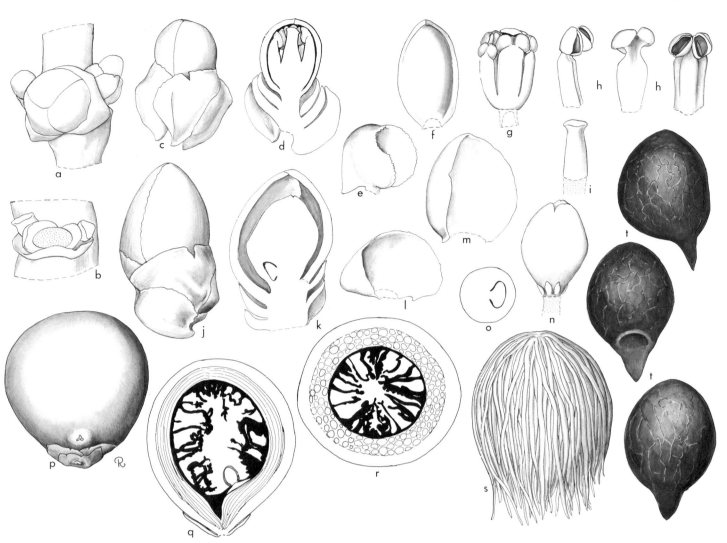

89.—**Vonitra. a,** triad ×9; **b,** triad, flowers removed to show scars, subtending bract, and bracteoles ×12; **c,** staminate bud ×15; **d,** staminate bud in vertical section ×15; **e,** staminate sepal ×15; **f,** staminate petal ×15; **g,** androecium ×15; **h,** stamen in 3 views ×22½; **i,** pistillode ×15; **j,** pistillate bud ×12; **k,** pistillate bud in vertical section ×12; **l,** pistillate sepal ×12; **m,** pistillate petal ×12; **n,** gynoecium and staminodes ×12; **o,** ovary in cross-section ×12; **p,** fruit ×2¼; **q,** fruit in vertical section ×2¼; **r,** fruit in cross-section ×2¼; **s,** endocarp ×2¼; **t,** seed in 3 views ×2¼. *Vonitra fibrosa*: **a-o,** *Moore 9034*; *V. utilis*: **p-t,** *Moore 9005A.*

coriaceous, rounded apically, gibbous and keeled dorsally, broadly imbricate; petals 3, distinct, valvate, a little longer than the sepals, nerved when dry; stamens 6, filaments thick, erect, ± in 2 series, not inflexed at the apex in bud, anthers basifixed, rounded, didymous, introrse; pollen elliptic or circular, monosulcate, with foveolate or fossulate, tectate exine; pistillode ± equalling the stamens, angled, columnar, truncate, briefly trilobed. Pistillate flowers in bud usually more than twice as long as the staminate flowers at anthesis, symmetrical, ± obovoid; sepals 3, distinct, rounded, gibbous and keeled dorsally near the base, broadly imbricate; petals 3, distinct, rounded, about twice as long as the sepals, broadly imbricate; staminodes 6, minute, toothlike; gynoecium unilocular, uniovulate, ovoid, stigmas 3, low, appressed, ovule laterally attached, form unknown. Fruit subglobose or obovoid with basal stigmatic remains sometimes barely visible under the apex of one petal; epicarp smooth, mesocarp with a thick fleshy layer including pale sclerosomes over a thick endocarp of robust, branching and interlacing fibers in several layers, the fleshy portion rotting away to leave the frayed, fiber-covered seed. Seed eccentrically obovoid, rounded at the top, narrowed abruptly near the base on the side opposite the stigmatic remains to a sharp point, raphe branches ascending from the base and much anastomosing, endosperm ruminate; embryo lateral below the middle in the narrowed area. Germination and eophyll unrecorded. Cytology not studied.

Anatomy.—The only study is by Damiani (1929), reported by Tomlinson (1961). Hypodermal layers are probably absent; fibers are in small strands adjacent to epidermal layers or solitary.

Distribution.—Four species endemic to Madagascar.

Ecology.—Tropical rain forest at altitudes of 0–900 m above sea level.

Common Names and Uses.—Piassava or vonitra palm (*V. fibrosa*). The apex is usually edible, and the fruit sometimes eaten, but the most important product is the fiber of the leaf sheaths from *V. utilis* and *V. fibrosa*.

Notes.—*Vonitra* can often be recognized by the dichotomous branching which occurs in only six other unrelated genera of palms (Moore and Uhl 1982) and also by the large untidy mass of sheath fibers which enclose the base of the crown.

Perrier de la Bâthie transferred *Chrysalidocarpus nossibensis* to *Vonitra* but it seems unlikely that he was right. As illustrated by Beccari (1914a, p. 42), the staminate flowers of *C. nossibensis* are as large as the pistillate buds, and the stamens, though young, and with filaments described as not reflexed at the apex, have anthers quite unlike those of *Vonitra*. Furthermore, *V. nossibensis* is unbranched and the ligule does not disintegrate into fibers. The above description includes the aberrant features of *V. nossibensis* but further study is required.

Taxonomic Accounts.—Beccari (1914a), Jumelle and Perrier de la Bâthie (1945).

Plate.—*55C; Fig. G.20.*

90. **CHRYSALIDOCARPUS** H. A. Wendland, Botanische Zeitung 36:117. 1878. Type: **C. lutescens** H. A. Wendland.

Phlogella Baillon, Bulletin Mensuel de la Société Linnéenne de Paris 2:1174. 1894. Type: *P. humblotiana* Baillon (=*C. humblotiana* (Baillon) Beccari).

Macrophloga Beccari, Palme del Madagascar 47. 1914 ("1912"). Type: *M. decipiens* (Beccari) Beccari (*Chrysalidocarpus decipiens* Beccari).

Small to moderate or tall, solitary or clustered, unarmed, pleonanthic, monoecious palms. Stem erect, sometimes producing aerial branches in extra-axillary positions, rarely swollen (*C. decipiens*), prominently ringed with leaf scars. Leaves pinnate, abscising neatly or marcescent; sheaths tubular at first, usually splitting opposite the petiole, not usually forming a conspicuous crownshaft but crownshaft well developed in some (e.g. *C. lutescens*),

sometimes with a pair of ligulelike auricles, often variously waxy and/or scaly; petiole very short, elongate, channeled adaxially, rounded abaxially, usually scaly and/or waxy like the sheath; rachis adaxially angled, abaxially rounded, sometimes conspicuously curved; leaflets singlefold, numerous, acute, rarely bifid, linear to lanceolate, rigid, flexuous or curved, regularly arranged or grouped and fanned within the groups giving a plumose appearance, the margins often thickened, adaxially glabrous, abaxially often with ramenta along midrib, and sometimes with minute scales and wax between the main veins, transverse veinlets obscure. Inflorescences interfoliar, occasionally becoming infrafoliar with age, branched to 3–4 orders, protandrous; peduncle elongate, often tomentose; prophyll short, 2-keeled, tubular, splitting for a short distance at the tip, often ± included by the leaf sheath, caducous; peduncular bract often inserted well above the prophyll, elongate, tubular in bud, often beaked, frequently tomentose, caducous; rachis longer or shorter than the peduncle; rachis bracts inconspicuous, low, rounded or conspicuous; rachillae elongate, slender, spreading, glabrous or tomentose, bearing rather crowded, spirally or subdistichously arranged, rounded, thick, somewhat deflexed bracts, the proximal subtending triads, the distal subtending solitary or paired staminate flowers; floral bracteoles rounded, minute. Staminate flowers ± symmetrical, larger than the pistillate buds at anthesis; sepals 3, distinct, imbricate, dorsally keeled; petals 3, distinct, valvate, exceeding the sepals, ± acute; stamens 6, filaments distinct, awl-shaped, erect or briefly inflexed in bud, anthers dorsifixed, ± versatile, latrorse; pollen elliptic, monosulcate, with scabrate to reticulate, tectate exine; pistillode 3-angled, conical, trifid at the tip. Pistillate flowers ± ovoid; sepals 3, distinct, imbricate, rounded; petals 3, distinct, longer than the sepals, imbricate except at the very tips where briefly valvate; staminodes 6, toothlike; gynoecium unilocular, uniovulate, stigmas 3, briefly recurved, ovule laterally attached, form unknown. Fruit ellipsoidal or globose with basal stigmatic remains; epicarp smooth when fresh, drying pebbled, mesocarp thin, fleshy, overlying a shell of prominent interlocking fibers, ascending from the base abaxially and branching in curves laterally towards other fibers ascending adaxially from the base, all adnate to the seed. Seed basally attached, raphe branches ascending, branching and anastomosing, endosperm homogeneous; embryo lateral or subbasal. Germination adjacent-ligular; eophyll bifid. *n* = 14 (*C. lutescens*, Gassner 1941, Eichhorn 1957). *n* = 16 (*C. lutescens*, Read 1966, Sharma and Sarkar 1957. *C. madagascariensis*, Aryavand 1977, Read 1966).

Anatomy.—Leaf (Tomlinson 1961), only *C. lutescens* studied.

Distribution.—About 20 species, in Madagascar, Comores Islands, and Pemba Island off the coast of Tanzania; two species, *C. glaucescens* and *C. cabadae* known only in cultivation.

Ecology.—Very varied, occurring from sea level to altitudes of 2000 m, some species confined to

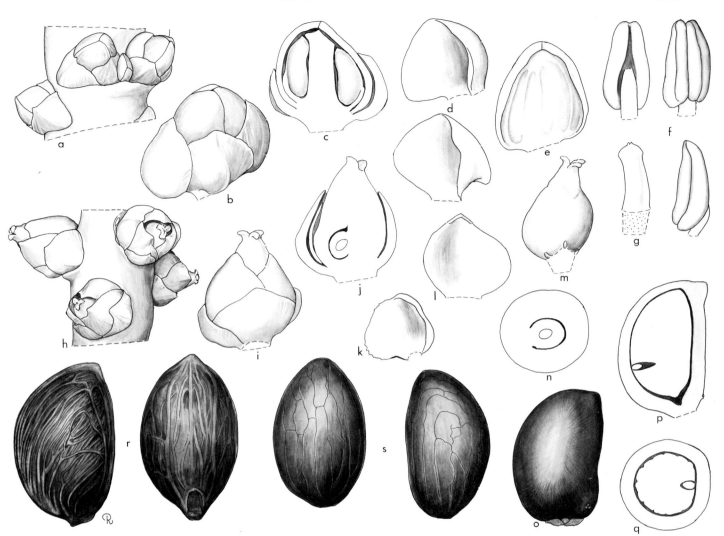

90.—**Chrysalidocarpus. a,** portion of rachilla with triads ×6; **b,** staminate bud ×12; **c,** staminate bud in vertical section ×12; **d,** staminate sepal in 2 views ×12; **e,** staminate petal, interior view ×12; **f,** stamen in 3 views ×12; **g,** pistillode ×12; **h,** portion of rachilla with triads, staminate flowers fallen ×6; **i,** pistillate flower ×9; **j,** pistillate flower in vertical section ×9; **k,** pistillate sepal ×9; **l,** pistillate petal ×9; **m,** gynoecium and staminodes ×9; **n,** ovary in cross-section ×12; **o,** fruit ×2¼; **p,** fruit in vertical section ×2¼; **q,** fruit in cross-section ×2¼; **r,** endocarp in 2 views ×3; **s,** seed in 2 views ×3. *Chrysalidocarpus lutescens*: **a-g,** *Moore 9018*; **h-n,** *Read 1410*; **o-s,** *Moore s.n.*

littoral forest, others to lowlands, and others to montane forest including rocky and mossy facies. *C. lutescens,* occurring in the wild on sand dunes and along watercourses, is now one of the most widespread and tolerant of all cultivated palms. Little is known of the natural history of *Chrysalidocarpus* species.

Common Names and Uses.—Areca palm, golden cane palm, yellow bamboo palm (*C. lutescens*), Cabada palm (*C. cabadae*). The apex of some species is bitter and inedible but of others is excellent and exploited as food. *C. lutescens* is a widespread and important ornamental.

Notes.—The genus is much in need of a modern reassessment. *Macrophloga* was separated by Beccari (1914a) based on material of *Chrysalidocarpus decipiens* with ruminate endosperm; however, this new genus is now thought to have been based on a mixture.

Taxonomic Accounts.—Beccari (1914a), Jumelle and Perrier de la Bâthie (1945).

Plate.—55D; Fig. G8.

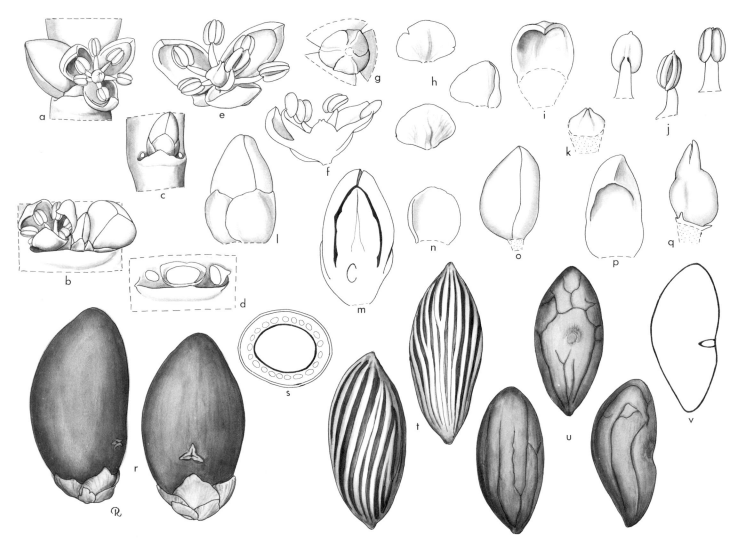

91.—Neophloga. a, portion of rachilla with pair of staminate flowers ×7½; b, portion of rachilla with triad ×7½; c, triad, staminate flowers fallen ×7½; d, triad, flowers removed to show subtending bract and bracteoles ×7½; e, staminate flower ×12; f, staminate flower in vertical section ×12; g, staminate calyx, bottom view ×12; h, staminate sepals ×12; i, staminate petal ×12; j, stamen in 3 views ×18; k, pistillode ×18; l, pistillate bud ×15; m, pistillate flower in vertical section ×15; n, pistillate sepal ×15; o, pistillate bud, calyx removed ×15; p, pistillate petal ×15; q, gynoecium ×15; r, fruit in 2 views ×4½; s, fruit in cross-section ×4½; t, endocarp in 2 views ×4½; u, seed in 3 views ×4½; v, seed in vertical section ×4½. Neophloga lanceolata: all from Moore 9000.

91. NEOPHLOGA Baillon, Bulletin Mensuel de la Société Linnéenne de Paris 2:1173. 1894. Type: N. pygmaea Pichi-Sermolli (N. commersoniana Beccari 1914, (non (Martius) Baillon 1895).

Dypsidium Baillon, Bulletin Mensuel de la Société Linnéenne de Paris 2:1172. 1894. Lectotype: D. catatianum Baillon (see Beccari and Pichi-Sermolli 1955) (=Neophloga catatiana (Baillon) Beccari).

Haplodypsis Baillon, Bulletin Mensuel de la Société Linnéenne de Paris 2:1167. 1894. Type: H. pervillei Baillon (=Neophloga pervillei (Baillon) Beccari).

Haplophloga Baillon, Bulletin Mensuel de la Société Linnéenne de Paris 2:1168. 1894. Type: H. poivreana Baillon (=Neophloga poivreana (Baillon) Beccari).

Slender or diminutive, solitary or clustered, unarmed, pleonanthic, monoecious palms. Stem eventually bare, ringed with leaf scars, often bearing hairs. Leaves few, pinnate, entire or bifid; sheaths tubular, often forming a crownshaft, glabrous or variously scaly or hairy, often terminating in a triangular ligule opposite the petiole or in 2 lateral auricles; petiole well developed or absent; leaflets few to many, regular or grouped, single-fold or many-fold, acute, acuminate, or praemorse, lanceolate to almost sigmoid, the apical pair usually compound and with lobed or praemorse tips, or blade entire and shallowly to deeply bifid, with lobed tips, blade glabrous or hairy. Inflorescences solitary, interfoliar, unbranched or branching to 1–2 orders; prophyll tubular, inserted at the base of the peduncle or higher, 2-keeled, membranous, variously scaly or hairy, persistent; peduncular bract 1 (rarely 2), inserted above and usually longer than the prophyll, tubular, sometimes enclosing the inflorescence in bud, persistent or deciduous; peduncle flattened, much longer than the rachis; rachis bearing spirally arranged first-order branches, all branches glabrous or conspicuously hairy; rachillae slender, pendulous or spreading, bearing spirally arranged, usually rather distant, superficial triads throughout their length except at the tip where bearing paired or solitary staminate flowers; bracts subtending triads conspicuous, rounded to triangular, liplike; floral bracteoles very small. Staminate flowers relatively large; sepals 3, distinct, imbricate, rounded to broadly triangular, dorsally keeled; petals 3, distinct, boat-shaped, valvate, striate; stamens 6, equal, filaments slender, sometimes inflexed at the tip, anthers narrow, elongate, medifixed, apically pointed, versatile; pollen elliptic to subcircular, monosulcate or rarely trichotomosulcate, with scabrate to finely reticulate, tectate exine; pistillode conspicuous, conical or columnar, trifid, ± as long as filaments. Pistillate flowers slightly larger than staminate; sepals 3, distinct, imbricate, ± rounded; petals 3, distinct, broadly triangular, basally imbricate, briefly valvate at the tip; staminodes 6, small, toothlike; gynoecium pure white, ± oblong in bud, trilocular, 2 locules aborting, stigmas 3, triangular, connivent in bud, obliquely apical and spreading at anthesis, uniovulate, ovule laterally attached, form unknown. Fruit brightly colored, usually red, ovoid to narrow-ellipsoidal, sometimes curved, stigmatic remains basal or lateral near the base; epicarp smooth, mesocarp fleshy with an inner fibrous layer, endocarp thin. Seed conforming to the fruit shape, basally attached, raphe branches few, anastomosing, endosperm homogeneous; embryo lateral in the middle or near the base. Germination and eophyll not recorded. Cytology not studied.

Anatomy. — See Tomlinson (1961) for a summary of some brief notes on the anatomy of the leaf, stem, and root by Achilli (1913).

Distribution. — About 29 species confined to Madagascar.

Ecology. — Diminutive palms of the undergrowth in lowland and montane tropical rain forest, including mossy forest.

Common Names and Uses. — Ambosa, Ambolo. Species of *Neophloga* do not appear to have precise local uses but all species are highly decorative and would make excellent ornamentals.

Notes. — *Neophloga* is scarcely separable from *Chrysalidocarpus*; however, until more observations are made in the field and floral morphology is better understood, we feel it best to maintain two genera.

Taxonomic Account. — Jumelle and Perrier de la Bâthie (1945).

Plate. — 56A.

92. **NEODYPSIS** Baillon, Bulletin Mensuel de la Société Linnéenne de Paris 2:1772. 1894. Type: **N. lastelliana** Baillon.

Small, moderate or tall, solitary or clustering, unarmed, pleonanthic, monoecious palms. Stem erect, never branched, conspicuously ringed with leaf scars. Leaves pinnate, neatly abscising, sometimes conspicuously 3-ranked; sheaths usually splitting opposite the petiole, a crownshaft not always developed, sometimes with a ligulelike structure opposite the petiole, glabrous to very densely covered with scales and/or white wax; petiole absent to well developed, abaxially rounded, adaxially channeled, bearing indumentum like the sheath; rachis straight or curved, adaxially angled or with 2 lateral grooves, abaxially rounded or strongly angled, indumentum as on the sheath; leaflets single-fold, numerous, acute to acuminate, often briefly bifid, ± linear, rigid or flexuous, regularly arranged or grouped and fanned within the group giving a plumose appearance, margins sometimes thickened, glabrous or with conspicuous ramenta along the abaxial midrib, sometimes also with minute scattered scales and abundant wax, transverse veins sometimes conspicuous. Inflorescences usually large, interfoliar or infrafoliar or becoming infrafoliar with age, branched to 3 orders; peduncle short or long, large, winged, and sometimes swollen at the base; prophyll tubular, 2-keeled, large, very coriaceous to woody, glabrous, scaly, or hairy, splitting apically; peduncular bract 1, tubular, ± beaked, longer than the prophyll, enclosing the inflorescence in bud, splitting longitudinally and deciduous, indumentum as on the prophyll; rachis shorter or longer than the peduncle; rachis bracts low, collarlike, inconspicuous; first-order branches spirally arranged, the proximal branched, the distal unbranched, proximal branches with bare portion at base, all branches variously hairy or glabrous; rachillae numerous, short to elongate, bearing spirally arranged, rather conspicuous, triangular bracts forming the lower lips of shallow crowded pits, each enclosing a triad or near the tips of the rachillae enclosing paired or solitary staminate flowers. Staminate flowers ± oblong in bud, symmetrical; sepals 3, distinct, imbricate, ± rounded, dorsally keeled; petals 3, twice to 4 times as long as sepals, boat-shaped, valvate, basally connate (? always); stamens 6, ± equal, filaments long, tapering, inflexed at the apex, anthers dorsifixed, versatile, oblong, latrorse; pollen elliptic, monosulcate, with scabrate, tectate exine; pistillode conspicuous, 3-angled, pointed. Pistillate flowers not larger than the staminate; sepals distinct, imbricate, laterally winged; petals 3, twice as long as the sepals, distinct, imbricate except for thickened valvate tips; staminodes 6, strapshaped or toothlike; gynoecium gibbous, unilocular but

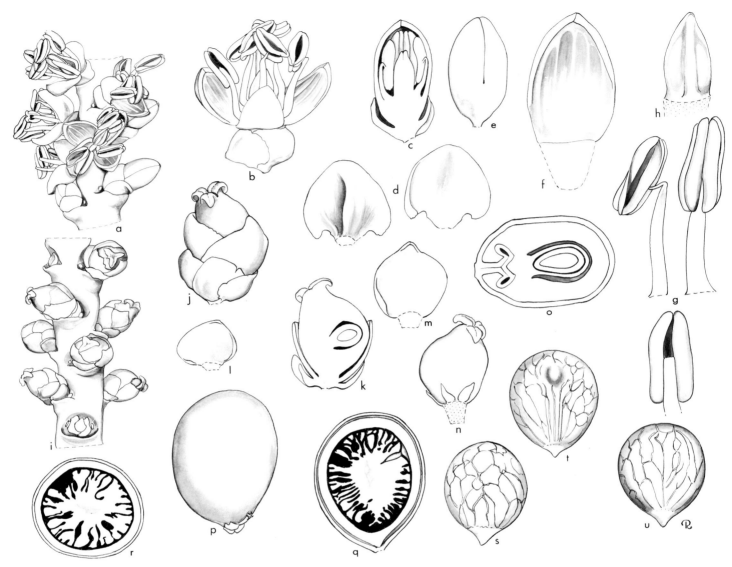

92.—**Neodypsis. a,** portion of rachilla at staminate anthesis ×3; **b,** staminate flower ×6; **c,** staminate bud in vertical section ×6; **d,** staminate sepals in 2 views ×12; **e,** staminate flower, sepals removed ×6; **f,** staminate petal, interior view ×12; **g,** stamen in 3 views ×12; **h,** pistillode ×12; **i,** portion of rachilla at pistillate anthesis ×3; **j,** pistillate flower after fertilization ×6; **k,** pistillate flower in vertical section ×6; **l,** pistillate sepal, interior view ×6; **m,** pistillate petal, interior view ×6; **n,** gynoecium and staminodes ×6; **o,** ovary in cross-section ×12; **p,** fruit ×1½; **q,** fruit in vertical section ×1½; **r,** fruit in cross-section ×1½; **s, t, u,** seed in 3 views ×1½. *Neodypsis decaryi*: all from *Read 827bis*.

with 2 small abortive locules, uniovulate, stigmas 3, triangular, becoming reflexed, ovule laterally attached, form unknown. Fruit ovoid, broadly ellipsoidal, or globose, stigmatic remains basal, perianth persistent; epicarp smooth, mesocarp fleshy with or without an inner fibrous layer, endocarp thin. Seed basally attached, obovoid, sometimes pointed at the base, raphe branches numerous, loosely anastomosing, endosperm very shallowly to deeply ruminate; embryo lateral above or below the middle. Germination adjacent-ligular; eophyll bifid. $n = 16$ (*N. decaryi*, Eichhorn 1957, Read 1966).

Anatomy.—Only the leaf of *N. decaryi* has been studied and the anatomy of the blade resembles that of other members of the Dypsidinae (Tomlinson 1961).

Distribution.—Fourteen species confined to Madagascar.

Ecology.—Mesophyll forest and tropical rain forest including mossy montane rain forest at altitudes from sea level to 2000 m.

Common Names and Uses. — Madagascar three-sided palm, triangle palm (*N. decaryi*). The apex can be eaten but is poisonous in some species. Several species are extremely elegant ornamentals.

Notes. — At present, *Neodypsis* is separable from *Chrysalidocarpus* only by the ruminate endosperm; this is obviously of questionable value. A careful study of the Madagascar palms is planned and until then, the genera are maintained.

Taxonomic Account. — Jumelle and Perrier de la Bâthie (1945).

Plate. — 56B; Figs. G.4, G.5.

Antongilia H. Jumelle, Annales de l'Institut Botanico-Géologique Colonial de Marseille. ser. 4. 6(2): 19. 1928. Type: **A. perrieri** H. Jumelle.

Antongilia was separated from *Neodypsis* by Jumelle on the basis of two characters: the anthers, which are described as sagittate, basifixed, and strongly spreading at the base, and the strangely fibrous endocarp. Beccari and Pichi-Sermolli (1955) follow Jumelle but comment that there is little in Jumelle's description to indicate whether there really are any differences except in the anthers. The type, *Perrier 11946,* has 6 ± equal stamens; however they are neither basifixed nor strongly sagittate, but are ± dorsifixed (perhaps not inflexed), and with a distinct pistillode in the middle. We can see no reason why this is not a species of *Neodypsis,* albeit an unusual one.

93. **Phloga** Noronha ex J. D. Hooker in Bentham & J. D. Hooker, Genera Plantarum 3:877, 909. 1883. Type: **P. nodifera** (Martius) Noronha ex Salomon (*Dypsis nodifera* Martius).

Small, solitary or clustering, unarmed, pleonanthic, monoecious palms. Stem ± erect, slender, conspicuously ringed with leaf scars. Leaves numerous, irregularly pinnate; sheaths tubular, not forming a well defined crownshaft, neatly abscising, apically with or without a ligulelike structure opposite the petiole, bearing dense caducous scales or tomentum; petiole absent or very short; rachis elongate, adaxially grooved near the base, abaxially rounded, angled distally, covered in caducous scales or tomentum; leaflets single-fold, numerous, threadlike at the base of the leaf, otherwise lanceolate and abruptly acuminate in a reflexed drip-tip, arranged in opposite or alternate groups of 2–7 or, rarely near the base solitary and almost regularly arranged, crowded within the groups, the insertion on the rachis usually grossly swollen, blade adaxially glabrous, abaxially with sparse minute scales along the main veins, transverse veinlets not visible. Inflorescences solitary, infrafoliar, usually several in various stages of development on the same stem, erect in bud, later spreading, branched to 3 orders basally, to 1 order

distally, apparently protandrous; peduncle elongate, ± crescentic to elliptic in cross-section, winged at the very base, densely tomentose; prophyll tubular, somewhat flattened, 2-keeled, almost as long as the peduncle, enclosing the inflorescence in bud, thinly coriaceous, variously scaly, persistent, splitting at the tip allowing the inflorescence to expand; peduncular bract 1, inserted some distance above the prophyll, slightly protruding through the split prophyll apex, tubular, deciduous leaving a persistent low collar; rachis equalling or longer than the peduncle; rachis bracts numerous, very small, triangular, not sheathing, spirally arranged; first-order branches with a short to elongate bare basal portion; rachillae slender, flexuous, curved, elongate, minutely scaly, bearing spirally arranged, small, triangular or rounded, membranous bracts forming the lower lip of shallow pits, each bearing a triad except at the very tips of the rachillae where bearing solitary or paired staminate flowers only; floral bracteoles small, membranous, minutely toothed. Staminate flowers very small (among the smallest in the family), ± globose; sepals 3, distinct, imbricate, ± rounded, membranous, minutely toothed, abaxially keeled; petals 3, valvate, ± striate, ± twice as long as the sepals, broadly triangular, basally briefly connate; stamens 6, in 2 whorls of 3, filaments distinct, very fleshy, ± spindle-shaped, anthers rounded, didymous, ± divergent or pendulous, very small, introrse, the connective short and thickened; pollen elliptic to circular, monosulcate, with intectate, baculate exine; pistillode very small, 3-lobed or conical. Pistillate flowers slightly larger than the staminate, ± ovate-conical; sepals 3, distinct, imbricate, abaxially keeled, ± rounded, ± membranous; petals 3, distinct, ± rounded, broadly imbricate except at the short valvate tips; staminodes 6, minute, toothlike; ovary globose-gibbous, stigmas 3, slightly eccentric, slender, fertile locule 1, ovule apparently ± lateral, form unknown. Fruit 1-seeded, slightly asymmetrical, narrowly ellipsoidal, apparently bright red, the stigmatic remains basal, perianth whorls persistent; epicarp smooth, mesocarp thin, fleshy, internally with numerous longitudinal fibers, endocarp thin, ± fibrous. Seed ± ellipsoidal, basally attached, raphe branches sparse, anastomosing, endosperm deeply ruminate; embryo lateral. Germination and eophyll not recorded. Cytology not studied.

Anatomy. — See Tomlinson (1961) for a summary of leaf anatomy as described by Achilli (1913). Tomlinson notes that *Neophloga, Phloga,* and *Dypsis* are almost identical in leaf anatomy.

Distribution. — Two species endemic to Madagascar.

Ecology. — Lowland to montane rain forest at altitudes of 0–2000 m above sea level.

Common Names and Uses. — Common names unknown. The stems of *P. gracilis* are apparently used in the manufacture of blow pipes. Both species are very elegant and would make fine ornamental subjects.

Notes. — Like so many of the Madagascar genera *Phloga* remains poorly known.

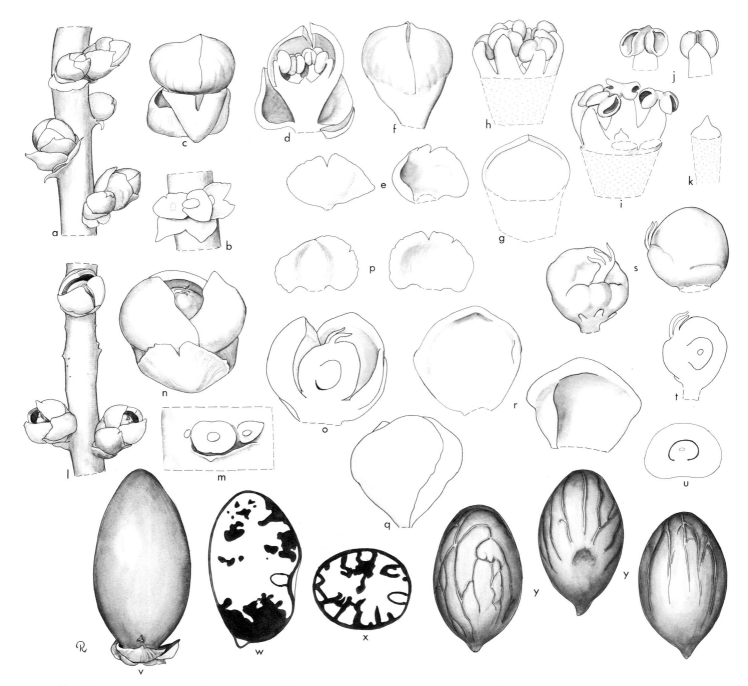

93.—**Phloga. a,** portion of rachilla with triads ×7½; **b,** triad, flowers removed to show subtending bract and bracteoles ×12; **c,** staminate bud ×15; **d,** staminate bud in vertical section ×15; **e,** staminate sepal in 2 views ×15; **f,** staminate bud, sepals removed ×15; **g,** staminate petal ×15; **h,** androecium ×22½; **i,** androecium, two stamens removed to show pistillode ×22½; **j,** stamen in 2 views ×22½; **k,** pistillode ×22½; **l,** portion of rachilla at pistillate anthesis ×6; **m,** triad, flowers removed to show subtending bract and bracteoles ×12; **n,** pistillate flower ×15; **o,** pistillate flower in vertical section ×15; **p,** pistillate sepal in 2 views ×15; **q,** pistillate petal in 2 views ×15; **r,** pistillate petal in 2 views ×15; **s,** gynoecium in 2 views ×15; **t,** gynoecium in vertical section ×15; **u,** ovary in cross-section ×15; **v,** fruit ×6; **w,** seed in vertical section ×6; **x,** seed in cross-section ×6; **y,** seed in 3 views ×6. *Phloga nodifera*: **a, b** and **v-y,** *Baron 4465*; **c-u,** *Baron 1881*.

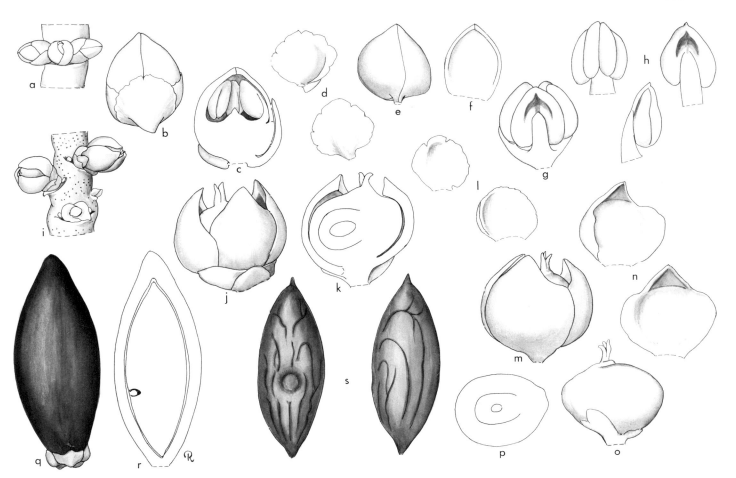

94.—**Dypsis. a,** triad ×7½; **b,** staminate bud ×18; **c,** staminate bud in vertical section ×18; **d,** staminate sepal in 2 views ×18; **e,** staminate buds, sepals removed ×18; **f,** staminate petal ×18; **g,** androecium ×24; **h,** stamen in 3 views ×24; **i,** portion of rachilla, all staminate and lowermost pistillate flower fallen, note bracts and bracteoles ×6; **j,** pistillate flower ×15; **k,** pistillate flower in vertical section ×15; **l,** pistillate sepals ×15; **m,** pistillate flower, sepals removed ×15; **n,** pistillate petal in 2 views ×15; **o,** gynoecium ×15; **p,** ovary in cross-section ×15; **q,** fruit ×4½; **r,** fruit in vertical section ×4½; **s,** seed in 2 views ×4½. *Dypsis louvelii*: **a–f** and **i–s,** *Moore 9021;* **g** and **h,** *Moore 9905.*

Taxonomic Account.—Jumelle and Perrier de la Bâthie (1945).

Plate.—56C.

94. **DYPSIS** Noronha ex Martius, Historia Naturalis Palmarum 3:180. 1837. Lectotype: **D. forficifolia** Martius (see Beccari and Pichi-Sermolli 1955).

Adelodypsis Beccari, Botanische Jahrbücher für Systematik 38 (Beiblatt 87):16. 1906. Type: *A. gracilis* (Bory) Beccari (*Dypsis gracilis* Bory) (=*D. pinnatifrons* Martius).

Trichodypsis Baillon, Bulletin Mensuel de la Société Linnéenne de Paris 2:1165. 1894. Type: *T. hildebrandtii* Baillon (=*Dypsis hildebrandtii* (Baillon) Beccari).

Moderate to slender or diminutive, solitary or clustered, unarmed, pleonanthic, monoecious palms. Stem even-tually bare, ringed with leaf scars, occasionally with hairs. Leaves few, pinnate or entire and bifid; sheaths tubular, often forming a crownshaft, variously scaly or hairy, often terminating in a triangular ligule opposite the petiole or in 2 lateral auricles; petiole well developed or absent, variously scaly or hairy; leaflets few to many, regular or grouped, single-fold or many-fold, acute, acuminate, or sometimes with a long tip, lanceolate to sigmoid, the apical pair usually compound and with lobed tips, or blade entire and shallowly to very deeply bifid, glabrous to hairy. Inflorescences solitary, interfoliar, unbranched, or branching to 2, or rarely to 4 orders; peduncle flattened, shorter or longer than the rachis; prophyll tubular, inserted at the base or higher on the peduncle; peduncular bract 1, usually inserted some distance above and longer than the prophyll, not enclosing the inflorescence; rachis shorter or longer than the peduncle, bearing spirally arranged first-order branches, all branches glabrous to conspicuously hairy; rachillae slender, sometimes very short, more often elongate, flexuous or rigid, bearing spirally arranged, usually rather distant triads throughout their length, except at the tip where bearing solitary or paired staminate flowers, flowers rarely slightly sunken in pits; rachilla bracts rounded or triangular, sometimes conspicuously ciliate-hairy. Staminate flowers minute; sepals 3, distinct, imbricate, striate, sometimes with ciliate margins; petals 3, distinct, valvate, boat-shaped, not more than 3 times as long as the sepals, usually shorter; androecium of 3 types, fertile stamens always 3: 1) in subgenus *Dypsis* stamens antesepalous, filaments very short, hardly joined at the base, anther locules more or less adnate to the thick connective, abortive stamens absent; 2) in subgenus *Trichodypsis,* fertile stamens antepetalous, alternating with rudimentary stamens, filaments connate briefly in a short cupule, anthers as above; 3) in subgenus *Adelodypsis,* stamens antesepalous, abortive stamens lacking, filaments linear, not connate at the base, anthers pendulous; pollen elliptic to circular, monosulcate, with intectate, baculate exine; pistillode minute, trifid, much shorter than to equalling the stamens or not evident. Pistillate flowers similar to the staminate; sepals 3, distinct, rounded, imbricate, irregularly splitting; petals 3, distinct, imbricate with minutely triangular valvate tips; staminodes 6, minute, toothlike; gynoecium gibbous, stigmas 3, awl-shaped, slightly eccentric, 2 locules aborting, 1 with laterally attached ovule, form unknown. Fruit ovoid to narrowly spindle-shaped, straight or curved, usually asymmetrical, bright red at maturity, stigmatic remains lateral near the base; epicarp smooth, mesocarp fleshy, fibrous, endocarp very thin. Seed conforming to shape of the fruit, erect, basally attached, raphe branches large, few, endosperm homogeneous; embryo lateral near the base. Germination and eophyll unrecorded. Cytology not studied.

Anatomy. — Leaf anatomy of a few species has been examined (Tomlinson 1961).

Distribution. — Twenty-one species endemic to Madagascar.

Ecology. — Lowland to montane rain forest.

Common Names and Uses. — Dypsis palms. Stems of some species have been used in the manufacture of blow pipes; many species are beautiful in form and would make elegant ornamentals.

Notes. — These are among the smallest palms and have quite remarkable staminate flowers, having only three stamens in various arrangements. However, relationships between the three sections of the genus and between the genus and other members of the Dypsidinae need further study.

Taxonomic Account. — Jumelle and Perrier de la Bâthie (1945).

Plate. — *56D; Figs. G.20, G.21.*

Euterpeinae J. Dransfield & N. Uhl, Principes 30: 9. 1986. Type: **Euterpe.**

Small to large, unarmed; crownshafts present or not well differentiated; leaves pinnate or pinnately ribbed; leaflets

Map 35. — **Distribution of Euterpeinae.**

entire; inflorescences infrafoliar, rarely interfoliar, branched to 1 order or rarely spicate; prophyll not basally adnate to the peduncle; peduncular bract slightly to markedly exserted from the prophyll before anthesis; staminate flowers usually asymmetrical, ± acute; filaments usually inflexed; petals of pistillate flowers imbricate; gynoecium pseudomonomerous; stigmatic remains various.

This subtribe of six genera includes all the pseudomonomerous members of the Areceae in the New World except *Roystonea* (Map 35). They inhabit lowland or montane rain forest from the West Indies south through Central America to Peru, Paraguay and Argentina. The genera share pinnate or pinnately veined leaves, inflorescences branched to 1 order or rarely spicate, a unilocular gynoecium, and rather thin fruit walls. *Euterpe* and *Prestoea,* and *Oenocarpus* and *Jessenia* seem more closely related to each other than to other genera of the group. The lack of a crownshaft (as in some of these taxa), superficial triads of flowers present throughout the rachillae, the simple fruit wall, and chromosome numbers of 18 are characters that appear to be unspecialized in the pseudomonomerous members of the Areceae.

Key to the Genera of the Euterpeinae

1 Inflorescences hippuriform (resembling a horse's tail); adaxial surface of the rachis lacking branches, rachillae all lateral or abaxial, curved and pendulous; prophyll much shorter than the peduncular bract, the latter terete, beaked; embryo large, about ⅔ as long as the seed 2

1 Inflorescences not hippuriform; the rachis bearing spirally inserted branches on all sides, or spicate; prophyll and peduncular bracts nearly equal or unequal; embryo small, much less than ½ as long as the seed 3

2 Lower surfaces of leaflets waxy; staminate flowers with 6 stamens; endosperm usually homogeneous. Central and South America .... 98. **Oenocarpus**

2 Lower surfaces of leaflets with peltate, sickle-shaped, or doubly sickle-shaped hairs; staminate flowers with 9–20 stamens; endosperm ruminate. Panama and South America north of the Amazon .... 99. **Jessenia**

3 Inner stamens markedly adnate to the pistillode in staminate flowers; sepals of pistillate flowers connate basally; stigmatic remains basal in fruit. Costa Rica to Peru .... 100. **Hyospathe**

3 Stamens not adnate to the pistillode in staminate flowers; sepals of pistillate flowers imbricate; stigmatic remains apical or lateral 4

4 Acaulescent or stem very short; inflorescence spicate; stigmatic remains apical. Costa Rica and northern Panama .... 97. **Neonicholsonia**

4 Stems short, moderate, or tall; inflorescence branched to 1 order; stigmatic remains lateral 5

5 Crownshaft clearly defined; petiole short; inflorescence branches densely white to dark brown-tomentose, spreading, pendulous from a somewhat dorsiventrally flattened rachis, usually not markedly enlarged at the base; prophyll and peduncular bract about equal or unequal, peduncular bract beaked, inserted close to prophyll; flowers often borne in pits. Lesser Antilles, Central and South America .... 95. **Euterpe**

5 Crownshaft usually not clearly defined except in a few species but then leaf sheaths tubular but partly open; petiole usually long; inflorescence branches glabrous to lightly hairy or scaly, stiffly ascending or divaricate in all directions, often markedly bulbous at the base; prophyll and peduncular bract markedly unequal, the peduncular bract longer, terete and beaked, usually inserted some distance above the prophyll; flowers superficial. West Indies, Nicaragua south to Brazil and Peru .... 96. **Prestoea**

95. EUTERPE Martius, Historia Naturalis Palmarum 2:28. 1823; emended 3:165. 1837; 3:230 (ed. 2). 1845 (conserved name). Type: **E. oleracea** Martius (conserved type).

Catis O. F. Cook, Bulletin of the Torrey Botanical Club 28:557. 1901. Type: *C. martiana* O. F. Cook (illegitimate name) (= *Euterpe oleracea* Martius).

Plectis O. F. Cook, Bulletin of the Torrey Botanical Club 31:352. 1904. Type: *P. oweniana* O. F. Cook (=*Euterpe macrospadix* Oersted).

Rooseveltia O. F. Cook, Smithsonian Miscellaneous Collections 98(7):21. 1939. Type: *R. frankliniana* O. F. Cook (=*Euterpe macrospadix* Oersted).

Moderate to large, solitary or clustered, unarmed, pleonanthic, monoecious palms. Stem erect, sometimes slender, obscurely to distinctly ringed with leaf scars, gray to white, base sometimes enlarged. Leaves few in crown, often spreading, pinnate; sheath elongate, tubular, usually forming a prominent crownshaft, smooth, variously glaucous, tomentose, or with scales, with or without a prominent, fibrous, adaxial ligule; petiole very short to moderate, slender, deeply concave adaxially, or flat with a central ridge, rounded abaxially, with scattered dark brown to blackish, branched scales or deciduous tomentum on both surfaces, usually denser adaxially; rachis slender, rounded abaxially, channeled adaxially near the base, distally angled, with dark brown to blackish scales more numerous adaxially; leaflets ± pendulous, narrow, lanceolate, single-fold, tips long-attenuate, pointed, midrib conspicuous, 1 or 2 pairs of large veins also evident, deciduous tattered scales often prominent abaxially along midribs and larger veins, other elliptic scales present or absent abaxially and near the base adaxially, transverse veinlets not evident. Inflorescences axillary, infrafoliar at anthesis, erect in bud, branched to 1 order; peduncle short, often dorsiventrally compressed, covered with scales, tomentum, or hairs, minutely brown-dotted or rarely glabrous; prophyll tubular, elongate, flattened dorsiventrally, inserted obliquely near the base of the peduncle, chartaceous, with scattered sometimes black, tattered-peltate scales, or ± glabrous, margins with wide flat keels, tip usually rounded, splitting abaxially below the tip; peduncular bract about as long as or longer than the prophyll, tubular, chartaceous, with scales as on the prophyll, tip pointed, hard, a second, incomplete, rather long, pointed peduncular bract sometimes present; rachis shorter or longer than the peduncle, covered with dense white, yellow to dark red tomentum; rachillae moderate to long, often slender, becoming pendulous, covered with dense white, orange, or dark brownish tomentum, and bearing rather close or distant, spirally arranged bracts, the proximal somewhat elongate, pointed, the distal smaller, often rounded, each subtending a triad of flowers at the base or more distally on the rachilla a pair of staminate or a single staminate flower, the pistillate flower sunken in a pit and surrounded by 2 rounded, stiff bracteoles, one usually larger, the 2 staminate flowers of the triad in shallow indentations above the pistillate flower. Staminate flowers elongate, pointed in bud; sepals 3, distinct, broadly imbricate, irregular, rounded to ± pointed, margins often tattered; petals 3, distinct, unequal, asymmetrical, valvate, the tips with short solid points; stamens 6, filaments short, linear, sometimes wider basally, anthers elongate, sagittate, medifixed, latrorse; pollen elliptic, monosulcate or sometimes trichotomosulcate, with finely reticulate or foveolate, tectate exine; pistillode 3-lobed, columnar. Pistillate flowers ovoid; sepals 3, distinct, imbricate, margins often lacerate, from ca. ¼ to ⅔ as long as the petals; petals 3, distinct, imbricate, margins irregular, tips with solid points; staminodes absent (? always); gynoecium ovoid, unilocular, uniovulate, stigmas 3 short, fleshy, recurved,

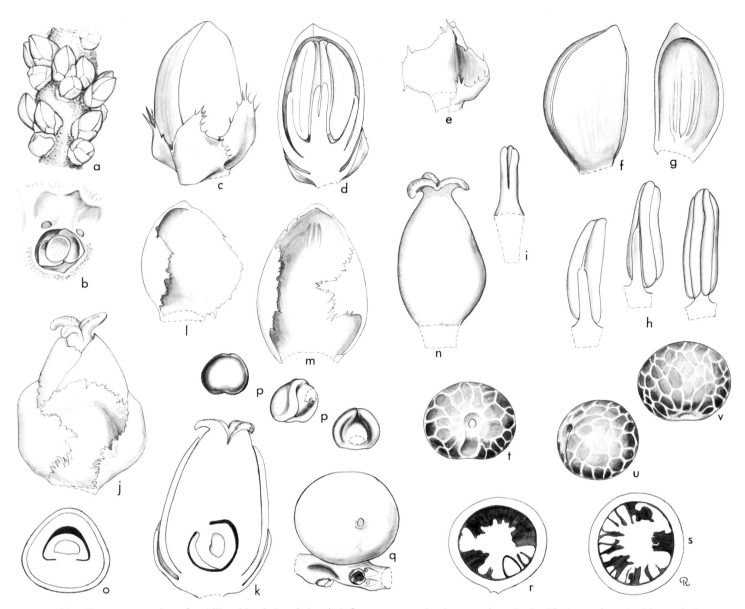

95.—**Euterpe. a,** portion of rachilla with triads ×3; **b,** triad, flowers removed ×6; **c,** staminate bud ×12; **d,** staminate bud in vertical section ×12; **e,** staminate sepal, interior view ×12; **f,** staminate flower, sepals removed ×12; **g,** staminate petal, interior view ×12; **h,** stamen in 3 views ×12; **i,** pistillode ×12; **j,** pistillate flower ×12; **k,** pistillate flower in vertical section ×12; **l,** pistillate sepal, interior view ×12; **m,** pistillate petal, interior view ×12; **n,** gynoecium ×12; **o,** ovary in cross-section ×12; **p,** ovule in 3 views ×12; **q,** fruit ×1½; **r,** fruit in vertical section ×1½; **s,** fruit in cross-section ×1½; **t, u, v,** seed in 3 views ×1½. *Euterpe cuatrecasana:* all from *Moore & Parthasarathy 9404.*

ovule probably hemianatropous, laterally attached. Fruit subglobose, small to moderate, single-seeded, stigmatic remains lateral to subapical; epicarp smooth, minutely pebbled when dry, mesocarp rather thin with radially arranged sclereid bundles and an inner layer of thin flat fibers, endocarp thin, crustaceous, tanniniferous. Seed globose, laterally attached, hilum elongate, ± 2-lobed, raphe branches forming a network, endosperm ruminate or homogeneous; embryo subbasal. Germination adjacent-ligular; eophyll bifid or pinnate with narrow leaflets. $n = 18$ (*E. oleracea,* Read and Moore 1967).

Anatomy.—Species studied (*E. broadwayae, E. oleracea,* Tomlinson 1961) lacked a hypodermis, had characteristic arrangements of fibrous bundles, and were considered rather distinct among arecoid palms. Further study of leaf anatomy is needed to determine whether such distinctions hold and how the species may vary. Floral anatomy has not been examined. See Elias de Paula (1975) for anatomy of root, leaflets, and fruits of *E. oleracea*.

Distribution. — About 28 species from the Lesser Antilles and Central America south through Brazil to Peru. A single distinctive species, *E. dominicana,* occurs in the Lesser Antilles.

Ecology. — Lowland rain forest and montane forests and swamps, often along rivers, but sometimes at higher elevations. *Euterpe* shares with *Geonoma* the widest altitudinal range of any palm in Colombia, both have species occurring in the swamps of Pacific shores and others reaching over 3000 m on mountain slopes (Dugand 1961).

Common Names and Uses. — Assai palms, Manaco. The "cabbage" is edible and much prized, being sweet and succulent and the most common source of hearts of palm in the Americas. Fruits of some species are used in preserves and beverages. Unopened inflorescences are made into pickles. The hard outer part of the stem may be used as planks, and leaves for thatch.

Notes. — A new treatment is much needed. In particular the differences between *Euterpe* and *Prestoea* need further study. See notes under *Prestoea*.

Taxonomic Accounts. — Burret (1929b). See also Moore (1963c), Read (1979), Galeano-Garces (1986).

Fig. — *G.12.*

96. **PRESTOEA** J. D. Hooker in Bentham & J. D. Hooker, Genera Plantarum 3:875, 899. 1883. (conserved name). Type: **P. pubigera** (Grisebach & H. A. Wendland) J. D. Hooker (*Hyospathe pubigera* Grisebach & H. A. Wendland).

Martinezia Ruiz & Pavon, Florae Peruvianae et Chilensis Prodromus. 148. 1794. Lectotype: *M. ensiformis* Ruiz & Pavon (see Burret 1933) (=*Prestoea ensiformis* (Ruiz & Pavon) H. E. Moore).

Oreodoxa Willdenow, Mémoires de l'Académie Royale des Sciences (Berlin) 1804:34. 1807. Lectotype: *O. acuminata* Willdenow (see Klotzsch, Linnaea 20:448. 1847) (rejected name) (=*Prestoea acuminata* (Willdenow) H. E. Moore).

Acrista O. F. Cook, Bulletin of the Torrey Botanical Club 28:555. 1901. Type: *A. monticola* O. F. Cook (=*Prestoea montana* (Graham) Nicholson).

Euterpe J. Gaertner *sensu* Beccari (non Martius)

Pomona College Journal of Economic Botany 2: 351. 1912.

Euterpe sect. *Euterpe* subsect. *Leiostachys* Burret, Botanische Jahrbücher für Systematik 63:50. 1929.

Euterpe sect. *Meteuterpe* Burret, Notizblatt des Botanischen Gartens und Museums zu Berlin-Dahlem 14:328. 1939.

Small to moderate, solitary or clustered, unarmed, pleonanthic, monoecious tree palms. Stem slender or relatively stout, brown or gray, sometimes swollen basally, leaf scars prominent or obscure, adventitious roots present or absent. Leaves regularly or irregularly pinnate, or undivided, curving or erect; sheath tubular, splitting opposite the petiole, usually not forming a distinct crownshaft (but *P. allenii* has a definite crownshaft), often scaly or tomentose, becoming glabrous; petiole usually elongate, rarely short, often slender, channeled adaxially, rounded abaxially, both surfaces densely dark tomentose or scaly, rachis channeled at the base, flat to ridged adaxially, rounded abaxially, densely tomentose (? always); leaflets long, narrow, opposite or subopposite, regularly arranged in one plane, shorter basally and distally, sometimes curved, tips pointed, edges often thickened, single-fold or several-fold distally or in partly entire leaves, midribs of folds prominent adaxially, other veins small, ± equal or 1–2 pairs slightly larger, blade adaxially ± glabrous, abaxially lightly tomentose, whitish dotlike hairs usually abundant, large to small tattered scales along the midrib and sometimes along larger veins, often waxy, transverse veinlets not evident. Inflorescences usually interfoliar in bud, becoming infrafoliar at anthesis or in fruit, branched to 1 order; peduncle short or long; prophyll markedly shorter than the peduncular bract, tubular, 2-keeled laterally, ± flat, splitting apically and dorsi-ventrally so as sometimes to appear bifid, inserted at the base of the peduncle, chartaceous to coriaceous, variously scaly; peduncular bract several times longer than the prophyll, terete, with a long hard beak, usually inserted some distance above the prophyll, chartaceous or coriaceous; rachis longer or shorter than the peduncle, bearing spirally arranged, short, thin, membranous or stiff, rounded or pointed bracts, each subtending a rachilla; rachillae slender, moderate to elongate, erect at first, becoming divaricate or stiffly ascending, sometimes markedly swollen or bulbous basally, rachis and rachillae densely covered with soft pale hairs or with dark red or brown tomentum or glabrous; rachilla bracts very shallow, membranous, subtending triads of flowers basally and paired to solitary staminate flowers distally, flowers superficial or in a slight depression, triads with the staminate flowers only slightly larger than and lateral to the pistillate, rarely (*P. cuatrecasasii*) the pistillate flower surrounded by 2 large bracteoles. Staminate flowers symmetrical or asymmetrical, ovoid, stalked or sessile; sepals 3, distinct and shortly imbricate basally or united in a low cupule, margins smooth or hairy with tufts of hairs at the tips, usually keeled to some extent; petals 3, ovate, distinct, valvate, tips valvate or appressed, margins smooth or hairy with tufts of hairs at the tips; stamens 6, filaments terete, briefly inflexed at the apex, anthers linear,

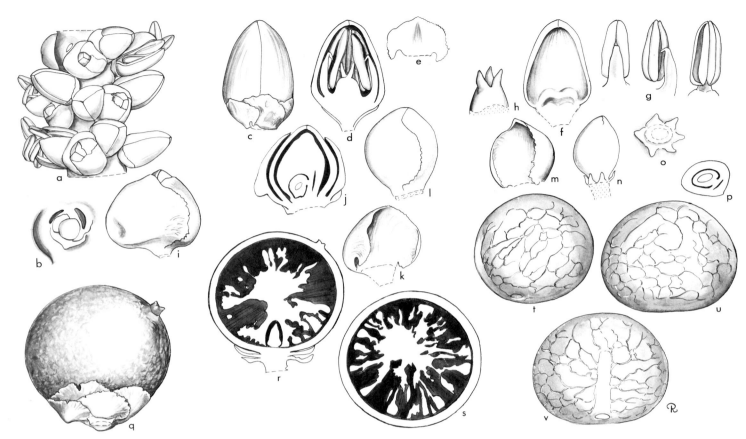

96.—**Prestoea. a,** portion of rachilla with staminate flowers and pistillate buds ×3; **b,** triad, flowers removed ×6; **c,** staminate bud ×6; **d,** staminate bud in vertical section ×6; **e,** staminate sepal ×6; **f,** staminate petal, interior view ×6; **g,** stamen in 3 views ×6; **h,** pistillode ×6; **i,** pistillate bud ×6; **j,** pistillate bud in vertical section ×6; **k,** pistillate sepal, interior view ×6; **l,** pistillate flower, sepals removed ×6; **m,** pistillate petal ×6; **n,** gynoecium and staminodes ×6; **o,** staminodes ×6; **p,** ovary in cross-section ×6; **q,** fruit ×3; **r,** fruit in vertical section ×3; **s,** fruit in cross-section ×3; **t, u, v,** seed in 3 views ×3. *Prestoea montana*: all from *Fischer & Ernst 858.*

acute or bifid apically, sagittate or free basally, dorsifixed slightly below the middle, latrorse; pollen elliptic, monosulcate, with finely reticulate or foveolate, tectate exine; pistillode columnar or trifid, light or dark. Pistillate flowers broadly ovoid; sepals 3, distinct, imbricate, rounded, margins smooth or hairy; petals 3, distinct, broadly imbricate, rounded, tips valvate; staminodes 6, small, tooth-like; gynoecium ovoid, asymmetrical, unilocular, uniovulate, style not evident, stigmas 3, appressed or reflexed, ovule large, basal, form unknown. Fruit rounded, dark purple to black at maturity (? always), perianth persistent, stigmatic remains subapical or near the middle; epicarp smooth or slightly irregular, mesocarp fleshy, with an inner layer of wide flat fibers, endocarp thin, crustaceous. Seed globose, laterally attached, hilum elongate, raphe branches numerous, anastomosing to form a network, endosperm ruminate or rarely (*P. cuatrecasasii, P. schultesiana*) homogeneous; embryo subbasal. Germination adjacent-ligular; eophyll bifid (e.g. *P. montana*) or pinnate (e.g. *P. decurrens*). n = 18 (*P. decurrens, P. longipetiolata,* Read and Moore 1967).

Anatomy.—Not studied.

Distribution.—About 28 species distributed throughout the West Indies, and from Nicaragua southward in Central America, and into Brazil and Peru. One extremely variable species (*P. montana*) is widespread in the Lesser Antilles and may be considered as several subspecies on further study (Read 1979).

Ecology.—Mostly on well drained slopes at moderate to rather high elevations. *P. montana* in the Lesser Antilles occurs in moist montane forest above 900 m.

Common Names and Uses.—Mountain cabbage palm (*P. montana*). The "cabbage" is edible (Hodge 1965), and some species are desirable ornamentals.

Notes.—The separation of *Prestoea* from *Euterpe* is still not clear. As delimited here (see key) there

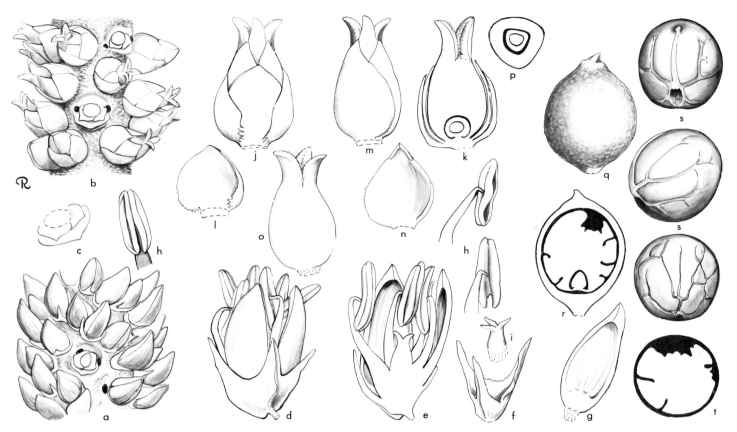

97.—**Neonicholsonia. a,** portion of spike at staminate anthesis ×3; **b,** portion of spike at pistillate anthesis ×3; **c,** bracteoles surrounding pistillate flower ×6; **d,** staminate flower ×6; **e,** staminate flower in vertical section ×6; **f,** staminate calyx ×6; **g,** staminate petal, interior view ×6; **h,** stamen in 3 views ×6; **i,** pistillode ×6; **j,** pistillate flower ×6; **k,** pistillate flower in vertical section ×6; **l,** pistillate sepal, interior view ×6; **m,** pistillate flower, sepals removed ×6; **n,** pistillate petal, interior view ×6; **o,** gynoecium ×6; **p,** ovary in cross-section ×6; **q,** fruit ×3; **r,** fruit in vertical section ×3; **s,** seed in 3 views ×3; **t,** seed in cross-section ×3. *Neonicholsonia watsonii:* all from *Huttleston 1943.*

are still some exceptional species which may be misplaced. Considerable field work and careful observation of all taxa is needed.

Taxonomic Accounts.—A complete treatment is much needed. See Read (1979), Moore (1980b), and Henderson (1986b).

Plate.—57A.

97. **NEONICHOLSONIA** Dammer, Gardeners' Chronicle series 3, 30:178. 1901. Lectotype: **N. watsonii** Dammer (see H. E. Moore 1951).

Bisnicholsonia O. Kuntze in Post and O. Kuntze, Lexicon Generum Phanerogamarum, 621 and inserenda. 1903 (superfluous name).

Woodsonia, L. H. Bailey, Gentes Herbarum 6:262. 1943. Type: *W. scheryi* L. H. Bailey (=*N. watsonii* Dammer).

Small, acaulescent or short, solitary (? always), unarmed, pleonanthic, monoecious palm. Stem rhizomatous, or very short, sheathed by leaf bases. Leaves pinnate; sheaths short, thin. fibrous, opening opposite the petiole, not forming a crownshaft; petiole moderate, slender, 4-sided; rachis 4-sided basally, distally angled adaxially, rounded abaxially, glabrous; leaflets lanceolate or linear, rather short, tapering to a point, opposite to subopposite, single-fold, distal pair sometimes united basally, thin and papery, adaxially glabrous, abaxially lightly waxy-tomentose, midrib prominent, transverse veinlets not evident or visible and short. Inflorescences solitary, interfoliar, spicate; peduncle very long, slender; prophyll short, 2-keeled laterally, splitting apically; peduncular bract much longer than the prophyll, terete, slender, beaked, splitting abaxially; flower bearing portion also elongate but shorter than the peduncle, densely hairy becoming glabrous, bearing spirally arranged, closely crowded, shallow, pointed bracts each subtending a triad basally and pairs or single staminate flowers distally; floral bracteoles conspicuous, shallow, pointed, the outer markedly larger than the inner. Staminate flowers lateral to the pistillate, somewhat variable, ovoid, curved in bud; sepals 3, basally connate for ½ their length in a short erect cupule with 3 long, narrow pointed tips, keeled or not; petals 3, distinct, valvate, about twice as long as the sepals, striate, grooved adaxially, narrow or rather broad, tips thickened; stamens 6, distinct or briefly connate basally, filaments awl-shaped, somewhat enlarged basally and adnate to pistillode, antesepalous filaments shorter, anthers elongate, medifixed, basally ± sagittate, versatile, latrorse, connective ± prolonged in a tip; pollen elliptic, monosulcate or rarely trichotomosulcate, with coarsely reticulate, tectate exine; pistillode short or slender and elongate, trifid apically or throughout. Pistillate flowers ovoid; sepals 3, distinct, partially imbricate, margins somewhat fringed, tips pointed, striate; petals like the sepals but tips thickened, valvate; staminodes lacking; gynoecium ovoid, unilocular, uniovulate, style not evident, stigma with 3 fleshy lobes, briefly reflexed, papillose adaxially, ovule basally attached, form unknown. Fruit ovoid, black when mature, irregular, remnants of 2 abortive carpels present, stigmatic remains apical to subapical forming a distinct beak; epicarp thin, smooth, mesocarp thin, composed of large, flat fibers, endocarp thin, crustaceous. Seed globose, hilum basal, raphe branches few, large, deeply sunken making the endosperm ruminate peripherally; embryo large, basal to subbasal. Germination adjacent-ligular; eophyll bifid, the tips further divided. $n = 18$ (Read 1966).

Anatomy.—Not studied.

Distribution.—One variable species in Panama and Nicaragua.

Ecology.—Found only in rain forest at low elevations from 0–250 m.

Common Names and Uses.—Not recorded.

Notes.—This palm is poorly known and certainly worthy of further study. The low habit and spicate inflorescence apparently led Moore (1973a) to consider it highly evolved in the *Euterpe* alliance. The peripheral rumination of the seed appears to result from deeply impressed raphe branches.

Taxonomic Account.—Moore (1951).

Fig.—*G.23.*

98. OENOCARPUS Martius, Historia Naturalis Palmarum 2:21. 1823. Lectotype: **O. bacaba** Martius (see H. E. Moore 1963c).

Moderate to large, solitary or clustered, unarmed (except for sharp fibers of leaf sheaths), pleonanthic, monoecious palms. Stem erect, densely covered in fibrous leaf sheaths, when mature becoming bare except rarely (*O. circumtextus*) fibrous network persistent, leaf scars smooth, flush with stem basally, swollen and prominent distally, a small mass of slender roots sometimes present basally. Leaves pinnate, spirally arranged or distichous, suberect when young, becoming spreading; sheath tightly clasping but not forming a distinct crownshaft, splitting at least partially opposite the petiole, thick, leathery, lightly furrowed adaxially, glabrous or scaly abaxially, margins disintegrating into moderate, uniform fibers; petiole short,

rarely elongate, channeled adaxially, rounded abaxially; leaflets regularly arranged in one plane or irregularly clustered, broadly lanceolate, acute to tapering, single-fold, blade adaxially glabrous, abaxially usually waxy, sparsely to densely covered in some species with needlelike to blunt hairs, midrib prominent, intermediate veins conspicuous, transverse veinlets not evident. Inflorescences interfoliar in bud, becoming infrafoliar, hippuriform (shaped like a horse's tail), protandrous, branched to 1 order laterally and abaxially, adaxial branches absent; peduncle short to elongate, flattened, tomentose; prophyll short, wide, adaxially flattened, 2-keeled, splitting abaxially, margins broadly toothed; peduncular bract much longer than the prophyll, terete, beaked, scaly; rachis longer than the peduncle but short, tapering, bearing spirally arranged, very small, slightly sunken, pointed to scalloped, thin bracts, adaxial ones abortive and evident only in young stages, lateral and abaxial bracts subtending rachillae; rachillae ± flexuous, pendulous, short to elongate, straight to slightly undulate, slender, tapering, bearing triads of flowers basally and pairs to single staminate flowers distally, rarely completely staminate, flowers borne in shallow depressions; rachilla bracts low, rounded with a short point, slightly sunken; floral bracteoles similar to rachilla bracts. Staminate flowers asymmetrical, pointed in bud; sepals 3, distinct, valvate, imbricate or briefly connate basally; petals 3, distinct, ovate, somewhat asymmetrical, valvate; stamens 6, filaments terete, slender, straight or variously curved and bent, distinctly inflexed at the apex, anthers elongate, basally free and sagittate, rounded or blunt apically, dorsifixed, versatile, connective not extending above locules, latrorse; pollen elliptic, monosulcate, with scabrate or reticulate, tectate exine; pistillode bifid or trifid. Pistillate flowers shorter than the staminate; sepals 3, distinct, suborbicular, imbricate, hooded; petals 3, distinct, imbricate except for valvate apices when young, otherwise like the sepals; staminodes toothlike or lacking; gynoecium ovoid, briefly stalked, unilocular, uniovulate, style short, cylindrical, bearing 3 fleshy stigmas, reflexed at anthesis, papillose adaxially. Fruit ellipsoidal to globose, dark purple when ripe, perianth persistent, stigmatic remains apical to slightly eccentric; epicarp smooth or minutely pebbled, waxy, mesocarp fleshy, oily, with internal fibers adnate to and covering the seed, endocarp apparently lacking. Seed ovoid-ellipsoidal to globose, hilum basal, raphe lateral, branches parallel, indistinct, endosperm homogeneous, striate, with central parenchymatous cavity; embryo basal, very large, extending through the endosperm into central cavity. Germination adjacent-ligular; eophyll bifid. Cytology not studied.

Anatomy.—Not studied.

Distribution.—Eight species ranging from Costa Rica and Panama to the Amazon and Orinoco Valleys in Colombia, Ecuador, Venezuela, Guyana, Surinam, French Guiana, Brazil, Peru, and Bolivia.

Ecology.—Rain forest species found on sandy soil of *terra firme* areas, along river margins.

Common Names and Uses.—Bacaba. Important for pericarp oil; the mesocarp provides a creamy

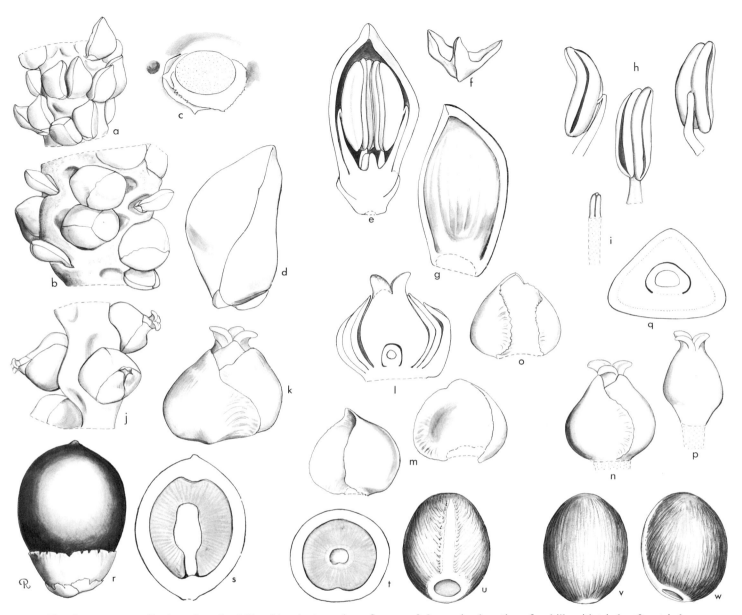

98.—**Oenocarpus. a,** distal portion of rachilla with paired staminate flowers ×3; **b,** proximal portion of rachilla with triads ×3; **c,** triad, flowers removed to show bracteoles ×6; **d,** staminate bud ×12; **e,** staminate bud in vertical section ×12; **f,** staminate calyx ×12; **g,** staminate petal, interior view ×12; **h,** stamen in 3 views ×12; **i,** pistillode ×12; **j,** portion of rachilla at pistillate anthesis ×3; **k,** pistillate flower ×6; **l,** pistillate flower in vertical section ×6; **m,** pistillate sepals in 2 views ×6; **n,** pistillate flower, sepals removed ×6; **o,** pistillate petal ×6; **p,** gynoecium ×6; **q,** ovary in cross-section ×12; **r,** fruit ×1½; **s,** fruit in vertical section ×1½; **t,** fruit in cross-section ×1½; **u, v, w,** seed in 3 views ×1½. *Oenocarpus mapora* subsp. *mapora:* **a–c,** *Moore et al. 8412;* **d–i,** *Moore et al. 8406;* **j–q,** *Moore et al. 8415;* **r–w,** *Moore & Parthasarathy 9479.*

drink. The "cabbage" is edible and good and the trunk is used for construction and spears. For more details see Balick (1980, 1985, 1986).

Notes.—Most closely related to *Jessenia* from which it differs in lacking sicklelike trichomes on abaxial leaf surfaces, in having only six stamens with filaments definitely inflexed in bud, and in homogeneous rather than ruminate endosperm.

Taxonomic Account.—Balick (1980, 1986).

Plate.—57B, C.

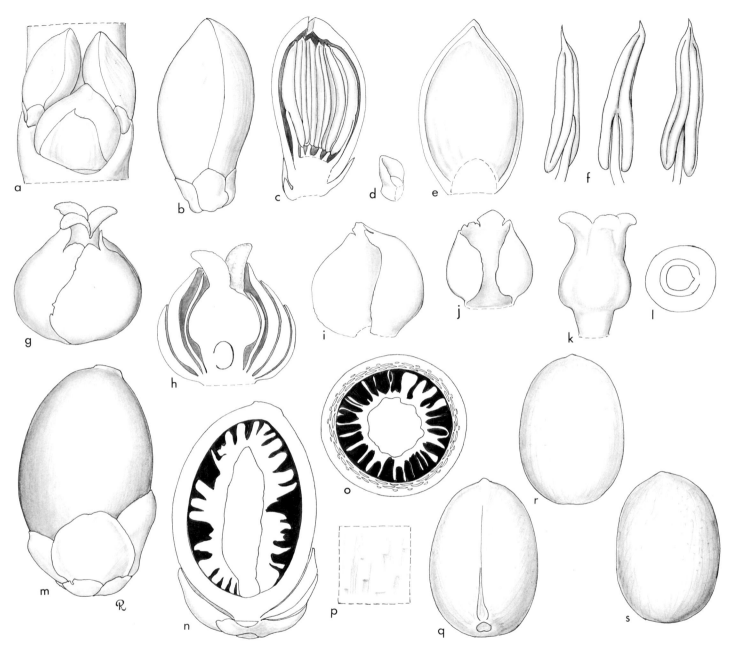

99.—**Jessenia. a,** portion of rachilla with triad ×3; **b,** staminate bud ×6; **c,** staminate bud in vertical section ×6; **d,** staminate sepal ×6; **e,** staminate petal ×6; **f,** stamen in 3 views ×9; **g,** pistillate flower ×6; **h,** pistillate flower in vertical section ×6; **i,** pistillate sepal ×6; **j,** pistillate petal ×6; **k,** gynoecium ×6; **l,** ovary in cross-section ×6; **m,** fruit ×1½; **n,** fruit in vertical section ×1½; **o,** fruit in cross-section ×1½; **p,** detail of fruit wall, much enlarged; **q, r, s,** seed in 3 views ×1½. *Jessenia bataua: a-f, Moore & Parthasarathy 9476; g-s, Steyermark & Fernandez 99604.*

99. JESSENIA H. Karsten, Linnaea 28:387. 1857. Type: *J. polycarpa* H. Karsten = **J. bataua** (Martius) Burret (*Oenocarpus bataua* Martius).

Large to massive, solitary, unarmed (except for sharp fibers on upper parts of leaf sheaths), pleonanthic, monoe-cious palm. Stem erect, stout, clothed in leaf sheaths, and sharp fibers, becoming bare and ringed with obscure or prominent leaf scars. Leaves numerous, ascending at first, later spreading, pinnate; sheath not forming a crownshaft, with a short ligule in front of the petiole, thick, leathery, lightly furrowed adaxially, glabrous abaxially, sheath tubular at first, later splitting opposite the petiole and disintegrating marginally into masses of hairlike black or brown fibers and fewer stout, sharp, knitting-needlelike fibers; petiole short, channeled adaxially, rounded abaxially; rachis deeply grooved adaxially at the base, 4-sided near the center, flat to concave, becoming triangular distally, with deciduous scales; leaflets drooping to stiffly spreading, single-fold, regularly arranged in a single plane, opposite to subalternate, broadly linear, acute, ± glabrous adaxially, densely covered abaxially with persistent, shining, pale, straw-colored or brownish, membranous, orbicular to transversely elliptical or sickle-shaped, medifixed scales, or with scattered, whitish, waxy. sickle-shaped hairs, midrib largest but other intermediate veins also large, transverse veinlets not evident. Inflorescences hippuriform (shaped like a horse's tail), solitary, interfoliar in bud becoming infrafoliar, branched to 1 order, protandrous; peduncle short, very stout; prophyll large, 2-keeled, ± beaked, adaxially flat, abaxially rounded, margins irregularly toothed, opening apically, adaxially glabrous, abaxially with deciduous tomentum; peduncular bract much longer than the prophyll, terete, beaked, splitting abaxially, striate, shed early with the prophyll, both surfaces covered in deciduous tomentum; rachis short, stout, lacking rachillae on the adaxial surface but often with empty rachis bracts and small bulges or warts, bearing crowded, spirally arranged rachillae on the lateral and abaxial sides; rachis bracts very small, flat, triangular; rachillae, long, slender, somewhat flexuous, pendulous, glabrous, bearing spirally arranged, rather distant triads of flowers in depressions basally or up to ⅔ the rachilla length, and closer pairs of staminate flowers distally, the rachilla equal or smaller in diameter where staminate, rarely an inflorescence completely staminate with a distally sterile part; rachilla bracts low, rounded, pointed or blunt, often scarcely distinguishable; floral bracteoles very small, inconspicuous, ± triangular. Staminate flowers lateral to and slightly above the pistillate, smaller than the pistillate; sepals 3, very short, connate and adnate basally to the receptacle, and there fleshy and slightly inflated, distinct, imbricate, broadly pointed above; petals 3, distinct, ovate, somewhat asymmetrical, valvate, fibrous, not depressed adaxially; stamens (7–8) 9–20, filaments awl-shaped, rather short, slightly inflexed at the tips, anthers elongate, dorsifixed just below the middle, free and somewhat sagittate basally, connective with a pronounced tip; pollen elliptic, monosulcate, with scabrate or reticulate, tectate exine; pistillode short, trifid. Pistillate flowers larger than the staminate at anthesis; sepals 3, broadly imbricate, margins irregular; petals 3, similar to the sepals but with briefly valvate apices, much thinner than the sepals in bud but becoming fleshy at maturity; staminodes lacking; gynoecium shortly stalked, trilobed, usually unilocular, uniovulate (rarely bilocular, biovulate, according to Balick, pers. comm.), style short, thick, bearing 3 large, fleshy stigmas, papillose adaxially, reflexed at anthesis, ovule basal, erect, anatropous. Fruit 1(–2)-seeded, large, oblong-ellipsoidal to almost globose, violet-purple to blackish with a glaucous bloom at maturity, perianth persistent, stigmatic remains apical to subapical; epicarp smooth, mesocarp fleshy with inner bands of large flat fibers, inner layer adnate to the seed. Seed ellipsoidal,

hilum basal, raphe narrow, tapering, endosperm ruminate, hollow in center; embyro basal, very large, extending beyond the middle of the seed. Germination adjacent ligular; eophyll bifid. Cytology not studied.

Anatomy.—Not studied.

Distribution.—A single species with two subspecies, the type subspecies in Panama, the Amazon and Orinoco Valleys, Andean foothills and Pacific coast; the other in northern Venezuela, Trinidad, Guyana, and Surinam (Balick, pers. comm.).

Ecology.—Rain forest palms occurring in large stands in periodically flooded areas and also on upland which is not inundated.

Common Names and Uses.—Seje palm, mille pesos palm, for local names see Balick (1985). Important as a source of a high quality edible oil for local consumption. The oil is very similar to olive oil and is also used medicinally (Plotkin and Balick 1984). Fruit produce a milklike drink important as a source of protein (Balick and Gershoff 1981). The "cabbage" is excellent; leaves provide material for thatch and carrying baskets, and the wood has various uses.

Notes.—Most closely related to *Oenocarpus,* see p. 361.

Taxonomic Account.—Balick (1980, 1986).

Plate.—57D.

100. HYOSPATHE Martius, Historia Naturalis Palmarum 2:1. 1823. Type: **H. elegans** Martius.

Small or rarely moderate, solitary or clustering, graceful, unarmed, pleonanthic, monoecious palms. Stem slender, ringed with conspicuous, sometimes oblique, rather distant leaf scars. Leaves regularly pinnate, entire and bifid, or bi- or trijugate; sheath usually forming a short to long crownshaft, not splitting opposite the petiole until shed, margin irregular, chartaceous, striate, adaxially grooved, glabrous, abaxially with scattered scales; petiole moderate, slender, abaxially rounded, with hairs or deciduous scales; rachis adaxially ridged, abaxially ridged or rounded, also scaly; leaflets lanceolate to falcate, pointed, often somewhat curved apically, alternate, single-fold, several-fold or many-fold, bearing scattered deciduous scales along abaxial ribs and sometimes basally on adaxial ribs, surfaces similar or dissimilar in color, midrib prominent, 1–2 pairs of parallel veins also conspicuous in some species, transverse veinlets conspicuous or obscure. Inflorescence solitary, branched to 1 order, branches stiff or pendulous; peduncle short or long, slender; prophyll 2-keeled laterally, tapering to a rather blunt point, chartaceous, splitting dorsiventrally and apically to become bifid, inserted above the base of the peduncle; peduncular bracts 1–2, terete, much longer than or about as long as the prophyll, beaked, splitting abaxially, inserted somewhat above the prophyll; rachis much shorter to rarely longer than the peduncle; rachis bracts very short, obscure, subtending spirally in-

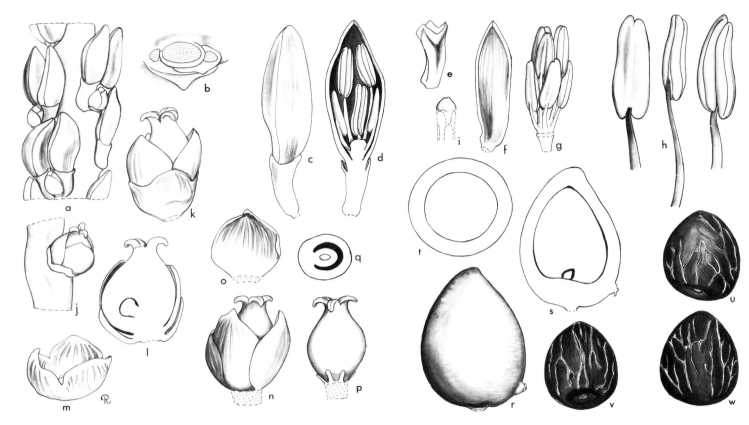

100.—**Hyospathe. a,** portion of rachilla with triads ×3; **b,** triad, flowers removed to show bracts ×9; **c,** staminate bud ×6; **d,** staminate bud in vertical section ×6; **e,** staminate calyx ×6; **f,** staminate petal, interior view ×6; **g,** androecium ×6; **h,** stamen in 3 views ×12; **i,** pistillode ×6; **j,** portion of rachilla at pistillate anthesis ×6; **k,** pistillate flower ×12; **l,** pistillate flower in vertical section ×12; **m,** pistillate calyx ×12; **n,** pistillate flower, calyx removed ×12; **o,** pistillate petal, interior view ×12; **p,** gynoecium and staminodes ×12; **q,** ovary in cross-section ×12; **r,** fruit ×3; **s,** fruit in vertical section ×3; **t,** fruit in cross-section ×3; **u, v, w,** seed in 3 views ×3. *Hyospathe weberbaueri:* **a-i,** *Moore et al. 9500; H. elegans:* **j-q,** *Guppy G-651;* **r-w;** *Moore et al. 9508.*

serted rachillae; rachillae slender, rather distant or crowded, moderate to short and stiff or long and pendulous, sometimes undulate apically, bearing spirally arranged triads of flowers nearly throughout and paired to solitary staminate flowers distally; floral bracteoles shallow, rounded. Staminate flowers lateral to the pistillate, sessile or stalked, narrow, elongate; sepals 3, united in a tube, adnate basally for at least ⅔ their length to the receptacle to form a stalklike base, free tips short, broadly triangular; petals 3, distinct, narrowly ovate, asymmetrical, curved basally, pointed distally; stamens 6, the 3 antesepalous with shorter filaments, free or shortly joined with the pistillode, the 3 antepetalous with filaments much longer, adnate to the pistillode nearly to its apex, filaments awl-shaped, anthers moderately long, dorsifixed near the base, latrorse, united throughout; pollen elliptic, monosulcate or rarely trichotomosulcate, with scabrate, tectate exine; pistillode narrowly ovoid with 2 stigmatic lobes. Pistillate flower ovoid, shorter than the staminate; sepals 3, united in a cupule for ca. ⅔ their length, tips broad, pointed, striate; petals 3, distinct, ovate, moderately imbricate, striate, tips pointed; staminodes 6, small, straplike; gy-

noecium ovoid, unilocular, uniovulate, narrowed to a short tubular style, stigmas 3, recurved at anthesis, ovule basal, laterally attached, form unknown. Fruit ovoid to cylindrical, pointed, asymmetrical, black at maturity, stigmatic remains basal; epicarp smooth, lightly mottled, mesocarp fibrous, endocarp thin, crustaceous. Seed narrow, ovoid, ± pointed, hilum basal, raphe branches anastomosing, endosperm homogeneous; embryo rather large, basal. Germination adjacent-ligular; eophyll bifid. Cytology not studied.

Anatomy.—Not studied.

Distribution.—About 17 species ranging from Costa Rica to Peru.

Ecology.—In rain forest in swamps or on dry ground at low elevations but also on the slopes of Andes in Colombia between 1000–2000 m (Dugand 1961).

Common Names and Uses.—Hog palm (*H. concinna*), Ubim palm (*H. elegans*). These palms would make handsome ornamentals.

Notes.—No recent taxonomic treatment exists. Several authors note the beauty of the palms. It seems surprising that their ornamental potential has not been exploited. The difference in length of antesepalous and antepetalous stamens and the adnation of the antepetalous filaments to the pistillode are distinctive and unusual in the family as a whole.

Taxonomic Accounts.—Burret (1929c) and Bailey and Moore (1949).

Fig.—G.20.

Roystoneinae J. Dransfield & N. Uhl, Principes 30: 7. 1986. Type: **Roystonea.**

Robust, unarmed; leaves pinnate, leaflets entire; crownshaft well developed; inflorescences infrafoliar, branched to 4 orders; pistillate flowers with petals connate basally, valvate distally; staminodes connate in a cupule adnate to the petals; gynoecium pseudomonomerous; fruit with basal stigmatic remains.

The subtribe contains the single genus *Roystonea,* confined to islands of the Caribbean and to the neighboring mainland (Map 36). The connate petals with valvate, distinct lobes, an adnate staminodial ring in the pistillate flower, and an undivided eophyll are unusual in the Areceae. The relationships of *Roystonea* are not obvious.

101. ROYSTONEA O. F. Cook, Science, ser. 2, 12: 479. 1900. Type: **R. regia** (Kunth) O. F. Cook (=*Oreodoxa regia* Kunth).

Oreodoxa of many authors, not Willdenow.

Tall, stout, solitary, unarmed, pleonanthic, monoecious palms. Stem columnar, variously tapered or swollen, tan, gray, or white, ringed by prominent or obscure leaf scars. Leaves pinnate; sheath tubular, large, forming a prominent crownshaft; petiole relatively short, channeled adaxially, rounded abaxially; leaflets narrow, elongate, tapering to a point, single-fold, held in one plane or variously inserted, crowded or in groups, rather thin, midrib only or midrib and other longitudinal veins raised abaxially, hairs frequent and scales prominent along the midrib, transverse veinlets evident abaxially. Inflorescences infrafoliar, massive, branched to 3(–4) orders; peduncle very short, stout; prophyll tubular, elongate, strongly 2-keeled laterally, truncate, leathery, green, splitting apically; peduncular bract 2 to 3 times as long as the prophyll, terete, pointed, glabrous, leathery, green, splitting longitudinally; rachis much longer than the peduncle, bearing small, pointed, spirally inserted bracts; rachillae very long, slender and pendulous or short, stout and variously divaricate, straight or undulate, white when first exposed due to copious free scales; rachilla bracts spirally arranged, small, membranous, tapered, subtending widely spaced triads of flowers proximally and paired or solitary staminate flowers distally; floral bracteoles small, thin, membranous. Staminate flowers nearly symmetrical, larger than the pistillate buds at anthesis; sepals 3, distinct, triangular, im-

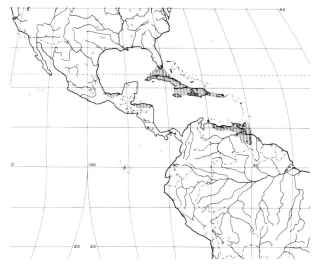

Map 36.—**Distribution of Roystoneinae.**

bricate, very short; petals 3, distinct, ovate, valvate, about 10 times the length of the sepals, tips thickened; stamens 6–12, filaments awl-shaped, erect in bud; anthers elongate, versatile, sagittate basally, dorsifixed near the middle, latrorse, connective tanniniferous; pollen elliptic, monosulcate, with foveolate or fossulate, tectate exine; pistillode subglobose or trifid. Pistillate flowers nearly conical to shortly ovoid; sepals 3, distinct, very short, broadly imbricate, rounded; petals 3, ovate, connate about ½ their length, valvate distally, more than twice as long as the sepals; staminodes 6, connate in a 6-lobed cupule adnate to the corolla basally; gynoecium subglobose, unilocular, uniovulate, style not distinct, stigmas 3, recurved, ovule laterally attached, form unknown. Fruit obovoid to oblong-ellipsoidal or subglobose, stigmatic remains nearly basal, perianth persistent; epicarp smooth, thin, mesocarp of pale parenchyma over a layer of thin, flat, anastomosing fibers next to the endocarp, endocarp thin, horny, fragile, somewhat operculate at the base, roughened and often ± adherent to the seed adaxially. Seed ellipsoidal, brown, hilum large, circular, lateral, raphe branches fine, radiating from the hilum, endosperm homogeneous; embryo nearly basal. Germination adjacent-ligular; eophyll entire. $n =$ 18 (*R. altissima, R. elata, R. princeps,* Read 1966; *R. oleracea,* Sharma and Sarkar 1957; *R. regia,* Eichhorn 1957, Sharma and Sarkar 1957). $n = 19$ (*R. regia,* Satô 1946, questionable count).

Anatomy.—Leaf (Tomlinson 1961). Tomlinson found the anatomy of the lamina different from that of other members of the Areceae, especially in the abundance of fibers; however, many of the New Caledonian genera also have abundant nonvascular fibers.

Distribution.—About ten to twelve species found throughout the islands of the Caribbean and bordering continental areas such as Florida, Mexico,

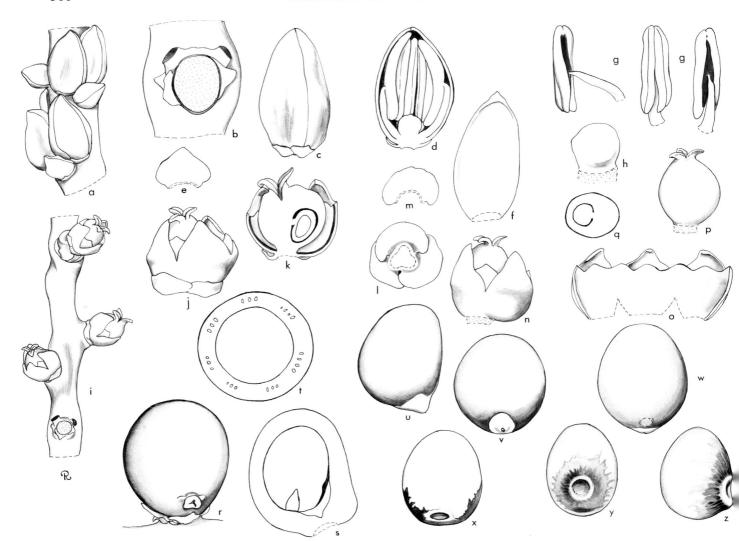

101.—**Roystonea. a,** portion of rachilla with triads ×3; **b,** triad, flowers removed ×6; **c,** staminate bud ×6; **d,** staminate bud in vertical section ×6; **e,** staminate sepal ×6; **f,** staminate petal, interior view ×6; **g,** stamen in 3 views ×6; **h,** pistillode ×12; **i,** portion of rachilla at pistillate anthesis ×3; **j,** pistillate flower ×6; **k,** pistillate flower in vertical section ×6; **l,** pistillate calyx, interior ×6; **m,** pistillate sepal, exterior view ×6; **n,** pistillate flower, calyx removed ×6; **o,** pistillate corolla and staminodes, expanded, interior view ×6; **p,** gynoecium ×6; **q,** ovary in cross-section ×6; **r,** fruit ×3; **s,** fruit in vertical section ×3; **t,** fruit in cross-section ×3; **u, v, w,** endocarp in 3 views ×3; **x, y, z,** seed in 3 views ×3. *Roystonea sp.:* all from *Read 602.*

eastern Central America, and northern South America.

Ecology. — Primarily palms of the lowlands. Some species are thought to be indicators of good soil conditions. Most of their original habitats are now cleared for agriculture.

Common Names and Uses. — Royal palms, mountain cabbage palm (*R. altissima*). *Roystonea* species are among the most elegant of the large palms and are widely cultivated in both hemispheres. Fruits are high in oil content and are used as pig food. The "cabbage" of *R. oleracea* is edible.

Notes. — See subtribe.

Taxonomic Accounts. — No recent treatment exists. One is certainly much needed but will be difficult because the species have been widely cultivated and disseminated by man and may have hybridized. See Bailey (1935a), Bailey and Moore (1949), and Read (1979).

Plate. — *58A; Figs. G.3, G.4, G.5.*

Archontophoenicinae J. Dransfield & N. Uhl. Principes 30:8. 1986. Type: **Archontophoenix.**

Moderate to robust or tall, unarmed; leaves pinnate, leaflets entire; crownshaft always well developed; inflorescences branched to 2–3 orders; prophyll and peduncular bract similar; staminate flowers ± asymmetrical, filaments erect or inflexed in bud; petals of pistillate flower imbricate; gynoecium pseudomonomerous; fruit with apical stigmatic remains; endocarp lacking an operculum; embryo basal.

Seven genera make up this rather homogeneous subtribe; one genus occurs in Australia, one on Lord Howe Island, one in New Zealand and neighboring islands, and four in New Caledonia (Map 37). These are medium-sized palms showing less diversity in habit and leaf form than is seen in the other subtribes of the Areceae. Leaves are strictly pinnate with long or more usually short and often massive petioles. A distinct crownshaft is present. The inflorescence has a very short and stout peduncle and rachillae which are stout and stiffly divaricate or more slender and pendulous at first but becoming divaricate when fruiting. The fruits have flat, anastomosing fibers in the inner layers of the mesocarp. All the genera except *Rhopalostylis* have more than six stamens. Variation occurs primarily in symmetry of the staminate flowers and in the pistillodes. Leaf anatomy of the four New Caledonian genera is distinctive and is thought to indicate that they may have originated from a single ancestor (Uhl and Martens in prep.).

The distribution pattern of the subtribe has been considered common to rain forest taxa that radiated throughout Australasia in the Late Cretaceous and Early Tertiary before the development in the Miocene of extensive archipelagic links with Malesia (Holloway 1979). Their relationship to other palms is not clear.

Key to the Genera of the Archontophoenicinae

1 Staminate flowers asymmetrical, acute; sepals narrow, acute to acuminate, very briefly imbricate basally, 3–4 or more times as long as wide; stamen filaments markedly inflexed at the apex in bud; pistillode as long as the stamens in bud; fruit not appearing pebbled when dry, mesocarp with elongate sclereids 2

1 Staminate flowers symmetrical or if asymmetrical, sepals definitely imbricate basally, acute to rounded, less than 2 times as long as wide; stamen filaments ± erect at the apex in bud; pistillode various or absent; fruit drying with a pebbled appearance, mesocarp with a shell of short, pale, flat sclereids 3

2 Floral triads borne basally, paired to solitary staminate flowers borne distally on the rachillae; stamens 6 to 12;

Map 37.—**Distribution of Archontophoenicinae.**

protandrous; pistillode slender, cylindrical; mesocarp lacking tannin cells. Lord Howe Island . . . . **104. Hedyscepe**

2 Floral triads borne nearly throughout the rachillae; stamens 9–12; protogynous; pistillode rounded at the base; mesocarp with tannin cells. New Zealand, Chatham, Norfolk, and Raoul Islands . . . . 105. **Rhopalostylis**

3 Leaves few, in 4 ranks; staminate flowers nearly symmetrical; pistillode as long as the stamens; bracteoles surrounding the pistillate flower sepallike, about as long as the rachilla bracts; fruit lacking tannin cells. New Caledonia . . . . 108. **Actinokentia**

3 Leaves numerous, in more than 4 ranks; staminate flowers symmetrical or asymmetrical; pistillode shorter than stamens in bud, or lacking; bracteoles surrounding the pistillate flower unequal, not sepallike; fruit with or without tannin cells 4

4 Staminate flowers asymmetrical with prominent pistillode, more than half as long as the stamens in bud 5

4 Staminate flowers symmetrical or asymmetrical, pistillode short, trifid or lacking, much less than half as long as the stamens, or lacking 6

5 Stamens ca. 34–37; fruit ellipsoidal, lacking tannin cells; seed with homogeneous endosperm. New Caledonia . . . . 106. **Kentiopsis**

5 Stamens ca. 12–13; fruits globose to ellipsoidal, with dispersed tannin cells; seed with ruminate endosperm. Eastern Australia . . . . 102. **Archontophoenix**

6 Staminate flowers symmetrical; sepals imbricate, broadly rounded; petals rounded; pistillode short, trifid; mesocarp with tannin cells between an outer layer of sclereids and an inner layer of fibers, fibers adherent to the mesocarp only at the base. New Caledonia . . . . 107. **Mackeea**

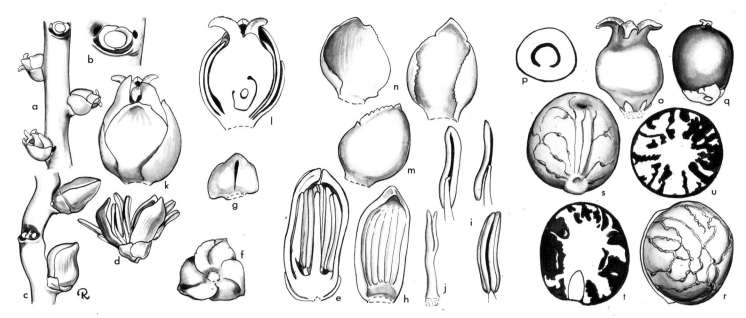

102.—**Archontophoenix. a,** portion of rachilla with triads, staminate flowers fallen ×1½; **b,** triad, flowers removed ×6; **c,** portion of rachilla with paired staminate flowers ×3; **d,** staminate flower ×3; **e,** staminate flower in vertical section ×6; **f,** staminate calyx ×6; **g,** staminate sepal ×6; **h,** staminate petal, interior view ×6; **i,** stamen in 3 views ×6; **j,** pistillode ×6; **k,** pistillate flower ×6; **l,** pistillate flower in vertical section ×6; **m,** pistillate sepal, exterior view ×6; **n,** pistillate petal in 2 views ×6; **o,** gynoecium and staminodes ×6; **p,** ovary in cross-section ×6; **q,** fruit ×1½; **r, s,** seed in 2 views ×3; **t,** seed in vertical section ×3; **u,** seed in cross-section ×3. *Archontophoenix alexandrae*: **a–p,** *Moore & Stephens 9249*; **q–u,** *White 3364*.

6 Staminate flowers asymmetrical; sepals acute; petals angled; pistillode lacking; mesocarp with dispersed tannin cells, fibers often thickened, adherent to the endocarp throughout. New Caledonia .... 103. **Chambeyronia**

102. ARCHONTOPHOENIX H. A. Wendland & Drude, Linnaea 39:182, 211. 1875. Lectotype: **A. alexandrae** (F. v. Mueller) H. A. Wendland & Drude (*Ptychosperma alexandrae* F. v. Mueller) (See O. F. Cook 1915a and Beccari and Pichi-Sermolli 1955).

Loroma O. F. Cook, Journal of the Washington Academy of Sciences 5:117. 1915. Type: *L. amethystina* O. F. Cook (=*Archontophoenix cunninghamiana* (H. A. Wendland) H. A. Wendland & Drude).

Moderate to tall, solitary, unarmed, pleonanthic, monoecious palms. Stem columnar, graceful, rather slender, slightly or strongly swollen basally, leaf scars obscure or prominent, often raised, distant or close. Leaves pinnate, erect or spreading, sometimes twisted about 90 degrees basally; sheaths tubular, forming a prominent crownshaft, thick, leathery, green, rusty-brown or purplish-red, often somewhat swollen basally; petiole short, grooved adaxially, rounded abaxially; rachis very long, similar to the petiole near the base, becoming flat adaxially and grooved laterally, scaly and minutely brown-dotted; leaflets lanceolate, elongate, tips irregularly pointed, single-fold, green or whitish abaxially due to very small silvery scales, ra-

menta large, dark-brown, often twisted or divided, medifixed or basifixed, present or lacking abaxially along the midrib, the midrib and large veins prominently or obscurely brown-dotted, midrib and several pairs of veins prominent abaxially, transverse veinlets not apparent. Inflorescences infrafoliar, erect in bud, becoming horizontal or drooping, with pendulous branches, branched to 3(–4) orders, protandrous; peduncle very short, stout; prophyll tubular, elongate, somewhat dorsiventrally flattened, 2-keeled laterally, briefly beaked, rather thin; peduncular bract like the prophyll but not keeled, prophyll and peduncular bract caducous; rachis moderate, tapering; rachis bracts low, ± ruffled to prominent, sharply pointed; rachillae somewhat divaricate and pendulous, bearing spirally arranged, rather thick, basally cupular, low and rounded or short pointed bracts subtending triads of flowers nearly throughout the rachillae, a few paired and solitary staminate flowers present distally; floral bracteoles low, rounded. Flowers pale lavender to purplish or cream to yellow. Staminate flowers asymmetrical, borne lateral to the pistillate in the triads; sepals 3, distinct, imbricate, broadly ovate, keeled, tips pointed; petals 3, distinct, ca. 5 times as long as the sepals, narrowly ovate, grooved adaxially, tips thicker, pointed; stamens ca. 12–14 (8 or 9–24 according to Hooker, Bailey), filaments short, awl-shaped, erect apically in bud, anthers elongate, linear, dorsifixed near the middle, erect in bud, later versatile, bifid basally, pointed to slightly emarginate distally, latrorse, the connective elongate, tanniniferous; pollen elliptic, monosulcate, with finely reticulate, tectate exine; pistillode more than half as long to as long as the stamens, trifid or cylindrical. Pistillate flowers symmetrical, ovoid; sepals 3, distinct, broadly imbricate, tips briefly pointed;

petals 3, distinct, imbricate except for prominent valvate tips; staminodes 3, toothlike, borne on one side of the gynoecium; gynoecium irregularly ovoid, unilocular, uniovulate, style indistinct, stigmas 3, recurved, ovule laterally attached, form unknown. Fruit globose to ellipsoidal, pink to red, stigmatic remains apical; epicarp smooth, mesocarp thin, soft, fleshy with flattened, conspicuously branched and interlocking, longitudinal fibers, endocarp thin, smooth, fragile, not operculate. Seed ellipsoidal to globose, basally attached, hilum basal, elongate, raphe branches numerous, anastomosing, endosperm ruminate; embryo basal. Germination adjacent-ligular; eophyll bifid. $n = 16$ (*A. alexandrae*, Read 1965a, 1966; Sarkar 1970). $n = 14$ (*A. alexandrae*, *A. cunninghamiana*, Eichhorn 1957).

Anatomy.—Leaf (Tomlinson 1961). In *A. alexandrae* guard cells are dumbbell-shaped (Solereder and Meyer 1928). Guard cells have the outer walls thickened; such thickenings also characterize all of the New Caledonian members of the subtribe, *Actinokentia*, *Chambeyronia*, *Kentiopsis*, and *Mackeea* (Uhl and Martens in prep.).

Distribution.—Two species of eastern Australia from the southern coast of New South Wales to the northern coast of Queensland. *A. alexandrae* is known to be variable and 3–5 new species may need to be described.

Ecology.—Rain forest in warm-temperate to tropical regions at sea level to elevations of about 1200 m, often in wet gullies, on stream banks or edges of swamps on various soils.

Common Names and Uses.—Alexander palm, King palm (*A. alexandrae*); piccabean palm, bangalow palm (*A. cunninghamiana*). Grown commercially as ornamentals in many warm-temperate and tropical regions.

Notes.—Perhaps most closely related to *Chambeyronia* but differs in having pendulous rachillae, an elongate pistillode, and ruminate endosperm.

Taxonomic account.—Bailey (1935b).

Plates.—20A, 58B; Figs. G.4, G.12.

103. CHAMBEYRONIA Vieillard, Bulletin de la Société Linnéenne de Normandie, sér. 2. 6:229. 1873.

Lectotype: **C. macrocarpa** (Brongniart) Vieillard ex Beccari (*Kentiopsis macrocarpa* Brongniart) (see Beccari 1920 and Beccari and Pichi-Sermolli 1955).

Moderate, solitary, unarmed, pleonanthic, monoecious palms. Stem erect, ringed with leaf scars, enlarged at the base but roots not prominent. Leaves regularly pinnate, curved, spreading, often red when first exposed; sheath tubular, forming a prominent crownshaft, with or without a shallow notch opposite the petiole, glabrous adaxially, lightly or densely covered in scales abaxially; petiole chan-

neled adaxially, rounded abaxially, with scattered small brown scales; leaflets acute to acuminate, single-fold, wide, waxy or glabrous adaxially, small brown scales scattered abaxially, midrib and marginal ribs large, transverse veinlets obscure or evident. Inflorescences infrafoliar, protandrous, branched to 2(–3) orders basally, to 1 order distally; peduncle very short; prophyll tubular, completely encircling the peduncle and enclosing the peduncular bract, caducous, dorsiventrally flattened, with 2 wide lateral keels, chartaceous, glabrous adaxially, lightly or densely scaly abaxially; peduncular bract lacking keels and thinner, with a more definite beak, otherwise like the prophyll; rachis longer than the peduncle bearing spirally arranged, low or prominent, pointed bracts subtending branches or rachillae; rachillae rather stout, tapering, sinuous, lightly or densely scaly; rachilla bracts prominent, spreading or ascending, spirally arranged, subtending triads of flowers basally and paired or solitary staminate flowers distally, the triads rather distant, sometimes appearing as though impressed in the axis; bracteoles surrounding the pistillate flower unequal, not sepallike, the larger one shorter or exceeding the triad bract. Staminate flowers asymmetrical to subsymmetrical; sepals 3, distinct, acute to long pointed; petals 3, distinct, valvate, asymmetrical, angled, and strongly nerved to nearly symmetrical and smooth when dry; stamens 19–55, filaments awl-shaped, briefly inflexed, anthers erect in bud, linear, dorsifixed, bifid basally, emarginate apically, latrorse, the connective elongate; pollen elliptic, one end sometimes dilated, monosulcate or rarely trichotomosulcate, with reticulate-foveolate, tectate exine; pistillode lacking. Pistillate flowers symmetrical; sepals 3, distinct, broadly imbricate, acute; petals 3, distinct, broadly imbricate with prominently valvate apices; staminodes 3, small, toothlike, borne at one side of the gynoecium; gynoecium with 3 spreading stigmas, unilocular, uniovulate, ovule laterally attached, hemianatropous. Fruit subglobose to ovoid, with apical stigmatic remains; epicarp smooth, underlain by a mesocarp of oblique, short, pale sclereids over parenchyma with dispersed tannin cells and stout, flat, longitudinal, anastomosing fibers adherent to the endocarp, endocarp thin, fragile, not operculate. Seed attached by an elongate lateral hilum, raphe branches numerous, anastomosing, endosperm homogeneous; embryo basal. Germination adjacent-ligular; eophyll bifid. $n = 16$ (*C. macrocarpa*, Johnson 1985).

Anatomy.—In leaf anatomy *C. macrocarpa* is distinguished from other members of the Archontophoenicinae in New Caledonia by a large fibrous strand of ca. 15 cells between each two vascular bundles. *C. lepidota* is the only species of the Archontophoenicinae to have thick cuticles on both upper and lower leaf surfaces, perhaps associated with the more exposed habitat (Uhl and Martens in prep.).

Distribution.—Two species in New Caledonia.

Ecology.—*C. macrocarpa* is found in wet forest or gallery forest nearly throughout New Caledonia. *C. lepidota*, however, occurs on schistose soils only in the northeastern part of the island.

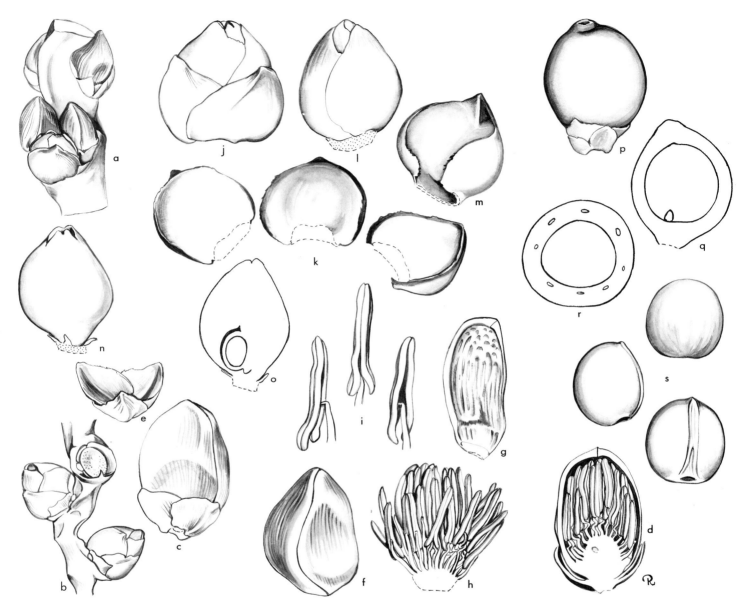

103.—**Chambeyronia. a,** portion of rachilla with triads ×1½; **b,** portion of rachilla with triads, all flowers fallen (top) and staminate flowers fallen (bottom) ×1½; **c,** staminate bud ×3; **d,** staminate bud in vertical section ×3; **e,** staminate sepals ×3; **f,** staminate bud, sepals removed ×3; **g,** staminate petal, interior view ×3; **h,** androecium ×3; **i,** stamen in 3 views ×6; **j,** pistillate bud ×3; **k,** pistillate sepals ×3; **l,** pistillate bud, sepals removed ×3; **m,** pistillate petal ×3; **n,** gynoecium and staminodes ×3; **o,** gynoecium in vertical section ×3; **p,** fruit ×1½; **q,** fruit in vertical section ×1½; **r,** fruit in cross-section ×1½; **s,** seed in 3 views ×1½. *Chambeyronia macrocarpa*: all from *Moore et al. 9335.*

Common Names and Uses.—Common names unknown. *C. macrocarpa* is probably the most widely cultivated New Caledonian palm.

Notes.—Closely related to *Archontophoenix* and *Hedyscepe* but differing in more numerous stamens and large floral bracteoles. See also notes under *Archontophoenix.*

Taxonomic Account.—Moore and Uhl (1984). *Plates.*—*20B; 58C.*

104. **HEDYSCEPE** H. A. Wendland & Drude, Linnaea 39:178, 203. 1875. Type: **H. canterburyana** (C. Moore & F. v. Mueller) H. A. Wendland & Drude (*Kentia canterburyana* C. Moore & F. v. Mueller).

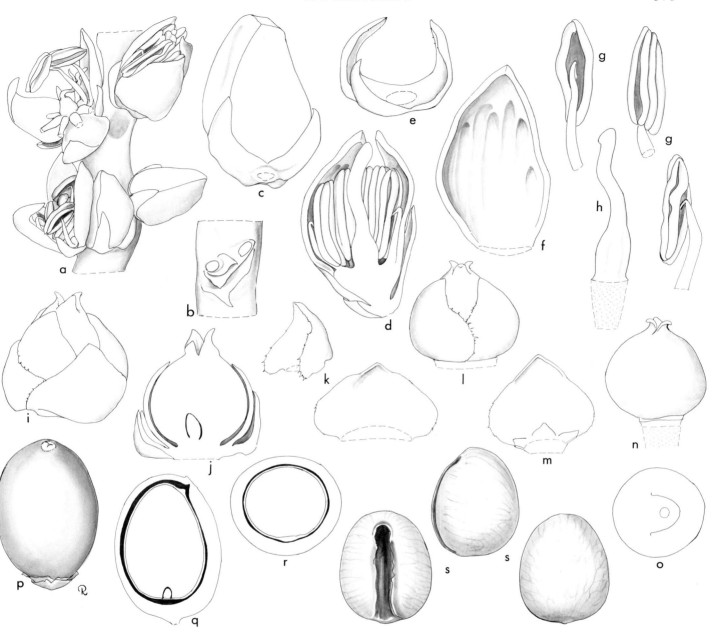

104.—**Hedyscepe. a,** portion of rachilla with paired staminate flowers ×3; **b,** portion of rachilla, paired staminate flowers removed to show scars and bracteoles ×6; **c,** staminate bud ×6; **d,** staminate bud in vertical section ×6; **e,** staminate calyx ×6; **f,** staminate petal, interior view ×6; **g,** stamen in 3 views ×6; **h,** pistillode ×7½; **i,** pistillate flower ×4½; **j,** pistillate flower in vertical section ×4½; **k,** pistillate sepal in 2 views ×4½; **l,** pistillate flower, sepals removed ×4½; **m,** pistillate petal with staminodes, interior view ×4½; **n,** gynoecium ×4½; **o,** ovary in cross-section ×4½; **p,** fruit ×1; **q,** fruit in vertical section ×1; **r,** fruit in cross-section ×1; **s,** seed in 3 views ×1. *Hedyscepe canterburyana*: **a–h,** *Shick s.m.*; **i–o,** *Darian s.n.*; **p–s,** *Moore & Shick 9252.*

Solitary, moderate, unarmed, pleonanthic, monoecious palm. Stem rather stout, conspicuously ringed with narrow, raised, whitish leaf scars. Leaves pinnate, stiff, arching; sheath forming a prominent crownshaft, thick, striate, densely covered with white tomentum and scattered small brown scales; petiole very short, stout, adaxially grooved, abaxially rounded; leaflets subopposite, rather short, lanceolate, pointed, proximal and distal leaflets distinctly narrower and shorter, stiff, ± erect, single-fold, adaxially glabrous, abaxially tomentose along the margins and scaly along the ribs on both surfaces, midrib and 3 pairs of veins raised adaxially, transverse veinlets not evident. Inflorescences solitary, infrafoliar, protandrous, branched to 1(–3) orders; peduncle short, ± flat, stout, horizontal; prophyll tubular, dorsiventrally flattened, pointed but not tapering, with 2 flat lateral keels, chartaceous, deciduous; peduncular bract like the prophyll but not keeled, also caducous; ca. 3 wide ridgelike bracts above the peduncular bract; rachis rather short but longer than the peduncle, bearing low, pointed, spirally arranged bracts subtending rachillae; rachillae divaricate, stout, bearing triads of flowers nearly throughout, distally with a few pairs and single staminate flowers; floral bracteoles, low, rounded. Staminate flowers asymmetrical; sepals 3, distinct, slightly imbricate and bulbous or connate basally, narrow, elongate, widely separated, tapering distally, keeled; petals 3, distinct, variously angled, valvate; stamens 9–10 (–12) according to J. D. Hooker) in 2 series, antesepalous stamens solitary, antepetalous stamens paired, filaments awl-shaped, markedly inflexed at the apex in bud, anthers erect in bud, large, variously curved, linear, emarginate apically, bifid basally, latrorse, connective elongate, tanniniferous; pollen elliptic, monosulcate, with finely reticulate, tectate exine; pistillode with a rounded ovarian part and long terete style about as high as the stamens. Pistillate flowers symmetrical, ovoid; sepals 3, distinct, imbricate, rounded; petals 3, distinct, imbricate with briefly valvate apices; staminodes 3, small, toothlike, borne on one side of the gynoecium (?); gynoecium unilocular, uniovulate, ovoid with 3 recurved stigmas, ovule basally attached, form unknown. Fruit broadly ellipsoidal, deep dull red when ripe, stigmatic remains apical; epicarp smooth, mesocarp with a prominent layer of longitudinal, slender fibers over parenchyma and dispersed tannin cells and flat, long fibers adherent to the endocarp, endocarp crustaceous, thin, fragile, not operculate. Seed laterally attached by a broad elongate hilum, raphe branches numerous, anastomosing, endosperm homogeneous; embryo basal. Germination adjacent-ligular; eophyll bifid. Cytology not studied.

Anatomy. — Not studied.

Distribution. — One species endemic to Lord Howe Island.

Ecology. — Found on high cliffs above the sea, most common on the more exposed ridges at 600–750 m elevation.

Common Names and Uses. — Big mountain palm, Canterbury umbrella palm. Excellent as an ornamental for cool, dry, sea coast areas; also grown as a house plant.

Notes. — Closely related to *Rhopalostylis*. Differs in having triads nearly throughout the rachillae, more than six stamens, and a pistillode with a rounded ovarian base. Also differs in being protandrous; *Rhopalostylis* is protogynous.

Taxonomic Account. — No treatment since the original description of Wendland and Drude (1875).

Plate. — 58D.

105. RHOPALOSTYLIS H. A. Wendland & Drude, Linnaea 39:180, 234. 1875. Type: **R. baueri** H. A. Wendland & Drude.

Eora O. F. Cook, Journal of Heredity 18:409. 1927. Type: *E. sapida* (H. A. Wendland & Drude) O. F. Cook (=*R. sapida* H. A. Wendland & Drude).

Moderate to tall, solitary, unarmed, pleonanthic, monoecious palms. Stem erect, smooth, green to gray, closely ringed with prominent leaf scars, sometimes enlarged and bearing exposed roots at the base. Leaves pinnate, ascending and erect or somewhat arched, often twisted; sheath forming a prominent, rather short and somewhat bulbous crownshaft, enlarged basally or ± straight, sheath with definite diagonal nerves, and small brown scales; petiole very short, channeled adaxially, rounded abaxially; rachis like the petiole proximally, becoming channeled laterally and ridged adaxially, densely covered with small to medium brown scales; leaflets subopposite, forward pointing, stiff, lanceolate, tapering, often curved distally, single-fold, adaxially glabrous, abaxially and marginally somewhat tomentose, large scales present along the midrib, midrib evident adaxially, midrib and 1 pair of veins near the margins raised abaxially, transverse veinlets not evident. Inflorescence infrafoliar, spreading, ± pendulous in fruit, branched to 3 orders; peduncle very short, dorsiventrally flattened, stout; prophyll tubular, elongate, rather short and broad, with 2 flat, lateral keels, broadly pointed distally, thin, papery, deciduous; peduncular bract like the prophyll but not keeled, deciduous with the prophyll; rachis longer than the peduncle, stout, tapering, bearing spirally arranged, sometimes prominent bracts, bracts basally wide, tapering to a point, subtending rachillae; rachillae divaricate, short, stout, with or without a short bare portion, bearing triads of flowers basally and paired to solitary staminate flowers on a short distal portion; rachilla bracts pointed, thick, striate, semicircular, tightly enclosing the lower half of the pistillate flower; floral bracteoles short, rounded, or somewhat pointed. Staminate flowers asymmetrical, borne laterally and somewhat distally to the pistillate; sepals 3, distinct, briefly imbricate basally, narrow, tapering, somewhat keeled; petals 3, distinct, only slightly or markedly longer than the sepals, curved, adaxially grooved, tips thick, pointed; stamens 6, filaments markedly inflexed in bud, terete, joined briefly basally, anthers erect in bud, linear, dorsifixed near the middle, emarginate apically, bifid basally, latrorse, connective elongate, tanniniferous; pollen elliptic, monosulcate, with foveolate to fossulate, tectate exine; pistillode slender, cylindrical, about as long as the stamens. Pistillate flowers symmetrical, ovoid; sepals 3, distinct, imbricate, truncate with a central point; petals 3, distinct, broadly imbricate basally with prominent valvate apices; staminodes lacking or toothlike; gynoecium ellipsoidal, unilocular, uniovulate, style not distinct, stigmas 3, recurved, conspicuous, ovule very large, laterally attached, form unknown. Fruit globose or ellipsoidal, red when ripe, stigmatic remains apical, perianth persistent, spreading; epicarp smooth, mesocarp with a thin layer of sclereids and many flat, longitudinal fibers adherent to the

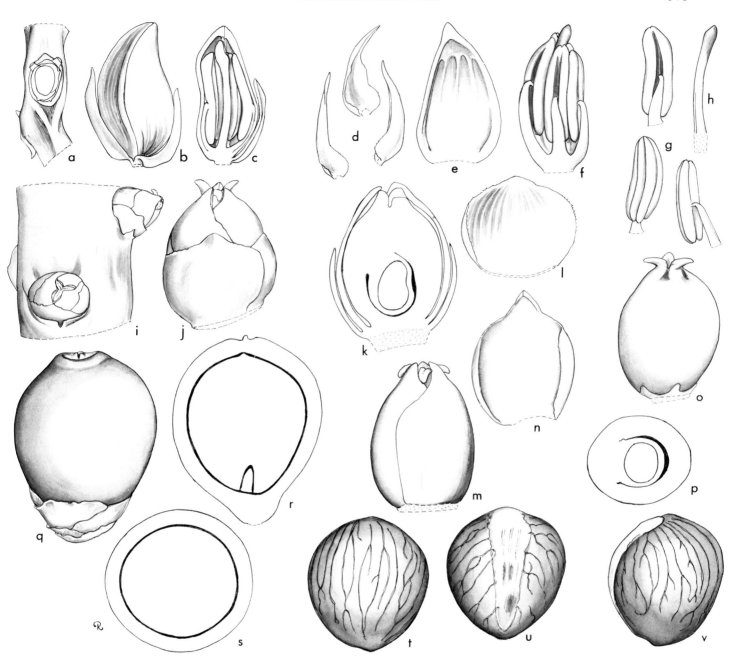

105.—**Rhopalostylis. a,** portion of rachilla with triad, flowers removed ×3; **b,** staminate bud ×6; **c,** staminate bud in vertical section ×3; **d,** staminate sepals ×6; **e,** staminate petal, interior view ×6; **f,** androecium and pistillode ×6; **g,** stamen in 3 views ×6; **h,** pistillode ×6; **i,** portion of rachilla at pistillate anthesis ×3; **j,** pistillate flower ×6; **k,** pistillate flower in vertical section ×6; **l,** pistillate sepal, interior view ×6; **m,** pistillate flower, sepals removed ×6; **n,** pistillate petal, interior view ×6; **o,** gynoecium and staminodes ×6; **p,** ovary in cross-section ×6; **q,** fruit ×3; **r,** fruit in vertical section ×3; **s,** fruit in cross-section ×3; **t, u, v,** seed in 3 views ×3. *Rhopalostylis baueri*: **a–h,** *Leyden s.n.*; **i–v,** *Osbourne s.n.*

endocarp, endocarp thin, fragile, not operculate, white or ± tan colored. Seed ellipsoidal or globose, laterally attached by an elongate, rather wide, tapering hilum, raphe branches few or numerous, moderate to fine, anastomosing, endosperm homogeneous; embryo basal, often ex-

actly so. Germination adjacent-ligular; eophyll bifid. Cytology not studied.

Anatomy.—Leaf (Tomlinson 1961). Floral anatomy not studied.

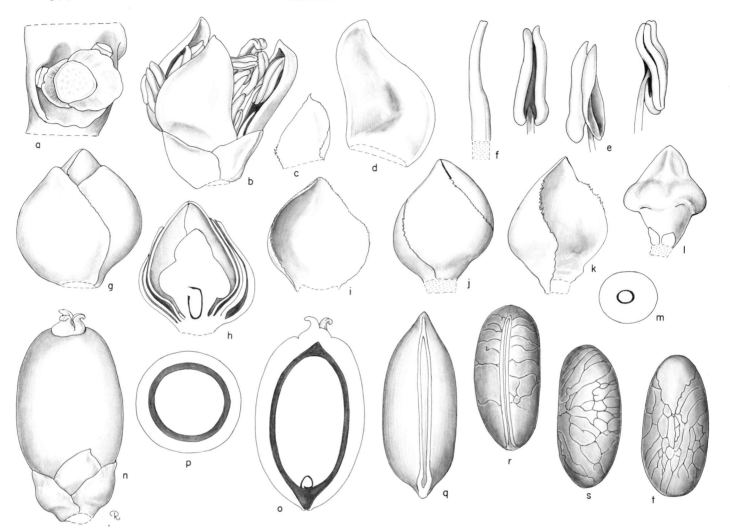

106.—**Kentiopsis. a,** triad, flowers removed to show bract, bracteoles, and pedicels of staminate flowers ×6; **b,** staminate flower ×6; **c,** staminate sepal ×6; **d,** staminate petal, interior view ×6; **e,** stamen in 3 views ×9; **f,** pistillode ×9; **g,** pistillate bud ×6; **h,** pistillate bud in vertical section ×6; **i,** pistillate sepal, interior view ×6; **j,** pistillate bud, sepals removed ×6; **k,** pistillate petal ×6; **l,** gynoecium and staminodes ×6; **m,** ovary in cross-section ×6; **n,** fruit ×3; **o,** fruit in vertical section ×3; **p,** fruit in cross-section ×3; **q,** endocarp, fibers attached ×3; **r, s, t,** seed in 3 views ×3. *Kentiopsis oliviformis*: **a,** *Moore et al. 10071*; **b-m,** *MacKee 25644*; **n-t,** *Moore 10457* and *Schmid 1222.*

Distribution. — Variously considered as three species or two species, one with two varieties; distributed in New Zealand, Chatham Island, Norfolk Island, and Raoul (Sunday) Island.

Ecology. — Chiefly in dense lowland forests, usually not far from the sea in a mild, warm-temperate climate with abundant moisture.

Common Names and Uses. — Nikau palm (*R. sapida*), norfolk palm (*R. baueri*). Used extensively by the Maoris for thatch and basket weaving. The terminal bud is edible. The palms are striking ornamentals in suitably moist climates.

Notes. — Very similar and obviously closely related to *Hedyscepe*; see notes under *Hedyscepe*.
Taxonomic account. — Bailey (1935c).
Plate. — 20C, D.

106. **KENTIOPSIS** Brongniart, Comptes Rendus Hebdomadaires des Séances de l'Académie des Sciences 77:398. 1873. Lectotype: **K. oliviformis** (Brongniart & Gris) Brongniart (*Kentia oliviformis* Brongniart & Gris) (see Beccari 1920).

Solitary, tall, unarmed, pleonanthic, monoecious palm. Stem erect, thick basally, gray, ringed with ± prominent, rather close leaf scars. Leaves pinnate, spreading, neatly abscising; sheaths forming a prominent crownshaft; petiole channeled adaxially, rounded abaxially; leaflets regularly arranged, lanceolate, acute to acuminate, single-fold, adaxially glabrous, abaxially densely covered with small pale scales, midrib prominent, marginal rib second in size to midrib, transverse veinlets not evident. Inflorescences infrafoliar, branched to 3 orders basally, 2–1 orders distally, protandrous; peduncle very short; prophyll and peduncular bract caducous, prophyll completely encircling the peduncle and enclosing the peduncular bract, briefly beaked, flat, keeled laterally, rather thin, chartaceous, both surfaces densely covered in whitish deciduous tomentum; peduncular bract like the prophyll but lacking keels; rachis elongate, longer than the peduncle, bearing spirally arranged, low, rounded, ± ruffled bracts subtending the branches and rachillae; rachillae rather slender, moderate and about equal in length, bearing spirally arranged prominent, rounded, liplike bracts subtending flowers borne in triads of 2 staminate and a pistillate nearly throughout the rachillae, a few paired or solitary staminate flowers present distally; bracteoles surrounding the pistillate flower low, unequal, rounded, not sepallike. Staminate flowers asymmetrical; sepals 3, distinct, ± deltoid, ± acute, imbricate basally, scarcely higher than wide; petals 3, valvate, angled, acute; stamens ca. 34–37 (18–24 according to Brongniart, 15–18 according to Beccari), filaments erect at the apex in bud, anthers erect in bud, linear, dorsifixed, emarginate apically, bifid basally, latrorse, the connective elongate; pollen elliptic or triangular, monosulcate or trichotomosulcate, with finely pitted, tectate exine; pistillode nearly as high as the stamens (lacking, according to Beccari), with an attenuate, sometimes briefly trifid apex. Pistillate flowers symmetrical; sepals 3, distinct, broadly imbricate; petals 3, distinct, broadly imbricate with valvate apices; staminodes 3, small, toothlike, borne at one side of the gynoecium; gynoecium pseudomonomerous, with 3 prominent, recurved stigmas, unilocular, uniovulate, ovule pendulous. Fruit ellipsoidal, red at maturity with apical stigmatic remains; epicarp smooth, mesocarp consisting of a shell of pale, short, ellipsoidal sclereids over pale parenchyma with a few included longitudinal fibers and at maturity a layer of tannin cells adjacent to flat, anastomosing fibers adherent to the endocarp, endocarp thin, fragile, not operculate. Seed attached by an elongate hilum, the raphe branches numerous, anastomosing, endosperm homogeneous; embryo basal. Germination adjacent-ligular (?); eophyll bifid. Cytology not known.

Anatomy. — The midribs of the leaflets have a high, wide, asymmetrically truncate adaxial projection three times as long or longer than the pointed abaxial projection; fibrous strands are scattered, and there is no tannin in the palisade (Uhl and Martens in press).

Distribution. — One species in southwest central New Caledonia.

Ecology. — *Kentiopsis* has a very restricted distribution on non-ultrabasic rocks.

Common Names and Uses. — None recorded, but certainly of ornamental value.

Notes. — *Kentiopsis* is distinct from other members of the Archontophoenicinae in its asymmetrical staminate flowers with angled petals and markedly unequal bracteoles surrounding the pistillate flower. It is perhaps most closely related to *Mackeea*.

Taxonomic Account. — Moore and Uhl (1984).

Plate. — *59A.*

107. MACKEEA H. E. Moore, Gentes Herbarum 11: 304. 1978. Type: **M. magnifica** H. E. Moore.

Solitary, tall, unarmed, pleonanthic, monoecious palm. Stems erect, gray, slightly conic-expanded at base with leaf scars prominent but not indented in lower portion, more congested above. Leaves pinnate, spreading not arching; sheath forming a crownshaft, not swollen at the base, thick, fibrous, ± woody, with gray scales abaxially; petiole ridged adaxially, rounded abaxially; rachis ridged adaxially, flattened abaxially, tomentose; leaflets regularly arranged in 1 plane, acute, single-fold, somewhat leathery, upper surface with elevated midrib, lower surface with many prominent veins, marginal ribs second in size to the midrib, small scales on adaxial ribs, midrib with membranous, medifixed, tattered ramenta abaxially, transverse veinlets not evident. Inflorescences infrafoliar, spreading, protandrous, stiffly branched to 2(–3) orders basally, to 1 order distally; peduncle very short, stout, tomentose; prophyll and peduncular bract caducous, prophyll completely encircling the peduncle at insertion, markedly 2-keeled but scarcely beaked apically, chartaceous, bearing deciduous tomentum and scales abaxially; peduncular bract lacking keels, beaked, otherwise similar to and completely enclosed by the prophyll; rachis longer than the peduncle; rachis bracts subtending the lower branches reduced to low ruffled ridges, those subtending rachillae and upper branches acute; rachillae rather slender, medium and equal in length, bearing spirally arranged, low rounded bracts subtending triads of 2 staminate flowers and a pistillate flower, nearly to the apex of the rachillae, the distal few nodes with paired or solitary staminate flowers only; bracteoles surrounding the pistillate flower unequal, one as high as the rachilla bract, the other nearly twice as high. Staminate flowers nearly symmetrical; sepals 3, distinct, rounded, keeled toward the base; petals 3, distinct, spreading at anthesis, subacute and thickened at the apex; stamens 32–38, filaments awl-shaped, erect to briefly inflexed at the apex in bud, slightly shorter than the anthers, anthers linear-oblong, dorsifixed, emarginate to briefly bifid at the base and apex, introrse, connective dark; pollen elliptic, monosulcate, with finely reticulate, tectate exine; pistillode much shorter than the stamens, trifid. Pistillate buds ovoid; sepals 3, distinct, rounded, hairy in bud, broadly imbricate; petals 3, distinct, broadly imbricate except for the short valvate apices; staminodes mostly 2–3, toothlike, borne at one side of the gynoecium; gynoecium with 3 recurved stigmas, unilocular, uniovulate, ovule pendulous, arillate, probably hemianatropous. Fruit ellipsoidal, with apical stigmatic remains; epicarp smooth when fresh, drying minutely pebbled, thin, mesocarp with abun-

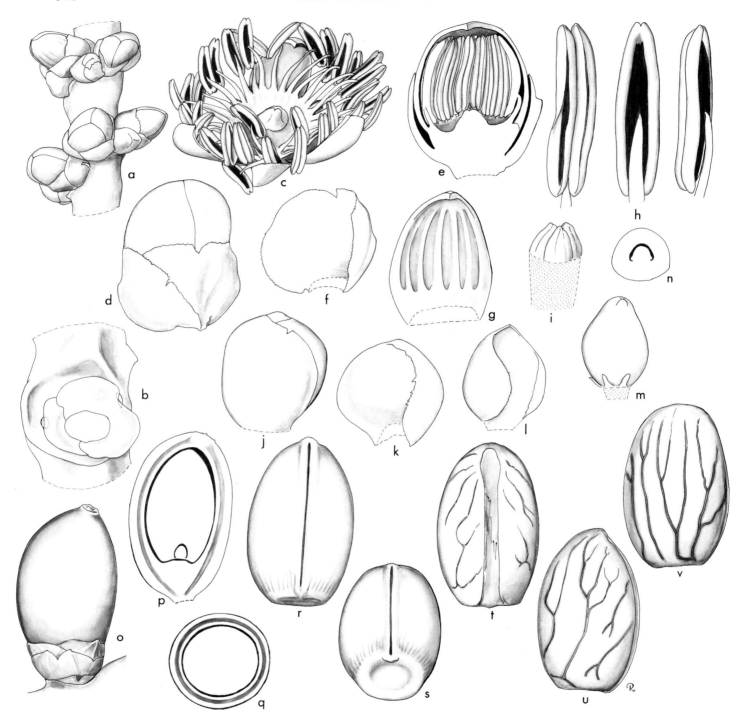

107.—**Mackeea. a,** portion of rachilla with triads, flowers in bud ×2¼; **b,** triad, flowers removed to show bracteoles around pistillate bud ×4½; **c,** staminate flower at anthesis ×4½; **d,** staminate bud ×6; **e,** staminate bud in vertical section ×6; **f,** staminate sepal ×6; **g,** staminate petal, interior view ×6; **h,** stamen in 3 views ×12; **i,** pistillode ×12; **j,** pistillate bud ×6; **k,** pistillate sepal ×6; **l,** pistillate petal ×6; **m,** gynoecium and staminodes ×6; **n,** ovary in cross-section ×6; **o,** fruit ×2¼; **p,** fruit in vertical section ×2¼; **q,** fruit in cross-section ×2¼; **r, s,** endocarp in 2 views ×3; **t, u, v,** seed in 3 views ×3. *Mackeea magnifica*: **a–n,** *MacKee 26471*; **o–v,** *Moore & Schmid 10054*.

dant short sclereids at an angle to the epicarp and external to a heavily tanniniferous layer with included, flat longitudinal fibers, these adherent to the endocarp only basally, endocarp glassy, fragile, with longitudinal groove and round basal invagination but not operculate. Seed ellipsoidal, hilum linear, raphe branches descending and anastomosing, endosperm homogeneous; embryo basal. Germination adjacent-ligular; eophyll bifid. Leaves of juvenile individuals distichously arranged. Cytology not studied.

Anatomy.—See characteristics of leaf anatomy of the Archontophoenicinae under *Actinokentia* (Uhl and Martens in press). In *Mackeea* cells of the upper hypodermal layer are larger than those of second adaxial layer and a large and often several small fibrous strands alternate with vascular bundles.

Distribution.—One species endemic to northeastern New Caledonia.

Ecology.—Wet montane forest or gallery forest on schistose rocks.

Common Names and Uses.—Not recorded.

Notes.—*Mackeea magnifica* is the tallest and stateliest palm in New Caledonia. It differs from other members of the Archontophoenicinae in having fibers of the mesocarp adnate only basally to the endocarp.

Taxonomic Account.—Moore and Uhl (1984).

Plate.—*59B.*

108. **ACTINOKENTIA** Dammer, Botanische Jahrbücher für Systematik 39:20. 1906. Lectotype: **A. divaricata** (Brongniart) Dammer (*Kentiopsis divaricata* Brongniart) (see Beccari 1920).

Solitary, small to moderate, unarmed, pleonanthic, monoecious palms. Stem slender, erect, prominently ringed with somewhat sunken leaf scars, sometimes with prickly roots. Leaves pinnate; sheaths thick, forming a crownshaft; petiole short, rounded abaxially, channeled adaxially, or elongate and terete; leaflets regularly arranged, lanceolate, acute to tapering, single-fold, adaxially waxy or glabrous, abaxially waxy tomentose with large ramenta along the midribs, midribs conspicuous, second largest ribs those along margins, transverse veinlets not evident. Inflorescences infrafoliar, protandrous, divaricately branched to 3 orders basally, 2–1 orders distally; peduncle short; prophyll tubular, pointed, rather thin, indistinctly 2-keeled, completely encircling the peduncle at insertion and enclosing the peduncular bract, caducous; peduncular bract like the prophyll but lacking keels; rachis longer than the peduncle bearing spirally arranged, spreading, acute bracts subtending branches and rachillae; rachilla bracts prominent, rounded, liplike and shorter than the flowers or acute and exceeding the flowers, subtending triads basally, paired or solitary staminate flowers distally, in broadened depressions in the rachillae; bracteoles surrounding the pistillate flower sepallike, outermost brac-

teole prominent, ca. ½ as long or as long as the inner bracteoles. Staminate flowers symmetrical, larger at anthesis than the pistillate buds; sepals 3, distinct, broadly imbricate and rounded, scarcely longer than broad, the outer often prominently keeled or pouchlike near the apex; petals 3, distinct, valvate, boat-shaped; stamens 19–50, filaments erect or nearly so at the apex in bud, anthers erect in bud, linear, dorsifixed, slightly emarginate apically, bifid basally, latrorse, the connective elongate; pollen elliptic, monosulcate, with finely reticulate, tectate exine; pistillode as long as the stamens in bud, tapered to a slender apex from a broad base. Pistillate buds usually well developed at staminate anthesis, symmetrical; sepals 3, distinct, broadly imbricate and rounded; petals 3, distinct, imbricate except for briefly valvate apices; staminodes 3, small, toothlike, borne at one side of the gynoecium; gynoecium unilocular, uniovulate, stigmas 3, prominent, recurved, ovule pendulous, hemianatropous. Fruit ellipsoidal with apical stigmatic remains; epicarp smooth, mesocarp underlain by a shell of short, pale sclereids, elliptic in outline at surface, the sclereid shell over parenchyma with flat, anastomosing longitudinal fibers adherent to the endocarp, tannin cells lacking, or few and interspersed among the fibers, endocarp thin, fragile, not operculate. Seed attached by an elongate hilum, raphe branches anastomosing, endosperm homogeneous; embryo basal. Germination and eophyll not recorded. Cytology not known.

Anatomy.—An adaxial hypodermis of two large cells, a marginal rib second in size to the midrib and guard cells with markedly thickened outer walls characterize these species and the other three members of the Archontophoenicinae in New Caledonia. *Actinokentia* is distinct from all other New Caledonia palms in a symmetrical, adaxially truncate, abaxially pointed midrib (Uhl and Martens in prep.).

Distribution.—Two species in New Caledonia.

Ecology.—The two species of *Actinokentia* occur in wet forests on serpentine soils from 60–1000 m in the southern part of the island. Individuals are small relative to those of other genera in the Archontophoenicinae and seldom reach the forest canopy. Where *A. divaricata* and *A. huerlimannii* are sympatric on the flanks of Mont Nekando, they appear to occupy different habitats and exposures, the first on the slopes descending to the Ngoye River, the second in a thicket beside the ridge trail.

Common Names and Uses.—Common names unknown. *A. divaricata* was reported to be introduced into cultivation in Europe more than a century ago. A new introduction was observed flowering and fruiting in late June 1980 at the Wahiawa Botanic Garden of the Honolulu Botanic Garden System (see also Baker 1980).

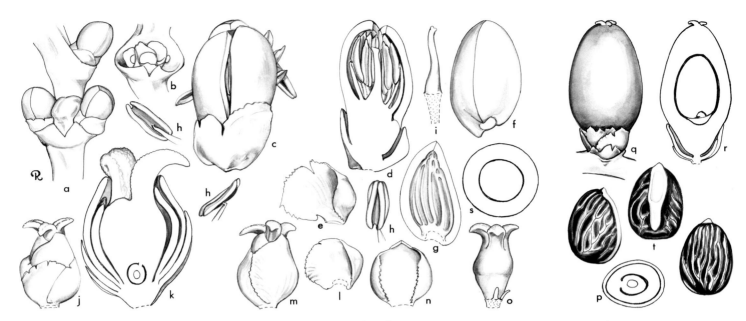

108.—**Actinokentia. a,** portion of rachilla with triad ×3; **b,** triad, flowers removed to show bracts ×3; **c,** staminate flower ×6; **d,** staminate flower in vertical section ×6; **e,** staminate sepal ×6; **f,** staminate bud, sepals removed ×6; **g,** staminate petal, interior view ×6; **h,** stamen in 3 views ×6; **i,** pistillode ×6; **j,** pistillate flower ×3; **k,** pistillate flower in vertical section ×6; **l,** pistillate sepal ×3; **m,** pistillate flower, sepals removed ×3; **n,** pistillate petal, interior view ×3; **o,** gynoecium and staminodes ×3; **p,** ovary in cross-section ×9; **q,** fruit ×1½; **r,** fruit in vertical section ×1½; **s,** fruit in cross-section ×1½; **t,** seed in 3 views ×1½. *Actinokentia divaricata*: all from *Moore et al. 9340.*

Notes.—Leaves of the two species are so different in morphology that *A. huerlimannii* was thought at first to belong in another genus. Foliar anatomy is strikingly similar, however, as are flowers and fruits. Small size and few leaves in the crown help to distinguish the genus.

Taxonomic Account.—Moore and Uhl (1984).
Plate.—59C; Fig. G.19.

Cyrtostachydinae J. Dransfield & N. Uhl, Principes 30:8. 1986. Type: **Cyrtostachys.**

Moderate to tall, unarmed; leaves pinnate, leaflets entire; crownshaft well developed; inflorescences infrafoliar, branched to 3 orders; peduncle very short, basal branches sharply divaricate; prophyll and peduncular bract similar, both caducous; triads borne in pits with rounded lips; staminate flowers symmetrical, rounded in bud, petals connate in the basal ⅓; filaments connate basally, inflexed in bud; petals of pistillate flower imbricate; gynoecium pseudomonomerous; fruit with apical stigmatic remains; embryo basal.

Cyrtostachys, the only genus in the subtribe, is Papuasian with one representative, *C. renda,* occurring west of Wallace's Line (Map 38). The strongly divaricate inflorescence branches are distinctive, as are the rachilla pits, and the connate petals and filaments in the staminate flowers. The genus is isolated with no clear relatives.

109. CYRTOSTACHYS Blume, Bulletin des Sciences Physiques et Naturelles en Néerlande 1:66. 1838. Type: **C. renda** Blume.

Solitary or clustered, moderate to tall, unarmed, pleonanthic, monoecious palms. Stems erect, bare, conspicuously ringed with leaf scars, often bearing a mass of adventitious roots at the base, where clustering, the clump rather close, or more rarely diffusely spreading by stolons. Leaves pinnate, neatly abscising; sheaths tubular, forming a well defined crownshaft, brilliantly orange-red colored in 1 species (*C. renda*), glabrous or scaly; petiole short to long, adaxially channeled or flattened, abaxially rounded or angled, glabrous or scaly; rachis like the petiole but

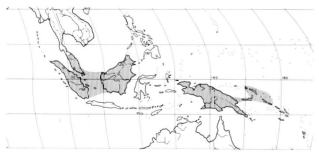

Map 38.—**Distribution of Cyrtostachydinae.**

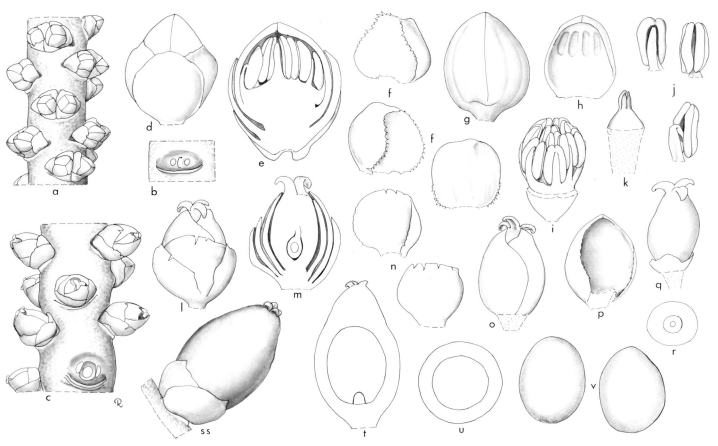

109.—**Cyrtostachys. a,** portion of rachilla with paired staminate flowers in pit ×3; **b,** detail of pit, flowers removed ×3; **c,** portion of rachilla in pistillate flower ×3; **d,** staminate bud ×9; **e,** staminate bud in vertical section ×12; **f,** staminate sepals ×9; **g,** staminate bud, sepals removed ×9; **h,** staminate petal, interior view ×9; **i,** androecium ×9; **j,** stamen in 3 views ×12; **k,** pistillode ×12; **l,** pistillate flower ×6; **m,** pistillate flower in vertical section ×6; **n,** pistillate sepals in 2 views ×6; **o,** pistillate flower, sepals removed ×6; **p,** pistillate petal ×6; **q,** gynoecium and staminodes ×6; **r,** ovary in cross-section ×6; **s,** fruit ×4; **t,** fruit in vertical section ×4; **u,** fruit in cross-section ×4; **v,** seed in 2 views ×4. *Cyrtostachys renda*: all from *Moore & Meijer 9157.*

angled adaxially; leaflets always single-fold, acute or acuminate, regularly arranged, often stiff, sometimes ascending, sometimes slightly paler beneath, ± glabrous adaxially, abaxially often with ramenta along the midvein and sometimes minutely dotted between the veins, transverse veinlets conspicuous or obscure. Inflorescence apparently protandrous, infrafoliar, highly branched to 3 orders, rather diffuse and spreading; peduncle usually very short, ± oval in cross-section; prophyll enclosing the inflorescence until leaf fall, borne just above the winged base of the peduncle, tubular, 2-keeled, ± lanceolate, with winged margins, splitting, soon caducous; peduncular bract borne just above the prophyll, completely enclosing the inflorescence, splitting longitudinally like the prophyll, caducous; subsequent bracts very inconspicuous, incomplete, low, triangular; rachis longer than the peduncle; first-order branches robust, spreading, with a short bare portion at the base, then branching to produce diverging rachillae or second-order branches; second-order branch-

es, when not rachillae, also with short bare portion and then branching to produce rachillae; rachillae elongate, cylindrical, rather robust, glabrous, papillose, minutely roughened or indumentose, often brightly colored, expanding long before anthesis; rachilla bracts low, triangular, spirally arranged, rather crowded, each partially enclosing a shallow pit bearing a triad of flowers, triads borne throughout the length of the rachillae; floral bracteoles membranous, very small and inconspicuous. Staminate flowers with 3, distinct, imbricate, broad, strongly keeled sepals with minutely toothed margins (? always); petals about twice as long as sepals, united at the very base to ca. ⅓ their length, distally with 3 triangular, valvate tips; stamens 9–15, the filaments awl-shaped, connate basally, apically inflexed in bud, anthers dorsifixed, latrorse; pollen elliptic or circular, monosulcate, with scabrate, finely reticulate, fossulate, or verruculate, tectate exine; pistillode almost as long as filaments, narrow, elongate, trifid. Pistillate flowers about the same size as or slightly larger than the staminate; sepals 3, distinct, rounded, imbricate, the margins minutely toothed (? always); petals 3, slightly larger than the sepals, distinct, imbricate proximally, asymmetrical, rounded with short triangular valvate tips; staminodal ring membranous, very low, bearing short truncate or irregularly triangular teeth; gynoecium unilocular, ellipsoidal with 3 short recurved stigmas, ovule pendulous from the apex of the locule, form unknown. Fruit 1-seeded, broad to narrow-ellipsoidal, usually black, the perianth whorls persistent, stigmatic remains apical; epicarp smooth, contrasting with the rachilla, mesocarp thin, oily, with abundant longitudinal fiber bundles, endocarp thin, closely adhering to the seed. Seed globose or ellipsoidal, apically attached, the hilum orbicular, endosperm homogeneous; embryo basal. Germination adjacent-ligular; eophyll bifid with narrow lobes. $n = 16$ (*C. renda*, Sarkar 1970).

Anatomy.—Tomlinson (1961) found that leaves of *Cyrtostachys* could be distinguished from those of other arecoid palms by the sinuous epidermal cell walls and fibrous hypodermis.

Distribution.—Eight species, *C. renda* (synonym *C. lakka*) in the Peninsular Malaysia, south Thailand, Sumatra, and Borneo and very widely cultivated, all other species in New Guinea and Melanesia.

Ecology.—*C. renda* is exclusive to peat swamp forest, usually near the coast, where it can be a conspicuous component of the vegetation; other species may be found in lowland rain forest and at altitudes up to about 500 m.

Fossil record.—Pollen referable to *Cyrtostachys* has been recorded from Upper Miocene deposits in Borneo (Muller 1972).

Common Names and Uses.—Sealing wax palm, pinang rajah (*C. renda*). *C. renda* is a commercially important ornamental. Locally its trunk is also used as a source of laths for supporting *Nypa* leaf thatch. The larger New Guinea species may supply timber.

Notes.—The relationships of *Cyrtostachys* are not obvious, hence its separation in a subtribe of its own.

Taxonomic Account.—There is no monographic account of the genus.

Plates.—*21A; 59D.*

Linospadicinae J. D. Hooker in Bentham & J. D. Hooker, Genera Plantarum 3:872, 876. 1883. ('*Linospadiceae*'). Type: **Linospadix.**

Small and slender to moderate, unarmed; crownshaft not present; leaves pinnate or pinnately ribbed, leaflets entire or irregularly bifid; inflorescences interfoliar, sometimes multiple, always spicate; prophyll persistent, inserted at the very base of the peduncle and included in the leaf sheaths; peduncular bract inserted near the base

Map 39.—**Distribution of Linospadicinae.**

of the peduncle and persistent or inserted distally and caducous; triads borne in deep pits; staminate flowers symmetrical or nearly so; petals of pistillate flowers imbricate; gynoecium pseudomonomerous; fruit with apical stigmatic remains; embryo basal.

The subtribe contains four closely related genera confined to New Guinea and the Moluccas, Australia, and Lord Howe Island (Map 39). These small and usually slender, or tall, rather robust (*Howea*) pinnate-leaved palms can be recognized by the lack of a crownshaft and particularly by the spicate inflorescences with triads of flowers enclosed in deep pits. The flowers of the four genera are remarkably similar. Staminate flowers have imbricate sepals, longer valvate petals, six or often many stamens, and small, slender, or no pistillodes. Pistillate flowers have imbricate sepals, extremely imbricate petals with valvate tips, small staminodes, and a pseudomonomerous gynoecium. Stigmatic remains are apical in the fruits.

It could be argued that the four genera should be regarded as four subgenera of a single genus but they can easily be separated by solitary or clustered habit, position of the peduncular bract, adnation of the endocarp to the seed, and homogeneous versus ruminate endosperm.

The spicate inflorescences and the often deep pits

with large closing bracts are similar to those of the New World Geonomeae. However, flower structure in the Geonomeae is very different: sepals and petals are thin, elongate, and connate, the gynoecium is trilocular (except in *Geonoma*), staminodes are specialized, and styles very long. The affinities of the four closely related genera of Linospadicinae are clearly with the pseudomonomerous Areceae.

Key to the Genera of the Linospadicinae

1 Peduncular bract inserted near the base of the peduncle, ± flattened, opening apically, shorter than and not enclosing the spike before anthesis, ± persistent and marcescent; filaments mostly inflexed, anthers dorsifixed; endocarp adherent to the seed. Moluccas to New Guinea . . . . 110. **Calyptrocalyx**
1 Peduncular bract inserted at the tip of the peduncle, tubular, enclosing the spike in bud, marcescent or caducous, leaving a ruffled scar on the peduncle; filaments not inflexed, anthers basifixed; endocarp adherent or free from the seed 2
2 Stems solitary, stout; leaflets always single-fold; staminate flower with 30–70 stamens; endocarp thick, cartilaginous, not adhering to the seed; endosperm homogeneous. Lord Howe Island . . . . 113. **Howea**
2 Stems usually clustered, usually slender; leaflets 1 to many-fold; staminate flower with 6–15 stamens; endocarp thin, adhering to the seed; endosperm homogeneous or ruminate 3
3 Leaflets single-fold; seed with ruminate endosperm, raphe extending the length of the seed, the branches reticulate. Australia . . . . 112. **Laccospadix**
3 Leaflets 1 to several-fold or the blade undivided, seed with homogeneous endosperm, raphe extending ⅓ the length of the seed or less, the branches free or anastomosing. New Guinea and Australia . . . . 111. **Linospadix**

110. CALYPTROCALYX Blume, Bulletin des Sciences Physiques et Naturelles en Néerlande 1:66. 1838. Type: **C. spicatus** (Lamarck) Blume (*Areca spicata* Lamarck).

Linospadix Beccari ex J. D. Hooker in Bentham & J. D. Hooker, Genera Plantarum 3:903. 1883 (Non H. A. Wendland 1875). Lectotype: *L. arfakiana* Beccari (see Beccari and Pichi-Sermolli 1955) (=*Calyptrocalyx* sp.).

Paralinospadix Burret, Notizblatt des Botanischen Gartens und Museums zu Berlin-Dahlem 12:331. 1935. Lectotype: *P. arfakiana* (Beccari) Burret (*Linospadix arfakiana* Beccari) (see Beccari and Pichi-Sermolli 1955).

Solitary or more often clustering, small to moderate, unarmed, pleonanthic, monoecious palms. Stem erect, becoming bare, conspicuously ringed with leaf scars. Leaves undivided with bifid apices and pinnately ribbed, or pinnate, marcescent or neatly abscising, a crownshaft scarcely developed; sheaths soon splitting opposite the petiole, scaly

or not, the margins usually fibrous; petiole short or long, adaxially channeled, abaxially rounded; lamina bifid with acute or lobed tips, or leaflets 1–several ribbed, acute, acuminate or sometimes toothed, concolorous, variously scaly or glabrous. Inflorescences solitary or multiple, interfoliar, protandrous, spicate; peduncle winged at the base, erect, elongate; prophyll inserted at the very base, ± included within the sheaths, common to all axes where inflorescences multiple, tubular, flattened, ±2-winged, tending to disintegrate into fibers apically; peduncular bract inserted near the peduncle base, tubular, open apically, shorter than the spike and not enclosing it, persistent or rotting on the inflorescence; spike short to elongate bearing a dense spiral of low, rounded bracts forming the lower lips of usually deep floral pits, each enclosing a triad except at the apex where enclosing paired or solitary staminate flowers, flowers exserted one at a time; floral bracteoles small, included. Staminate flowers sessile or briefly pedicellate; sepals 3, distinct, imbricate, often keeled; petals 3, distinct, about twice as long as the sepals, valvate, marked within by stamen impressions; stamens 6–120 or more, filaments elongate, linear, erect or usually inflexed at the apex in bud, anthers dorsifixed, erect or versatile, mostly deeply sagittate basally, latrorse; pollen elliptic, monosulcate, with finely reticulate, tectate exine; pistillode sometimes lacking or slender and ± club-shaped, about as long as stamens. Pistillate flowers ± globular; sepals 3, distinct, imbricate; petals 3, distinct, exceeding the sepals, broadly imbricate except at the minutely valvate tips; staminodes (2–)3–6; gynoecium unilocular, uniovulate, ellipsoidal with apical buttonlike or trifid stigmas, ovule hemianatropous, attached laterally above the middle of the locule. Fruit small to large, usually bright red at maturity, perianth whorls persistent, stigmatic remains apical; epicarp smooth, mesocarp fleshy or dry, white or pink, endocarp thin, closely adhering to the seed. Seed subbasally to laterally attached, hilum short to elongate, raphe branches anastomosing, endosperm homogeneous or ruminate; embryo basal. Germination adjacent-ligular; eophyll bifid. $n = 16$ (*C*. sp. as *Paralinospadix stenoschista*, Read 1966; *C. spicatus*, Sarkar 1970).

Anatomy.—Leaf (Tomlinson 1961).

Distribution.—About 38 species, one widespread in the Moluccas, the remainder in New Guinea.

Ecology.—Undergrowth palms of primary rain forest occurring at elevations from sea level to ca. 1000 m in mountains, usually on montane slopes with well drained soils, more rarely along streams or sometimes gregarious in swampy or poorly drained areas.

Common Names and Uses.—Not recorded.

Notes.—Distinctions between *Calyptrocalyx* and *Paralinospadix* based on ruminate versus homogeneous endosperm and stamen filaments erect versus inflexed at the apex in bud are not satisfactory. *Paralinospadix merrilliana,* the only species in Burret's *Paralinospadix* section *Atopocarpa,* has ruminate endosperm while the range from erect to in-

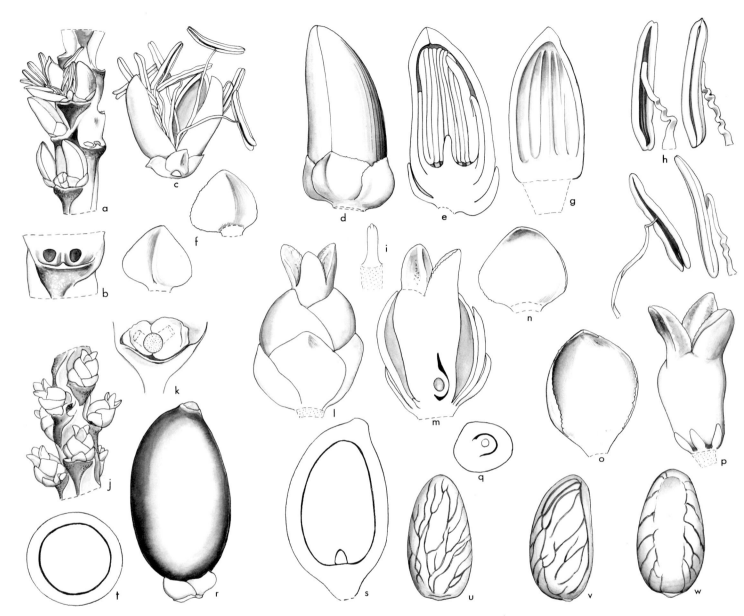

110.—**Calyptrocalyx. a,** portion of rachilla with triads ×3; **b,** scars of paired staminate flowers ×6; **c,** staminate flower ×6; **d,** staminate bud ×12; **e,** staminate bud in vertical section ×12; **f,** staminate sepal in 2 views ×12; **g,** staminate petal, interior view ×12; **h,** stamen in 4 views ×12; **i,** pistillode ×12; **j,** portion of rachilla at pistillate anthesis ×3; **k,** triad, flowers removed to show bracteoles ×6; **l,** pistillate flower ×12; **m,** pistillate flower in vertical section ×12; **n,** pistillate sepal, interior view ×12; **o,** pistillate petal, interior view ×12; **p,** gynoecium and staminodes ×12; **q,** ovary in cross-section ×12; **r,** fruit ×3; **s,** fruit in vertical section ×3; **t,** fruit in cross-section ×3; **u, v, w,** seed in 3 views ×3. *Calyptrocalyx* sp. (*Paralinospadix hollrungii*): **a-q,** *Moore et al. 9274*; **r-w,** *Moore et al. 9265.*

flexed stamen filaments may be found in a single flower of *C. spicatus.* A more useful division might be based on the manner in which the flowers are borne, whether in shallow or deep pits, but again sharp contrasts are difficult to make. Size alone, or solitary versus clustered stems, are not meaningful characteristics, though size is sometimes useful in the field. The structure of the inflorescence and the insertion of major bracts, however, are constant features binding together a series of species that exhibit marked differences in habit, foliage, and to some degree in habitat.

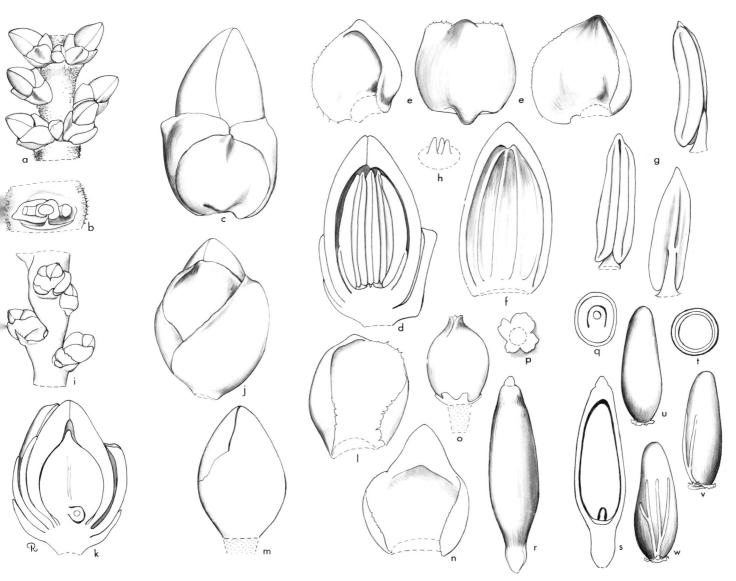

111.—**Linospadix. a,** portion of rachilla with triads ×3; **b,** triad, flowers removed to show bracteoles ×6; **c,** staminate bud ×12; **d,** staminate bud in vertical section ×12; **e,** staminate sepals ×12; **f,** staminate petal, interior view ×12; **g,** stamen in 3 views ×12; **h,** pistillode ×25; **i,** portion of rachilla in pistillate bud ×3; **j,** pistillate bud ×12; **k,** pistillate bud in vertical section ×12; **l,** pistillate sepal, interior view ×12; **m,** pistillate bud, sepals removed ×12; **n,** pistillate petal, interior view ×12; **o,** gynoecium and staminodes ×12; **p,** staminodes from below ×12; **q,** ovary in cross-section ×12; **r,** fruit ×3; **s,** fruit in vertical section ×3; **t,** fruit in cross-section ×3; **u, v, w,** seed in 3 views ×3. *Linospadix monostachya:* **a-q,** *Moore 9232; L. albertisiana:* **r-w,** *Brass 6893.*

Taxonomic Account.—For a partial synopsis see Burret (1935a).

Plate.—*60A, B.*

111. Linospadix H. A. Wendland in H. A. Wendland & Drude, Linnaea 39:177, 198. 1875. Type: **L. monostachya** (Martius) H. A. Wendland ('*monostachyos*') (*Areca monostachya* Martius).

Bacularia F. v. Mueller ex J. D. Hooker, Botanical Magazine 6644. 1882. Superfluous name. Type: *B. monostachya* (Martius) F. v. Mueller ex J. D. Hooker.

Small to very small, solitary or clustered, unarmed, pleonanthic, monoecious palms. Stem erect, slender, eventually becoming bare, conspicuously ringed with leaf scars. Leaves bifid to pinnate, neatly abscising or marcescent, a crownshaft not well developed; sheaths soon splitting opposite the petiole, bearing scattered scales, the margins often becoming fibrous, a tattering ligule some-times present; petiole very short to long, usually scaly; rachis very short to long; blade bifid with acute, acuminate or lobed tips, or divided into 1–several fold leaflets, the leaflets regular or irregular, acute, acuminate, bifid or ir-regularly lobed and praemorse, often bearing minute scales on both surfaces, transverse veinlets usually obscure. In-florescences solitary, interfoliar, ± erect, protandrous, un-branched; peduncle winged at the base; prophyll inserted near the base of the peduncle, tubular, 2-keeled, ± in-cluded within the subtending leaf sheath, persistent, be-coming tattered and fibrous; peduncular bract 1, inserted in the distal part of the peduncle or at its very tip, tu-bular, ± beaked, ± enclosing the spike in bud, soon split-ting longitudinally, deciduous; spike short to elongate, variously scaly, bearing dense to lax, spirally arranged, broad, ± triangular bracts forming the lower lips of very shallow floral pits, each bearing a triad except at the tip where bearing solitary or paired staminate flowers, the flowers exposed, not enclosed by the pit; floral bracteoles minute. Staminate flowers ± sessile, ± symmetrical, both of a triad apparently developing ± at the same time; sepals 3, distinct, broadly imbricate, ± keeled; petals 3, distinct, about twice as long as the sepals, with very thick valvate tips, internally marked with stamen impressions; stamens 6–12 erect, filaments very short, anthers dorsifixed, ± linear, apically acute, basally ± sagittate, latrorse; pollen elliptic, monosulcate, with finely reticulate, tectate exine; pistillode very small, minutely 3-pointed. Pistillate flow-ers eventually much larger than the staminate; sepals 3, distinct, broadly imbricate; petals 3, distinct, slightly ex-ceeding the sepals, with broad imbricate bases and con-spicuous, thickened, triangular, valvate tips; staminodes 3–6, irregularly lobed and toothlike; gynoecium unilocu-lar, uniovulate, ± ovoid, with 3 short stigmas, becoming recurved, ovule laterally attached near the base, hemianat-ropous (? always). Fruit ellipsoidal to spindle-shaped, bright red (? always) at maturity, perianth whorls persistent, the stigmatic remains apical; epicarp smooth, mesocarp thin, fleshy, with thin fibers next to the endocarp, endocarp very thin, closely adhering to the seed. Seed subbasally attached, the raphe extending ca. ⅓ the seed length, or less, the branches free or anastomosing, endosperm ho-mogeneous; embryo basal. Germination adjacent-ligular; eophyll bifid. Cytology not known.

Anatomy. — Not studied.

Distribution. — About 11 species, some five species in New Guinea, the rest in Australia.

Ecology. — Minute to small palms of the under-growth of tropical rain forest, especially at higher elevations.

Common Names and Uses. — Walking stick palms. Stems of *L. monostachya* have been used as walking sticks. The "cabbage" is edible and the mesocarp, though thin, is pleasantly acid to the taste.

Notes. — Several taxa in Queensland appear to be undescribed.

Taxonomic Account. — The only recent synopsis is Burret (1935a).

Plate. — 60C.

112. LACCOSPADIX Drude & H. A. Wendland, Nachrichten von der Königlichen Gesellschaft der Wissenschaften und von der Georg-Augusts-Uni-versität 1875:59. 1875. Type: **L. australasica** H. A. Wendland & Drude.

Small to moderate, solitary or clustering, unarmed, pleonanthic, monoecious palm. Stem erect, becoming bare, conspicuously ringed with leaf scars. Leaves pinnate, mar-cescent; sheaths soon splitting opposite the petiole, bear-ing scattered scales, the margins becoming fibrous; petiole long, adaxially channeled, abaxially rounded, bearing scattered scales; rachis curved, scaly like the petiole; leaf-lets numerous, single-fold, conspicuously plicate, acute or acuminate, adaxially and abaxially with minute scattered scales, abaxially with conspicuous ramenta along the main ribs, transverse veinlets not visible. Inflorescences soli-tary, interfoliar, protandrous, unbranched; peduncle winged at the base, erect, elongate, bearing scattered ca-ducous scales; prophyll inserted at the base of the pedun-cle, flattened, tubular, 2-winged, ± included within the leaf sheaths, tending to disintegrate into fibers apically; peduncular bract 1, inserted near the tip of the peduncle, enclosing the spike in bud, splitting longitudinally, decid-uous at anthesis; rachis ± equalling the peduncle, pen-dulous, bearing a slightly spiralled series of prominent, rounded bracts forming the lower lips of the floral pits; floral pits enclosing triads except at the apex where en-closing paired or solitary staminate flowers only, flowers exserted one at a time; floral bracteoles 3, ± sepallike. Staminate flowers borne on very short flattened pedi-cels, ± symmetrical; sepals 3, distinct, keeled, ± chaffy, with irregular margins; petals 3, ± twice as long as the sepals, distinct, triangular-ovate, valvate, marked within by anther impressions; stamens 9–12, erect, filaments very short, anthers ± elongate, basifixed, latrorse; pollen ellip-tic, monosulcate, with finely reticulate, tectate exine; pis-tillode minute, trifid. Pistillate flowers ± globular; sepals 3, distinct, ± chaffy, with irregular margins; petals similar to but longer than sepals, distinct, broadly imbricate ex-cept at the valvate, triangular tip; staminodes 3, small, ± triangular; gynoecium unilocular, uniovulate, ovoid-ellip-soidal, tipped with 3, short, recurved stigmas, ovule at-tached laterally near the base, campylotropous. Fruit el-lipsoidal when fresh, red at maturity, perianth whorls persistent, the stigmatic scar apical; epicarp smooth, me-socarp thin, fleshy, overlying stout longitudinal fibers, en-docarp thin, adherent to seed. Seed laterally attached with short oblong hilum, the raphe ± extending the length of the seed, the raphe branches anastomosing, endosperm deeply ruminate; embryo basal. Germination adjacent-ligular; eophyll bifid. *n* = 16 (Read 1965a).

Anatomy. — Not studied.

Distribution. — One species widespread in tropical rain forest in northeastern Queensland, Australia; the possibility of a second species cannot be dis-counted.

Ecology. — Occurs in shaded, humid rain forest on mountain ranges and tablelands at altitudes of 800–1400 m above sea level.

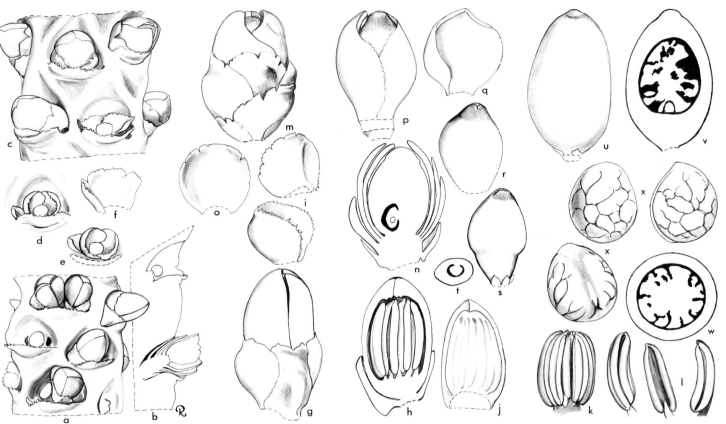

112.—**Laccospadix. a,** portion of rachilla at staminate anthesis × 3; **b,** portion of rachilla at staminate anthesis in vertical section × 3; **c,** portion of rachilla in pistillate bud, staminate flowers fallen × 3; **d,** triad, flowers removed × 2; **e,** triad, flowers and lip removed × 3; **f,** bracteole subtending pistillate flower × 3; **g,** staminate bud × 6; **h,** staminate bud in vertical section × 6; **i,** staminate sepal in 2 views × 6; **j,** staminate petal, interior view × 6; **k,** androecium × 4; **l,** stamen in 3 views × 6; **m,** pistillate flower with bracteoles × 6; **n,** pistillate flower, sepals removed × 6; **o,** pistillate sepal, interior view × 6; **p,** pistillate flower, sepals removed × 6; **q,** pistillate petal, interior view × 6; **r,** gynoecium × 6; **s,** gynoecium and staminodes × 6; **t,** ovary in cross-section × 6; **u,** fruit × 3; **v,** fruit in vertical section × 3; **w,** fruit in cross-section × 3; **x,** seed in 3 views × 3. *Laccospadix australasica*: all from *Moore & Volk 9240*.

Common Names and Uses.—Atherton palm. Rather infrequently cultivated as an ornamental.

Notes.—A very attractive palm because of the long spikes of red fruits.

Taxonomic Account.—There is no recent published assessment of infraspecific variation.

Plate.—See Front Dust Cover.

113. HOWEA Beccari, Malesia 1:66. 1877. ('Howeia'). Lectotype: **H. belmoreana** (C. Moore & F. v. Mueller) Beccari (*Kentia belmoreana* C. Moore & F. v. Mueller) (see O. F. Cook 1926 and Beccari and Pichi-Sermolli 1955).

Grisebachia Drude & H. A. Wendland, Nachrichten von der Königlichen Gesellschaft der Wissenschaften und von der Georg-Augusts-Universität 1875:55. 1875 (Non Klotzsch 1838). Lectotype: *G. belmoreana* (C. Moore & F. v. Mueller) Drude & H. A. Wendland (*Kentia belmoreana* C. Moore & F. v. Mueller) (see O. F. Cook 1926 and Beccari and Pichi-Sermolli 1955).

Denea O. F. Cook. Journal of the Washington Academy of Sciences 16:395. 1926. Type: *D. forsteriana* (F. v. Mueller) O. F. Cook (*Kentia forsteriana* F. v. Mueller = *Howea forsteriana* (F. v. Mueller) Beccari).

Moderate, solitary, unarmed, pleonanthic, monoecious palms. Stem erect, bare, conspicuously marked with close, horizontal or oblique leaf scars, the base sometimes expanded into a knob. Leaves pinnate, neatly abscising but not forming a crownshaft; sheath well developed, splitting longitudinally opposite the petiole, disintegrating into an interwoven mass of fine fibers; petiole short to moderately long, flattened or slightly channeled adaxially, abaxially ± angled, sparsely to densely scaly; rachis ± rounded to angled abaxially, adaxially angled, scaly as the petiole·

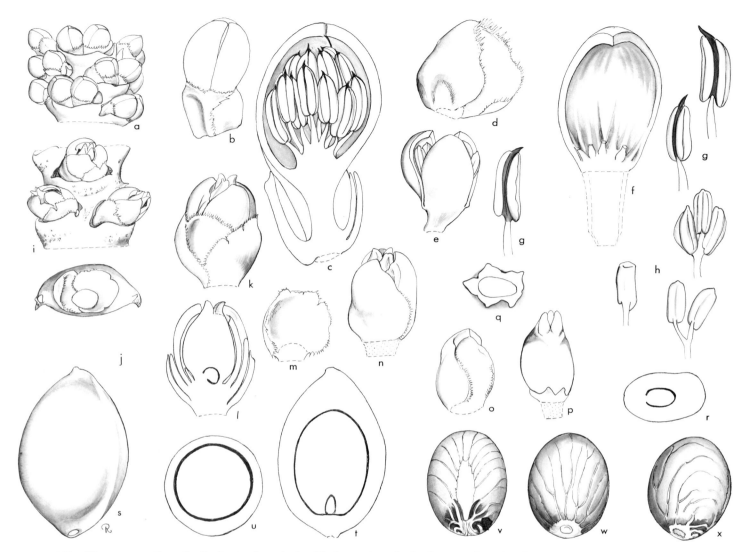

113.—**Howea. a,** portion of spike in staminate bud ×1½; **b,** staminate bud ×3; **c,** staminate bud in vertical section ×6; **d,** staminate sepal ×6; **e,** staminate flower, sepals removed ×3; **f,** staminate petal, interior view ×6; **g,** normal stamen in 3 views ×6; **h,** unusual solitary and branched stamens with diminished connective ×6; **i,** portion of spike at pistillate anthesis ×1½; **j,** view into pit to show bracteoles ×3; **k,** pistillate flower ×3; **l,** pistillate flower in vertical section ×3; **m,** pistillate sepal, interior view ×3; **n,** pistillate flower, sepals removed ×3; **o,** pistillate petal, interior view ×3; **p,** gynoecium and staminodes ×3; **q,** staminodes ×3; **r,** ovary in cross-section ×6; **s,** fruit ×1½; **t,** fruit in vertical section ×1½; **u,** fruit in cross-section ×1½; **v, w, x,** seed in 3 views ×1½. *Howea forsteriana:* **a-h,** *Bailey 9053;* **i-r,** Sydney Botanic Garden; **s-x,** *Moore 9254.*

leaflets numerous, single-fold, regularly arranged, curved or stiffly ascending, acute, acuminate or minutely bifid, adaxially with sparse scattered scales, abaxially ± glabrous or rather densely dotted with scales and bearing abundant floccose indumentum and ramenta along the midrib, transverse veinlets obscure. Inflorescences interfoliar, sometimes becoming infrafoliar after leaf fall, short or almost as long as the leaves, spicate, solitary or compound with up to 3–8 borne together on a common axillary boss, erect at first, later pendulous, protandrous; peduncle ± elliptic in cross-section, much shorter than or ± equalling the rachis, densely scaly; prophyll tubular, membranous; peduncular bract inserted near to or some distance from the prophyll, enclosing the inflorescence until anthesis, ± membranous, tubular, later splitting down its length, disintegrating and falling, leaving a low collar; rachis robust, scaly, densely covered with spirally arranged, ± spreading, low, rounded or triangular, rigid, coriaceous bracts, each forming a lip to a floral pit, enclosing a triad of flowers, except at the very tips where pits enclosing paired staminate flowers; floral bracteoles ± sepallike. Staminate flowers partially exserted one at a time from the pit at anthesis; sepals 3, distinct, imbricate, usually keeled, ± rounded, the margins toothed; corolla with a stalklike base ± as long as the sepals, and 3 ovate, valvate lobes; stamens 30–70 or more, filaments elongate, variously connate at the base for much of their length, the connective sometimes prolonged into a point, anthers elongate, ± latrorse; pollen elliptic, monosulcate, with scabrate, tectate exine; pistillode absent. Pistillate flowers ± globular; sepals 3, distinct, imbricate, rounded, the margins toothed; petals 3, distinct, basally strongly imbricate, the tips briefly valvate; staminodes 3–6, forming a low, irregularly lobed, membranous ring, or irregularly separated as triangular or bifid flanges; gynoecium unilocular, uniovulate, tipped with 3 short stigmas ± reflexed at anthesis, ovule laterally attached, campylotropous. Fruit ovoid, sometimes faintly ridged, 1-seeded, shiny dark green at first, turning dull yellowish-green or reddish-brown, perianth whorls persistent, stigmatic remains apical; epicarp smooth, mesocarp rather thinly fleshy with abundant longitudinal fibers, endocarp cartilaginous, not adhering to the seed. Seed laterally attached, raphe extending ⅓ the length of the seed or less, endosperm homogeneous; embryo basal. Germination adjacent-ligular; eophyll bifid. $n = 16$ (*H. forsteriana*, Venkatasubban 1945, Sharma and Sarkar 1957). $n = 18$ (*H. belmoreana*, Satô 1946).

Anatomy. — The two species can be distinguished by leaf anatomy (Tomlinson 1961).

Distribution. — Two easily distinguished species endemic to Lord Howe Island.

Ecology. — *H. forsteriana* is abundant on the island in lowland forest on sandy areas; *H. belmoreana* can be found with the former as scattered individuals, but becomes abundant at higher elevations up to about 450 m above sea level.

Common Names and Uses. — Kentia palms, Howea palms, sentry palms. Both species, but especially *H. forsteriana,* are important as commercially grown ornamentals.

Notes. — The two species of *Howea* are the largest palms in the Linospadicinae. *Howea belmoreana* is distinguished by curved leaves with erect leaflets and by a single inflorescence in each leaf axil, while *H. forsteriana* has rather flat leaves with drooping leaflets and several inflorescences in each leaf axil. Flowers and fruits mature slowly so that several inflorescences in different stages are often present on a single tree.

Taxonomic Account. — Bailey (1939a).

Plate. — 60D.

Ptychospermatinae J. D. Hooker in Bentham & J. D. Hooker, Genera Plantarum 3:872, 874. 1883. (*'Ptychospermeae'*). Type: **Ptychosperma.**

Small, moderate or tall; unarmed; leaves pinnate or rarely pinnately ribbed; crownshaft well developed; leaflets lanceolate or linear to cuneate, apically acute, oblique, truncate, or often praemorse, sometimes longitudinally divided; inflorescences infrafoliar; prophyll and pedun-

Map 40. — **Distribution of Ptychospermatinae.**

cular bract similar, inserted close together or peduncular bract large, inserted above, and exserted from the prophyll; staminate flowers larger than the pistillate with rounded, boat-shaped petals; stamens numerous, pistillode large, often bottle-shaped, or small, conic, trifid; petals of pistillate flowers imbricate; gynoecium pseudomonomerous; fruit with apical stigmatic remains; seed sometimes irregularly angled; embryo basal.

This subtribe is widespread in east Malesia extending to Fiji, Samoa, and Australia, with one outlying species of *Veitchia* in the Philippines (Map 40). The nine genera are well defined by the presence of prominent crownshafts, usually praemorse leaflets, symmetrical staminate flowers with often large, bottle-shaped pistillodes, and rather large fruits with apical stigmatic remains. Within the subtribe leaflets vary in shape and seeds are rounded to angled. Relationships among the genera and of the genera to other subtribes are not well understood.

Key to the Genera of the Ptychospermatinae

1 Leaflets of juvenile leaves entire, cuneate, several-nerved, leaflets of mature leaves divided longitudinally into 7–17 linear segments; peduncular bract similar to and included within the prophyll, prophyll and peduncular bract caducous 2

1 Leaflets in both juvenile and mature leaves cuneate, truncate, acute, acuminate, or oblique, undivided; peduncular bract similar to or longer than and inserted well above and protruding from the prophyll, prophyll and peduncular bract marcescent 3

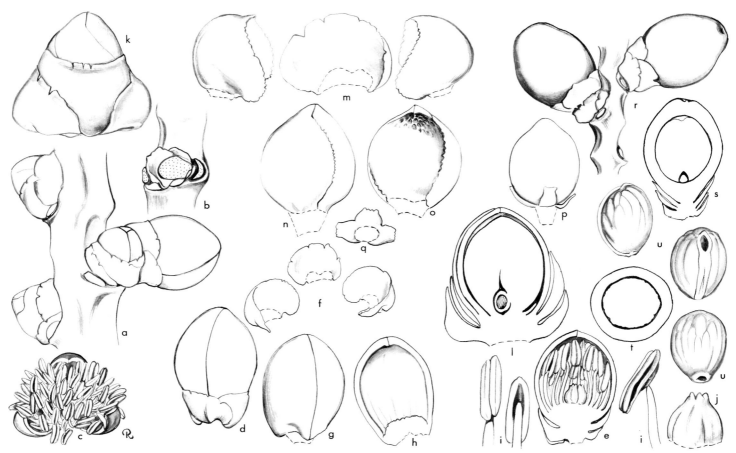

114.—**Drymophloeus. a,** portion of rachilla with triads ×3; **b,** triad, flowers removed ×3; **c,** staminate flower at anthesis ×1½; **d,** staminate bud ×3; **e,** staminate bud in vertical section ×3; **f,** staminate sepals ×3; **g,** staminate bud, sepals removed ×3; **h,** staminate petal, interior view ×3; **i,** stamen in 3 views ×3; **j,** pistillode ×9; **k,** pistillate bud ×6; **l,** pistillate bud in vertical section ×6; **m,** pistillate sepals ×6; **n,** pistillate bud, sepals removed ×6; **o,** pistillate petal ×6; **p,** gynoecium and staminodes ×6; **q,** staminodes ×6; **r,** portion of rachilla in fruit ×1½; **s,** fruit in vertical section ×1½; **t,** fruit in cross-section ×1½; **u,** seed in 3 views ×1½. *Drymophloeus subdistichus*: all from *Moore & Whitmore 9300.*

2 Stem slightly bottle-shaped; primary leaflets regularly arranged, divided into 11–17 segments, lacking white woolly scales abaxially; outer endocarp with large, conspicuously branched, tough black fibers; endosperm homogeneous. Australia .... 119. **Wodyetia**

2 Stem moderate to slender, not bottle-shaped; primary leaflets clustered, divided into 7–9 segments, bearing white woolly scales abaxially; outer endocarp with sparsely branched, thin, terete, straw-colored fibers; endosperm ruminate. Australia .... 118. **Normanbya**

3 Seed rounded in cross-section 4

3 Seed angled or grooved in cross-section 6

4 Leaflets broadly to narrowly wedge-shaped or broadly lanceolate to obovate; peduncular bract terete and prominently beaked, inserted well above and becoming exserted from the prophyll. Halmahera, Ceram, Ambon, to New Guinea, the Solomon Islands, and possibly to Fiji and Samoa .... 114. **Drymophloeus**

4 Leaflets lanceolate, medium to narrow; peduncular bract similar to and included within the prophyll 5

5 Leaflets wide in the middle or throughout, moderate to rather short, truncate, oblique, acute, or acuminate, chaffy ramenta present abaxially near the base of the midribs; mesocarp with several series of fibrous bundles, ± rounded in section, next to the endocarp. New Hebrides, Fiji, Philippine Islands .... 116. **Veitchia**

5 Leaflets narrow, long, usually with 2–4 rather short jagged points, lacking chaffy ramenta on midribs; mesocarp with a single series of large, flat fibrous bundles closely adherent to the endocarp. Northern Territory, Australia .... 115. **Carpentaria**

6 Peduncle elongate; peduncular bract inserted well above and exserted from the prophyll; fruit often angled and tapered at both ends; seed irregularly angled in cross-section, acute. Fiji Islands, Samoa .... 117. **Balaka**

6 Peduncle short, peduncular bract similar to and included in the prophyll; fruit ovoid; seed 3–5-furrowed in cross-section, acute and truncate or pointed at both ends 7

7 Leaflets 3-pronged at the apex, the center prong the longest; anthers basifixed, not versatile; fruit very strongly

5-angled when dry; the seed with 5 acute ridges. Eastern New Guinea .... 122. **Brassiophoenix**

7 Leaflets acute, oblique, truncate, or 2-pronged and concave apically; anthers dorsifixed, sagittate basally; fruit rounded or irregularly ridged when dry; seed with 5 rounded or irregular ridges 8

8 Seed rounded apically and with 5 rounded ridges; endocarp thin, fibrous or if somewhat bony then not elaborated and staminate flowers with short, conic-ovoid pistillode. Moluccas, New Guinea, northeastern Australia, D'Entrecasteaux and Louisiade archipelagos, Solomon Islands, Micronesia .... 120. **Ptychosperma**

8 Seed pointed apically, with irregular ridges; endocarp very thick, hard; pistillode always bottle-shaped. New Guinea, Bismarck Archipelago, Solomon Islands . 121. **Ptychococcus**

114. DRYMOPHLOEUS Zippelius, Algemene Konsten Letter-bode 1829(19):297. 1829. Lectotype: **D. oliviformis** (Giseke) Miquel (*Areca oliviformis* Giseke) (see Beccari and Pichi-Sermolli 1955).

Coleospadix Beccari, Annales du Jardin Botanique de Buitenzorg 2:90. 1885. Lectotype: *C. litigiosa* (Beccari) Beccari (*Ptychosperma litigiosum* Beccari) (see Beccari and Pichi-Sermolli 1955) (=*Drymophloeus litigiosus* (Beccari) H. E. Moore).

Saguaster O. Kuntze, Revisio Generum Plantarum 2:734. 1891. Type: *S. oliviformis* (Giseke) O. Kuntze (=*Drymophloeus oliviformis* (Giseke) Miquel).

Solfia Rechinger, Repertorium Specierum Novarum Regni Vegetabilis 4:232. 1907.

Type: *S. samoensis* Rechinger (=*Drymophloeus samoensis* (Rechinger) Beccari ex Martelli).

Rehderophoenix Burret, Notizblatt des Botanischen Gartens und Museums zu Berlin-Dahlem 13:86. 1936. Type: *R. pachyclada* Burret (=*Drymophloeus pachycladus* (Burret) H. E. Moore).

Small to rarely moderate, solitary, unarmed, pleonanthic, monoecious palms. Stem erect, slender, ringed with rather widely spaced leaf scars, sometimes short stilt roots present basally. Leaves pinnate, arching slightly, few in crown; sheath rather thick, forming a slender crownshaft, glabrous adaxially, abaxially densely covered with whitish tomentum and small red-brown scales, becoming minutely brown-dotted; petiole short, slender, adaxially deeply channeled, abaxially rounded, covered with deciduous tomentum and pale or dark scales; rachis long, slender, adaxially often sharply pointed or ridged and rounded, abaxially rounded, densely covered with brown tattered scales or tomentum; leaflets subopposite to alternate, in one plane, single-fold, broadly or narrowly wedge-shaped, or broadly lanceolate to narrowly obovate, distal pair sometimes broader and united or small and narrow, leaflets distally variously lobed or oblique, raggedly praemorse, adaxially glabrous except for a few scales near bases of major veins, abaxially densely covered with small scales on minor veins, major veins with ramenta toward the base, or lacking scales except on midrib, midvein and a

pair of large veins along or close to the margins prominent, margins densely covered with caducous tomentum and scales, transverse veinlets not evident. Inflorescences infrafoliar, branched to 1 or basally to 2–3 orders; peduncle relatively slender, elongate, elliptical in cross-section; prophyll deciduous, tubular, slender, dorsiventrally flattened, with 2, narrow, lateral keels, pointed, splitting apically and for a short distance abaxially to release the peduncular bract, densely covered with multibranched or pale-margined brown scales; peduncular bract tubular, slender, much longer than the prophyll, with a long rather flat, pointed tip, densely covered with scales like the prophyll; rachis shorter than the peduncle, angled, tapering, bearing rather few, distant, spirally arranged triads of flowers basally, and pairs of a pistillate and one staminate, or a single staminate flower distally; floral bracteoles low, rounded or truncate. Staminate flowers borne laterally toward the lower side of the pistillate flower in rounded indentations in the rachillae; sepals 3, distinct, imbricate, irregularly but strongly keeled, margins thin, variously notched; petals 3, distinct, ovate, valvate, evenly thickened, adaxially grooved, reflexed at anthesis; stamens numerous, 25 to more than 200, filaments moderate, awl-shaped, anthers elongate, sagittate basally, uneven, sometimes divided apically, medifixed, versatile, latrorse; pollen elliptic or triangular, monosulcate or trichotomosulcate, with finely punctate, tectate exine; pistillode with 3 short, rounded, 3-angled lobes or ovoid attenuate to ⅔ as long as the stamens, usually shortly trifid apically. Pistillate flowers broadly ovoid; sepals 3, distinct, imbricate, hooded, edges minutely toothed or variously notched; petals 3, twice as long as the sepals in late bud, distinct, ovate, imbricate, lateral margins shortly fringed, tips thick, valvate; staminodes 3, shortly joined basally, wide, truncate and bifid or uneven distally; gynoecium symmetrical, ovoid, tapering distally, unilocular, uniovulate, stigmas 3, recurved, ovule attached laterally or pendulous from the top of the locule, form unknown. Fruit ellipsoidal to ovoid, red at maturity, stigmatic remains apical; epicarp thin, smooth, becoming wrinkled when dry, mesocarp fleshy, fibrous, with stinging crystals, fibers adherent to the thin, rather smooth endocarp. Seed ovoid, surface smooth, hilum apical, raphe much branched, branches somewhat sunken, endosperm homogeneous or ruminate; embryo basal. Germination adjacent-ligular; eophyll bifid, or entire, ovate, margins toothed. $n = 16$ (*D. samoensis,* Essig 1971; *D. beguinii,* Read 1966).

Anatomy.—Leaf (Tomlinson 1961), fruit (Essig 1977b).

Distribution.—About 15 species extending from Halmahera, Ceram, Ambon to New Guinea, the Solomons, and possibly to Fiji and Samoa.

Ecology.—Understory palms in rain forests where rainfall is high.

Common Names and Uses.—Common names unknown. The black wood of the trunk is used for making spears, arrowheads, and other items. Some species are grown as ornamentals in moist tropical areas.

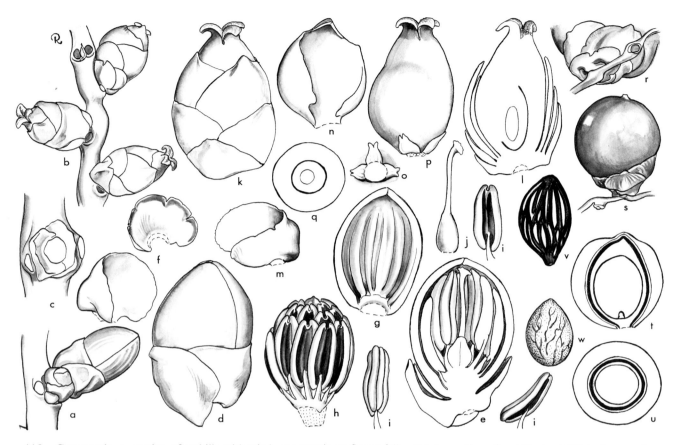

115.—**Carpentaria. a,** portion of rachilla with triad, one staminate flower fallen ×3; **b,** portion of rachilla in pistillate flower ×3; **c,** triad, flowers removed ×6; **d,** staminate bud ×6; **e,** staminate bud in vertical section ×6; **f,** staminate sepals in 2 views ×6; **g,** staminate petal, interior view ×6; **h,** androecium ×6; **i,** stamen in 3 views ×6; **j,** pistillode ×6; **k,** pistillate flower ×6; **l,** pistillate flower in vertical section ×6; **m,** pistillate sepal ×6; **n,** pistillate petal ×6; **o,** staminodes ×6; **p,** gynoecium and staminodes ×6; **q,** ovary in cross-section ×6; **r,** perianth in fruit ×3; **s,** fruit ×1½; **t,** fruit in vertical section ×1½; **u,** fruit in cross-section ×1½; **v,** fibers over endocarp ×1½; **w,** seed ×1½. *Carpentaria acuminata:* all from *Moore & Spence 9228.*

Notes.—Closely related to *Ptychosperma* but differing in a longer peduncle, a peduncular bract which is inserted well above and longer than the prophyll, and in seeds rounded, not lobed in cross-section. Tomlinson (1961) has noted similarity to *Ptychosperma* in leaf anatomy.

Taxonomic Accounts.—No overall treatment of species exists and obviously considerable field work will be necessary to produce one. See Moore (1953, 1969b).

Plate.—61A; Fig. G.3.

115. **CARPENTARIA** Beccari, Annales du Jardin Botanique de Buitenzorg 2:128. 1885. Type: **C. acuminata** (H. A. Wendland & Drude) Beccari (*Kentia acuminata* H. A. Wendland & Drude).

Moderate or tall, solitary, unarmed, pleonanthic, monoecious palm. Stem erect, moderate, smooth, gray, ringed with leaf scars. Leaves pinnate, arching or drooping, tips becoming pendulous; sheath forming a prominent crownshaft; petiole very short, deeply channeled adaxially, rounded abaxially, covered with small brown scales; rachis channeled basally to ridged; leaflets abaxially shallowly convex, ± clustered basally, opposite to subopposite distally, long, narrow lanceolate, tips oblique to truncate, praemorse, often with 2–4 longer prongs, the proximal sometimes tapering to a single or double point, adaxially lightly tomentose, abaxially covered with small brown-centered scales, midrib the only prominent nerve on both surfaces, larger abaxially, transverse veinlets not apparent. Inflorescences infrafoliar, horizontal, appearing rather large, branched to 3 orders basally, to 2–1 orders distally; peduncle very short, stout, flattened, bearing deciduous brown tomentum; prophyll tubular (not seen), caducous; peduncular bract tubular, caducous, shortly beaked, splitting abaxially, adaxially glabrous, abaxially densely to lightly covered in stellate brown scales, scar of 1 incomplete peduncular bract present; rachis much longer than the peduncle, elongate, tapering, bearing many (more than

20) ± angled first-order branches, each subtended by a very small, ridgelike bract; rachillae rather short, slender, spreading, bearing spirally arranged, distant triads of flowers for ⅔ their length and paired to solitary staminate flowers distally; floral bracteoles large, low, rounded. Staminate flowers lateral to the pistillate, symmetrical, ovoid; sepals 3, distinct, broadly imbricate, irregularly rounded, somewhat gibbous; petals 3, distinct, rather broadly ovate, valvate, evenly thickened, adaxially grooved; stamens ca. 33, filaments erect in bud, short, awl-shaped, anthers oblong-elliptical, bifid basally, emarginate apically, dorsifixed near the base, latrorse, connective broad, tanniniferous; pollen elliptic, monosulcate, with finely reticulate, tectate exine; pistillode bottle-shaped, as long as the stamens in bud. Pistillate flowers ovoid; sepals 3, distinct, imbricate, rounded, margins variously split; petals 3, distinct, broadly ovate and imbricate, tips thick, valvate, opening briefly apically to expose the stigmas at anthesis; staminodes 3, toothlike, bifid apically; gynoecium asymmetrical, ovoid with a bulge on one side, unilocular, uniovulate, stigmas 3, fleshy, recurved at anthesis, ovule very large, laterally attached, form unknown. Fruit ovoid when fresh, red at maturity, stigmatic remains apical, perianth persistent; epicarp smooth, becoming wrinkled when dry, mesocarp fleshy over a layer of broad, flat fibers anastomosing distally and closely appressed to the endocarp, endocarp thin, glasslike. Seed attached laterally, ovoid, ± pointed, round in cross-section, hilum elongate, raphe branches anastomosing, endosperm homogeneous; embryo basal. Germination adjacent-ligular; eophyll bifid. *n* = 16 (Read 1965a).

Anatomy.—Fruit (Essig 1977b).

Distribution.—One species in Northern Territory, Australia.

Ecology.—Found in rain forests along banks of streams at low elevations, usually near brackish water estuaries.

Common Names and Uses.—Carpentaria palm. A handsome ornamental but requires humid tropical or subtropical conditions. Widely planted in northeastern Australia and southern Florida in parks and along streets.

Notes.—Very closely related to *Veitchia*; differs in thinner and narrower lanceolate leaflets which are often four pointed and lack ramenta on their midribs, and in having only one series of fibers in the mesocarp. The species of *Veitchia*, as far as is known, have leaflets with large marginal veins which are not present in *Carpentaria* and the peduncle bears the scar of a second incomplete peduncular bract which is lacking in *Carpentaria*. These may be specific rather than generic differences but we have maintained the genus until further study of the variation within *Veitchia* can be undertaken.

Taxonomic Account.—Beccari (1885).

Plate.—61B; Figs. G.16, G.20.

116. VEITCHIA H. A. Wendland in Seemann, Flora Vitiensis 270. 1868. (Conserved name). Type: **V. joannis** H. A. Wendland (conserved type).

Vitiphoenix Beccari, Annales du Jardin Botanique de Buitenzorg 2:9. 1885. Type: *V. filifera* (H. A. Wendland) Beccari (*Ptychosperma filiferum* H. A. Wendland) (=*Veitchia filifera* (H. A. Wendland) H. E. Moore).

Adonidia Beccari, Philippine Journal of Science 14: 329. 1919. Type: *A. merrillii* (Beccari) Beccari (*Normanbya merrillii* Beccari) (=*Veitchia merrillii* (Beccari) H. E. Moore).

?*Kajewskia* Guillaumin, Journal of the Arnold Arboretum 13:113. 1932. Type: *K. aneityensis* Guillaumin (? =*Veitchia spiralis* H. A. Wendland).

Moderate to tall, solitary, unarmed, pleonanthic, monoecious palms. Stem moderate, sometimes wide at the base, ringed with close leaf scars, becoming longitudinally striate, covered in gray scales or smooth, gray to brown. Leaves pinnate, spreading or partially erect; sheaths forming a prominent crownshaft, covered with deciduous gray to brown tomentum; petiole short, adaxially channeled, abaxially rounded, densely covered with deciduous tomentum at least basally, often bearing dark brown to black tattered scales in various, sometimes diagnostic patterns at the apex; rachis elongate, flat to ridged adaxially, rounded abaxially, tomentose; leaflets regularly or irregularly arranged, single-fold, tapered from middle to base and usually to the apex, apically oblique, truncate, acute, or acuminate and variously toothed, the upper margin usually longest, midrib and marginal veins prominent, midrib bearing ramenta abaxially, otherwise abaxial surface covered in pale scales with brown centers, shining red scales, or glabrous, transverse veinlets not evident. Inflorescences infrafoliar, branched to 3 or 4 orders basally, fewer orders distally, branches variously tomentose; peduncle short, stout, dorsiventrally compressed; prophyll and peduncular bract caducous, prophyll tubular, rather thin, 2-keeled laterally; peduncular bract like the prophyll but lacking keels, briefly beaked, scar of an incomplete peduncular bract usually present; rachis longer than the peduncle, tapering, stiff, bearing very short bracts subtending branches and rachillae; rachillae medium to long, slightly to markedly flexuous, bearing spirally, or distally subdistichous triads nearly throughout, or triads only near the base of the rachillae and distally flower clusters of paired or solitary staminate flowers; floral bracteoles very small or conspicuous, short, rounded, margins notched. Staminate flowers bullet-shaped; sepals 3, distinct, imbricate, rounded, ± hooded; petals 3, slightly asymmetrical to symmetrical, valvate, more than twice as long as the sepals; stamens numerous, to over 100, filaments awl-shaped, long, slender, united at the base, not inflexed apically, anthers linear, basifixed or dorsifixed and then bases deeply sagittate, acute, emarginate, or bifid apically, latrorse; pollen elliptic, monosulcate, with finely reticulate or fossulate, tectate exine; pistillode attenuate from a bulbous base, as long as the stamens, usually bifid or trifid apically. Pistillate flowers ovoid; sepals 3, distinct, thick, imbricate,

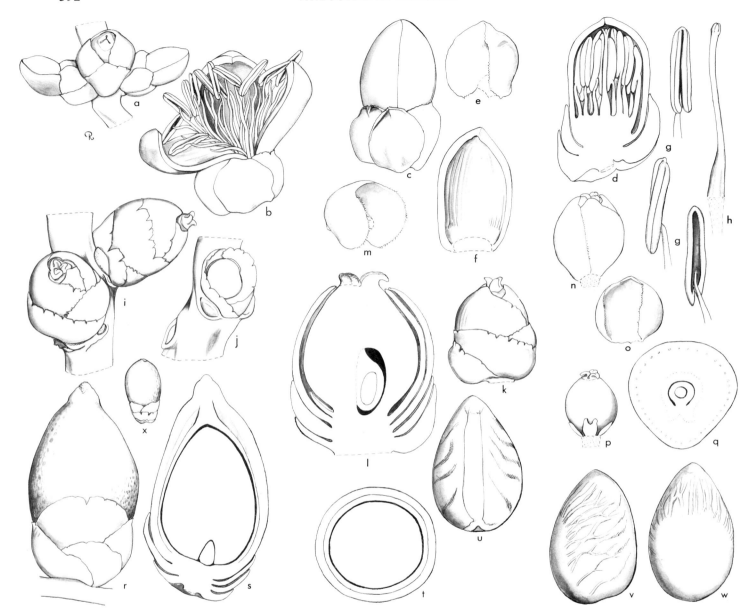

116.—**Veitchia. a,** portion of rachilla with triad ×1½; **b,** staminate flower ×3; **c,** staminate bud ×3; **d,** staminate bud in vertical section ×3; **e,** staminate sepal ×3; **f,** staminate petal, interior view ×3; **g,** stamen in 3 views ×6; **h,** pistillode ×6; **i,** rachilla at pistillate anthesis ×3; **j,** triad, flowers removed to show bracteoles ×3; **k,** pistillate flower ×3; **l,** pistillate flower in vertical section ×6; **m,** pistillate sepal ×3; **n,** pistillate flower, sepals removed ×3; **o,** pistillate petal ×3; **p,** gynoecium and staminodes ×3; **q,** ovary in cross-section ×6; **r,** fruit ×1; **s,** fruit in vertical section ×1; **t,** fruit in cross-section ×1; **u, v, w,** seed in 3 views ×1; **x,** fruit ×1. *Veitchia joannis*: **a-h** and **r-w,** *Moore & Koroiveibau 9351*; *V. simulans*: **i-q,** *Moore & Koroiveibau 9352*; *V. sessilifolia*: **x,** *Moore & Koroiveibau 9348*.

margins notched; petals 3, distinct, broadly imbricate, only slightly longer than the sepals, apices shortly valvate, margins notched; staminodes 3–6, toothlike, usually variously connate; gynoecium irregularly ovoid, unilocular, uniovulate, style thick, stigmas 3, sessile, recurved at anthesis, ovule large, laterally attached, form unknown. Fruit ovoid, beaked, small to moderately large, red or orange-red at maturity, perianth whorls enlarged, persistent, stig-

matic remains apical; epicarp thin, sometimes appearing lined or pebbled when dry, mesocarp yellowish, thin-fleshy, with 2–several layers of slender to large fibers and ground tissue sclerified near the endocarp, endocarp thin to thick, chartaceous, cartilaginous or nearly glasslike, fragile, in some species fracturing transversely. Seed ovoid to ellipsoidal, truncate basally, rounded to pointed apically, attached laterally, hilum elongate, raphe branches descend-

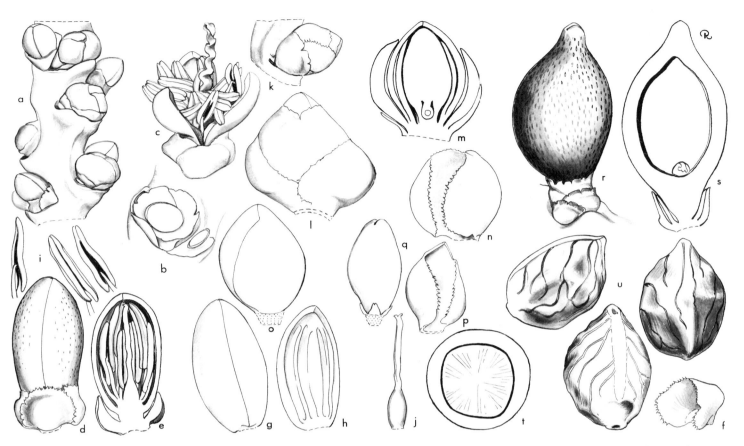

117.—**Balaka. a,** portion of rachilla with triads ×3; **b,** triad, flowers removed ×6; **c,** staminate flower at anthesis ×6; **d,** staminate bud ×6; **e,** staminate bud in vertical section ×6; **f,** staminate sepal ×6; **g,** staminate bud, sepals removed ×6; **h,** staminate petal, interior view ×6; **i,** stamen in 3 views ×6; **j,** pistillode ×6; **k,** portion of rachilla with pistillate bud ×3; **l,** pistillate bud ×6; **m,** pistillate bud in vertical section ×6; **n,** pistillate sepal ×6; **o,** pistillate bud, sepals removed ×6; **p,** pistillate petal ×6; **q,** gynoecium and staminodes ×6; **r,** fruit ×3; **s,** fruit in vertical section ×3; **t,** fruit in cross-section ×3; **u,** seed in 3 views ×3. *Balaka longirostris*: **d-q,** *Moore & Koroiveibau 9362*; *B. microcarpa*: **a-c** and **r-u,** *Moore et al. 9359.*

ing from the apex and sides, simple, forked, or branched and much anastomosed, endosperm where known usually homogeneous, ruminate in *V. merrillii*; embryo basal. Germination adjacent-ligular; eophyll bifid. *n* = 16 (*V. sessilifolia, V. vitiensis,* Read 1965a; *V. merrillii, V. montgomeryana,* Read 1966).

Anatomy.—Leaf (Tomlinson 1961), fruit (Essig 1977b).

Distribution.—About 18 species in the New Hebrides, Fiji, and Philippine Islands; ten species are endemic to Fiji.

Ecology.—Found from near sea level to cloud forests at 1000 m in dense or light forest; *V. merrillii* grows on karst limestone cliffs.

Common Names and Uses.—Christmas palm, Manila palm (*V. merrillii*). Several species are elegant ornamentals. The leaves have been used for thatch and the trunks as wood for rafters, spears, and canoes. The heart is edible as a salad and the

inflorescence and seed are also said to be edible in *V. vitiensis.*

Notes.—Several species of *Veitchia* are inadequately known (see Moore 1979). The genus is distinguished from other Ptychospermatinae by the combination of similar prophyll and peduncular bracts, lanceolate leaflets, and rounded rather than angled seeds. It is most closely related to *Carpentaria* (see notes under that genus).

Taxonomic Accounts.—Moore (1957a, 1979).

Plates.—*21B; 61C.*

117. **BALAKA** Beccari, Annales du Jardin Botanique de Buitenzorg 2:91. 1885. Lectotype: **B. perbrevis** (H. A. Wendland) Beccari (*Ptychosperma perbreve* H. A. Wendland) (see Beccari and Pichi-Sermolli 1955).

Small to moderate, solitary, unarmed, pleonanthic,

monoecious palms. Stem erect, slender, ringed with rather prominent leaf scars. Leaves pinnate, somewhat arched and spreading; sheath tubular, forming a prominent crownshaft, covered with brown scales; petiole very short to moderate, nearly terete or channeled adaxially, rounded abaxially, covered in tattered brown scales; rachis channeled to ridged adaxially, rounded abaxially, densely covered in tattered, brown scales; leaflets elongate to sigmoid or wedge-shaped and little tapered, alternate in one plane, single-fold, oblique or truncate apically, praemorse, with brown scales along ribs abaxially and scattered on bases of ribs adaxially, several veins about equal in size or midrib and marginal veins prominent, transverse veinlets not evident. Inflorescences infrafoliar, branched to 2 orders basally, 1 order distally, spreading; peduncle long; prophyll rather short and slender, 2-keeled laterally, slightly beaked, opening apically; peduncular bract inserted well above and much longer than the prophyll, terete, beaked, both bracts usually caducous before anthesis and bearing brown scales or tomentum; rachis shorter than the peduncle, bearing spirally arranged, pointed bracts subtending rachillae; rachillae rather short, bearing distichously arranged, low, rounded bracts subtending triads of flowers nearly throughout, a few solitary staminate flowers distally; floral bracteoles prominent, margins somewhat jagged. Staminate flowers symmetrical, bullet-shaped in bud; sepals 3, distinct, glabrous or red-brown tomentose, rounded, imbricate, margins toothed; petals 3, briefly united at the base, ovate, valvate, grooved adaxially; stamens numerous (24–50), filaments erect in bud, awl-shaped, anthers elongate, dorsifixed near the base, bifid apically, briefly sagittate basally, latrorse; pollen elliptic, monosulcate, with finely reticulate or fossulate, tectate exine; pistillode bottle-shaped with a long neck, often ± flexuous apically at anthesis. Pistillate flowers ovoid; sepals 3, distinct, imbricate, margins toothed; petals 3, distinct, widely imbricate, toothed laterally, pointed apically; staminodes usually 6, small, ± united, toothlike with jagged tips; gynoecium ovoid, unilocular, uniovulate, stigmas apparently short, ovule pendulous, form unknown. Fruit irregularly ovoid, tapered distally or at both ends, often angled, ± beaked, reddish-orange at maturity, drying pebbled, stigmatic remains apical; epicarp thin, mesocarp with outer sclereid layer, inner fleshy layer, and a single series of vascular bundles with thick fibrous sheaths next to the endocarp, endocarp thin, not operculate. Seed elongate, pointed, ridged, 4–5-angled in cross-section, hilum elongate, lateral, raphe branches few, endosperm homogeneous, embryo basal. Germination and eophyll not recorded. Cytology not studied.

Anatomy. — Fruit (Essig 1977b).

Distribution. — About seven species, five endemic to Fiji and two in Samoa.

Ecology. — These palms occur in various types of forest up to about 1000 m altitude.

Common Names and Uses. — Balaka palms. The straight stems have been used for walking sticks and spears and the kernel is reported to be edible. Some species (e.g. *B. seemannii*) are widely grown as ornamentals in Fiji and elsewhere.

Notes. — Closely related to *Veitchia* and *Ptychosperma,* differing from the former in ridged seeds and often angled and tapered fruit, and from the latter in a more elongate peduncle and in a peduncular bract that is exserted well above and much longer than the prophyll.

Taxonomic Account. — Moore (1979).

Plate. — *61D; Figs. G.19, G.21.*

118. **NORMANBYA** F. v. Mueller ex Beccari, Annales du Jardin Botanique de Buitenzorg 2:91, 170, 171. 1885. Lectotype: *N. muelleri* Beccari (illegitimate name) (*Cocos normanbyi* W. Hill = **Normanbya normanbyi** (W. Hill) L. H. Bailey) (see H. E. Moore 1963c).

Moderate to tall, solitary, unarmed, pleonanthic, monoecious palm. Stem erect, moderate, ringed with distinct leaf scars, vertically striate, gray, bulbous basally. Leaves pinnate, plumose, loosely arching; sheath forming a prominent crownshaft, pale, ashy gray, brownish near the top; petiole short or nearly lacking, channeled adaxially, rounded abaxially, densely covered with whitish tomentum and scattered brown, tattered scales; rachis long, arching, ± rounded adaxially and abaxially, densely covered in tattered brown scales; leaflets single-fold, irregularly arranged, divided nearly to the base into 7–9 linear segments, with or without midribs and with 1–3 large veins, apices of segments praemorse, only outermost 2 of each group with thickened margins, blade appearing dark green adaxially, bluish-white abaxially, adaxial surface glabrous, abaxial densely covered with uniseriate, medifixed scales, transverse veinlets not evident. Inflorescences infrafoliar, divaricate, somewhat pendulous in fruit, branched to 2 (? more) orders; peduncle short; prophyll tubular, rather narrow, 2-keeled laterally; peduncular bract like the prophyll, both deciduous; rachis bracts low, ridgelike, subtending spirally arranged, stout, angled branches and terete rachillae; rachilla bracts low, ridgelike, subtending triads basally, paired and solitary staminate flowers distally; floral bracteoles low, rounded. Staminate flowers symmetrical, bullet-shaped in bud, borne lateral to the pistillate on short, laterally-flattened stalks; sepals 3, distinct, imbricate, rounded, upper margins ± truncate, minutely toothed; petals 3, distinct, valvate, ovate, evenly thickened; stamens 24–40, filaments short, awl-shaped, anthers elongate, shortly bifid apically, dorsifixed almost at the base, ± introrse, connective elongate, tanniniferous; pollen elliptic, monosulcate, with scabrate, tectate exine; pistillode flask-shaped with long narrow neck, slightly longer than the stamens, apically expanded. Pistillate flowers ovoid; sepals 3, distinct, broadly imbricate, rounded with short pointed tips, margins slightly fringed; petals 3, like the sepals but longer and with short valvate tips; staminodes 3, broadly toothlike; gynoecium narrowly ovoid, unilocular, uniovulate, narrowing shortly above the ovarian region to 3, large reflexed stigmas, ovule pendulous, form unknown. Fruit ovoid to obpyriform, pointed distally, dull salmon-pink to purplish-brown at maturity, stigmatic remains apical forming a short beak;

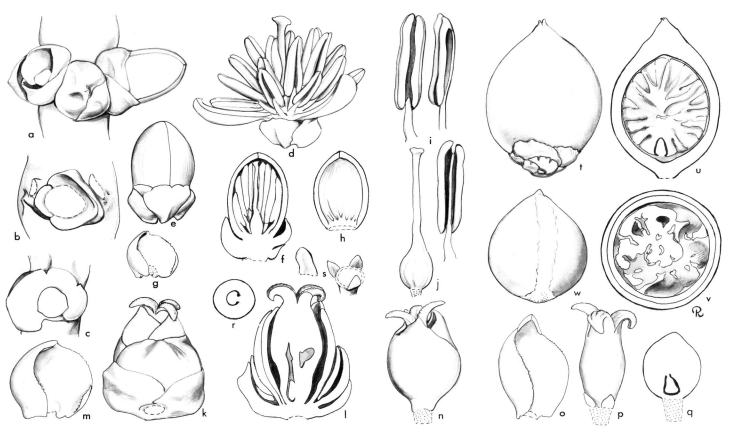

118.—**Normanbya. a,** portion of rachilla showing triad ×3; **b,** triad, flowers removed to show bracts ×3; **c,** scar of pistillate flower with enlarged bracteole ×3; **d,** staminate flower ×3; **e,** staminate bud ×3; **f,** staminate bud in vertical section ×3; **g,** staminate sepal ×3; **h,** staminate petal, interior view ×3; **i,** stamen in 3 views ×6; **j,** pistillode ×6; **k,** pistillate flower ×3; **l,** pistillate flower in vertical section ×3; **m,** pistillate sepal ×3; **n,** pistillate flower, sepals removed ×3; **o,** pistillate petal ×3; **p,** gynoecium and staminodes ×3; **q,** gynoecium in vertical section ×3; **r,** ovary in cross-section ×3; **s,** staminodes ×6; **t,** fruit ×1; **u,** fruit in vertical section ×1; **v,** fruit in cross-section ×1; **w,** seed ×1. *Normanbya normanbyi*: **a-b** and **e-j,** *Moore et al. 9246*; **c-d** and **k-r,** *Nur s.n.*; **s-w,** *Moore 7015*.

epicarp somewhat fleshy, drying wrinkled, mesocarp rather thin, with longitudinal, branched, straw-colored fibers adherent to the smooth endocarp. Seed laterally attached with a long unbranched raphe, hilum lateral, endosperm ruminate; embryo basal. Germination adjacent-ligular; eophyll bifid. Cytology not studied.

Anatomy. —Leaf (Tomlinson 1961).

Distribution. —One species in rain forests of northern Queensland, Australia.

Ecology. —*Normanbya* grows in moist Complex and Simple Mesophyll Vine Forest with an annual rainfall of 3000 mm, close to rivers and streams, often in swampy areas and usually in gravelly alluvial soils, in areas where dry periods are not more than 40 days long.

Common Names and Uses. —Black palm. The hard, dark wood was used by aborigines for making spears. It is a handsome ornamental requiring a warm moist, somewhat protected location.

Notes. —*Normanbya* can be immediately recognized by the irregularly arranged, longitudinally divided leaflets with 7–9 segments. *Wodyetia* has a similar leaf but with regularly arranged leaflets divided into more (11–17) segments. In *Normanbya* the leaflets also bear white woolly scales abaxially, the outer endocarp has a few thin fibers rather than many large fibers, and the endosperm is ruminate rather than homogeneous. Structurally the leaves of *Normanbya* and *Wodyetia* become ± bipinnate by the longitudinal splitting of a single leaflet. They may be developmentally different from the bipinnate leaves of *Caryota* where development of both primary and secondary leaflets is similar (Periasamy 1967). Such division of leaflets is unusual in palms occurring elsewhere only in certain genera of the Iriarteeae.

Taxonomic Account. —Bailey (1935c).

Plate. —*62A; Fig. G.14.*

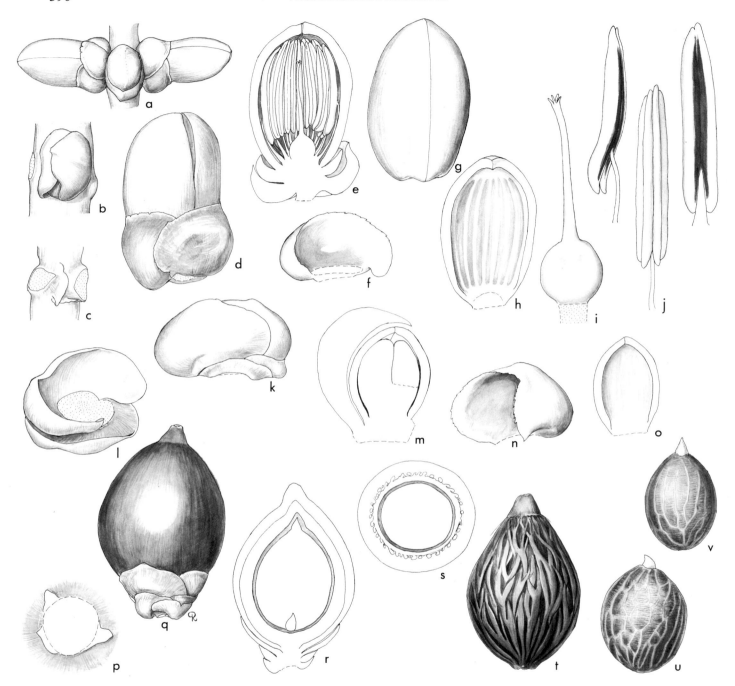

119.—**Wodyetia. a,** portion of rachilla with triad ×2¼; **b,** triad, staminate flowers removed, pistillate bud enclosed by bracts ×6; **c,** distal portion of rachilla, pair of staminate flowers removed to show scars and bracts ×6; **d,** staminate bud ×4½; **e,** staminate bud in vertical section ×4½; **f,** staminate sepal ×4½; **g,** staminate bud, sepals removed ×4½; **h,** staminate petal, interior view ×4½; **i,** pistillode ×9; **j,** stamen in 3 views ×9; **k,** pistillate bud and 2 basal bracts ×4½; **l,** bracts from base of pistillate flower ×6¾; **m,** pistillate bud in vertical section ×9; **n,** pistillate sepal ×4½; **o,** pistillate petal, interior view ×9; **p,** fruit in basal view ×1½; **q,** mature fruit ×1; **r,** fruit in vertical section ×1; **s,** fruit in cross-section ×1; **t,** outer endocarp showing large forking fibers ×1; **u, v,** seed in 2 views ×1. *Wodyetia bifurcata:* all from *Irvine 2184.*

119. **WODYETIA** A. K. Irvine, Principes 27:161. 1983.
Type: **W. bifurcata** A. K. Irvine.

Moderate, solitary, unarmed, pleonanthic, monoecious palm. Stem columnar, slightly bottled-shaped, closely ringed with leaf scars, light gray. Leaves pinnate, appearing plumose and oblong-elliptical in outline; sheath tubular forming a prominent crownshaft, elongate, green, splitting opposite the petiole, covered with a grayish-white tomentum; petiole short, stout, adaxially slightly concave to flat, abaxially rounded; rachis much longer than the petiole, adaxially becoming angled, abaxially rounded, petiole and rachis covered with grayish-white to brown, tattered-peltate scales and larger ramenta; leaflets single-fold, regularly arranged, divided into several linear segments, or deeply lobed, each segment usually with 1 (2–4) main ribs, apices coarsely praemorse sometimes obliquely so, or with 2–several small teeth, rarely pointed, tapering, terminal leaflets single or paired, adaxially glabrous, abaxially densely covered with very small whitish scales, transverse veinlets not evident. Inflorescences infrafoliar, horizontal in bud, becoming ± pendulous in fruit, branched to 4 orders basally, 2–1 orders distally; peduncle short, wide, ± flattened; prophyll tubular, dorsiventrally flattened, with 2 flat lateral keels, rather narrow, tapering from the base to a blunt point, caducous; peduncular bract like the prophyll but not keeled, 4–5 small, incomplete bracts present above the peduncular bract; rachis much longer than the peduncle bearing distant, stout, angled, spirally arranged branches subtended by small, pointed, or wrinkled bracts; rachillae rather short, cylindrical, bearing widely spaced triads basally and paired or solitary staminate flowers distally; floral bracteoles small, narrow, imbricate. Staminate flower symmetrical, bullet-shaped in bud; sepals 3, distinct, imbricate, rounded, inflated, margins finely toothed; petals 3, distinct, broadly ovate, valvate, very hard, about twice as long as the sepals; stamens 60–71, filaments slender, terete, short, anthers elongate, narrow, slightly bifid apically, unevenly sagittate basally, dorsifixed near the base, latrorse, connective elongate, tanniniferous; pollen elliptic, monosulcate, with punctate, tectate exine; pistillode bottle-shaped with a long neck, terminated by 4–5 short, linear lobes or papillae. Pistillate flowers (buds only seen), ovoid; sepals 3, distinct, broadly imbricate, rounded, margins finely tattered; petals 3, distinct, imbricate, hooded, valvate distally; staminodes 6, very small, triangular with short filaments; gynoecium conic-ovoid, unilocular, uniovulate, stigmas 3, apices rounded. Fruit globose-ovoid, orange-red at maturity, stigmatic remains apical forming a conical beak; epicarp thin with very short, stout fibers below the epidermal layer, mesocarp fleshy, orange-yellow when ripe, thin with longitudinal fibers, some forked, endocarp complex with outer distinctive thick, flat, branched fibers and an inner layer of horizontal fibers. Seed ellipsoidal, beaked, raphe branches medium, anastomosing, slightly impressed, endosperm homogeneous; embryo basal. Germination adjacent-ligular; eophyll bifid. $n = 16$ (Johnson 1985).

Anatomy. — Not studied.
Distribution. — One species in northeastern Queensland, Australia, confined to the southwest, south and southeast sides of the Melville Range.

Ecology. — Forming the canopy in open woodland communities of rain forest in coarse, loose granite sand, among huge granite boulders.

Common Names and Uses. — Foxtail palm. Seems destined to become a handsome ornamental for periodically dry, relatively cool climates.

Notes. — The divided leaflets and large black, pericarp fibers are the distinguishing characters. The genus is most closely related to *Normanbya*. See notes under *Normanbya*.

Taxonomic Account. — Irvine (1983).

Plate. — 62B.

120. **PTYCHOSPERMA** Labillardière, Mémoires de la Classe des Sciences Mathématiques et Physiques de l'Institut National de France 1808(2):252. 1809.
Type: **P. gracile** Labillardière.

Seaforthia R. Brown, Prodromus Florae Novae Hollandiae 267. 1810. Type: *S. elegans* R. Brown (=*Ptychosperma elegans* (R. Brown) Blume).

Drymophloeus subgenus *Actinophloeus* Beccari, Malesia 1:42. 1877.

Actinophloeus (Beccari) Beccari, Annales du Jardin Botanique de Buitenzorg 2:126. 1885. Lectotype: *A. ambiguus* (Beccari) Beccari (*Drymophloeus ambiguus* Beccari) (=*Ptychosperma ambiguum* (Beccari) Beccari).

Romanowia Sander ex André, Revue Horticole 71:262. 1899. Type: *R. nicolai* Sander ex André (*Ptychosperma nicolai* (Sander ex André) Burret) (see Moore 1963c).

Ponapea Beccari, Botanische Jahrbücher für Systematik 59:13. 1924. Type: *P. ledermanniana* Beccari (=*Ptychosperma ledermannianum* (Beccari) H. E. Moore & Fosberg).

Strongylocaryum Burret, Notizblatt des Botanischen Gartens und Museums zu Berlin-Dahlem 13:95. 1936. Type: *S. macranthum* Burret (=*Ptychosperma salomonense* Burret).

Small to moderate, solitary or clustered, unarmed, pleonanthic, monoecious palms. Stems erect, usually slender, smooth, often gray, obscurely or conspicuously ringed with leaf scars. Leaves pinnate, rather short, vertical to ± horizontal, relatively few in the crown; sheath elongate, forming a prominent crownshaft, bearing tattered, peltate, or tufted scales and tomentum, the sheath apex with or without a triangular or ligulate, sometimes divided appendage opposite or to one side of the petiole; petiole short or elongate, channeled adaxially, usually rounded abaxially, tomentose or with scales; rachis longer than the petiole, adaxially ridged, abaxially rounded, variously scaly; leaflets regularly or irregularly arranged, or clus-

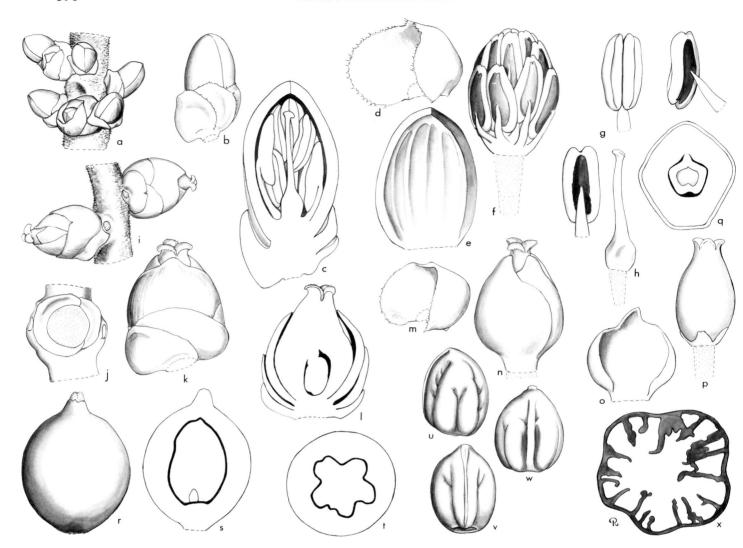

120.—**Ptychosperma. a,** portion of rachilla with triads ×3; **b,** staminate bud ×6; **c,** staminate bud in vertical section ×12; **d,** staminate sepal ×12; **e,** staminate petal, interior view ×12; **f,** androecium ×12; **g,** stamen in 3 views ×12; **h,** pistillode ×12; **i,** portion of rachilla in pistillate flower ×3; **j,** triad, flowers removed to show bracteoles ×6; **k,** pistillate flower ×6; **l,** pistillate flower in vertical section ×6; **m,** pistillate sepal ×6; **n,** pistillate flower, sepals removed ×6; **o,** pistillate petal, interior view ×6; **p,** gynoecium and staminodes ×6; **q,** ovary in cross-section ×12; **r,** fruit ×3; **s,** fruit in vertical section ×3; **t,** fruit in cross-section ×3; **u, v, w,** seed in 3 views ×3; **x,** seed in cross-section ×6. *Ptychosperma caryotoides*: **a–q,** *Moore & Womersley 9279*; *P. macarthurii*: **r–w,** *Moore 6023*; *P. elegans*: **x,** *White 7761*.

tered, single-fold, wedge-shaped, linear or wider medially, apices obliquely or concavely praemorse, or praemorse and notched, the margins extending beyond the midrib, midrib always prominent, marginal ribs thickened, usually glabrous adaxially, the large or small distal leaflets linear to broadly wedge-shaped, ramenta present or absent along abaxial ribs, transverse veinlets evident (? always). Inflorescences infrafoliar, branched usually to 2, 3, or 4(–6) orders, protandrous; peduncle usually short but elongate in *P. tagulense* and *P. palauense,* angled, glabrous, or with scales and tomentum throughout; prophyll tubular, dorsiventrally flattened, keeled laterally, attached at the base

of the peduncle, splitting apically, then abaxially, early caducous; peduncular bract tubular, similar to, attached close to, and enclosed by the prophyll, often with a hard short or tapering beak, splitting abaxially, early caducous, an incomplete peduncular bract usually present; rachis longer than the peduncle except where peduncle elongate; rachis bracts triangular to ligulate, or short, stubby, in horizontal furrows, spirally arranged; rachillae elongate, often fleshy, bearing spirally arranged bracts similar to the rachis bracts, subtending triads basally and paired to solitary staminate flowers distally, from as few as 4 to more than 100 clusters per rachilla depending on the species;

floral bracteoles short, rounded. Staminate flowers bullet-shaped to ovoid, lateral to the pistillate in triads; sepals 3, distinct, broadly imbricate, sometimes gibbous, margins fringed, tips shortly pointed; petals 3, distinct, ovate, rather thick, fibrous, valvate, grooved adaxially, 3–4 times as long as the sepals; stamens 9–over 100, arranged in alternating antesepalous whorls of 3 and antepetalous whorls of several (Uhl and Moore 1980), filaments short, awl-shaped, not inflexed, anthers linear-lanceolate, strongly often unevenly sagittate basally, bifid apically, dorsifixed near the middle, versatile, latrorse, connective elongate, tanniniferous; pollen elliptic or rarely subtriangular, monosulcate or rarely trichotomosulcate, with finely reticulate, tectate exine; pistillode bottle-shaped with a long neck, irregularly cleft apically, or short, conic-ovoid, trifid or tripapillate apically. Pistillate flowers shorter than the staminate, conic-ovoid; sepals 3, distinct, broadly imbricate, sometimes gibbous, marginally fringed; petals 3, distinct, broadly imbricate, tips valvate, thick, pointed, opening slightly but not reflexed at anthesis; staminodes toothlike, linear or united, then broad, toothed or ribbed, and scale-like; gynoecium conic-ovoid, unilocular, rarely bi- or trilocular, stigmas 3, short, reflexed at anthesis, ovule hemianatropous, 5-angled, pendulous, funicle long, bearing a short aril. Fruit globose to ellipsoidal, red, orange or purple-black at maturity, stigmatic remains apical, forming a beak, perianth persistent; epicarp granular due to short or long, oblique, fibrous bundles and interspersed brachysclereids, mesocarp fleshy, mucilaginous or tanniniferous, sometimes with irritant needle crystals, endocarp fibrous with vascular bundles with large fibrous sheaths at several levels and extending into the inner mesocarp or united in a single layer (*P. salomonense*), usually adherent to the seed. Seed longitudinally 5-grooved or angled, rarely 3-grooved or rounded in cross-section, hilum lateral, raphe branches few, sparsely branched, endosperm homogeneous or ruminate; embryo basal. Germination adjacent-ligular; eophyll bifid. $n = 16$ (*P. elegans, P. macarthurii, P. sanderianum,* Eichhorn 1953, 1957; Read 1965a, 1966; Satô 1946; Sarkar 1970; Sharma and Sarkar 1957).

Anatomy.—Fruit (Essig 1977b), leaf (Tomlinson 1961), inflorescence and flower development (Uhl 1976a, b), stamen development (Uhl and Moore 1980), correlations of anatomy with pollination (Uhl and Moore 1977a).

Distribution.—Twenty-eight species centered in New Guinea and the D'Entrecasteaux and Louisiade archipelagos but extending eastwards from the Moluccas to the Solomon Islands and southwards from the Caroline Islands to northeastern Australia. A number of other species have been described but are as yet poorly known.

Ecology.—Each of the four subgenera and the two sections of subgenus *Actinophloeus* has a distinct range and habitat. The center of diversity of subgenus *Ptychosperma* and the two sections of subgenus *Actinophloeus* is the mountainous southeastern tip of New Guinea, where each of the groups has a number of endemic taxa. *P. palauense,* the only species in subgenus *Korora* and possibly the most primitive, apparently occurs on limestone, an unusual habitat. Other species inhabit coastal or swampy lowland forests, and others the better drained edges of these areas or foothills. *P. vestitum* is exceptional in occurring in fresh-water swamps. Pollination in *P. macarthurii* is mostly by bees of the genus *Nomia* (Halictidae) which are attracted to flowers of both sexes by nectar (Essig 1973).

Common Names and Uses.—Solitaire palm (*P. elegans*), Macarthur palm (*P. macarthurii*). Some species make elegant ornamentals but need plentiful moisture and protection from winds. Essig (1978) notes reports of use of the wood for bows, arrowheads, and spears, and that the fruit of some species has been a poor substitute for betel nut.

Notes.—Large areas in the range of the genus are still unexplored botanically and new species may be discovered in future as noted by Essig (1978). *Ptychosperma* is considered (Essig 1978) to have coevolved with *Ptychococcus* and *Brassiophoenix* to which it seems closely related. About 12 species had been introduced into cultivation through the 1950's; seven of these have been in cultivation for over 100 years and are widely distributed around the world. Growers should be aware of the possibility of hybridization which has been common among the cultivated species (Essig 1975b).

Taxonomic Account.—Essig (1978).

Plate.—62C; Figs. G.13, G.15, G.20.

121. PTYCHOCOCCUS Beccari, Annales du Jardin Botanique de Buitenzorg 2:100. 1885. Lectotype: **P. paradoxus** (Scheffer) Beccari (*Drymophloeus paradoxus* Scheffer) (see Burret 1928a).

Moderate, solitary, unarmed, pleonanthic, monoecious palms. Stem slender to moderate, ringed with leaf scars, gray or brownish. Leaves pinnate, spreading to ascending, blade ± horizontal basally but twisting toward an arched apex; sheath forming a long crownshaft, margins oblique, lacking a ligule, covered in dense, partially deciduous scales or tomentum; petiole very short, channeled adaxially, rounded abaxially, densely tomentose; rachis adaxially flat basally, with a central ridge at midlength to ridged distally, abaxially rounded, densely tomentose; leaflets lanceolate, single-fold, apically very oblique, truncate, or somewhat pointed, and toothed, red-brown or pale scales on both surfaces, denser abaxially and along veins, midrib prominent, marginal ribs also large and sometimes (? always) densely tomentose, transverse veinlets not evident. Inflorescences solitary, infrafoliar, stiff, usually several clustered below the crownshaft, horizontal in flower, drooping in fruit, branched to 3 orders basally, fewer orders distally, all branches densely scaly, becoming gla-

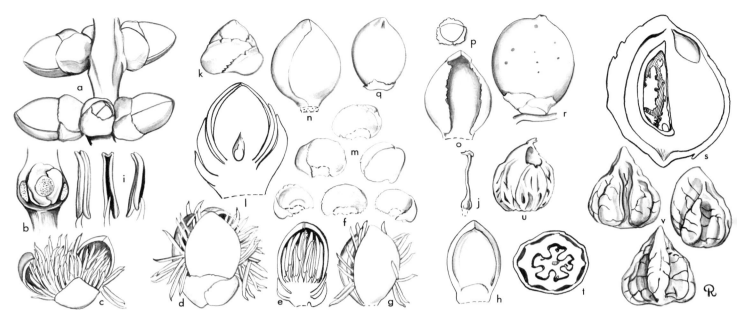

121.—**Ptychococcus. a,** portion of rachilla with triads ×1½; **b,** triad, flowers removed ×1½; **c,** staminate flower from above ×1½; **d,** staminate flower, lateral view ×1½; **e,** staminate bud in vertical section ×1½; **f,** staminate sepals ×1½; **g,** staminate flower, sepals removed ×1½; **h,** staminate petal, interior view ×1½; **i,** stamen in 3 views ×3; **j,** pistillode ×1½; **k,** pistillate bud ×1½; **l,** pistillate bud in vertical section ×3; **m,** pistillate sepals ×1½; **n,** pistillate bud, sepals removed ×3; **o,** pistillate petal ×3; **p,** staminodes ×3; **q,** gynoecium and staminodes ×3; **r,** fruit ×½; **s,** fruit in vertical section ×1; **t,** fruit in cross-section ×½; **u,** endocarp ×½; **v,** seed in 3 views ×1. *Ptychococcus lepidotus*: all from *Moore et al. 9259.*

brous; peduncle short, stout, dorsiventrally compressed; prophyll tubular, 2-keeled laterally, slightly beaked, bearing deciduous tomentum; peduncular bract like the prophyll but lacking keels, second partial peduncular bract present in young stages; rachis longer than the peduncle bearing very short, wide, rounded bracts subtending distant branches and rachillae; rachillae rather short, sometimes zigzag, bearing very short rounded bracts subtending distant triads of large flowers, flowers borne nearly throughout the rachillae, projecting on either side of the rachillae; floral bracteoles irregular, rounded, those surrounding the pistillate flower of medium height; scar of pistillate flower very large compared to those of staminate flowers. Staminate flowers slightly asymmetrical; sepals 3, distinct, imbricate, keeled dorsally toward a gibbous base, margins split and bearing hairs; petals 3, distinct, valvate, ovate, glabrous or densely covered in small membranous scales; stamens numerous (–100), filaments short, awl-shaped, anthers elongate, notched apically, deeply bifid basally, dorsifixed near the base, ± introrse, connective tanniniferous; pollen elliptic, monosulcate, with finely reticulate, tectate exine; pistillode bottle-shaped with neck as long as the stamens, apically with a few short pointed tips. Pistillate flowers ovoid, smaller than the staminate at anthesis; sepals 3, distinct, imbricate, rounded, sometimes covered with small hairs; petals 3, distinct, broadly imbricate with short, thick valvate tips, sometimes densely scaly; staminodes 3, ± united in a low semicupule; gynoecium ovoid, unilocular, uniovulate, style not differentiated, stigma 3-lobed, ovule pendulous, 5-angled, form unknown. Fruit ovoid, prominently wrinkled and angled when dry, orange to red at maturity, perianth persistent

as a large cupule, stigmatic scar slightly eccentric; epicarp with short oblique fibrous bundles and interspersed brachysclereids, mesocarp fleshy with tanniniferous cells and vascular bundles lacking fibrous sheaths, endocarp with large keel, deeply grooved between 3 lateral and 2 ventral ridges, wall hard, thick. Seed 5-lobed, like the endocarp in shape, hilum round, apical, raphe branches thin, endosperm with shallow marginal ruminations and a deep intrusion in the rapheal lobes; embryo basal. Germination adjacent-ligular; eophyll bifid, tips toothed. $n = 16$ (*P. lepidotus*, Read 1965a).

Anatomy.—Leaf (Tomlinson 1961).

Distribution.—Seven species, all rather poorly known, have been described; six are found in New Guinea and one in the Solomon Islands.

Ecology.—In rain forest along rivers in the lowlands and on mountain ridges.

Common Names and Uses.—Common names unknown. The wood is extremely tough and used for bows, arrows, and building. The seed is said to be edible.

Notes.—Closely related to *Ptychosperma,* differing in having a thick hard endocarp and seeds pointed at both ends with sharp or irregular, not rounded ridges.

Taxonomic Accounts.—No recent assessment exists. See Moore (1965a) and Essig (1977b).

Plate.—62D; Fig. G.23.

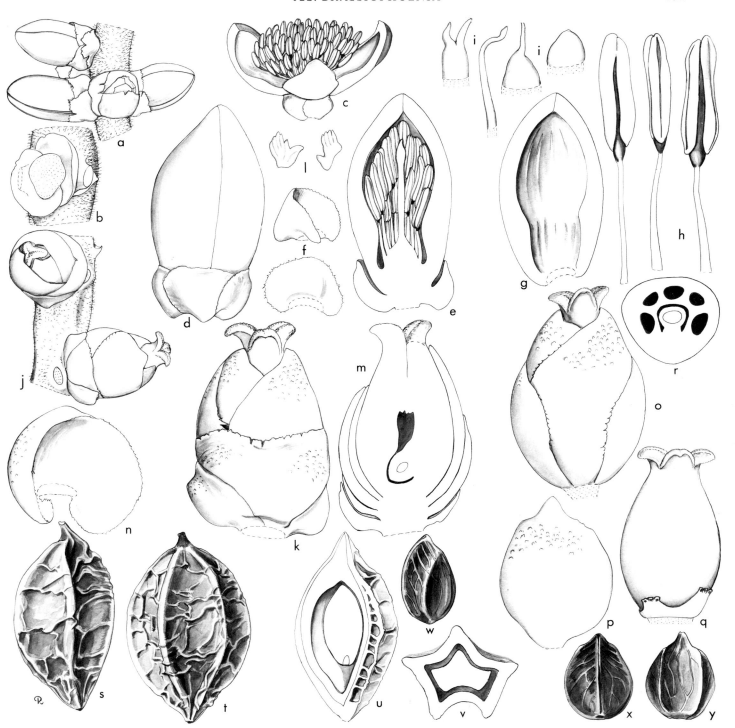

122.—**Brassiophoenix. a,** portion of rachilla with triads ×3; **b,** triad, flowers removed to show bracteoles ×3; **c,** staminate flower ×3; **d,** staminate bud ×6; **e,** staminate bud in vertical section ×6; **f,** staminate sepals in 2 views ×6; **g,** staminate petal, interior view ×6; **h,** stamen in 3 views ×18; **i,** pistillodes of various forms ×6; **j,** portion of rachilla in pistillate flower ×3; **k,** pistillate flower ×6; **l,** scales from pistillate perianth, much enlarged; **m,** pistillate flower in vertical section ×6; **n,** pistillate sepal ×6; **o,** pistillate flower, sepals removed ×6; **p,** pistillate petal, exterior view ×6; **q,** gynoecium and staminodes ×6; **r,** ovary in cross-section ×6; **s, t,** fruit in 2 views ×1½; **u,** fruit in vertical section ×1½; **v,** fruit in cross-section ×1½; **w, x, y,** seed in 3 views ×1½. *Brassiophoenix schumannii:* **a,** *Read 1476; Brassiophoenix* sp.: **b-r,** *Read 809; B. drymophloeoides:* **s-y,** *Darbeyshire 964.*

122. BRASSIOPHOENIX Burret, Notizblatt des Botanischen Gartens und Museums zu Berlin-Dahlem 12:345. 1935. Type: **B. drymophloeoides** Burret.

Small to moderate, solitary, unarmed, pleonanthic, monoecious palms. Stem slender, erect, ringed with leaf scars, light gray to brown. Leaves pinnate, spreading to erect; sheath forming a crownshaft, sometimes bearing a triangular appendage opposite the petiole, glaucous or densely white tomentose and minutely dotted; petiole very short, slender, deeply channeled adaxially, rounded abaxially, densely white tomentose, minutely brown-dotted, and bearing dark curly ramenta; rachis slender, adaxially ridged in the center, rounded abaxially, densely covered in dark or red-brown tattered scales; leaflets single-fold, wedge-shaped, apically trilobed, the center lobe much prolonged, all lobes toothed, basally bearing dark chaffy scales as the rachis, glaucous abaxially, midrib and marginal ribs large, transverse veinlets not evident. Inflorescences infrafoliar, branched to 2(–3) orders basally, densely dark or white-woolly tomentose throughout; peduncle short, dorsiventrally flattened; prophyll tubular, short, 2-keeled laterally, splitting apically; peduncular bract twice as long as the prophyll, tubular, exserted at maturity, 1 or 2 additional incomplete, ribbonlike or triangular to elongate peduncular bracts present; rachis longer than the peduncle bearing very short, spirally arranged bracts subtending branches and rachillae; rachillae rather short, thick in the middle, bearing very short, spirally arranged bracts subtending triads of flowers nearly throughout the rachillae, triads distant, staminate flowers projecting laterally, much wider than the rachillae; floral bracteoles 3, the first small, pointed, the second 2 large, rounded. Staminate flowers bullet-shaped in bud; sepals 3, distinct, short, rounded, imbricate, gibbous basally, edges toothed; petals 3, distinct, ovate, valvate, thick, tapering to a blunt point; stamens numerous (ca. 100–230), inserted on a conical receptacle, filaments long, slender, anthers elongate, basifixed, latrorse, connective tanniniferous, prolonged basally between the anthers; pollen elliptic, monosulcate, with finely reticulate, tectate exine; pistillode small, conical, sometimes with a short terete neck. Pistillate flowers ovoid; sepals 3, distinct, thickened dorsally, broadly imbricate, bearing large scales, margins split irregularly; petals 3, distinct, about twice as long as the sepals at anthesis, otherwise like the sepals, tips thick, shortly valvate; staminodes joined basally into a shallow ring bearing short 3-lobed projections; gynoecium ovoid, unilocular, uniovulate, style not differentiated, stigma 3-lobed, fleshy, papillose, reflexed at anthesis, ovule laterally attached, pendulous, form unknown. Fruit ellipsoidal, tapered at both ends, wrinkled and ridged when dry, pale yellow-orange or red at maturity, stigmatic remains apical; epicarp with short, single, oblique fibrous bundles and interspersed brachysclereids, mesocarp fleshy, endocarp hard, thick, ridged. Seed laterally attached, irregular with 5 ridges, pointed distally, hilum elongate, raphe branches curved, somewhat anastomosing, endosperm homogeneous; embryo basal. Germination adjacent-ligular; eophyll bifid, tips toothed. $n = 16$ (*B.* sp., Read 1966; *B. schumannii*, Johnson 1985).

Anatomy.—Not studied.

Distribution.—Two species in New Guinea.

Ecology.—Both species are inhabitants of mixed lowland rain forest.

Common Names and Uses.—Common names unknown. Handsome ornamentals.

Notes.—Distinguished from other genera of Ptychospermatinae by the three-pronged leaflets and by the basifixed anthers with the connective basally enlarged. The endocarp is hard as in *Ptychococcus* but lacks unsheathed vascular bundles and is thus distinct anatomically (Essig 1977b). In leaf form, *Brassiophoenix* seems closest to *Drymophoeus*, but resembles *Ptychosperma* in inflorescence structure and *Ptychococcus* in fruit, and therefore represents a different combination of characters within the subtribe.

Taxonomic Account.—Essig (1975a).

Plate.—*63A; Figs. G.15, G.16, G.19.*

Arecinae

Diminutive to large, unarmed; crownshaft usually developed; leaves pinnate or pinnately ribbed; leaflets entire, bifid, deeply lobed or praemorse; inflorescence usually infrafoliar, branching to 3 orders; prophyll and peduncular bract where present, similar, inserted close together, opening ± simultaneously, peduncular bract absent in *Nenga, Pinanga,* and *Areca*; staminate flowers asymmetrical, corolla usually ± pointed; pistillate flowers smaller than the staminate or rarely larger, petals imbricate or connate; gynoecium pseudomonomerous; fruit with apical stigmatic remains; seed basally or laterally attached; embryo basal.

The eight genera forming the type subtribe of the type tribe exhibit considerable diversity. These are diminutive to very tall palms distributed from Asia to Papuasia (Map 41). A crownshaft is usually developed, but is absent in some undergrowth species of *Nenga, Pinanga,* and *Areca*. A peduncular bract is present in all genera except *Nenga, Pinanga,* and *Areca* where the inflorescence is enclosed by the prophyll alone. These three genera are predominantly West Malesian except for a few species of *Pinanga* and several very distinctive species of *Areca* which occur east of Wallace's Line. *Pinanga* is a large genus with relatively uniform inflorescence morphology; it does, however, display quite extraordinary diversity in pollen structure. *Areca*, on the other hand, has much less variable pollen morphology but there is great diversity in inflorescence morphology, particularly in Bornean species. *Loxococcus*, endemic to Sri Lanka and perhaps the most isolated genus both in distribution and in inflorescence and floral morphology, is of interest in possessing an incomplete, poorly developed peduncular

Triads usually very few in number at the base of each rachilla, rarely numerous; seed basally attached with circular hilum. Southeast Asia to Solomon Islands . 130. **Areca**
7 Triads numerous, often occupying ¾ the rachilla length; seed laterally attached with narrow longitudinal hilum. Indochina to West Malesia .... 128. **Nenga**

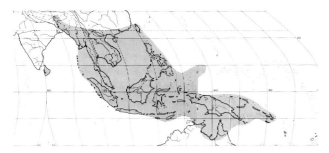

Map 41.— **Distribution of Arecinae.**

bract. Papuasian *Gronophyllum, Siphokentia, Hydriastele,* and *Gulubia* are very closely related to each other and difficult to define; it is possible that with further field work a revised circumscription may become necessary.

Key to the Genera of the Arecinae

1 Inflorescence bearing 2 large bracts, the prophyll and a similar peduncular bract, the peduncle later bearing 2 circular scars at the base 2
1 Inflorescence bearing only 1 large bract, the peduncle later bearing a single circular scar 6
2 Peduncular bract distinctly shorter than the prophyll, scarcely sheathing the inflorescence; rachillae bearing spirally arranged triads in the proximal ½–¾, distally bearing paired or solitary staminate flowers. Sri Lanka .... 123. **Loxococcus**
2 Peduncular bract ± as large as the prophyll; rachillae bearing opposite and decussate or whorled, very rarely spirally arranged triads ± throughout their length 3
3 Pistillate flower bearing connate sepals and petals. Moluccas .... 125. **Siphokentia**
3 Pistillate flower bearing distinct sepals and petals 4
4 Inflorescence protandrous; petals of pistillate flowers more than twice as long as the sepals, with conspicuous long, valvate tips. Moluccas, New Guinea, and Australia .... 124. **Gronophyllum**
4 Inflorescence protogynous; petals of pistillate flower less than twice as long as the sepals with very short valvate tips 5
5 Robust solitary palms; leaves large; leaflets acute or irregularly bilobed at the tip. Moluccas and New Guinea to Solomons, New Hebrides, Fiji, Palau, and Australia ... . 127. **Gulubia**
5 Moderate, usually clustered palms; leaves short; leaflets conspicuously praemorse at the tip. New Guinea, Bismarcks, Australia .... 126. **Hydriastele**
6 Inflorescence protogynous, spicate or branched to 1 order only; rachillae bearing distichous or more rarely spirally arranged triads throughout their length. Southeast Asia to New Guinea .... 129. **Pinanga**
6 Inflorescence protandrous (in a few *Areca* spp. recorded as protogynous but perhaps erroneously so), spicate or branched to 1–3 orders; rachillae bearing triads proximally and paired or solitary, spirally arranged, distichous or unilateral staminate flowers distally, or rachillae unisexual 7

123. **Loxococcus** H. A. Wendland & Drude, Linnaea 39:185. 1875. Type: **L. rupicola** (Thwaites) H. A. Wendland & Drude ex J. D. Hooker (*Ptychosperma rupicolum* Thwaites).

Moderate, solitary, unarmed, pleonanthic, monoecious palm. Stem erect, rather slender, conspicuously ringed with leaf scars, sometimes slightly swollen at the base. Leaves stiff, pinnate, neatly abscising; sheaths forming a well defined crownshaft, bearing sparse scales; petiole usually very short, adaxially channeled, abaxially rounded, sparsely scaly; rachis adaxially becoming angled distally, abaxially rounded: leaflets mostly single-fold except for the terminal pair and, rarely, the basal pair, regularly arranged, generally rather stiff and coriaceous, linear, close, the apices praemorse, truncate or oblique, glabrous adaxially, abaxially paler with very thin, white, caducous indumentum and conspicuous ramenta along the midrib near the base, midrib prominent, transverse veinlets not visible. Inflorescences infrafoliar, rather short, stiff, spreading, branching to 2 orders basally, to 1 order distally, apparently protandrous; peduncle short, the base bulbous and with 2 clasping wings; prophyll borne just above the base of the peduncle, narrow, ovate, beaked, laterally 2-keeled, entirely enclosing the inflorescence until leaf fall, then splitting longitudinally, bearing abundant, scattered scales; peduncular bract borne just above the prophyll, much shorter than the prophyll, lanceolate, acuminate, apparently not completely sheathing the inflorescence, incompletely encircling the peduncle, scaly as the prophyll; 1 or 2 small, triangular, acuminate, open, peduncular bracts sometimes present; rachis stiffly projecting upward, much longer than the peduncle, bearing spirally arranged small, triangular, acuminate bracts subtending branches and rachillae; rachillae rather flexuous, short, stout, deep crimson at anthesis, glabrous, bearing spirally arranged, very small, low, triangular bracts subtending flower groups, flowers borne in triads for ½–¾ the rachilla length, with solitary or paired staminate flowers distally; floral bracteoles minute. Staminate flowers somewhat asymmetrical, ± fleshy; sepals 3, distinct, imbricate, broadly triangular, keeled, the margins minutely toothed; petals 3, elongate, unequal, briefly connate basally, valvate, tips triangular; stamens 12, filaments short, slender, distinct, anthers ± sagittate at the base, elongate, latrorse; pollen elliptic, monosulcate, with scabrate, tectate exine; pistillode ± conical, domed, or 3-angled with 3 short slender appendages (? vestigial stamens). Pistillate flowers ± globular; sepals 3, distinct, imbricate, short, broad, keeled; petals 3, distinct, imbricate, the tips minutely valvate at anthesis, about twice as long as sepals; staminodial ring low, membranous, with ca. 9, irregular, triangular lobes; gynoecium unilocular, uniovulate, spherical, stigmas 3, reflexed apically, ovule

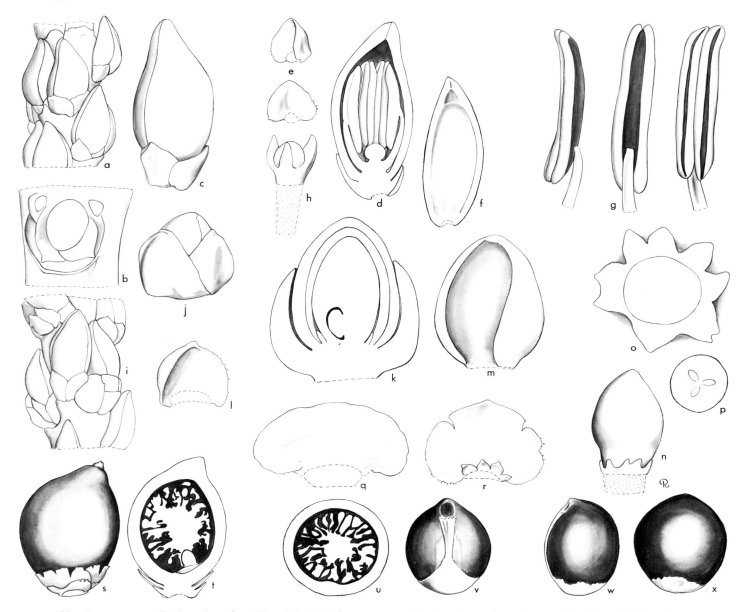

123.—**Loxococcus. a,** distal portion of rachilla ×3; **b,** triad, flowers removed to show bracteoles ×6; **c,** staminate bud ×6; **d,** staminate bud in vertical section ×6; **e,** staminate sepal in 2 views ×6; **f,** staminate petal, interior view ×6; **g,** stamen in 3 views ×12; **h,** pistillode ×12; **i,** triads from inflorescence in bud ×3; **j,** pistillate bud ×6; **k,** pistillate bud in vertical section ×12; **l,** pistillate sepal, interior view ×6; **m,** pistillate petal ×12; **n,** gynoecium and staminodes ×12; **o,** staminodes ×24; **p,** ovary in cross-section ×12; **q,** sepal in fruit, interior view ×6; **r,** petal and staminodes in fruit, interior view ×6; **s,** fruit ×1½; **t,** fruit in vertical section ×1½; **u,** fruit in cross-section ×1½; **v, w, x,** seed in 3 views ×1. *Loxococcus rupicola*: all from *Moore et al. 9031.*

laterally attached, form unknown. Fruit reddish-brown at maturity, ± spherical with a short, broad, slightly eccentric beak tipped with the stigmatic remains, perianth whorls persistent; epicarp smooth, mesocarp thin with numerous longitudinal, pale fibers, becoming free basally after disintegration of epicarp, endocarp thin, not adhering to the seed. Seed globose, basally and laterally attached with a ± circular, basal, slender, lateral hilum running ± the length of the seed, endosperm deeply ruminate; embryo basal. Germination and eophyll not recorded. *n* = 16 (Sharma 1970).

Anatomy.—Not studied.

Distribution.—One species in Sri Lanka.

Ecology.—On cliffs, rocks and steep slopes in humid rain forest at altitudes of 300–1600 m.

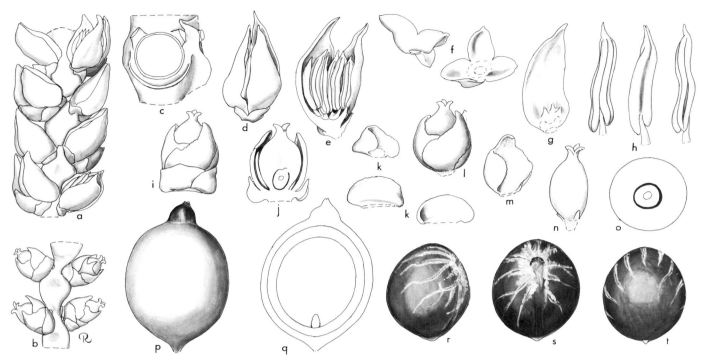

124.—**Gronophyllum. a,** portion of rachilla in staminate flower ×1½; **b,** portion of rachilla in pistillate flower ×1½; **c,** triad, flowers removed ×6; **d,** staminate flower ×3; **e,** staminate flower in vertical section ×3; **f,** staminate calyx in 2 views ×6; **g,** staminate petal, interior view ×3; **h,** stamen in 3 views ×6; **i,** pistillate flower ×3; **j,** pistillate flower in vertical section ×3; **k,** pistillate sepals ×3; **l,** pistillate flower, sepals removed ×3; **m,** pistillate petal, interior view ×3; **n,** gynoecium and staminodes ×3; **o,** ovary in cross-section ×6; **p,** fruit ×3; **q,** fruit in vertical section ×3; **r, s, t,** seed in 3 views ×3. *Gronophyllum chaunostachys:* all from *Moore et al. 9258* and *Hoogland & Craven 10934.*

Common Names and Uses.—Dotalu. Seed is rarely used as a substitute for betel.

Notes.—*Loxococcus* is a rather poorly known genus. Though handsome, it seems to be in few collections. It may be regarded as one of the simpler members of the Arecinae. The reduced peduncular bract is significant, perhaps showing the beginning of a trend leading to complete loss as displayed in *Nenga, Pinanga,* and *Areca.*

Taxonomic Account.—Beccari and Pichi-Sermolli (1955).

Plate.—63B.

124. GRONOPHYLLUM Scheffer, Annales du Jardin Botanique de Buitenzorg 1:135. 1876. Type: **G. microcarpum** Scheffer.

Kentia Blume, Bulletin des Sciences Physiques et Naturelles en Néerlande 1:64. 1838. (Non *Kentia* Adanson 1763). Type: *K. procera* Blume (=*Gronophyllum procerum* (Blume) H. E. Moore).

Nengella Beccari, Malesia 1:32. 1877. Lectotype: *N. montana* Beccari (see Burret 1936b) (=*Gronophyllum montanum* (Beccari) Essig & Young).

Leptophoenix Beccari, Annales du Jardin Botanique de Buitenzorg 2:82. 1885. Lectotype: *L. pinangoides* (Beccari) Beccari (*Nenga pinangoides* Beccari) (see Beccari and Pichi-Sermolli 1955) (=*Gronophyllum pinangoides* (Beccari) Essig & Young).

Tall, moderate, or small, solitary or clustered, unarmed, pleonanthic, monoecious palms. Stems erect, slender or moderate, bare, conspicuously ringed with leaf scars. Leaves pinnate, neatly abscising; sheaths elongate, forming a well defined crownshaft, usually densely covered in scales and hairs, sometimes with a ligulelike projection; petiole short to long, adaxially channeled near the base, distally rounded, abaxially rounded, usually densely scaly; rachis straight or conspicuously curved, adaxially ± angled, abaxially rounded, scaly as the petiole; leaflets few to numerous, regularly arranged or grouped, linear-lanceolate to cuneate, composed of 1–several folds, apically acute, bifid or conspicuously praemorse, apical pair ± several-fold, divergent, adaxial and abaxial surfaces bearing scattered minute scales, sometimes also with bands of deciduous chaffy scales along major ribs, transverse veinlets often conspicuous. Inflorescences infrafoliar, solitary at each node, but often several in different stages of flowering or fruiting at one time, branching to 1–3 orders, rarely spicate, usually horse-tail like, protandrous; peduncle short, winged at the base, often becoming bulbous in fruit; prophyll compressed, entirely enclosing inflorescence in bud, 2-keeled, briefly beaked, thin, membranous to coriaceous, splitting longitudinally and deciduous; peduncular bract 1, similar to the prophyll but not 2-keeled, deciduous; rachis longer or shorter than the peduncle; subsequent bracts usually very small, only rarely long, narrowly triangular; first-order branches (where present) proximally often with a basal bare portion and very few to several branches, distally unbranched; rachillae slender, usually elongate, very few to very numerous, ± straight or flexuous, bearing sparse or dense triads throughout their length, triads either opposite and decussate, or in alternating whorls of 3, at the very tips of the rachillae sometimes bearing solitary or paired staminate flowers; rachilla bracts low, rounded or triangular; floral bracteoles low, rounded. Staminate flowers ± asymmetrical; sepals 3, ± triangular, keeled, basally briefly united; petals 3, ca. 4–5 times as long as the sepals, ± fleshy, triangular, very briefly united at the base; stamens 6–9, shorter than or ± equalling the petals, filaments short, anthers basifixed, elongate, latrorse; pollen elliptic, monosulcate or rarely trichotomosulcate, with finely or coarsely reticulate, tectate exine; pistillode minute, trifid. Pistillate flowers smaller than the staminate, ± conical in bud; sepals 3, distinct, broadly triangular, ± keeled, coriaceous; petals 3, distinct, at least twice as long as the sepals, broadly imbricate, with relatively large, conspicuous, thickened, triangular, valvate tips closely appressed in bud, the tips persisting or eroding into fibers in fruit; staminodes 3 (? always), toothlike, minute; gynoecium unilocular, uniovulate, globose to narrow-ellipsoidal, stigmas 3, low, sessile or borne on a low short style, ± erect, ovule laterally attached near the tip of the locule, form unknown. Fruit globose to narrowly ellipsoidal, straight or curved, bright red to purplish-black, sometimes briefly beaked, stigmatic remains apical, perianth whorls persistent, the petal tips reflexed or appressed to the fruit; epicarp smooth or slightly pebbled, mesocarp thin, with abundant tannin cells, and longitudinal fiber bundles, endocarp thin, crustose or obsolescent. Seed laterally attached with short to elongate hilum, raphe branches sparsely anastomosing, endosperm homogeneous or ruminate; embryo basal. Germination adjacent-ligular; eophyll bifid. Cytology not studied.

Anatomy.—Not studied.

Distribution.—About 33 species distributed from Sulawesi through the Moluccas to New Guinea, the Bismarck Archipelago, and Australia.

Ecology.—Very varied, occurring from lowland forest at sea level to montane mossy forest, as undergrowth palms to emergents, on a variety of rocks including serpentine and limestone.

Common Names and Uses.—Pinang salea (*G. microcarpum*). Trunks of the larger species are sometimes used in house construction in New Guinea.

Notes.—The delimitation of genera of Papuasian palms in the Arecineae has proved to be very problematic, and the solution presented here may not prove to be satisfactory. *Siphokentia*, easily separated from *Gronophyllum* because of the gamosepalous, gamopetalous pistillate flowers, could well be more closely related to true *Gronophyllum* than some of the palms first described under *Kentia* but now included in *Gronophyllum*. The characters of the pistillate corolla associated with the protandrous state have traditionally been given great emphasis in the separation of genera. However, the use of this character gives genera which include palms of disparate habit, leaf, and fruit structure, and similar associations of characters occur in the closely related complex of *Hydriastele* and *Gulubia*. The inclusion of *Nengella* in *Gronophyllum* seems entirely justified, the main difference being in size.

Taxonomic Accounts.—Burret (1936a, b) and Essig and Young (1985).

Plate.—63C.

125. SIPHOKENTIA Burret, Notizblatt des Botanischen Gartens und Museums zu Berlin-Dahlem 10:198. 1927. Type: **S. beguinii** Burret.

Moderate, solitary, unarmed, pleonanthic, monoecious palms. Stems rather slender, erect, bare, conspicuously ringed with leaf scars. Leaves pinnate, neatly abscising; sheaths tubular, closely sheathing, forming a well defined crownshaft, densely covered with scaly and floccose indumentum, bearing an irregularly tattering ligule apically, petiole relatively short, channeled adaxially, rounded abaxially, densely scaly as the sheath; rachis ± curved, angled adaxially, rounded abaxially; blade sometimes entire, more usually regularly to irregularly divided into 1–several fold, praemorse leaflets, the terminal pair several-fold, adaxially glabrous, abaxially paler, densely brown-dotted, and bearing ramenta on main veins, transverse veinlets inconspicuous. Inflorescence solitary, infrafoliar, ± curved at anthesis, branching to 1 order, apparently protandrous; peduncle very short, bulbous based, with 2 crescentic wings clasping the stem; prophyll borne just above the base, tubular, narrowly ovate, beaked, 2-keeled, membranous, glabrous, entirely enclosing the inflorescence until leaf fall, then splitting longitudinally and falling; peduncular bract borne just above the prophyll, ± as long as and similar to the prophyll but scarcely 2-keeled; rachis longer than the peduncle; rachis bracts inconspicuous, incompletely sheathing, triangular; rachillae rather few (rarely more than 16), ± curved at anthesis, later pendulous, bearing spiral (rarely) or opposite and decussate triads throughout their length; rachilla bracts low, triangular, becoming more prominent after flowering, eventually the rachillae swelling somewhat at each node; floral bracteoles low, rounded. Staminate flowers somewhat asymmetrical, fleshy; calyx with a short stalklike base, with 3 short triangular, keeled lobes; petals 3, much exceeding the calyx, narrow, triangular, acuminate, briefly connate basally; stamens 9–10, about ½ the length of the petals, filaments slender, very short, variously epipetalous

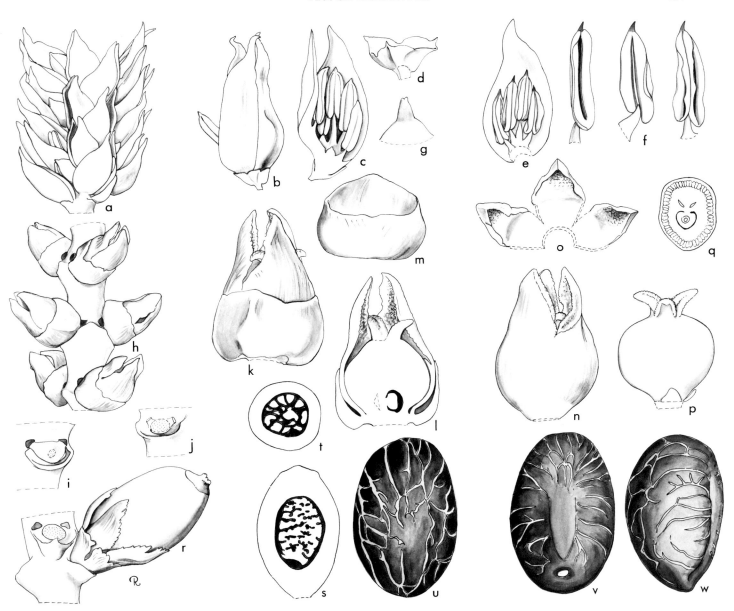

125.—**Siphokentia. a,** portion of rachilla at staminate anthesis ×1½; **b,** staminate flower ×3; **c,** staminate flower in vertical section ×3; **d,** staminate calyx ×6; **e,** staminate petal with stamens, interior view ×3; **f,** stamen in 3 views ×6; **g,** pistillode ×12; **h,** portion of rachilla at pistillate anthesis with scars of staminate flowers ×3; **i, j,** triads with flowers removed in 2 views ×3; **k,** pistillate flower ×6; **l,** pistillate flower in vertical section ×6; **m,** pistillate calyx ×6; **n,** pistillate flower, calyx removed ×6; **o,** pistillate corolla, interior view, expanded ×3; **p,** gynoecium and staminodes ×6; **q,** ovary in cross-section ×6; **r,** fruit and floral scars ×3; **s,** fruit in vertical section ×3; **t,** fruit in cross-section ×3; **u, v, w,** seed in 3 views ×6. *Siphokentia beguinii:* all from *Moore et al. 9386.*

and connate, connective prolonged into a short point, anthers elongate, latrorse; pollen elliptic, monosulcate, with coarsely reticulate, tectate exine; pistillode minute or absent. Pistillate flowers much shorter than the staminate; calyx tubular, striate, very briefly 3-lobed distally; corolla about 2–3 times as long as the calyx, tubular in the proximal ca. ½, distally with 3 striate, somewhat undulate, thin, narrow, triangular, loosely imbricate, valvate-tipped lobes; staminodes 3(–6?), minute, spathulate or triangular; gynoecium unilocular, uniovulate, ± spherical, stigmas 3, fleshy, reflexed, ovule laterally attached near the base, ± hemianatropous. Fruit ovoid, shiny, reddish (? always) at maturity, with a short beak and apical stigmatic remains, perianth whorls persistent, the corolla lobes becoming tattered; epicarp smooth, mesocarp with 2 layers of fibers, the outer cartilaginous, giving a ridged appearance to dried

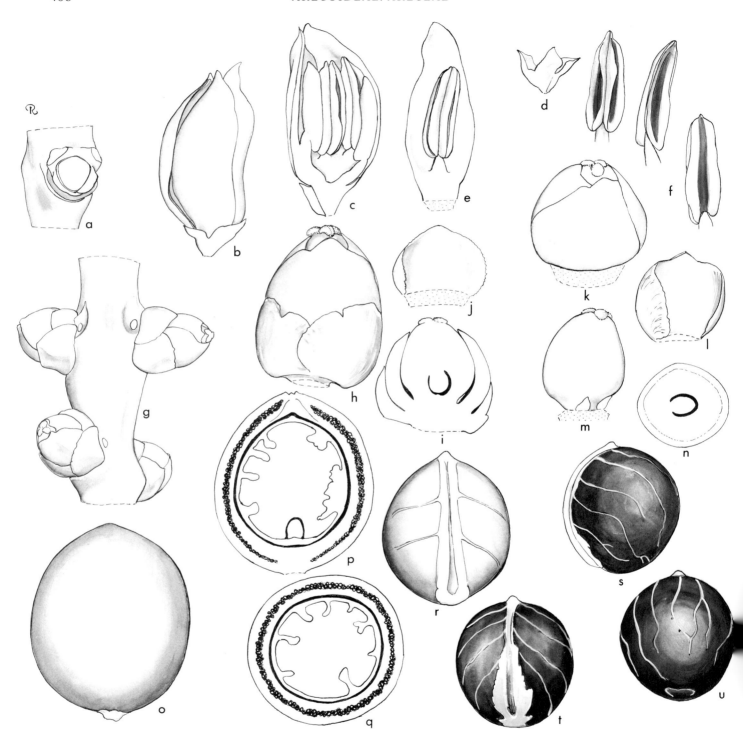

126.—**Hydriastele. a,** triad, flowers removed ×6; **b,** staminate bud ×6; **c,** staminate bud in vertical section ×6; **d,** staminate calyx ×6; **e,** staminate petal with stamen, interior view ×6; **f,** stamen in 3 views ×6; **g,** portion of rachilla with triads, staminate flowers removed ×6; **h,** pistillate flower ×12; **i,** pistillate flower in vertical section ×12; **j,** pistillate sepal ×12; **k,** pistillate flower, sepals removed ×12; **l,** pistillate petal ×12; **m,** gynoecium with staminodes ×12; **n,** ovary in cross-section ×12; **o,** fruit ×6; **p,** fruit in vertical section ×6; **q,** fruit in cross-section ×6; **r,** seed showing elongate hilum ×6; **s, t, u,** seed in 3 views ×6. *Hydriastele* sp.: all from *Moore 9271.*

fruit, the inner slender, anastomosing, endocarp membranous closely adhering to the seed. Seed basally attached, with elongate lateral raphe, and coarse anastomosing fibers, endosperm ruminate; embryo basal. Germination and eophyll not recorded. *n* = 16 (*S. beguinii*, Read 1966).

Anatomy.—Not studied.

Distribution.—Two species known from Halmahera, Obi Island, and Kahatola Island, all in the northwest Moluccas; the two taxa possibly not distinct.

Ecology.—Recent collections by de Vogel suggest the genus is confined to lowland rain forest developed on ultrabasic rock.

Common Names and Uses.—Common names unknown. Widespread in enthusiasts' collections.

Notes.—See comments under *Gronophyllum*.

Taxonomic Accounts.—Burret (1927) and Moore (1953).

Plate.—*63D.*

126. **HYDRIASTELE** H. A. Wendland & Drude, Linnaea 39:180, 208. 1875. Type: **H. wendlandiana** (F. v. Mueller) H. A. Wendland & Drude (*Kentia wendlandiana* F. v. Mueller).

Adelonenga J. D. Hooker in Bentham & J. D. Hooker, Genera Plantarum 3:885. 1883. Lectotype: *A. variabilis* (Beccari) Beccari (*Nenga variabilis* Beccari) (=*H. variabilis* (Beccari) Burret) (see Beccari and Pichi-Sermolli 1955).

Small to moderate, usually clustered, unarmed, pleonanthic, monoecious palms. Stems erect, usually forming rather close clumps, bare, conspicuously ringed with leaf scars. Leaves pinnate, neatly abscising; sheaths elongate, forming a well defined crownshaft, usually densely scaly or tomentose, and/or waxy, a ligulelike prolongation sometimes present opposite or at the base of the petiole; petiole short to long, adaxially channeled, abaxially rounded, usually conspicuously scaly; rachis adaxially channeled or angled near the base, distally angled, abaxially rounded, usually scaly as the petiole; leaflets usually ± regularly arranged, sometimes ± grouped, mostly single-fold but a few 2–3-fold, the terminal pair usually broad, several-fold, the rest parallel sided or somewhat wedge-shaped, irregularly and conspicuously praemorse at the tips, adaxially glabrous, abaxially with scattered ramenta along the main veins, transverse veinlets obscure. Inflorescences infrafoliar, branching to 1–2 orders, protogynous; peduncle short, winged at the base, sometimes becoming swollen; prophyll compressed, entirely enclosing the inflorescence in bud, 2-keeled, with a conspicuous apical beak, thin, papery when dry, glabrous or scaly, soon drying on exposure, splitting longitudinally on the abaxial face and abscising together with the peduncular bract; peduncular bract 1, rarely 2, similar to and entirely enclosed by the prophyll, tubular, enclosing the inflorescence in bud; subsequent bracts inconspicuous; rachis usually not exceeding the peduncle, bearing inconspicuous rachis bracts subtending few to many crowded, ± spirally arranged first-order branches, the proximal bearing a few branches or all unbranched; rachillae elongate, usually ± straight, of ± equal length, tending to curve downwards, bearing throughout their length opposite and decussate pairs of triads of cream-colored or pinkish-tinged flowers, except at the very tip where bearing solitary or paired staminate flowers; rachilla bracts very inconspicuous, low, ± rounded. Staminate flowers asymmetrical; sepals 3, short, triangular, joined into a cup for ca. ½ their length; petals 3, fleshy, distinct, except at the very base, valvate, 4–5 times as long as the calyx, narrow, triangular, 1 usually larger than the other 2; stamens 6, epipetalous, filaments very short, fleshy, anthers elongate, erect, basifixed, latrorse; pollen elliptic, monosulcate, with scabrate or coarsely reticulate, tectate exine; pistillode absent. Pistillate flowers globose, much smaller than the staminate; sepals 3, distinct, rounded, broadly imbricate; petals 3, distinct, not more than twice as long as the sepals, rounded, broadly imbricate except for very small valvate tips; staminodes 3 (? always), toothlike, minute; gynoecium ± globose or ovoid, unilocular, uniovulate, stigmas 3, low, sessile, ovule laterally attached near apex of locule, form unknown. Fruit ellipsoidal to globose, small, bright to dull red or purplish, ± symmetrical with apical stigmatic remains; epicarp smooth, sometimes drying ridged, mesocarp thinly fleshy with a conspicuous tanniniferous layer, and internally with numerous fine, longitudinal, fibrovascular bundles, endocarp thin. Seed ovoid or globose, laterally attached with elongate hilum, raphe branches sparse, anastomosing, endosperm homogeneous or shallowly to deeply ruminate; embryo basal. Germination adjacent-ligular; eophyll bifid with minutely praemorse tips. *n* = 16 (*H.* sp., Read 1966).

Anatomy.—Not studied.

Distribution.—About eight species in New Guinea, Bismarck Archipelago, and northern Australia.

Ecology.—Lowland to upland tropical rain forest. One species (represented by *Brass 13608, 13700*) occurs as a rheophyte in Irian Jaya, and has very slender leaflets. Pollination has been studied by Essig (1973) who showed that curculionid beetles are probably the pollinators.

Common Names and Uses.—Common names not recorded. Stems have been used, split, as spears; several species are cultivated as ornamentals.

Notes.—See notes under *Gronophyllum* and *Gulubia*.

Taxonomic Account.—Burret (1937a).

Plate.—*21C, D.*

127. **GULUBIA** Beccari, Annales du Jardin Botanique de Buitenzorg 2:128, 131, 134. 1885. Lectotype: **G. moluccana** (Beccari) Beccari (*Kentia moluccana* Beccari) (see Beccari and Pichi-Sermolli 1955).

Gulubiopsis Beccari, Botanische Jahrbücher für Systematik 59:11. 1924. Type: *G. palauensis* Beccari

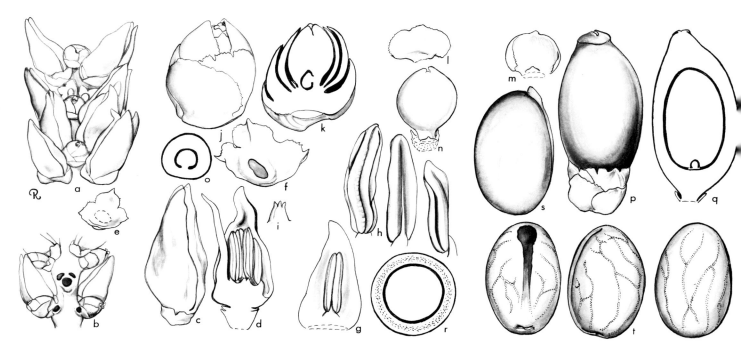

127.—**Gulubia. a,** portion of rachilla with triads in staminate bud ×1½; **b,** portion of rachilla, some buds removed to show scars ×1½; **c,** staminate bud ×3; **d,** staminate bud in vertical section ×3; **e,** staminate calyx, interior view ×3; **f,** staminate calyx, exterior view ×6; **g,** staminate petal with stamen, interior view ×3; **h,** stamen in 3 views ×6; **i,** pistillode ×6; **j,** pistillate flower ×6; **k,** pistillate flower in vertical section ×6; **l,** pistillate sepal, exterior view ×3; **m,** pistillate petal, interior view ×3; **n,** gynoecium and staminodes ×6; **o,** ovary in cross-section ×8; **p,** fruit ×3; **q,** fruit in vertical section ×3; **r,** fruit in cross-section ×3; **s,** endocarp ×3; **t,** seed in 3 views ×3. *Gulubia hombronii:* all from *Moore et al. 9296.*

(=*Gulubia palauensis* (Beccari) H. E. Moore & Fosberg).

Paragulubia Burret, Notizblatt des Botanischen Gartens und Museums zu Berlin-Dahlem 13:84. 1936. Type: *P. macrospadix* Burret (=*Gulubia macrospadix* (Burret) H. E. Moore).

Tall, solitary, unarmed, pleonanthic, monoecious palms. Stems erect, rather robust, bare, conspicuously ringed with leaf scars. Leaves pinnate, a relatively large number in the crown, neatly abscising; sheaths forming a well defined crownshaft, elongate, variously scaly or glabrous; petiole short, adaxially channeled, abaxially rounded, variously glabrous or scaly; rachis straight or conspicuously curved, adaxially channeled near the base, distally angled, abaxially rounded, variously scaly like the petiole; leaflets very numerous, pendulous or horizontal or ascending, straight or curved, regularly arranged, linear-lanceolate, single-fold, acute or very briefly bifid at the tip, adaxial surface glabrous, abaxially with or without minute dotlike scales and large ramenta along the main vein near the base, transverse veinlets obscure. Inflorescences infrafoliar, solitary at each node, but often several in different stages of flowering and fruiting at one time, branching to 1–3 orders proximally, to 1 order distally, protogynous; peduncle short, winged basally, often becoming swollen in fruit; prophyll compressed, entirely enclosing inflorescence in bud, 2-keeled, ± rounded at the tip, thin, membranous, splitting longitudinally and abscising; peduncular bract 1 or vestigial, inserted some distance from the prophyll, slightly to much smaller than the prophyll, complete or incomplete, triangular to lanceolate, deciduous; rachis longer or shorter than the peduncle; rachis bracts very small; first-order branches with a short to long basal bare portion, glabrous; rachillae few to numerous, elongate, straight or flexuous, eventually pendulous in fruit, bearing very close to rather distant, opposite and decussate triads of white to rose-pink flowers throughout the rachilla except at the very tip, where sometimes solitary or paired staminate flowers; rachilla bracts, low, rounded; floral bracteoles minute. Staminate flowers asymmetrical; sepals 3, short, ± triangular, briefly joined at the base; petals 3, valvate in bud, or the margins not meeting in *G. palauensis*; 4–5 times as long as the sepals, narrow, triangular, the outward facing petal larger than the others, ± fleshy, briefly united at the base; stamens 6–24, shorter or longer than the petals, filaments very short, anthers elongate, basifixed, erect, latrorse; pollen elliptic, monosulcate, with finely to coarsely reticulate and granulate, tectate exine; pistillode absent, or very small, trifid. Pistillate flowers globose, much smaller than the staminate; sepals 3, distinct, rounded, broadly imbricate, sometimes with toothed margins; petals 3, distinct, not more than twice as long as the sepals, rounded, broadly imbricate except at the very small valvate tips, the margins sometimes toothed or ciliate; staminodes usually 3(1–6) tooth-like; gynoecium globose to conical, unilocular, uniovulate, stigmas 3, short, sessile, ovule lateral, form unknown. Fruit ellipsoidal to globose, small, bright or dull red or blue-gray with pale stripes, ± symmetrical with apical stigmatic remains; epicarp smooth or drying ridged, mesocarp thin with a prominent tanniniferous layer and straight, little-branched, longitudinal fibrovascular bundles, in *G. costata* forming prominent ribs, endocarp thin. Seed globose to ellipsoidal, laterally attached with narrow elongate hilum, and sparse, anastomosing raphe branches, endosperm homogeneous or ruminate (*G. macrospadix* only); embryo basal. Germination adjacent-ligular; eophyll bifid. $n = 16$ (*G. costata, G. hombronii,* Read 1965a).

Anatomy.—Fruit anatomy (Essig 1982).

Distribution.—Nine species distributed from the Moluccas to New Guinea, Bismarck Archipelago, Solomon Islands, Australia, New Hebrides, Fiji, and Palau.

Ecology.—Lowland to upland and montane tropical rain forest. *G. palauensis* occurs on limestone ridges.

Common Names and Uses.—Common names unknown. Essig (1982) records the use of trunks for floorboards and side panels of houses in New Guinea.

Notes.—*Gulubia* differs from *Hydriastele* in its solitary emergent habit only, *Gronophyllum* and *Hydriastele* are also protogynous; pistillate petals of these genera are short and the stigmas are exposed when the inflorescence bracts open. See comments under *Gronophyllum.*

Taxonomic Account.—Essig (1982).

Plate.—64A.

128. NENGA H. A. Wendland & Drude, Linnaea 39: 182. 1875. Type: *Pinanga nenga* (Blume ex Martius) Blume (*Areca nenga* Blume ex Martius) (=**N. pumila** (Martius) H. A. Wendland (*Areca pumila* Martius)).

Moderate, solitary or clustered, acaulescent or erect, unarmed, pleonanthic, monoecious palms. Stem slender, short, rarely exceeding 5 m in height with short or elongate internodes and conspicuous leaf scars, stilt roots frequent. Leaves pinnate; sheaths usually forming a well defined crownshaft with leaves neatly abscising, or leaves marcescent and crownshaft poorly developed (*N. gajah*); petiole usually well developed, flattened or grooved adaxially, rounded or angled abaxially; leaflets with 1–several folds, linear to sigmoid, acute or acuminate, the terminal pair obscurely lobed, lobes corresponding to the folds, the adaxial ribs often bearing ramenta on the under surface, transverse veinlets obscure. Inflorescence infrafoliar or interfoliar (*N. gajah*), erect or pendulous, branching to 1 order, rarely to 2 orders or unbranched, protandrous; peduncle short in species with infrafoliar inflorescences, long

where inflorescences interfoliar (*N. gajah*); prophyll thin, membranous, enclosing the inflorescence in bud, splitting and falling at anthesis or thick, almost woody, persistent, eventually rotting; peduncular bracts incomplete, small, triangular; rachillae bearing spirally arranged minute bracts subtending triads proximally, solitary or paired staminate flowers distally, or triads confined to central rachilla and lateral rachillae with staminate flowers only, flowers not or only slightly sunken in the rachillae; floral bracteoles minute. Staminate flowers fleshy, sessile; sepals 3, connate at the very base, shorter than, almost as long as, or far exceeding the corolla; corolla with slightly stalklike base or not, with 3 long, valvate lobes; stamens 6, borne at the base of the corolla lobes, filaments short, anthers oblong to linear, latrorse; pollen elliptic or circular, monosulcate, the sulcus sometimes very short, with coarsely to extremely coarsely reticulate, sometimes also granular or minutely echinate, tectate exine; pistillode absent. Pistillate flowers sessile, globular; sepals 3, distinct, imbricate; petals 3, distinct, imbricate; staminodes absent or minute; gynoecium globose or columnar, uniloculate, uniovulate, style lacking, stigmas 3, massive, fleshy, divergent, ovule laterally attached, form unknown. Fruiting rachillae usually not differing greatly in color from flowering ones. Fruit ovoid to obpyriform, dull to brightly colored, stigmatic remains apical; epicarp smooth, dull or shiny, mesocarp thin, fleshy, sweet, endocarp composed of longitudinal fibers adhering to the seed, becoming free at both ends (*N. pumila*) or at one end only, the fibers enclosing a solid parenchymatous mass of varying size distal to the seed. Seed with longitudinal hilum and raphe branches anastomosing, endosperm deeply ruminate; embryo basal. Germination adjacent-ligular; eophyll bifid. Cytology not studied.

Anatomy.—Not studied.

Distribution.—Five species ranging from Vietnam and Burma to Sumatra, the Malay Peninsula, Borneo, and Java.

Ecology.—All species are confined to primary tropical rain forest and are found from sea level to altitudes of about 1400 m. *N. pumila* sometimes occurs in peat swamp forest.

Fossil Record.—Fossil pollen referable to *Nenga* has been recorded from lower Miocene deposits in Borneo (Muller 1979).

Common Names and Uses.—Pinang palms. Stems are sometimes used split, as laths.

Notes.—*Nenga* is closely related to *Pinanga* and *Areca. N. gajah* is an extraordinary, aberrant species which nevertheless seems to belong in the genus; most of its peculiarities seem to be related to the interfoliar position of the inflorescence which in turn is related to the short internodes and marcescent leaves. Such an anomalous habit is also found in a few species of *Areca* and *Pinanga.*

Taxonomic Account.—Fernando (1983).

Plate.—64B, C.

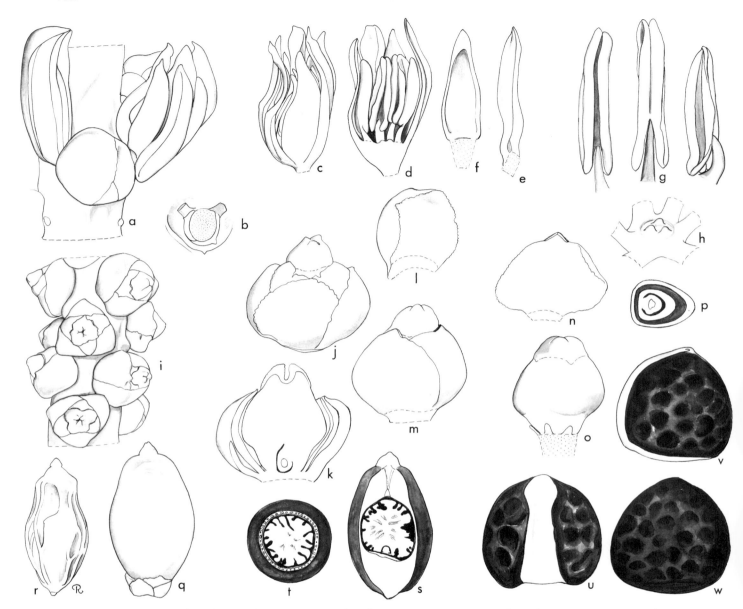

128.—**Nenga. a,** portion of rachilla showing triad ×3; **b,** triad, flowers removed ×3; **c,** staminate flower ×3; **d,** staminate flower in vertical section ×3; **e,** staminate sepal ×3; **f,** staminate petal, interior view ×3; **g,** stamen in 3 views ×6; **h,** pistillode ×6; **i,** portion of rachilla in pistillate flower ×3; **j,** pistillate flower ×3; **k,** pistillate flower in vertical section ×3; **l,** pistillate sepal ×3; **m,** pistillate flower, sepals removed ×3; **n,** pistillate petal, interior view ×3; **o,** gynoecium and staminodes ×3; **p,** ovary in cross-section ×3; **q,** fruit ×1½; **r,** dry fruit ×1½; **s,** fruit in vertical section ×1½; **t,** fruit in cross-section ×1½; **u, v, w,** seed in 3 views × 3. *Nenga grandiflora:* **a-h,** *Moore & Pennington 9061; N. pumila:* **i-p,** *Moore & Pennington 9071;* **q-w,** *Moore & Pennington 9056.*

129. **Pinanga** Blume, Bulletin des Sciences Physiques et Naturelles en Néerlande 1:65. 1838. Lectotype: **P. coronata** (Blume ex Martius) Blume (*Areca coronata* Blume ex Martius) (see Beccari and Pichi-Sermolli 1955).

Cladosperma Griffith, Notulae ad Plantas Asiaticas 3:165. 1851. Type: *C. paradoxa* (Griffith) Beccari

(*Areca paradoxa* Griffith) (=*Pinanga paradoxa* (Griffith) Scheffer).

Ophiria Beccari, Annales du Jardin Botanique de Buitenzorg 2:128. 1885. Type: *O. paradoxa* (Griffith) Beccari (*Areca paradoxa* Griffith) (=*Pinanga paradoxa* (Griffith) Scheffer).

Pseudopinanga Burret, Notizblatt des Botanischen

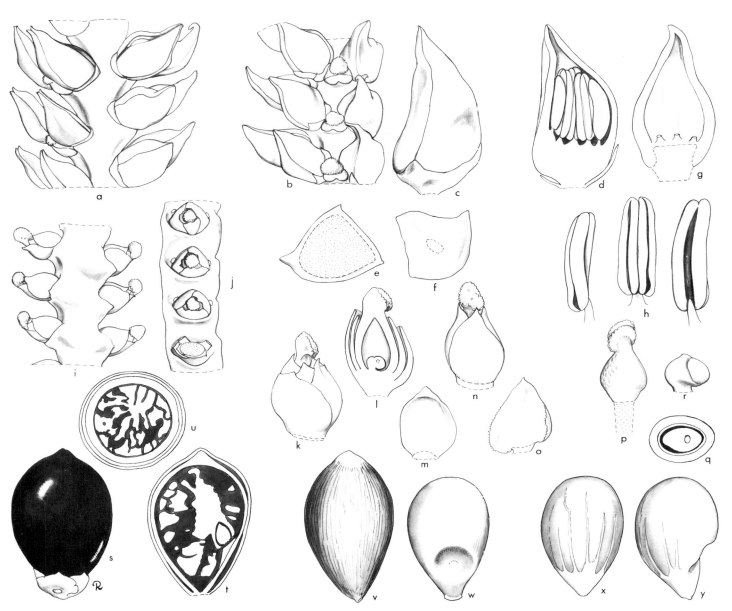

129.—**Pinanga. a, b,** portion of rachilla with triads in 2 views ×3; **c,** staminate bud ×6; **d,** staminate bud in vertical section ×6; **e, f,** staminate calyx, interior (**e**) and exterior (**f**) views ×6; **g,** staminate petal, interior view ×6; **h,** stamen in 3 views ×12; **i, j,** portion of rachilla at pistillate anthesis in 2 views ×3; **k,** pistillate flower ×6; **l,** pistillate flower in vertical section ×6; **m,** pistillate sepal, interior view ×6; **n,** pistillate flower, calyx removed ×6; **o,** pistillate petal, interior view ×6; **p,** gynoecium ×6; **q,** ovary in cross-section ×12; **r,** ovule ×12; **s,** fruit ×3; **t,** fruit in vertical section ×3; **u,** fruit in cross-section ×3; **v,** endocarp ×3; **w, x, y,** seed in 3 views ×3. *Pinanga coronata*: **a-r,** *Read 822* and *825*; **q-y,** *Moore s.n.*.

Gartens und Museums zu Berlin-Dahlem 13:188. 1936. Type: *P. insignis* (Beccari) Burret (*Pinanga insignis* Beccari).

Very small to robust, solitary or clustered, acaulescent or erect, unarmed, pleonanthic, monoecious palms. Stem very slender to moderate, with elongate or short internodes and conspicuous leaf scars, occasionally stilt-root- ed. Leaves undivided and pinnately ribbed, with or without an apical notch, or pinnate; sheaths tubular, forming a well defined crownshaft, with leaves neatly abscising, very rarely leaves marcescent and crownshaft not well developed; petiole present or absent, adaxially rounded or channeled, abaxially rounded, glabrous or variously indumentose; leaflets 1 to several-fold, regularly to irregularly arranged, acute, acuminate, or lobed, the lobes corresponding to the folds, the apical leaflets almost always lobed, blade occasionally mottled, sometimes paler beneath, often with a wide variety of scales and hairs, transverse veinlets usually obscure. Inflorescence mostly infrafoliar, rarely interfoliar in acaulescent species with marcescent leaves, very rarely bursting through marcescent leaf sheaths (*P. simplicifrons*), usually rapidly becoming pendulous, occasionally erect, protogynous, unbranched or branching to 1 order only; peduncle usually short, dorsiventrally flattened, glabrous or tomentose; prophyll thin, membranous, 2-keeled, enclosing the inflorescence in bud, quickly splitting to expose the flowers except in *P. simplicifrons* and *P. cleistantha* where persistent and enclosing inflorescence up to almost mature fruiting; peduncular bracts absent; rachis usually longer than the peduncle; rachis bracts triangular, usually very inconspicuous; rachillae bearing spiral or distichous triads throughout, or triads in 4 or 6 vertical rows, or, more rarely, spiral proximally and distichous distally; triads sometimes partially sunken in the axis of the rachilla, but well defined pits not present; floral bracteoles minute. Staminate flowers asymmetrical, sessile, rarely stalked at the base, very rarely the stalk of one flower much longer than the other (*P. cleistantha*); calyx cupular with 3 triangular, frequently unequal lobes; petals 3, triangular, frequently unequal, joined briefly basally, valvate in bud, much exceeding the calyx lobes, usually very fleshy; stamens rarely 6, usually 12–30, filaments short, anthers linear, latrorse; pollen elliptic or ± circular, monosulcate, the sulcus sometimes extended, meridionosulcate, or trichotomosulcate, the exine intectate and granulate, baculate, or with extraordinary urn-shaped bodies (urceoli), or exine semitectate and perforate, finely to coarsely reticulate, rugulate, clavate, or echinate; pistillode absent. Pistillate flowers usually globose, symmetrical, much smaller than the staminate; sepals 3, membranous, striate, imbricate, distinct, or connate proximally with 3 broad, sometimes imbricate lobes distally; petals 3, distinct, imbricate, membranous; staminodes absent; gynoecium unilocular, uniovulate, globose, stigma usually convolute, sessile or on a short style, ovule basally attached, anatropous. Fruiting rachillae usually brightly colored (reddish or orange). Fruit globose, or ellipsoidal to spindle-shaped, sometimes narrow spindle-shaped and curved (*P. salicifolia* and others), bright crimson, scarlet, orange or black, very rarely dull brown or green, frequently passing through pink to crimson to black at maturity, stigmatic remains apical; epicarp usually smooth, shiny, with a silky sheen, or dull, mesocarp usually thin, fleshy, sweet, rarely greatly expanding (e.g. *P. keahii*), endocarp of longitudinal fibers, usually adhering to the seed, becoming free at the basal end only (see *Nenga*), fruit without a solid beak. Seed conforming to the fruit shape, but usually slightly hollowed at the base, with conspicuous basal hilum and anastomosing raphe branches, endosperm deeply ruminate or, very rarely subruminate or homogeneous; embryo basal. Germination adjacent-ligular; eophyll bifid or rarely entire with a minute apical cleft. *n* = 16 (*P. kuhlii,* Read 1966, Sarkar 1970; *P. patula,* Sarkar 1970). *n* = 14 (*P. kuhlii, P. coronata,* Eichhorn 1957, 1953; *P. disticha,* Gassner 1941).

Anatomy. — Leaf (Tomlinson 1961).

Distribution. — About 120 species ranging from the Himalayas and south China to New Guinea, with the greatest diversity in the wet areas of the Sunda Shelf; very poorly represented in Papuasia.

Ecology. — Almost all species are plants of the forest undergrowth; a few massive species such as *P. insignis* contribute to the lower part of the forest canopy. In altitude the genus ranges from sea level to ca. 2800 m in the mountains. Some species may be associated with various rock types including limestone and ultrabasics, but the greatest diversity appears to be in primary forest developed on sandstones on Borneo, where in some rich localities as many as nine species may be found growing sympatrically.

Common Names and Uses. — Pinang, Bunga. Stems may be used as laths, and leaves as thatch; fruit are rarely used as a betel substitute.

Notes. — This is a wonderfully protean genus as far as habit is concerned but seems to show rather little variation in inflorescence presentation and form. The pollen, however, is extremely varied (Ferguson et al. 1983). Pollination, where casually observed, appears to be by beetles.

Taxonomic Accounts. — Beccari (1886) is the last monograph and many species have been described since, e.g. by Furtado (1934) and Dransfield (1980b). A modern monographic account is much needed.

Plates. — 22A, B; 64D; Figs. G.21, G.23.

130. **ARECA** Linnaeus, Species Plantarum 1189. 1753. Type: **A. catechu** Linnaeus.

Mischophloeus Scheffer, Annales du Jardin Botanique de Buitenzorg 1:115, 134. 1876. Type: *M. paniculatus* (Scheffer) Scheffer (*Areca paniculata* Scheffer) (=*A. vestiaria* Giseke).

Gigliolia Beccari, Malesia 1:171. 1877. (Non Barbosa Rodrigues). Lectotype: *G. insignis* Beccari (=*A. insignis* (Beccari) J. Dransfield).

Pichisermollia H. Monteiro-Neto, Rodriguesia 41: 198. 1976. Type: *P. insignis* (Beccari) H. Monteiro-Neto (*Gigliolia insignis* Beccari).

Very small to moderate, solitary or clustered, acaulescent to erect, unarmed, pleonanthic, monoecious palms. Stem slender to moderate, occasionally stilt-rooted, internodes very short to elongate, leaf scars often conspicuous. Leaves undivided and pinnately ribbed, with or without an apical notch, or pinnate; sheaths forming a well defined crownshaft with leaves neatly abscising, or rarely crownshaft not well developed when leaves marcescent or the sheaths partly open; petiole present or ab-

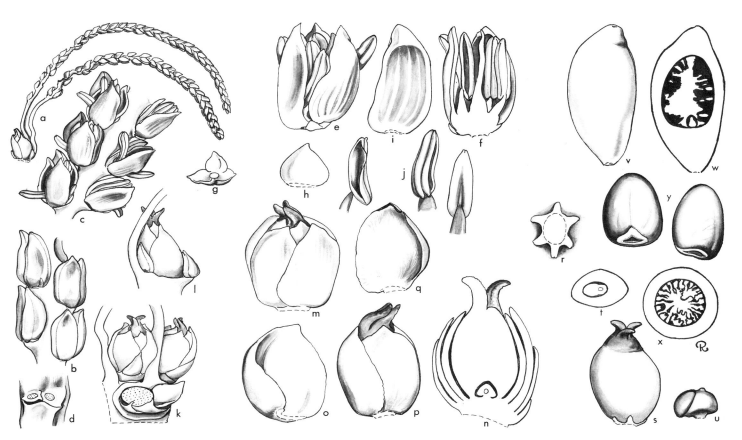

130.—**Areca. a,** rachillae ×½; **b, c,** portion of rachilla with staminate buds and flowers ×3; **d,** bracteoles subtending staminate flowers ×6; **e,** staminate flower ×6; **f,** staminate flower in vertical section ×6; **g,** staminate calyx ×6; **h,** staminate sepal, exterior view ×12; **i,** staminate petal, interior view ×6; **j,** stamen in 3 views ×6; **k,** bases of rachillae with pistillate flowers ×1½; **l,** pistillate flower with 2 sterile staminate flowers ×1½; **m,** pistillate flower ×3; **n,** pistillate flower in vertical section ×3; **o,** pistillate sepal, interior view ×3; **p,** pistillate flower, sepals removed ×3; **q,** pistillate petal, interior view ×3; **r,** staminodes ×3; **s,** gynoecium and staminodes ×3; **t,** ovary in cross-section ×3; **u,** ovule ×6; **v,** fruit ×1; **w,** fruit in vertical section ×1; **x,** fruit in cross-section ×1; **y,** seed in 2 views ×1. *Areca macrocalyx*: all from *Moore & Whitmore 9303*.

sent, adaxially channeled or rounded, abaxially rounded, glabrous or variously indumentose; leaflets regularly or irregularly arranged, 1–several fold, acute, acuminate or lobed, the lobes corresponding to the folds, the apical pair almost always lobed, held in one plane, very rarely (*A. insignis*) with a basal auricle reflexed across the rachis, blade variously scaly or hairy, transverse veinlets obscure. Inflorescences erect or pendulous, mostly infrafoliar, rarely interfoliar in acaulescent species with marcescent leaves, in one species sometimes bursting through marcescent leaf sheaths (*A. jugahpunya*), branched to 3 orders basally, fewer orders distally, very rarely spicate, protandrous (or very rarely recorded as protogynous); peduncle very short to long; prophyll thin, membranous, enclosing the inflorescence in bud, quickly splitting and falling, other bracts very inconspicuous; rachis shorter or longer than the peduncle; rachillae glabrous or variously indumentose; rachilla bracts minute; triads confined to the proximal part of the main axis, or to the proximal part of each order of

branching, or rarely to a subdistal part of the main axis only; rachillae otherwise bearing solitary or paired staminate flowers arranged spirally, distichously, or in 2 approximate rows on one side of the rachilla, the rachilla tips sometimes devoid of flowers. Staminate flowers frequently minute, sessile, or with a stalk formed from the receptacle; calyx with 3 distinct, slightly imbricate, triangular sepals, or cupular with 3 triangular lobes; corolla with 3 triangular, valvate petals, rarely briefly connate at the base, much longer than the sepals; stamens free or briefly epipetalous, 3, 6, 9 or up to 30 or more, filaments short to elongate, anthers linear or sinuous, sometimes very irregular, latrorse or rarely opening by apical pores; pollen elliptic or circular, monosulcate with the sulcus short to extensive, trichotomosulcate, monoporate (ulcerate), or triporate, with perforate, foveolate, or finely to coarsely reticulate tectate or intectate exine; pistillode present and conspicuous as a trifid column as long as the stamens, or minute, or often absent. Pistillate flowers sessile, usually much larger than the staminate, ± globular; sepals 3, distinct, imbricate; petals similar to the sepals, 3, distinct, sometimes valvate at the very tip, otherwise imbricate; staminodes 3–9 or absent; gynoecium unilocular, uniovulate, globose to ovoid, stigmas 3, fleshy, triangular, ± reflexed at anthesis, ovule anatropous, basally attached. Rachilla distal to pistillate flowers drying after anthesis, portions bearing fruit sometimes becoming brightly colored. Fruit globose, ovoid, or spindle-shaped, often brightly colored, rarely dull brown or green, stigmatic remains apical; epicarp smooth, shiny or dull, mesocarp thin to moderately thick, fleshy or fibrous, endocarp composed of robust longitudinal fibers, usually closely appressed to the seed, becoming free at the basal end or not. Seed conforming to the fruit shape or slightly hollowed at the base, with basal hilum and raphe branches anastomosing, endosperm deeply ruminate; embryo basal. Germination adjacent-ligular; eophyll bifid or rarely entire with a minute apical cleft. $n = 16$ (*A. catechu* Satô 1946, Sharma and Sarkar 1956, Read 1966); *A. triandra* Janaki Ammal 1945, Sharma and Sarkar 1957).

Anatomy. — Leaf, stem, root (Tomlinson 1961); gynoecium (Uhl and Moore 1971).

Distribution. — About 60 species, distributed from India and south China through Malesia to New Guinea and the Solomon Islands; one species recorded for Australia but this probably based on a cultivated specimen.

Ecology. — Most species are small to moderate palms of the undergrowth of tropical rain forest. *A. catechu,* the betel nut, is very widespread as a crop plant and seems to tolerate open conditions. Some species of *Areca* have very narrow ecological limits; for example, *A. rheophytica* is confined to the banks of fast-flowing streams on ultrabasic rock in Sabah, Borneo. *A triandra* is a polymorphic species occurring from India to Borneo; some of the entities within this complex taxon have rather precise habitat requirements.

Fossil Record. — *Retimonocolpites pluribaculatis* Salard-Cheboldaeff from the Maestrichtian of Cameroon has been referred to *Areca* and stated to be close to *A. ipot* (Muller 1981). In view of the great number of parallelisms in pollen form in the palms and the very limited distribution of *A. ipot* (Philippines), equating this pollen record with *Areca* seems questionable.

Common Names and Uses. — Betel nut palm, pinang, bunga, jambe. *Areca catechu* is economically important and widely cultivated, sometimes on a plantation scale. The endosperm, sliced, is chewed with leaves of *Piper betle* Linnaeus, lime and other ingredients; it contains the alkaloid arecaine which acts as a mild narcotic. The practice of betel-chewing is widespread and often has ceremonial significance. The fruit are also used as a source of tannin in dyeing, medicinally, and, rarely, as toothbrushes. The apex is edible and the flowers often used as ceremonial decoration. The leaf sheath may be utilized making containers, and other species may serve as substitutes in betel-chewing. Several species are cultivated as ornamentals.

Notes. — *Pichisermollia* has recently been included in *Areca* (Dransfield 1984c). As circumscribed here, *Areca* is a remarkably variable genus with very distinctive sections. The variation in Borneo is particularly noteworthy.

Taxonomic Accounts. — Furtado (1933) and Dransfield (1984c).

Plates. — 22C, D; 65A, B; also in 69C; Figs. G.4, G.19.

Iguanurinae J. D. Hooker in Bentham & J. D. Hooker, Genera Plantarum 3:872, 876. 1883. ('*Iguanureae*'). Type: **Iguanura.**

Diminutive to very large, unarmed; crownshafts often present; leaves pinnate or pinnately ribbed; leaflets when present entire or praemorse; inflorescences inter- or infrafoliar, spicate or branched up to 4 orders; prophyll tubular or incomplete; peduncular bract usually similar to and inserted near the prophyll; triads sometimes borne in pits; staminate flowers ± symmetrical; pistillodes usually prominent; pistillate flower with imbricate petals; gynoecium pseudomonomerous; fruit with apical, lateral, or basal stigmatic remains; endocarp with a well defined operculum covering the embryo; seed basally or laterally attached; embryo basal or lateral.

The Iguanurinae include 27 genera which are found predominantly in the islands of the western Pacific, straddling Wallace's line, but mainly to the east (Map 42). *Bentinckia* reaches southern India, and *Dictyosperma* is endemic to the Mascarene Islands. Scattered over thousands of square miles, the subtribe shows great diversity in habit, inflorescence form, flower, and fruit structure. What holds the group together is the presence of an operculum at the base of the endocarp and an absence of spines. A few genera (*Alsmithia, Cyphosperma, Burretiokentia, Veillonia, Physokentia*) have extraordinarily sculptured endocarps but the significance of the sculpturing is not evident. The closest relatives of the Iguanurinae are the Oncospermatinae, the only other subtribe possessing an operculum, but distinguished by spines, at least in the juvenile state. Since several members of the Oncospermatinae display what appears to be some loss of spines, it seems possible that some members of the Oncospermatin-

Map 42.—**Distribution of Iguanurinae.**

ae may be more closely related to certain genera of Iguanurinae than to each other.

Key to the Genera of the Iguanurinae

1 Prophyll completely encircling the peduncle at insertion, leaving a circular scar when caducous; stamens 6 or more 2

1 Prophyll incompletely encircling the peduncle at insertion, opening abaxially, leaving an incomplete scar upon falling; stamens always 6 20

2 Seed irregularly ridged, furrowed and sculptured with adherent fibers .... 143. **Alsmithia**

2 Seed ± small, not ridged or sculptured 3

3 Staminate flowers borne in vertically oriented pairs sunken in distinct depressions distally, smaller than and lateral to the pistillate flowers proximally on the rachillae; fruit large, with apical stigmatic remains. Fiji .... 131. **Neoveitchia**

3 Staminate flowers borne in horizontally oriented pairs distally, lateral to pistillate flowers proximally on the rachillae; fruit moderate, rarely large with apical, lateral, or basal stigmatic remains 4

4 Inflorescence interfoliar; fruit covered with prominent corky warts; stigmatic remains basal in fruit 5

4 Inflorescence interfoliar, or infrafoliar, fruit smooth or merely pebbled to granulose when dry; stigmatic remains various 6

5 Peduncular bract inserted near the base of the peduncle; fruit more than 2.5 cm in diameter. Marquesas Islands .... 132. **Pelagodoxa**

5 Peduncular bract inserted at the apex of the peduncle; fruit 1.5 cm in diameter or less. New Guinea .... 137. **Sommieria**

6 Flowers borne in laterally compressed pits, the staminate on long, hairy pedicels; fruit with stigmatic remains lateral in lower ¼; seeds ridged and grooved. Southern India and Nicobar Islands .... 138. **Bentinckia**

6 Flowers sessile or impressed in the rachillae but neither in laterally compressed pits nor the staminate with hair covered pedicels; stigmatic remains apical to basal; seeds smooth 7

7 Leaflets several-ribbed with praemorse apices or leaf blades, when not divided with toothed margins; inflorescences usually interfoliar; triads shallowly to deeply sunken in depressions in the rachillae. Thailand, Peninsular Malaysia, Borneo, Java, Sumatra ... 133. **Iguanura**

7 Leaflets 1-ribbed with acute or acuminate apices; inflorescences various; triads superficial 8

8 Seed with ruminate endosperm 9

8 Seed with homogeneous endosperm 12

9 Leaf sheaths splitting opposite the petiole, not forming a prominent crownshaft; inflorescences interfoliar, at least in bud, sometimes infrafoliar at anthesis or in fruit; the peduncle elongate, prominent, usually as long as the rachis or longer. Philippines to Micronesia, New Guinea, Solomon Islands .... 136. **Heterospathe**

9 Leaf sheaths tubular, forming a prominent crownshaft; inflorescence infrafoliar; peduncle usually much shorter than the rachis 10

10 Inflorescence lacking branches adaxially except at the apex, branched to 1 order only and the lower branches ±

ascending, not divaricate from the rachis at a 90° angle; fruit black at maturity. Mascarene Islands . . . . .146. **Dictyosperma**

10 Inflorescence with branches spirally arranged, the lower branches abruptly divaricate at about a 90° angle from the rachis and again once- or twice-branched; fruit yellow, orange, or red 11

11 Stamens 6–9; pistillode prominent. Nicobar Islands, Peninsular Malaysia, Moluccas, New Guinea to the Solomon Islands . . . . 145. **Rhopaloblaste**

11 Stamens 15–30 or more; pistillode minute or lacking. New Guinea, Solomon Islands . . . . 147. **Actinorhytis**

12 Staminate flowers mostly larger than the pistillate; stamen filaments inflexed at the apex in bud; anthers dorsifixed, with elongate connective, not didymous 13

12 Staminate flowers mostly smaller than the pistillate; stamen filaments erect in bud; anthers didymous 18

13 Stamens 12; fruit with basal stigmatic remains, lacking a shell of sclereids. New Caledonia . . . . .140. **Cyphokentia**

13 Stamens 6; fruit various 14

14 Endocarp minutely pitted; seed with lateral embryo. New Caledonia . . . . 149. **Alloschmidia**

14 Endocarp not pitted; seed with basal embryo 15

15 Leaf sheaths split opposite the petiole; inflorescence interfoliar. Lord Howe Island . . . . 135. **Lepidorrhachis**

15 Leaf sheaths forming a prominent crownshaft; inflorescence infrafoliar 16

16 Inflorescence densely tomentose; fruit with apical stigmatic residue. Ryukyu Islands . . . . 144. **Satakentia**

16 Inflorescence glabrous or at most minutely hairy; fruit with subapical to nearly basal stigmatic remains 17

17 Stilt roots usually developed; staminate flowers markedly asymmetrical, with short, trifid pistillode and acute sepals and petals; fruit lacking sclereids but with prominent, often greatly thickened fibers. New Ireland to Samoa . . . . 142. **Clinostigma**

17 Stilt roots not developed; staminate flowers symmetrical, with pistillode as long as stamens in bud and rounded sepals and petals; fruit with a layer of short sclereids beneath the exocarp. New Caledonia . . . . . . .141. **Moratia**

18 Fruit ellipsoidal with basal stigmatic remains; sclereids lacking in mesocarp but tannin cells present. New Caledonia . . . . 134. **Brongniartikentia**

18 Fruit globose or nearly so with lateral stigmatic remains; mesocarp with a shell of short sclereids beneath the exocarp 19

19 Leaf sheaths with minute scales, split opposite the petiole and not forming a crownshaft; peduncle short; fruit small, 1.4–1.6 cm in diameter, with tannin cells interior to sclereid layer. New Caledonia . . . . .139. **Clinosperma**

19 Leaf sheaths densely scaly, tubular and forming a prominent crownshaft; peduncle elongate; fruit large, ca. 3.2 cm in diameter, lacking tannin cells. New Caledonia . . . . 148. **Lavoixia**

20 Seed terete or 2-lobed in cross-section, ovoid, ellipsoidal, globose or rarely kidney-shaped in outline 21

20 Seed irregular in cross-section, externally angled or intricately ridged, furrowed, and sculptured 23

21 Fruit with apical stigmatic remains 22

21 Fruit with lateral stigmatic remains. New Caledonia . . . . .152. **Basselinia**

22 Stilt roots prominent and stout; pistillode of staminate

flower shorter than stamens; fruit often curved apically. New Caledonia . . . . 151. **Campecarpus**

22 Stilt roots not prominently developed; pistillode of staminate flower longer than stamens, columnar; fruit straight. New Caledonia and Loyalty Islands . . . . 150. **Cyphophoenix**

23 Leaf sheaths split opposite the petiole in bud, not forming a prominent crownshaft; inflorescence among the leaves in bud, becoming infrafoliar in fruit; peduncle elongate, much exceeding the rachis; prophyll and peduncular bract ± persistent, at length marcescent; inflorescence branches with long bare basal portions, prominently swollen at the insertion, stiffly and divaricately branched to 1 order or the distal undivided. Fiji and New Caledonia . . . . .153. **Cyphosperma**

23 Leaf sheaths forming a prominent crownshaft; inflorescence infrafoliar; peduncle shorter than the rachis; prophyll and peduncular bracts caducous; inflorescence branches without a long basal bare portion, nor swollen at the insertion 24

24 Staminate flowers symmetrical; pistillode thick, columnar, longer than the stamens in bud, expanded into a broadly capitate apex; fruit subglobose with stigmatic remains lateral in upper third, the surface minutely granular-papillate. New Caledonia . . . . 154. **Veillonia**

24 Staminate flowers slightly to markedly asymmetrical, the pistillode elongate-conic to angled-columnar, shorter than the stamens in bud, not broadly capitate; fruit smooth or drying pebbled but not granular-papillose 25

25 Bracteoles surrounding the pistillate flower sepallike; anthers with locules not continuous but interrupted by sterile connectivelike areas; fruit drying densely pebbled and shouldered; mesocarp not readily separable from the stony, intricately sculptured, 4-angled endocarp with a dorsal groove flanked by 2 ridges. New Caledonia . . . . 155. **Burretiokentia**

25 Bracteoles surrounding the pistillate flower very narrow, rarely (*P. dennisii*) with a slender limb but never sepallike; locules of anthers continuous; fruit globose or subglobose or collapsing and drying wrinkled but not pebbled; mesocarp with a shining inner layer adjacent to and readily separated from the endocarp, endocarp sharply 4-angled to variously ridged and sculptured but always with a dorsal ridge. New Britain to Fiji . . . . 156. **Physokentia**

131. NEOVEITCHIA Beccari, Le Palme della Nuova Caledonia 9. 1920; and Webbia 5:77. 1921. Type: **N. storckii** (H. A. Wendland) Beccari (*Veitchia storckii* H. A. Wendland).

Moderate, solitary, unarmed, pleonanthic, monoecious tree palm. Stem erect, becoming bare, conspicuously ringed with leaf scars. Leaves pinnate, neatly abscising; leaf sheath ± split opposite the petiole, not forming a well developed crownshaft, bearing scattered scales, the mouths irregularly fibrous; petiole flattened or shallowly channeled adaxially, abaxially rounded, bearing scattered caducous scales; rachis ± curved, densely minutely-dotted abaxially, deciduously floccose adaxially; leaflets numerous, regularly arranged, single-fold, acute, with conspic-

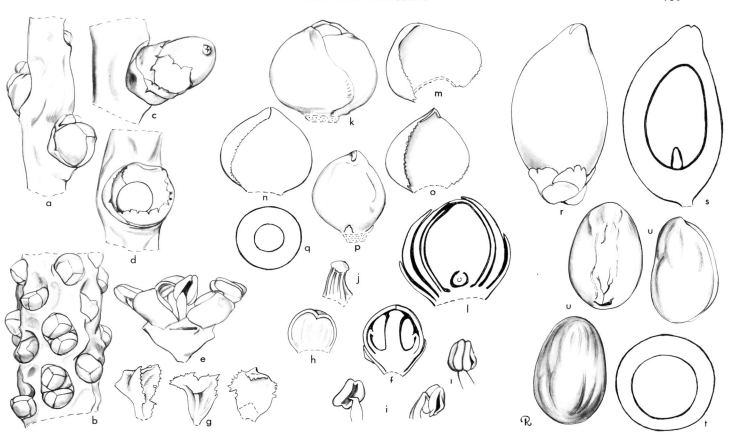

131.—**Neoveitchia. a,** portion of rachilla with triads ×1½; **b,** portion of rachilla with paired, superposed, staminate buds ×3; **c,** portion of rachilla with very young fruit ×1½; **d,** bracteoles subtending pistillate flower ×1½; **e,** staminate flower, expanded ×6; **f,** staminate bud in vertical section ×6; **g,** staminate sepals ×6; **h,** staminate petal, interior view ×6; **i,** stamen in 3 views ×6; **j,** pistillode ×6; **k,** pistillate bud ×3; **l,** pistillate bud in vertical section ×3; **m,** pistillate sepal ×3; **n,** pistillate bud, sepals removed ×3; **o,** pistillate petal ×3; **p,** gynoecium and staminodes ×3; **q,** ovary in cross-section ×6; **r,** fruit ×1; **s,** fruit in vertical section ×1; **t,** fruit in cross-section ×1; **u,** seed in 3 views ×1. *Neoveitchia storckii:* all from *Moore & Koroiveibau 9360.*

uously thickened margins, adaxially glabrous, abaxially with few ramenta along the midrib near the base, transverse veinlets not visible. Inflorescences infrafoliar, branching to 3 orders, apparently protandrous; peduncle winged at the base, somewhat swollen, rapidly tapering, distally ± circular in cross-section; prophyll inserted near the base of the peduncle, tubular, flattened, strongly 2-keeled, splitting apically long before anthesis while still enclosed within the leaf sheath, allowing the peduncular bract to protrude, eventually deciduous; peduncular bract about twice as long as the prophyll, beaked, tubular, entirely enclosing the inflorescence, splitting longitudinally at anthesis, then deciduous, 1 (or 2) very much smaller, incomplete, ± triangular, peduncular bracts also present; rachis ± the same length as the peduncle; rachis bracts spirally arranged, small, low, triangular; first-order branches with a basal bare portion; rachillae rather stiff, curved, eventually pendulous, somewhat angled, basally bearing rather few, distant, ± superficial triads, the 2 staminate flowers ± distal (rather than lateral) to the pistillate flower, distally the rachilla bearing ±7 vertical series

of floral pits, each partially enclosing a vertical (rather than lateral) pair of staminate flowers, the staminate portion of the rachilla deciduous at fruiting stage; floral bracteoles small, included within the pits. Staminate flowers asymmetrical, those originating from triads with flattened pedicels, those from staminate pairs ± sessile; sepals 3, strongly keeled or winged, distinct, strongly imbricate, or frequently 1 distinct, and 2 joined for ¾ their length into a 2-keeled prophyll-like structure, or all 3 joined but retaining 2 distinct imbricate margins, the margins coarsely toothed; petals 3, distinct, triangular-ovate, valvate, smooth; stamens 6, filaments distinct, rather short, narrow, fleshy, inflexed in bud, anthers short, rectangular, medifixed, ± versatile, latrorse, the connective broad, conspicuous; pollen elliptic, monosulcate, with finely punctate, tectate exine; pistillode columnar, striate, truncate, as long as the stamens. Pistillate flowers very much larger than the staminate, ± spherical; sepals 3, distinct, broadly imbricate; petals 3, distinct, broadly imbricate except for the minute, triangular, valvate tips; staminodes 3, very small, triangular, toothlike; gynoecium unilocular, uniovulate, ovoid, stigmas 3, very small, reflexed, ovule laterally attached, form unknown. Fruit ellipsoidal, rather large, becoming reddish-yellow at maturity, perianth whorls persistent, stigmatic remains apical; epicarp smooth, mesocarp fleshy with abundant close longitudinal fibers, endocarp thin, bony, closely adhering to the seed, operculum, small, circular. Seed laterally attached, hilum elongate, running ± the length of the seed, raphe branches abundant, anastomosing, endosperm homogeneous; embryo basal. Germination and eophyll not recorded. Cytology not studied.

Anatomy. — Not studied.

Distribution. — A single species, confined to a very limited area in Naitasiri Province, Viti Levu, Fiji Islands, where it is in danger of extinction.

Ecology. — Now only known in valley bottom secondary forest.

Common Names and Uses. — Unleito. Trunks have been used as posts in house construction; the young fruit is eaten.

Notes. — The arrangement of the staminate flowers, one above the other, is unique. Although *Neoveitchia* is obviously a member of the Iguanurinae, its relationships within the subtribe are obscure.

Taxonomic Accounts. — Moore (1957b, 1979).

Plate. — 65C, D.

132. **PELAGODOXA** Beccari in Bois, Revue Horticole series 2, 15:302. 1917. Type: **P. henryana** Beccari.

Moderate, solitary, unarmed, pleonanthic, monoecious palm. Stem erect, bare, ringed with close leaf scars. Leaves pinnately ribbed, undivided except for the bifid apex, but often split by wind; leaf sheaths soon splitting opposite the petiole, not forming a crownshaft, densely tomentose, with an irregular ligule at the mouth, disintegrating into fine fibers; petiole relatively short, adaxially channeled, abaxially ± rounded, densely covered in tomentum; rachis curved, densely tomentose; blade adaxially bright, shiny green, glabrous, abaxially with a thin felt of gray tomentum, distal margin shallowly lobed, the lobes corresponding to the major folds and minutely toothed, transverse veinlets obscure. Inflorescences solitary, interfoliar, much shorter than the leaves, branching to 2 orders, protandrous; peduncle ± oval in cross-section, exserted from the leaf sheaths; prophyll short, inserted near the base of the peduncle, only partially enclosing the inflorescence in bud, splitting abaxially near the tip, beaked, strongly 2-keeled, coriaceous to sub-woody, densely tomentose, tending to disintegrate into fibers; peduncular bract longer than the prophyll, inserted just above the prophyll, tubular, beaked, enclosing the inflorescence in bud, densely tomentose; subsequent bracts rather small, incomplete, broad, triangular; rachis only slightly longer than the peduncle; all inflorescence axes tomentose; rachillae stiff, relatively thick, gradually tapering to a pointed tip, bearing spirally arranged, shallow pits, the rachilla bracts forming low triangular lips to the pits, pits in the proximal

ca. ¼–⅓ of rachillae containing triads, distally containing paired or solitary staminate flowers, the rachilla bracts at the tips of the rachillae more prominent than at the base; floral bracteoles low, rounded, inconspicuous, included within the pits. Staminate flowers small, ± globular, ± symmetrical, only partially exserted from the pit; sepals 3, distinct, imbricate, strongly keeled, rather chaffy; petals 3, about twice as long as the sepals, united proximally and adnate to the receptacle forming a stalklike base, distally ± triangular-ovate, striate, valvate; stamens 6, the filaments united basally to the pistillode forming a solid column above the insertion of the free portion of petals, free filaments fleshy, triangular, gradually tapering to the connective, anthers short, medifixed, basally sagittate, latrorse, the connective prolonged in a brief point; pollen elliptic, monosulcate, with rugulate, tectate exine; pistillode pyramidal. Pistillate flowers globose, at anthesis larger than the staminate, tending to crack open the floral pits; sepals 3, distinct, broad, rounded, imbricate; petals 3, distinct, broadly imbricate except for brief, triangular valvate tips, very briefly joined basally to form a short broad stalk with the receptacle; staminodes 3, triangular, flattened, very small; gynoecium unilocular, uniovulate, rounded, stigmas 3, short, reflexed, ovule laterally attached, campylotropous. Fruit large, spherical, perianth whorls persistent, stigmatic remains basal, the fruit surface cracked into low, pyramidal, corky warts; epicarp obsolescent at maturity, mesocarp massively corky with abundant radiating fibers, endocarp thin, woody. Seed basally attached with rounded hilum, endosperm homogeneous with a large central hollow; embryo basal. Germination adjacent-ligular; eophyll bifid. $n = 14$ (Johnson 1985). $n = 16$ (Read and Moore 1967).

Anatomy. — Leaf (Tomlinson 1961), easily recognized by a unique arrangement of cells around the stomata; otherwise isolated from other reduplicate palms.

Distribution. — One species, confined to the Marquesas Islands where very rare.

Ecology. — In dense rain forest at about 135 m above sea level, in a humid valley.

Common Names and Uses. — Enu, vahani. The young endosperm is said to be eaten; the palm is cultivated and much sought after as an ornamental.

Notes. — This is an extraordinary genus with an unusual distribution. The huge bifid leaf, the connate petals in the staminate flower, stamens adnate to the pistillode, and the corky-warted fruit represent a combination of characters found in no other genus. Its relationships probably lie with *Heterospathe* but it does remain very isolated. *P. mesocarpa*, based on a single fruit, is surely conspecific with *P. henryana*.

Taxonomic Accounts. — See Martelli (1932) and Gillett (1971), for an account of the genus in the wild.

Plates. — 23B; 66A.

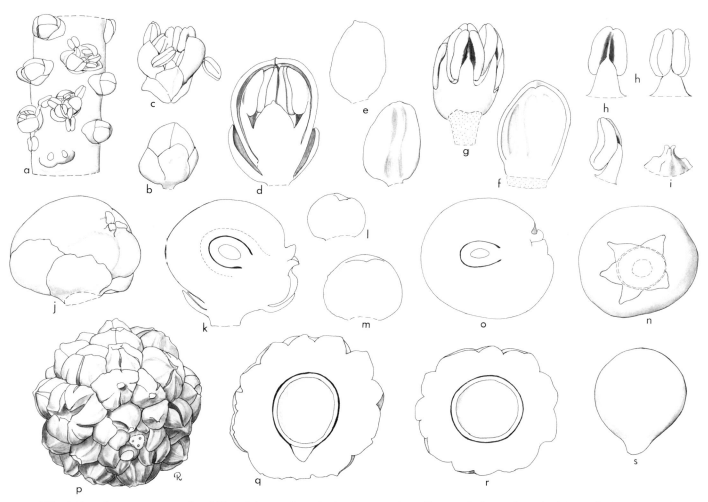

132.—**Pelagodoxa. a,** portion of rachilla ×3; **b,** staminate bud ×6; **c,** staminate flower ×6; **d,** staminate bud in vertical section ×12; **e,** staminate sepal in 2 views ×12; **f,** staminate petal ×12; **g,** androecium ×12; **h,** stamen in 3 views ×12; **i,** pistillode ×24; **j,** pistillate flower ×6; **k,** pistillate flower in vertical section ×6; **l,** pistillate sepal ×6; **m,** pistillate petal ×6; **n,** gynoecium, bottom view to show staminodes ×6; **o,** ovary in cross-section ×6; **p,** fruit ×¾; **q,** fruit in vertical section ×¾; **r,** fruit in cross-section ×¾; **s,** seed ×¾. *Pelagodoxa henryana:* **a-o,** *Moore 9400;* **p-s,** *Read s.n.*

133. IGUANURA Blume, Bulletin des Sciences Physiques et Naturelles en Néerlande 1:66. 1838. Type: **I. leucocarpa** Blume.

Slackia Griffith, Calcutta Journal of Natural History 5:468. 1845. Type: *S. geonomiformis* Griffith (=*Iguanura wallichiana* (Wallich ex Martius) J. D. Hooker).

Small, solitary or clustered, acaulescent or erect, unarmed, pleonanthic, monoecious palms. Stems rarely exceeding about 4 m in height, with very short to elongate internodes, leaf scars inconspicuous, stilt roots sometimes present. Leaves undivided and pinnately ribbed, with or without an apical notch, or regularly to irregularly pinnate, marcescent or neatly abscising; sheaths usually splitting opposite the petiole and persistent, not forming a crownshaft, or rarely neatly abscising and a crownshaft devel-

oped, variously tomentose, a tattering ligule sometimes present; petiole present or absent, variously indumentose as the rachis; expanding blades frequently reddish-tinged, leaflets 1–several fold, the tips or margins in entire blades irregularly praemorse, the main ribs frequently bearing scales or hairs, scattered or in bands, the blade with conspicuous longitudinal veins, transverse veinlets inconspicuous. Inflorescences usually interfoliar or infrafoliar (in species with a crownshaft), solitary, protandrous, spicate or branching to 1 or 2 orders, emerging long before anthesis, erect at first, becoming curved or pendulous; peduncle very short to very long; prophyll 2-keeled, tubular, short, usually enclosed within the leaf sheath, frequently marcescent, often indumentose; peduncular bract attached a short distance above the prophyll, usually much exceeding it, otherwise similar, marcescent, rarely neatly abscising, subsequent peduncular bracts very inconspicuous; rachis usually much shorter than the peduncle; ra-

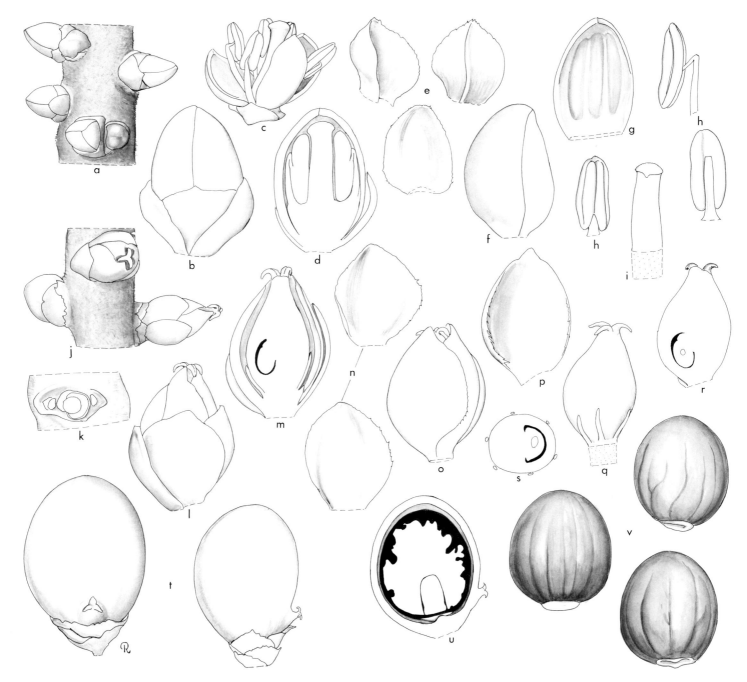

133.—**Iguanura. a,** portion of rachilla with staminate and smaller pistillate buds ×4½; **b,** staminate bud ×12; **c,** staminate flower ×7½; **d,** staminate bud in vertical section ×12; **e,** staminate sepals ×12; **f,** staminate bud, sepals removed ×12; **g,** staminate petal, interior view ×12; **h,** stamen in 3 views ×12; **i,** pistillode ×12; **j,** portion of rachilla with pistillate flowers ×4½; **k,** triad, flowers removed to show bracts and scars ×7½; **l,** pistillate flower ×7½; **m,** pistillate flower in vertical section ×7½; **n,** pistillate sepal in 2 views ×7½; **o,** pistillate flower, sepals removed ×7½; **p,** pistillate petal ×7½; **q,** gynoecium and staminodes ×7½; **r,** gynoecium in vertical section ×7½; **s,** ovary in cross-section ×7½; **t,** fruit in 2 views ×4½; **u,** fruit in vertical section ×4½; **v,** seed in 3 views ×4½. *Iguanura wallichiana*: **a–i,** *Moore 9063*; **j–s,** *Moore 9072*; **t–v,** *Kunstler 7999*.

chillae rarely exceeding about 20 in number, usually fewer, very slender to moderately robust, glabrous or densely tomentose, bearing distant or dense, spirally arranged triads, superficial or, more usually, sunken in pits, each subtended by a low rachilla bract, forming the lower lip of the pit, an upper lip sometimes also differentiated, the pits frequently bearing sparse or abundant hairs, distalmost bracts subtending paired or solitary staminate flowers; floral bracteoles very small, included within the pits; flowers opening singly, in pit-bearing species the flowers exserted one at a time. Staminate flowers sessile, ± globular in bud, symmetrical, abscising after anthesis usually leaving the calyx behind; sepals 3, distinct, imbricate, membranous, ± striate, often keeled, often ciliate-margined, sometimes tomentose, scarcely exserted from the pit; petals 3, valvate, twice as long as the sepals, somewhat hooded, very briefly joined at the base; stamens 6, filaments slender, elongate, fleshy, inflexed in bud, anthers ± oblong, the margins sometimes undulate, ± versatile, latrorse; pollen elliptic, monosulcate, with perforate, tectate exine; pistillode conspicuous, columnar, as long as the petals, fleshy. Pistillate flower ± globular, slightly larger than the staminate; sepals 3, distinct, broadly imbricate, rounded, ± striate; petals 3, distinct, exceeding the sepals, broadly imbricate, with minute, triangular, valvate tips, ± striate; staminodes 6, slender, flattened; gynoecium unilocular, uniovulate, slightly asymmetrical, ± ovoid, stigmas 3, large, fleshy, reflexed, ovule laterally attached, hemianatropous. Fruit ovoid, ellipsoidal, bilobed, or narrowly spindle-shaped and straight or curved, or even flat and 5-pointed, smooth when fresh, smooth or ridged when dry, green, white, brownish or pink turning brilliant red at maturity, the stigmatic remains basal, perianth whorls persistent; epicarp smooth, shiny, mesocarp fleshy, endocarp well developed, woody, smooth or variously ridged, with a basal rounded operculum. Seed conforming to the shape of the endocarp, attached at one side near the base, the hilum ± circular, raphe branches spirally ascending, anastomosing, endosperm homogeneous or ruminate; embryo basal. Germination adjacent-ligular; eophyll ± entire, with praemorse margins, with or without a small apical notch. n = 16 (*I. wallichiana*, Johnson 1985).

Anatomy. — Not studied.

Distribution. — About 18 species in Sumatra, Peninsular Malaysia, south Thailand and Borneo, many of them very local and poorly known.

Ecology. — All species are plants of the undergrowth of primary tropical rain forest; they may be found at altitudes from sea level to about 1200 m in the mountains. They often occur gregariously. In Peninsular Malaysia, *I. wallichiana* is extraordinarily widespread, yet in Sumatra it is local, for no obvious reason. In Borneo many taxa are known from very restricted areas. *I. melinauensis* and *I. elegans* are found in rich alluvial soil developed at the base of limestone hills, but are not confined to this habitat; neither do they appear to be true calcicoles. Ants, flies, bees and wasps are frequent visitors to the staminate flowers of *I. wallichiana* (Kiew

1972), but of these, ants seem to be the most consistent visitors of pistillate flowers.

Common Names and Uses. — Pinang. Species of *Iguanura* are seldom used except in a casual way, e.g. the leaves may be used for thatching overnight shelters. Roots and fruit of *I. wallichiana* have been attributed with contraceptive properties (Burkill 1966). All species are very decorative, but appear to be difficult to cultivate.

Notes. — The small size and usual lack of a crownshaft help to distinguish this genus. *Iguanura* seems to be most closely related to *Heterospathe*. The most remarkable feature of the genus is undoubtedly the range of fruit shape. Although the genus has been recently monographed, many species, including the type, are very poorly known and represented in herbaria by few specimens.

Taxonomic Accounts. — Kiew (1976, 1979).

Plates. — 23A; 66B; Fig. G.19.

134. **BRONGNIARTIKENTIA** Beccari, Le Palme della Nuova Caledonia 48. 1920; and Webbia 5:116. 1921. Type: **B. vaginata** (Brongniart) Beccari (*Cyphokentia vaginata* Brongniart).

Small or moderate, solitary, unarmed, pleonanthic, monoecious palms. Stem erect, slender, green or brown, ringed with prominent, irregular, indented leaf scars, sometimes enlarged at maturity by the persistent fibrous stubs of old inflorescences. Leaves sometimes in 3 ranks, regularly pinnate, spreading or arching; sheaths usually ± deeply split opposite the petiole, not forming a crownshaft, covered with deciduous, sparse indumentum or persistent dense tomentum and twisted spathulate, basifixed scales; petiole long or short, rounded abaxially, shallowly channeled adaxially, or nearly cylindrical, covered with deciduous brown tomentum, becoming minutely brown-dotted; rachis angled adaxially, rounded abaxially; leaflets stiff, single-fold, leathery when dry, acute, or somewhat rounded, or the distalmost very briefly bifid at the apex, the midrib and 1–3 veins on each side prominent on the upper surface, transverse veinlets not evident. Inflorescences protandrous, interfoliar in bud or at anthesis, becoming infrafoliar at anthesis or in fruit, branched to 1 or 2(–3) orders, erect or curved and pendulous; peduncle short or long; prophyll completely encircling the peduncle, narrow, 2-keeled laterally, tubular, pointed, short, open apically; peduncular bract inserted close to or some distance above the prophyll, terete, slightly to markedly exceeding the prophyll, blunt-tipped, thin, both prophyll and peduncular bract ± lightly tomentose, persistent, and marcescent (*B. vaginata*) or deciduous and the peduncular bract leaving a rufflike base (*B. lanuginosa*); rachis about equal to or much shorter than the peduncle, somewhat angled and ± rugose when dry, bearing spirally inserted, distant, short, rounded to acute bracts subtending branches and rachillae; first-order branches with a prominent bare basal portion; rachillae slender, bearing spirally ar-

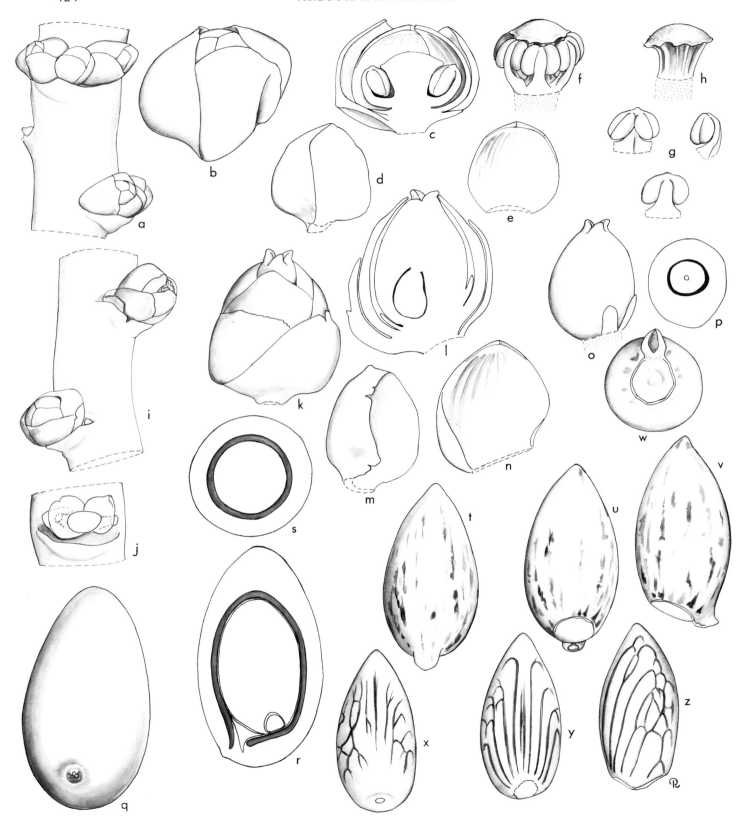

ranged shallow, liplike, acute bracts, each subtending a triad in the lower ½ to ⅔ of each rachilla and paired to solitary staminate flowers distally; floral bracteoles sepallike and prominent. Staminate flowers symmetrical, very small; sepals 3, distinct, broadly imbricate; petals 3, distinct, valvate, slightly longer than the sepals; stamens 6, filaments short, stout, erect, not inflexed, anthers didymous with separated locules inserted at the apex of the filament, introrse; pollen elliptic, monosulcate, with perforate, tectate exine; pistillode longer than the stamens, angled-capitate at the apex. Pistillate flowers slightly larger than the staminate; sepals 3, distinct, broadly imbricate; petals 3, distinct, imbricate except the briefly valvate apices, slightly longer than the sepals; staminodes 3, clustered at one side of the gynoecium opposite the fertile locule; gynoecium unilocular, uniovulate, eccentrically ovoid with 3 short, recurved stigmas, the ovule pendulous, probably hemianatropous. Fruit ovoid-ellipsoidal, green when immature, red at maturity, with subbasal stigmatic remains; epicarp smooth, mesocarp with a granular pale layer, a layer of anastomosing longitudinal fibers, and a layer of red tannin cells against the endocarp, endocarp thin, vitreous, fragile, operculate basally. Seed ellipsoidal, hilum round, basal, raphe branches ascending, endosperm homogeneous; embryo basal. Germination and eophyll not recorded. Cytology not studied.

Anatomy.—In leaf anatomy the genus is distinguished by the combination of two adaxial and one abaxial hypodermal layers, and obovate midribs with wide truncate or crescentic fibrous sheaths about equal in height above and below the lamina. Leaves of *B. vaginata* have more tannin and more fibrous strands than those of *B. lanuginosa* (Uhl and Martens in prep.).

Distribution.—Two species in New Caledonia.

Ecology.—*B. vaginata* occurs in wet forests on peridotitic soils in southern New Caledonia. *B. lanuginosa* occurs on schists and siliceous soils in a limited region of northeastern New Caledonia. Plants of the latter species are generally shorter and often stouter than those of *B. vaginata* and the inflorescences are borne below the leaves at anthesis.

Common Names and Uses.—Not recorded.

Notes.—*Brongniartikentia* stands apart among New Caledonian palms in several respects. Inflorescences are often borne among the leaves, at least in bud, and the leaf sheaths do not form a tubular

crownshaft but split to a greater or lesser degree opposite the petiole. These characteristics are shared only with *Cyphosperma* among palms of the island. *Brongniartikentia* does not have the highly sculptured endocarp and seed characteristic of *Cyphosperma,* and the prophyll completely encircles the peduncle, instead of being incompletely circling.

Taxonomic Account.—Moore and Uhl (1984).
Plate.—66C; *Fig. G.19.*

135. **LEPIDORRHACHIS** (H. A. Wendland & Drude) O. F. Cook, Journal of Heredity 18:408. 1927 ('*Lepidorhachis*'). Type: **L. mooreana** (F. v. Mueller) O. F. Cook (*Kentia mooreana* F. v. Mueller).
Clinostigma section *Lepidorrhachis* H. A. Wendland & Drude, Linnaea 39:218. 1875. Type: *C. mooreanum* (F. v. Mueller) H. A. Wendland & Drude.

Small to moderate, solitary, unarmed, pleonanthic, monoecious palm. Stem thick, short, green, prominently ringed with close leaf scars. Leaves pinnate, ascending; sheath inflated at the base, deeply split opposite the petiole, not forming a distinct crownshaft, densely brown-scurfy toward the apex and petiole; petiole short, shallowly channeled adaxially, rounded abaxially, densely brown-scurfy; rachis adaxially channeled to ridged, abaxially rounded, densely tomentose; leaflets regularly arranged, alternate, single-fold, acute, stiff, ascending from the rachis, the midrib and 2–3 secondary nerves on each side prominent adaxially, margins thickened, bearing scales along ribs on both surfaces, transverse veinlets not evident. Inflorescences interfoliar in bud, becoming infrafoliar at anthesis, branched to 3 orders basally, fewer distally, densely covered with basifixed, twisted, simple to forked or tattered, brown, membranous scales; peduncle very short; prophyll tubular, 2-keeled, open apically, apparently completely encircling at the base; peduncular bract tubular, beaked, exserted from the prophyll; rachis longer than the peduncle, bearing short, wide, acute bracts subtending rather distant, spirally arranged branches and rachillae; rachillae short, bearing flowers in triads nearly throughout or staminate flowers paired or solitary toward the apex, the triads superficial, each subtended by an acute bract. Staminate flowers slightly asymmetrical; sepals 3, distinct, imbricate basally, keeled, ± rounded apically; petals 3, distinct, slightly asymmetrical, about twice as long as the sepals, strongly nerved when dry; stamens 6,

134.—**Brongniartikentia. a,** portion of rachilla in staminate bud ×6; **b,** staminate bud ×15; **c,** staminate bud in vertical section ×15; **d,** staminate sepal ×15; **e,** staminate petal, interior view ×15; **f,** androecium and pistillode ×15; **g,** stamen in 3 views ×15; **h,** pistillode ×15; **i,** portion of rachilla at pistillate anthesis ×6; **j,** triad, flowers removed to show bracteoles, pedicels of staminate flowers indicated by dotted lines ×6; **k,** pistillate flower at anthesis ×12; **l,** pistillate flower in vertical section ×12; **m,** pistillate sepal ×12; **n,** pistillate petal, interior view ×12; **o,** gynoecium and staminodes ×12; **p,** ovary in cross-section ×12; **q,** fruit ×3; **r,** fruit in vertical section ×3; **s,** fruit in cross-section ×3; **t, u, v, w,** endocarp in 4 views ×3; **x, y, x,** seed in 3 views ×2. *Brongniartikentia lanuginosa*: a–h and q–z, *Moore & Schmid 10037*; i–p, *Moore et al. 9967.*

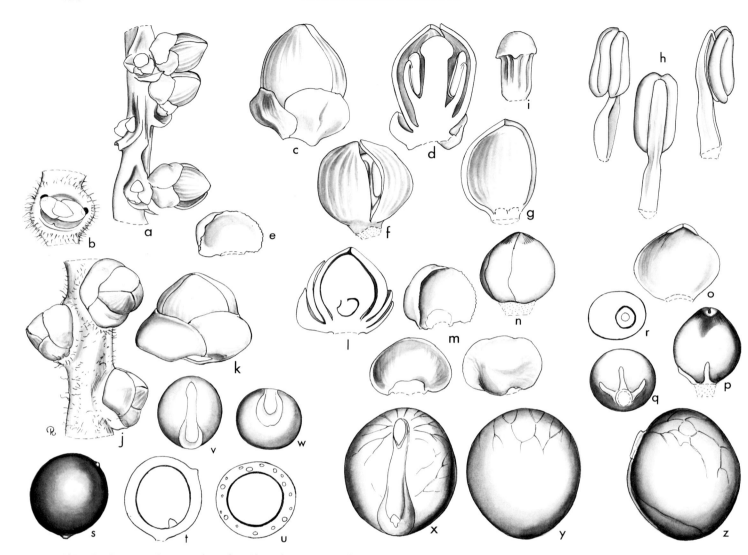

135.—**Lepidorrhachis. a,** portion of rachilla with staminate flowers ×5; **b,** triad, flowers removed to show bracteoles and scars ×3; **c,** staminate bud ×10; **d,** staminate bud in vertical section ×10; **e,** staminate sepal ×10; **f,** staminate bud, sepals removed ×10; **g,** staminate petal, interior view ×10; **h,** stamen in 3 views ×15; **i,** pistillode ×10; **j,** rachilla with pistillate buds ×3; **k,** pistillate bud ×6; **l,** pistillate bud in vertical section ×6; **m,** pistillate sepals ×6; **n,** pistillate bud, sepals removed ×6; **o,** pistillate petal ×6; **p,** gynoecium and staminodes ×6; **q,** gynoecium and staminodes, basal view ×6; **r,** ovary in cross-section ×1½; **s,** fruit ×1½; **t,** fruit in vertical section ×1½; **u,** fruit in cross-section ×1½; **v, w,** endocarp with operculum in 2 views ×1½; **x, y, z,** seed in 3 views ×3. *Lepidorrhachis mooreana*: all from *Moore & Shick 9250.*

filaments distinct, inflexed in bud, anthers oblong in outline, latrorse; pollen elliptic, monosulcate, with finely punctate, tectate exine; pistillode narrowly cylindrical, expanded apically, slightly longer than the stamens in bud. Pistillate flowers symmetrical; sepals 3, distinct, broadly rounded and imbricate; petals 3, distinct, imbricate with briefly valvate apices, strongly nerved when dry; staminodes 3, on one side of the gynoecium; gynoecium unilocular, uniovulate, subglobose, stigmas recurved, ovule pendulous, probably hemianatropous. Fruit globose or nearly so, red at maturity, stigmatic remains lateral in the upper ⅓–¼; epicarp smooth, drying granular over included sclerosomes, mesocarp fleshy, thin, with included longitudinal fibers except along the rapheal region, endocarp thin, fragile, operculate. Seed globose, with elongate raphe, hilum apical, short, elliptic, vasculature prominent, branched, the branches anastomosing abaxially, endosperm homogeneous; embryo subbasal. Germination and eophyll unrecorded. Cytology not studied.

Anatomy.—Gynoecium with many bundles of sclereids peripherally (Uhl unpubl.). Leaf anatomy not studied.

136.—**Heterospathe. a,** portion of rachilla with triads ×3; **b,** portion of rachilla, staminate flowers fallen ×3; **c,** triad, flowers removed ×6; **d,** staminate bud ×12; **e,** staminate bud in vertical section ×12; **f,** staminate sepal, interior view ×12; **g,** staminate petal, interior view ×12; **h,** stamen in 3 views ×12; **i,** pistillate flower ×6; **j,** pistillate flower in vertical section ×12; **k,** pistillate sepal ×6; **l,** pistillate flower, sepals removed ×6; **m,** pistillate petal, interior view ×6; **n,** gynoecium and staminodes ×6; **o,** ovary in cross-section ×6; **p,** fruit ×3; **q,** fruit in vertical section ×3; **r,** fruit in cross-section ×3; **s,** seed in 3 views ×3. *Heterospathe humilis*: all from *Moore et al. 926.*

Distribution.—One species on Lord Howe Island.

Ecology.—Found only in low mossy forest at high elevations.

Common Names and Uses.—Little Mountain Palm. A handsome ornamental. The fruit is favored by rats and must be protected.

Notes.—The rather short stout stem, stiff ascending leaflets, lack of a crownshaft, and red fruits are characteristic. The restriction of this palm to high elevations on Lord Howe Island is noteworthy.

Taxonomic Account.—No recent treatment.

Plate.—66D.

136. HETEROSPATHE Scheffer, Annales du Jardin Botanique de Buitenzorg 1:141. 1876. Type: **H. elata** Scheffer.

Ptychandra Scheffer, Annales du Jardin Botanique de Buitenzorg 1:140. 1876. Type: *P. glauca* Scheffer (=*Heterospathe glauca* (Scheffer) H. E. Moore).

Barkerwebbia Beccari, Webbia 1:281. 1905. Type: *B. elegans* Beccari (=*Heterospathe* sp. not formally transferred).

Dwarf to moderate, solitary or sometimes clustered, unarmed, pleonanthic, monoecious palms. Stem creeping or erect, sometimes basally expanded, gray-green to brown, leaf scars prominent. Leaves pinnate, rarely bifid, erect, becoming spreading, often reddish when young; sheath splitting abaxially and not forming a well defined crownshaft, margins fibrous, acute, glaucous or not; leaflets acute to acuminate, single-fold, prominent, midrib elevated, marginal ribs often thickened, veins adaxially ± waxy or glabrous, abaxially tomentose or brown-dotted, with or without basifixed ramenta on midrib. Inflorescences interfoliar or infrafoliar at anthesis, branched to 1–4 orders basally, fewer distally, with reddish-brown, deciduous tomentum; peduncle prominent, elongate, elliptic in cross-section; prophyll persistent, attached near the base and completely encircling the peduncle, tubular, 2-keeled laterally, ± dorsiventrally flattened, splitting abaxially and apically; peduncular bract attached below or sometimes above the middle of the peduncle, terete, beaked, enclosing the inflorescence in bud, greatly exceeding the prophyll, splitting abaxially and caducous or marcescent as the inflorescence matures; rachis short to elongate, bearing spirally arranged, short, pointed bracts subtending a few simple rachillae, or several branches with basal bare portions; rachillae slender, bearing sessile or slightly depressed, spirally arranged triads subtended by spreading liplike bracts throughout the rachillae, or with paired or solitary staminate flowers toward the apex of the rachillae; bracteoles of the staminate flowers small, bracteoles surrounding the pistillate flower 2, spreading to cupular and imbricate. Staminate flowers slightly to markedly asymmetrical; sepals 3, distinct, broadly imbricate and rounded, ± keeled dorsally and gibbous basally; petals 3, distinct, valvate, usually about twice as long as the sepals, prominently lined when dry, ± acute, one usually somewhat larger than the others; stamens 6–36 or more, distinct, the filaments awl-shaped and strongly inflexed at the apex, anthers oblong in outline, dorsifixed and versatile at anthesis, latrorse; pollen elliptic, monosulcate, with finely reticulate, tectate exine; pistillode either small and conical, or columnar, prominent, nearly as long as the stamens, sometimes with an expanded apex. Pistillate flowers symmetrical, ± same size as the staminate; sepals 3, distinct, broadly imbricate, rounded; petals 3, distinct, broadly imbricate with briefly valvate apices; staminodes 3, toothlike; gynoecium unilocular, uniovulate, short, soft, expanded upward into a thick stylar region below 3 recurved, short stigmas, the ovule lateral at top of locule, pendulous, hemianatropous. Fruit globose to ellipsoidal, small to large, orange to red when mature, stigmatic remains eccentrically apical or subapical to lateral; epicarp smooth but drying granular over short sclerosomes in the thinly fleshy mesocarp, with flattened anastomosing fibers, endocarp thin, operculate, shining within, not adherent to the seed. Seed globose to ellipsoidal, attached apically and laterally by the elongate hilum extending nearly the length of the seed, raphe branches simple to anastomosing, endosperm ruminate; embryo basal. Germination adjacent-ligular; eophyll bifid where known. $n = 16$ (*H. humilis* (?), Read 1965a, 1966; *H. elata,* Read 1966, Sharma and Sarkar 1957).

Anatomy.—Leaf (*H. elata,* Tomlinson 1961).

Distribution.—About 32 species from the Philippines and Micronesia to eastern Indonesia and to the Solomon Islands, including 16 species in New Guinea.

Ecology.—Inhabitants of lowland and montane rain forests. Many species are undergrowth palms; a few contribute to the forest canopy.

Common Names and Uses.—Sagisi palm. Fruit of *H. elata* is chewed as a betel substitute in the Philippines; the "cabbage" is said to be edible and the split petioles and leaflets are used in weaving.

Notes.—A widespread genus of the western fringe of the Pacific; although it occurs in Palawan (Dransfield, pers. obs.) the genus has not yet been found in Borneo. It seems to be a relatively unspecialized member of the Iguanurinae; more detailed study of the species is needed and should be rewarding.

Taxonomic Account.—Moore (1969c). No satisfactory key to species exists.

Plates.—23C; 67A.

137. **SOMMIERIA** Beccari, Malesia 1:66. 1877. Lectotype: **S. leucophylla** Beccari (see Beccari and Pichi-Sermolli 1955).

Small, solitary, acaulescent to short-stemmed, unarmed, pleonanthic, monoecious palms. Stem eventually erect, becoming bare, ringed with very close leaf scars, sometimes also bearing bunches of aerial roots. Leaves numerous, entire, bifid, sometimes with 2 pairs of segments, pinnately ribbed, marcescent; leaf sheaths densely tomentose, eventually splitting irregularly opposite the petiole and disintegrating into an interwoven mass of fibers, the mouth (? always) prolonged into a fibrous ligule; petiole usually short, adaxially channeled, abaxially rounded, variously tomentose; rachis adaxially channeled near the base, distally angled, abaxially rounded, gradually tapering; blade divided to produce a large, bifid part and 1 pair of narrow acuminate basal segments, or simply bifid, the apical margins lobed, the lobes corresponding to the major folds, or subentire, adaxially minutely scaly (? always), abaxially glabrous or densely white-tomentose, transverse veinlets obscure. Inflorescences ± erect, interfoliar, solitary, ± equalling the leaves, branching to 1 order, protandrous; peduncle very long, slender, ± elliptical in cross-section; prophyll scarcely exserted from the subtending leaf sheath, 2-keeled, tubular, splitting along the abaxial face, the tip somewhat beaked, sometimes tattering into fibers at the tip; peduncular bract 1, tubular, borne at the tip of the peduncle, ± enclosing the rachillae before anthesis, membranous, splitting down one side to the base and becoming lanceolate, apparently sometimes persisting, sometimes deciduous; rachis very short; rachillae few in number (less than 12), spirally arranged, pendulous, ± stiff, slender, elongate, each subtended by a minute first-order bract, the surface of the rachilla densely dark brown-tomentose, flowers arranged in triads, sunken within pits ± throughout the entire length of the rachilla; the rachilla bracts low, minutely toothed, forming the lower lips of the pits; floral bracteoles minute. Staminate flowers ± symmetrical, the base somewhat stalked; sepals 3, distinct, rounded, imbricate, hooded, strongly keeled, ± striate; petals 3, ± twice as long as the sepals, distinct, ovate-triangular, valvate, scarcely opening at anthesis; stamens 6, filaments minutely connate basally, fleshy, awl-shaped, inflexed in bud (? always), the antesepalous much longer than the antepetalous, at anthesis spreading between the petals, the antepetalous included, anthers short, rectangular, medifixed, ± versatile, latrorse; pollen elliptic, monosulcate, with scabrate, tectate exine; pistillode ± as long as petals, columnar, ± angled. Pistillate flowers eventually larger than the staminate, the sepals, 3, distinct or briefly connate, rounded, strongly imbricate; petals ± equalling the sepals, 3, distinct or briefly connate, rounded, imbricate except for the short, triangular, valvate tips; staminodes 3–6, toothlike; gynoecium unilocular, uniovulate, ovoid, stigmas 3, apical, reflexed, ovule form not known. Fruit small, spherical, perianth whorls persistent, the stigmatic remains basal; epicarp smooth, brown early in development, soon cracking, obsolescent at maturity, mesocarp cracked to form pyramidal to hexagonal, corky warts, brown-tipped, pink-sided and white-based when fresh, drying dull brown throughout, endocarp thin, bony, operculate, closely adhering to the seed. Seed basally attached, spherical, hilum ± circular, raphe branches sparsely anastomosing, endosperm homogeneous; embryo subbasal. Germination adjacent-ligular; eophyll bifid. $n = 17$ (*S. affinis,* Johnson 1985).

Anatomy.—Not studied.

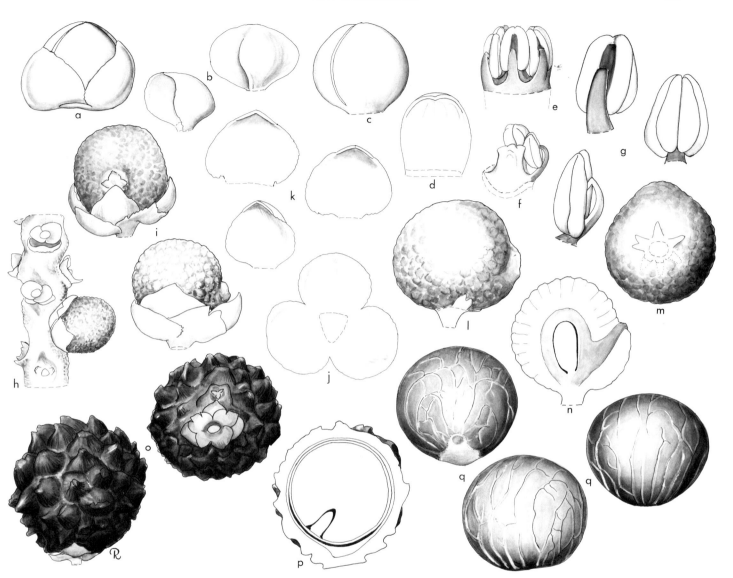

137.—**Sommieria. a**, staminate bud ×12; **b**, staminate sepal in 2 views ×12; **c**, staminate bud, calyx removed ×12; **d**, staminate petal ×12; **e**, androecium ×12; **f**, pistillode with 2 stamens ×12; **g**, stamen in 3 views ×24; **h**, rachilla with young fruit ×6; **i**, young fruit in 2 views ×12; **j**, pistillate calyx ×12; **k**, pistillate petals ×12; **l**, gynoecium of young fruit ×12; **m**, base of gynoecium with staminodes ×12; **n**, young fruit in vertical section ×12; **o**, mature fruit in 2 views ×4; **p**, mature fruit in vertical section ×4; **q**, seed in 3 views ×5. *Sommieria leucophylla*: **a-g**, *Beccari 607*; *S. affinis*: **h-q**, source unknown.

Distribution.—Three poorly known species confined to New Guinea; all three are found in Irian Jaya, only *S. affinis* occurs in Papua New Guinea.

Ecology.—All species are confined to the undergrowth of humid tropical rain forest.

Common Names and Uses.—Not recorded.

Notes.—*Sommieria* is closely related to *Heterospathe,* especially to the short-stemmed, under growth taxa with sparsely branched inflorescences. Although so distinctive in its fruit, the genus remains poorly known, and we are much in need of well collected material.

Taxonomic Accounts.—Beccari (1877), Hay (1984). There has been no reassessment of the delimitation of species.

Plate.—67B.

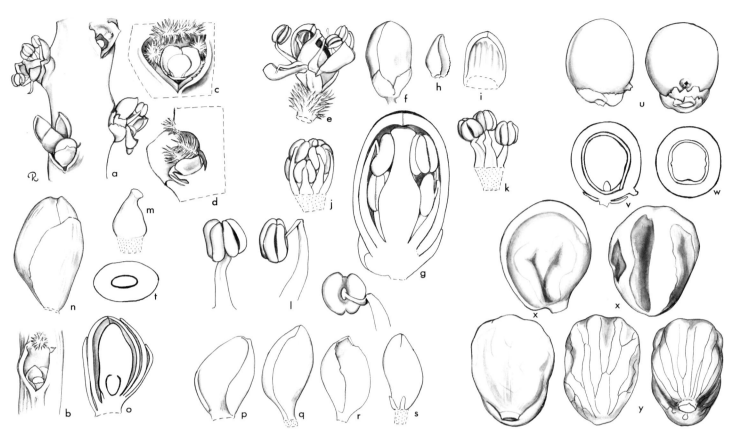

138.—**Bentinckia. a,** portion of rachilla with staminate flowers in pits ×3; **b,** pit, flowers removed to show bracts ×3; **c,** pit, expanded ×3; **d,** pit in vertical section ×3; **e,** staminate flower and pedicel ×6; **f,** staminate bud ×6; **g,** staminate bud in vertical section ×12; **h,** staminate sepal ×6; **i,** staminate petal, interior view ×6; **j,** androecium ×6; **k,** portion of androecium, interior view ×6; **l,** stamen in 3 views ×12; **m,** pistillode ×6; **n,** pistillate bud ×6; **o,** pistillate bud in vertical section ×6; **p,** pistillate sepal ×6; **q,** pistillate flower, sepals removed ×6; **r,** pistillate petal ×6; **s,** gynoecium and staminodes ×6; **t,** ovary in cross-section ×12; **u,** fruit ×1½; **v,** fruit in vertical section ×1½; **w,** fruit in cross-section ×1½; **x,** endocarp in 3 views ×3; **y,** seed in 2 views ×3. *Bentinckia nicobarica:* **a-m** and **u-y,** *Moore 6097;* **n-t,** *Bailey 582.*

138. **BENTINCKIA** A. Berry in Roxburgh, Flora Indica (edition 2) 3:621. 1832. Type: **B. condapanna** A. Berry.

Keppleria Martius ex Endlicher, Genera Plantarum 251. 1837. Type not designated.

Moderate, solitary, unarmed, pleonanthic, monoecious palms. Stem moderate, closely ringed with leaf scars, brown. Leaves pinnate, somewhat arching to spreading, becoming pendulous, neatly abscising; sheaths thick, striate, tubular, forming a conspicuous crownshaft, ± glabrous; petiole very short, stout, adaxially channeled, abaxially rounded; rachis elongate, angled adaxially, rounded abaxially; leaflets single-fold, basal leaflets sometimes united, alternate, lanceolate, acute or acuminate, tips bifid, with small, brown scales on both surfaces, and long, pale ramenta near the base adaxially, along ribs abaxially and midrib raised adaxially, transverse veinlets not evident. Inflorescences infrafoliar, branched to 3 orders ba-

sally, fewer distally, somewhat pendulous at anthesis; peduncle very short, dorsiventrally flattened; prophyll and peduncular bract inserted close together at base of peduncle, both caducous, chartaceous, tomentose; prophyll tubular, rather wide, 2-keeled laterally, tapering slightly to a blunt tip, splitting abaxially; peduncular bract like the prophyll but beaked and lacking keels; rachis longer than the peduncle, bearing rather distant, spirally arranged, short, sometimes pointed bracts subtending branches and rachillae, glabrous except for a dense tuft of short hairs in bract axils; rachillae rather stiff, moderate, tapering, bearing spirally arranged, low, rounded bracts subtending triads of flowers nearly throughout, a few paired or solitary staminate flowers distally; flowers borne in vertical, laterally compressed pits, inner surfaces of pits densely hairy; floral bracteoles about equal, shallow, rounded. Staminate flowers slightly asymmetrical, sepals 3, distinct, scarcely imbricate, narrow, ± acute, membranous; petals 3, asymmetrical and angled, ± strongly nerved; stamens 6, those opposite the sepals usually shorter than those opposite the petals, the filaments awl-shaped, inflexed at the apex in bud, the inflexed portion very slender, anthers elliptic to oblong or nearly quadrate, basifixed, the connective very short, latrorse; pollen elliptic, monosulcate, with finely reticulate, tectate exine; pistillode ovoid with expanded capitate tip when fresh, as long as the stamens in bud. Pistillate flowers ± symmetrical; sepals 3, distinct, imbricate, ± rounded apically, nearly as long as the petals in bud, glumaceous, petals 3, broadly imbricate with very briefly valvate apices; staminodes 3–6, awl-shaped or narrowly deltoid; gynoecium ellipsoidal, asymmetrical, unilocular but vestigial locules evident, uniovulate, stigmas 3, recurved, papillose, ovule pendulous, probably hemianatropous. Fruit globose-obovoid, black or purplish at maturity, with stigmatic remains near the base in lower ¼; epicarp smooth but drying dimpled, mesocarp fleshy with sclerosomes, the principal fibers 4, 1 short from base to stigmatic remains, 1 looped over the endocarp and 2 laterally branched and anastomosing toward the apex, endocarp operculate, thickish, less fragile than in most genera, grooved abaxially from operculum to apex and laterally, attachment directly connected to the operculum. Seed shining brown, conspicuously grooved abaxially and laterally with raphe branches ascending adaxially, arched over the seed and laterally, anastomosing adaxially, hilum round, endosperm homogeneous; embryo basal. $n = 16$ (*B. nicobarica*, Read 1966; *B. condapanna*, Sarkar 1970).

Anatomy.—Leaf with single layered hypodermal layers, two more or less distinct adaxial palisade layers, and numerous small (2–3 cell) fibrous strands, usually hypodermal (Tomlinson 1961).

Distribution.—Two species, one in Tranvancore, India and one in the Nicobar Islands.

Ecology.—*B. condapanna* grows at 1000–1400 m at the edge of high peaks in the Travancore hills; *B. nicobarica* apparently grows at somewhat lower elevations along with *Areca catechu, Pinanga manii,* and *Rhopaloblaste augusta. B. condapanna* is endangered because wild elephants feed on young foliage and because of deforestation especially in the Palni Hills.

Common Names and Uses.—Bentinckia palm. The inflorescence of *B. condapanna* has been used in religious ceremonies.

Notes.—The genus is the only member of the subtribe to be represented in the Indian subcontinent; *B. condapanna* must be regarded as an ancient relict. The grooved seed shows similarities with those of several members of the Ptychospermatinae.

Taxonomic Account.—Gamble (1935). No recent treatment exists.

Plate.—67C.

139. CLINOSPERMA Beccari, Le Palme della Nuova Caledonia 51. 1920; and Webbia 5:119. 1921.

Type: **C. bracteale** (Brongniart) Beccari (*Cyphokentia bractealis* Brongniart).

Moderate, solitary, unarmed, pleonanthic, monoecious palm. Stem erect, irregularly ringed with prominent broad leaf scars and bases of old inflorescences towards the summit, often not obviously ringed below, internodes elongate, brown. Leaves regularly pinnate, spreading; sheaths split ¾ to nearly to the base, not forming a prominent crownshaft, glabrous adaxially, glaucous with brown, membranous, tattered scales abaxially; petiole rounded in section, except directly above the sheath where shallowly concave, bearing reddish-brown or dotlike scales; rachis angled adaxially, abaxially rounded, with deciduous tomentum; leaflets acute, single-fold, midrib prominent and squared adaxially, prominent abaxially, ramenta lacking, 2 other veins elevated, all veins often dotted or with small pale scales abaxially, transverse veinlets not evident. Inflorescences infrafoliar at anthesis, compact, branched to 3 orders basally, to 1 order distally, densely scaly throughout or only in branch axils; peduncle short; prophyll completely encircling the peduncle at insertion, prominently 2-keeled laterally, slightly beaked, chartaceous, enclosing the similar, briefly beaked peduncular bract in bud, a second, large, open, pointed peduncular bract often present, prophyll and peduncular bract caducous; rachis longer than the peduncle, bearing spirally inserted bracts subtending rachillae; rachillae short to moderate, very slender, bearing low, acute bracts subtending triads in the lower ⅓, more rarely in lower ½–⅝, and often rounded bracts subtending paired or solitary staminate flowers distally; bracteoles surrounding the pistillate flower unequal, brown, somewhat sepallike, the shorter about as long as the subtending bract, the longer exceeding the bract. Staminate flowers symmetrical, depressed; sepals 3, distinct, basally imbricate, rounded, gibbous dorsally near the apex; petals 3, distinct, valvate; stamens 6, distinct, filaments flattened, not inflexed at the apex in bud, anthers yellow, nearly as long as the filaments, ± didymous from a short, darkened connective; pollen elliptic, monosulcate, with perforate, tectate exine; pistillode fleshy, as long as the stamens, about as wide as high, slightly expanded apically in a 3-lobed cap, lobes rounded. Pistillate flowers about twice as long as the staminate at anthesis; sepals 3, distinct, broadly imbricate, rounded, somewhat gibbous dorsally towards the apex; petals 3, distinct, imbricate except for briefly valvate apices; staminodes 3, at one side of the gynoecium; gynoecium ovoid, unilocular, uniovulate, ovule pendulous, form unknown. Fruit eccentrically globose, with stigmatic remains lateral at about the middle; epicarp smooth, mesocarp of pale, fleshy parenchyma over a solid shell of pale sclerosomes underlain by pale parenchyma with flat, slender, ± anastomosing fibers and irregularly flattened tannin cells, endocarp fragile, vitreous, eccentrically globose, with short groove and rounded basal operculum. Seed light brown, hilum short, raphe branches ascending and curved laterally from raphe, anastomosing somewhat abaxially, endosperm homogeneous; embryo basal. Germination and eophyll not recorded. Cytology not known.

Anatomy.—Tannin and fibrous strands are both

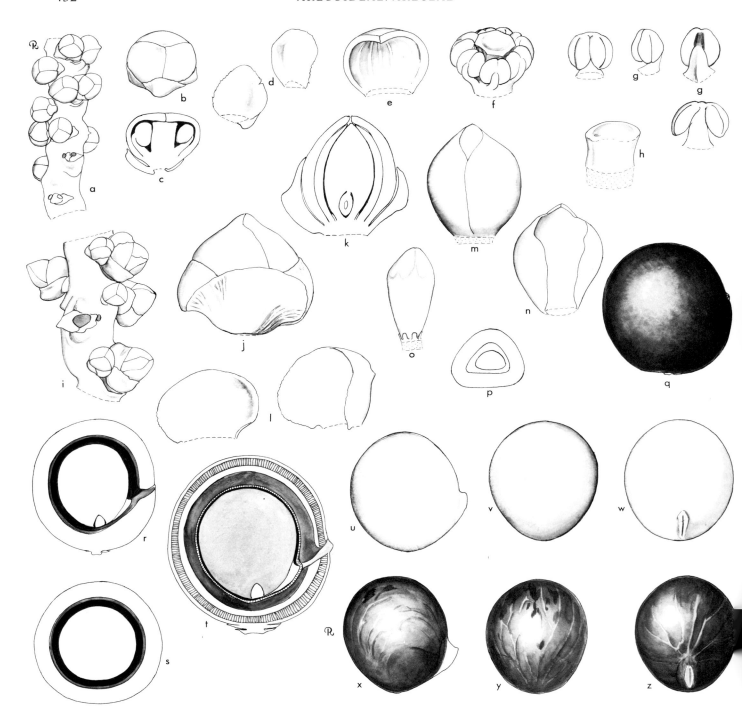

139.—**Clinosperma. a,** portion of rachilla with paired staminate flowers ×6; **b,** staminate bud ×12; **c,** staminate bud in vertical section ×12; **d,** staminate sepals, interior and exterior views ×12; **e,** staminate petal, interior view ×12; **f,** androecium and pistillode ×12; **g,** stamen in 4 views, one with locules spread to show attachment ×18; **8,** pistillode ×18; **i,** portion of rachilla with triads ×6; **j,** pistillate bud ×12; **k,** pistillate bud in vertical section ×12; **l,** pistillate sepals in 2 views ×12; **m,** pistillate bud, sepals removed ×12; **n,** pistillate petal ×12; **o,** gynoecium and staminodes ×12; **p,** ovary in cross-section ×18; **q,** fruit ×3; **r,** fruit in vertical section ×3; **s,** fruit in cross-section ×3; **t,** fruit in vertical section, pericarp regions diagrammatic ×4½; **u, v, w,** endocarp in 3 views ×3; **x, y, z,** seed in 3 views ×3. *Clinosperma bracteale*: **a-h** and **q,** *MacDaniels s.n.*; **i-p,** *Lavoix 23*; **r-z,** *Moore et al. 9970.*

lacking in leaves. Midribs of leaflets have long narrow extensions of the adaxial fibrous sheath (Uhl and Martens in prep.). Floral anatomy has not been reported.

Distribution. —One species in New Caledonia.

Ecology. —*Clinosperma* is found in wet forests on serpentine soils and schists in southern New Caledonia.

Common Names and Uses. —Not recorded.

Notes. —*Clinosperma* is distinctive in its compact inflorescence with acuminate rachis bracts, triads mostly borne in the lower one-third of the rachillae, and pistillate flowers larger than staminate at staminate anthesis. The staminate flowers, like those of *Brongniartikentia,* have didymous anthers and the fruit, with its internal shell of sclereids, is very similar to that of *Basselinia,* from which it differs in many other respects. Indumentum of the inflorescence is variable but characteristic minute, tattered scales are usually evident at least in axils of the branches.

Taxonomic Account. —Moore and Uhl (1984).

Plate. —*67D.*

140. CYPHOKENTIA Brongniart, Comptes Rendus Hebdomadaires des Séances de l'Académie des Sciences 77:399. 1873. Lectotype: **C. macrostachya** Brongniart (see Beccari 1920).

Dolichokentia Beccari, Le Palme della Nuova Caledonia 45. 1920; and Webbia 5:113. 1921. Type: *D. robusta* (Brongniart) Beccari (*Cyphokentia robusta* Brongniart = *C. macrostachya* Brongniart).

Moderate, solitary (or exceptionally with 2–3 stems), unarmed, pleonanthic, monoecious palm. Stem erect, not prominently ringed, enlarged at the base, yellow or whitish, brown-spotted. Leaves regularly pinnate, gracefully spreading; sheaths tubular, forming a prominent, white-waxy crownshaft; petiole short, concave adaxially, rounded abaxially, glabrous; rachis concave adaxially near base, becoming angled distally, rounded abaxially, often somewhat curved, glabrous; leaflets acute, slightly arched from rachis, single-fold stiff, apparently waxy on both surfaces, midrib and a lateral vein on each side elevated and prominent adaxially, secondary veins numerous, large ribs clothed basally with ramenta, transverse veinlets not evident. Inflorescences infrafoliar, branched to 2(–3) orders basally and fewer distally, branches pendulous, protandrous; peduncle very short, ±recurved; prophyll wide, tubular, broadly 2-keeled laterally, completely encircling the peduncle and enclosing the briefly beaked, similar peduncular bract, both caducous; rachis elongate, bearing very low and rounded to scarcely evident bracts subtending branches and rachillae; rachillae variously compressed in bud, very long, slender, tapering, pendulous, distant, bearing low, rounded, liplike bracts subtending flowers in triads nearly throughout the rachillae, and paired or solitary staminate flowers distally; bracteoles surrounding pistillate flowers sepallike, imbricate, about as high as bracts of the triad. Staminate buds nearly symmetrical; sepals 3, distinct, slightly imbricate basally, small, rounded, gibbous at base and keeled dorsally; petals 3, distinct, valvate, broadly ovate in outline, not markedly fibrous, grooved on inner surface; stamens 12, filaments incurved, awl-shaped, briefly inflexed at the apex in bud, about as long as the anthers, anthers oblong in outline, dorsifixed, briefly bifid at base and apex, latrorse; pollen elliptic, monosulcate, with finely reticulate, tectate exine; pistillode as long as the anthers in bud, somewhat 3-angled and expanded into a 3-angled, flat apex. Pistillate flowers not seen at anthesis; sepals 3, distinct, rounded, imbricate basally in fruit and then ca. 2 mm. high; petals 3, distinct, imbricate except briefly for the valvate tips, nerved in fruit; staminodes 5–6, toothlike; gynoecium ovoid, unilocular, uniovulate, ovule not known. Fruit ellipsoidal, red at maturity, with stigmatic remains below the middle about ⅓ from the base; epicarp smooth, drying somewhat wrinkled but not regularly pebbled, thin, not tanniniferous, overlying a shell of very short sclereids external to a fleshy layer of mesocarp, mesocarp with longitudinal flat fibers, and a tanniniferous layer adjacent to the endocarp, endocarp vitreous, thickish, with a round, basal operculum and lateral beak. Seed nearly ellipsoidal, hilum near the base, round, raphe branches ascending from the base; endosperm homogeneous; embryo basal. Germination and eophyll unrecorded. Cytology not known.

Anatomy. —*Cyphokentia* is similar to *Moratia* in leaf structure but with cuticles of medium thickness, guard cells not sunken, and vascular bundles absent in sheath of midrib (Uhl and Martens in prep.).

Distribution. —One species in New Caledonia.

Ecology. —*C. macrostachya* is a somewhat variable species that occurs over a wide range on soil derived from both serpentines and schists.

Common Names and Uses. —Not recorded.

Notes. —Fruits of *Cyphokentia* cannot be distinguished from those of *Brongniartikentia.* However, the two genera are abundantly distinct in the morphology of the inflorescence and staminate flowers. *Cyphokentia* resembles *Moratia* in several respects as noted under that genus.

Taxonomic Account. —Moore and Uhl (1984).

Plate. —*68A.*

141. MORATIA H. E. Moore, Gentes Herbarum 12: 18. 1980. Type: **M. cerifera** H. E. Moore.

Moderate, solitary, unarmed, pleonanthic, monoecious palm. Stem erect, stout, usually prominently ringed, orange when young, becoming brown. Leaves regularly pinnate, curved to spreading, neatly abcising; sheath tubular, forming a prominent crownshaft, white-waxy; petiole channeled adaxially, rounded abaxially, brown-scaly to dotted; rachis angled adaxially, rounded abaxially, with

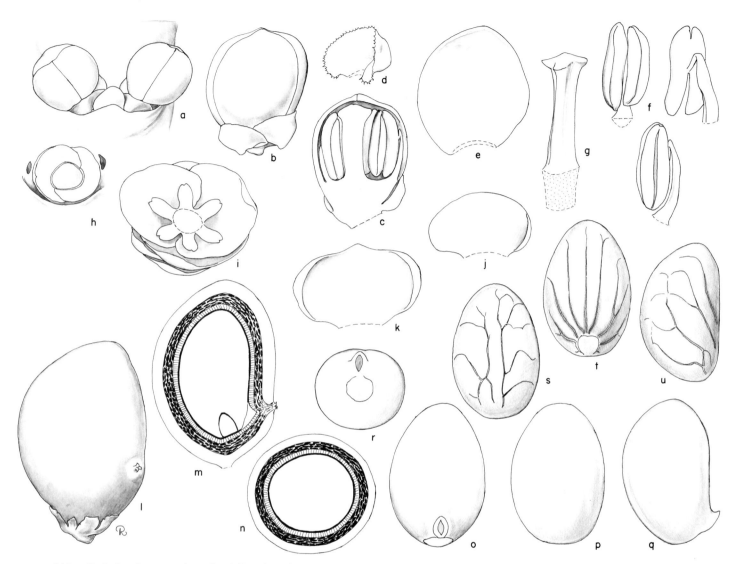

140.—**Cyphokentia. a,** portion of rachilla with triad ×6; **b,** staminate bud ×9; **c,** staminate bud in vertical section ×9; **d,** staminate sepal ×12; **e,** staminate petal, interior view ×9; **f,** stamen in 3 views ×12; **g,** pistillode ×12; **h,** triad, flowers removed to show bracteoles surrounding pistillate flower ×6; **i,** interior view of perianth, fruit removed, to show staminodes ×8; **j,** pistillate sepal, in fruit ×9; **k,** pistillate petal, in fruit ×9; **l,** fruit ×3¾; **m,** fruit in vertical section ×3¾; **n,** fruit in cross-section ×3¾; **o, p, q,** endocarp in 3 views ×3¾; **r,** endocarp in basal view to show operculum ×3¾; **s, t, u,** seed in 3 views ×3¾. *Cyphokentia macrostachya:* **a-g,** *MacKee 23888;* **h-u,** *Moore et al. 10032.*

scales like the petioles; leaflets regularly arranged, acute, single-fold, coriaceous, ramenta prominent on midrib and often on veins toward the base beneath, lower surface waxy, a midrib and a vein on each side prominent on both surfaces, transverse veinlets not evident. Inflorescences infrafoliar, branched to 2–3 orders basally, to 1–2 orders distally, lowest branches subopposite, spreading, markedly protandrous; peduncle very short, stout, dorsiventrally flattened; prophyll tubular, 2-keeled laterally, beaked, completely encircling the peduncle, enclosing the peduncular bract; peduncular bract tubular, equalling the prophyll, both chartaceous and caducous; rachis longer than the peduncle, bearing short, acute bracts subtending branches and rachillae; rachillae long, slender, spreading, bearing rounded, crescent-shaped bracts subtending flowers borne in triads proximally, and pairs or solitary staminate flowers distally; bracteoles surrounding the pistillate flower about equal, ± sepallike, about as high as the bract of the triad. Staminate buds symmetrical; sepals 3, distinct, imbricate, rounded, gibbous dorsally and prominently keeled toward the base; petals 3, distinct, valvate, subacute, impressed internally in conformity with the stamens, smooth externally when dry; stamens 6, filaments inflexed at the apex in bud, anthers dorsifixed, oblong in outline, emarginate at apex, briefly bifid at base, with prominent connective; pollen elliptic, monosulcate, with

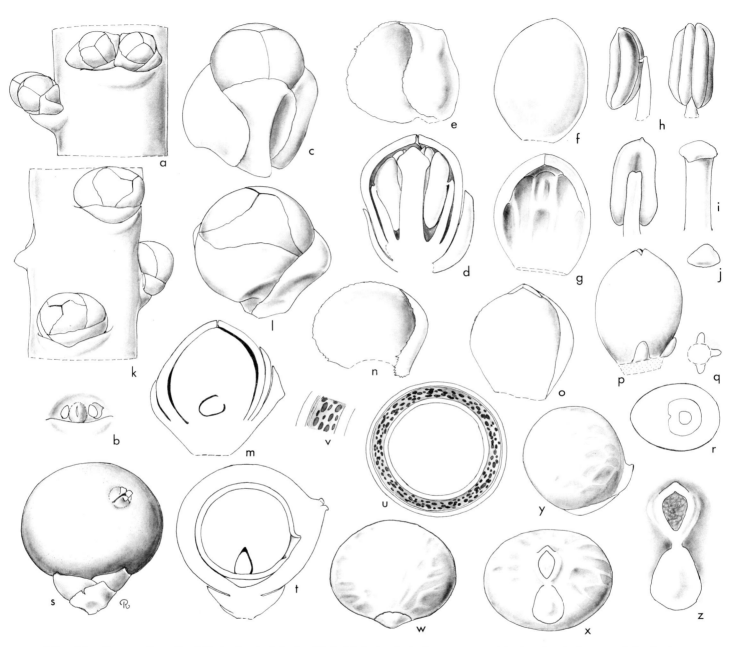

141.—**Moratia. a,** portion of rachilla in staminate bud ×4½; **b,** triad, staminate flowers removed to show bracteoles around developing pistillate bud ×4½; **c,** staminate bud ×12; **d,** staminate bud in vertical section ×12; **e,** staminate sepal ×12; **f, g,** staminate petals, exterior (**f**) and interior (**g**) views ×12; **h,** stamen in 3 views ×12; **i,** pistillode ×12; **j,** apex of pistillode ×12; **k,** portion of rachilla with pistillate buds ×4½; **l,** pistillate bud ×9; **m,** pistillate bud in vertical section ×9; **n,** pistillate sepal ×9; **o,** pistillate petal ×9; **p,** gynoecium and staminodes ×9; **q,** staminodes ×9; **r,** ovary in cross-section ×9; **s,** fruit ×3; **t,** fruit in vertical section ×3; **u,** fruit in cross-section ×3; **v,** section of fruit wall ×6; **w, x, y,** endocarp in 3 views ×3; **z,** point of seed attachment and operculum ×4½. *Moratia cerifera*: all from *Moore & Morat 10400.*

finely reticulate, tectate exine; pistillode as high as the stamens in bud, angled-columnar, with expanded, 3-angled apex. Pistillate buds very small at staminate anthesis, at maturity larger than the staminate flowers; sepals 3, distinct, imbricate, rounded; petals 3, distinct, imbricate

except for the briefly valvate apices, prominently tanniniferous; staminodes 3, toothlike, borne at one side of the gynoecium; gynoecium ovoid, unilocular, uniovulate, stigmas 3, reflexed at anthesis, ovule pendulous, probably hemianatropous. Fruit depressed-globose, wider than high

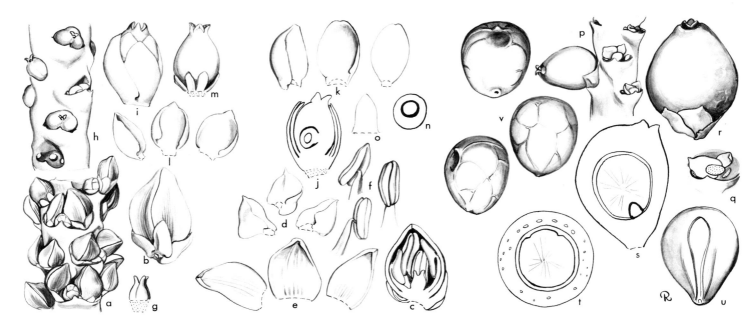

142.—**Clinostigma. a,** portion of rachilla with triads ×3; **b,** staminate bud ×6; **c,** staminate bud in vertical section ×6; **d,** staminate sepals ×6; **e,** staminate petals ×6; **f,** stamen in 3 views ×6; **g,** pistillode ×6; **h,** portion of rachilla in young fruit ×3; **i,** pistillate flower ×6; **j,** pistillate flower in vertical section ×6; **k,** pistillate sepals ×6; **l,** pistillate petals ×6; **m,** gynoecium and staminodes ×6; **n,** ovary in cross-section ×6; **o,** staminode ×12; **p,** portion of rachilla in fruit ×3; **q,** triad, fruit removed to show floral scars and bracteoles ×6; **r,** fruit ×6; **s,** fruit in vertical section ×6; **t,** fruit in cross-section ×6; **u,** endocarp ×6; **v,** seed in 3 views ×6. *Clinostigma exorrhizum:* all from *Moore & Koroiveibau 9355.*

or thick, with stigmatic remains lateral near the middle, drying with prominent rounded ridges; epicarp very minutely roughened when fresh, mesocarp with a thin layer of pale parenchyma lacking tannin cells, external to a thin shell of pale, flat sclereids, these covering a thick layer of parenchyma with abundant tannin cells and a few longitudinal flat fibers, endocarp similar to fruit in shape, rather thick and vitreous, not ridged or angled or sculptured but with a discernible pattern of thickened branches, radiating from the hilum, prominent, short, ± ellipsoidal, above a short, ± spathulate operculum. Seed subglobose, broader than thick or high, raphe branches ascending and anastomosing from the flattened base, endosperm homogeneous; embryo basal. Germination not recorded; eophyll bifid. Cytology not studied.

Anatomy.—Leaves of *Moratia* have a remarkably thick adaxial cuticle, four times as high as the epidermal cells (Uhl and Martens in prep.).

Distribution.—One species in New Caledonia.

Ecology.—*Moratia* occurs in wet forests on schistose soils, in the northeastern part of the island. The trunk is much higher and thicker in the forest near 500 meters on Mont Panié than at higher elevations in more exposed forest, where it occurs to ca. 900 m.

Common Names and Uses.—Not recorded.

Notes.—The leaf sheaths are often bright orange under the wax and orange within. *Cyphokentia* may

be confused with *Moratia* in the field because both have white-waxy leaf sheaths and prophylls. Staminate flowers of *Moratia,* however, are dark red and have only six stamens, while those of *Cyphokentia* are rose colored with 12 stamens. The pistillate flowers of the two may be distinguished by the six staminodes of *Cyphokentia* versus three for *Moratia* and usually by the orange inner and sometimes outer surface of the leaf sheath in *Moratia.* The two genera are closely related and are extremely similar in foliar anatomy.

Taxonomic Account.—Moore and Uhl (1984).

Plate.—68B; *Fig. G.21.*

142. CLINOSTIGMA H. A. Wendland, Bonplandia 10:196. 1862. Type: **C. samoense** H. A. Wendland.

Exorrhiza Beccari, Annales du Jardin Botanique de Buitenzorg 2:128. 1885. Type: *E. wendlandiana* Beccari (=*Clinostigma exorrhizum* (H. A. Wendland) Beccari).

Bentinckiopsis Beccari, Le Palme della Nuova Caledonia 45. 1920; and Webbia 5:113. 1921. Lectotype: *B. carolinensis* (Beccari) Beccari (*Cyphokentia carolinensis* Beccari) (see Beccari and Pichi-Sermolli 1955). (=*Clinostigma carolinense* (Beccari) H. E. Moore & Fosberg.)

Clinostigmopsis Beccari in Martelli, Atti della Societa Toscana di Scienze Naturali di Pisa, Memorie 44:161. 1934. Lectotype: *C. thurstonii* (Beccari) Beccari (=*Clinostigma thurstonii* Beccari) (see Beccari and Pichi-Sermolli 1955).

Tall, robust, solitary, unarmed, pleonanthic, monoecious palms. Stem erect, often longitudinally fissured, densely and conspicuously ringed with leaf scars, new internodes glaucous, sometimes with prominent prickly stilt roots. Leaves pinnate; sheaths tubular, forming a prominent crownshaft, ± glaucous; petiole mostly short, concave adaxially, rounded abaxially, glaucous; rachis flat adaxially, rounded abaxially, glaucous when young; leaflets single-fold, regularly arranged, ± arched to pendulous from the rachis, with a prominent elevated midrib and 1–2 secondary ribs on each side above, all the veins rather densely covered abaxially with minute, pale-margined, brown-centered, membranous scales and often with large ramenta on the midrib below, margins nearly parallel, tapering gradually to an acuminate apex, this often frayed and bifid in age. Inflorescences infrafoliar, branched to 3 orders basally, to 2–1 orders distally, or to 1 order only; peduncle short, wide, flat, glaucous, frequently becoming swollen; prophyll tubular, thin, 2-keeled, completely encircling the peduncle, enclosing the thin, beaked peduncular bract; both caducous; rachis longer than the peduncle, tapering, glaucous when young, bearing spirally arranged, conspicuous, pointed bracts each subtending a first-order branch; first-order branches with a short bare portion basally, bearing very small pointed, spirally arranged bracts subtending rachillae; rachillae long, very slender, bearing rather close, spirally arranged acute bracts subtending triads of flowers nearly throughout or only in the lower ⅓ to ½, staminate flowers paired or solitary toward the apex, the axis somewhat impressed above the triad; floral bracteoles unequal in size, the third largest, often exceeding the triad bract. Staminate flowers markedly asymmetrical, one ebracteolate, the other subtended by a low spreading bracteole; sepals 3, distinct, basally imbricate, acute, laterally compressed and dorsally keeled toward the base; petals 3, distinct, valvate, asymmetrical, acute, prominently lined centrally but the margins ± veinless and pale when dry; stamens 6, filaments distinct, awl-shaped, equal, or those opposite the sepals inserted lower than those opposite the petals, the filaments inflexed at the apex in bud, the anthers versatile at anthesis, acute to emarginate or deeply bifid at the apex, equally or unequally bifid at the base; pollen elliptic, monosulcate, with finely reticulate, tectate exine; pistillode short, broadly conical, trifid. Pistillate flowers symmetrical, ovoid; sepals 3, distinct, ± boat-shaped, broadly imbricate; petals 3, distinct, slightly longer than the sepals, broadly imbricate with very briefly valvate apices; staminodes (5–) 6, membranous, toothlike; gynoecium ovoid, unilocular, uniovulate, with 3, short recurved stigmas, the ovule laterally attached, form unknown. Fruit ovoid to ellipsoidal and terete to laterally compressed, red when mature, the stigmatic remains eccentrically apical to lateral or rarely bas-

al; epicarp smooth but often drying granulose-wrinkled over fibers, mesocarp with prominent, sometimes greatly thickened (*C. ponapense*), longitudinal fibers and a thin layer of red sclerosomes (*C. exorrhizum*) over a thin, crustaceous, fragile endocarp, this neither angled nor sculptured except for a thickened apical cap opposite the hilum, tapered downward to a narrow operculum opposite the embryo. Seed obovoid to ellipsoidal, sometimes somewhat compressed laterally, hilum rounded to elongate, basal or extending along one side of the seed, raphe branches few, unbranched or loosely anastomosing; endosperm homogeneous; embryo basal. Germination adjacent-ligular; eophyll bifid or entire. $n = 18$ (*C. savoryanum*, M. Ono and Masuda 1981). $n = 16, 32$ (*C. savoryanum* as *Exorrhiza savoryana*, Satô 1946).

Anatomy. — Unknown.

Distribution. — About 13 species from the Bonin and Caroline Islands to Samoa, Fiji Islands, New Hebrides (Banks Group), the Solomon Islands, and New Ireland.

Ecology. — The species are found in montane rain forests, usually in dense forests on crests and ridges; *C. harlandii* is not known below 1000 m and is almost perpetually in clouds or mist.

Common Names and Uses. — Common names unknown. Split stems are used for house building. All species are very elegant and would make fine ornamentals.

Notes. — *Clinostigma* occurs in a great arc through the western Pacific, a most interesting distribution pattern. It is a relatively unspecialized member of the Iguanurinae.

Taxonomic Accounts. — Moore (1969b, 1979), Dransfield (1982b).

Plate. — 68C.

143. ALSMITHIA H. E. Moore, Principes 26:122. 1982. Type: **A. longipes** H. E. Moore.

Solitary, moderate, unarmed, pleonanthic, monoecious palm. Stem erect, rather irregularly ringed with leaf scars; sheaths not forming a distinct crownshaft, soon splitting opposite the petiole, bearing minute scales; petiole very long, adaxially channeled, abaxially rounded, bearing peltate scales; rachis curved, adaxially angled, abaxially rounded; leaflets single-fold, regularly arranged in one plane, acute, lacking both scales and ramenta. Inflorescences solitary, axillary, interfoliar, erect, branching to 2 orders, protandrous, or rarely entirely staminate; peduncle elongate, flattened, tomentose; prophyll flattened, completely encircling the peduncle at insertion, ± persistent, tubular at the base, unilaterally splitting at the apex, minutely scaly; peduncular bract inserted some distance from and much exceeding the prophyll, splitting along one side, soon deciduous, minutely scaly; subsequent bracts small, acute to rounded; rachis ± equalling the peduncle, bearing spirally arranged first-order branches, with bare proximal sections; rachillae slender, flexuous, downy, creamy white

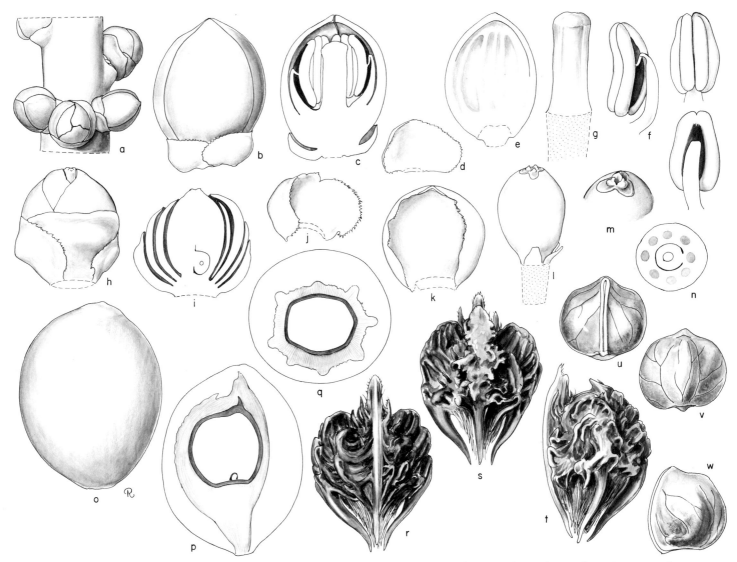

143.—**Alsmithia. a,** portion of rachilla with triads ×3; **b,** staminate bud ×7½; **c,** staminate bud in vertical section ×7½; **d,** staminate sepal ×7½; **e,** staminate petal, interior view ×7½; **f,** stamen in 3 views ×9; **g,** pistillode ×9; **h,** pistillate flower ×6; **i,** pistillate flower in vertical section ×6; **j,** pistillate sepal ×6; **k,** pistillate petal ×6; **l,** gynoecium and staminodes ×6; **m,** stigmas ×12; **n,** ovary in cross-section ×9; **o,** fruit ×1½; **p,** fruit in vertical section ×1½; **q,** fruit in cross-section ×1½; **r, s, t,** endocarp and adnate fibers in 3 views ×1½; **u, v, w,** seed in 3 views ×1½. *Alsmithia longipes:* all from *Moore et al. 10545.*

at anthesis, becoming red-brown to green, proximally bearing spirally arranged triads, distally bearing solitary or paired staminate flowers, rarely bearing staminate flowers throughout; rachilla bracts low, rounded; floral bracteoles ± rounded. Staminate flower buds symmetrical; sepals 3, distinct, imbricate, rounded, minutely ciliate; petals 3, distinct, valvate; stamens 6, filaments awl-shaped, inflexed at the tip in bud, anthers oblong, dorsifixed, briefly bifid at base, latrorse; pollen elliptic, monosulcate, with rugulate, tectate exine; pistillode narrow, conical, slightly shorter than the stamens in bud, rounded at the tip. Pistillate flowers ovoid; sepals 3, distinct, broadly imbricate,

rounded, minutely ciliate; petals 3, distinct, broadly imbricate except for the minute valvate tips; staminodes 3, narrow triangular; gynoecium obovoid, unilocular, uniovulate, stigmas 3, low, linear, scarcely exserted, ovule pendulous, hemianatropous. Fruit ellipsoidal, red at maturity, stigmatic remains apical; epicarp smooth when fresh, drying irregular and lined, mesocarp parenchymatous, thick, with many short oblique fibers beneath the epicarp, tannin cells not obvious, endocarp thin, fragile, with thickened adnate fibers, irregularly sculptured, ridged and grooved, beaked at the apex, with a mass of slender fibers within a framework of thickened fibers at the base, oper-

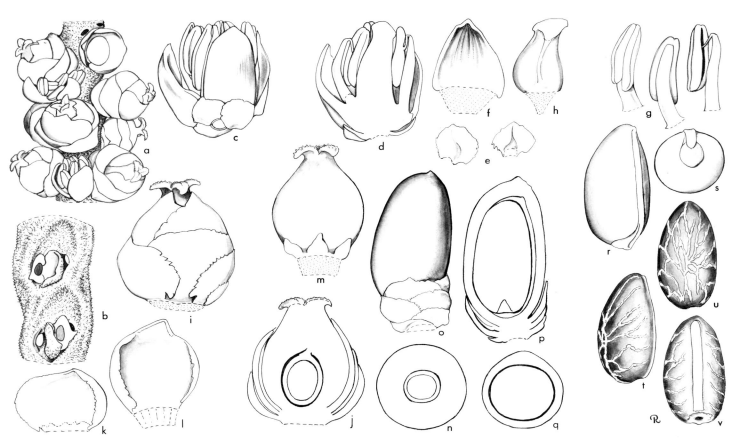

144.—**Satakentia. a,** portion of rachilla with staminate and pistillate flowers ×3; **b,** triads, flowers removed to show bracteoles ×3; **c,** staminate flower ×6; **d,** staminate flower in vertical section ×6; **e,** staminate sepals, exterior and interior views ×6; **f,** staminate petal, interior view ×6; **g,** stamen in 3 views ×6; **h,** pistillode ×6; **i,** pistillate flower ×6; **j,** pistillate flower in vertical section ×6; **k,** pistillate sepal, interior view ×6; **l,** pistillate petal, interior view ×6; **m,** gynoecium and staminodes ×6; **n,** gynoecium in cross-section ×6; **o,** fruit ×3; **p,** fruit in vertical section ×3; **q,** fruit in cross-section ×3, **r,** endocarp with operculum ×3; **s,** operculum ×3; **t, u, v,** seed in 3 views ×3. *Satakentia liukiuensis*: **a** and **i-n,** *Murata s.n.*; **b-h,** *Moore et al. 9382*; **o-v,** *Yamakawa s.n.*

culum basal, rounded. Seed angled in cross-section, briefly beaked with elongate hilum adaxially, 3 rounded ridges laterally and abaxially, basally flattened, raphe branches anastomosing laterally and apically, endosperm homogeneous, embryo basal. Germination and eophyll not recorded. Cytology not known.

Anatomy.—Not studied.

Distribution.—Monotypic, confined to the island of Taveuni in the Fiji Islands.

Ecology.—Occurs in wet forest on ridges and steep slopes at altitudes of 300–500 m above sea level.

Common Names and Uses.—Not recorded.

Notes.—The extremely long petioles and sculptured endocarps distinguish this genus. Endocarps of the New Caledonian genera, *Cyphosperma, Veillonia,* and *Burretiokentia* are similar but prophylls are incomplete rather than encircling. *Alsmithia* is little known.

Taxonomic Account.—Moore, Phillips, and Vodonaivalu (1982).

Plate.—24A, B.

144. SATAKENTIA H. E. Moore, Principes 13:5. 1969.
Type: **S. liukiuensis** (Hatusima) H. E. Moore (*Gulubia liukiuensis* Hatusima).

Moderate, solitary, unarmed, pleonanthic, monoecious palm. Stem erect, usually enlarged and with a mass of adventitious roots at the base, columnar above, green to brown, longitudinally striate, ringed with close leaf scars. Leaves pinnate, spreading; sheaths tubular, forming a prominent crownshaft; petiole short, adaxially channeled with a central ridge, abaxially rounded; rachis elongate, flattened adaxially, rounded abaxially, tomentose; leaflets regularly arranged, acute, single-fold, midrib evident abaxially, marginal nerves thickened, usually 2(–3) secondary ribs, and numerous tertiary veins on each side, glabrous adaxially, ramenta present abaxially near the base of the midrib, transverse veinlets not evident. Inflorescences infrafoliar, densely and minutely stellate-tomentose, branched to 2 orders basally, to 1 order distally; peduncle short, stout; prophyll tubular, terete, 2-keeled laterally, beaked in bud, enclosing the tubular, terete, beaked peduncular bract, both splitting abaxially and caducous at anthesis, sometimes a prominent third, and even a fourth, incomplete peduncular bract developed; rachis about as long as the peduncle, tapering, densely tomentose, angled, bearing spirally inserted, rather large, acute bracts subtending basal branches and smaller rounded bracts subtending distal branches; rachillae elongate, slender, stiff, bearing spirally arranged, low, rounded bracts subtending flowers borne in triads of 2 staminate and 1 pistillate in the lower ¼ to ⅓ of the rachillae, paired to solitary staminate flowers distally. Staminate flowers slightly asymmetrical; sepals 3, distinct, imbricate, ± rounded; petals 3, distinct, valvate, more than twice as long as the sepals; stamens 6, filaments distinct, awl-shaped, inflexed at the apex in bud, anthers oblong in outline, latrorse; pollen elliptic, monosulcate, with finely reticulate, tectate exine; pistillode as long as the stamens, cylindrical, with obliquely subcapitate apex. Pistillate flowers ovoid; sepals 3, distinct, broadly imbricate; petals 3, distinct, imbricate, with shortly valvate apices; staminodes 3, toothlike, on one side of the gynoecium; gynoecium ovoid, unilocular, uniovulate, stigmas 3, recurved at anthesis, ovule pendulous, anatropous. Fruit ovoid-ellipsoidal with eccentrically apical stigmatic remains; epicarp smooth but drying longitudinally lined, mesocarp with numerous flat longitudinal fibers in thin flesh and some red-brown stone cells near the apex, endocarp thin, fragile, operculate at the base of the elongate hilar seam, not adherent to the seed. Seed ellipsoidal, hilum elongate, raphe branches anastomosing, endosperm homogeneous; embryo basal. Germination adjacent-ligular; eophyll bifid. Cytology not known.

Anatomy.—Not studied.

Distribution.—One species on Ishigaki Island (Yonehara) and Iriomote Island (Hoshitate, Nakama River, Sonai), Yoeyama Group of the Ryukyus.

Ecology.—On slopes of hills or rarely near sea level.

Common Names and Uses.—Noyashi and Yaeyama-yashi. Cultivated as an ornamental. The "cabbage" is said to have been eaten during World War II.

Notes.—Very closely related to *Clinostigma* (and possibly scarcely distinct) but differing in the tomentose inflorescence, the staminate flowers with a well developed pistillode, and the fruit with more or less apical stigmatic remains.

Taxonomic Account.—Moore (1969a).

Plate.—68D.

145. **RHOPALOBLASTE** Scheffer, Annales du Jardin Botanique de Buitenzorg 1:137. 1876. Type: *R.*

hexandra Scheffer = **R. ceramica** (Miquel) Burret (*Bentinckia ceramica* Miquel).

Ptychoraphis Beccari, Annales du Jardin Botanique de Buitenzorg 2:90. 1885. Type: *P. singaporensis* (Beccari) Beccari (*Ptychosperma singaporense* Beccari) (=*Rhopaloblaste singaporensis* (Beccari) H. E. Moore).

Small to large, solitary or clustered, unarmed, pleonanthic, monoecious palms. Stem short or tall, often enlarged at the base but uniform and moderate to slender above, clearly ringed with leaf scars, brown or gray. Leaves pinnate; sheaths tubular, forming a crownshaft, or crownshaft not defined, ± densely covered with deciduous tomentum; petiole short to elongate; channelled adaxially, rounded abaxially; rachis rounded abaxially, angled above towards the apex, the sheath, lower surface of petiole and rachis usually densely covered with peltate scales with tattered interlocking margins, the upper surface of petiole and rachis usually with basifixed, twisted, entire or tattered, membranous scales persisting about the bases of the leaflets and where protected elsewhere; leaflets spreading or pendulous, with a pulvinus at the base, linear, acutely to acuminately and obliquely bifid apically, the midrib and one or more secondary ribs on each side prominent abaxially, minutely brown-dotted and at least the midrib with prominent dull brown, basifixed or medifixed, twisted, membranous scales basally or throughout, transverse veinlets not evident. Inflorescences borne below the leaves, branched to 3 orders basally, fewer orders distally, peduncle short; the prophyll 2-keeled, tubular, enclosing the similar peduncular bract, both usually ± tomentose at least when young, and caducous; rachis short to prominent but as long as or longer than the peduncle; basal branches usually abruptly divaricate, spreading at an angle of about 90° to the rachis (*R. singaporensis* often at an acute angle); bracts subtending the branches often prominent, pointed, rachilla bracts prominent or not, subtending triads nearly throughout; bracteoles surrounding the pistillate flower subequal or unequal, prominent and sepallike. Staminate flowers symmetrical or nearly so at anthesis but in bud the outer sepal prominent and largely enfolding the remainder of the perianth; sepals 3, distinct, broadly imbricate at anthesis, rounded, ± gibbous and keeled dorsally; petals 3, distinct, valvate; stamens 6–9, the filaments very briefly connate basally or ± distinct, strap-shaped, narrowed and prominently inflexed at the apex in bud, the anthers narrowly elliptic in outline, medifixed, emarginate apically and basally, the connective prominent the entire length of the anther, latrorse; pollen elliptic or circular, monosulcate, with foveo-fossulate or finely reticulate, tectate exine; pistillode conical to columnar and ± angled, the apex briefly 3-lobed and sometimes somewhat expanded. Pistillate flowers broader than high in bud and with the outer sepal usually enfolding the remainder of the perianth as in the staminate; sepals 3, distinct, broadly imbricate, rounded; petals 3, distinct, broadly imbricate basally, the short valvate apices erect and scarcely exceeding the sepals at anthesis but the petals in fruit generally nearly twice as long as the sepals; staminodes mostly 6, obtuse, ± deltoid, membranous, often united in pairs

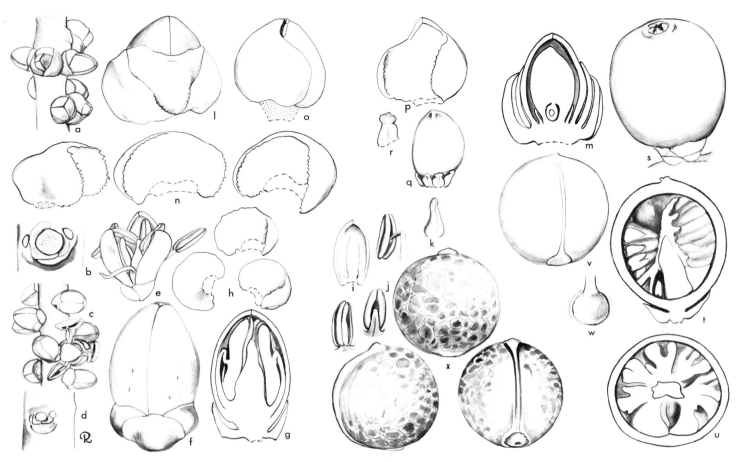

145.—**Rhopaloblaste. a,** portion of rachilla with triads ×1½; **b,** triad, flowers removed ×3; **c,** portion of rachilla with paired and solitary staminate flowers ×1½; **d,** scars and bracteoles of paired staminate flowers ×3; **e,** staminate flower at anthesis ×3; **f,** staminate bud ×6; **g,** staminate bud in vertical section ×6; **h,** staminate sepals ×6; **i,** staminate petal, interior view ×3; **j,** stamen in 3 views ×3; **k,** pistillode ×3; **l,** pistillate bud ×6; **m,** pistillate bud in vertical section ×6; **n,** pistillate sepals ×6; **o,** pistillate bud, sepals removed ×6; **p,** pistillate petal ×6; **q,** gynoecium and staminodes ×6; **r,** staminode ×12; **s,** fruit ×1½; **t,** fruit in vertical section ×1½; **u,** fruit in cross-section ×1½; **v,** endocarp ×1½; **w,** operculum ×3; **x,** seed in 3 views ×1½. *Rhopaloblaste elegans:* all from *Moore & Whitmore 9310.*

or irregularly united or united in a membranous, lobed ring; gynoecium irregularly ovoid, unilocular, uniovulate, stigmas erect to recurved between the valvate apices of the petals at anthesis, the ovule (in *R. ceramica*) hemianatropous, broader laterally, attached adaxially (in the ventral angle) and pendulous from the top of the locule. Fruit ovoid or ellipsoidal to subglobose, orange-yellow to red at maturity, with apical or stigmatic remains; epicarp smooth, mesocarp lacking fiber sclereids or tannin cells, with flattened longitudinal fibers in one or usually more than one layer against the yellowish, fragile endocarp, this impressed over the hilum and with a round basal operculum. Seed brown, with a lightly to deeply impressed hilum along the adaxial side, raphe branches anastomosing, endosperm deeply ruminate; embryo basal, large. Germination adjacent-ligular, eophyll finely pinnate. $n =$ 16 (*R. ceramica*, Read 1965a; and as *R. hexandra*, Sarkar 1970).

Anatomy.—Leaf (Tomlinson 1961).

Distribution.—Six species in the Nicobar Islands, Peninsular Malaysia, and Singapore, the Moluccas, New Guinea, and Solomon Islands.

Ecology.—All species inhabit rain forest at relatively low elevations.

Common Names and Uses.—Kerinting (*R. singaporensis*). Widely grown as ornamentals.

Notes.—Few collections have been made from the wild and more are desirable. The distribution pattern is of considerable interest, suggesting immigration into the Malesian region from two directions (see Dransfield 1981b).

Taxonomic Account.—Moore (1970).

Plate.—69A.

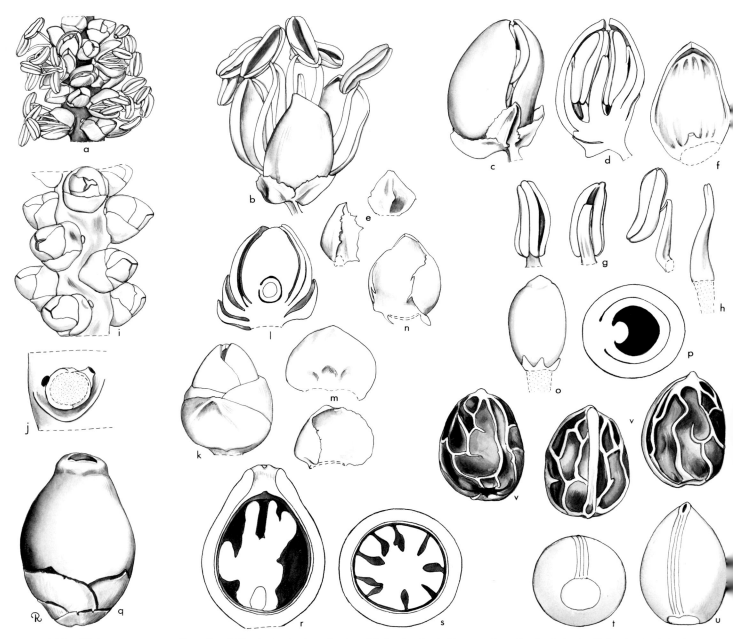

146.—**Dictyosperma. a,** portion of rachilla at staminate anthesis ×1½; **b,** staminate flower ×6; **c,** staminate bud ×6; **d,** staminate bud in vertical section ×6; **e,** staminate sepal in 2 views ×6; **f,** staminate petal, interior view ×6; **g,** stamen in 3 views ×6; **h,** pistillode ×6; **i,** portion of rachilla at pistillate anthesis ×3; **j,** triad, flowers removed ×6; **k,** pistillate flower ×6; **l,** pistillate flower in vertical section ×6; **m,** pistillate sepals in 2 views ×6; **n,** pistillate petal, interior view ×6; **o,** gynoecium and staminodes ×6; **p,** ovary in cross-section ×12; **q,** fruit ×3; **r,** fruit in vertical section ×3; **s,** fruit in cross-section ×3; **t, u,** endocarp in 2 views showing operculum ×3; **v,** seed in 3 views ×3. *Dictyosperma album*: all from *Read 831.*

146. **DICTYOSPERMA** H. A. Wendland & Drude, Linnaea 39:181. 1875. Type: **D. album** (Bory) H. A. Wendland & Drude ex Scheffer (*Areca alba* Bory).
Dicrosperma H. A. Wendland & Drude ex W. Watson, Gardeners' Chronical, series 2, 24:362. 1885. (Type as above).
Linoma O. F. Cook, Journal of the Washington Academy of Sciences 7:123. 1917. Type: *L. alba*

(Bory) O. F. Cook (*Areca alba* Bory = *Dictyosperma album* (Bory) H. A. Wendland & Drude.

Stout, solitary, unarmed, pleonanthic, monoecious palm. Stem erect, sometimes enlarged at the base, brown or gray, often vertically fissured. Leaves pinnate, spreading, with arched, ± pendulous leaflets; sheath tubular, forming a prominent crownshaft, thinly to densely white, gray or brown tomentose; petiole very short, nearly flat to slightly rounded adaxially, abaxially rounded, tomentose marginally and adaxially, the scales with blackish centers and pale, tattered-twisted margins, deciduous, leaving dotlike scars; rachis adaxially angled with scales as on the petiole, abaxially rounded; leaflets lanceolate, acute, single-fold, subopposite, regularly arranged, abaxially with pale to dark brown, twisted, basifixed or medifixed membranous ramenta on the midrib, midrib conspicuous adaxially, transverse veinlets not evident. Inflorescences infrafoliar, protandrous, as many as 6 present below the crownshaft, erect in bud, branched to 1 order, branches stiff, ascending; peduncle very short, dorsiventrally compressed, gray-brown tomentose; prophyll tubular, bluntly pointed, rather wide, shortly 2-keeled laterally, glabrous or with deciduous gray tomentum, splitting adaxially, caducous; peduncular bract like the prophyll, lacking keels, beaked, rather thin, fibrous; rachis longer than the peduncle, stout, tapering, ± densely covered with twisted hairs or glabrous, bearing acute or low rounded bracts subtending rachillae on 3 sides, lacking rachillae adaxially, at least toward the base; rachillae moderate, tapering, stiff, ascending, becoming recurved, glabrous or hairy only at the base, bearing triads in the lower ½–⅘, and paired staminate flowers distally; floral bracteoles low, flattened, not sepallike. Staminate flowers sessile or briefly pedicellate, yellow to maroon, asymmetrical; sepals 3, distinct, slightly imbricate at the base only, acute, keeled and ± gibbous towards the base; petals 3, distinct, valvate, ovate, acute, with an outer layer of thick fibers and tannin cells; stamens 6, filaments stout, inflexed at the apex in bud, anthers dorsifixed near the middle, becoming versatile, linear-lanceolate, briefly bifid at the apex, more deeply bifid basally, the locules in bud separated by a very narrow sterile portion, latrorse; pollen elliptic or rarely irregular, monosulcate, with finely reticulate, tectate exine, rarely with small, supratectal spines; pistillode nearly as long as the stamens, tapered to a slender tip from a broad base. Pistillate flowers ovoid, smaller than the staminate; sepals 3, distinct, imbricate, broadly rounded; petals 3, distinct, broadly imbricate, very briefly valvate at the apex; staminodes 3, small, triangular, at one side of the gynoecium; gynoecium ovoid, unilocular, uniovulate, stigmas scarcely differentiated, not exserted or recurved, ovule large, prominently vascularized, attached laterally in upper part of locule, hemianatropous. Fruit ovoid or ovoid-ellipsoidal, black or purplish at maturity, stigmatic remains apical; epicarp smooth when fresh, wrinkled but not pebbled when dry, mesocarp with an external and an internal layer of elongate, vertically oriented parenchyma cells with some flat, thin, longitudinal fibers between the layers, cells of the inner layer longer and overlying a layer of contiguous thickened fibers and a thin layer of ± isodiametric tannin cells adherent to the endocarp, endocarp horny, with round

basal operculum and scar of seed attachment extending the length of the adaxial side to the acute apex. Seed ovoid-ellipsoidal, acute, brown, with elongate hilum and only slightly anastomosing raphe branches descending from the apex, endosperm deeply ruminate; embryo basal. Germination adjacent-ligular; eophyll bifid. $n = 16$ (Read 1966, Sharma and Sarkar 1957).

Anatomy.—The leaf has a one-layered hypodermis below each surface and a well developed three to four layered adaxial palisade. Fibers are frequent in large bundles mostly next to the adaxial hypodermis. See Tomlinson (1961).

Distribution.—One species in the Mascarene Islands.

Ecology.—Grows from sea level to 600 m or more, nearly extinct in the wild state, cultivated on Mauritius and Réunion and elsewhere.

Common Names and Uses.—Princess palm, hurricane palm. Frequently grown as an ornamental.

Notes.—This is a very isolated genus in both distribution and relationships. The operculate endocarp clearly links it to the Iguanurinae, but within the subtribe its relationships are not clear. In many ways, *Dictyosperma* is rather unspecialized. It may be related to *Clinostigma*. There is also some similarity in inflorescence, and indeed in some aspects of flower form with some members of the Euterpeinae, but these may represent parallels.

Taxonomic Accounts.—Moore and Guého (1980, 1984).

Plate.—*69B; Fig. G.23.*

147. ACTINORHYTIS H. A. Wendland & Drude, Linnaea 39:184. 1875. Type: **A. calapparia** (Blume) H. A. Wendland & Drude ex Scheffer (*Areca calapparia* Blume).

Tall, solitary, unarmed, pleonanthic, monoecious tree palms. Stem erect, bare, conspicuously marked with leaf scars, with a large mass of roots at the base. Leaves pinnate, arching, neatly abscising; sheaths tubular, forming a long, slender, well defined crownshaft, bearing scattered caducous scales, the mouth with a short ligule; petiole very short in mature individuals (long in juveniles), adaxially channeled or flattened, abaxially rounded, densely caducously tomentose; rachis conspicuously down curved toward the tip; leaflets very numerous, close, regularly arranged, single-fold, acute, acuminate or briefly bifid, the margins thickened, adaxially glabrous, abaxially with minute dotlike scales and conspicuous ramenta along the midrib, transverse veinlets obscure. Inflorescences infrafoliar, erect in bud, becoming horizontal or pendulous, branching to 3 orders proximally, to 1 order distally, protandrous; peduncle short, winged at the very base, grossly swollen just above the base in the center, caducously tomentose; prophyll inserted near the base of the peduncle,

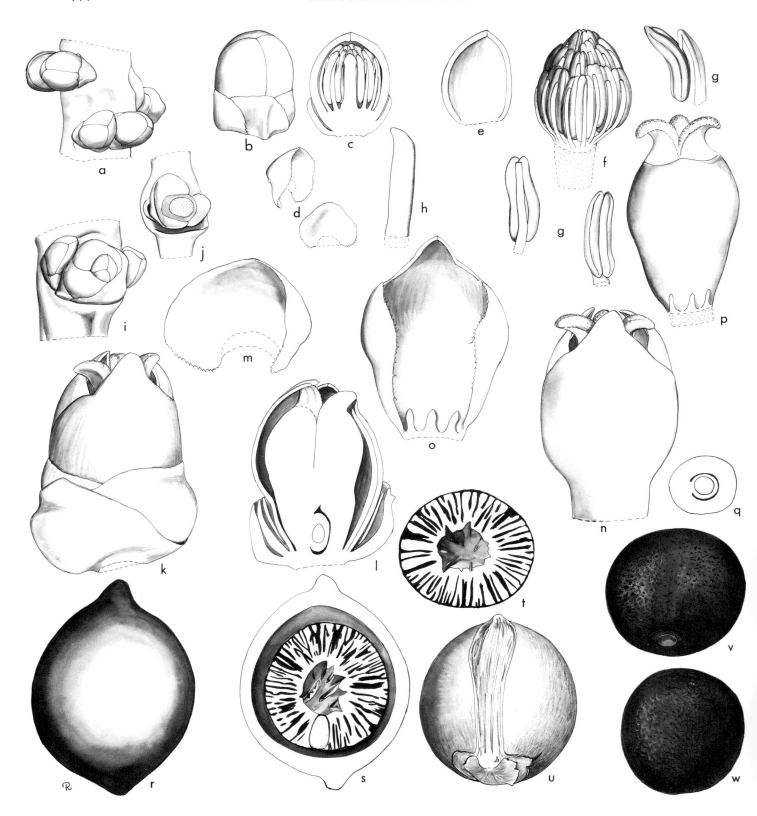

tubular, beaked, 2-keeled, entirely enclosing the inflorescence in bud, sparsely scaly, splitting abaxially, deciduous; peduncular bract, inserted just above the prophyll, similar to the prophyll but scarcely 2-winged, deciduous; subsequent bracts low, triangular, inconspicuous; rachis longer than the peduncle, ± elliptic in cross-section, bearing relatively few, large, spirally arranged first-order branches, with conspicuous, bare, proximal portions; rachillae rather stiff, elongate, bearing spirally arranged triads in the proximal ½ to ⅔, and paired or solitary staminate flowers distally, or rarely, bearing only staminate flowers; rachilla bracts low, rounded, quite conspicuous, tending to form very shallow pits; floral bracteoles sepallike. Staminate flowers asymmetrical in bud; sepals 3, distinct, imbricate, ± triangular-tipped, keeled; petals 3, distinct, ± ovate, valvate, ±2–3 times as long as the sepals; stamens 24–33 or more, exserted at anthesis, filaments slender, elongate, inflexed at the tip, anthers medifixed, narrow oblong, ± versatile, latrorse; pollen elliptic, monosulcate, with finely reticulate, tectate exine; pistillode columnar, ± as long as the stamens in bud, shorter when stamens exserted. Pistillate flowers globular, at anthesis much larger than the staminate; sepals 3, distinct, imbricate, rounded; petals 3, ± twice as long as the sepals, distinct, broadly imbricate with conspicuous, triangular, valvate tips; staminodes 3, narrow triangular, flattened; gynoecium ovoid to obovoid, unilocular, uniovulate, stigmas 3, large, fleshy, recurved, ovule laterally attached near the apex of the locule, hemianatropous. Fruit very large, ovoid, ± beaked, green turning red at maturity, perianth whorls persistent, stigmatic remains apical; epicarp smooth, mesocarp with thin flesh and abundant anastomosing fibers adhering to the endocarp, endocarp closely adhering to the seed, thin, ± bony with circular operculum. Seed globose, with lateral, longitudinal hilum, endosperm deeply ruminate, with a central, irregular hollow; embryo basal. Germination adjacent-ligular; eophyll bifid. Cytology not known.

Anatomy. — Leaf (Tomlinson 1961).

Distribution. — Two species, *A. calapparia,* native to New Guinea and the Solomon Islands and *A. poamau* in the Solomon Islands. *A. calapparia* has become widespread in Southeast Asia.

Ecology. — In the wild, the two species are plants of lowland tropical rain forest at altitudes up to about 1000 m above sea level.

Common Names and Uses. — Pinang penawar, pinang mawar. *A. calapparia* is widely planted in Southeast Asia and Malesia; it is extremely decorative, but the main reason for its cultivation by villagers is as a magic or medicinal plant. The seed may also be chewed as a betel substitute. Uses of *A. poamau* have not been recorded.

Notes. — These are large palms with arching leaves, very slender crownshafts, conical masses of roots at the base of the trunks and large, widely spreading inflorescences below the leaves. These characters and the large fruits, the largest in the subtribe, are distinctive.

Taxonomic Account. — There has been no recent assessment of the genus.

Plate. — 69C.

148. LAVOIXIA H. E. Moore, Gentes Herbarum 11: 296. 1978. Type: **L. macrocarpa** H. E. Moore.

Moderate, solitary, unarmed, pleonanthic, monoecious palm. Stem erect, brown, much enlarged at the base, leaf scars wide, not impressed. Leaves regularly pinnate, stiff, spreading; sheaths tubular for some time but becoming deeply split opposite the petiole, and then not forming a prominent crownshaft, glabrous adaxially, covered abaxially with prominent, dark brown, scurfy scales; petiole short, adaxially shallowly channeled near the base, rounded distally and abaxially, nearly circular in cross-section; rachis angled adaxially, rounded abaxially; leaflets stiff, somewhat ascending, single-fold, acute, adaxially glabrous, abaxially with scattered, minute scales and large ramenta along the midrib, midrib and marginal ribs prominent, 2 pairs of lateral veins also large, transverse veinlets not evident. Inflorescences infrafoliar, spreading, branched to 2 orders basally, to 1 order distally, protandrous; peduncle dorsiventrally flattened, short; prophyll completely encircling the peduncle at its insertion, tubular, with 2, wide, flat, lateral keels, splitting apically, covered with dense tomentum and branched scales, caducous; peduncular bract enclosing the inflorescence in bud, beaked, longer than the prophyll, tomentose throughout and distally covered with large ramenta, also caducous; rachis longer than the peduncle, bearing spirally inserted, low, rounded or ruffled bracts subtending first-order branches and rachillae; rachillae slender, tapering, bearing spirally arranged, low, rounded bracts subtending triads in the basal ½ or ⅔ and paired or solitary staminate flowers distally, flowers somewhat sunken in the axis; bracteoles surrounding the pistillate flower brown, sepallike, imbricate. Staminate buds symmetrical; sepals 3, distinct, im-

---

147.—**Actinorhytis. a,** portion of rachilla with paired staminate buds ×3; **b,** staminate bud ×6; **c,** staminate bud in vertical section ×6; **d,** staminate sepals in 2 views ×6; **e,** staminate petal, interior view ×6; **f,** androecium ×6; **g,** stamen in 3 views ×12; **h,** pistillode ×12; **i,** portion of rachilla with triad ×3; **j,** triad, flowers removed to show bracteoles ×3; **k,** pistillate flower ×6; **l,** pistillate flower in vertical section ×6; **m,** pistillate sepal, interior view ×6; **n,** pistillate flower, sepals removed ×6; **o,** pistillate petal with staminodes, interior view ×6; **p,** gynoecium and staminodes ×6; **q,** ovary in cross-section ×6; **r,** fruit ×1; **s,** fruit in vertical section ×1; **t,** seed in cross-section ×1; **u,** endocarp with basal operculum ×1; **v, w,** seed in 2 views ×1. *Actinorhytis calapparia*: **a-h** and **r-w,** *Whitmore BSIP 4169*; **i-q,** *Bailey s.n.*

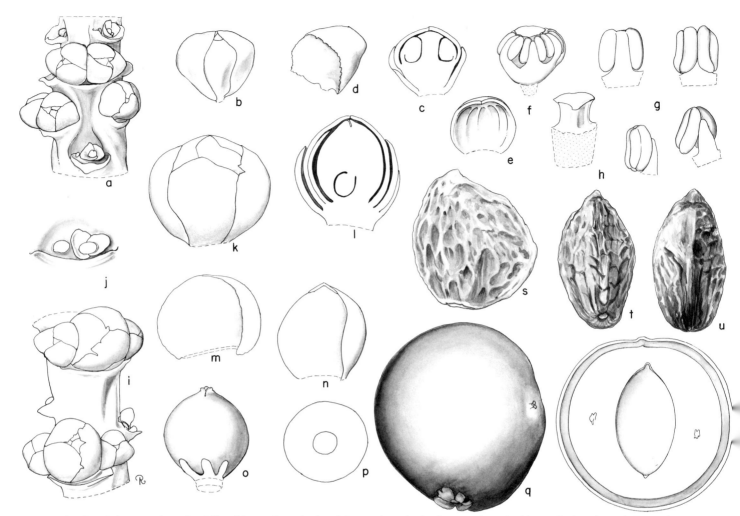

148.—**Lavoixia. a,** portion of rachilla with staminate buds ×6; **b,** staminate bud ×9; **c,** staminate bud in vertical section ×9; **d,** staminate sepal ×9; **e,** staminate petal, interior view ×9; **f,** androecium and pistillode ×9; **g,** stamen in 4 views ×15; **h,** pistillode ×15; **i,** portion of rachilla with triads ×6; **j,** triad, flowers removed to show bracteoles ×9; **k,** pistillate bud ×9; **l,** pistillate flower in vertical section ×9; **m,** pistillate sepal ×9; **n,** pistillate petal ×9; **o,** gynoecium and staminodes ×9; **p,** ovary in cross-section ×9; **q,** fruit ×1½; **r,** fruit in vertical section, seed not formed ×1½; **s, t, u,** seed in 3 views ×1½. *Lavoixia macrocarpa:* **a–h,** *Schmid 4578;* **i–p,** *Moore 10464;* **q** and **r,** *Schmid 1616.*

bricate, rounded, gibbous dorsally toward the base; petals 3, distinct, valvate; stamens 6, filaments flat, erect at the apex in bud, anthers didymous from a short connective; pollen elliptic, monosulcate, with finely reticulate, tectate exine; pistillode slightly exceeding the stamens, expanded in a flat, slightly lobed cap. Pistillate flowers subglobose, larger than the staminate; sepals 3, distinct, broadly imbricate, rounded; petals 3, distinct, imbricate except for briefly valvate apices, scarcely exceeding the sepals; staminodes 3, toothlike, borne at one side of the gynoecium; gynoecium ovoid, unilocular, uniovulate, stigmas small, ovule pendulous, curved, probably hemianatropous. Fruit subglobose, large, with stigmatic remains lateral at about the middle; epicarp smooth over a thin shell of short sclereids perpendicular to the surface and a thick parenchymatous layer lacking tannin cells, endocarp thin, oper-

culate, adherent to the seed. Seed laterally compressed, attached basally, variously indented, pointed apically, endosperm homogeneous; embryo basal. Germination and eophyll not recorded. Cytology not studied.

Anatomy.—In leaf anatomy *Lavoixia* is distinctive because of an abundance of tannin and a lack of fibrous bundles in the mesophyll (Uhl and Martens in prep.).

Distribution.—One species in New Caledonia.

Ecology.—*Lavoixia* is known only from wet forest on steep rocky slopes at ca. 500 m on Mt. Panié. Only one population is known, consisting in 1980 of four individuals.

Common Names and Uses.—Not known.

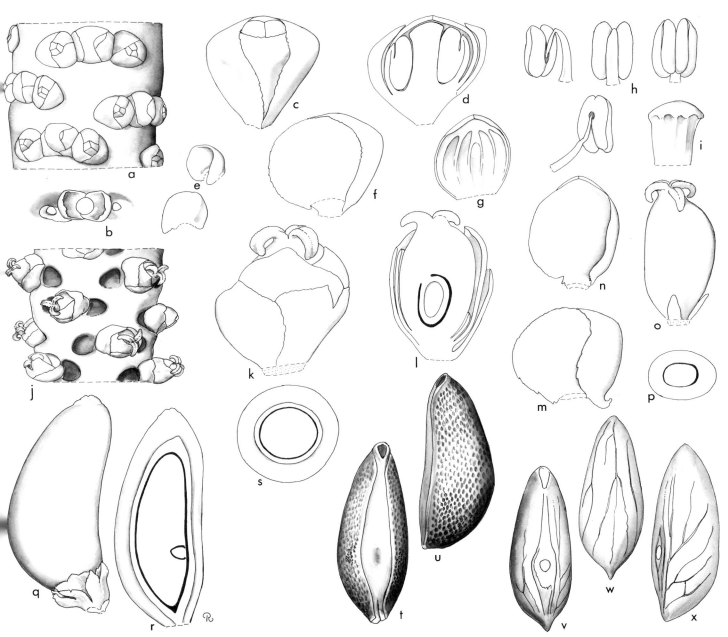

149.—**Alloschmidia. a,** portion of rachilla with triads, flowers in bud ×6; **b,** triad, flowers removed to show bracteoles ×6; **c,** staminate bud ×15; **d,** staminate bud in vertical section ×15; **e,** bracteoles ×12; **f,** staminate sepal ×15; **g,** staminate petal, interior view ×15; **h,** stamen in 4 views ×15; **i,** pistillode ×15; **j,** portion of rachilla at pistillate anthesis ×6; **k,** pistillate flower ×12; **l,** pistillate flower in vertical section ×12; **m,** pistillate sepal ×12; **n,** pistillate petal ×12; **o,** gynoecium and staminodes ×12; **p,** ovary in cross-section ×12; **q,** fruit ×4½; **r,** fruit in vertical section ×4½; **s,** fruit in cross-section ×4½; **t, u,** endocarp in 2 views ×4½; **v, w, x,** seed in 3 views ×4½. *Alloschmidia glabrata*: all from *Moore et al. 9957.*

Notes.—A very rare palm, known only from one locality in New Caledonia, distinguished by the very large fruits and laterally compressed sculptured seeds.
Taxonomic Account.—Moore and Uhl (1984).
Plate.—69D.

149. ALLOSCHMIDIA H. E. Moore, Gentes Herbarum 11:293. 1978. Type: **A. glabrata** (Beccari) H. E. Moore (*Basselinia glabrata* Beccari).

Moderate, solitary, unarmed, pleonanthic, monoecious palm. Stem slender, ringed with slightly impressed leaf scars, internodes long at the base, short distally, brown, longitudinally lined, prickly adventitious roots sometimes developed at the base. Leaves pinnate, spreading; sheaths tubular, forming a crownshaft with scattered, caducous scales; petiole short, flat adaxially, rounded abaxially, margins sharp, bearing brown-centered scales; rachis angled adaxially, rounded abaxially, with similar scales; leaflets borne in 1 plane, single-fold except near the base and tip where several-fold, acute to acuminate, both surfaces bearing scales, becoming brown-dotted, ramenta present abaxially on the midrib, midrib prominent, lateral and marginal veins thickened, transverse veinlets not evident. Inflorescences interfoliar, pendulous, branched to 3 orders basally, to 1 order distally, protandrous; peduncle short, stout, recurved; prophyll inserted at the base of the peduncle, tubular, shortly 2-keeled laterally, chartaceous, completely encircling the peduncle basally, enclosing the peduncular bract, caducous; peduncular bract inserted near the prophyll, briefly beaked like the prophyll, tomentose distally, an incomplete peduncular bract inserted distally; rachis somewhat longer than the peduncle, bearing low, usually rounded bracts subtending branches and rachillae; rachillae long, slender, all about equal in length, bearing triads in a curved horizontal line nearly throughout, staminate and pistillate flowers about the same size in bud, sunken in conspicuous depressions, with no obvious subtending bract or lip but with minute trichomes on the distal side; floral bracteoles equal, sepallike, exceeding the depression, the outer rounded and slightly shorter. Staminate flowers ± symmetrical; sepals 3, distinct, imbricate, thickened and dark dorsally; petals 3, distinct, valvate; stamens 6, filaments awl-shaped, markedly inflexed at the apex in bud, anthers dorsifixed, oblong, latrorse; pollen elliptic, monosulcate, with finely reticulate, tectate exine; pistillode triangular-columnar with rounded triangular apex, slightly exceeding stamens. Pistillate flowers about the same size as the staminate; sepals 3, distinct, broadly imbricate, thickened and dark dorsally; petals 3, distinct; imbricate with briefly valvate apices; staminodes 3, toothlike, borne at one side of the gynoecium; gynoecium ellipsoidal, unilocular, uniovulate, with short, recurved stigmas, ovule pendulous, briefly arillate, probably hemianatropous. Fruit ellipsoidal, with apical stigmatic remains, falling from perianth which persists on the rachilla; epicarp smooth, underlain by tannin cells, a shell of pale, flattish, very short sclereids, a few thin, pale, longitudinal fibers, and an inner tanniniferous layer, endocarp fragile, minutely reticulate, narrowly ovoid-ellipsoidal, with an elongate operculum and produced in a basal point. Seed narrowly ovoid-ellipsoidal, hilum elongate, in upper ⅔, raphe branches few, descending, scarcely anastomosing; endosperm homogeneous; embryo lateral, below the middle. Germination adjacent-ligular; eophyll bifid. Cytology not studied.

Anatomy.—*Alloschmidia* belongs to a group of New Caledonian genera having single adaxial and abaxial hypodermal layers in leaves. Leaves of *Alloschmidia* also lack fibrous strands but are almost completely tanniniferous (Uhl and Martens in prep.).

Distribution.—One species in northeastern New Caledonia.

Ecology.—*Alloschmidia* occurs in wet forests on schists or micaschists in Ton-Non Massif and Panié Massif, mostly at elevations from 240–1170 m, but in one locality at only 10 m.

Common Names and Uses.—Common names unknown. The vegetative bud is recorded as edible.

Notes.—*Alloschmidia glabrata* is unusual on several counts. The prominently pedunculate inflorescences are often numerous and in all stages of flower and fruit, forming a dark mass beneath the crownshaft, the flowers are borne in horizontal lines in depressions lacking an obvious bracteal lip, the endocarp is unique in its pitting, and the lateral position of the embryo is unusual in the Areceae.

Taxonomic Account.—Moore and Uhl (1984).

Plate.—70A.

150. CYPHOPHOENIX H. A. Wendland ex J. D. Hooker in Bentham & J. D. Hooker, Genera Plantarum 3:893. 1883. Lectotype: *Kentia elegans* Brongniart & Gris = **C. elegans** (Brongniart & Gris) H. A. Wendland ex Salomon (see Beccari 1920).

Moderate, solitary, unarmed, pleonanthic, monoecious palms. Stems erect, prominently ringed, smooth, yellowish, green or gray, sometimes enlarged at the base. Leaves regularly pinnate, straight or arched, spreading; sheaths forming a prominently and diagonally ribbed, somewhat inflated crownshaft, covered outside and inside with pale, gray, brown or red tomentum and persistent or deciduous scales; petiole channeled adaxially, rounded abaxially, tomentose to glabrous adaxially, with tomentum and scales abaxially; rachis flat to angled adaxially with broad margins basally, becoming nearly deltoid in section apically, rounded abaxially, minutely dotted adaxially, tomentose and scaly abaxially; leaflets stiff, single-fold, coriaceous when dry, obliquely acute to acuminate or rarely bifid, margins not thickened, abaxially with medifixed ramenta with tattered and twisted margins, prominent toward the base on the midrib, with or without small brown scales, midrib prominent and elevated adaxially, secondary veins scarcely prominent, transverse veinlets not evident. Inflorescences infrafoliar, stiffly branched to 1 or 2(–3) orders basally, fewer orders distally, protandrous; peduncle short; prophyll incompletely encircling the peduncle, open abaxially, 2-keeled laterally, caducous, tomentose; peduncular bract completely encircling the peduncle and enclosing the inflorescence in bud, slightly exceeding the prophyll, also caducous and tomentose; rachis much exceeding the peduncle, angled, minutely striate when dry, bearing spirally arranged, low rounded bracts subtending several divaricate branches, the lower ones with a prominent bare base; rachillae long, curved, slender, bearing

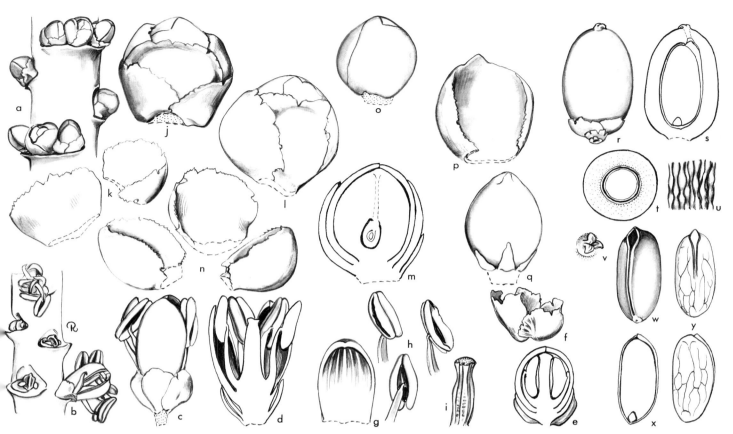

150.—**Cyphophoenix. a,** portion of rachilla with triads ×3; **b,** portion of rachilla with paired staminate flowers, most fallen ×3; **c,** staminate flower ×6; **d,** staminate flower in vertical section ×6; **e,** staminate bud in vertical section ×6; **f,** staminate sepals ×6; **g,** staminate petal, interior view ×6; **h,** stamen in 3 views ×6; **i,** pistillode ×6; **j,** pistillate bud with subtending bracteoles ×6; **k,** bracteoles subtending pistillate flower ×6; **l,** pistillate bud ×6; **m,** pistillate bud in vertical section ×6; **n,** pistillate sepals ×6; **o,** pistillate bud, sepals removed ×6; **p,** pistillate petal, interior view ×6; **q,** gynoecium and staminodes ×6; **r,** fruit ×1½; **s,** fruit in vertical section ×1½; **t,** fruit in cross-section ×1½; **u,** portion of dried exocarp, much enlarged; **v,** stigmatic remains ×3; **w,** endocarp ×1½; **x,** endocarp in vertical section ×1½; **y,** seed in 2 views ×1½. *Cyphophoenix elegans*: all from *Moore et al. 9323.*

prominent, rounded, liplike bracts subtending triads in the lower ⅓–½ of each rachilla, and paired or solitary staminate flowers distally; bracteoles about the pistillate flower prominent, marginally imbricate, ½ the length of the sepals. Staminate flowers symmetrical, borne on very short, straplike pedicels in triads, but ± sessile in the distal pairs; sepals 3, distinct, imbricate, broadly rounded or becoming crenulate apically, keeled dorsally and ± compressed laterally toward the base; petals 3, distinct, about twice as long as the sepals, valvate, scarcely acute at apex, ± lined when dry; stamens 6, filaments distinct, awl-shaped, the slender apex inflexed in bud, anthers versatile at anthesis, emarginate apically, bifid ca. ½ their length basally, basifixed but appearing dorsifixed; pollen elliptic, monosulcate, with finely reticulate, tectate exine; pistillode nearly columnar, angled and grooved, at least when dry, very briefly 3-lobed at apex. Pistillate flowers symmetrical; sepals 3, distinct, broadly imbricate and rounded, nearly as high as the petals; petals 3, distinct, longer than the sepals, strongly imbricate except for the very briefly valvate or subvalvate apices; staminodes 3, distinct, awl-shaped, flat; gynoecium ovoid when fresh, unilocular, uniovulate, stigmas 3, recurved, short, the ovule pendulous, probably hemianatropous. Fruit ovoid to oblong-ellipsoidal, yellow with black tip at maturity, stigmatic remains almost exactly apical; epicarp smooth but drying densely pebbled over a layer of short, pale, obliquely oriented fibers, mesocarp ± dry, with numerous slender, elongate, red tannin cells intermixed with the fibers and beneath the fibers against the endocarp, endocarp thin, crustaceous, fragile, oblong-ellipsoidal, circular in cross-section, neither angled nor sculptured, operculum circular, basal. Seed oblong-ellipsoidal, circular in cross-section, hilum obovoid, apical, tapered toward the base, raphe branches weakly or strongly anastomosing, endosperm homogeneous; embryo basal. Germination adjacent-ligular; eophyll apparently bifid. Cytology not studied.

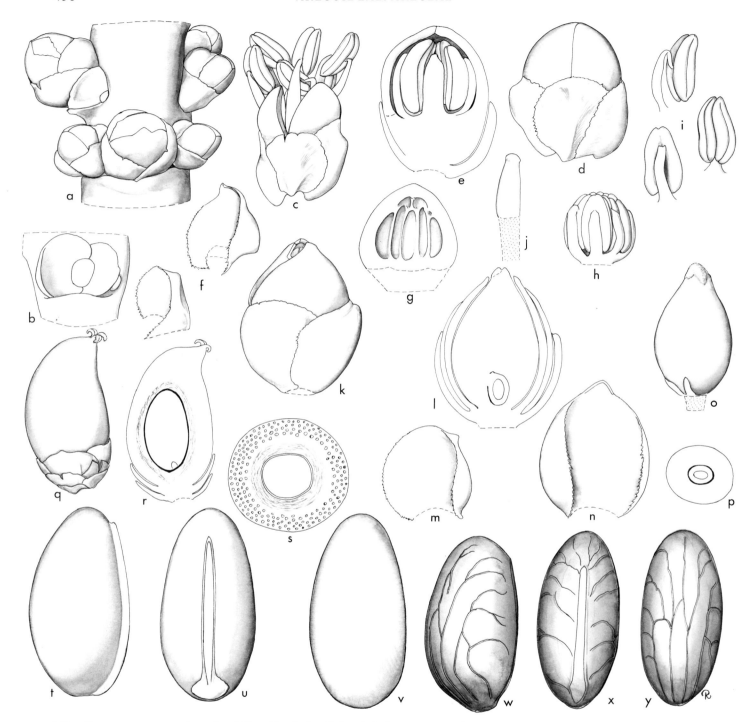

151.—**Campecarpus. a,** portion of rachilla with triads ×3; **b,** triad, flowers removed to show bracteoles ×6; **c,** staminate flower at anthesis ×4½; **d,** staminate bud ×6; **e,** staminate bud in vertical section ×6; **f,** staminate sepals in 2 views ×6; **g,** staminate petal, interior view ×6; **h,** androecium ×6; **i,** stamen in 3 views ×6; **j,** pistillode ×6; **k,** pistillate flower ×4½; **l,** flower in vertical section ×4½; **m,** pistillate sepal ×4½; **n,** pistillate petal ×4½; **o,** gynoecium and staminodes ×4½; **p,** ovary in cross-section ×4½; **q,** fruit ×1½; **r,** fruit in vertical section ×1½; **s,** fruit in cross-section ×2¼; **t, u, v,** endocarp in 3 views ×3; **w, x, y,** seed in 3 views ×3. *Campecarpus fulcitus:* **a-j,** *Moore et al. 9334;* **k-p,** *Moore et al. 9337;* **q-v,** *Moore et al. 10009;* **w-y,** *Balansa 1960.*

Anatomy.—*Cyphophoenix* shares the following features of leaf anatomy with *Campecarpus* and *Veillonia*: vascular bundles in uneven rows, many small vascular bundles present, lower bundle sheaths crescentic, wider then upper sheaths. These three genera are the only palms in New Caledonia having two-layered upper and lower hypodermal layers. *Cyphophoenix* differs from the others in that cells of the upper hypodermal layer are strikingly large and inner hypodermal layers of both surfaces are interrupted by distinctive rows of fibrous strands (Uhl and Martens in prep.).

Distribution.—Two species, one in New Caledonia and one in the Loyalty Islands.

Ecology.—*Cyphophoenix elegans* is a component of gallery forest in a limited area of northeastern New Caledonia, where it occurs on schistose rocks in marked contrast to the raised coral of Lifou Island on which *C. nucele* grows.

Common Names and Uses.—Not recorded.

Notes.—Differences between *Cyphophoenix elegans* and *C. nucele* appear to be constant and sufficient to warrant specific status. As in *Brongniartikentia,* each species is confined to a particular edaphic situation and the two are separated by a long distance. Seed of *C. nucele* has been introduced into cultivation in the United States where it may be expected to do especially well on the coral rocks of southern Florida.

Taxonomic Account.—Moore and Uhl (1984).

Plate.—70B.

151. **CAMPECARPUS** H. A. Wendland ex Beccari, Le Palme della Nuova Caledonia 28. 1920; and Webbia 5:96. 1921. Type: **C. fulcitus** (Brongniart) H. A. Wendland ex Beccari (*Kentia fulcita* Brongniart).

Moderate, solitary, unarmed, pleonanthic, monoecious palm. Stem erect, prominently and deeply ringed with leaf scars, above a mass of brown, rather close prop roots. Leaves regularly pinnate, spreading to nearly erect; sheaths forming a crownshaft, somewhat inflated basally, densely tomentose; petiole short, shallowly channeled adaxially, rounded abaxially, densely scaly, becoming dotted; rachis concave adaxially, becoming ridged distally and then nearly triangular in section, rounded abaxially with scales as the petiole; leaflets borne horizontally in one rank on each side, single-fold, acute, leathery, with small dots and at least the midrib bearing dark brown, membranous, tattered, medifixed ramenta nearly to the apex, midrib elevated and flattened adaxially, midrib and 2 lateral veins prominent abaxially, transverse veinlets not evident. Inflorescences infrafoliar, branched to 2 orders basally, to 1 order distally, protandrous; peduncle short, ± dorsiventrally compressed; prophyll incompletely encircling the peduncle at insertion, tubular, 2-keeled laterally, tomentose apically, caducous; peduncular bract exceeding the prophyll and enclosing the inflorescences in bud, tubular, beaked, glabrous, caducous; rachis longer than the peduncle, bearing rounded to acute, spreading bracts subtending rachillae; rachillae stout, ± pendulous, tomentose, bearing projecting, rounded, or ± acute bracts subtending flowers borne in triads in the lower ca. ⅔ of each rachilla, and paired or solitary staminate flowers distally; bracteoles surrounding the pistillate flower sepallike, imbricate. Staminate flowers ± symmetrical; sepals 3, distinct, broadly imbricate, rounded, somewhat gibbous basally and keeled centrally; petals 3, distinct, valvate, thick, marked within by impressions of anthers; stamens 6, filaments rather stout, broad, briefly inflexed at the apex in bud, anthers dorsifixed, exserted and versatile at anthesis, oblong-ovate in outline, briefly bifid at apex, more deeply bifid at base, latrorse, connective tanniniferous; pollen elliptic, monosulcate, with finely reticulate, tectate exine; pistillode shorter than the stamens in bud, narrowly pyramidal, with acutely 3-angled apex. Pistillate flowers larger than the staminate, symmetrical; sepals 3, distinct, broadly imbricate, rounded; petals 3, distinct, broadly imbricate except for the briefly valvate apices; staminodes 3, borne at one side of gynoecium, small, toothlike; gynoecium ovoid, unilocular, uniovulate, stigmas 3, recurved at anthesis, ovule pendulous, probably hemianatropous. Fruit narrowly ovoid with curved apex, stigmatic remains eccentrically apical; epicarp smooth, mesocarp fleshy, with numerous, longitudinal flat fibers external to a tanniniferous layer and elongate tannin cells in white parenchyma adjacent to the endocarp, endocarp vitreous, fragile, with longitudinal adaxial ridge and rounded basal operculum. Seed ellipsoidal, hilum elongate, raphe branches arching from the hilum toward the abaxial side and base, endosperm homogeneous; embryo basal. Germination and eophyll not recorded. Cytology not studied.

Anatomy.—Leaf anatomy shows similarities to that of *Cyphophoenix* and *Veillonia* as explained under *Cyphophoenix.* In *Campecarpus* cells of the upper adaxial hypodermal layer often have thick apparently lignified walls and some are tanniniferous (Uhl and Martens in prep.).

Distribution.—One species in New Caledonia.

Ecology.—*Campecarpus* occurs in wet forests on serpentine rocks in southern New Caledonia.

Common Names and Uses.—Not recorded.

Notes.—*Campecarpus* is distinguished by the often prominent stilt roots, incomplete prophyll, and stout rachillae.

Taxonomic Account.—Moore and Uhl (1984).

Plate.—70C.

152. **BASSELINIA** Veillard, Bulletin de la Société Linnéenne de Normandie série. 2, 6:230. 1873. Lectotype: **B. gracilis** (Brongniart & Gris) Veillard (*Kentia gracilis* Brongniart & Gris) (see Beccari 1920).

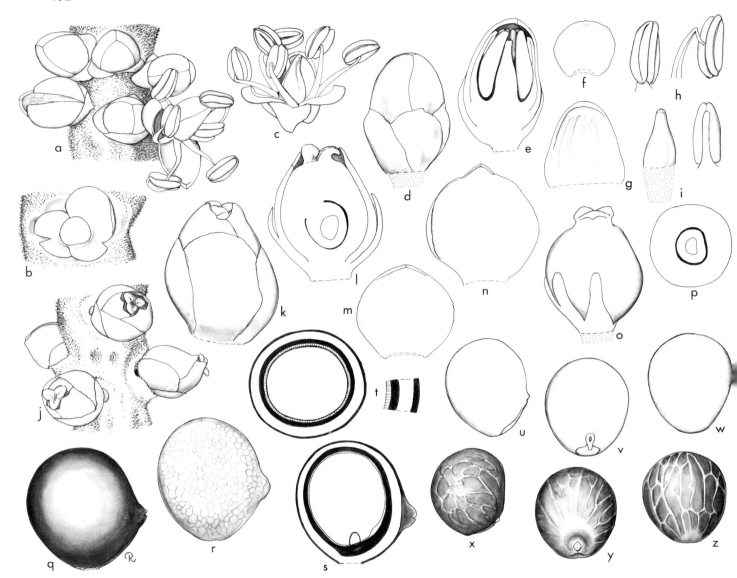

152.—**Basselinia. a,** portion of rachilla with triads ×4½; **b,** triad, flowers removed to show bracteoles ×6; **c,** staminate flower at anthesis ×4½; **d,** staminate bud ×7½; **e,** staminate bud in vertical section ×7½; **f,** staminate sepal ×7½; **g,** staminate petal, interior view ×7½; **h,** stamen in 3 views ×7½; **i,** pistillode ×7½; **j,** portion of rachilla with pistillate flowers ×4½; **k,** pistillate flower ×7½; **l,** pistillate flower in vertical section ×7½; **m,** pistillate sepal, interior view ×7½; **n,** pistillate petal, interior view ×7½; **o,** gynoecium and staminodes ×7½; **p,** ovary in cross-section ×7½; **q,** fruit ×3; **r,** fruit with epidermal layer removed to show sclereids ×3; **s,** fruit in vertical section ×3; **t,** fruit in cross-section ×3, and part of wall, enlarged; **u, v, w,** endocarp in 3 views ×3; **x, y, z,** seed in 3 views ×3. *Basselinia sordida:* **a-p,** *Moore et al. 10072; B. velutina:* **q-z,** *Moore et al. 9964.*

Microkentia H. A. Wendland ex J. D. Hooker in Bentham & J. D. Hooker, Genera Plantarum 3: 895. 1883. Lectotype: *Basselinia gracilis* (Brongniart & Gris) Vieillard (see Beccari 1920).

Nephrocarpus Dammer, Botanischer Jahrbücher für Systematik 39:21. 1906. Type: *N. schlechteri* Dammer (=*Basselinia pancheri* (Brongniart & Gris) Vieillard (*Kentia pancheri* Brongniart & Gris)).

Small to stout, solitary or clustered, unarmed, pleonanthic, monoecious palms. Stem erect, usually ± prominently ringed, internodes glabrous, scaly, or densely tomentose. Leaves pinnate or entire and pinnately ribbed, spreading to ascending; sheaths sometimes partly open but forming a prominent crownshaft, variously scaly and tomentose; petiole channeled adaxially, rounded abaxially; rachis angled adaxially, abaxially rounded; leaflets soft or coriaceous when dry, ± regularly arranged, acute, single or several-fold, or the blade undivided except at the apex, bearing small dotted scales over ribs and surface abaxially (scales large and dense in *B. vestita*), scales usually only on veins adaxially, midrib prominent, bearing ramenta abaxially, lateral and marginal veins prominent or not, transverse veinlets not evident. Inflorescences infrafoliar, branched to 1 or 2 orders; peduncle short; prophyll incompletely encircling the peduncle, shortly 2-keeled laterally, rather thin, open abaxially; peduncular bract tubular, complete, somewhat exserted from the prophyll, ± beaked; rachis longer than the peduncle; rachis and rachillae glabrous to scaly or tomentose; bracts subtending the branches, rachillae, and triads low, rounded to acute, flowers sometimes obscured by hairs; rachillae moderate, stiff, ± spreading, bearing flowers horizontally aligned in triads in the lower ½–¾ or more, and paired or solitary staminate flowers distally; bracteoles surrounding the pistillate flower equal or unequal, brown, sepallike. Staminate buds symmetrical; sepals 3, distinct, imbricate, ± acute to rounded; petals 3, distinct, valvate; stamens 6, filaments inflexed at the apex in bud, anthers dorsifixed, bifid at the base and apex, latrorse; pollen elliptic, monosulcate, with finely reticulate, tectate exine; pistillode nearly as high as the stamens in bud, angled-cylindrical, narrowed to slightly expanded at the apex. Pistillate flowers smaller than, equalling or larger than the staminate; sepals 3, distinct, imbricate, rounded; petals 3, distinct, imbricate except for the briefly valvate apices; staminodes 3 at one side of the gynoecium, small; gynoecium unilocular, uniovulate, stigmas 3, prominent, recurved, ovule ± pendulous, usually hemianatropous. Fruit subglobose to ellipsoidal, sometimes bilobed, red or black, with lateral to subapical stigmatic remains; epicarp smooth or drying pebbled, mesocarp with a thin layer of small, irregular tannin cells external to a thin layer of short sclereids over abundant ellipsoidal tannin cells and a few flat, thin fibers, endocarp thin, vitreous, fragile, with a rounded, basal operculum. Seed globose to kidney-shaped or rounded, hilum and raphe short, the raphe branches anastomosing laterally, endosperm homogeneous; embryo basal. Germination adjacent-ligular; eophyll bifid (where known). Cytology not studied.

Anatomy.—The two sections of *Basselinia* are distinct in leaf anatomy. *B. deplanchei, B. gracilis, B. pancheri,* and *B. vestita* form a very coherent group similar in epidermal, hypodermal, mesophyll, and guard cell structure, and differing only in distribution of fibrous strands and minor characteristics of midribs. Differences are similar to those separating species of *Actinokentia, Brongniartikentia,* and *Burretiokentia.* The six species of section *Taloua,* except for *B. sordida* are strikingly and distinctively fibrous, in contrast to the species of sec-

tion *Basselinia* which all have large amounts of tannin (Uhl and Martens in prep.).

Distribution.—Eleven species, locally or widely distributed in New Caledonia.

Ecology.—Ten species of *Basselinia* are restricted to either serpentine or schistose soils, the eleventh, *B. gracilis,* occurs on both soil types and is the most widely distributed palm in New Caledonia.

Common Names and Uses.—Common names not recorded. All species would make elegant ornamentals but apparently are difficult to grow.

Notes.—The genus *Basselinia* is divided into two sections. The extremes are so different in general aspect that they were at one time thought to represent two or even three distinct genera. However, the species differ among themselves less than the complex as a unit does from other genera in the Iguanurinae.

Taxonomic Account.—Moore and Uhl (1984).
Plates.—25A–D; 70D; 71A.

153. CYPHOSPERMA H. A. Wendland ex J. D. Hooker in Bentham & J. D. Hooker, Genera Plantarum 3:895. 1883. Lectotype: *Cyphokentia balansae* Brongniart = **C. balansae** (Brongniart) H. A. Wendland ex Salomon (see Beccari 1920).

Taveunia Burret, Occasional Papers of the Bernice P. Bishop Museum 11:12. 1935. Type: *T. trichospadix* Burret (=*Cyphosperma trichospadix* (Burret) H. E. Moore).

Moderate, solitary, unarmed, pleonanthic, monoecious palms. Stem erect, ± prominently ringed with irregular leaf scars. Leaves regularly pinnate, or bifid or irregularly divided, ± 3-ranked, spreading or ± erect; sheaths split opposite the petiole, not forming a crownshaft, glabrous; petiole short, stout, channeled to ± flat adaxially, rounded abaxially; rachis adaxially channeled above the base, becoming nearly triangular in section with a narrow ridge toward the apex, rounded abaxially, with scales and tomentum; leaflets when present, acute, single-fold, with elevated midrib, adaxially with 2 lateral veins and many secondary veins with or without linear scales, prominently veined abaxially with deciduous tomentum, ramenta sometimes present, transverse veinlets inconspicuous. Inflorescences interfoliar but persisting below the leaves, arched in flower, pendulous in fruit, branched to 2 orders basally, to 1 order distally, branches and rachillae with a prominent pulvinus at the base, protandrous; peduncle somewhat dorsiventrally compressed and elliptical in cross-section, elongate, much exceeding the bracts at anthesis; prophyll tubular, short, incompletely encircling the peduncle abaxially, 2-keeled laterally, chartaceous, open apically, ± glabrous, marcescent; peduncular bract with tubular base, much longer than the prophyll, beaked, covered

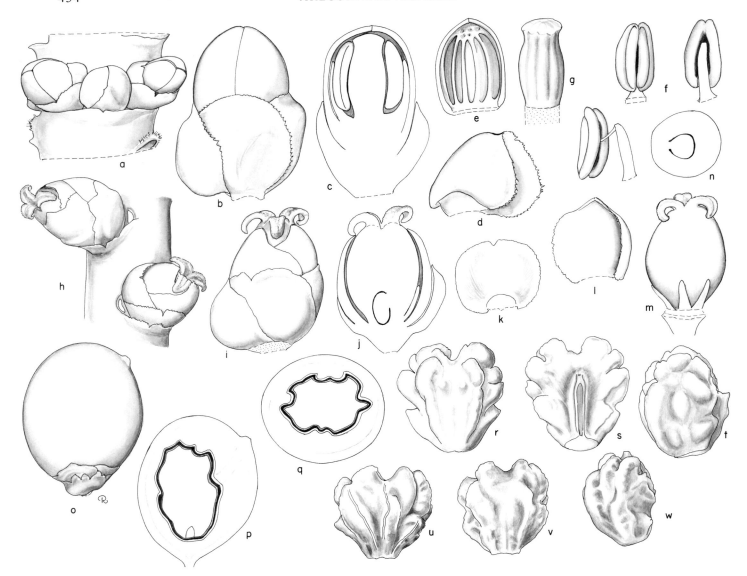

153.—**Cyphosperma. a,** portion of rachilla with triad ×6; **b,** staminate bud ×12; **c,** staminate bud in vertical section ×12; **d,** staminate sepal ×12; **e,** staminate petal, interior view ×12; **f,** stamen in 3 views × 12; **g,** pistillode ×12; **h,** portion of rachilla at pistillate anthesis, staminate flowers fallen ×6; **i,** pistillate flower × 7½; **j,** pistillate flower in vertical section × 7½; **k,** pistillate sepal × 7½; **l,** pistillate petal × 7½; **m,** gynoecium and staminodes × 7½; **n,** ovary in cross-section ×9; **o,** fruit ×3; **p,** fruit in vertical section ×3; **q,** fruit in cross-section ×3; **r, s, t,** endocarp in 3 views ×3; **u, v, w,** seed in 3 views ×3. *Cyphosperma balansae:* **a–g,** *Moore et al. 10073;* **h–w,** *Moore et al. 10033.*

with deciduous tomentum, also marcescent; rachis bearing low, acute to rounded bracts subtending branches and rachillae; rachillae distant, slender, moderate, tomentose throughout or glabrous except for patches of stiff, pale brown hairs in the upper and lateral parts of pit cavities, bearing acute or rounded bracts subtending partially sunken triads nearly throughout the rachillae, with paired or solitary staminate flowers in the upper ¼ or less; bracteoles surrounding the pistillate flower nearly equal, imbricate, nearly as long as the bract subtending the triad. Staminate flowers symmetrical; sepals 3, distinct, rounded, imbri-

cate, gibbous basally and centrally keeled; petals 3, distinct, valvate; stamens 6, filaments flattened, inflexed at the apex in bud, erect at anthesis, anthers oblong, latrorse dorsifixed, briefly emarginate at the base and apex; pollen elliptic, monosulcate, with scabrate, tectate exine; pistillode overtopping the stamens in bud, nearly columnar, apex expanded, 3-grooved. Pistillate flowers larger than the staminate; sepals 3, distinct, rounded, imbricate; petals 3, distinct, imbricate except for briefly valvate apices; staminodes 3, distinct, toothlike at one side of gynoecium; gynoecium unilocular, uniovulate, ellipsoidal, stigmas 3, recurved, ovule pendulous, form not known. Fruit broadly ellipsoidal, with stigmatic remains lateral in upper ¼–⅓; epicarp smooth when fresh, drying pebbled, mesocarp fleshy, with short fiber bundles nearly perpendicular to the epicarp, whitish parenchyma with dispersed, elongate, irregular tannin cells and thin, flat fibers, near but not adnate to the endocarp, endocarp thin, vitreous, fragile, irregularly sculptured, ridged, and grooved. Seed irregularly sculptured like the endocarp, hilum linear, endosperm homogeneous; embryo basal. Germination adjacent-ligular; eophyll bifid. $n = 16$ (*C. trichospadix,* Read 1965).

Anatomy. — In leaf anatomy *C. balansae* is distinguished by small fibrous strands in both upper and lower hypodermal layers. A two-layered upper and single layered lower hypodermis in shared with *Brongniartikentia, Clinosperma,* and *Lavoixia* (Uhl and Martens in prep.).

Distribution. — Three species, two in Fiji, one in New Caledonia.

Ecology. — On schists, graywackes, and peridotites in northeastern and northwestern New Caledonia, and in dense forests at elevations from 600 m or less to 900 m in Fiji.

Common Names and Uses. — Not recorded.

Notes. — *Cyphosperma* is readily distinguished from *Burretiokentia* and *Veillonia* in New Caledonia and from *Physokentia* in Fiji to New Britain, which share the characteristic incompletely encircling prophyll and sculptured endocarp and seed, by the lack of crownshaft and the long-pedunculate inflorescence with marcescent bracts and strongly pulvinate branches. *Alsmithia* also has a sculptured endocarp but differs in having very long petioles and a complete prophyll.

Taxonomic Accounts. — Beccari and Pichi-Sermolli (1955), Moore (1979), and Moore and Uhl (1984).

Plate. — *71B; Fig. G.18.*

154. VEILLONIA H. E. Moore, Gentes Herbarum 11: 299. 1978. Type: **V. alba** H. E. Moore.

Moderate, solitary, unarmed, pleonanthic, monoecious palm. Stem erect, somewhat expanded at the base and sometimes with a mass of exposed roots, green or gray-brown below, often white-waxy distally, leaf scars prominent, ± indented. Leaves regularly pinnate, spreading; sheaths tubular, forming a prominent, bulging crownshaft, white-waxy, densely covered in red-brown scales; petiole channeled adaxially, minutely brown-dotted, rounded abaxially; rachis angled adaxially, bearing brown scales, rounded abaxially; leaflets acute, acuminate, or the distalmost very briefly bifid, single-fold, abaxially with dot-like scales and scattered, medifixed or basifixed, twisted, membranous ramenta on the midrib and veins, midrib and 2 lateral veins prominent, transverse veinlets not ev-

ident. Inflorescences infrafoliar, branched to 1–2 orders basally, to 1 order distally, erect in bud, branches becoming pendulous, protandrous; peduncle very short, dorsiventrally compressed, white-waxy, tomentose; prophyll incompletely encircling the peduncle at insertion, shallowly 2-keeled laterally, with a short beak, often split into 2 halves, rather thin, often white-waxy, caducous; peduncular bract tubular, beaked, much exceeding the prophyll, woody; rachis longer than the peduncle, bearing spirally arranged, rounded or often acute, sometimes conspicuous bracts subtending branches and rachillae; rachillae long, tapering, and stiffly pendulous, bearing prominent, spreading, rounded bracts subtending triads in the lower ½ of the rachilla or more, and bearing paired or solitary staminate flowers distally; bracteoles surrounding the pistillate flowers prominent, sepallike. Staminate flowers symmetrical; sepals 3, distinct, broadly imbricate, slightly keeled dorsally; petals 3, distinct, valvate; stamens 6, filaments strongly inflexed at the apex in bud, anthers oblong, dorsifixed, bifid at base and apex, latrorse, the locules lacking a sterile central portion; pollen elliptic, monosulcate, with finely reticulate, tectate exine; pistillode longer than the stamens in bud, fluted-columnar, expanded into a rounded apex. Pistillate flowers subglobose, larger than the staminate; sepals 3, distinct, broadly imbricate, rounded; petals 3, distinct, imbricate except for the briefly valvate apices; staminodes 3, toothlike, borne at one side of the gynoecium; gynoecium ovoid, unilocular, uniovulate, stigmas 3, prominent, recurved at anthesis, the ovule pendulous, probably hemianatropous. Fruit eccentrically ovoid, with stigmatic remains subapical, drying with a pebbled surface; epicarp hard, minutely papillate, over a layer of sclereids, mesocarp soft, with numerous shining, red, ellipsoidal tannin cells and a few, pale, flat fibers, endocarp fragile, highly sculptured with an adaxial ridge and basal operculum framed by lateral, ± flat areas, and with 2 lateral and 2 abaxial irregular crests and a dorsal groove. Seed sculptured like the endocarp, with an elongate lateral hilum, endosperm homogeneous; embryo basal. Germination and eophyll not recorded. Cytology not studied.

Anatomy. — *Veillonia* shares features of leaf anatomy with *Campecarpus* and *Cyphophoenix* (see *Cyphophoenix*). Leaves of *Veillonia* lack palisade layers and have small fibrous strands and scattered tanniniferous cells in the center of the lamina (Uhl and Martens in prep.).

Distribution. — One species endemic to New Caledonia.

Ecology. — The genus is known only from the Panié Massif, where it occurs on gneissic or schistose soils.

Fossil record. — Unknown.

Common Names and Uses. — Not recorded.

Notes. — *Veillonia alba* is unusual in the Iguanurinae because of the minutely papillate epidermis of the fruit. It is most closely related to *Burretiokentia,* from which it differs in having symmetrical sta-

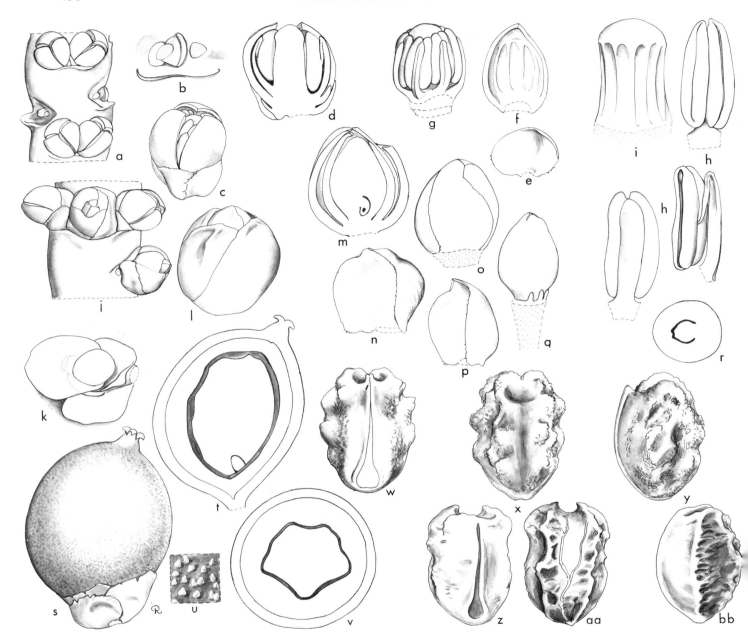

154.—**Veillonia. a,** portion of rachilla with paired staminate flowers ×3; **b,** dyad, staminate flowers removed to show bracteoles ×6; **c,** staminate bud ×6; **d,** staminate bud in vertical section ×6; **e,** staminate sepal, interior view ×6; **f,** staminate petal, interior view ×6; **g,** androecium and pistillode ×6; **h,** stamen in 3 views ×12; **i,** pistillode ×12; **j,** portion of rachilla with triads ×3; **k,** triad, flowers removed to show bracteoles and arrangement of flowers ×6; **l,** pistillate bud ×6; **m,** pistillate bud in vertical section ×6; **n,** pistillate petal ×6; **o,** pistillate bud, sepals removed ×6; **p,** pistillate petal ×6; **q,** gynoecium and staminodes ×6; **r,** ovary in cross-section ×12; **s,** fruit ×3; **t,** fruit in vertical section ×3; **u,** fruit wall, much enlarged; **v,** fruit in cross-section ×3; **w, x, y,** endocarp in 3 views ×3; **z, aa, bb,** seed in 3 views ×3. *Veillonia alba*: all from *Schmid 1615*.

minate flowers with a columnar pistillode longer than the stamens in bud and expanded into a capitate apex, anther sacs lacking the characteristic sterile connectivelike center of *Burretiokentia,* and the

leaf sheath, upper part of trunk, prophyll, and peduncular bract usually white-waxy.

Taxonomic Account.—Moore and Uhl (1984). *Plates.—71C.*

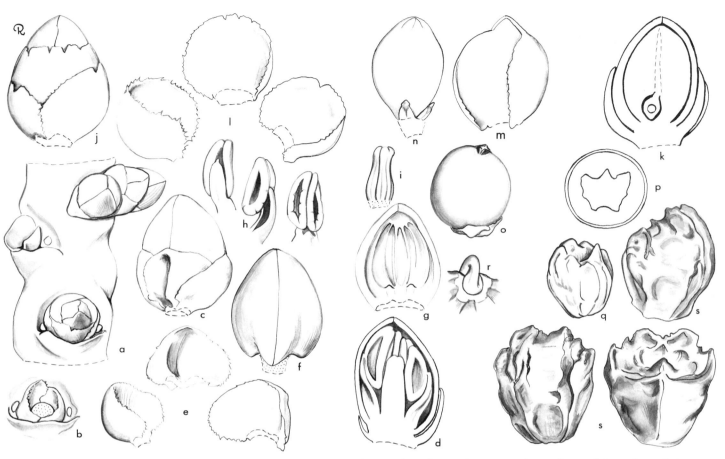

155.—**Burretiokentia. a,** portion of rachilla with complete triad, with staminate flowers fallen, and with all flowers fallen ×3; **b,** triad, flowers removed ×3; **c,** staminate bud ×6; **d,** staminate bud in vertical section ×6; **e,** staminate sepals ×6; **f,** staminate bud, sepals removed ×6; **g,** staminate petal, interior view ×6; **h,** stamen in 3 views ×6; **i,** pistillode ×6; **j,** pistillate bud ×6; **k,** pistillate bud in vertical section ×6; **l,** pistillate sepals ×6; **m,** pistillate petal ×6; **n,** gynoecium and staminodes ×6; **o,** fruit ×1½; **p,** fruit in cross-section ×1½; **q,** endocarp ×1½; **r,** operculum of endocarp ×3; **s,** seed in 3 views ×3. *Burretiokentia vieillardii*: all from *Moore et al. 9334.*

155. **BURRETIOKENTIA** Pichi-Sermolli in Beccari & Pichi-Sermolli, Webbia 11:122. 1955. Type: **B. vieillardii** (Brongniart & Gris) Pichi-Sermolli (*Kentia vieillardii* Brongniart & Gris).

Rhynchocarpa Beccari, Le Palme della Nuova Caledonia 37. 1920; and Webbia 5:105. 1921 (Non Schrader ex Endlicher 1839). Type: *R. vieillardii* (Brongniart & Gris) Beccari (*Kentia vieillardii* Brongniart & Gris) (=*Burretiokentia vieillardii* (Brongniart & Gris) Pichi-Sermolli).

Moderate to large, solitary, slender, unarmed, pleonanthic, monoecious palms. Stem erect with prominent nodal scars, green or brown, often slightly expanded basally, prickly adventitious roots sometimes present. Leaves regularly pinnate, spreading; sheaths tubular, usually forming a prominent crownshaft, more rarely split opposite the petiole, covered with scales or tomentum, obliquely lined; petiole short, shallowly channeled adaxially, rounded abaxially, margins sharp, densely scaly or minutely dotted; rachis angled adaxially, rounded abaxially, scaly or minutely dotted on both surfaces; leaflets stiff, acute, single-fold, 1(–2) lateral veins on each side prominent adaxially, the midrib and numerous veins prominent abaxially, densely scaly when young, becoming dotted in age, ramenta usually abundant along ribs, transverse veinlets not evident. Inflorescences infrafoliar, branched to 1(–2) orders, protandrous; peduncle short; prophyll incompletely encircling the peduncle at insertion, open abaxially, caducous; peduncular bract thin, inserted close to and not much exceeding the prophyll, completely enclosing the inflorescence in bud, also caducous; rachis angled, longer than the peduncle, bearing low bracts subtending glabrous to densely tomentose branches and rachillae; rachillae appearing rather stout, arching and spreading, bearing spirally arranged, low, rounded, somewhat spreading bracts subtending triads in the lower ½–⅔ of each rachilla and paired or solitary staminate flowers distally; bracteoles surrounding the pistillate flower prominent, nearly equal, sepallike, exceeding the subtending bract. Staminate flowers not at all or slightly to markedly asymmetrical, often developing well before the pistillate buds or these abortive and the inflorescence wholly staminate; sepals 3, distinct, imbricate, rounded, and the outer usually keeled dorsally; petals 3, distinct, valvate, about twice as long as the sepals, drying lined; stamens 6, filaments flattened, of uniform width or tapered distally from a broad base, inflexed at the apex in bud, anthers dorsifixed, briefly bifid at the apex, bifid nearly ½ their length basally, the connective dark, each locule with a central sterile connectivelike area marked with included raphides; pollen elliptic, monosulcate, with finely reticulate, tectate exine; pistillode ca. ½ as long as the stamens or a little more to equalling them in bud, trilobed, sometimes deeply so, not much expanded at apex. Pistillate flowers shorter than the staminate; sepals 3, distinct, broadly imbricate; petals 3, distinct, not much longer than sepals, imbricate except for the briefly valvate apices; staminodes 3, toothlike, borne at one side of the gynoecium; gynoecium unilocular, uniovulate, ovoid, stigmas 3, recurved, ovule pendulous, hemianatropous. Fruit globose to ellipsoidal, green when immature, becoming red at maturity, smooth when fresh, pebbled and usually irregularly shouldered and angled when dry, the stigmatic remains apical or eccentrically apical; epicarp thin, mesocarp with a dense layer of elongate, oblique sclereids over a densely tanniniferous layer and a few flat, longitudinal fibers against the endocarp, endocarp irregularly sculptured, with an adaxial keel and an abaxial groove between lateral ridges, operculum basal rounded. Seed irregular, sculptured like the endocarp, hilum linear, lateral, endosperm homogeneous; embryo basal. Germination not recorded; eophyll probably bifid. Cytology not studied.

Anatomy. — In leaf anatomy *Burretiokentia* is like *Moratia, Cyphokentia, Alloschmidia,* and *Basselinia* in having single adaxial and abaxial hypodermal layers. In *Burretiokentia* adaxial hypodermal cells are very large, twice as long and four to five times as wide as the epidermal cells (Uhl and Martens in prep.).

Distribution. — Two species in New Caledonia.

Ecology. — *B. vieillardii* is widely distributed from the southeast to northeast New Caledonia in moist forests on serpentine or schists. *B. hapala* occurs in wet forests or gallery forests on calcareous and schistose soils from 50–400 m in northern New Caledonia.

Common Names and Uses. — Not recorded.

Notes. — Distinguished by an incomplete prophyll and strikingly sculptured endocarp, *Burretiokentia* seems most closely related to *Veillonia* (see notes under that genus). *B. vieillardii* is one of the most common palms in New Caledonia; the prominently ringed glossy, green or brown stems are conspicuous.

Taxomomic Account. — Moore and Uhl (1984).

Plates. — 24D; 71D.

156. **PHYSOKENTIA** Beccari in Martelli, Atti della Societa Toscana de Scienze Naturali di Pisa, Memorie 44:152. 1934. Lectotype: **P. tete** (Beccari) Beccari (*Cyphosperma tete* Beccari) (see Burret 1935b).

Goniosperma Burret, Occasional Papers of the Bernice P. Bishop Museum 11(4):10. 1935. Type: *G. vitiense* Burret (=*Physokentia thurstonii* Beccari) (*Cyphosperma thurstonii* Beccari).

Solitary, small to moderate, unarmed, pleonanthic, monoecious palms. Stem erect, ringed with leaf scars, stilt roots conspicuously developed, forming a cone supporting the stem base. Leaves pinnate, neatly abscising; sheaths tubular, forming a conspicuous crownshaft, usually bearing a dense covering of ± caducous, floccose tomentum, the mouth lacking a ligule; petiole absent or short, ± rounded, variously clothed in scales and/or tomentum; rachis variously scaly or tomentose like the petiole; leaflets regularly arranged, single-fold, acute or acuminate (or minutely lobed in *P. tete*) or blade irregularly divided into 1-several-fold, narrow to broad, ± sigmoid leaflets, the proximal acute or acuminate, the distal, including the apical pair, shallowly lobed, the lobes corresponding to the adaxial ribs, blade adaxially glabrous or with minute, dotlike scales along the main veins, abaxially rather densely covered in minute, dotlike scales, the main ribs also bearing numerous conspicuous ramenta, transverse veinlets inconspicuous. Inflorescences solitary, infrafoliar, branching to 2 (rarely 3) orders proximally, to 1 order distally, apparently protandrous; peduncle short, winged at the base, narrow elliptic in cross-section; prophyll inserted near the base of the peduncle, open abaxially in bud, not completely encircling the peduncle at the insertion; peduncular bract inserted just above and exceeding the prophyll, completely encircling the peduncle, tubular, enclosing the inflorescence in bud, ± beaked, splitting abaxially, abscising with the prophyll at anthesis; rachis longer than the peduncle, but itself relatively short, bearing ca. 12–20, spirally arranged, first-order branches; rachis bracts inconspicuous; rachillae spreading, curved or ± pendulous, somewhat flexuous, ± angled, bearing spirally arranged triads of white to red flowers in the proximal ca. ⅓, distally bearing solitary or paired staminate flowers, rarely rachillae bearing only staminate flowers; rachilla bracts prominent, rounded to acute, often ± reflexed; bracteoles membranous, rounded, or rarely (*P. dennisii*) each prolonged into a slender process, sometimes ciliate-margined. Staminate flowers briefly pedicellate, ± asymmetrical; sepals 3, distinct, imbricate, ± broad, triangular, keeled, the margins often coarsely toothed; petals 3, distinct or very briefly joined at the base, valvate; stamens 6, filaments slender, elongate, prominently inflexed at the apex in bud; anthers oblong-linear, medifixed, versatile, latrorse; pollen elliptic, monosulcate, with finely reticulate or scabrate, tectate exine; pistillode conspicuous, elongate, conical or columnar, ± trifid. Pistillate flowers ± globular, sessile; sepals 3, distinct, imbricate; petals 3, distinct, broadly imbricate with short valvate triangular tips; staminodes 3, toothlike; gynoecium ovoid, unilocular, uniovulate, stigmas 3, short, recurved, ovule laterally attached, hemianatropous. Fruit globose or subglobose, red or black

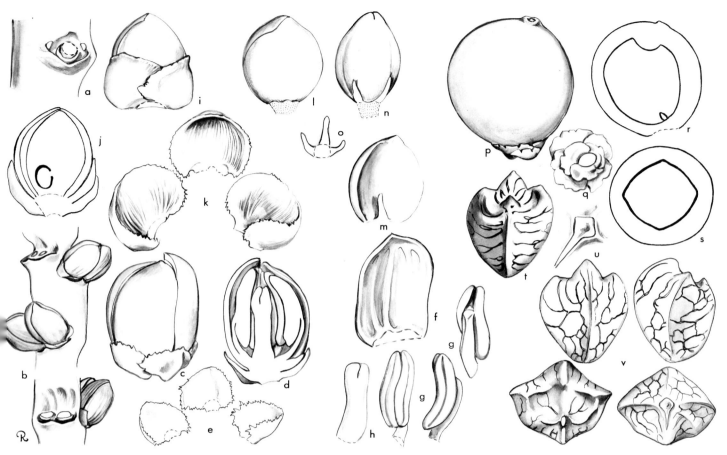

156.—**Physokentia. a,** portion of rachilla with triad, flowers removed ×3; **b,** portion of rachilla with paired staminate flowers in 2 views ×3; **c,** staminate bud ×6; **d,** staminate bud in vertical section ×6; **e,** staminate sepals ×6; **f,** staminate petal, interior view ×6; **g,** stamen in 3 views ×6; **h,** pistillode ×6; **i,** pistillate bud ×6; **j,** pistillate bud in vertical section ×6; **k,** pistillate sepals ×6; **l,** pistillate bud, sepals removed ×6; **m,** pistillate petal and staminode, interior view ×6; **n,** gynoecium and staminodes ×6; **o,** staminodes ×6; **p,** fruit ×1½; **q,** fruiting perianth ×1½; **r,** fruit in vertical section ×1½; **s,** fruit in cross-section ×1½; **t,** endocarp ×1½; **u,** operculum ×3; **v,** seed in 4 views ×1½. *Physokentia thurstonii:* **b–h,** *Moore & Koroiveibau 9347;* **p–v,** *Moore & Koroiveibau 9353; P. rosea:* **a** and **i–o,** *Moore & Koroiveibau 9363.*

at maturity, stigmatic remains eccentrically apical; perianth whorls persistent, epicarp smooth, or drying wrinkled, mesocarp fleshy with few flat fibers and numerous sclereids, easily separated from the endocarp, endocarp thin or thick, variously angled or ridged and sculptured, always with a prominent adaxial keel and a sharp to obtuse abaxial ridge, operculum to 4-angled. Seed conforming to the endocarp shape, laterally attached with elongate, narrow hilum, raphe branches ± horizontal, loosely anastomosing, endosperm homogeneous or ruminate; embryo basal. Germination not recorded; eophyll bifid. Cytology not studied.

Anatomy.—Not studied.

Distribution.—Seven species in the Fiji Islands, New Hebrides, Solomon Islands, and New Britain.

Ecology.—Confined to undergrowth of rain forest at low to high elevations; *P. whitmorei* is found in

forest developed on ultrabasic rock, and *P. dennisii* has been recorded on soils overlying limestone.

Common Names and Uses.—For common names see Moore (1969d).

Notes.—*Physokentia* is one of the most highly specialized members of the Iguanurinae. The incompletely encircling prophyll and highly sculptured endocarp resemble those of *Cyphosperma, Burretiokentia,* and *Veillonia. Alsmithia* also has a sculptured endocarp but the prophyll is complete.

Taxonomic Account.—Moore (1969d).

Fig.—G.23.

157. **GONIOCLADUS** Burret, Notizblatt des Botanischen Gartens und Museums zu Berlin-Dahlem 15:86. 1940. Type: **G. petiolatus** Burret.

Moderate, solitary, unarmed, pleonanthic, monoecious palm. Stem erect. Leaves pinnate, neatly abscising; sheaths tubular, forming a conspicuous crownshaft; petiole short, adaxially channeled, abaxially rounded; rachis densely covered with caducous, powdery indumentum; leaflets single-fold, apparently regularly arranged, acute or acuminate, adaxially minutely dotted with scales along ribs, abaxially paler and minutely dotted throughout, also with conspicuous ramenta along the midrib. Inflorescences infrafoliar, branched to 3 orders; peduncle short, flattened; prophyll thin, papery, glabrous, oblanceolate, with a well defined beak; peduncular bract inserted close to the prophyll, lanceolate, briefly acuminate, slightly longer than the prophyll, both caducous; branches glabrous, ± flattened; rachillae attenuate to an almost spinelike apex, bearing spirally arranged triads nearly to the tip. Staminate flower buds symmetrical, rounded; sepals 3 imbricate; petals 3, valvate; stamens 6; filaments very short, (?)erect in bud; pistillode columnar, flattened-capitate, scarcely exceeding the stamens. Pistillate flowers symmetrical; sepals 3, distinct, imbricate; petals 3, distinct, imbricate; staminodes few, small; gynoecium unilocular, uniovulate, ovule unknown. Young fruit with eccentric stigmatic remains; epicarp densely granulose when dry, mesocarp with dense transverse sclerosomes. Other parts unknown. Cytology not studied.

Anatomy.—Not studied.

Distribution.—One species, collected in 1937 on the Rairaimatuku Plateau, Viti Levu, Fiji. The holotype and duplicates were destroyed in Berlin during the Second World War. Attempts by H. E. Moore, Jr. to relocate the palm were unsuccessful, but *Physokentia rosea* was found at the type locality of *Goniocladus petiolatus* (Moore 1979).

Ecology.—*G. petiolatus* was collected in rain forest at an elevation of 1158 m.

Common Names and Uses.—Not recorded.

Notes.—Several features of the incomplete protologue suggest a strong affinity with *Physokentia* and indeed *P. rosea* grows at the type locality. However, *Goniocladus* differs from *P. rosea* in the inflorescence branching to three rather than two orders, in the rachillae bearing triads throughout most of their length, rather than in the proximal ¼–½, in the flattened, capitate rather than trifid pistillode, and in the fruit having transverse sclerosomes. Because of this *Goniocladus* is not included in synonymy with *Physokentia* but remains incompletely known.

Taxonomic Accounts.—Burret (1940), Moore (1979).

Oncospermatinae J. D. Hooker in Bentham & J. D. Hooker, Genera Plantarum 3:872, 874. 1883. ('*Oncospermeae*'). Type: **Oncosperma.**

Small to robust, spiny (at least when juvenile); crownshaft present or absent; leaves pinnate or pinnately ribbed; leaflets entire or praemorse; inflorescences inter- or infrafoliar, branched to 4 orders; triads rarely borne in pits; staminate flowers symmetrical or asymmetrical, rarely open early in development; pistillate flowers with imbricate petals; gynoecium pseudomonomerous; fruit with apical, lateral, or basal stigmatic remains; endocarp with a well defined operculum covering the embryo; embryo basal.

The Oncospermatinae includes eight genera, five of them found only in the Seychelles, two in the Mascarene Islands, and the eighth, *Oncosperma,* in Sri Lanka, Southeast Asia, and west Malesia with one or two species transgressing Wallace's Line (Map 43). The whole subtribe displays remarkable diversity in floral and fruit morphology and, indeed, even in habit. *Deckenia* is noteworthy for the presence of "congenitally" open flowers. The absence of the subtribe in Madagascar seems to emphasize further the extraordinary nature of the island's palm flora. Relationships of this subtribe are discussed above under the Iguanurinae.

Key to the Genera of the Oncospermatinae

1 Leaves with leaflets all single-fold, acute or acuminate; sheaths usually forming a conspicuous crownshaft; inflorescence usually infrafoliar; peduncular bract enclosed by the prophyll, both inserted close together, splitting and usually caducous at anthesis; peduncle short, usually ± equalling the rachis; rachillae straight or coiled and twisted in bud; staminate flowers asymmetrical, sepals acute ... 2

1 Leaves with blades undivided, bifid, or irregularly to regularly divided into leaflets, these usually with more than 1 rib, acute, bifid or praemorse; sheaths not forming a conspicuous crownshaft; inflorescences interfoliar or becoming infrafoliar in age; peduncular bract caducous, inserted some distance from the prophyll and exceeding it, prophyll persistent; peduncle elongate, usually much longer than the rachis; rachillae straight in bud; staminate flowers symmetrical or asymmetrical, sepals rounded .. 5

2 Triads borne in six vertical rows, each triad subtended by a saucerlike bract, the bracts obscured by the staminate flowers, but becoming conspicuous when the flowers have fallen; fruit ovoid with apical or eccentrically apical stigmatic remains, perianth persistent, ± ½ as high as the fruit; seed with homogeneous endosperm. Mascarene Islands .... 161. **Tectiphiala**

2 Rachilla bracts not saucerlike; fruit ellipsoidal to globose, with lateral to basal stigmatic remains, perianth persistent, less than half as high as the fruit; endosperm homogeneous or ruminate 3

3 Staminate flower open early in development with ca. 9 stamens, scarcely exceeding the petals; pistillode conspicuous, slender, elongate, trifid; fruit ellipsoidal with basal stigmatic remains. Seychelles .... 158. **Deckenia**

3 Staminate flower closed in bud, stamens 6–12; pistillode shorter than the stamens and petals; fruit globose to ellipsoidal with lateral stigmatic remains 4

4 Stamens exserted at anthesis; pistillode minutely trifid; seed with homogeneous endosperm. Mascarene Islands .... 159. **Acanthophoenix**

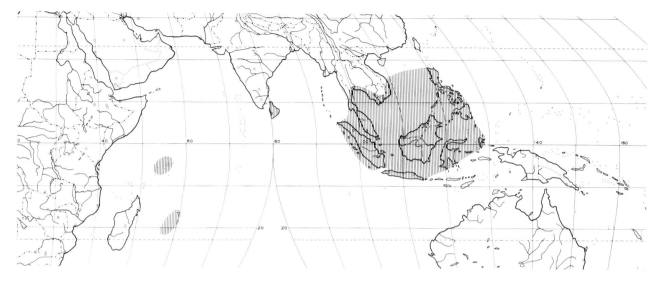

Map 43.—Distribution of Oncospermatinae.

4 Stamens included at anthesis; pistillode deeply trifid; seed with ruminate endosperm. Sri Lanka to Sulawesi and Moluccas .... 160. **Oncosperma**
5 Leaflets or blade praemorse; staminate flowers with petals about twice as long as the sepals; stamens 6; pistillode large, truncate, 3-angled and lobed, about as high as the petals 6
5 Leaflets or blade lobes acute or acuminate; staminate flowers with petals about 4 times as long as the sepals; stamens 18 or more; pistillode not truncate, angled or lobed 7
6 Leaf blade appearing almost undivided, the leaflets scarcely separated; fruit large, 2–2.5 cm in diameter, the endocarp conspicuously ridged and crested; seed ± ridged, raphe branches anastomosing. Seychelles .... 162. **Verschaffeltia**
6 Leaflets clearly separated; fruit small, ca. 5 mm in diameter or less; endocarp not ridged; seed not ridged, the raphe branches few, ascending. Seychelles .. 163. **Roscheria**
7 Leaf blade usually undivided although lobed marginally, the lobes bifid; inflorescence branching to 2 orders; staminate flowers asymmetrical; stamens ca. 18, the filaments tapered, anthers ± versatile; pistillode small, slender; fruit ovoid. Seychelles .... 164. **Phoenicophorium**
7 Leaf pinnate, with rather distant, mostly 2–3-ribbed, acute or acuminate leaflets; inflorescence branching to 1 order; staminate flowers symmetrical; stamens 40–50, the filaments expanded distally, anthers not versatile; pistillode ovoid, minutely trifid; fruit subglobose. Seychelles .... 165. **Nephrosperma**

158. DECKENIA H. A. Wendland ex Seemann, Gardeners' Chronicle 1870:561. 1870. Type: **D. nobilis** H. A. Wendland ex Seemann.

Robust, solitary, spiny, pleonanthic, monoecious palm. Stem erect, tall, spiny when juvenile, becoming distally unarmed at maturity, conspicuously ringed with leaf scars, slightly swollen at the base, with abundant adventitious roots. Leaves pinnate, neatly abscising; sheaths tubular, forming a well defined crownshaft, densely spiny when young, unarmed or minutely roughened near the petiole at maturity, densely white-tomentose; petiole relatively short, flattened or channeled adaxially, abaxially rounded, bearing abundant, caducous, shaggy hairs, also spiny in juveniles; rachis robust, gradually tapering, hairy and, in juveniles, spiny like the petiole; leaflets numerous, all single-fold, regularly arranged, rather stiff, elongate, acuminate, somewhat plicate, adaxially bearing caducous tomentum when young, abaxially densely covered with minute, dotlike scales and abundant, conspicuous ramenta along the major longitudinal veins, transverse veinlets obscure. Inflorescences solitary, infrafoliar, erect in bud, branching to 2 orders at the base, to 1 order distally, protandrous; peduncle relatively short, winged at the base, elliptic in cross-section, glabrous; prophyll inserted just above the base of the peduncle, tubular, elliptic, very briefly beaked, 2-keeled, splitting along one face, caducous, usually very densely armed with erect, rather soft, short to long, golden-colored spines; peduncular bract very similar to the prophyll, but less prominently 2-keeled, also caducous; rachis longer than the peduncle, it and its branches twisted in bud, becoming straight, rachis and peduncle remaining erect, the branches becoming pendulous; first-order branches numerous, rather crowded, spirally arranged; rachillae numerous, elongate, pendulous, flexuous, bearing rather crowded, spirally arranged, superficial triads throughout their length except at the extreme tips. Staminate flowers ± globular, open early in development; sepals 3, narrow, triangular, keeled, joined briefly at the base; petals 3, triangular, sometimes briefly connate in a somewhat stalklike base; stamens 6–9, filaments very short and broad, adnate to the petals, anthers medifixed, tightly recurved and/or twisted, latrorse; pollen elliptic, monosulcate, with intectate, clavate exine; pistillode columnar longer than the petals, trifid, very conspicuous at first, becoming less conspicuous at anthesis. Pistillate flowers globular; sepals 3, distinct, rounded, imbricate; petals 3, distinct, rounded, imbricate, with minute, triangular, valvate tips; staminodes 6, minute, toothlike; gynoecium globular or ovoid, unilocular, uniovulate, stigmas 3, re-

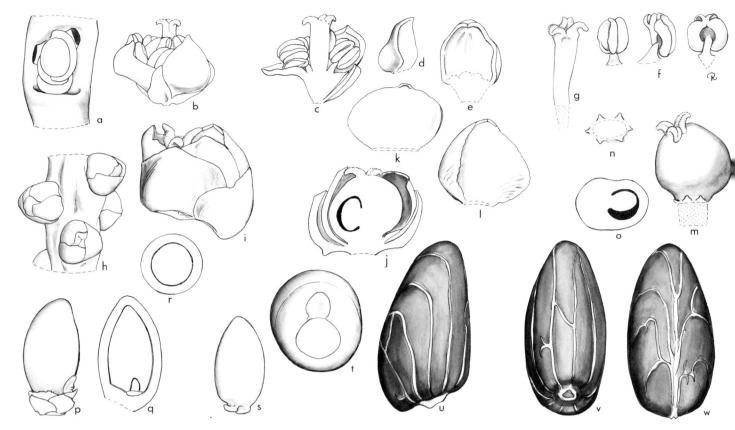

158.—**Deckenia. a,** portion of rachilla with triad, flowers removed to show bracteoles ×6; **b,** staminate flower ×12; **c,** staminate flower in vertical section ×12; **d,** staminate sepal ×12; **e,** staminate petal, interior view ×12; **f,** stamen in 3 views ×12; **g,** pistillode ×12; **h,** portion of rachilla with pistillate buds ×6; **i,** pistillate flower ×12; **j,** pistillate flower in vertical section ×12; **k,** pistillate sepal ×12; **l,** pistillate petal, interior view ×12; **m,** gynoecium and staminodes ×12; **n,** staminodes ×12; **o,** ovary in cross-section ×12; **p,** fruit ×3; **q,** fruit in vertical section ×3; **r,** fruit in cross-section ×3; **s,** endocarp ×3; **t,** base of endocarp and operculum ×6; **u, v, w,** seed in 3 views ×6. *Deckenia nobilis:* **a-g,** *Vaughan 806*; **h-o,** *Furtado 31123*; **p-w,** *Squibb s.n.*

flexed, ovule laterally attached, ?hemianatropous. Fruit relatively small, narrowly ovoid, black at maturity, perianth whorls persistent, the stigmatic remains conspicuous as an eccentric, basally rounded pad; epicarp smooth, drying longitudinally ridged, mesocarp thin, with few, large, longitudinal fibers corresponding to the ridges when dry, endocarp thin, cartilaginous, with a basal circular operculum. Seed very narrowly ovoid, basally attached, with a small circular hilum, and sparse raphe branches only rarely anastomosing, endosperm homogeneous; embryo basal. Germination adjacent ligular; eophyll bifid. Cytology not known.

Anatomy.—Leaf, petiole, root (Tomlinson 1961).

Distribution.—One species confined to the Seychelles Islands.

Ecology.—*D. nobilis* occurs at altitudes from sea level to nearly 600 m, but grows gregariously mostly on knolls and ridges at about 300 m altitude; its massive litter prevents regeneration and there is usually no undergrowth under dense stands.

Common Names and Uses.—Cabbage palm, palmiste. The "cabbage" is eaten and the leaf sheaths used for making containers.

Notes.—*Deckenia* is more closely related to *Acanthophoenix* of the Mascarenes than to the other Seychelles members of the Oncospermatinae. The staminate flowers are unusual in opening early in development and in their globular shape and ± connate petals with adnate stamen filaments and curved or twisted anthers.

Taxonomic Account.—Bailey (1942).

Plates.—*26B; 72A.*

159. **ACANTHOPHOENIX** H. A. Wendland, Flore des Serres et des Jardins de l'Europe 16:181. 1867. Lectotype: **A. rubra** (Bory) H. A. Wendland (*Areca rubra* Bory) (see Beccari and Pichi-Sermolli 1955).

Robust, solitary, spiny, pleonanthic, monoecious palm. Stem erect, usually unarmed, rarely spiny on new growth,

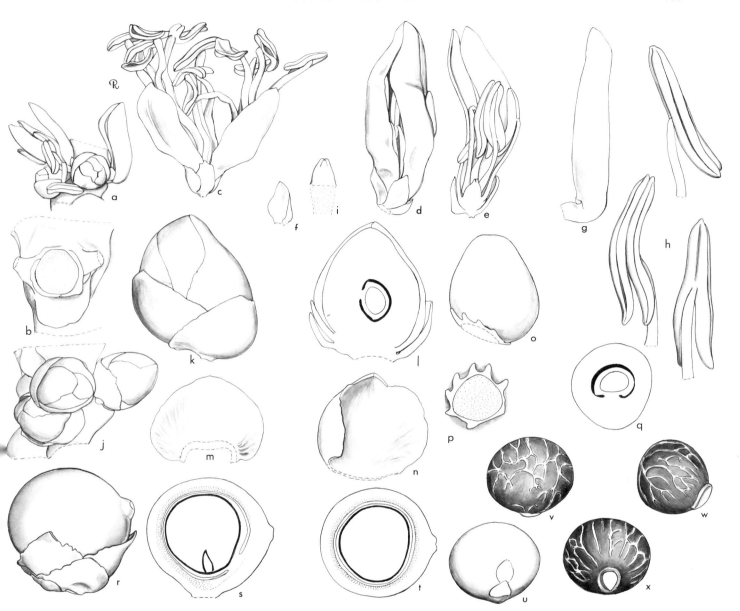

159.—**Acanthophoenix. a,** portion of rachilla with triads ×3; **b,** triad, flowers removed to show bracteoles ×6; **c,** staminate flower ×3; **d,** staminate bud ×6; **e,** staminate bud in vertical section ×6; **f,** staminate sepal ×6; **g,** staminate petal ×6; **h,** stamen in 3 views ×12; **i,** pistillode ×12; **j,** rachilla in pistillate flower ×3; **k,** pistillate bud ×6; **l,** pistillate bud in vertical section ×6; **m,** pistillate sepal ×6; **n,** pistillate petal ×6; **o,** gynoecium and staminodes ×6; **p,** staminodes and base of gynoecium ×6; **q,** ovary in cross-section ×6; **r,** fruit ×3; **s,** fruit in vertical section ×3; **t,** fruit in cross-section ×3; **u,** endocarp with operculum ×3; **v, w, x,** seed in 3 views ×3. *Acanthophoenix rubra*: **a, b** and **d–i,** *Vaughan 852*; **c** and **j–x,** *Vaughan 851a.*

conspicuously ringed with leaf scars, slightly swollen at the base. Leaves pinnate, neatly abscising; sheaths tubular, forming a well defined crownshaft, bearing abundant tomentum and black, rather fragile spines, rarely very sparsely armed, ligule absent; petiole rather short, adaxially flattened or shallowly channeled, abaxially rounded, tomentose or glabrous, ± unarmed to densely armed with black spines, especially in juveniles; rachis glabrous or scaly, tomentose or bearing ramenta; leaflets elongate, single-fold, acute, regularly arranged, ± pendulous, with white wax abaxially, adaxially usually armed with slender, bulbous-based bristles along the midrib near the base, rarely also armed abaxially, abaxially bearing minute dotlike scales and conspicuous ramenta along the main vein near the insertion, sometimes with white wax, transverse veinlets obscure. Inflorescences solitary, infrafoliar, protandrous, erect in bud, branching to 2 orders near the base, to 1 order distally; peduncle short, winged at the base, tomentose to becoming glabrous, unarmed or armed with flat, dark brown, straight or sinuous spines; prophyll inserted near the base of the peduncle, tubular, elliptic, briefly beaked, 2-keeled, completely enclosing the inflorescence in bud, unarmed or rarely spiny, glabrous or tomentose, splitting along one face, deciduous; peduncular bract 1, inserted just above and similar to the prophyll but less conspicuously 2-keeled, also caducous; rachis much longer than the peduncle, rachis bracts very inconspicuous, low, triangular, glabrous to tomentose, often spiny; first-order branches spirally arranged, rather distant; rachillae ivory-white to reddish at anthesis, becoming green in fruit, elongate, pendulous, sinuous, bearing very inconspicuous to prominent, spirally arranged, triangular bracts, each subtending a triad throughout the rachilla length except at the very tip where subtending solitary or paired staminate flowers; floral bracteoles low, very inconspicuous. Staminate flowers often briefly pedicellate, asymmetrical, white, cream-colored to red; sepals 3, distinct or briefly connate, imbricate, short, acute, ± keeled; petals 3, basally ± briefly connate, valvate, 3–4 times as long as the sepals, ± elliptic, fleshy; stamens (4–) 6–12, exserted at anthesis, filaments slender to wide, elongate, often coiled in bud but not inflexed, anthers dorsifixed, linear, basally sagittate, versatile, latrorse; pollen elliptic, monosulcate, with tectate, reticulate exine; pistillode ± ovoid, short, briefly to deeply trifid. Pistillate flowers ± ovoid; sepals 3, distinct, imbricate, broad, rounded; petals 3, distinct, imbricate except for the minute, valvate, triangular tips; staminodes 6–9, toothlike or absent; gynoecium unilocular, uniovulate, ovoid, stigmas broad, ovule large, pendulous, campylotropous. Fruit borne with persistent perianth whorls, ellipsoidal to subglobose, black at maturity, with lateral to subapical stigmatic remains; epicarp smooth or slightly pebbled when dry, mesocarp with tanniniferous parenchyma overlying a shell of short sclereids, external to a layer of tanniniferous parenchyma with included thin, flat, longitudinal fibers, endocarp thin, crustaceous, fragile, with circular basal operculum. Seed globose, attached laterally near the base, hilum circular, raphe branches ascending and anastomosing, endosperm homogeneous; embryo basal. Germination adjacent-ligular; eophyll bifid or pinnate. $n = 16$ (Essig 1971b). $n = 18$ (Sarkar 1970).

Anatomy. — Not studied.

Distribution. — One perplexingly variable species confined to Mauritius and Réunion, once common, now exceedingly rare in the wild; elsewhere cultivated, but not very common.

Ecology. — Grows at altitudes from near sea level to 1350 m; the wild populations are so small and disturbed that few generalizations can be made about its ecology.

Common Names and Uses. — Palmiste rouge. The "cabbage" is eaten, this being responsible for the palm's near extinction.

Notes. — *Acanthophoenix* is most closely related to

Tectiphiala and *Deckenia* but distinct, most especially, in the structure of the staminate flower.

Taxonomic Account. — Moore and Guého (1980).

Plates. — *26A; 72B.*

160. **ONCOSPERMA** Blume, Bulletin des Sciences Physiques et Naturelles en Néerlande 1:64. 1838. Type: *O. filamentosum* Blume = **O. tigillarium** (Jack) Ridley (*Areca tigillaria* Jack).

Keppleria C. F. Meisner, Plantarum Vascularium Genera 1:355; 2:266. 1842 (Non Martius ex Endlicher 1837). Type: *K. tigillaria* (Jack) C. F. Meisner (*Areca tigillaria* Jack).

Tall, usually clustered, spiny, pleonanthic, monoecious palms. Stem erect, often very tall, becoming bare, ringed with leaf scars, frequently armed with scattered or dense, robust spines, the spines tending to erode with age, in one species (*O. fasciculatum*) the stems sometimes branching aerially. Leaves pinnate, neatly abscising; leaf sheaths tubular, closely sheathing, forming a well defined crownshaft, bearing abundant tomentum and spines of varying lengths, the distal margins tending to tatter irregularly; petiole usually robust, adaxially concave or flattened, abaxially rounded, usually densely armed with short to long spines and indumentum; rachis adaxially angled, rounded abaxially; marginal reins sometimes well developed and persisting as pendulous strips at the base of the rachis, leaflets very numerous, single-fold, acute or acuminate, regularly arranged, pendulous or not, or distinctly grouped and held in different planes (*O. fasciculatum*), lacking spines, bearing bands of caducous scales adaxially, abaxially with ramenta along the midvein, and sometimes with abundant dotlike scales. Inflorescences solitary, infrafoliar, branching to 2 orders near the base, to 1 order distally, protandrous, erect in bud; peduncle short, broad, winged at the base, horizontal at anthesis, sparsely to densely tomentose, unarmed or sparsely to densely armed with straight spines; prophyll inserted just above the base of the peduncle, robust, tubular, flattened, 2-keeled, briefly beaked, completely enclosing the inflorescence until anthesis, coriaceous to ± woody, densely indumentose, very sparsely to very densely covered in short or long, straight or twisted spines; peduncular bract 1, inserted just above and similar to the prophyll but only slightly 2-keeled and usually more sparsely armed; rachis longer than the peduncle, bearing few to numerous, pendulous, first-order branches; rachis bracts very inconspicuous; rachillae long, slender to rather robust, flexuous, pendulous, glabrous, bearing spirally arranged, low triangular bracts each subtending a triad, or in the distal portion of the rachilla, subtending solitary or paired staminate flowers. Staminate flowers asymmetrical, sessile or sometimes slightly stalked at the base; sepals 3, ± acute, keeled, imbricate, basally briefly connate or ± distinct; petals 3, acute or acuminate, valvate, much longer than the sepals, distinct or briefly connate at the base; stamens shorter than the petals, 6–9 (?12 recorded, but not found by us), briefly epipetalous or ± free, the filaments short, thick, sometimes connate at the base in a very short ring, an-

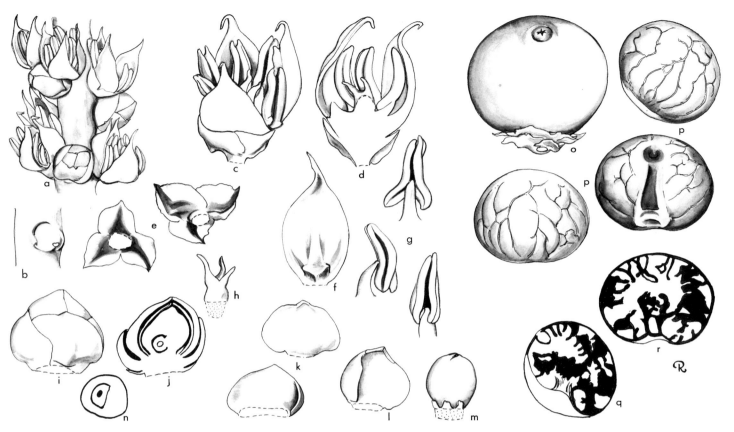

160.—**Oncosperma. a,** portion of rachilla with triads ×3; **b,** triad, flowers removed ×3; **c,** staminate flower ×6; **d,** staminate flower in vertical section ×6; **e,** staminate calyx in 2 views ×6; **f,** staminate petal, interior view ×6; **g,** stamen in 3 views ×6; **h,** pistillode ×6; **i,** pistillate bud ×6; **j,** pistillate bud in vertical section ×6; **k,** pistillate sepal, exterior and interior views ×6; **l,** pistillate petal ×6; **m,** gynoecium and staminodes ×6; **n,** ovary in cross-section ×6; **o,** fruit ×3; **p,** seed in 3 views ×3; **q,** seed in vertical section ×3; **r,** seed in cross-section ×3. *Oncosperma tigillarium:* **a-n,** *Moore & Meijer 9183;* **o-r,** *Moore & Meijer 9221.*

thers ± medifixed, basally sagittate, latrorse; pollen elliptic or circular, monosulcate or sometimes trichotomosulcate, with tectate exine bearing supratectal, knoblike processes; pistillode shorter or longer than the stamens, deeply trifid. Pistillate flowers ± globular; sepals 3, distinct, rounded, imbricate; petals 3, distinct, rounded, imbricate at the base, the tips valvate; staminodes 6 (? always), very small, toothlike; gynoecium unilocular, uniovulate, ± globose or ovoid, the stigmas apical, scarcely prominent, ovule form unknown. Fruit spherical, dark blue-black, with lateral or subapical stigmatic remains; epicarp smooth or pebbled, mesocarp thinly fleshy, without fibers, endocarp thin, crustaceous, closely adherent to the seed, with a round basal operculum. Seed attached by an elongate lateral hilum, raphe branches anastomosing, partially embedded in the endosperm, endosperm deeply ruminate; embryo subbasal. Germination adjacent-ligular; eophyll bifid. $n = 16$ (*O. tigillarium* as *O. filamentosum,* Sharma and Sarkar 1957).

Anatomy.—Leaf, root (Tomlinson 1961).

Distribution.—Five species, one endemic to Sri Lanka, two endemic to the Philippines, and two widespread in Southeast Asia and west Malesia, reaching Sulawesi, the Philippines, and western Moluccas.

Ecology.—*O. tigillarium* is characteristic of the landward fringe of mangrove forest, and is also rarely found on poor sandy soils inland; *O. horridum, O. platyphyllum* and *O. gracilipes* are characteristic of hilly sites inland. *O. fasciculatum* occurs on steep slopes at altitudes of 300–1000 m above sea level. Species of *Oncosperma* frequently occur gregariously and are very conspicuous; their heavy, spiny litter must play an important role in sylvigenic cycles. Little is known of the natural history of these common palms. (See House 1984).

Fossil Record.—Fruits attributed to *Oncosperma* occur in the Eocene London Clay flora of Great Britain (see Chandler 1961–64); pollen of *Oncosperma* has been reported from Oligocene deposits in Borneo (Muller 1964, 1970).

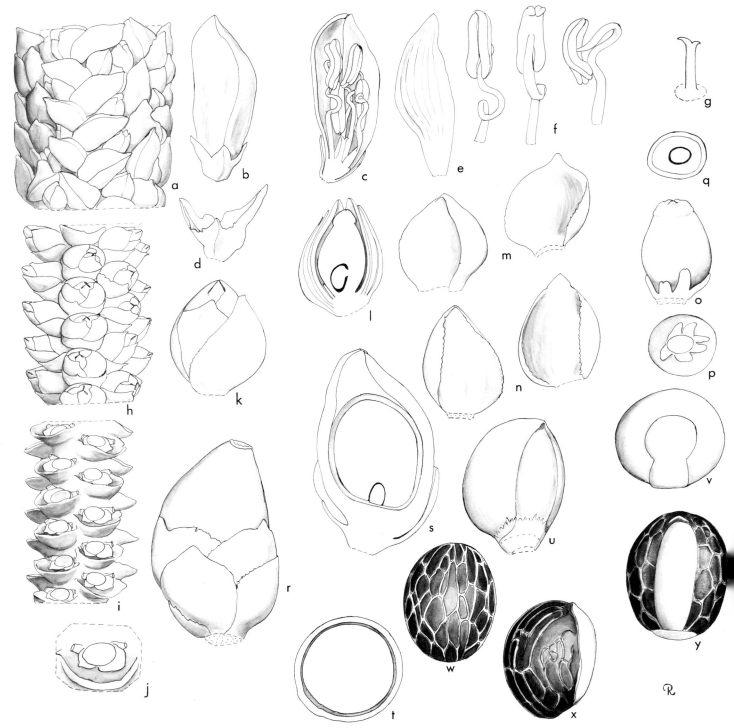

161.—**Tectiphiala. a,** portion of rachilla in staminate bud ×2; **b,** staminate bud ×4½; **c,** staminate bud in vertical section ×4½; **d,** staminate calyx ×7½; **e,** staminate petal, exterior view ×4½; **f,** stamen in 3 views ×6; **g,** pistillode ×7½; **h,** portion of rachilla in pistillate bud ×2; **i,** portion of rachilla, flowers removed to show prominent subtending bracts ×2; **j,** triad, flowers removed to show bracteoles and staminate pedicels ×4½; **k,** pistillate bud ×4½; **l,** pistillate bud in vertical section ×4½; **m,** pistillate sepal in 2 views ×4½; **n,** pistillate petal in 2 views ×4½; **o,** gynoecium and staminodes ×4½; **p,** staminodes at base of gynoecium ×4½; **q,** ovary in cross-section ×4½; **r,** fruit ×4½; **s,** fruit in vertical section ×4½; **t,** fruit in cross-section ×4½; **u,** endocarp ×4½; **v,** endocarp with operculum ×4½; **w, x, y,** seed in 3 views ×4½. *Tectiphiala ferox:* all from *Moore & Guého 9925.*

Common Names and Uses.—Nibung (*O. tigillarium*), bayas (*O. horridum*). The "cabbage" of most species is excellent and widely collected. The trunks of *O. tigillarium* are extremely durable and have been used (with spines removed) as telegraph poles, and split as flooring. Sheaths are sometimes used as buckets. Despite their spines all species are very elegant ornamentals.

Notes.—The affinities of *Oncosperma* are with *Tectiphiala*, *Deckenia*, and *Acanthophoenix* rather than with the other members of the subtribe. These genera share regularly pinnate leaves, distinct crownshafts, similar and caducous prophylls and peduncular bracts, rather short peduncles, and asymmetrical staminate flowers.

Taxonomic Account.—There is no recent overview of the genus.

Plate.—72C; Fig. G.23.

161. TECTIPHIALA H. E. Moore, Gentes Herbarum 11(4):285. 1978. Type: **T. ferox** H. E. Moore.

Moderate, solitary or clustered, spiny, pleonanthic, monoecious palm. Stem erect, bearing persistent leaf bases basally, distally free of leaf bases, ringed with leaf scars and abundant long spines with bulbous bases. Leaves pinnate, neatly abscising in mature individuals; sheaths tubular, forming a crownshaft, bearing an untidy ligule, and very densely covered in spines of varying length and abundant dark hairs; petiole rather short, adaxially with short spines, abaxially hairy; rachis bearing stiff hairs on both surfaces or on the adaxial surface alone; leaflets singlefold, very coriaceous, acute, arranged in close or distant fascicles, and fanned within the groups, adaxially glabrous, abaxially with a very dense covering of white scales, the midnerve bearing scattered ramenta, transverse veinlets obscure. Inflorescences solitary, infrafoliar, erect in bud, becoming ± pendulous, branching to 1 order, protandrous; peduncle covered in short spines at the base, above the insertion of the peduncular bract bearing a variety of short to very long spines; prophyll inserted just above the base of the peduncle, tubular, 2-keeled, completely enclosing the inflorescence in bud, splitting along the ventral midline and abscising, densely covered in stiff dark hairs; peduncular bract 1, inserted just above the prophyll, similarly hairy, abscising before anthesis; rachis scarcely evident; rachillae 3–5, congested at the apex of the peduncle, straight or flexuous, flattened and spiny at the base; rachilla bracts arranged in ca. 6 vertical rows throughout most of the rachilla length, prominent, approximate, projecting, saucerlike, rounded, each subtending a triad except at the very tip of the rachilla where subtending solitary or paired staminate flowers; bracteoles surrounding the pistillate flower unequal, one much larger than the other. Staminate flowers asymmetrical, acute, very briefly stalked, obscuring the rachilla bracts; sepals 3, often unequal, acute, briefly connate at the base; petals 3, distinct, strongly nerved when dry, angled, acute, valvate; stamens 6(–7), ± equalling the petals, filaments ± cylindrical, ± twisted and coiled, erect at the tip, anthers dorsifixed, briefly bifid at the tip, deeply bifid at the base, latrorse; pollen elliptic to nearly circular, monosulcate, with tectate, reticulate to scrobiculate exine; pistillode usually apparent, ½ as long as the stamens, trifid or oblique. Pistillate flowers in bud ± obscured by the staminate flowers; sepals 3, distinct, broadly imbricate, ± acute; petals 3; distinct, scarcely exceeding the sepals, broadly imbricate with briefly valvate tips; staminodes 6(–7), small, toothlike or linear; gynoecium ovoid, unilocular, uniovulate, the stigmas not prominent, ovule large, pendulous, probably hemianatropous. Fruit asymmetrically ovoid, dark blue-black, with apical stigmatic remains; epicarp smooth, underlain by longitudinal sclereids over a layer of tannin cells, endocarp thin with round basal operculum. Seed attached by an elongate elliptical hilum, raphe branches anastomosing, endosperm homogeneous; embryo basal. Germination and eophyll not known. Cytology not studied.

Anatomy.—Not studied.

Distribution.—A single species endemic to Mauritius.

Ecology.—*Tectiphiala* grows in relict scrub in mostly wet, more or less acid situations at elevations of ca. 570–650 m.

Common Names and Uses.—Common names not recorded. The "cabbage" is edible.

Notes.—*Tectiphiala* is most closely related to *Acanthophoenix* but differs especially in the remarkable saucerlike bracts that subtend the triads of the flowers.

Taxonomic Account.—Moore (1978b).

Plate.—26C.

162. VERSCHAFFELTIA H. A. Wendland, L'Illustration Horticole 12 (Miscellanées):5. 1865. Type: **V. splendida** H. A. Wendland.

Regelia Hortorum ex H. A. Wendland, L'Illustration Horticole 12 (Miscellanées) 6. 1865 (Non Schauer 1843). Type: *R. magnifica* Hortorum ex H. A. Wendland (= *Verschaffeltia splendida* H. A. Wendland).

Moderate, solitary, spiny when young, becoming less spiny at maturity, pleonanthic, monoecious palm. Stem erect, becoming bare, conspicuously ringed with leaf scars, the juvenile very densely armed with long black spines, the adult more sparsely armed with rings of reflexed spines, the base of the trunk supported on a cone of robust stilt roots. Leaves large, neatly abscising, bifid, pinnately ribbed and lobed, irregularly split into approximate several-fold leaflets; sheath becoming open, not forming a crownshaft, very densely black-spiny in juveniles, unarmed in adults, the margins irregularly ligulelike; petiole short, glabrous, heavily armed as is the rachis in juveniles, unarmed in adults, adaxially deeply grooved, abaxially rounded; blade unsplit in juveniles, irregularly split in adults, the margins deeply lobed up to ½ the blade depth into reduplicate segments, the segment tips irregularly praemorse, blade adaxially glabrous, abaxially with sparse, minute, dotlike

162.—**Verschaffeltia. a,** distal portion of rachilla with staminate buds and scars ×4½; **b,** staminate flower at anthesis ×12; **c,** staminate bud ×12; **d,** staminate bud in vertical section ×12; **e,** staminate sepals in 2 views ×12; **f,** staminate bud, sepals removed ×12; **g,** staminate petal, interior view ×12; **h,** stamen in 3 views ×12; **i,** pistillode ×12; **j,** basal portion of rachilla with triads, staminate flowers removed (top), all flowers removed (bottom), to show scars and bracteoles ×7½; **k,** pistillate flower ×12; **l,** pistillate flower in vertical section ×12; **m,** pistillate sepal in 2 views ×12; **n,** pistillate flower, sepals removed ×12; **o,** pistillate petal ×12; **p,** gynoecium and staminodes ×12; **q,** ovary in cross-section ×12; **r,** fruit ×1½; **s,** endocarp ×1½; **t,** base of endocarp and operculum ×1½; **u,** endocarp in vertical section ×1½; **v,** endocarp in cross-section ×1½; **w, x, y,** seed in 3 views ×1½. *Verschaffeltia splendida:* **a-q,** *Moore 10098;* **r,** *Squibb 4963;* **s-y,** *Moore s.n.*

scales and conspicuous, large, tattered ramenta along adaxial ribs, transverse veinlets obscure. Inflorescences solitary, interfoliar, branching to 2 (rarely 3) orders proximally, 1 order distally, protandrous; peduncle elongate, ± rounded in cross-section, densely tomentose like other inflorescence axes, winged at the base; prophyll inserted some distance from the base of the peduncle, very large, ± persistent, coriaceous, tubular, 2-keeled, the keels tending to become irregularly split or toothed, apically splitting to almost ½ the length, unarmed, bearing scattered scales; peduncular bract 1, inserted some distance above the prophyll, deciduous, similar to the prophyll but thinner and not 2-keeled; rachis shorter than the peduncle; rachis bracts minute, triangular, inconspicuous; first-order branches numerous, with a swollen base and short bare section; rachillae numerous, spreading, flexuous or rigid, somewhat sinuous, bearing spirally arranged superficial triads except at the very tip where bearing solitary or paired staminate flowers. Staminate flowers small, globular, symmetrical; sepals 3, distinct, imbricate, rounded; petals 3, distinct, ± broadly triangular, valvate, ± twice as long as sepals; stamens 6, filaments distinct, ± fleshy, rather short, anthers rounded, medifixed, ± versatile, latrorse; pollen elliptic, monosulcate, with reticulate, tectate exine; pistillode large, truncate, 3-angled, trifid, about as long as the petals. Pistillate flowers larger than the staminate, ± globular; sepals 3, distinct, imbricate, ± broad, rounded, irregularly splitting; petals 3, distinct, broad, rounded, imbricate, with very short, triangular, valvate tips; staminodes 6, with flattened, ribbonlike filaments and wide, flattened tips; gynoecium ovoid, unilocular, uniovulate, stigmas 3, short, reflexed, ovule laterally attached, ?hemianatropous. Fruit 1-seeded, moderate, spherical, brownish green, perianth whorls persistent, stigmatic remains basal; epicarp smooth, roughened when dry, mesocarp with a crustose layer just below the epicarp, and relatively thin flesh beneath, fibers sparse attached to endocarp, endocarp thin, cartilaginous, bearing conspicuous, irregular flanges and ridges, and a rounded basal operculum. Seed conforming to the endocarp shape, conspicuously ridged when immature, slightly ridged at maturity, basally attached with rounded hilum, raphe branches sparse, anastomosing, endosperm deeply ruminate, with a small central hollow; embryo basal. Germination adjacent-ligular; eophyll bifid, spiny. $n = 18$ (Sarkar 1970).

Anatomy. — Leaf, root (Tomlinson 1961).

Distribution. — A single species confined to the islands of Mahé, Silhouette, and Praslin in the Seychelles.

Ecology. — *V. splendida* grows in relic forests on slopes between 300 and 600 m above sea level; more rarely it occurs in river valleys below 300 m altitude. It seems to be confined to steep hillsides and precipitous ravines, where it usually occurs as solitary individuals, rarely in colonies.

Common Names and Uses. — Latanier latte. Trunks have been used in house construction. The genus is also widespread in cultivation as an ornamental.

Notes. — *Verschaffeltia* is obviously related to *Phoenicophorium, Roscheria,* and *Nephrosperma* but is nevertheless very distinct. *Verschaffeltia* is distinguished by a nearly undivided leaf with praemorse margins and by large fruits with a ridged endocarp. It seems closely related to *Roscheria* which has a leaf with large separated leaflets but a small fruit and seeds lacking ridges.

Taxonomic Account. — Bailey (1942).

Plate. — *72D; Fig. G.3.*

163. ROSCHERIA H. A. Wendland ex I. B. Balfour in J. G. Baker, Flora of Mauritius and the Seychelles 386. 1877. Type: **R. melanochaetes** (H. A. Wendland) H. A. Wendland ex I. B. Balfour (*Verschaffeltia melanochaetes* H. A. Wendland).

Small or moderate, solitary, spiny when young, sparsely armed at maturity, pleonanthic, monoecious palm. Stem erect, becoming bare, conspicuously ringed with leaf scars, the juvenile bearing rings of black spines, at maturity unarmed or with very few, scattered, weak spines, the stem base sometimes with aerial roots. Leaves irregularly pinnate, neatly abscising; sheaths tubular, forming a well defined crownshaft, covered in scattered brown scales and armed with scattered, short, black spines, spines much more dense near the base of the petiole; petiole adaxially deeply channeled, abaxially rounded, densely armed along the margins near the base with short, easily detached, black spines; rachis unarmed, bearing scattered scales; blade entire, bifid in juveniles, at maturity irregularly divided into 1–several-fold leaflets, those with single ribs acuminate, those with several ribs truncate, praemorse, adaxially glabrous, abaxially bearing abundant minute, dotlike scales and conspicuous ramenta along the major ribs, transverse veinlets obscure. Inflorescences solitary, interfoliar at first, becoming infrafoliar after leaf fall, copiously branching to 3, very rarely to 4 orders proximally, to fewer orders distally; peduncle elongate, crescentic in cross-section, winged at the base; prophyll inserted some distance from the base, membranous to coriaceous, tubular, persistent, flattened, 2-keeled, briefly split at the tip, unarmed, bearing scattered small scales; peduncular bract inserted some distance above the prophyll, usually much exceeding it, very sparsely scaly, tubular at first, later splitting along much of its length and expanding, eventually falling; rachis usually shorter than the peduncle; rachis bracts all minute, triangular, very inconspicuous; branches of all orders with a short to long portion free of branches or flowers, all axes scaly; first-order branches subdistichous, the proximal longer than the distal; rachillae slender, rather short, flexuous, bearing spirally arranged, minute bracts subtending triads in the middle portion and paired or solitary staminate flowers distally, the flowers not at all sunken. Staminate flowers very small, globular in bud; sepals 3, ± distinct, imbricate, broad, triangular, ± keeled; petals 3, distinct, valvate, more than twice as long as the sepals, broad, triangular; stamens 6, filaments connate basally to form a low ring, the distinct portions short, broad, triangular, anthers very small,

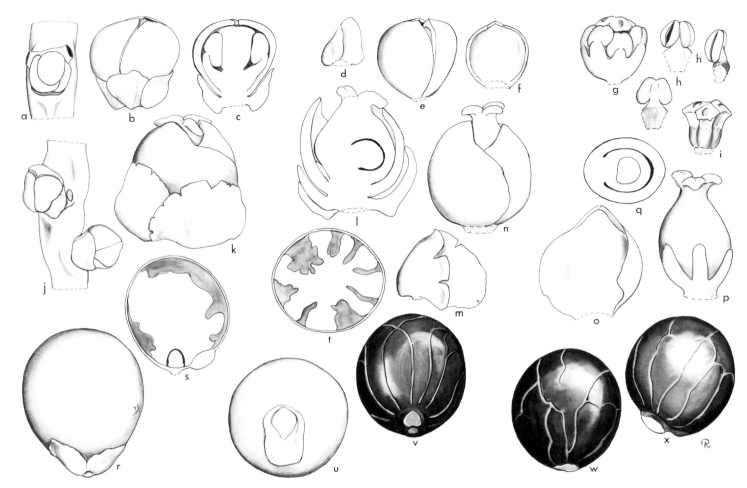

163.—**Roscheria. a,** portion of rachilla with triad, flowers removed to show bracteoles ×12; **b,** staminate bud ×18; **c,** staminate bud in vertical section ×18; **d,** staminate sepal ×18; **e,** staminate flower, sepals removed ×18; **f,** staminate petal ×18; **g,** androecium ×18; **h,** stamen in 3 views ×18; **i,** pistillode ×18; **j,** portion of rachilla with pistillate buds ×12; **k,** pistillate flower ×18; **l,** pistillate flower in vertical section ×18; **m,** pistillate sepal ×18; **n,** pistillate flower, sepals removed ×18; **o,** pistillate petal, interior view ×18; **p,** gynoecium and staminodes ×18; **q,** ovary in cross-section ×18; **r,** fruit ×6; **s,** fruit in vertical section ×6; **t,** fruit in cross-section ×6; **u,** endocarp and operculum ×6; **v, w, x,** seed in 3 views ×6. *Roscheria melanochaetes:* all from *Squibb s.n.*

rounded, medifixed, ± versatile, latrorse; pollen elliptic, monosulcate, with reticulate, tectate exine; pistillode relatively large, truncate, 3-angled. Pistillate flowers larger than the staminate; sepals 3, distinct, thick, imbricate, broad, rounded, the margins irregularly splitting; petals 3, distinct, broad, triangular, the tips briefly valvate, otherwise imbricate; staminodes 6, toothlike, ± united basally; gynoecium asymmetrical, ovoid, unilocular, uniovulate, stigma apical, 3-lobed, ovule laterally attached, form unknown. Fruit small, globular or ellipsoidal, red at maturity, perianth whorls persistent, stigmatic remains subbasal; epicarp smooth, mesocarp very thin, with a layer of anastomosing fibers and abundant raphides, endocarp relatively thick, bony, smooth, with basal operculum. Seed basally attached with rounded hilum, raphe branches sparse, anastomosing, endosperm deeply ruminate; embryo basal. Germination and eophyll not recorded. $n = 16$ (Sarkar 1970).

Anatomy.—Not studied.

Distribution.—Monotypic, confined to Mahé and Silhouette Islands in the Seychelles.

Ecology.—An undergrowth palm of mountain rain forest, very rarely found below 500 m altitude; at ca. 750 m it can form pure stands on very steep slopes in the undergrowth of *Northia* forest.

Common Names and Uses.—Latanier hauban. Uses not recorded.

Notes.—An elegant small palm with a distinctive habit.

Taxonomic Account.—Bailey (1942).

Plate.—26D.

164. **PHOENICOPHORIUM** H. A. Wendland, L'Illustration Horticole 12 (Miscellanées):5. 1865. Type:

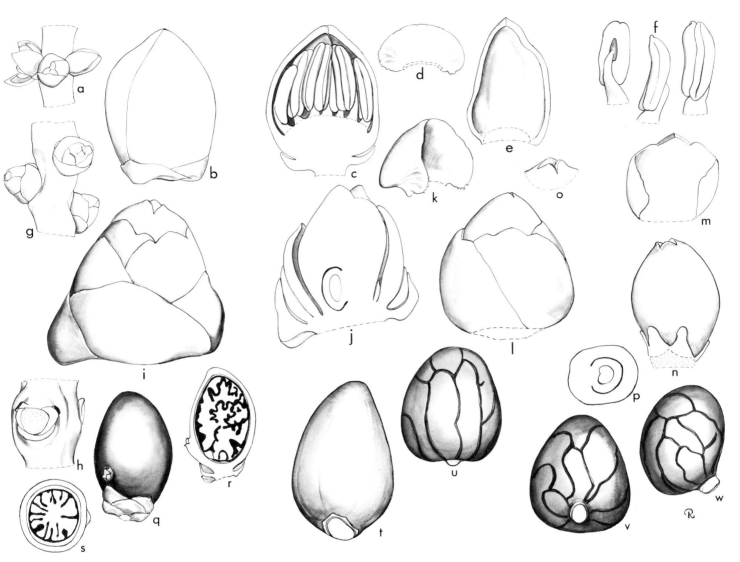

164.—**Phoenicophorium. a,** portion of rachilla with triad ×3; **b,** staminate bud ×12; **c,** staminate bud in vertical section ×12; **d,** staminate sepal ×12; **e,** staminate petal, interior view ×12; **f,** stamen in 3 views ×12; **g,** portion of rachilla at pistillate anthesis ×3; **h,** triad, flowers removed to show scars and bracteoles ×6; **i,** pistillate flower ×12; **j,** pistillate flower in vertical section ×12; **k,** pistillate sepal ×12; **l,** pistillate flower, sepals removed ×12; **m,** pistillate petal ×12; **n,** gynoecium and staminodes ×12; **o,** stigmas ×12; **p,** ovary in cross-section ×12; **q,** fruit ×3; **r,** fruit in vertical section ×3; **s,** fruit in cross-section ×3; **t,** endocarp and operculum ×6; **u, v, w,** seed in 3 views ×6. *Phoenicophorium borsigianum*: all from *Read 1550*.

P. sechellarum H. A. Wendland (illegitimate name) (=**P. borsigianum** (K. Koch) Stuntz) (*Astrocaryum borsigianum* K. Koch).

Stevensonia Duncan ex I. B. Balfour in J. G. Baker, Flora of Mauritius and the Seychelles 388. 1877. Type: *S. grandifolia* Duncan ex I. B. Balfour (=*Phoenicophorium borsigianum* (K. Koch) Stuntz).

Moderate, solitary, spiny when young, sparsely armed or ± unarmed at maturity, pleonanthic, monoecious palm. Stem erect, becoming bare, conspicuously ringed with leaf scars, the juvenile bearing abundant black spines, usually ± unarmed at maturity. Leaves large, bifid, lobed and pinnately ribbed but not pinnatifid, neatly abscising; sheaths becoming open, not forming a well defined crownshaft, covered in abundant tomentum, easily detached spicules, and scattered, large black spines when young, becoming markedly less spiny as maturity is reached, sheath margin irregularly ligulelike, tattering; petiole well developed, adaxially channeled, abaxially rounded, sparsely scaly, in juveniles bearing abundant, large, black spines abaxially; rachis bearing black spines in the proximal region in juveniles; blade bifid, with very conspicuous, pinnate ribs, splitting along abaxial ribs to ⅛ to ⅓ the rib length into briefly bifid lobes, sometimes split further by wind, blade bright green, often reddish-tinged, adaxially glabrous, abaxially with abundant dotlike scales and large ramenta along the adaxial folds near the rachis, transverse veinlets obscure. Inflorescences solitary, interfoliar, branching to 1–2 orders proximally, to 1 order distally, protandrous; peduncle elongate, winged at the base, oval in cross-section, unarmed, glabrous; prophyll inserted some distance from the base of the peduncle, persistent, very coriaceous, tubular, 2-keeled, the keels tending to be irregularly split or toothed, splitting apically for a short distance, scaly or sparsely tomentose, unarmed or armed with sparse to abundant, short, black spines; peduncular bract 1, inserted some distance above the prophyll but included within it, ± woody, conspicuously beaked, deciduous, unarmed, minutely scaly, tubular at first then splitting along ± its entire length; rachis much shorter than the peduncle; rachis bracts minute, triangular, inconspicuous; first-order branches spirally arranged, crowded, ± pendulous, their bases somewhat swollen; rachillae glabrous, slender, elongate, flexuous, with a very short, bare area at the base, above this bearing spirally arranged, superficial triads, except near the tip where bearing solitary or paired staminate flowers; bracteoles minute, rounded. Staminate flowers slightly asymmetrical; sepals 3, distinct, imbricate, low, ± rounded, keeled; petals about 4–5 times as long as the sepals, 3, distinct, valvate; stamens 15–18, filaments short in bud, at anthesis becoming elongate, slender, anthers elongate, medifixed, basally sagittate, latrorse; pollen elliptic, monosulcate, with tectate exine bearing supratectal spines; pistillode absent. Pistillate flowers ± globular, about the same size as the staminate; sepals 3, distinct, imbricate, rounded, ± keeled; petals 3, distinct, rounded, imbricate, with short, triangular, valvate tips; staminodes 6, toothlike; gynoecium asymmetrically ovoid, unilocular, uniovulate, stigmas 3, apical, very low, ovule laterally attached, ?campylotropous. Fruit 1-seeded, relatively small, ovoid to ellipsoidal, red, with persistent perianth whorls, and subbasal stigmatic remains; epicarp shiny, mesocarp thinly fleshy with a thick layer of tannin cells external to the endocarp, endocarp thin, cartilaginous, with basal round operculum. Seed ovoid, basally attached, with rounded hilum and sparse, anastomosing raphe branches, endosperm deeply ruminate; embryo basal. Germination adjacent-ligular; eophyll lanceolate, entire. $n = 16$ (Read 1966, Sarkar 1970).

Anatomy. — Leaf (Tomlinson 1961 as *Stevensonia*).

Distribution. — One variable species, widespread in the Seychelles Islands.

Ecology. — *P. borsigianum* occurs abundantly from sea level to altitudes of about 300 m, above which it becomes much rarer. It occasionally occurs in pure stands, and seems to be relatively tolerant of disturbance. It is frequently planted as an ornamental.

Common Names and Uses. — Latanier feuille. A much prized ornamental, used in the Seychelles for thatch.

Notes. — The leaf is very distinctive being undivided but lobed marginally, the lobes acuminate or acute, not praemorse as in *Vershaffeltia* and *Roscheria*.

Taxonomic Account. — Bailey (1942).
Plate. — *73A; Fig. G.24.*

165. NEPHROSPERMA I. B. Balfour in J. G. Baker, Flora of Mauritius and the Seychelles 386. 1877. Type: **N. vanhoutteanum** (H. A. Wendland ex Van Houtte) I. B. Balfour (*Oncosperma vanhoutteanum* H. A. Wendland ex Van Houtte).

Moderate, solitary, spiny when young, unarmed or only very sparsely armed when mature, pleonanthic, monoecious palm. Stem erect, becoming bare, conspicuously ringed with leaf scars, unarmed. Leaves pinnate, neatly abscising; sheaths tubular, becoming open, not forming a well defined crownshaft, densely tomentose, bearing abundant, black spines in juveniles, ± unarmed or very sparsely armed in mature individuals, sheath margin irregularly ligulelike, tattering; petiole well developed, adaxially channeled, abaxially rounded, bearing white indumentum and scattered scales, and few bristles near the base; rachis curved; leaflets rather regularly arranged, neatly curved, distant, composed usually of 2–3 folds, acute or acuminate, adaxially glabrous, abaxially with numerous, minute, dotlike scales and abundant ramenta along the adaxial ribs, transverse veinlets obscure; expanding leaf flushed red. Inflorescences solitary, interfoliar, branching to 1 order only, protandrous; peduncle very long (±½ the length of the leaves or more), erect at first, becoming curved, winged at the base, ± oval in cross-section, unarmed, scaly; prophyll inserted near the base of the peduncle, persistent, coriaceous, tubular, 2-keeled, the wings tending to be irregularly split or toothed, splitting apically for a short distance, covered with rather dense scales and scattered white wax, armed with short weak bristles and spines or rarely unarmed; peduncular bract, inserted a short distance from the prophyll, elongate, with a conspicuous long beak, tubular at first, then splitting along its length, deciduous, scaly and spiny as the prophyll; rachis shorter than the peduncle, scaly, bearing rather lax, spirally arranged rachillae; rachis bracts minute; rachillae scaly, with a pronounced swelling and bare section at the base, very long, spreading, slender, bearing distant, spirally arranged, superficial triads throughout, except at the tip where bearing solitary or paired staminate flowers; floral bracteoles minute. Staminate flowers symmetrical; sepals 3, distinct, imbricate, rounded, irregularly splitting, keeled; petals about 3–4 times as long as the sepals, 3, distinct, valvate, ± boat-shaped; stamens ca. 40–50, filaments elongate, anthers very small, rounded, with a broad connective, not versatile, latrorse; pollen elliptic, monosulcate, with finely reticulate, tectate exine; pistillode ovoid, conspicuous, minutely but clearly trifid at its tip. Pistillate flowers globular; sepals 3, distinct, imbricate, low, ± rounded, thick, tending to split irregularly; petals 3, distinct, imbricate, ± rounded, with short triangular, valvate tips; staminodes 6, small, toothlike; gynoecium ± obpyriform, unilocular, uniovulate, with minute apical stigmas, ovule laterally attached, form unknown. Fruit relatively small, spherical to somewhat kidney shaped, red, perianth

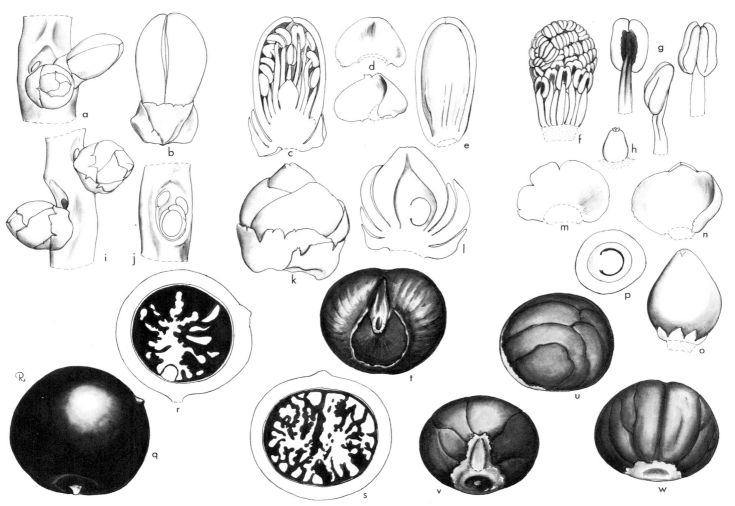

165.—**Nephrosperma. a,** portion of axis with triad, one staminate flower fallen ×3; **b,** staminate bud ×6; **c,** staminate bud in vertical section ×6; **d,** staminate sepal in 2 views ×6; **e,** staminate petal, interior view ×6; **f,** androecium ×6; **g,** stamen in 3 views ×12; **h,** pistillode ×6; **i,** portion of rachilla at pistillate anthesis ×3; **j,** triad, flowers removed ×3; **k,** pistillate flower ×6; **l,** pistillate flower in vertical section ×6; **m,** pistillate sepal, interior view ×6; **n,** pistillate petal, interior view ×6; **o,** gynoecium and staminodes ×6; **p,** ovary in cross-section ×6; **q,** fruit ×3; **r,** fruit in vertical section ×3; **s,** fruit in cross-section ×3; **t,** endocarp and operculum ×3; **u, v, w,** seed in 3 views ×3. *Nephrosperma vanhoutteanum*: **a-h** and **q-w,** *Read 1557*; **i-p,** *Moore 9033*.

whorls persistent, stigmatic remains lateral; epicarp shiny, smooth, mesocarp thinly fleshy with a layer of slender fibers next to the endocarp, endocarp very thin, cartilaginous, with a thin, ± rounded operculum. Seed ± globose, somewhat kidney shaped, attached laterally near the base, with an oblong hilum, raphe branches distant, slightly embedded in the endosperm, endosperm deeply ruminate; embryo basal. Germination adjacent-ligular; eophyll bifid. *n* = 16 (Read 1966, Sharma and Sarkar 1957).

Anatomy. —Leaf (Tomlinson 1961).

Distribution. —One species confined to the Seychelles Islands; elsewhere widely cultivated.

Ecology. —A lowland species, not occurring above 500 m altitude, growing on rocky slopes; also found in some secondary forest types.

Common Names and Uses. —Latanier mille-pattes. Uses not recorded apart from its being an ornamental.

Notes. —The staminate flowers are, perhaps, the most specialized within the Oncospermatinae because of the large number of stamens (40–50) and the large pistillode.

Taxonomic Account. —Bailey (1942).

Plate. —27A, B.

Sclerospermatinae J. Dransfield & N. Uhl, Principes 30:9. 1986. Type: **Sclerosperma.**

Massive, unarmed, short stemmed or acaulescent; crownshaft absent; leaves large, bifid or regularly or irregularly pinnate, margins entire or praemorse; inflores-

Map 44.— **Distribution of Sclerospermatinae.**

cences interfoliar, spicate or branched to 2 orders, condensed; peduncle short, stout; prophyll small, peduncular bracts 1 complete and several incomplete; rachis short, stout; flowers, at least the staminate, borne in shallow to deep depressions in thick rachillae; sepals usually narrow, not touching; pistillate flowers with imbricate petals; gynoecium pseudomonomerous; fruit with apical or lateral stigmatic remains; embryo basal.

The Sclerospermatinae consist of two very peculiar genera, *Marojejya* in Madagascar and *Sclerosperma* in west Africa (Map 44). Both genera have flowers in triads and pseudomonomerous gynoecia, therefore belonging to tribe Areceae. *Sclerosperma* is acaulescent and *Marojejya* has a short to tall stem. Leaves of both genera are massive, bifid, or pinnately divided. The condensed inflorescences are unusual in bearing numerous incomplete peduncular bracts; that of *Sclerosperma* is unbranched but that of *Marojejya* is branched to one order. There are many differences in flowers and fruits. The shared peculiarities of these genera may be the result of parallel evolution.

Key to the Genera of the Sclerospermatinae

1 Inflorescence spicate bearing flowers of both sexes; stamens numerous. West Africa . . . . **Sclerosperma**
1 Inflorescences branched to 1 order, usually unisexual; stamens 6. Madagascar . . . . **Marojejya**

166. SCLEROSPERMA G. Mann & H. A. Wendland, Transactions of the Linnean Society of London 24:427. 1864. Type: **S. mannii** H. A. Wendland.

Short or acaulescent, clustering, unarmed, pleonanthic, monoecious palms. Stem if evident, creeping or erect, rather stout, closely ringed with leaf scars. Leaves reduplicate, bifid or divided, very large, deeply bifid in juveniles, ascending; sheath rather short, splitting opposite the petiole, margins fibrous; petiole long, slender, adaxially channeled, abaxially rounded; leaflets when present, alternate, of several very narrow folds, midribs prominent, marginal ribs next largest, blade adaxially dark, abaxially glaucous and with small scales along the veins, folds apically praemorse, margins minutely toothed, transverse veinlets not evident. Inflorescences interfoliar, concealed among the leaf bases and sometimes partially obscured by accumulated debris, spicate; peduncle very short, elliptic in cross-section, densely tomentose; prophyll rather short, strongly 2-keeled, becoming fibrous; peduncular bract longer than the prophyll, tubular, forming a fibrous net around the flowers, apparently opening distally and inflorescence becoming partially exserted, 2 incomplete, pointed peduncular bracts borne laterally just below the flowers; rachis longer than the peduncle, but short, stout, bearing a few (ca. 12) triads of flowers at the base and about 13 rows of staminate flowers distally, triads each subtended by a shallow pointed fibrous bract, the distal staminate flowers by small acute bracts; floral bracteoles present in triads, flat, ± rounded and partially united. Staminate flowers in triads ± pedicellate and asymmetrical, distal flowers sessile, symmetrical; sepals 3, distinct, imbricate basally, elongate, tapering, truncate apically or with a short central point; petals 3, distinct, valvate but tips flattened and buds truncate apically, thick; stamens ca. 60, filaments very short, ± triangular, anthers elongate, basifixed, latrorse, connective prominent, apiculate; pollen ± triangular, triporate, with reticulate, tectate exine; pistillode lacking. Pistillate flowers larger than the staminate, broadly ovoid; sepals 3, connate in a 3-lobed, glabrous cupule or margins of 2 sepals distinct and imbricate, somewhat angled by mutual pressure; petals 3, distinct, asymmetrical, broadly imbricate with thick valvate tips; staminodes 6, very small, triangular; gynoecium ovoid, unilocular, uniovulate, covered in thin brown scales, bearing a large, caplike, 3-angled stigma; ovule ± pendulous, probably campylotropous. Fruit globose, depressed apically around a short beak of stigmatic remains, purplish but probably black at maturity; epicarp thin, mesocarp thin, parenchymatous with silica (?) inclusions, endocarp bony, thick, irregularly and shallowly pitted externally, with basal pore region. Seed globose, somewhat rough, hilum elongate, endosperm homogeneous; embryo basal. Germination remote-tubular; eophyll bifid. Cytology not studied.

Anatomy. — Silica bodies hat-shaped. Otherwise the leaf like arecoid palms anatomically (Tomlinson 1961).

Distribution. — Three species in west Africa.

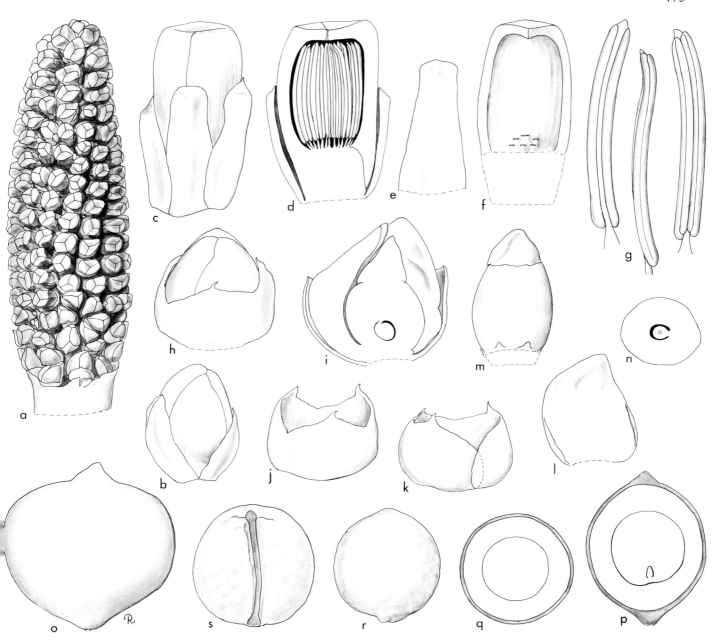

166.—**Sclerosperma. a,** inflorescence ×½; **b,** staminate bud from triad ×4½; **c,** staminate bud from distal portion of inflorescence ×4½; **d,** distal staminate bud in vertical section ×4½; **e,** staminate sepal ×4½; **f,** staminate petal, with stamens removed, interior view ×4½; **g,** stamen in 3 views ×9; **h,** pistillate bud ×3; **i,** pistillate bud in vertical section ×4½; **j, k,** pistillate calyx in 2 views ×3; **l,** pistillate petal, interior view ×3; **m,** gynoecium and staminodes ×4½; **n,** ovary in cross-section ×4½; **o,** fruit ×1½; **p,** fruit in vertical section ×1; **q,** fruit in cross-section ×1; **r,** endocarp ×1; **s,** seed ×1½. *Sclerosperma mannii*: all from *Moore & Enti 9899.*

Ecology.—Best developed in low, wet, swampy areas but does ascend onto slopes; found on sandy loam which is often waterlogged although friable when dry.

Common Names and Uses.—Common names not recorded. Leaves are used for thatch and the seeds are eaten.

Notes.—This is a most remarkable palm with no

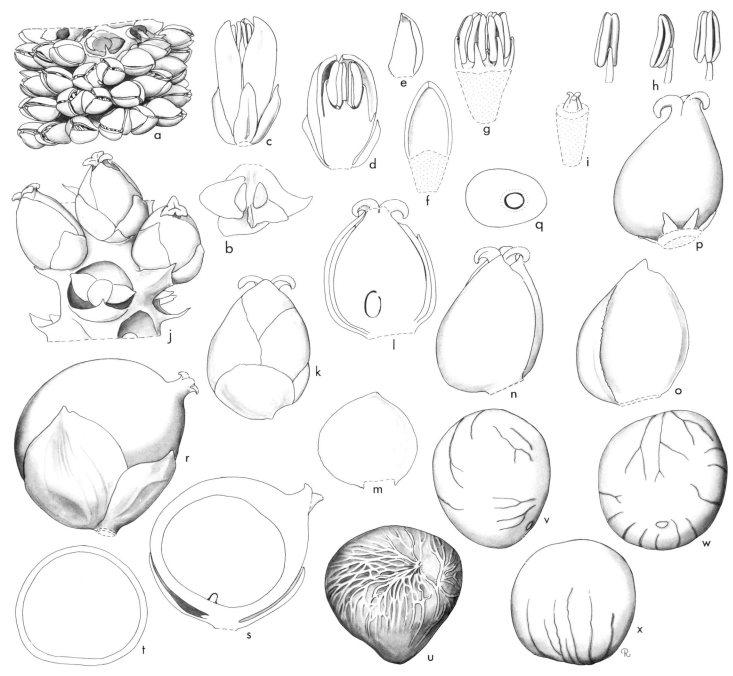

167.—**Marojejya. a,** portion of staminate rachilla ×3; **b,** bracteoles of staminate dyad ×6; **c,** staminate flower ×6; **d,** staminate flower in vertical section ×6; **e,** staminate sepal, interior view ×6; **f,** staminate petal, interior view ×6; **g,** androecium ×6; **h,** stamen in 3 views ×6; **i,** pistillode ×6; **j,** portion of pistillate rachilla ×2¼; **k,** pistillate flower ×9; **l,** pistillate flower in vertical section ×9; **m,** pistillate sepal ×9; **n,** pistillate flower, sepals removed ×9; **o,** pistillate petal ×9; **p,** gynoecium and staminodes ×9; **q,** ovary in cross-section ×9; **r,** fruit ×2¼; **s,** fruit in vertical section ×2¼; **t,** fruit in cross-section ×2¼; **u,** endocarp and fibers ×2¼; **v, w, x,** seed in 3 views ×2¼. *Marojejya insignis*: all from *Moore 9901.*

clear relatives. In several respects *Sclerosperma* shows similarities to *Marojejya* but these may be parallels. The presence of such an extraordinary palm in west Africa argues for the presence in the past of a much more diverse palm flora in Africa. We believe the position of *Sclerosperma* will not be understood until we have more detailed knowledge of the palms of Madagascar.

Taxonomic Account.—No recent treatment exists.

Plate.—*73B, C.*

167. MAROJEJYA Humbert, Mémoires de l'Institut Scientifique de Madagascar, Série B, Biologie Vegetale 6:92. 1955. Type: **M. insignis** Humbert.

Stout, solitary, unarmed, monoecious, pleonanthic palms. Stem erect, obscurely ringed with leaf scars, internodes short, sometimes with short root spines. Leaves numerous, massive, pinnate or entire, the crown often filled with fibers; sheath with or without rounded auricles; petiole absent or thick and wide at the base, gradually tapering to the rachis, adaxially channeled, abaxially rounded, densely covered with caducous, dense brown scales; rachis adaxially deeply channeled, abaxially rounded basally, becoming laterally channeled distally, densely scaly at the base, blade undivided for ca. ¼ to the entire length, where not entire, distally irregularly divided into decurrent, 1–several-nerved, obtuse leaflets, the blade eventually splitting irregularly, abaxially with scattered irregular bands of caducous, chocolate-brown scales, numerous fine, longitudinal veins between the major ribs, transverse veinlets not evident. Inflorescences unisexual (but see below), hidden among the leaf bases beneath debris, branching to 1 order, staminate and pistillate inflorescences basically similar but staminate with more numerous slender and longer branches; peduncle large, slightly flattened, short, densely covered in dark brown scales; prophyll tubular, 2-keeled, strongly flattened, splitting longitudinally, thinly coriaceous, bearing numerous caducous, dark brown scales; basal peduncular bract similar to the prophyll but smaller, subsequent peduncular bracts numerous, crowded, spirally arranged, incomplete, acute to acuminate, stiff, ± erect, gradually diminishing in size distally; rachis shorter than the peduncle, bearing spirally arranged rachillae, each subtended by a conspicuous, acute or acuminate bract; staminate rachillae ± equal in length, stout, catkinlike, somewhat flexuous, densely covered in brown tomentum; rachilla bracts conspicuous, paired, narrow, triangular, subtending densely crowded, paired staminate flowers except near the base and at the tip where solitary staminate flowers present, flowers abortive at the very base, rarely a few pistillate flowers present at the base (as a monstrosity), distal bracts forming pits; floral bracteoles 2, well developed, acute, ciliate margined. Staminate flowers rather small, somewhat asymmetrical due to close packing; sepals 3, free, unequal, narrow, ovate, keeled, chaffy, ciliate margined, tending to be widely separated; petals 3, ± boat-shaped, valvate, coriaceous, connate ba-

sally for ⅓ their length and adnate to the receptacle; stamens 6, filaments basally connate, the distinct portions flattened, tapering, elongate, inflexed at the tip, anthers medifixed, ± versatile, latrorse; pollen elliptic, monosulcate, with foveolate, tectate exine; pistillode small, 3 lobed. Pistillate rachillae shorter, thicker, and fewer than the staminate, densely brown tomentose, bearing crowded, spirally arranged, triangular bracts forming the lower lips of shallow pits, each pit bearing 3 membranous bracteoles, 2 very small abortive staminate flowers and a large solitary pistillate flower. Pistillate flowers much larger than the staminate, obpyriform, somewhat asymmetrical; sepals 3, distinct, somewhat chaffy, ovate with triangular tips, ± striate; petals 3, distinct, similar to the sepals but larger and with short, triangular, valvate tips; staminodes 6, narrow, triangular; gynoecium gibbous, unilocular, uniovulate, gradually tapering to 3, large, triangular, recurved stigmas, ovule large, pendulous, campylotropous. Fruit asymmetrically globular, perianth persistent, stigmatic remains forming a large lateral beak; epicarp smooth, mesocarp thin, granular, endocarp composed of several layers of broad, soft anastomosing fibers closely adhering to the seed. Seed irregularly rounded, flattened, or ± kidney-shaped, smooth or grooved and ridged, subapically attached, endosperm homogeneous; embryo basal, opposite the fruit attachment. Germination adjacent-ligular; eophyll bifid, with or without a petiole. Cytology unknown.

Anatomy.—*Marojejya* has a distinct area of tannin surrounded by fibrous and vascular bundles around the locule. The ovule is unusually large (Uhl unpublished).

Distribution.—Two species endemic to northeastern Madagascar.

Ecology.—Hill slopes and swamps in tropical rain forest to about 900 m altitude.

Common Names and Uses.—Not recorded.

Notes.—*Marojejya* is an extraordinary genus, perhaps related to *Sclerosperma*. We still know very little about its natural history and its relationships may only become apparent after more careful work on Madagascan palms.

Taxonomic Accounts.—Humbert (1955), Dransfield and Uhl (1984a).

Plates.—*27C; 73D; Fig. G.6.*

Areceae incertae sedis

Because material is scanty or unavailable, it is not possible to place the following two genera within subtribes in the formal taxonomic hierarchy. Both *Carpoxylon* and *Masoala* appear to be pseudomonomerous and hence members of tribe Areceae. They are included here as genera of uncertain affinity (see notes under each genus).

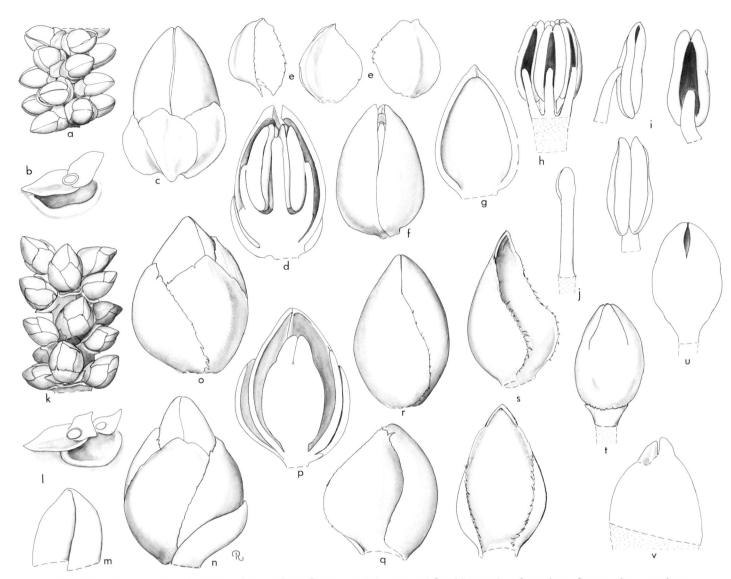

168.—**Masoala. a,** portion of rachilla with staminate flowers ×1½; **b,** scar and floral bracteoles of staminate flower ×3; **c,** staminate bud ×6; **d,** staminate bud in vertical section ×6; **e,** staminate sepals ×6; **f,** staminate flower, sepals removed ×6; **g,** staminate petal ×6; **h,** androecium ×6; **i,** stamen in 3 views ×7½; **j,** pistillode × 7½; **k,** portion of rachilla with triads ×1½; **l,** triad, flowers removed to show scars and bracteoles, scar of left staminate flower hidden ×3; **m,** bract subtending pistillate flower ×6; **n,** pistillate bud with subtending bract ×6; **o,** pistillate bud ×6; **p,** pistillate bud in vertical section ×6; **q,** pistillate sepal ×6; **r,** pistillate bud, sepals removed ×6; **s,** pistillate petal in 2 views ×6; **t,** gynoecium ×6; **u,** gynoecium in vertical section ×6; **v,** vertical section of part of an older gynoecium. *Masoala madagascariensis:* all from *Perrier de la Bâthie 11938.*

168. MASOALA H. Jumelle, Annales de l'Institut Botanico-Géologique Colonial de Marseille série 5, 1(1):8. 1933. Type: **M. madagascariensis** H. Jumelle.

Robust, solitary, unarmed, pleonanthic, monoecious palm. Stem erect, short, covered with remains of the leaf sheaths. Leaves large, reduplicately pinnate, apparently marcescent; sheaths tubular, sparsely tomentose, atten-uate distally, the margins smooth, ligule absent; petiole relatively short, adaxially deeply channeled, abaxially rounded, sparsely tomentose; rachis adaxially ridged, abaxially rounded or flattened; leaflets numerous, regularly arranged, linear, single-fold except at the very tip where sometimes 2-fold, the midrib strong, the tips briefly bifid, adaxially glabrous, abaxially minutely dotted, bearing several large, brown ramenta along the midrib, transverse veinlets obscure. Inflorescences solitary, interfoliar, branching to 2 orders; peduncle elongate, semicircular or crescent-shaped in cross-section, sparsely tomentose; prophyll inserted some distance above the base of the peduncle, large, flattened, narrow, elliptical, beaked, strongly 2-keeled, coriaceous, sparsely tomentose, splitting longitudinally along the abaxial face, persistent; peduncular bract similar to the prophyll but not 2-keeled, caducous, incomplete peduncular bracts several, membranous, relatively large, triangular, open; rachis longer than the peduncle, bearing spirally arranged, short triangular bracts each subtending a first-order branch; proximal first-order branches with a short bare portion distally, bearing 1–2 branches; rachillae ± straight, rather thick, elongate, bearing spirally arranged, very slightly sunken triads, each subtended by a thick, coriaceous, low triangular bract through most of the rachilla length, or bearing more crowded, more sunken pairs of staminate flowers towards the rachilla tips, or distal rachillae entirely staminate; floral bracteoles conspicuous, ± triangular. Staminate flowers symmetrical; sepals 3, distinct, imbricate, coriaceous, triangular, keeled; petals 3, distinct, triangular, about 3 times as long as the sepals, coriaceous; stamens 6, filaments slender, distinct, anthers elongate, basifixed, latrorse; pollen elliptic, monosulcate, with rugulate, tectate exine; pistillode columnar, ± equalling the stamens in length. Pistillate flowers ovoid, much larger than the staminate; sepals 3, distinct, broadly imbricate, triangular, keeled, coriaceous, shiny; petals 3, distinct, imbricate with valvate tips, triangular, coriaceous, striate; staminodes absent; gynoecium ovoid, ? locules, ? ovules, stigmas 3, large, triangular, appressed in bud. Fruit unknown. Cytology not studied.

Anatomy. — Not studied.

Distribution. — A single species known from a single collection from the Masoala peninsula in northeastern Madagascar.

Ecology. — *Masoala* is presumed to be a palm of tropical rain forest at low elevations.

Common Names and Uses. — Not recorded.

Notes. — Jumelle and Perrier de la Bâthie describe a strong, truncate, undulate margined staminodial cupule to 3 mm high surrounding the ovary but we have found no trace of this; we attribute the supposed staminodial ring to possible differential shrinkage of the wall of the ovary. The genus remains very poorly known, and the lack of a staminodial cupule removes the one really distinctive floral character of the genus as described by Jumelle. Until *Masoala* is recollected and studied in more detail, its position remains in doubt.

Taxonomic Account. — Jumelle and Perrier de la Bâthie (1945).

169. **CARPOXYLON** H. A. Wendland & Drude, Linnaea 39:177. 1875. Type: **C. macrospermum** H. A. Wendland & Drude.

Habit, vegetative parts, and inflorescence unknown. Fruit large, ± ovoid-ellipsoidal, somewhat asymmetrical, single-seeded, with eccentrically apical, conical stigmatic remains; epicarp smooth, thin, mesocarp thinly fibrous, the innermost fibers adherent to the thick, woody endocarp, endocarp thicker above the raphe. Seed ± oblong-ovoid, flattened at the raphe, hilum impressed, ± subbasal, raphe branches numerous, radiating, diverging, many ascending, all anastomosing, endosperm homogeneous; embryo basal. Cytology, not known.

Anatomy. — Not studied.

Distribution. — One species in Aneityum, Vanuatu (New Hebrides).

Ecology. — Not known.

Uses. — Not known.

Notes. — *Carpoxylon* is known only from the descriptions and illustration of the fruit and seed by Wendland and Drude (1875). Although it seems certain that the palm belongs to Arecoideae: Areceae, its closer relationships cannot be understood until it is recollected. It has been searched for, e.g. by Hodel (Hodel 1982) but without success. Burret (1932a) referred the poorly known taxon *Kajewskia aneityensis* Guillaumin to *Carpoxylon,* but Moore (1957a) has suggested that *Kajewskia* is almost certainly synonymous with *Veitchia spiralis* H. A. Wendland. The fruit of *Carpoxylon* as described by Wendland and Drude cannot be included in *Veitchia* because of the woody endocarp and eccentrically apical stigmatic remains.

Taxonomic Accounts. — H. A. Wendland & Drude (1875), Beccari & Pichi-Sermolli (1955).

COCOEAE Martius in Endlicher, Genera Plantarum 254. 1837. ("*Cocoineae*").

Slender to very robust, acaulescent to erect, pleonanthic palms; crownshaft lacking; leaves pinnate or pinnately ribbed, reduplicate, leaflets acute, obliquely lobed or praemorse; inflorescence unisexual or bisexual, spicate or branched to 1 or very rarely 2 orders, never multiple, bearing a short prophyll, usually included within the leaf sheaths and a usually very much longer, frequently very thick, woody peduncular bract; flowers superficial or occasionally in pits; petals of pistillate flowers imbricate or connate; staminodes usually connate in a conspicuous ring; gynoecium with 3 or rarely more locules and ovules; fruit sometimes very large, 1–several seeded, never lobed; endocarp with 3 or more well defined pores.

The Cocoeae includes 22 genera arranged in five subtribes and represents the cocosoid major group of Moore with *Beccariophoenix* added. The distribution is predominantly New World but there are a few members of the Old World (Map 45). The tribe presents such a distinctive facies that it has long been differentiated from other palms as a

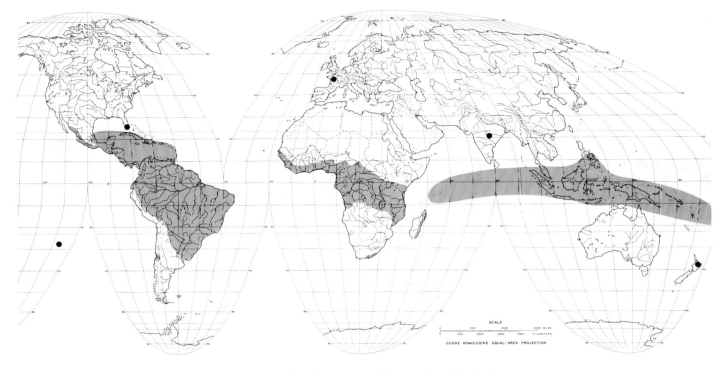

Map 45.—**Distribution of Cocoeae:** fossils in black

subfamily or family, yet similarities in habit and general aspects of the inflorescence with other tribes in the Arecoideae, particularly the Areceae, are overwhelming. The genera are characterized, above all else, by the presence of an endocarp with three or more clearly defined pores. Along with the pores go a suite of other characters; the inflorescence is usually branched to one order only (rarely spicate), the prophyll usually inconspicuous, being hidden among the leaf sheaths, and the peduncular bract well developed and large, frequently woody, and sometimes cowllike. There is usually a rather thick staminodial ring in the pistillate flower. The very small ovules are situated in the extreme base of a triovulate or rarely multiovulate gynoecium. The fruit, when more than one-seeded, is never lobed. The occurrence of fossils in New Zealand and Easter Island suggests that the tribe was even more widely distributed in the past.

The differences between the five subtribes are displayed in the following key.

Key to the Subtribes of the Cocoeae

1 Unarmed palms except for the sometimes sharply toothed petiole margins, petals of pistillate flowers always free and broadly imbricate 2
1 Spiny palms, armed in some or all parts with soft to mostly stout spines, or when rarely unarmed (some spp. of *Bac-*

tris), then the petals of pistillate flowers connate . . . .
. . . . **Bactridinae**
2 Peduncular bract fibrous or woody; pistillate flowers deeply sunken in the rachillae; endocarp with pores at or above the middle . . . . **Elaeidinae**
2 Peduncular bract woody; pistillate flowers superficial; endocarp with pores at or below the middle 3
3 Peduncular bract borne at the tip of the peduncle, splitting longitudinally, circumscissile and deciduous at anthesis . . . . **Beccariophoenicinae**
3 Peduncular bract borne just above the insertion of the prophyll, splitting longitudinally, usually cowllike, persistent 4
4 Inflorescences normally of more than one kind on the same plant, androgynous and staminate, or sometimes also pistillate; pistillate flower sometimes with more than 3 carpels . . . . **Attaleinae**
4 Inflorescences not normally differentiated into androgynous and staminate; pistillate flower always trilocular and triovulate . . . . **Butiinae**

It seems most useful to provide a key to the genera of the whole tribe rather than separate keys for each subtribe.

Key to the Genera of the Cocoeae

1 Unarmed palms except for the sometimes sharply toothed petiole margins; corolla of pistillate flowers always of broadly imbricate petals; endocarp with pores above, at, or below the middle 2
1 Prickly palms, armed in some or all parts with soft to mostly stout spines, or when rarely unarmed (*Bactris* spp.), then the perianth of pistillate flowers with connate

petals; endocarp with pores at or above the middle except rarely basal in *Acrocomia* (*Acanthococos*), the pores more or less deeply impressed in the endocarp, usually covered by or plugged with fibers adherent to the endocarp, lacking a clearly demarcated and visible operculum; fruit always (?) 1-seeded; endosperm always homogeneous .. 17

2 Pistillate flowers not or only slightly sunken in the rachillae; endocarp with pores at or below the middle; peduncular bract woody 3

2 Pistillate flowers deeply sunken in the rachillae; endocarp with pores at or above the middle; peduncular bract fibrous or woody 16

3 Peduncular bract borne at the tip of the peduncle, splitting longitudinally, circumscissile and deciduous at anthesis; stamens 18–21, the filaments connate in a torus. Madagascar .... 170. **Beccariophoenix**

3 Peduncular bract borne near the prophyll insertion or higher, but not at the tip, not circumscissile, splitting abaxially but not deciduous at anthesis, persistent or marcescent; stamens 3–many, filaments variously free or connate. 4

4 Peduncular bract nearly smooth or finely striate but not deeply grooved; pores at or below the middle, not impressed in the endocarp, each with a clearly demarcated, thin operculum 5

4 Peduncular bract shallowly to deeply grooved; pores mostly near the base of and usually impressed in the endocarp, often covered by or plugged with fibers, sometimes with a clearly demarcated operculum 7

5 Petioles usually conspicuously toothed on the margin toward the base; staminate flowers with 6 stamens; fruit 1–3-seeded. Brazil to Paraguay .... 171. **Butia**

5 Petioles not toothed along the margin; staminate flowers with more than 6 stamens 6

6 Trunks always solitary, massive, up to 1 m in diameter or more; leaflets clustered; staminate flowers stalked, the sepals not imbricate, stamens 15–30. Coastal Central Chile ....172. **Jubaea**

6 Trunks often multiple, rather slender; leaflets ± regularly arranged; staminate flowers not stalked, sepals imbricate, stamens 8–16. Southeastern Africa ...... 173. **Jubaeopsis**

7 Inflorescences not normally differentiated into androgynous and staminate but instead the pistillate flowers borne at the base of, in the lower part of, or nearly throughout the rachillae or the spike, the staminate flowers lateral to the pistillate and usually pedicellate in the triads, sessile and paired or solitary in the upper part of the rachilla or spike; pistillate flowers always trilocular and triovulate 8

7 Inflorescences normally of more than one kind on the same plant, androgynous and staminate, or sometimes also pistillate; androgynous inflorescences with the pistillate flowers large and few at the base of short rachillae, the pistillate flowers accompanied by lateral or abortive staminate flowers and usually with some paired or solitary staminate flowers on the distal portion of the rachillae; staminate inflorescences with longer rachillae bearing staminate flowers only; pistillate flowers sometimes with more than 3 carpels, ovules, and stigmas 13

8 Triads separated on the inflorescence; sepals of staminate flowers rarely as long as the petals 9

8 Triads densely crowded on the lower portion of a spike, the terminal portion with staminate flowers only; brac-

teoles prominent; staminate flowers rather markedly asymmetrical, lateral to the closely packed pistillate flowers on the lower portion, and densely crowded on the terminal portion of the spike; sepals of staminate flowers linear, acute to acuminate, more than half as long as the petals, stamens 6–120 12

9 Stamens ca. 15; endocarp irregularly sculptured and roughened with 3 prominent crests at the apex. Ecuador and Bolivia .... 177. **Parajubaea**

9 Stamens 6; endocarp smooth or roughened but not irregularly sculptured externally 10

10 Pistillate flowers very large, globose-ovoid, the sepals and petals rounded without valvate apices, imbricate; staminate flowers with distinct sepals and 6 stamens; fruit very large, up to 25 cm long or more at maturity, with a very thick, fibrous mesocarp and thick, bony endocarp; seed normally 1, with liquid endosperm when young and a large, hollow interior when completely mature. Old World tropics, pantropical in cultivation ... .174. **Cocos**

10 Pistillate flowers ovoid or conic-ovoid, the sepals acute and ± hooded, the petals usually with conspicuously valvate apices 11

11 Leaflets densely white or pale brown tomentose abaxially, very narrow, close, and regularly arranged; anthers versatile, medifixed, filaments inflexed at the tip. Epicarp and mesocarp splitting regularly and longitudinally from the apex to the base into 3 sections at maturity, exposing the thin endocarp. Brazil .... 176. **Lytocaryum**

11 Leaflets lacking a dense covering of tomentum abaxially (very rarely thin indument present but then leaflets grouped); anthers only rarely versatile; epicarp and mesocarp not splitting at maturity; endocarp very thick, variously beaked, ridged, minutely pitted or invaginated. South America and Lesser Antilles .... 175. **Syagrus**

12 Plants usually without emergent stem; stamens 6–19; seed with homogeneous endosperm. Brazil, Paraguay .. .. 178. **Allagoptera**

12 Plants with prominent trunk; stamens 60–120; seed with ruminate endosperm. Brazil .... 179. **Polyandrococos**

13 Stamens much exserted from the staminate flowers, the corolla very small; fruits usually 1-seeded, the endocarp smooth and sharply pointed; stamens almost always 6. Trinidad to Brazil .... 183. **Maximiliana**

13 Stamens included, corolla of staminate flowers prominent and longer than the anthers; fruit (1–)3(–7)-seeded 14

14 Anthers irregularly twisted, sinuous or inrolled; stamens 6–ca. 50. Mexico to Brazil .... 182. **Orbignya**

14 Anthers straight; stamens 6 to many 15

15 Petals of staminate flowers more or less flattened, mostly ovate, oblong or lanceolate; stamens 6–75. Panama, Colombia to Brazil .... 180. **Attalea**

15 Petals of staminate flowers more or less rounded or angled in cross section, fleshy, narrow-elongate, awl-shaped; stamens usually 6. Mexico to Brazil .... 181. **Scheelea**

16 Flowers of both sexes consistently in the same inflorescence, the pistillate near the bases of rachillae; inflorescence long-peduncled, laxly branched. Brazil 184. **Barcella**

16 Flowers normally in separate inflorescences on the same plant; inflorescence short-peduncled, densely branched. Costa Rica to Brazil, Africa .... 185. **Elaeis**

17 Staminate flowers borne in pairs lateral to the pistillate

in basal triads on the rachillae, immediately above the triads in pairs, or mostly or entirely single, subtended by membranous bractlets united to form chambers resembling those of a honeycomb; staminate flowers with free sepals, petals free and valvate or adnate basally to the short floral receptacle then free and valvate; stamenfilaments inflexed at the apex in bud, the anthers dorsifixed and versatile; sepals of pistillate flowers free, petals free and broadly imbricate, or if sometimes partially connate basally and with an adnate staminodial tube, then at least the margins free and imbricate; fruit with abundant short fibers in the mesocarp, these strongly adherent to the smooth or only very shallowly pitted endocarp. Cuba and Mexico to Argentina . . . .
. . . . 186. **Acrocomia**

17 Staminate flowers and inflorescences various; sepals of the pistillate flowers distinct and imbricate or connate in a shallow to deep cupule; petals of pistillate flowers connate $\frac{1}{3}$–$\frac{1}{2}$ their length in a campanulate tube with prominent spreading or erect, valvate lobes, or more than $\frac{1}{2}$ their length in an urnlike, briefly 3-lobed, 3-toothed or even truncate tube; fruit lacking abundant short fibers adherent to the endocarp 18

18 Staminate flowers with stamen filaments erect, the basifixed anthers often sagittate basally; pistillode present; pistillate petals connate $\frac{1}{3}$–$\frac{1}{2}$ their length in a campanulate tube with prominent valvate lobes; staminodes connate and adnate to the corolla tube basally, but distinct or continued in a free, 3–6-lobed or -toothed or truncate tube sometimes nearly equalling the stigmas above 19

18 Staminate flowers with stamen filaments erect or inflexed at the apex or from nearly the middle in bud; pistillode usually lacking; pistillate petals connate beyond the middle or completely connate in a 3-lobed, 3-toothed, or truncate, urnlike or tubular corolla, the lobes, when developed, not spreading; staminodes free or united in a short tube but not adnate to the corolla 20

19 Trunks uniform in diameter; leaflets variously oblique or truncate, broad, and strongly toothed at the apex; sepals of staminate flowers distinct (except where united to the floral receptacle) and separated or imbricate; sepals of pistillate flowers distinct, imbricate; lobes of pistillate corolla spreading at anthesis. Lesser Antilles, South America from Brazil to Peru and Bolivia . . 188. **Aiphanes**

19 Trunk markedly ventricose; leaflets acute or acuminate; sepals of both pistillate and staminate flowers connate, cupular; lobes of pistillate corolla erect. Cuba . . . .
. . . . 187. **Gastrococos**

20 Staminate flowers often associated with the pistillate in triads basally or along the upper part of the rachilla but above these triads, paired or generally solitary and densely aggregated in a distinct terminal portion of the rachilla, each pair of flowers or each flower subtended by a prominent bract adnate to or coherent with adjacent bracts to form a cupule sometimes as high as the flowers; stamen filaments inflexed at the apex in bud; anthers dorsifixed, versatile. Mexico to Brazil . . . . 191. **Astrocaryum**

20 Staminate flowers not densely aggregated in a distinct terminal portion of the rachilla but associated with the pistillate in triads or irregularly interspersed among the triads and subtended by short, free bracteoles 21

21 Erect plants; peduncular bract inserted near the prophyll at the base of the peduncle; distal leaflets not modified as acanthophylls; flowers all or nearly all borne in triads or the staminate more numerous and irregularly interspersed among the triads; stamen filaments inflexed at the apex or from nearly the middle in bud, anthers mostly dorsifixed, versatile. Cuba and Mexico to Brazil . . . . .
. . . . 189. **Bactris**

21 Climbing plants; peduncular bract often inserted above the middle of the peduncle; distal leaflets usually very distant and modified into reflexed hooks (acanthophylls); flowers in triads nearly throughout the rachillae; stamen filaments erect in bud, short, anthers basifixed, erect, sagittate basally. Mexico to Brazil . . . . 190. **Desmoncus**

Multi-access Key to Genera of Cocoeae

Erect palms	170, (171), 172–174, (175), 176, 177, 179, (180–182), 183, (185), (186), 187, (188), (189), (191).
Climbing palms	190.
Acaulescent palms	(171), (175), 178, (180–182), 184, (185), (186), (188), (189), (191).
Clustered palms	173, (175), (178), (189), 190, (191).
Solitary palms	170–172, 174, (175), 176, 177, (178), 179–188, (189), (191).
Unarmed palms	170, (171), 172–174, (175), 176–178, (179), 180–184, (189).
Petiole armed with spine-like leaflet bases	185.
Petiole armed with marginal fiber teeth	(171), (175), (179).
Sheath, petiole, and/or leaflets armed with spines	186–188, (189), 190–191.
Reflexed acanthophylls present	190.
At least some mid-leaflets composed of more than one fold or blade bifid	(188), (189), (191).
Leaflets praemorse	179, 188, (189).
Leaflets or blade strongly discolorous	(175), 176, (178), 179, (186), 187, (189), (191).
Entirely staminate inflorescence present	180–183, 185.
Inflorescence spicate	(175), 178, 179, (188), (189).
Peduncular bract borne at the tip of peduncle	170.
Peduncular bract grooved	170, 174–184.
Staminate flowers borne in pits	179, 184–186, (188), 191.
Staminate flowers stalked	(171), 172, (175), (176), 178, (186), (188), (189).
Sepals of staminate flowers connate	(171), 172, (175), 176, 178, 179, (182), (183), 187, (188), 189, 190, (191).
Petals of staminate flowers connate	170 (basally), (171), (182), 186, 187, 189, 191.

Stamens more than six	170, 172, 173, 177, (178), 179, (180), (182), (183), (189), (190), (191).
Sepals of pistillate flowers connate	187, 189–191.
Petals of pistillate flowers connate	(186), 187–191.
Fruit more than one-seeded (monstrosities excluded)	(171), (175), (177), (180), (181), (182), (183).
Epicarp and mesocarp splitting along three lines exposing endocarp	176.
Endocarp irregular within or without	(175), 177, (182).
Endosperm ruminate	170, (175), (176), (179).

Beccariophoenicinae J. Dransfield & N. Uhl, Principes 30:10. 1986. Type: **Beccariophoenix.**

Very massive; unarmed, leaf regularly pinnate, leaflets acute; inflorescences branched to 1 rarely to 2 orders; peduncular bract borne at the top of the peduncle just below the rachillae, extremely thick and woody, splitting longitudinally and circumscissile, deciduous at anthesis; rachillae with large basal pulvini; fruit 1-seeded, endocarp rather thin with 3 pores; endosperm ruminate; embryo lateral near the base.

The subtribe consists of the single genus *Beccariophoenix* (Map 46). See notes under genus.

170. **BECCARIOPHOENIX** H. Jumelle & H. Perrier de la Bâthie, Annales de la Faculte des Sciences de Marseille 23(2):34. 1915. Type: **B. madagascariensis** H. Jumelle & H. Perrier de la Bâthie.

Robust, solitary, unarmed, pleonanthic, monoecious, tree palm. Stem erect. Leaves massive, pinnate, marcescent; sheath tubular at first, with a large, lateral obtuse lobe on each side, disintegrating into a mass of gray fibers; petiole absent; rachis adaxially channeled near the base, abaxially rounded, distally with 2 lateral grooves; leaflets single-fold, very numerous, ± regularly arranged, more slender and crowded at the base of the rachis than distally, ± rigid, acute, adaxially glabrous, abaxially sometimes covered with a thin layer of powdery white wax, transverse veinlets short, conspicuous. Inflorescences solitary, interfoliar, exserted from leaf sheaths, branching to 1(–2) orders; peduncle massive, elliptic in cross-section, densely gray-tomentose; prophyll inserted at the base of and shorter than the peduncle, thick, coriaceous, persistent, disintegrating into coarse interwoven fibers, strongly 2-keeled, tubular, splitting briefly at the tip; peduncular bract inserted at the apex of the peduncle, longer than the prophyll, extremely thick (up to 3 cm), woody, tubular, with a solid beak, splitting, longitudinally and circumscissile at the insertion, caducous, leaving a collarlike scar, adaxially smooth, shiny, abaxially tomentose and longitudinally shallowly grooved; rachis very short, bearing crowded, spirally arranged, short, triangular, acuminate,

Map 46.—**Distribution of Beccariophoenicinae.**

coriaceous bracts each subtending a first-order branch, the proximal few sometimes bearing 1 or 2 second-order branches; rachillae straight, rigid, rather thick, each with a large swelling at the very base, forming a spherical pulvinus, proximally with a very short bare portion, distally bearing subdistichous or strictly distichous flower groups, each subtended by a low triangular bract, the rachilla surface sparsely waxy or bare, flowers borne in triads throughout much of the rachilla length except near the tips where flowers solitary or paired and staminate, or near the base where flowers occasionally in 4's of 2 pistillate and 2 staminate; floral bracteoles well developed, broad, rounded, striate, rather coriaceous. Staminate flowers relatively very large, covered with white wax (?always), subsymmetrical; sepals 3, distinct, keeled, imbricate, coriaceous, rather short; petals 3, distinct except at the very base, valvate, strongly coriaceous to woody, ± boat-shaped, much longer than the sepals, somewhat striate, adnate at the very base to the floral axis; stamens 18–21, filaments short, slender at the base, adnate to the floral axis, anthers elongate, erect, ± basifixed, sometimes irregularly sagittate; pollen elliptic, monosulcate, with rugulate, perforate, tectate exine; pistillode absent or minute (Beccari and Pichi-Sermolli 1955). Pistillate flowers only slightly larger than the staminate, covered in thin wax (?always); sepals 3, distinct, broadly imbricate, hooded, strongly coriaceous, ± striate; petals 3, distinct, imbricate, thinly coriaceous, with very brief valvate tips; staminodes connate in a brief irregularly toothed ring; gynoecium trilocular, triovulate, obpyriform, stigmas 3, tightly appressed in bud, ovule form unknown. Fruit relatively large, 1-seeded, ± ovoid with a short triangular beak, the perianth segments persisting as a cupule; epicarp purplish with scattered brown tomentum, smooth, mesocarp rather dry with abundant longitudinal fibers, the outer fine, the inner broad

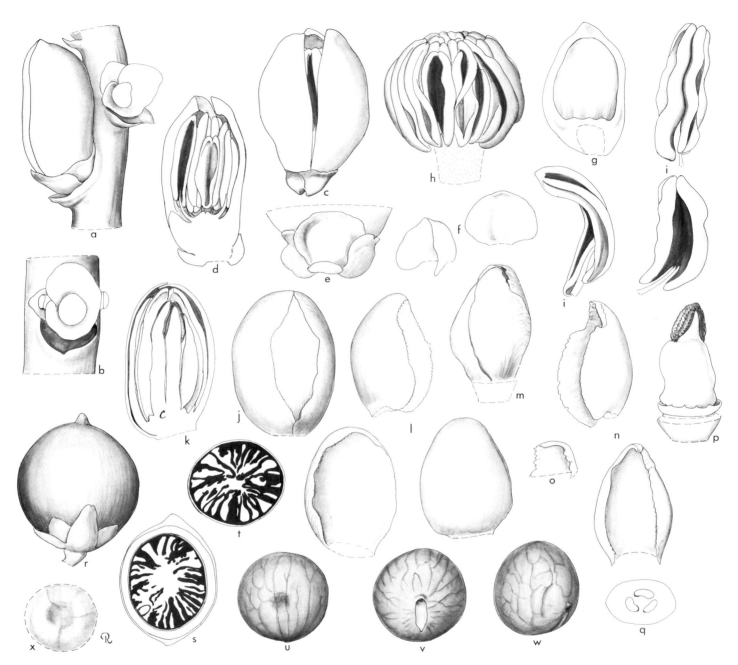

170.—**Beccariophoenix. a,** portion of staminate rachilla ×3; **b,** triad, flowers removed to show bracteoles and scars ×3; **c,** staminate flower ×3; **d,** staminate flower in vertical section ×3; **e,** staminate calyx ×4½; **f,** staminate sepal in 2 views ×4½; **g,** staminate petal, interior view ×3; **h,** androecium ×4½; **i,** stamen in 3 views ×4½; **j,** pistillate bud ×3; **k,** pistillate bud in vertical section ×3; **l,** pistillate sepals ×3; **m,** pistillate bud, sepals removed ×3; **n,** pistillate petal in 2 views ×3; **o,** pistillate petal tip ×3; **p,** gynoecium and staminodial cupule ×3; **q,** ovary in cross-section ×6; **r,** fruit ×1½; **s,** fruit in vertical section ×1½; **t,** fruit in cross-section ×1½; **u, v, w,** seed in 3 views ×1½; **x,** indentation in seed, enlarged. *Beccariophoenix madagascariensis*: all from *Humbert 20572.*

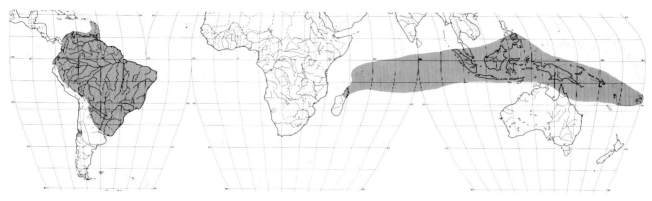

Map 47.—**Distribution of Butiinae.**

and flattened, easily separated from endocarp, endocarp woody, relatively thin, marked with 3 pores below the middle, 1 opposite the embryo. Seed broadly ovoid, attached near the base with a broad hilum, with numerous anastomosing raphe branches, endosperm deeply ruminate; embryo lateral below the equator. Germination and eophyll not known. Cytology not studied.

Anatomy.—Not studied.

Distribution.—A single species on the verge of extinction in eastern Madagascar.

Ecology.—Tropical rain forest at ca. 100–1000 m altitude.

Common Names and Uses.—Manarano, Maruala. The leaves are used in hat making. The destructive exploitation is thought to be responsible for the rarity of the palm.

Notes.—This is a spectacular and extraordinary palm. Characters suggesting affinities with the Cocoeae are the short peduncle, branched largely to 1 order, a prophyll and one peduncular bract, and an endocarp with defined pores. *Beccariophoenix* may be regarded as an ancient remnant of the line of evolution which gave rise to the Cocoeae. There seems now no doubt that the placement of *Beccariophoenix* by Beccari and Pichi Sermolli (1955) and Moore (1973a) together with members of the tribe Areceae was incorrect.

Taxonomic Accounts.—Beccari and Pichi-Sermolli (1955).

Figs. G.19, G.20.

Butiinae Saakov, Palms and their culture in the USSR 193. 1954. Type: **Butia.**

Diminutive to very large, unarmed except for the sometimes sharply toothed petiole margins; leaves pinnate, leaflets acute or oblique; inflorescence almost always bisexual; peduncular bract woody, inserted at the base of the peduncle, persistent; pistillate flowers not or only slightly sunken in the rachillae; petals of pistillate flowers broadly imbricate; endocarp with pores at or below the middle; endosperm homogeneous or ruminate.

This subtribe includes nine genera mostly from South America except for one species of *Syagrus* in the Lesser Antilles, the pantropical *Cocos* probably of Pacific origin, and *Jubaeopsis* in South Africa (Map 47). Fruits of a cocoid palm collected in Madagascar by Gerard Jean in 1983 were shown to us by Dr. M. E. Darian. Dransfield and Cooke made complete collections of the palm in October 1986. It belongs to subtribe Butiinae but further understanding of its relationships requires careful examination of flowers and fruiting material.

The delimitation of genera in this subtribe has caused many problems. Almost all species within the subtribe have at some time been included in the genus *Cocos*. We have adopted a more conservative approach than that of Beccari (1916) and Moore (1973a), and have recognized nine genera. We have reduced several genera to synonymy with *Syagrus,* which, however, remains distinct from *Cocos. Cocos* and *Syagrus* are obviously very closely related, but *Cocos* itself displays a unique assemblage of characters. The combination of very large globose-ovoid pistillate flowers with rounded sepals, and petals lacking valvate apices, and of very large fruit with liquid endosperm when young and a large central cavity at maturity is found nowhere else. The unusually thick fibrous mesocarp is also distinct.

The most specialized members of the subtribe are *Allagoptera* and *Polyandrococos*; in these two genera the inflorescence is spicate and the flowers, in particular the staminate, which are congested, misshapen, and stalked, with narrow divergent sepals, show remarkable divergence from those of less specialized genera such as *Butia* and *Syagrus*. The largest stamen number in the tribe is in *Polyandrococos*

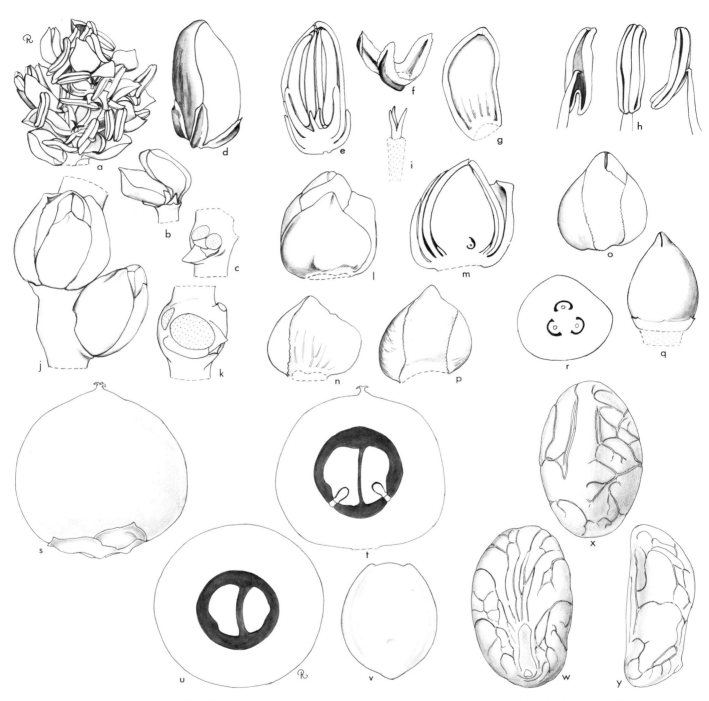

171.—**Butia. a,** portion of rachilla with staminate flowers ×3; **b,** staminate buds ×3; **c,** scars of paired staminate flowers with bract and bracteoles ×3; **d,** staminate bud ×6; **e,** staminate bud in vertical section ×6; **f,** staminate calyx ×6; **g,** staminate petal, interior view ×6; **h,** stamen in 3 views ×6; **i,** pistillode ×6; **j,** triad with pistillate buds ×3; **k,** triad, flowers removed to show bract and bracteoles ×3; **l,** pistillate bud ×3; **m,** pistillate bud in vertical section ×3; **n,** pistillate sepal ×3; **o,** pistillate bud, 2 sepals removed ×3; **p,** pistillate petal ×3; **q,** gynoecium and staminodial ring ×3; **r,** ovary in cross-section ×6; **s,** fruit ×1½; **t,** fruit in vertical section ×1½; **u,** fruit in cross-section ×1½; **v,** endocarp ×1½; **w, x, y,** seed in 3 views ×3. *Butia capitata*: **a-i,** *Moore s.n.*; **j-r,** *Read 906*; **s-y,** *Sheehan s.n.*

which has 60–120 stamens, borne on a remarkable elongate receptacle. The subtribe has been the subject of a phytochemical study by Williams, Harborne and Glassman (1983).

171. **BUTIA** (Beccari) Beccari, Agricoltura Coloniale 10:489. 1916. Lectotype: **B. capitata** (Martius) Beccari (*Cocos capitata* Martius) (see H. E. Moore 1963c).

Cocos subgenus *Butia* Beccari, Malpighia 1:352. 1887.

Syagrus section *Butia* (Beccari) Glassman, Fieldiana: Botany. 32:235. 1970 (Excluding *S. vagans* and *S. schizophylla*).

Small to large, solitary, armed or unarmed, pleonanthic, monoecious palms. Stem subterranean to erect, generally not tall, obscured by remains of leaf bases, eventually becoming bare, marked with close leaf scars, leaves pinnate, large, arching; sheaths tubular at first, disintegrating into a fibrous network, often densely tomentose; petiole short to long, channeled or flat adaxially, rounded or angled abaxially, proximally unarmed and bearing scattered fibers or armed with coarse spines decreasing in size distally until represented by short teeth, variously caducously scaly or glabrous, often glaucous; rachis usually curved, adaxially angled or flattened, rounded or flattened abaxially; leaflets single-fold, usually numerous, regularly arranged, held stiffly in the same plane, linear, acuminate, acute, obtuse or asymmetrical at the tips, frequently glaucous, usually with crowded ramenta on the abaxial surface of the main vein near the rachis, transverse veinlets obscure. Inflorescences solitary, interfoliar, shorter than the leaves, branching to 1 order, apparently protandrous; peduncle ± rounded in cross-section, short to long, ± glabrous or with scattered caducous scales; prophyll short, flattened, tubular, 2-keeled, usually hidden by the leaf sheaths, becoming fibrous with age, splitting at the tip, persistent; peduncular bract inserted near the prophyll, much longer, tubular, enclosing the inflorescence in bud, tightly sheathing proximally, beaked distally, splitting longitudinally along the abaxial face to expose the flowers, expanding distally and becoming cowllike, smooth or becoming longitudinally striate with age, adaxially glabrous, abaxially glabrous, scaly, or very densely tomentose; rachis shorter or longer than the peduncle, bearing spirally arranged, relatively few to very numerous rachillae, each subtended by an inconspicuous triangular bract; rachillae rather stiff, ± zig-zag, glabrous or minutely dotted, with a short to long, basal, bare portion, above which bearing few to numerous, spirally arranged triads proximally, paired or solitary staminate flowers distally, the distalmost rachillae sometimes entirely staminate, the flower groups close or relatively distant, superficial; rachilla bracts and floral bracteoles inconspicuous. Staminate flowers sessile or briefly pedicellate, slightly asymmetrical; sepals 3, distinct or jointed at the base, narrow, triangular, membranous, ± keeled, acute; petals 3, distinct, or very briefly connate at the base, valvate, at least 3 times as long as the sepals, ± fleshy, ovate to triangular; stamens 6, filaments distinct, awl-shaped, elongate, anthers elongate, medifixed, versatile, basally sagittate, introrse; pollen el-

liptic or subelliptic, monosulcate or trichotomosulcate, with foveolate or finely reticulate, tectate exine; pistillode shorter than the filaments, trifid. Pistillate flowers much larger than the staminate, globose to ovoid, ± symmetrical; sepals 3, distinct, broadly imbricate, coriaceous, somewhat keeled, triangular, the tips conspicuously hooded; petals 3, ± the same length as and similar to the sepals, distinct, broadly imbricate, the tips briefly valvate; staminodial ring well developed as a free, fleshy collar surrounding the base of the ovary, irregularly minutely lobed; gynoecium ± ovoid, trilocular, triovulate, stigmas 3, conspicuous, reflexed at anthesis, ovules hemianatropous, laterally attached to the ventral angles of the locules, septal canals present, opening at the bases of the stigmas. Fruit 1–3-seeded, spherical, oblate, or ovoid, yellow, brown, or purplish, with a short to long beak and apical stigmatic remains; epicarp smooth, mesocarp thin to thick, pulpy or fleshy, sometimes sweet, fibrous, endocarp thick, bony, with 1–3 developed cavities, the pores lateral below the equator or subbasal. Seed basally attached, conforming to the shape of the endocarp cavities, endosperm homogeneous, solid; embryo opposite the endocarp pore. Germination and eophyll not recorded. $n = 16$ (*Butia capitata* as *Cocos capitata* and *C. odorata*, *B. bonnetii*, Satô 1946; *B. capitata*, Janaki Ammal 1945, Read 1966).

Anatomy.—Leaf (Glassman 1979) and floral (Uhl and Moore 1971).

Distribution.—Eight well defined species and several poorly known taxa confined to cooler, drier areas of South America, in southern Brazil, Paraguay, Uruguay, and Argentina.

Ecology.—Often gregarious in grasslands, "campo rupestre," "cerrado," and woodlands in the lowlands.

Common Names and Uses.—Yatay palms, jelly palms, butia palms. Mesocarp of *B. capitata* is edible and can be made into jams; several species are widespread as slow growing cold-tolerant ornamentals.

Notes.—*Butia* seems most closely related to *Jubaea* but differs in having only six rather than numerous stamens and in the usually conspicuously toothed petioles.

Taxonomic Account.—Glassman (1979).

Plate.—74A; Figs. G.5, G.20.

172. **JUBAEA** Kunth in Humboldt, Bonpland & Kunth, Nova Genera et Species Plantarum 1: quarto edition 308; folio edition 247. 1816 ("1815"). Type: *J. spectabilis* Kunth = **J. chilensis** (Molina) Baillon (*Palma chilensis* Molina).

Molinaea Bertero, Mercurio Chileno 13:606. 1829. (Non Commerson ex A. L. Jussieu 1789). Type: *M. micrococos* Bertero (superfluous name).

Micrococos R. A. Philippi, Botanische Zeitung 17: 362. 1859. Type: *M. chilensis* (Molina) R. A. Philippi (*Palma chilensis* Molina).

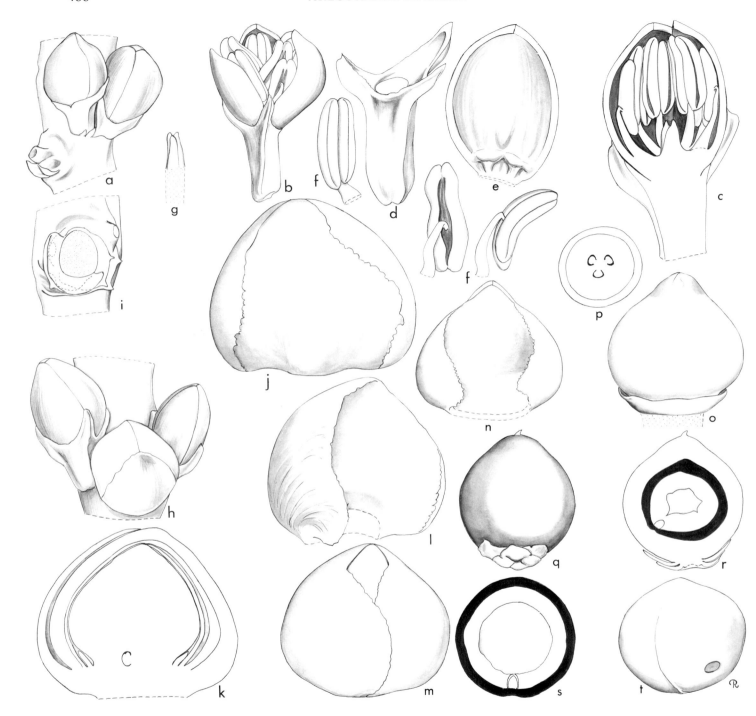

172.—**Jubaea. a,** portion of rachilla with staminate buds ×3; **b,** staminate flower ×3; **c,** staminate bud in vertical section ×6; **d,** staminate calyx and receptacle ×6; **e,** staminate petal, interior view ×6; **f,** stamen in 3 views ×6; **g,** pistillode ×6; **h,** portion of rachilla with triad ×3; **i,** triad, flowers removed to show bracteoles ×3; **j,** pistillate bud ×6; **k,** pistillate bud in vertical section ×6; **l,** pistillate sepal ×6; **m,** pistillate flower, sepals removed ×6; **n,** pistillate petal, interior view ×6; **o,** gynoecium and staminodial ring ×6; **p,** ovary in cross-section ×6; **q,** fruit ×1; **r,** fruit in vertical section ×1; **s,** endocarp and seed in cross-section ×1½; **t,** endocarp ×1½. *Jubaea chilensis:* **a-p,** *Moore 9366;* **q-t,** *Osborne s.n.*

Massive, solitary, unarmed, pleonanthic, monoecious palm. Stem erect, very stocky, eventually bare and marked with close, oblique leaf scars and vertical cracking. Leaves pinnate, many in the crown, neatly abscising in mature trunked individuals; sheaths soon disintegrating into fibers and eventually becoming open; petiole short to long, sometimes hardly distinguishable from the sheath, edged with disintegrated leaf sheath fibers except near the tip where almost smooth, adaxially flattened, abaxially rounded or angled, bearing thin or thick white wax or glabrous; rachis stiff or gently curving, proximally adaxial face flattened, angled distally, abaxially rounded, bearing scattered caducous scales distally; leaflets numerous, single-fold, close but irregularly grouped, held ± all in the same plane, linear, very stiff, the tips often with a reflexed hooklike flange representing a fragment of the rein, irregularly obliquely bifid or regularly bifid, thinly glaucous, adaxially bearing caducous scales along the main vein and very few scattered scales and wax on the blade surface, abaxially with abundant caducous scales and bifid ramenta throughout the length of the main vein, transverse veinlets obscure. Inflorescences solitary, interfoliar, large, branching to 1 order, protandrous; peduncle elongate, ± circular in cross-section, maroon when fresh, covered in dense, caducous tomentum; prophyll short, tubular, 2-keeled, enclosing the base of the peduncle, becoming fibrous with age; peduncular bract inserted near the prophyll, much exceeding it, enclosing the entire inflorescence in bud, tubular, woody, with a short solid beak, at anthesis splitting down ± the entire length, expanding and becoming cowl-shaped, adaxially smooth, glabrous, creamy-yellow when fresh, abaxially not grooved, only faintly striate, densely covered in soft, brown tomentum; rachis shorter than the peduncle, bearing numerous, elongate, spreading, spirally arranged rachillae, each subtended by a short, inconspicuous triangular bract; rachillae maroon, swollen at the very base and with a short basal bare portion, above which bearing numerous, spirally arranged triads in the proximal ca. $\frac{1}{8}$–$\frac{1}{4}$ and paired or solitary staminate flowers distally, the distalmost rachillae sometimes entirely staminate; floral bracteoles very small. Staminate flowers slightly asymmetrical; calyx with a solid, elongate, stalk-like base and 3, narrow, triangular keeled lobes; petals 3, much longer than the calyx, distinct, valvate, ± boat-shaped with triangular tips; stamens ca. 18, filaments slender, fleshy, elongate, cylindrical, apically inflexed, anthers medifixed, versatile, ± rectangular, latrorse; pollen elliptic, monosulcate, with tectate, foveolate exine; pistillode small, trifid. Pistillate flowers globular, only slightly larger than the staminate; sepals 3, distinct, rounded, broadly imbricate, the outermost ± keeled; petals 3, distinct, rounded, broadly imbricate except at the short triangular valvate tips; staminodial ring low, ± shallowly lobed, forming a collar surrounding the gynoecium; gynoecium trilocular, triovulate, ± broadly ovoid, stigmas closely appressed, ovules hemianatropous, laterally attached to the ventral angle of the locules. Fruit usually 1-seeded, orange-yellow, ± ovoid, with a short beak and apical stigmatic remains; epicarp smooth, mesocarp thick, fleshy, sweet, endocarp smooth, thick, bony, with 3 low crests and 3 pores lateral below the equator. Seed basally attached, closely adhering to the endocarp, endosperm homogeneous with large central cavity; embryo opposite one of the endocarp pores. Germination adjacent-ligular; eophyll entire, lanceolate. $n = 16$ (Sarkar 1970, Satô 1946, Read 1966).

Anatomy. — Leaf, readily identified by the anatomy of the lamina and showing some resemblances to *Butia* (Tomlinson 1961).

Distribution. — One species, now much restricted, and threatened in central Chile; widely cultivated in warm temperate regions.

Ecology. — Growing on sides of ravines and ridges in dry scrubby woodland.

Common Names and Uses. — Chilean wine palm. Formerly trunks of *Jubaea* were felled and tapped for wine and sugar, the yield from a single trunk being prodigious. The palm is a widespread and important ornamental in dry warm temperate regions.

Notes. — *Jubaea chilensis* is one of the most massive palms. It seems to be most closely related to *Jubaeopsis* and *Butia*. It differs from *Butia* in the lack of spines on the petioles, in stalked rather than sessile staminate flowers, and in having more than six stamens, and from *Jubaeopsis* in the solitary habit, and the stalked staminate flowers with connate sepals.

Dransfield et al. (1984) have reported the presence in the recent past of a now extinct palm on Easter Island. Though represented only by endocarps these are sufficient for the palm to be determined as belonging to the Butiinae and very closely related to *Jubaea*.

Taxonomic Account. — Glassman (1987).

Plates. — 28A; 74B.

173. JUBAEOPSIS Beccari, Webbia 4:171. 1913. Type: **J. caffra** Beccari.

Moderate, clustered, unarmed, pleonanthic, monoecious palm. Stems erect, branching at the base and also aerially by forking, bearing leaf sheath remains distally, eventually becoming bare, marked with close leaf scars. Leaves pinnate, arranged in 5 vertical rows, marcescent or neatly abscising; sheaths tubular, soon disintegrating into an interwoven mass of fibers; apparent petiole short to elongate, adaxially channeled, abaxially rounded, glabrous, the margins bearing leaf sheath fiber remains, or becoming smooth; rachis ± straight or curved, adaxially channeled near the base, angled distally, abaxially rounded or flattened; leaflets numerous, single-fold, close, regularly arranged, except at the very tip, stiff, held in one plane, linear, the tips mostly asymmetrically 2-lobed, except at the leaf tip where acute or sometimes hooked, thinly glaucous, adaxial surface bearing scattered, minute, dotlike scales, abaxially with scattered dotlike scales, and

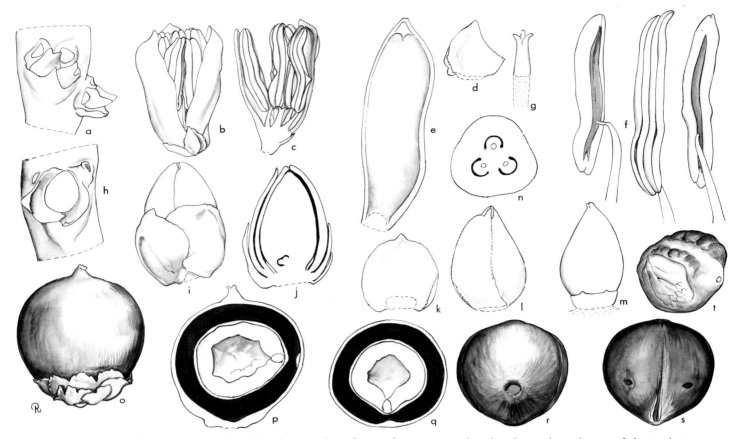

173.—**Jubaeopsis. a,** portion of rachilla with paired staminate flowers, flowers removed to show bracteoles and scars ×3; **b,** staminate flower ×3; **c,** staminate flower in vertical section ×3; **d,** staminate sepal ×6; **e,** staminate petal ×6; **f,** stamen in 3 views ×6; **g,** pistillode ×6; **h,** triad, flowers removed to show bracteoles and scars ×3; **i,** pistillate flower ×3; **j,** pistillate flower in vertical section ×3; **k,** pistillate sepal ×3; **l,** pistillate petal ×3; **m,** gynoecium and staminodial ring ×3; **n,** ovary in cross-section ×6; **o,** fruit ×1; **p,** fruit in vertical section ×1; **q,** fruit in cross-section ×1; **r, s,** endocarp in 2 views ×1; **t,** seed ×1. *Jubaeopsis caffra:* **a-n,** *Prosser s.n.;* **o-t,** *Codd s.n.*

a few large brown ramenta along the main vein, transverse veinlets conspicuous, sinuous. Inflorescences solitary, interfoliar, branching to 1 order, shorter than the leaves, protandrous; peduncle elongate, round in cross section; prophyll short, tubular, 2-keeled, enclosed within the leaf sheaths, splitting apically; peduncular bract inserted near the prophyll, tubular and entirely enclosing the inflorescence in bud, later splitting longitudinally along the abaxial face and expanding, becoming cowllike, woody, smooth, abaxially somewhat striate but not grooved, apically with a short, laterally flattened beak; rachis usually shorter than the peduncle, bearing numerous, spirally arranged, rather distant, spreading rachillae, each subtended by a low triangular bract; rachillae elongate, swollen at the very base and with a short or long basal bare portion, above which bearing few to numerous spirally arranged triads, distally bearing paired or solitary staminate flowers; rachilla bracts and floral bracteoles small, inconspicuous. Staminate flowers rather large, asymmetrical, sessile; sepals 3, distinct, unequal, imbricate, ± triangular, keeled; petals 3, distinct, very unequal, much larger than the sepals, boat-shaped with triangular tips, valvate; stamens (7–)8–16, filaments slender, fleshy, ± cylindrical, apically inflexed, anthers linear, basally sagittate, dorsifixed, introrse; pollen subelliptic or circular, monosulcate or trichotomosulcate, with punctate or vermiculate, tectate exine; pistillode small, irregularly trifid. Pistillate flowers ovoid, only slightly larger than the staminate; sepals 3, distinct, broad, rounded, with pointed tips, imbricate, somewhat irregularly keeled; petals 3, distinct, ± twice as long as the sepals, broad, rounded, imbricate except at the short valvate triangular tips; staminodial ring collarlike, very briefly toothed or consisting of several irregular toothlike lobes; gynoecium ± ovoid, trilocular, triovulate, stigmas 3, very short, ± triangular, ovules hemianatropous, laterally attached. Fruit 1-seeded, brown at maturity, globose with a short apical beak, stigmatic remains apical; epicarp smooth, mesocarp thin, fibrous, only slightly fleshy, easily separated from the endocarp at maturity, endocarp thick, bony, with 3 vertical grooves, the pores lateral just below the equator. Seed basally attached, somewhat irregular in shape, endosperm homogeneous with a large central cavity; embryo lateral, next to one of the endocarp pores. Germination remote tubular; eophyll entire, lanceolate. $n = 80-100$ (Robertson 1976).

Anatomy.—See Robertson (1976a, b) for embryology and (1977a) for anatomy and development of fruit and seed.

Distribution.—One species confined to the coastal reaches of two rivers in South Africa.

Ecology.—*J. caffra* grows gregariously on the steep north, rocky banks of the rivers, near sea-level.

Common Names and Uses.—Pondoland palm, Kafir palm. The endosperm may be eaten. Because of its rarity, *J. caffra* is sought after as a collector's item.

Notes.—*Jubaeopsis* is most closely related to *Jubaea* and *Butia*; it represents a remarkable relic of the evolution of the Cocoeae surviving in Southern Africa.

Taxonomic Account.—For a discussion of its morphology see Robertson (1977b). See Beccari (1913a) and Glassman (1987).

Plate.—*74C.*

174. Cocos Linnaeus, Species Plantarum 1188. 1753. Type: **C. nucifera** Linnaeus.
Calappa Steck, Dissertatio Inauguralis Medica de Sagu 9. 1757.
Coccus P. Miller, The Gardener's Dictionary Abridged from the Folio Edition 4. 1754.

Moderate, solitary, unarmed, pleonanthic, monoecious palm, sometimes flowering while still without an emergent trunk. Stem erect, often curved or slanting, becoming bare and conspicuously ringed with leaf scars. Leaves numerous, pinnate, neatly abscising; sheath fibrous, forming a woven supportive network with a conspicuous, tonguelike extension opposite the petiole, eventually disintegrating and becoming open; petiole short to long, adaxially channeled, abaxially rounded, bearing caducous tomentum abaxially; rachis elongate, curved or straight, adaxially angled near the tip, abaxially rounded, with caducous tomentum abaxially; leaflets very numerous, single fold, regularly arranged in one plane, usually rather stiff, linear, acuminate, usually bifid with slightly asymmetrical tips, adaxially glabrous, abaxially with abundant, dotlike scales and very small ramenta along the midrib, midrib prominent adaxially, transverse veinlets evident. Inflorescences solitary, interfoliar, axillary, branched to 1 order, protandrous; peduncle ± elliptic in cross-section, robust, elongate, bearing scattered scales; prophyll tubular, 2-keeled laterally, opening apically, becoming fibrous, tomentose, persistent, ± obscured by the leaf sheaths; peduncular bract inserted near the prophyll, very large, tubular, entirely enclosing the inflorescence in bud, splitting abaxially, becoming boat-shaped, beaked, thick, woody, adaxially smooth, abaxially with longitudinal, shallow grooves and caducous tomentum; rachis ± equalling the peduncle,

bearing spirally arranged rachillae, each subtended by an inconspicuous triangular bract and with a swollen base; rachillae robust, ± pendulous at first, later spreading with a basal bare portion and 0–a few basal triads and pairs or solitary staminate flowers distally; rachilla bracts and floral bracteoles inconspicuous. Staminate flowers ± asymmetrical, narrowly ovoid, moderate, sessile; sepals 3, distinct, rather unequal, imbricate, triangular, ± keeled; petals much longer than the sepals, thick, rather leathery, distinct, valvate, irregularly boat-shaped, acute; stamens 6, filaments rather short, distinct, awl-shaped, fleshy, ± erect, anthers deeply sagittate basally, shallowly so at the apex, elongate, medifixed, ± versatile, latrorse; pollen elliptic, monosulcate or occasionally trichotomosulcate, exine tectate, finely reticulate; pistillode with 3, slender, pointed lobes. Pistillate flowers very large, globose in bud, becoming very broadly ovoid at anthesis; sepals 3, distinct, imbricate, ± rounded; petals similar to and somewhat longer than the sepals, lacking valvate apices, very leathery; staminodial ring low, membranous, not lobed; gynoecium trilocular at the very base, triovulate, broadly ovoid, obscurely 3-angled, extremely fibrous distally, stigmas 3, very short, borne in a slight depression, ovule anatropous, very small, laterally attached. Fruit very large (except in unusual forms), ellipsoidal to broadly ovoid, indistinctly 3-angled, dull green, brown, brilliant-orange, yellow, to ivory-colored when ripe, perianth enlarging in fruit, stigmatic remains apical; epicarp smooth, mesocarp very thick and fibrous, dry, endocarp thick and woody, ± spherical to narrow ovoid, indistinctly 3-angled, with 3 longitudinal ridges, and 3, large, slightly sunken, basal pores, each with an operculum. Seed almost always 1 only, very large, with a narrow layer of homogeneous endosperm, and a large central cavity partially filled with fluid; embryo basal, opposite one of the endocarp pores. Germination adjacent-ligular; eophyll entire, broadly lanceolate. $n = 16$ (Gassner 1941, Janaki Ammal 1945, Read 1966, Satô 1946, Sharma and Sarkar 1957).

Anatomy.—Leaf, stems, root (Tomlinson 1961), leaf base (Tomlinson 1964).

Distribution.—A single species widely cultivated throughout the tropics and warmer subtropics. Origin uncertain but probably western Pacific (see Harries 1978, Gruezo and Harries 1984, Buckley and Harries 1984).

Ecology.—*C. nucifera* is often regarded as a strand plant but it will flower and fruit in humid equatorial regions at altitudes up to 900 m above sea level. Its natural habitat may well have been strand vegetation.

Common Names and Uses.—Coconut. One of the most important tropical crops with a multiplicity of uses both local and commercial.

Notes.—Gruezo and Harries (1984) and Buckley and Harries (1984) record the presence of wild-type coconuts in the Philippines and Australia respectively in apparently natural coastal forest and argue convincingly that these areas are exactly where *Co-*

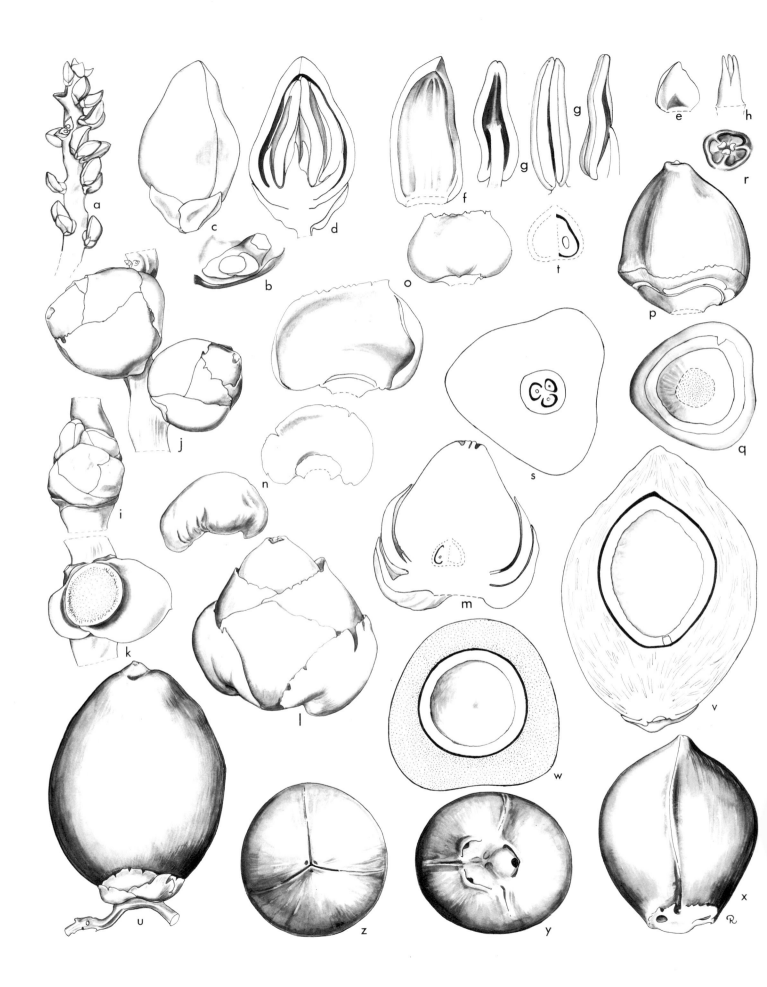

cos might be predicted to be native. *Cocos* is obviously very closely related to *Syagrus* but differs in the large pistillate flowers with rounded sepals and petals, in the large fruit with thick fibrous mesocarp, and in the endosperm.

The often slanting stems and graceful crowns of the coconut are largely responsible for palms being considered the hallmark of the tropics. Furthermore the coconut, one of the ten most important crop trees, is the mainstay of many people.

Taxonomic Accounts.—Glassman (1987), Harries (1978). See also Child (1974).

Plate.—28B; Figs. G.18, G.22.

175. SYAGRUS Martius, Palmarum Familia 18. 1824. Type: S. cocoides Martius.

Langsdorffia Raddi, Memorie di Matematica e di Fisica della Societa Italiana della Scienze 18(2): 345. 1820 (Non Martius, 1818). Type: *L. pseudococos* Raddi (=*Syagrus pseudococos* (Raddi) Glassman).

Platenia Karsten, Linnaea 28:250. 1856. Type: *P. chiragua* Karsten (=*Syagrus chiragua* (Karsten) H. A. Wendland).

Cocos subgenus *Arecastrum* Drude in Martius, Flora Brasiliensis 3(2):402. 1881.

Barbosa Beccari, Malpighia 1:349, 352. 1887. Type: *B. pseudococos* (Raddi) Beccari (*Langsdorffia pseudococos* Raddi) (=*Syagrus pseudococos* (Raddi) Glassman).

Rhyticocos Beccari, Malpighia 1:350, 353. 1887. Type: *R. amara* (N. J. Jacquin) Beccari (*Cocos amara* N. J. Jacquin) (=*Syagrus amara* (N. J. Jacquin) Martius).

Arikuryroba Barbosa Rodrigues, Plantas Novas Cultivadas no Jardim Botanico do Rio de Janeiro 1: 5. 1891. Type: *A. capanemae* Barbosa Rodrigues = *A. schizophylla* (Martius) L. H. Bailey (*Cocos schizophylla* Martius). (=*Syagrus schizophylla* (Martius) Glassman).

Arikury Beccari, Agricoltura Coloniale 10:445. 1916. Superfluous substitute name.

Arecastrum (Drude) Beccari, Agricoltura Coloniale 10:446. 1916. Type: *A. romanzoffianum* (Chamisso) Beccari (*Cocos romanzoffiana* Chamisso). (=*Syagrus romanzoffiana* (Chamisso) Glassman).

Chrysallidosperma H. E. Moore, Principes 7:109. 1963. Type: *C. smithii* H. E. Moore (=*Syagrus smithii* (H. E. Moore) Glassman).

Small to tall, solitary or clustered, unarmed or armed, pleonanthic, monoecious palms. Stem very short, subterranean to erect and tall, rarely stolonlike, sometimes swollen basally, distally obscured by leaf base remains, becoming bare, sometimes striate, and marked with inconspicuous or raised or impressed, oblique or circular conspicuous leaf scars. Leaves reduplicately pinnate, spirally arranged or, in *S. coronata*, ± arranged in 5 ranks, marcescent or neatly abscising; sheath disintegrating into an interwoven mass of fibers, the fibers slender to robust and flattened, rarely flattened and spinelike; petiole very short to long, adaxially channeled or flattened, abaxially rounded or angled, the margins smooth or bearing short caducous fibers, and rarely also bearing coarse spinelike fibers, surfaces variously glabrous, tomentose or scaly, sometimes waxy; rachis straight or curved, short to long, variously scaly, tomentose or glabrous; leaflets single-fold, few to very numerous, regularly or irregularly arranged, held in one or several planes, linear, moderately wide to very narrow, stiff or curved, the tips acute, acuminate or obtuse, symmetrical and shallowly bifid or asymmetrical; blade adaxially glabrous or with sparse scales or hairs, sometimes waxy, abaxially usually with conspicuous ramenta along the main vein, very rarely also with dense gray indumentum, transverse veinlets often conspicuous. Inflorescences solitary, interfoliar, rarely spicate, usually branching to 1 order, ?protandrous, much shorter than the leaves; peduncle ± elliptic in cross-section, short to long, glabrous or variously hairy or scaly; prophyll usually mostly concealed within the leaf sheaths, tubular, flattened, 2-keeled, splitting at the tip, becoming fibrous and disintegrating with age; peduncular bract persistent, much longer than the prophyll, usually inserted just above the prophyll, tubular, enclosing the inflorescence in bud, very rarely shorter than the expanded inflorescence, often ± spindle-shaped before splitting longitudinally along the abaxial face for most of its length, then expanding and becoming cowllike, beaked, usually ± woody, rarely thinly coriaceous or papery, glabrous or glaucous or pubescent, longitudinally grooved; rachis usually shorter than the peduncle or nearly equal (*S. coronata*), glabrous or hairy, bearing spirally arranged rachillae, each subtended by a

---

←

174.—**Cocos. a,** apical portion of rachilla with staminate buds ×⅔; **b,** pair of staminate flowers, flowers removed to show scars and bracteoles ×6; **c,** staminate bud ×6; **d,** staminate bud in vertical section ×6; **e,** staminate sepal, interior view ×6; **f,** staminate petal, interior view ×6; **g,** stamen in 3 views ×6; **h,** pistillode ×6; **i,** triad with pistillate bud and staminate flowers ×1½; **j,** lower portion of rachilla in pistillate flower ×1; **k,** triad, flowers removed to show bracteoles and scars ×1½; **l,** pistillate flower ×1½; **m,** pistillate flower in vertical section ×1½; **n,** pistillate sepals, interior and exterior views ×1½; **o,** pistillate petals, interior and exterior views ×1½; **p,** gynoecium and staminodial ring ×1½; **q,** basal view of gynoecium showing staminodial ring ×1½; **r,** stigmas ×3; **s,** ovary in cross-section ×1½; **t,** locule and ovule in vertical section ×3; **u,** fruit ×⅜; **v,** fruit in vertical section ×⅜; **w,** fruit in cross-section ×⅜; **x, y, z,** endocarp in 3 views ×½. *Cocos nucifera:* all from *Read s.n.* and *Moore s.n.*

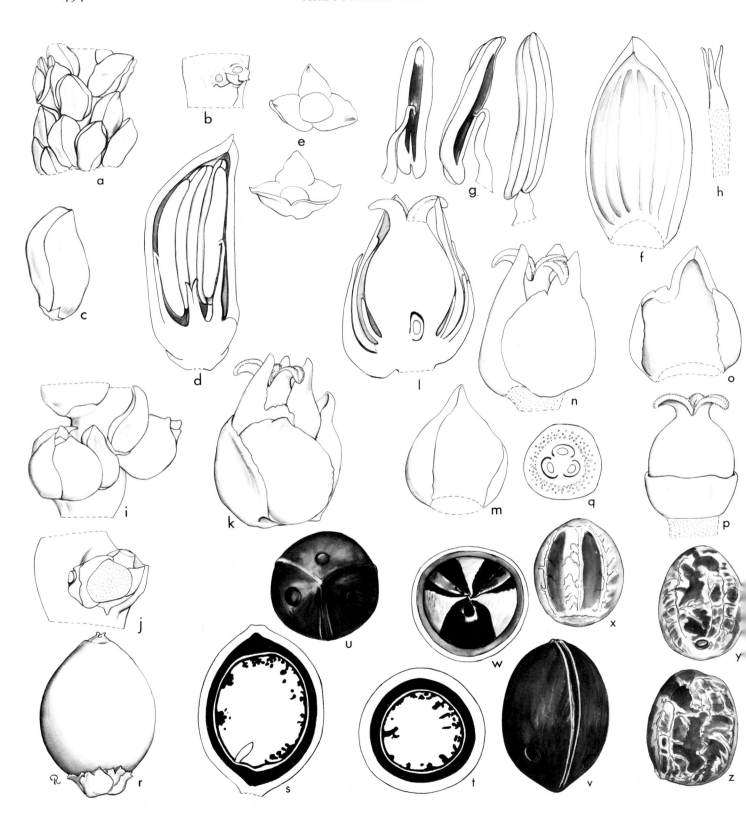

short, triangular, usually coriaceous bract; rachillae few to numerous, short or elongate, slender, straight or often twisted in bud, frequently zig-zag, glabrous or sparsely tomentose, bearing spirally arranged triads proximally, paired or solitary staminate flowers distally, or rarely, the distalmost rachillae bearing only staminate flowers; flower groups usually sessile, subtended by usually inconspicuous bracts; floral bracteoles minute. Staminate flowers usually ± asymmetrical; sepals 3, ± triangular, distinct and imbricate or briefly connate, rarely connate in a stalklike base; petals 3, distinct, valvate, ± thinly coriaceous or fleshy, much longer than the sepals, variously lanceolate, oblong, or ovate with acute tips, glabrous, tomentose, scaly or dotted; stamens 6, filaments distinct, or very briefly connate, relatively short, ± fleshy, anthers elongate, dorsifixed near the base or medifixed and ± versatile, introrse or latrorse; pollen elliptic, subelliptic, or subtriangular, monosulcate or trichotomosulcate, with finely reticulate or foveolate, tectate exine; pistillode minute, trifid or absent. Pistillate flowers slightly smaller to very much larger than the staminate flowers; sepals 3, distinct, broadly imbricate, triangular to ovate, acute or obtuse, fleshy to coriaceous, sometimes tomentose or scaly; petals 3, distinct, slightly shorter to slightly longer than the sepals, triangular or ovate, broadly imbricate at the base, with minute to moderately large and conspicuous valvate tips; staminodial ring membranous, low, ± 6-toothed, occasionally apparently absent; gynoecium columnar to conical or ovoid, trilocular, triovulate, glabrous or tomentose to scaly, the stigmas 3, reflexed, fleshy, ovules laterally attached to the central wall of the locules, ?anatropous. Fruit small to relatively large, 1–(rarely 2–) seeded, spherical, ovoid, or ellipsoidal, variously green, brown, yellow, or reddish, sometimes beaked, the perianth segments and staminodial ring persistent and sometimes enlarging as a cupule at the fruit base; epicarp smooth or longitudinally striate, glabrous or hairy, mesocarp fleshy or dry, with abundant longitudinal fibers, endocarp thick, woody, with basal or subbasal pores, sometimes beaked, sometimes with 3 longitudinal ridges, rarely with 3 irregular vertical bands of minute pores, endocarp cavity irregular or more usually circular, rarely triangular in cross-section, with 3, conspicuous, vertical lines, very rarely with a curved lateral protrusion into the seed (*S. romanzoffiana*). Seed conforming to the shape of the endocarp cavity, subbasally attached, endosperm homogeneous or ruminate, sometimes with a central cavity; embryo basal or subbasal opposite one of the endocarp pores. Germination adjacent-ligular or remote tubular; eophyll entire. *n* = 15 (*S. schizophylla* as *Arikuryroba schizophylla, S. vagans* as *S.* sp., Read 1966). *n* = 16 (*S. romanzoffiana* as *Arecastrum romanzoffianaum*, Janaki Ammal 1945, Sato 1946, Sar-

kar 1970, Read 1966; *S. comosa, S. coronata,* Read 1966; *S. schizophylla* as *Cocos schizophylla,* Sharma and Sarkar 1957.

Anatomy. — Leaf (Tomlinson 1961, Glassman 1987).

Distribution. — Thirty-two species recorded in South America from Venezuela southwards to Argentina with the greatest number of species in Brazil; one species in the Lesser Antilles.

Ecology. — Most species are confined to dry or semi-arid areas; these include all the acaulescent species. A few, usually treelike species are restricted to mesic and tropical rain forest. The acaulescent species are conspicuous components of several Brazilian arid vegetation types such as "cerrado" and "campo rupestre."

Common Names and Uses. — Syagrus palms, licury palm (*S. coronata*), Queen palm (*S. romanzoffiana*). Leaves of many species are used as thatch, those of *S. coronata* also yielding wax. The mesocarp of *S. oleracea* and *S. coronata* is edible, and the endosperm of *S. cocoides* and *S. coronata* can be used as a source of palm oil. The wood is also useful. For medicinal uses see Plotkin and Balick (1984). Many species are cultivated as ornamentals.

Notes. — After a great deal of deliberation we have decided to include several genera earlier recognized as distinct because of their ruminate endosperm (Moore 1973a). The basis for including the genera is the extraordinary variability of *Syagrus* itself and the unreliability of the endosperm character elsewhere in the family for separating genera. Thus *S. vagans* and *S. ruschiana* approach *Arikuryroba, S. inajai* differs from *Chrysallidosperma smithii* only in a few minor characters and the endosperm. The connate petals of *Rhyticocos* referred to by Read (1979) have not been found on our specimens, and the palm is otherwise rather like *Syagrus sancona* with a large ruminate endosperm. *Barbosa pseudococos* is very similar in flower and fruit characters to *S. stratinicola*. In broadening the concept of *Syagrus, Cocos* itself becomes very similar but, nevertheless, is distinct on the basis of the very few pis-

---

175. — **Syagrus. a,** portion of rachilla with paired staminate flowers × 3; **b,** scars of paired staminate flowers and bracteole × 6; **c,** staminate bud × 6; **d,** staminate flower in vertical section × 12; **e,** staminate calyx in 2 views × 12; **f,** staminate petal, interior view × 12; **g,** stamen in 3 views × 12; **h,** pistillode × 12; **i,** portion of rachilla with triads × 3; **j,** triad, flowers removed to show bracts × 6; **k,** pistillate flower × 6; **l,** pistillate flower in vertical section × 6; **m,** pistillate sepal × 6; **n,** pistillate flower, sepals removed × 6; **o,** pistillate petal, interior view × 6; **p,** gynoecium and staminodial ring × 6; **q,** ovary in cross-section × 6; **r,** fruit × 1½; **s,** fruit in vertical section × 1½; **t,** fruit in cross-section × 1½; **u, v, w,** endocarp in 3 views × 1½; **x, y, z,** seed in 3 views × 1½. *Syagrus schizophylla*: all from *Read 824.*

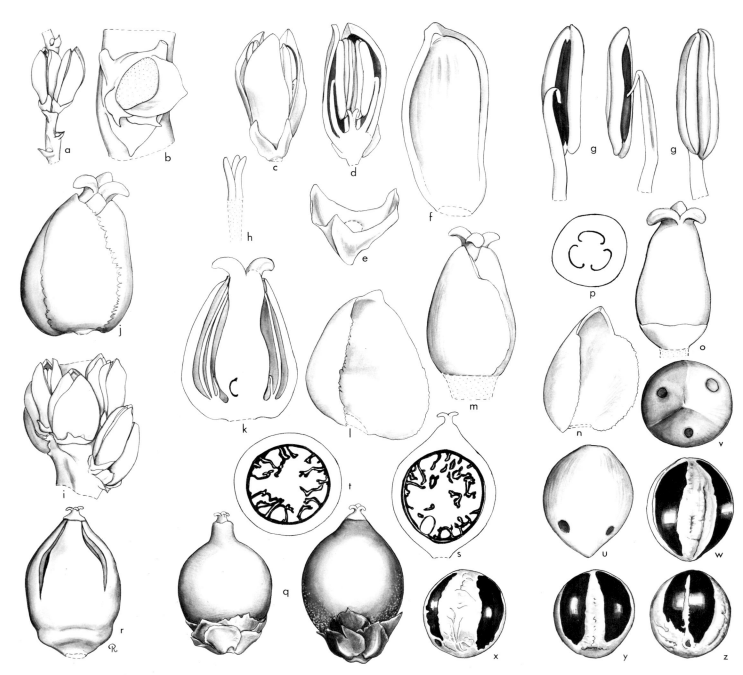

176.—Lytocaryum. a, distal portion of rachilla with paired staminate buds ×3; **b,** triad, flowers removed to show bracteoles ×6; **c,** staminate flower ×6; **d,** staminate flower in vertical section ×6; **e,** staminate calyx ×12; **f,** staminate petal, interior view ×12; **g,** stamen in 3 views ×12; **h,** pistillode ×12; **i,** portion of rachilla with triads ×3; **j,** pistillate flower ×6; **k,** pistillate flower in vertical section ×6; **l,** pistillate sepal ×6; **m,** pistillate flower, sepals removed ×6; **n,** pistillate petal ×6; **o,** gynoecium and staminodial ring ×6; **p,** ovary in cross-section ×18; **q,** two fruits ×1½; **r,** dried fruit with split pericarp ×1½; **s,** fruit in vertical section ×1½; **t,** fruit in cross-section ×1½; **u, v,** endocarp in 2 views ×1½; **w,** interior of endocarp, seed removed ×1; **x, y, z,** seed in 3 views ×1½. *Lytocaryum hoehnei*: **a–q** and **s–z,** *Eiten s.n.*; **r,** *Leandro & Toledo 51,606.*

tillate flowers which are distinctly ovoid and much larger than the staminate flowers and have rounded sepals and petals, and the extremely large fruit and very large seed with liquid endosperm when young.

Taxonomic Account.—Glassman (1987).

Plate.—*74D.*

176. LYTOCARYUM Toledo, Arquivos de Botanica do Estado de Saõ Paulo ser. 2, 2(1):6. 1944. Type: **L. hoehnei** (Burret) Toledo (*Syagrus hoehnei* Burret).

Glaziova Martius ex Drude, in Martius, Flora Brasiliensis 3(2):295. 1881 (Non Bureau 1868). Lectotype: *G. martiana* Glaziou ex Drude (illegitimate name) (=*Lytocaryum weddellianum* (H. A. Wendland) Toledo) (see H. E. Moore 1963c).

Microcoelum Burret & Potztal, Willdenowia 1:387. 1956. Lectotype: *M. martianum* (Glaziou ex Drude) Burret & Potztal (*Glaziova martiana* Glaziou ex Drude (illegitimate name) = *Lytocaryum weddellianum* (H. A. Wendland) Toledo (*Cocos weddellianum* H. A. Wendland, *M. weddellianum* (H. A. Wendland) H. E. Moore)).

Slender, solitary, unarmed, pleonanthic, monoecious palms. Stem erect, short, rarely exceeding 3 m, at first obscured by leaf sheath remains, later bare, closely ringed with leaf scars. Leaves pinnate, marcescent, graceful; leaf sheaths densely light or dark brown-hairy, with a triangular ligulelike projection opposite the petiole, later disintegrating into a fibrous network and splitting; petiole very short to elongate, adaxially flat to rounded, abaxially rounded or angled, fibrous along the margins, also with scattered thin indumentum and some coarse dark hairs; rachis neatly curved, usually bearing conspicuous, dark, coarse hairs adaxially; leaflets single-fold, numerous, slender, often extremely so, linear, close and regularly arranged, the tips asymmetrical, soft in texture, the adaxial surface dark green, abaxial surface covered with gray or pale brownish indumentum, with few to numerous ramenta along the midrib, transverse veinlets obscure. Inflorescences solitary, interfoliar, branching to 1 order, protandrous; peduncle short to elongate, elliptic in cross-section, sparsely to densely tomentose; prophyll tubular, flattened, 2-keeled, usually mostly concealed by the leaf sheaths, opening distally, becoming fibrous in age, light or dark brown tomentose; peduncular bract elongate, inserted just above and much longer than the prophyll, coriaceous to ± woody, entirely enclosing the inflorescence in bud, splitting longitudinally along the abaxial face and expanding, adaxial surface glabrous, smooth or tomentose, ± grooved, abaxial surface deeply grooved, densely light or dark brown-tomentose; rachis usually shorter than the peduncle, sparsely to densely tomentose like the peduncle, bearing numerous, spirally arranged rachillae, each subtended by a minute triangular bract; rachillae eventually widely spreading, slender, sparsely tomentose,

somewhat zig-zag, with a short to long basal bare portion, above which bearing few triads proximally and bearing paired or solitary staminate flowers distally, the distalmost rachillae shorter and sometimes entirely staminate; rachilla bracts and floral bracteoles inconspicuous. Staminate flowers small, ± symmetrical, sessile or borne on brief, slender pedicels; calyx with or without a solid, short to long stalklike base, and 3, membranous, keeled, narrow triangular, acute lobes; petals 3, distinct, valvate, ovate-triangular, acute, thinly coriaceous with scattered, caducous, dotlike scales; stamens 6, filaments slender or basally thickened, very briefly epipetalous, elongate, ± inflexed, anthers slender, ± oblong, basally sagittate, apically sometimes pointed, medifixed, versatile, latrorse; pollen elliptic, sometimes ± dilated at one end, monosulcate, with foveolate or finely reticulate, tectate exine; pistillode conspicuous, about ½ the height of the filaments, trifid or minute. Pistillate flower larger than the staminate, ± pyramidal; sepals 3, distinct, triangular, broadly imbricate, coriaceous, keeled, the tips ± hooded or not; petals ± equalling the sepals, 3, distinct, broadly imbricate at the base, abruptly narrowed at ± the midpoint to broad or narrow, tapering, valvate tips; staminodial ring thinly fleshy, irregularly 6-toothed or truncate; gynoecium ± pyramidal, trilocular, triovulate, brown-hairy, with a very short to long style and 3 stigmas appressed in bud, ovules laterally attached to the central axis, form unknown. Fruit globose to ovoid, 1-seeded, tinged pink or reddish, with a short beak and apical stigmatic remains; epicarp ± smooth, mesocarp thin, ± fibrous, it and the epicarp dehiscing along 3 vertical sutures to expose the endocarp, endocarp thin, rather fragile, marked with 3 vertical lines externally, internally with 3 shining broad bands, endocarp pores lateral near the base. Seed laterally attached with broad lateral hilum, endosperm homogeneous (*L. weddellianum* and *L. insigne*) or deeply ruminate (*L. hoehnei*), with or without a central hollow; embryo basal opposite an endocarp pore. Germination adjacent-ligular; eophyll pinnate. *n* = 16 (*L. weddellianum* as *Cocos weddelliana*, Eichhorn 1953).

Anatomy.—Not studied.

Distribution.—Three closely related species restricted to southeast Brazil. *L. weddellianum* is widespread as an ornamental.

Ecology.—Found in shady forest at altitudes of 800–1800 m.

Fossil Record.—Not known.

Common Names and Uses.—Common names not recorded. *L. weddellianum* is an important pot palm, sold in large quantities in Europe.

Notes.—The only difference between *Microcoelum* and *Lytocaryum* is the nature of the endosperm; otherwise the two taxa are very similar. Thus *Microcoelum* is placed in synonymy. *Lytocaryum* in the present sense has a combination of characters unusual in the subtribe Butiinae. The distinctive leaves with abundant rachis tomentum, together with

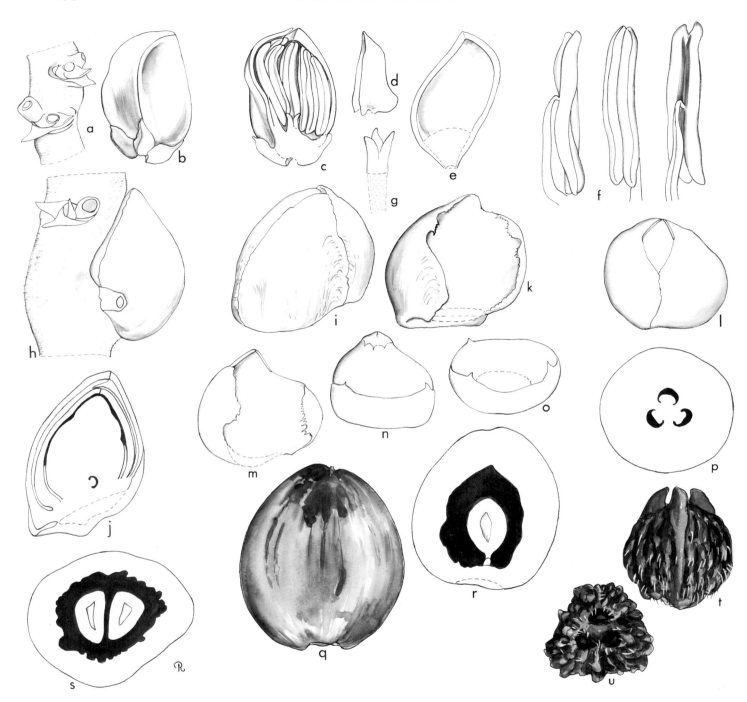

177.—**Parajubaea. a,** portion of rachilla with paired staminate flowers, flowers removed to show bracteoles and scars ×3; **b,** staminate bud ×3; **c,** staminate bud in vertical section ×3; **d,** staminate sepal ×6; **e,** staminate petal, interior view ×3; **f,** stamen in 3 views ×6; **g,** pistillode ×6; **h,** portion of rachilla with triads, all flowers but one pistillate bud removed to show scars and bracteoles ×3; **i,** pistillate flower ×3; **j,** pistillate flower in vertical section ×3; **k,** pistillate sepal ×3; **l,** pistillate flower, sepals removed ×3; **m,** pistillate petal ×3; **n,** gynoecium and staminodial ring ×3; **o,** staminodial ring ×3; **p,** ovary in cross-section ×6; **q,** fruit ×¾; **r,** fruit in vertical section ×¾; **s,** fruit in cross-section ×¾; **t, u,** endocarp in 2 views ×¾. *Parajubaea torallyi:* all from *Cardenas s.n.*

the strongly versatile anthers, the fruit with epicarp and mesocarp dehiscing by vertical sutures, and the thin rather fragile endocarp separate *Lytocaryum* from *Syagrus*.

Taxonomic Account. — See Glassman (1987).

Plate. — *75A.*

177. **PARAJUBAEA** Burret, Notizblatt des Botanischen Gartens und Museums zu Berlin-Dahlem 11: 48. 1930. Type: **P. cocoides** Burret.

Large, solitary, unarmed, pleonanthic, monoecious palms. Stem tall, stout or rather slender, gray, obscurely ringed with leaf scars. Leaves pinnate, slightly arching to pendulous, sometimes twisted, marcescent; sheath not forming a crownshaft, disintegrating into a mass of rather fine, brown fibers; petiole short, adaxially flat, abaxially rounded, glabrous, margins fibrous at least basally; rachis longer than the petiole, tapering, rounded adaxially, grooved laterally, rounded abaxially; leaflets distant, subopposite, narrow, elongate, single-fold, pointed distally, tips shortly bifid to oblique, glabrous adaxially, abaxially sparsely scaly and with linear ramenta along the midribs, midrib prominent adaxially, the only large vein, transverse veinlets not evident. Inflorescences interfoliar, erect, becoming pendulous in fruit, branched to 1 order; peduncle elongate, dorsiventrally flattened, glabrous; prophyll short, 2-keeled, opening apically, not exserted from the leaf sheath; peduncular bract much longer than the prophyll, narrowly tubular, tapering to a short apical beak, woody, deeply grooved, splitting abaxially and marcescent at least for a while, glabrous; several short, incomplete peduncular bracts present; rachis about as long as or shorter than the peduncle, bearing rather distant, spirally arranged, short, wide, centrally pointed bracts subtending rachillae; rachillae erect and closely appressed to the rachis, rather short, stout, sometimes zig-zag, enlarged basally, bearing spirally arranged, very short, wide, pointed bracts subtending a few triads (often 2) at the base and paired to solitary staminate flowers throughout most of the rachilla length; floral bracteoles short, rounded to pointed. Staminate flowers asymmetrical, ± pointed; sepals 3, distinct, imbricate basally, keeled, acute; petals 3, distinct, much larger than the sepals, angled, valvate; stamens ca. 15, filaments erect, awl-shaped, ± inflexed; anthers linear, emarginate apically, sagittate basally, dorsifixed near the middle, introrse; pollen elliptic, monosulcate, with finely punctate, tectate exine; pistillode short, briefly trifid. Pistillate flowers broadly ovoid, larger than the staminate; sepals 3, distinct, imbricate, margins irregular; petals 3, distinct, imbricate with briefly pointed, valvate tips; staminodes united in a shallow cupule with 3 pointed tips; gynoecium broadly ovoid, trilocular, triovulate, stigma short, rounded, trilobed, ovules laterally attached, form unknown. Fruit oblong-ovoid, beaked, perianth persistent on fresh fruit; epicarp smooth, mesocarp rather thin, fibrous, endocarp thick, very hard, with shining lines internally, externally irregularly sculptured with 3 prominent ridges (*P. torallyi*), or surface and thickness irregular, ridges not prominent (*P. cocoides*), pores 3, basal, sunken.

Seeds 1(–3), rounded, raphe elongate, lateral, endosperm homogeneous, hollow; embryo subbasal. Germination and eophyll not recorded. Cytology not known.

Anatomy. — Not studied.

Distribution. — Two species in Ecuador, Bolivia, and Colombia.

Ecology. — *P. torallyi* is found in humid ravines of spectacular sandstone mountains at high elevations (2400–2700 m) where it does not rain for ten months of the year. *P. cocoides* was described from 3000 m in the eastern Andes.

Common Names and Uses. — Common names not recorded. The mesocarp is fleshy and sweet and is eaten and the seed contains usable oil. These palms should make handsome ornamentals in cool and dry areas.

Notes. — *Parajubaea,* like most genera in subtribe Butiinae, is rather finely differentiated. The combination of the rather congested, closely adpressed rachillae, staminate flower with 15 stamens, and irregularly sculptured endocarp is not found elsewhere. The genus is probably most closely related to *Jubaea* or *Syagrus.*

Taxonomic Account. — No recent treatment exists but see Cardenas (1970).

Plate. — *75B.*

178. **ALLAGOPTERA** C. G. D. Nees in Wied-Neuwied, Reise nach Brasilien 2:335. 1821. Type: *A. pumila* C. G. D. Nees (=**A. arenaria** (Gomes) O. Kuntze (*Cocos arenaria* Gomes)) (see H. E. Moore 1963c).

Diplothemium Martius, Palmarum Familia 20. 1824. Lectotype: *D. maritimum* Martius (see H. A. Wendland 1854) (=*Allagoptera arenaria* (Gomes) O. Kuntze).

Small, acaulescent, usually clustered, unarmed, pleonanthic, monoecious palms. Stem erect, very short or subterranean. Leaf pinnate; sheath tubular, short, thin, becoming soft fibrous, usually floccose; petiole long, slender, shallowly channeled adaxially, rounded abaxially; rachis triangular in cross-section, glabrous or scaly; leaflets single-fold, inserted regularly or in groups, long, narrow, tapering, pointed, or 2-lobed and split apically, a midrib evident on both surfaces, large scales present or absent abaxially along the midrib, glabrous or glaucous throughout, or silvery beneath, transverse veinlets apparent adaxially. Inflorescences erect, unbranched; peduncle very long, slender; prophyll tubular, thin, dorsiventrally flattened, 2-keeled laterally, glabrous or scaly; peduncular bract 1, long, basally slender, sometimes appearing stalked, inflated above, tapering to a point, woody, ± plicate, splitting abaxially; rachis much shorter than the peduncle,

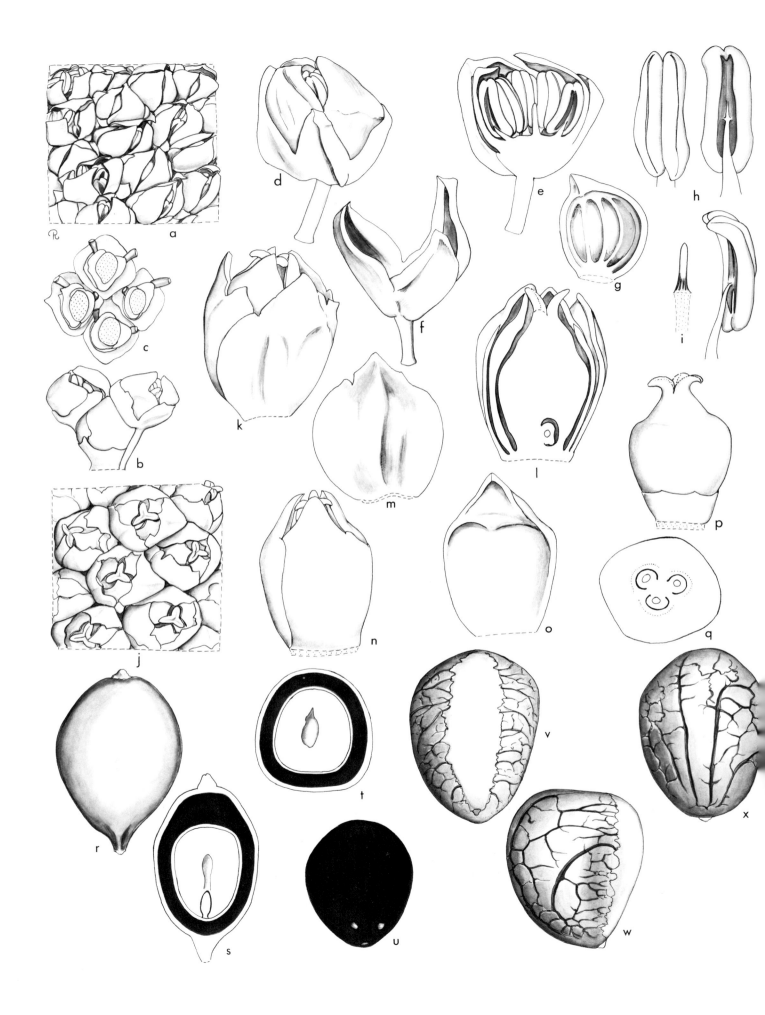

bearing closely appressed, spirally inserted, scarious bracts, subtending triads in the basal ½ and pairs of staminate flowers in the distal ½ of the spike. Staminate flowers large, chunky, ovoid and angled, those of the triads borne on long, ± flat pedicels curved around the pistillate flower, distal, paired staminate flowers sessile; sepals 3, narrow, connate basally for ca. ¼ their length, widely separated, pointed, keeled, margins entire or crenate; petals 3, distinct, irregular, angled, triangular, valvate, 2–4 times as long as the sepals, the tips thickened; stamens 6–ca. 19, filaments awl-shaped, ± united at the base, erect, anthers somewhat irregular, curved but not twisted, dorsifixed near the base of a prominent connective, latrorse; pollen elliptic, monosulcate, with foveolate to fossulate, tectate exine; pistillode lacking or slender, conical, ca. ½ as long as the stamens. Pistillate flowers slightly larger than the staminate; sepals 3, distinct, broadly imbricate, tips valvate in bud; petals 3, distinct, about as long as the sepals, broadly imbricate, tips valvate; staminodes connate in a low, shallowly-lobed cupule; gynoecium ovoid, trilocular, triovulate, stigmas narrow, recurved between the petal apices at anthesis, ovules laterally attached, anatropous. Fruit obovoid, angled by mutual pressure, usually 1-seeded, stigmatic remains represented by an apical knob, perianth enlarged and persistent; epicarp glabrous or with woolly scales, mesocarp fibrous and fleshy, endocarp hard but relatively thin, pores near the base. Seed obovoid, basally attached, hilum small, raphe wide with large curved and small anastomosing branches, endosperm hard, hollow, homogeneous; embryo basal. Germination not recorded; eophyll simple. $n = 16$ (*A. arenaria*, Read 1966).

Anatomy. — Not studied.

Distribution. — Probably five species in Brazil and Paraguay.

Ecology. — In loose sand on beaches, on dunes, in open tree and scrub woodlands, among rocks on sandstone hills, and in dry grassy or shrubby vegetation zones (cerrado).

Common Names and Uses. — For common names see Glassman (1972). Uses not recorded.

Notes. — One of the most specialized members of the Cocoeae, recognizable by its habit and striking spicate inflorescence bearing closely appressed pistillate flowers basally and staminate flowers distally.

Taxonomic Accounts. — See notes in Moore (1962a, 1963c).

Plates. — 75C; Figs. G.2, G.12.

179. **POLYANDROCOCOS** Barbosa Rodrigues, Contributions du Jardin Botanique de Rio de Janeiro 1:7. 1901. Lectotype: **P. caudescens** (Martius) Barbosa Rodrigues (*Diplothemium caudescens* Martius) (See H. E. Moore 1967a).

Moderate to tall, solitary, armed or unarmed, pleonanthic, monoecious palms. Stem rough, closely ringed with leaf bases. Leaves pinnate, marcescent; sheath tubular but splitting adaxially when young, appearing as a woody, slightly expanded base to the petiole, finely striate, covered with whitish, rusty spotted tomentum; petiole short, robust, deeply channeled adaxially, rounded abaxially, margins roughly toothed to spiny, tomentose abaxially like the sheath; rachis arched or straight, adaxially channeled, distally flattened, abaxially rounded; leaflets regularly arranged or grouped, in one or several planes, singlefold, glabrous adaxially, pale-waxy tomentose abaxially, leaflet tips irregularly bifid, lobed, almost praemorse or acuminate, midrib larger adaxially and the only prominent vein, transverse veinlets evident adaxially. Inflorescences solitary, interfoliar, pendulous, unbranched; peduncle elongate, circular in cross-section; prophyll tubular, 2-keeled, rather short, very fibrous, opening apically; peduncular bract 1, tubular, much longer than the prophyll, finely and deeply grooved, shorter or longer than the peduncle, with a long beak; rachis bearing close triads throughout the lower ½ or more of its length and pairs of staminate flowers distally, staminate flowers shed early, leaving a long, bare, pointed tip on the rachis at pistillate anthesis, bracts subtending triads ovate, pointed, those subtending staminate flower pairs with longer pointed tips, bracts adnate laterally to the rachis and to the bases of adjacent bracts, forming a curved depression surrounding the flower pairs, floral bracteoles inconspicuous. Staminate flowers asymmetrical, long, obovoid; sepals 3, linear, triangular, connate basally and adnate to the floral receptacle, very narrow and acuminate distally, ± keeled; petals 3, elongate, obovate, pointed, valvate, slightly longer, and much wider and thicker than the sepals, adnate basally to the floral receptacle; stamens numerous, 60–ca. 100, irregularly inserted on a conical floral receptacle, filaments cylindrical, elongate, flexible, variously bent and curved, sometimes a few joined together throughout their length, anthers elongate, sagittate basally, apiculate, dorsifixed at about ⅓ their length, versatile, introrse; pollen elliptic, dilated at one end, monosulcate, with finely reticulate tectate exine; pistillode apparently absent. Pistillate flowers smaller than the staminate, globose; sepals 3, distinct, ovate, broadly imbricate, tips pointed; petals 3, distinct, similar to the sepals but with longer, valvate tips, stam-

---

←

178. — **Allagoptera. a,** portion of spike at staminate anthesis × 3; **b,** triad × 3; **c,** triads, flowers removed to show bracteoles and staminate pedicels × 3; **d,** staminate flower × 6; **e,** staminate flower in vertical section × 6; **f,** staminate calyx and pedicel × 6; **g,** staminate petal, interior view × 6; **h,** stamen in 3 views × 12; **i,** pistillode × 12; **j,** portion of spike at pistillate anthesis × 3; **k,** pistillate flower × 6; **l,** pistillate flower in vertical section × 6; **m,** pistillate sepal, exterior view × 6; **n,** pistillate flower, sepals removed × 6; **o,** pistillate sepal, interior view × 6; **p,** gynoecium and staminodial cupule × 6; **q,** ovary in cross-section × 12; **r,** fruit × 2; **s,** fruit in vertical section × 2; **t,** fruit in cross-section × 2; **u,** endocarp × 2; **v, w, x,** seed in 3 views × 4. *Allagoptera arenaria*: **a-q,** *Read 955*; **r-x,** *Wilkinson 889.*

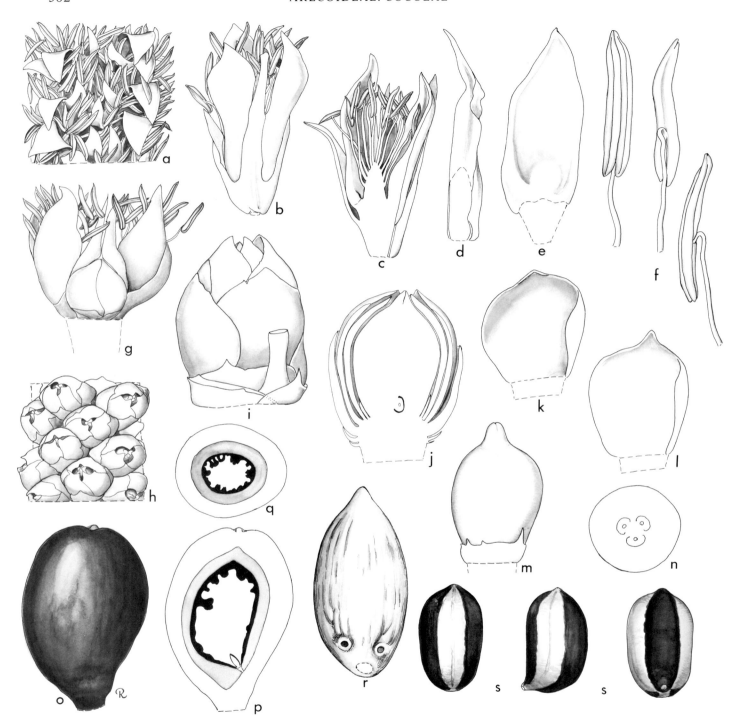

179.—**Polyandrococos. a,** portion of rachilla at staminate anthesis ×1½; **b,** staminate flower ×2; **c,** staminate flower in vertical section ×2; **d,** staminate sepal ×3; **e,** staminate petal, interior view ×3; **f,** stamen in 3 views ×6; **g,** portion of rachilla with triad × 1½; **h,** portion of rachilla at pistillate anthesis ×1; **i,** pistillate flower with bracteoles and pedicel of staminate flower ×3; **j,** pistillate flower in vertical section ×3; **k,** pistillate sepal, interior view ×3; **l,** pistillate petal, interior view ×3; **m,** gynoecium and staminodial ring ×3; **n,** ovary in cross-section ×6; **o,** fruit ×1; **p,** fruit in vertical section ×1; **q,** fruit in cross-section ×1; **r,** endocarp ×1½; **s,** seed in 3 views ×1. *Polyandrococos caudescens*: **a-n,** *Langlois s.n.*; **o-s,** *Read s.n.*

inodes united in a low, ± irregularly lobed ring; gynoecium obovoid, trilocular, triovulate, stigmas short, trifid; ovules laterally attached, ? anatropous. Fruit of moderate size, obovoid, angled, greenish-yellow, 1-seeded, stigmatic remains forming a beak; epicarp smooth, mesocarp fleshy-fibrous, endocarp thick, bony, smooth, with 3 pores near the base, internally with 3, broad, shining lines. Seed elongate, basally attached, beaked, endosperm shallowly ruminate with or without a central hollow; embryo subbasal. Germination not recorded; eophyll ovate, entire or briefly bifid. $n = 16$ (Read 1966).

Anatomy. — Not studied.

Distribution. — Two species in Brazil.

Ecology. — Found in open areas and in gallery forests.

Common Names and Uses. — Buri palm. Grown in botanic gardens in Rio de Janeiro, Jamaica, and elsewhere.

Notes. — The large unbranched inflorescence, at anthesis entirely covered by stamens, has a striking resemblance to that of *Phytelephas,* though there is no relationship. The genus is very poorly represented in herbaria and for a long time it was thought there was only a single species; however a second species, *P. pectinata* described in 1901 has been overlooked until recently.

Taxonomic Account. — Moore (1967a).

Plate. — 75D.

Attaleinae Drude in Engler & Prantl, Natürlichen Pflanzenfamilien 2, 3:27, 78. 1887. 'Attaleae.' Type: **Attalea.**

Acaulescent or erect, usually massive, unarmed; leaves pinnate, leaflet tips usually oblique; peduncular bract very thick and woody, borne at the base of the peduncle, persistent; inflorescences normally of more than one kind, androgynous and staminate, sometimes also pistillate; flowers superficial; pistillate flowers with imbricate petals; gynoecium sometimes with more than 3 carpels; endocarp pores ± basal; endosperm homogeneous.

Four genera occurring in Central and South America make up this subtribe (Map 48). Generic delimitation in the Attaleinae has been disputed and not all may agree with the treatment presented here. Traditionally five genera, *Attalea, Scheelea, Parascheelea, Orbignya* and *Maximiliana,* and *Markleya,* a putative intergeneric hybrid between *Scheelea* and *Maximiliana,* have been recognized. In a now controversial paper, Wessels Boer (1965) included all five genera in the single genus *Attalea* and made new combinations only for those taxa occurring in Suriname. Wessels Boer's treatment seems premature as far too little is known of these mostly

Map 48. — **Distribution of Attaleinae.**

large and cumbersome palms. The genera are characterized by the presence of more than one type of inflorescence, staminate, androgynous, and sometimes also pistillate occurring on a single tree. Gynoecia are often multicarpellate and endocarp pores are always basal.

Delimitation of the genera as recognized here, can only be accomplished if staminate flowers are present, but then there should be no difficulty in assigning material to genus. Characters of the fruit have yet to be proved consistent. Two apparent intermediates occur; they are the local upper Amazonian genus *Parascheelea* which we have shown (see below) to be linked to *Orbignya,* and a very poorly known palm of Haitai, *Attalea crassispatha* (see *Orbignya*).

180. **ATTALEA** Kunth in Humboldt, Bonpland & Kunth, Nova Genera et Species Plantarum 1: folio edition 248; quarto edition 309. 1816. Type: **A. amygdalina** Kunth.

Lithocarpos Targioni-Tozzetti, Memorie di Matematica e di Fisica della Societa Italiana delle Scienze Residente in Modena 20(2):312. 1833 (Non Blume 1825–26). Type: *L. cocciformis* Targioni-Tozzetti (illegitimate name) (*Cocos lapidea*

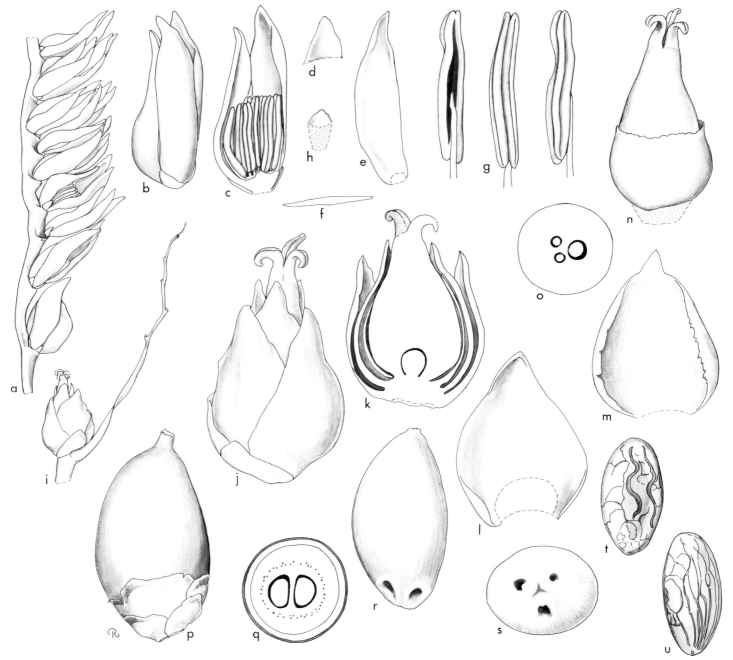

180.—**Attalea. a,** portion of staminate rachilla ×1½; **b,** staminate flower ×3; **c,** staminate flower in vertical section ×3; **d,** staminate sepal ×6; **e,** staminate petal ×3; **f,** staminate petal in cross-section ×6; **g,** stamen in 3 views ×6; **h,** pistillode ×6; **i,** pistillate rachilla ×½; **j,** pistillate flower ×1½; **k,** pistillate flower in vertical section ×1½; **l,** pistillate sepal ×1½; **m,** pistillate petal ×1½; **n,** gynoecium and staminodial cupule ×1½; **o,** ovary in cross-section ×1½; **p,** fruit ×½; **q,** fruit in cross-section ×½; **r, s,** endocarp in 2 views ×¾; **t, u,** seed in 2 views ×¾. *Attalea victoriana*: **a-h,** *Moore et al. 10196*; **i-u,** *Moore et al. 10199*.

J. Gaertner = *Attalea lapidea* (J. Gaertner) Burret).

Pindarea Barbosa Rodrigues, Plantas Novas Cultivadas no Jardim Botanico do Rio de Janeiro 5:

17. 1895 ("1896"). Type: *P. concinna* Barbosa Rodrigues (=*Attalea concinna* (Barbosa Rodrigues) Burret).

Sarinia O. F. Cook, National Horticultural Maga-

zine 21:78, 84. 1942. Type: *S. funifera* (Martius)
O. F. Cook (*Attalea funifera* Martius).

Ynesa O. F. Cook, National Horticultural Magazine
21: 71, 72, 84. Type: *Y. colenda* O. F. Cook (=
Attalea colenda (O. F. Cook) Balslev & Henderson) (see Balslev and Henderson 1987).

Small to massive, solitary, acaulescent or erect, unarmed, pleonanthic, monoecious palms. Stem subterranean to tall, usually becoming bare, obliquely marked with
leaf scars. Leaves massive, pinnate, marcescent; sheath
thick, finely or coarsely fibrous (in *A. funifera* producing
piassava); petiole lacking or short to elongate, adaxially
channeled, abaxially rounded, variously tomentose, rachis
adaxially channeled near the base, distally angled, abaxially rounded or flattened, abaxially variously tomentose;
leaflets inserted on the lateral faces or in shallow grooves;
leaflets numerous, linear-lanceolate, single-fold, regularly
arranged or in clusters of 2–5, irregularly lobed at the tips,
caducous scales abundant along the leaflet margins exposed in the sword leaf, midrib prominent, other longitudinal veins rather indistinct, transverse veinlets abundant, conspicuous. Inflorescences solitary, interfoliar, ±
erect or becoming pendulous, entirely staminate, entirely
pistillate, or with flowers of both sexes, branched to 1
order or branches short and flowers appearing ± sessile
on the main axis; peduncle short to long; prophyll obscured by leaf sheaths and not known, peduncular bract
tubular, entirely enclosing the inflorescence in bud with
a short to long solid beak, splitting abaxially, expanding
and usually becoming cowllike, thick and woody, abaxially deeply grooved, adaxially glabrous, abaxially densely
tomentose, long persistent, subsequent peduncular bracts
small, incomplete, triangular, ± coriaceous; rachis shorter
or longer than the peduncle, bearing spirally or unilaterally
arranged rachillae, each subtended by a short triangular
bract; staminate rachilla with a short to long basal bare
portion, above which bearing paired or solitary flowers,
spirally arranged (rarely) or in 2 rows on one side, glabrous
or floccose-tomentose, bisexual rachillae of two types,
either similar to the staminate but bearing a few basal
pistillate flowers or bearing 1 to several triads with a short
slender apical portion bearing fertile or sterile staminate
flowers, in the putative pistillate rachillae lacking all trace
of staminate flowers at maturity. Staminate flowers asymmetrical; sepals 3, distinct, triangular, very small, sometimes slightly imbricate basally; petals 3, distinct, much
longer than the sepals, ovate-triangular, acute, valvate;
stamens 3–75, usually much shorter than the petals, filaments slender, usually short, anthers ± straight, dorsifixed, sagittate basally, latrose; pollen elliptic or sub
triangular, monosulcate, trichotomosulcate, or tetrachotomosulcate, with scabrate or foveolate, tectate exine; pistillode minute or absent. Pistillate flowers very much larger
than the staminate, generally ovoid; sepals 3, distinct, ±
triangular, broadly imbricate, leathery; petals 3, distinct, rounded or ± triangular with triangular tips, glabrous or tomentose; staminodal ring large, coriaceous,
tomentose; gynoecium of 3–several connate carpels, ovoid
or obpyriform, style tapering, stigmatic lobes equal in
number to the carpels, linear, reflexed at anthesis, ovules
1 per carpel, basal, form unknown. Fruit ± ovoid, sometimes asymmetrical, 1–several seeded, with a short to
moderate beak and apical stigmatic remains, perianth and
staminodial ring persistent and enlarging; epicarp minutely grooved, bearing scales, mesocarp usually fleshy
and fibrous, endocarp very thick, stony, smooth without
or closely grooved, often with included fibers, the pores
subbasal, deeply impressed, ? always. Seed ellipsoidal or
laterally somewhat flattened, basally attached with fine
anastomosing raphe bundles, endosperm homogeneous,
solid (? always); embryo basal. Germination remote-tubular; eophyll entire, lanceolate. Most chromosome counts
cited under *Attalea* refer to species considered here to
belong to other attaleoid genera. *n* = 16 (*A. allenii,* Read
and Moore 1967).

Anatomy. — Leaf anatomy (Tomlinson 1961) is
very similar to that of *Scheelea.* Glassman (1977a)
finds that not all species of *Attalea, Scheelea,* and
Orbignya are distinct in leaf anatomy.

Distribution. — About 22 species occurring from
Panama southwards to Brazil and Peru. *Attalea
crassispatha* recorded from Haiti is regarded as not
belonging to *Attalea.* See notes under *Orbignya.*

Ecology. — Tropical rain forest to dry "campo rupestre" and "cerrado."

Common Names and Uses. — For common names
see Glassman (1972). These are palms with a multiplicity of uses, the most important being as a source
of oil (see Piñiero and Balick in press). For medicinal uses see Plotkin and Balick (1984).

Notes. — *Attalea* is distinguished by the triangular,
flattened petals of the staminate flower and the short
stamens with straight anthers.

Taxonomic Account. — Glassman (1977a).

Plate. — 76B.

181. **SCHEELEA** Karsten, Linnaea 28:264. 1857
("1856"). Lectotype: *S. regia* Karsten (see H. E.
Moore 1963c). (=**S. butyracea** (Mutis ex Linnaeus
filius) Karsten ex H. A. Wendland (*Cocos butyracea* Mutis ex Linnaeus filius)).

Robust to massive, solitary, acaulescent or erect, unarmed, pleonanthic, monoecious palms. Stem subterranean to erect and very tall, eventually bare, smooth, striate
inconspicuously ringed with oblique leaf scars. Leaves
pinnate, marcescent; sheath massive, thick, margins finely
or coarsely fibrous; petiole lacking or short to elongate,
adaxially channeled, abaxially rounded, variously tomentose; rachis often massive, adaxially channeled proximally, distally sharply angled (? always), abaxially rounded
or flattened, laterally flattened or grooved, adaxially glabrous, abaxially variously tomentose, margins often sharp;
leaflets very numerous, single-fold, sometimes regularly
arranged, more frequently grouped in 2's–5's, linear-lanceolate with irregular tips, surfaces apparently alike (? always), caducous scales abundant along margins exposed
in the swordleaf, midrib prominent, other longitudinal
veins rather indistinct, transverse veinlets conspicuous.

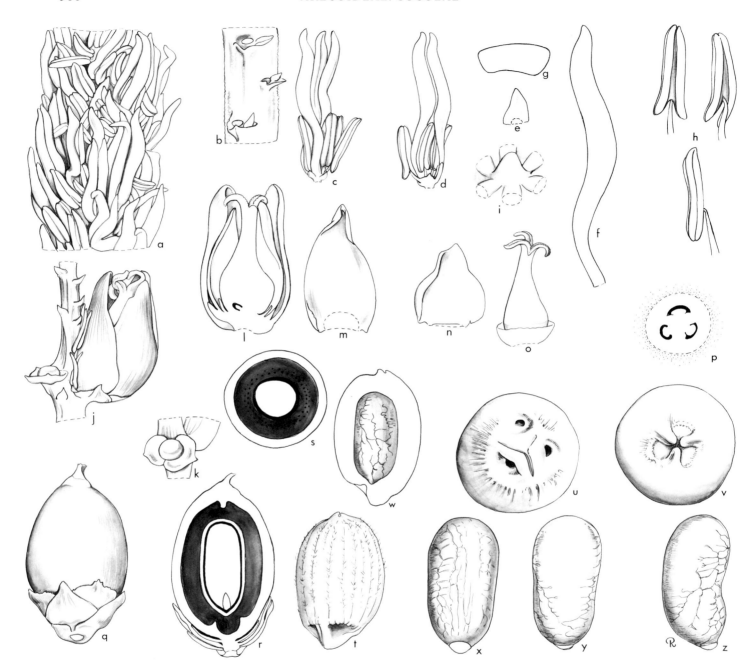

181.—**Scheelea. a,** portion of staminate rachilla ×3; **b,** scars of staminate flowers and bracteoles ×6; **c,** staminate flower ×3; **d,** staminate flower in vertical section ×3; **e,** staminate sepal ×12; **f,** staminate petal ×6; **g,** staminate petal in cross-section ×12; **h,** stamen in 3 views ×6; **i,** pistillode ×25; **j,** portion of rachilla with pistillate flower and abortive staminate flowers ×1; **k,** scar of pistillate flower and bracteoles ×1; **l,** pistillate flower in vertical section ×1; **m,** pistillate sepal, interior view ×1; **n,** pistillate petal, interior view ×1; **o,** gynoecium and staminodial cupule ×1; **p,** locules of ovary in cross-section ×6; **q,** fruit ×1; **r,** fruit in vertical section ×1; **s,** fruit in cross-section ×1; **t,** endocarp in lateral view ×1; **u, v,** endocarp in 2 views ×1½; **w,** endocarp in vertical section, seed removed ×1; **x, y, z,** seed in 3 views ×1½. *Scheelea* sp.: **a-i,** *Moore et al. 9510*; *S. rostrata*: **j-p,** *Moore et al. 6540*; *S. liebmannii*: **q-z,** *Moore 6229.*

Inflorescences solitary, interfoliar, ± erect or becoming pendulous, entirely staminate or with flowers of both sexes, branching to 1 order; peduncle moderate to very large, usually elongate; prophyll unknown; peduncular bract inserted near the base, tubular, entirely enclosing the inflorescence with a short to long terminal beak, splitting abaxially, expanding and becoming cowllike, thick, woody, long persistent, deeply grooved, adaxially glabrous, abaxially variously indumentose, subsequent peduncular bracts generally small, triangular, incomplete; rachis shorter (?) or usually longer than the peduncle, bearing numerous, spirally arranged rachillae, each subtended by a low triangular bract; staminate rachillae elongate, sometimes swollen at the base and with a basal bare portion (? always), above which bearing paired or solitary flowers, spirally or rarely unilaterally, each pair subtended by an inconspicuous to conspicuous triangular, coriaceous bract, bisexual rachillae with a basal bare portion and one to many triads, above which abruptly narrowing to a slender staminate portion or the rachillae as the staminate but bearing 1 or 2 basal triads, staminate flowers in the bisexual inflorescences sometimes apparently sterile. Staminate flowers generally elongate, often asymmetrical; sepals 3, distinct, triangular, minute; petals very much longer than the sepals, 3, distinct, very narrow, terete or planoconvex, fleshy; stamens 6, much shorter than the petals, filaments very slender, anthers straight, dorsifixed, relatively short, basally sometimes sagittate, latrorse, pollen elliptic to circular, monosulcate, with tectate, foveolate exine; pistillode inconspicuous or absent. Pistillate flowers much larger than the staminate, ± obovoid; sepals 3, distinct, rather broad, imbricate, coriaceous, ± pointed; petals 3, distinct, about as long as the sepals, broadly imbricate with short triangular tips, variously indumentose; staminodial ring large, thick, coriaceous, truncate; gynoecium of 3–several connate carpels, irregularly obpyriform, style narrow, stigmas as many as the carpels, papillose, hard, reflexed at anthesis, ovules as many as the carpels, basal, form unknown. Fruit rather small to large, ovoid, elongate, with persistent perianth, 1–5(–more?) seeded, briefly to prominently beaked, with apical stigmatic remains; epicarp minutely grooved, sparsely to densely scaly, mesocarp usually fleshy and fibrous, endocarp thick, bony, often with included fibers in rings or clusters, the pores subbasal, deeply impressed. Seed elongate, basally attached, raphe branches shortly anastomosing, endosperm homogeneous, solid (? always); embryo basal. Germination remote-tubular; eophyll entire, lanceolate. $n = 16$ (*S.* sp., Read 1966).

Anatomy. — Leaf (Tomlinson 1961, Glassman 1977c).

Distribution. — Twenty-eight species in Central America south to Brazil, Bolivia, and Peru.

Ecology. — Often abundant in open savannahs in drier regions but several species are adopted to tropical rain forest.

Common Names and Uses. — Yagua palm (*S. macrocarpa*). These are palms with a very wide range of uses such as for fiber, thatch, water scoops, and construction material, to cooking fuel oil, and medicines (Plotkin and Balick 1984).

Notes. — *Scheelea* is distinguished from other members of the Attaleinae by the staminate flowers with terete petals, stamens shorter than the petals, and straight anthers.

Taxonomic Account. — Glassman (1977c).

Plates. — 28C, D; 76C; Fig. G.5.

182. ORBIGNYA Martius ex Endlicher, Genera Plantarum 257. 1837. Conserved name. Type: **O. phalerata** Martius.

Parascheelea Dugand, Caldasia 1(1):10. 1940. Type: *P. anchistropetala* Dugand (=*Orbignya luetzelburgii* Burret).

Moderate to massive, solitary, acaulescent or erect, unarmed, pleonanthic, monoecious, occasionally androdioecious (A. Anderson, pers. comm.) palms. Stem subterranean to tall, usually becoming bare, striate, obscurely marked with large irregular leaf scars. Leaves pinnate, marcescent; sheath thick, massive, margins finely or coarsely fibrous; petiole lacking or short to elongate, adaxially channeled, abaxially rounded, variously tomentose; rachis often massive, adaxially channeled near the base with a rounded, central ridge, abaxially rounded, densely tomentose (? always), distally angled with a narrow to broad groove above the leaflet attachment; leaflets very numerous, single-fold, regularly arranged or in clusters of 2–4, linear-lanceolate with asymmetrical tips, sometimes briefly bifid, surfaces alike or the abaxial with thin indumentum, caducous scales abundant along the leaflet margins exposed in the sword leaf, midrib prominent abaxially, other longitudinal veins rather indistinct, transverse veinlets usually conspicuous. Inflorescences solitary, interfoliar, ± erect or becoming pendulous, entirely staminate, sometimes apparently entirely pistillate, or with flowers of both sexes, branching to 1 order; peduncle moderate to very large, usually elongate; prophyll ± woody, flattened, 2-keeled, tubular, irregularly splitting apically, becoming fibrous, usually entirely obscured by the leaf bases; peduncular bract, tubular, entirely enclosing the inflorescence in bud with a short to long, solid beak, splitting abaxially, expanding and becoming cowllike, thick and woody, abaxially deeply grooved, long persistent, adaxially glabrous, abaxially variously indumentose, subsequent peduncular bracts small, incomplete, triangular, ± coriaceous, rachis shorter or longer than the peduncle bearing spirally arranged, few to numerous rachillae, each subtended by a small to large, acute or acuminate, coriaceous bract; staminate rachillae often with a basal bare portion, above which bearing spirally or unilaterally arranged, paired or solitary flowers, each subtended by a small, pointed bract, bisexual rachillae often with a basal bare portion, above which bearing 1-several, large pistillate flowers sometimes in triads with accompanying staminate flowers, distally bearing few to many staminate flowers, these sometimes apparently sterile, sometimes lacking

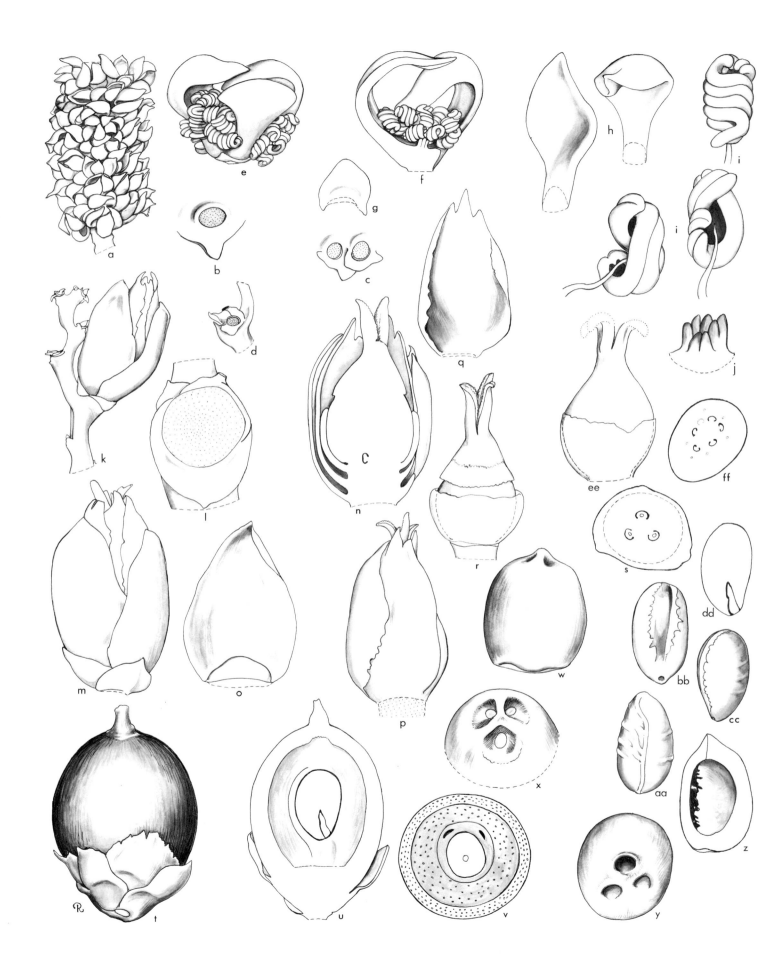

and the inflorescence entirely pistillate, occasionally the rachillae reduced to single pistillate flowers, ± sessile or on a short stalk, the abortive distal part of the rachilla appearing as a flattened stalk at the side of the pistillate flower. Staminate flowers often asymmetrical; sepals 3, distinct or basally connate, very small, ± membranous; petals (2) 3(–5), much longer than the sepals, broadly ovate to spathulate, rarely ± terete and hooklike, sometimes irregularly lobed, occasionally basally connate and adnate to the receptacle to form a solid column, thick leathery to fleshy and fibrous; stamens 6–30 (rarely more), much shorter than and included within the petals, filaments very slender, base sometimes expanded, anthers medifixed, irregular, the thecae separate or joined, coiled around each other, ± introrse; pollen elliptic to circular or subtriangular, monosulcate, the sulcus sometimes very short, or trichotomosulcate, with foveolate or fossulate, tectate exine; pistillode absent or very small, conical or 3–several-lobed. Pistillate flowers very much larger than the staminate, often massive; sepals 3, distinct, ovate, broadly imbricate, irregularly keeled, glabrous or tomentose, coriaceous; petals 3, distinct, somewhat exceeding the sepals, broadly imbricate with brief triangular tips, margins often irregularly lobed, coriaceous, glabrous or tomentose; staminodial ring very large, coriaceous, truncate or irregularly lobed; gynoecium with 3–7 carpels, often tomentose in the ovarian region, stylar region very fibrous, stigmas 3–7, hard, papillose, reflexed at anthesis, ovules as many as carpels, basal, anatropous. Fruit with persistent perianth and staminodial ring, 1-several-seeded, ovoid, frequently rather asymmetrical with a short to long apical beak and stigmatic remains; epicarp densely scaly, ± striate, mesocarp thin to thick, very hard and fibrous or sometimes pulpy, endocarp thin or usually very thick, hard, bony, enclosing 1-several seed chambers, sometimes with clusters of fibrous bundles, pores slightly above the base, superficial or sunken. Seed basally attached, spherical or narrow ellipsoidal, raphe branches fine, anastomosing, endosperm homogeneous often with a central lacuna; embryo basal. Germination remote-tubular; eophyll entire, lanceolate. $n = 16$ (*O. lydiae, O. cohune,* Sharma and Sarkar 1957, Satô 1946, Read 1966).

Anatomy.—Leaf (Tomlinson 1961, Glassman 1977b); gynoecium (Uhl and Moore 1971).

Distribution.—About 20 species in Central and South America, from Mexico south to Peru, Bolivia, and Brazil.

Ecology.—Varied, from humid tropical rain forest to savannah; some species adapted to periodic flooding. The local distribution frequently modified by man.

Common Names and Uses.—Babassu (*O. phalerata* and *O. oleifera*), Cohune (*O. cohune*). Uses are many, oil from seeds, petioles as wood, leaves for thatch and for making hats and umbrellas. Wine is made of sap from the terminal bud.

Notes.—*Orbignya* as delimited here, includes taxa of the Attaleinae with spirally twisted anthers. The anther thecae have frequently been reported as being separate but we have found this only rarely. *Parascheelea* was established by Dugand for a species with terete, curled, and hooked petals, joined at the base and adnate to the receptacle; *P. anchistropetala* has 6 stamens with highly coiled anthers. We have found that *O. cuatrecasana* and at least one other species of true *Orbignya* have the character of fused petals, and so the only absolute difference between *Parascheelea* and *Orbignya* is the terete, hooked, rather than flattened, spathulate petals. We believe this to be insufficient for the recognition of a separate genus and have included *Parascheelea* as a synonym of *Orbignya. Attalea crassispatha* (*Maximiliana crassipatha*) from Haiti, on which O. F. Cook based his invalidly published new genus *Bornoa,* has features suggesting relationships with *Orbignya* rather than *Attalea,* in particular the coiled anthers. The petals however are terete, straight and almost spinelike, unlike any other species of *Orbignya.* We do not feel confident in assigning this taxon to *Orbignya* or any other genus before more material is available. At present, the information concerning this Haitian palm tends further to obscure generic limits in the alliance, emphasizing the need for detailed studies. Hybridization is reported in the genus (Balick et al. 1987a, b).

Taxonomic Accounts.—Glassman (1977b), Anderson and Balick (in press).

Plates.—*76A, D; G.19.*

183. **MAXIMILIANA** Martius, Palmarum Familia 20. 1824 (Conserved name). Type: *M. martiana* Karsten (*M. regia* Martius (1826) (non *Maximilianea*

←

182.—**Orbignya. a,** portion of staminate rachilla ×1; **b,** bracteole and scar of staminate flower ×6; **c, d,** bracteoles and scars of paired staminate flowers in 2 views ×3; **e,** staminate flower ×3; **f,** staminate flower in vertical section ×3; **g,** staminate sepal ×12; **h,** staminate petals in 2 views ×3; **i,** stamen in 3 views ×12; **j,** pistillode ×12; **k,** portion of rachilla with pistillate flower ×1; **l,** bracteoles and scar of pistillate flower ×3; **m,** pistillate flower ×1½; **n,** pistillate flower in vertical section ×1½; **o,** pistillate sepal ×1½; **p,** pistillate flower, sepals removed ×1½; **q,** pistillate petal ×1½; **r,** gynoecium and staminodial cupule ×1½; **s,** ovary in cross-section ×1½; **t,** fruit ×¾; **u,** fruit in vertical section ×¾; **v,** fruit in cross-section ×¾; **w, x, y,** endocarp in 3 views × ¾; **z,** endocarp in vertical section, seed removed to show interior ×¾; **aa, bb, cc,** seed in 3 views ×¾; **dd,** seed in vertical section ×¾; **ee,** gynoecium and staminodial cupule ×1½; **ff,** ovary in cross-section ×1½. *Orbignya cohune*: **a-dd,** *Armour 151*; *O. speciosa*: **ee** and **ff,** *Read 912.*

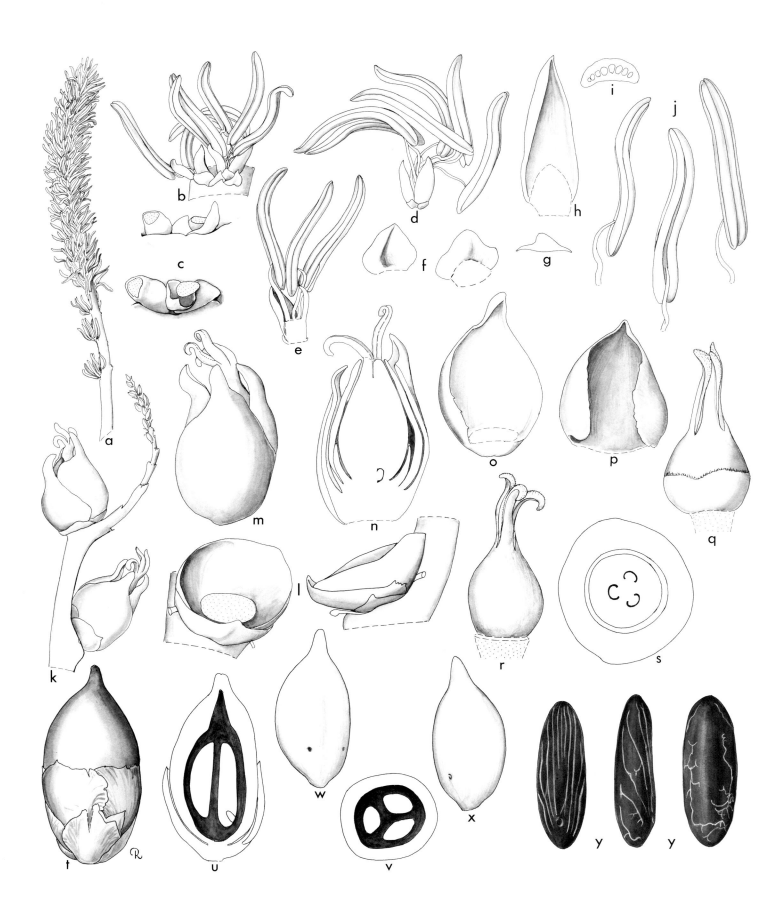

regia Martius (1819) = Cochlospermaceae) = **M. maripa** (Correa) Drude (*Palma maripa* Correa). *Englerophoenix* O. Kuntze, Revisio Generum Plantarum 2:728. 1891. Type: *E. regia* (Martius) O. Kuntze (illegitimate name) (*Maximiliana regia* Martius 1826, non 1819) (=*Maximiliana maripa* (Correa) Drude).

Massive, solitary, unarmed, pleonanthic, monoecious palm. Stem erect or decumbent, occasionally flowering when still very short, eventually becoming bare, obscurely ringed with leaf scars. Leaves pinnate, erect to slightly arching, massive, marcescent; sheath very long, disintegrating into a mass of coarse fibers; base of petiole very massive, long persistent; petiole elongate, adaxially channeled, abaxially rounded, the margins very sharp, sometimes bearing caducous tomentum; rachis elongate, adaxially channeled near the base, flattened or angled distally, abaxially rounded, the leaflets inserted in 2 conspicuous lateral grooves, the margins very sharp, abaxially with caducous indumentum; leaflets numerous, in groups of 2, 3–5(–9), in several planes giving the whole leaf a plumose appearance, stiff, linear lanceolate with unequal tips, the exposed margins with caducous brown scales when young, with prominent midrib and several pairs of longitudinal veins, transverse veinlets very numerous, evident adaxially. Inflorescences huge, solitary, interfoliar, bearing either staminate or both staminate and pistillate flowers, branching to 1 order; peduncle erect at first, becoming ± pendulous, ± circular in cross-section, bearing caducous tomentum; prophyll not seen; peduncular bract very large, long persistent, tubular at first, later splitting abaxially, expanding and becoming cowllike, entirely enclosing the inflorescence in bud, with a long solid beak, thick, woody, longitudinally deeply grooved except for the beak, adaxially smooth, abaxially with caducous indumentum, subsequent peduncular bracts very small, scalelike; rachis slightly longer than the peduncle, bearing numerous, spirally arranged or partially whorled rachillae, each subtended by small to moderate, membranous, triangular bracts; rachillae ± straight or coiled, the staminate rachillae slender with a short to long basal bare portion, distally bearing crowded, paired, or solitary flowers, rachilla bracts very small, membranous, sometimes also with indumentum distally, bisexual rachillae more robust than the staminate, with a very short to moderate basal bare portion, above which bearing several, rather distant pistillate flowers, each accompanied by 2 vestigial (? always) staminate flowers, distally rachillae abruptly narrowed, and bearing paired or solitary fertile or vestigial staminate flowers. Staminate flowers slightly asymmetrical, sessile; sepals 3, distinct, imbricate, or briefly connate, short, tri-

angular, keeled; petals 3, distinct, much longer than the sepals, lanceolate, pointed, adnate basally to the receptacle, rounded abaxially; stamens 6(–8 rarely), very conspicuous, much exceeding the petals, filaments slender, flexuous, anthers ± erect to somewhat versatile, straight, very long, dorsifixed near the base, latrorse; pollen elliptic, monosulcate, with foveolate or reticulate, tectate exine; pistillode lacking. Pistillate flower much larger than the staminate, ± ovoid, bracteoles 2, broad, rounded, keeled; sepals 3, distinct, coriaceous, ovoid, sometimes with thick beaks, imbricate, ± tomentose abaxially; petals 3, ± equalling or exceeding the sepals, very broad, imbricate, rounded, with very small triangular tips, margins sometime irregularly toothed, tomentose abaxially; staminodial ring very thick, fleshy, irregularly truncate, hairy abaxially and marginally; gynoecium of 3 connate carpels, triovulate, obpyriform, densely tomentose, style short or lacking, stigmas 3, elongate, reflexed, ovule form unknown. Fruit ovoid to obpyriform, briefly beaked, stylar remains apical, 1–3-seeded, perianth persistent, much enlarged; epicarp densely indumentose, mesocarp relatively thick, pulpy-fibrous, endocarp thick, bony, beaked with 3 pores lateral near the base. Seed narrow ellipsoidal, with coarse anastomosing raphe branches, endosperm with a narrow central hollow, (? always), homogeneous; embryo basal opposite a pore. Germination remote-tubular; eophyll lanceolate. Cytology not studied.

Anatomy.—Similar to *Attalea* and *Scheelea* in leaf anatomy (Tomlinson 1961).

Distribution.—One species in northern South America including Trinidad.

Ecology.—Coastal swamps and lowlands.

Common Names and Uses.—Maripa, Inajá, Curcurita. Locally much used for thatching, basketry, and matting. The peduncular bract is used as a container. The mesocarp provides a drink. The seeds are eaten toasted and produce an edible oil, which is good but liable to become rancid quickly. This is a magnificent palm suited for tropical landscaping.

Notes.—*Maximiliana* is distinguished from other genera of the Attaleinae by elongate anthers which greatly exceed the petals of the staminate flowers. *Markleya* Bondar, Arquivos Instituto Biologia Vegetal 15:50. 1957. Type: *M. dahlgreniana* Bondar was described by Bondar as an intergeneric hybrid between *Orbignya speciosa* (Martius) Barbosa Rodrigues and *Maximiliana maripa*. Wessels Boer (1965) disputed its hybrid status and recognized it

---

← 183.—**Maximiliana. a,** portion of staminate rachilla × ¾; **b,** dyad of staminate flowers × 4½; **c,** dyad, flowers removed to show bracteoles and scars, in 2 views × 12; **d,** staminate flower × 6; **e,** staminate flower in vertical section × 6; **f,** staminate sepal in 2 views × 18; **g,** staminate sepal in cross-section × 18; **h,** staminate petal × 18; **i,** staminate petal in cross-section × 18; **j,** stamen in 3 views × 6; **k,** portion of rachilla with 2 pistillate flowers, below, and staminate flowers, above × 1½; **l,** bract subtending pistillate flower and cupular bracteoles in 2 views × 2¼; **m,** pistillate flower × 2¼; **n,** pistillate flower in vertical section × 2¼; **o,** pistillate sepal × 2¼; **p,** pistillate petal × 2¼; **q,** gynoecium and staminodial cupule × 2¼; **r,** gynoecium × 2¼; **s,** ovary in cross-section × 4½; **t,** fruit × 1; **u,** fruit in vertical section × 1; **v,** fruit in cross-section × 1; **w, x,** endocarp in 2 views × 1; **y,** seed in 3 views × 1½. *Maximiliana maripa*: all from *Aba 401*.

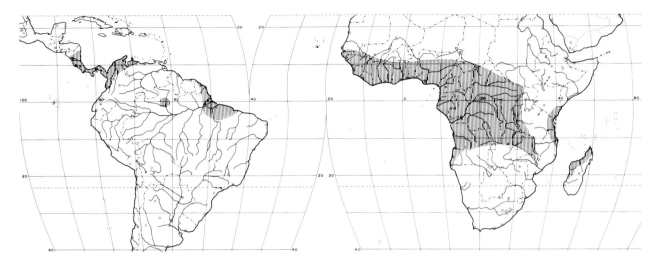

Map 49.—Distribution of Elaeidinae.

as a distinct species which he used, partly, as evidence for the inclusion of all members of Attaleinae in a single genus, *Attalea.* However Balick et al. (1987b) have shown that *Markleya* is indeed a hybrid.

O. F. Cook published the new generic name *Ethnora* based on *Maximiliana maripa,* in 1940 in the Journal of the Washington Academy of Science 20: 297. As the name appears without Latin description and postdates 1935, it is invalid and has no botanical standing.

Taxonomic Account.—Glassman (1978).
Plate.—77A; Fig. G.18.

Elaeidinae J. D. Hooker in Bentham & J. D. Hooker, Genera Plantarum 3:873, 882. 1883. ('*Elaeideae*'). Type: **Elaeis.**

Moderate to large; petioles armed with fibrous spines; leaves pinnate, leaflets acute; peduncular bract fibrous or long and woody (*Barcella*), borne at the base of the peduncle; flowers in deep pits; pistillate flowers with imbricate petals; fruit usually 1-seeded; endocarp pores at or above the middle; endosperm homogeneous.

Two genera, *Barcella* and *Elaeis,* make up the Elaeidinae, the former confined to Brazil, the latter

with two species, one in Central and South America, and one in Africa (Map 49). The Elaeidinae are distinguished by the enclosure of the flowers in pits, by a staminal tube formed by connate filaments, and by massive stigmas. The two genera seem closely related.

184. **BARCELLA** (Trail) Trail ex Drude in Martius, Flora Brasiliensis 3(2):459. 1881. Type: *B. odora* (Trail) Trail ex Drude (*Elaeis odora* Trail).
Elaeis subgenus *Barcella* Trail, Journal of Botany 15:80. 1877.

Moderate, solitary(?), acaulescent, unarmed, pleonanthic, monoecious palm. Stem very short, erect. Leaves arching or erect, pinnate, ?marcescent; sheath abaxially with caducous tomentum; petiole short, adaxially flattened, abaxially ± angled, the margins sharp, both surfaces glabrous; rachis adaxially angled, abaxially flattened; leaflets numerous, regularly arranged, single-fold, very gradually narrowed from near the base to a long acuminate tip, somewhat plicate, adaxially glabrous, abaxially bearing a few small ramenta along the main vein near the base, transverse veinlets conspicuous, very short. Inflorescences interfoliar, solitary, branching to 1 order, apparently protandrous; peduncle elongate, curving, ± circular or semicircular in cross-section, densely tomentose; prophyll short, thinly coriaceous, 2-keeled, acute, becoming fibrous dis-

→

184.—**Barcella. a,** portion of rachilla in staminate bud ×3; **b,** portion of rachilla, staminate buds removed to show pits ×6; **c,** vertical section of rachilla to show position of staminate bud in pit ×6; **d,** staminate bud ×12; **e,** staminate bud in vertical section ×12; **f,** staminate sepals in 2 views ×12; **g,** staminate bud, sepals removed ×12; **h,** staminate petal, interior view ×12; **i,** stamen in 3 views ×12; **j,** pistillode ×24; **k,** portion of rachilla with pistillate flowers and staminate pits ×3; **l,** pistillate flowers ×3; **m,** vertical section of rachilla to show position of pistillate flower in pit ×3; **n,** pistillate flower ×3; **o,** pistillate sepal ×3; **p,** pistillate petals ×3; **q,** gynoecium and staminodial cupule ×3, **r,** ovary in cross-section ×6; **s,** fruit in 2 views ×1; **t,** fruit in vertical section ×1; **u,** fibrous mesocarp ×1; **v,** endocarp in 4 views ×1; **w,** endocarp in vertical section ×1½; **x,** seed in 3 views ×3; **y,** seed in vertical section ×3. *Barcella odora*: **a–r,** *Rodrigues & Coelho 8394*; **s–y,** *Trail s.n.*

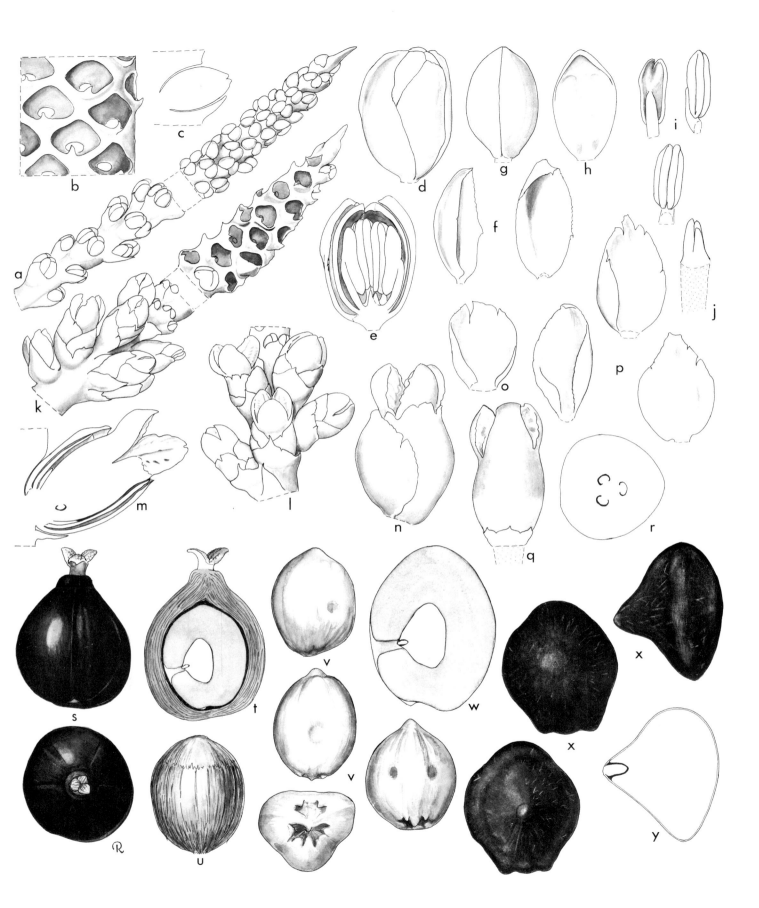

tally; peduncular bract much longer than the prophyll, ±
woody, enclosing the inflorescence in bud, splitting longitudinally allowing elongation of the peduncle and rachis,
beaked, striate abaxially, covered with minute scales; rachis
much shorter than the peduncle, bearing up to ca. 40,
crowded, rigid, spirally arranged, densely tomentose rachillae, each subtended by a triangular, acuminate bract;
proximal few rachillae expanded at the base and bearing
up to ca. 9 pistillate flowers, solitary or in triads, with
staminate flowers distally and all other rachillae bearing
dense spirals of paired staminate flowers, except at the
very tips where staminate flowers solitary, the pistillate
flowers ± superficial, each subtended by a triangular bract,
the staminate flowers, especially distally, sunken in pits,
the small triangular rachilla bracts forming the lower lips
of the pits, extreme tips of rachillae bare of bracts and
flowers, ± sharply pointed. Staminate flowers small; sepals
3, distinct, imbricate, membranous, narrow elliptic, abaxially keeled, hooded at the tips; petals 3, distinct, about
the same length as the sepals, valvate, ovate, striate; stamens 6, filaments broad, fleshy, united laterally to each
other to form a tube with 6, short, distinct, reflexed, abru-
ply narrowed tips, anthers ± rectangular, ± versatile, latrorse; pollen elliptic, somewhat irregular, monosulcate,
with scabrate, tectate exine; pistillode much shorter than
the connate filaments, columnar, trifid. Pistillate flowers
much larger than the staminate; sepals 3, distinct, ovate,
broadly imbricate, coriaceous, the margins tending to split
irregularly; petals 3, distinct, ovate, broadly imbricate except at the short valvate, triangular tips, ± coriaceous
except at the membranous, striate, irregular margins;
staminodes forming a membranous, 6-toothed ring; gynoecium ± columnar, trilocular, triovulate, with 3, massive, fleshy, 3-angled stigmas, ovule apparently orthotropous, attached centrally. Fruit moderately large, 1-seeded,
ovoid or basally angled by close packing, bright orange,
usually with a prominent apical beak bearing the stigmatic
remains; epicarp smooth, glabrous, mesocarp thick, fleshy,
oily, endocarp black, woody, ± 3-angled, traversed by
longitudinal fibers, with 3 lateral pores. Seed basally at-
tached(?), with a coarse network of fibers, endosperm homogeneous with a central cavity; embryo lateral near one
of the endocarp pores. Germination not known; eophyll
apparently entire, lanceolate. Cytology not studied.

Anatomy. — Not studied.

Distribution. — One species confined to a small area
of the banks of the Rio Negro and its tributaries in
Brazil.

Ecology. — Occurs on riverbanks at low altitude.

Common Names and Uses. — Common names not
recorded, uses many such as wood for construction
and leaves for weaving (Pinhiero and Balick in press)
but the greatest potential of this palm lies with possible hybridization with the African or American
species of *Elaeis.*

Notes. — *Barcella* and *Elaeis* are separated from
other Cocoeae by having the rather large pistillate

flowers deeply sunken in the rachillae and by endocarp pores at or above the middle. *Barcella* is
distinguished from *Elaeis* by the lack of spines on
the petiole and by the long peduncle, woody rather
than fibrous peduncular bract, and consistent presence of both staminate and pistillate flowers in the
inflorescence.

Taxonomic Accounts. — Trail (1877), Henderson
(1986c).

Fig. — G.21.

185. ELAEIS N. J. Jacquin, Selectarum Stirpium
    Americanarum Historia 280. 1763. Type: **E. gui-
    neensis** N. J. Jacquin.

Corozo N. J. Jacquin ex Giseke, Praelectiones in
    Ordines Naturales Plantarum 42, 92. 1792. Lec-
    totype: *C. oleifera* (Kunth) L. H. Bailey (*Alfonsia
    oleifera* Kunth) (see Bailey 1940) (=*Elaeis oleifera*
    (Kunth) Cortes).

Alfonsia Kunth in Humboldt, Bonpland & Kunth,
    Nova Genera et Species Plantarum 1: folio edition
    245; quarto edition 306. 1816. Type: *A. oleifera*
    Kunth (=*Elaeis oleifera* (Kunth) Cortes).

Moderate to robust, solitary, short to tall, armed, pleonanthic, monoecious palms. Stem procumbent or erect,
bearing persistent leaf bases, leaf scars wide, oblique,
eventually becoming bare, the internodes short. Leaves
many in the crown, pinnate, withering and not abscising
neatly except in tall-trunked individuals; sheath tubular
at first, later disintegrating into an interwoven mass of
fibers, those fibers attached to the base of the petiole remaining as regularly spaced, broad, flattened spines; petiole conspicuous, adaxially channeled, abaxially angled,
bearing caducous tomentum, the margins armed with regularly spaced fiber spines, distally (strictly speaking the
proximal part of the rachis) with margins armed with
short, triangular, bulbous-based spines representing the
pulvini and midribs of the proximal few vestigial leaflets,
the blades of which soon disintegrate on leaf expansion;
rachis curving or straight, adaxially angled, abaxially
curved or flattened; leaflets numerous, single-fold, regularly arranged or slightly grouped and held in different
planes, giving the whole leaf a plumose appearance, linear,
gradually tapering to acute tips, sometimes with bands of
caducous scales, midribs prominent, transverse veinlets
very short, inconspicuous. Inflorescences interfoliar, solitary, short and condensed, unisexual (except as monstros-
ities), usually several adjacent axils producing inflorescences of one sex followed by several producing the other
sex, branching to 1 order; peduncle short, ± elliptic in
cross-section; prophyll short, tubular and flattened,
2-keeled, tomentose, included within the subtending leaf
sheath, thick, traversed by numerous, thick, longitudinal
fibers, disintegrating distally into a mass of fibers, the
larger fibers spinelike; first peduncular bract inserted some
distance from the prophyll, tubular, fibrous, thinner than
the prophyll, distally disintegrating into a fibrous mass,

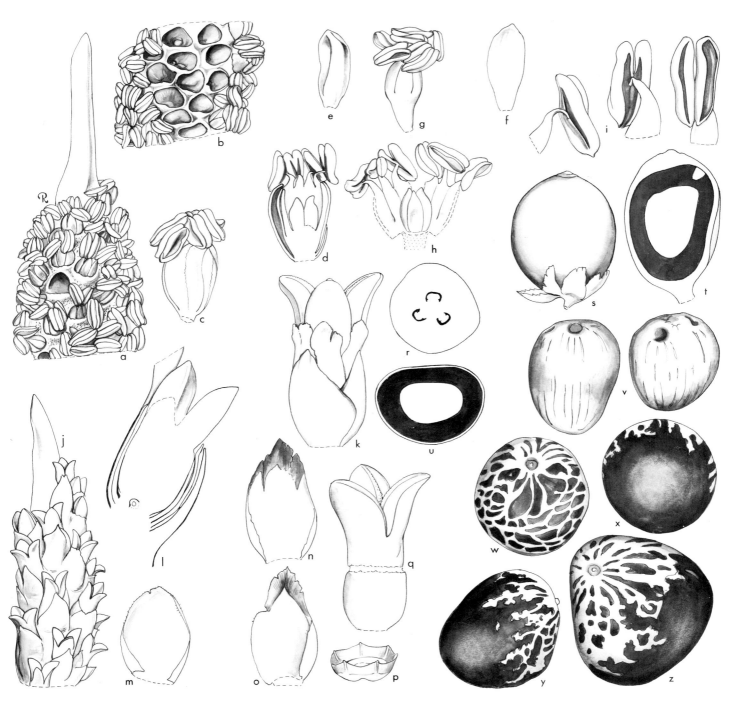

185.—**Elaeis. a,** terminal portion of staminate rachilla ×3; **b,** portion of staminate axis, flowers removed to show pits formed by bracts ×3; **c,** staminate flower ×6; **d,** staminate flower in vertical section ×6; **e,** staminate sepal ×6; **f,** staminate petal ×6; **g,** androecium ×6; **h,** androecium, expanded to show pistillode ×6; **i,** stamen in 3 views ×12; **j,** terminal portion of pistillate rachilla ×1; **k,** pistillate flower ×3; **l,** pistillate flower and portion of rachilla in vertical section ×3; **m,** pistillate bracteole ×3; **n,** pistillate sepal ×3; **o,** pistillate petal ×3; **p,** staminodial ring ×3; **q,** gynoecium ×3; **r,** gynoecium in cross-section ×6; **s,** fruit ×1½; **t,** fruit in vertical section ×1½; **u,** fruit in cross-section ×1½; **v,** endocarps showing variation in shape ×1½; **w, x, y, z,** seed in 4 views ×3. *Elaeis oleifera:* **a-r,** *Read 1388;* **s-z,** *Lindsay s.n.*

and splitting longitudinally, subsequent peduncular bracts small, not sheathing, narrow triangular, with sharp tips, striate; rachis shorter than, ± equalling, or slightly longer than the peduncle, tomentose, bearing numerous, spirally arranged, narrow triangular, membranous to coriaceous, acute bracts, each subtending a rachilla; staminate rachillae ± cylindrical, catkinlike, often somewhat angled due to close packing, tomentose, densely floriferous except at the ± spinelike tip where bare of flowers and bracts, the flowers solitary, borne in deep, spirally arranged pits, pistillate rachillae more massive than the staminate, bearing fewer flowers, the tips prolonged into a woody spine, each rachilla proximally bearing lax, ± superficial or only partially sunken, spirally arranged membranous rachilla bracts; bracts short, acute, or prolonged into a straight or flexuous spinelike tip, each subtending a solitary flower. Staminate flowers small, only slightly protruding from the pits at anthesis; sepals 3, distinct, unequal, ± rectangular, membranous, the edges not meeting in bud, abaxially keeled; petals 3, distinct, ± ovate, ± equalling the sepals, valvate, very thin; stamens 6, exserted at anthesis, filaments broad, fleshy, united laterally to form a tube, with 6 short, distinct, reflexed, abruptly narrowed tips, anthers ± rectangular, ± versatile, introrse; pollen elliptic or triangular, monosulcate, trichotomosulcate, or rarely tetrachotomosulcate, with reticulate, tectate exine; pistillode columnar, trifid, slightly shorter than the staminal tube. Pistillate flowers much larger than the staminate, borne with 2 acute or spine-tipped bracteoles; sepals 3, distinct, imbricate, rather thin; petals 3, distinct, imbricate, rather thin; staminodial ring low, 6-pointed, tanniniferous; gynoecium columnar to ovoid, trilocular, triovulate, stigmas 3, fleshy, reflexed, ±3-angled, ovules orthotropous, attached centrally. Fruit 1- (rarely more) seeded, ± ovoid but basally angled by close packing, variously orange or yellow, overlain with deep violet or black in exposed parts, apically beaked, stigmatic remains apical; epicarp smooth, mesocarp thick, fleshy, oily, fibrous, endocarp black, woody and very hard, variously ovoid, flattened or angled, with 3 apical pores. Seed basally attached with coarse, reticulate raphe branches, endosperm homogeneous, with or without a central cavity; embryo ± apical, opposite a pore. Germination adjacent-ligular; eophyll entire, lanceolate. $n = 16$ (*E. oleifera*, Read 1966; *E. guineensis*, Janaki Ammal 1945, Sharma and Sarkar 1957, Satô 1946).

Anatomy. — Leaf anatomy differs from that of other Cocoeae (Tomlinson 1961).

Distribution. — Two species, *E. guineensis,* native to the more humid areas of tropical Africa, possibly introduced in Madagascar, widespread throughout the humid tropics as the most productive oil crop, frequently naturalized; *E. oleifera* native to central and northern South America.

Ecology. — *E. oleifera* is frequent on poorly drained, sandy soils and in savannas; in Costa Rica it is found in palm swamp and mangrove communities (Allen 1956). *E. guineensis* is widespread on the margins of tropical rain forest and along watercourses in drier areas.

Fossil record. — Pollen referable to *Elaeis* has been recorded from the Miocene of West Africa.

Common Names and Uses. — African oil palm (*E. guineensis*), American oil palm (*E. oleifera*). *E. guineensis* is the most important commercial oil producing plant in the tropics, quite apart from its local uses as a source of wine, thatch, and building materials. Even waste endocarp has been used as road metalling. For further details see Hartley (1977) and for references (Johnson 1983b).

Notes. — *Elaeis* is notable as one of only two genera of the Cocoeae present in Africa and also for its distribution on either side of the Atlantic. See further notes under *Barcella.*

Taxonomic Accounts. — Beccari (1914b) and Zeven (1967).

Plates. — *77B; G.20.*

BACTRIDINAE J. D. Hooker in Bentham & J. D. Hooker, Genera Plantarum 3:873, 881. 1883 ('*Bactrideae*'). Type: **Bactris.**

Diminutive to very large, acaulescent, erect or climbing, armed in some or all parts with soft or mostly stout spines (very rarely unarmed, but then pistillate petals connate); leaves pinnate or pinnately ribbed, leaflets acute or praemorse; peduncular bract usually thick, borne at the base of the peduncle, persistent; petals of pistillate flowers connate or imbricate; fruit 1-seeded; endocarp pores at or above the middle except rarely (*Acrocomia*); endosperm always homogeneous.

This is a very diverse group consisting of six clearly demarcated genera, confined to the New World but abundant in South America (Map 50). There is great diversity in habit from massive palms with ventricose trunks to diminutive undergrowth palmlets, large acaulescent palms, and climbers. The subtribe is distinguished by having spines on some parts in nearly all members; only a few species of the very large genus *Bactris* are more or less unarmed, bearing a few bristles along the leaflet margins. *Acrocomia* is probably the least specialized in inflorescence form and in showing little connation of perianth parts; *Astrocaryum* with few pistillate flowers, staminate flowers in catkinlike branches, and the perianth members of pistillate flowers connate is the most advanced.

186. **ACROCOMIA** Martius, Historia Naturalis Palmarum 2:66. 1824. Type: *A. sclerocarpa* Martius

(illegitimate name) (*Cocos aculeata* N. J. Jacquin) = **A. aculeata** (N. J. Jacquin) Loddiges.

Acanthococos Barbosa Rodrigues, Palmae Hasslerianae Novae 1. 1900. Type: *A. hassleri* Barbosa Rodrigues (=*Acrocomia* sp.—formal transfer not yet made).

Dwarf to large, solitary, spiny, pleonanthic, monoecious palms. Stem very short, subterranean and geotropic, or erect, columnar or sometimes swollen, covered in persistent leaf bases and eventually becoming bare, or armed heavily with spines at first, soon becoming bare, eventually smooth, ringed with leaf scars. Leaves few to numerous, pinnate, marcescent or abscising neatly; sheath disintegrating into a mass of fibers, usually both spiny and finely bristly; petiole short or ± absent, adaxially channeled, abaxially rounded, usually spiny and finely bristly; rachis usually curved, armed with robust spines, especially along the margins, adaxially channeled near the base, angled distally, abaxially angled or rounded; leaflets numerous, single-fold, linear, acute or shallowly bifid, sometimes plicate, subregularly arranged (rarely) or grouped, usually held in different planes giving the leaf a plumose appearance, usually coriaceous, adaxially usually glabrous, abaxially glabrous, glaucous or pubescent, transverse veinlets obscure. Inflorescences axillary, interfoliar, shorter than the leaves, arching or becoming pendulous, branching to 1 order; peduncle ± oval in cross-section, often elongate, spiny and/or tomentose, rarely unarmed; prophyll tubular, 2-keeled, closely sheathing, usually remaining ± hidden within the leaf sheaths, soon tattering and splitting irregularly, glabrous or densely shaggy hairy, sometimes also spiny; peduncular bract inserted near the prophyll, much larger than the prophyll, persistent, tubular, enclosing the rachillae in bud, strongly beaked, woody, splitting along the abaxial face, then expanded or ± cowllike, abaxial surface densely shaggy tomentose, and often sparsely to densely spiny, spines sometimes restricted to near the beak, adaxial surface glabrous, often conspicuously pale yellow; rachis longer or shorter than the peduncle, variously spiny, tomentose, or glabrous, bearing few to numerous, spirally arranged rachillae, each subtended by a short triangular bract; rachillae short to elongate, straight or somewhat flexuous, often with a pulvinus (?nectariferous) at the base, usually cream-colored or yellowish, with a very short to long basal, bare portion, then bearing 1–several, rather distant spirally arranged triads, distal to these a few pairs of staminate flowers, in the distal portion bearing dense spirals of solitary staminate flowers, each flower group subtended by a short-triangular bract, those subtending the staminate flowers forming shallow pits; floral bracteoles small, mostly obscured within the pits. Flowers creamy yellow, usually rather strongly earthy smelling. Staminate flowers symmetrical or somewhat asymmetrical, those of the triads briefly stalked, those of distal portion of rachillae sessile; sepals 3, distinct, small, narrow to broadly triangular, sometimes irregularly ciliate; petals 3, distinct except at the very base, much longer than the sepals, ± boat-shaped, ± fleshy, valvate; stamens 6, filaments briefly ad-

Map 50.—**Distribution of Bactridinae.**

nate to the base of the petals, elongate, inflexed at the tip, anthers ± rectangular, medifixed, latrorse; pollen subtriangular or rarely elliptic, trichotomosulcate or rarely tetrachotomosulcate or monosulcate, with foveolate, fossulate, or reticulate, tectate exine; pistillode small, trifid. Pistillate flowers larger than the staminate, conic-ovoid; sepals 3, distinct, ± imbricate, broadly triangular; petals much longer than the sepals, 3, ± distinct except sometimes near the base, always with broad, imbricate, distinct margins, except for valvate tips; staminodes 6, united to form a staminodial ring, free, or briefly adnate to the petals, 6-toothed, usually bearing well developed but empty, rounded anthers; gynoecium irregularly ovoid, trilocular, triovulate, variously scaly or tomentose, stigmas 3, conspicuous, sometimes violet in color, reflexed beyond the petals at maturity, ovule laterally attached, ?orthotropous. Fruit usually 1-seeded, globose, or rarely somewhat pyriform, olive-green to yellow-brown, the stigmatic remains apical; epicarp smooth, or tomentose-bristly, mesocarp fleshy, with abundant short fibers adnate to the endocarp; endocarp very thick, stony, dark brown, with 3 pores ± at the equator. Seed basally attached, ± irregular, endosperm homogeneous, sometimes with a central hollow; embryo lateral opposite one of the pores. Germination adjacent-ligular; eophyll not recorded. $n = 15$ (*A. aculeata, A. spinosa,* Read 1966).

Anatomy.—Leaf (Tomlinson 1961), fruit (Vaughan 1960).

Distribution.—About 26 species have been described, but there are probably far fewer, distributed throughout the West Indies and from Mexico southwards to Argentina.

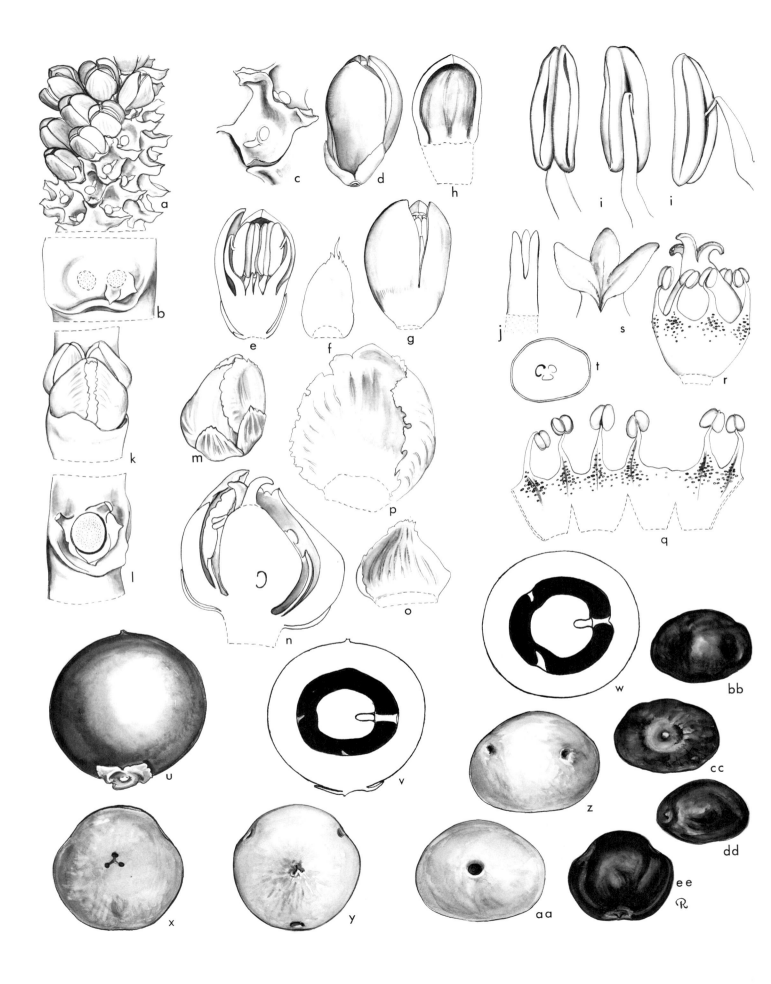

Ecology.—Species of *Acrocomia* usually avoid everwet regions and may be conspicuous components of savannah and man-made grasslands, the seed sometimes distributed by cattle. The three acaulescent species described in *Acanthococos* are palms of "cerrado."

Common Names and Uses.—Macaúba, Gru Gru (*A. aculeata*), Mbocayá totai (*A. totai*) Mucajá (*A. eriocantha*). *Acrocomia* is considered a genus of great potential (Lleras 1985). Starch can be extracted from the stem of *A. totai* (and probably other species too); leaves are used as a source of fiber for weaving hammocks and other articles. Fruit of many species are used as a source of oil (from the endosperm) and animal food and are sometimes sold for human consumption. The cabbage is edible. For medicinal uses see Plotkin and Balick (1984).

Notes.—*Acrocomia* seems to be the least specialized member of the subtribe in terms of inflorescence and flower structure. The rachillae bear shallow rather than deep pits and there is very little if any connation in the perianths and androecium. *Acanthococos,* described to include three acaulescent species, is distinctive only in its habit and is thus included in synonymy.

Taxonomic Accounts.—The genus is in need of a critical revision. Bailey's preliminary account (1941) is the most useful. See also Toledo (1952).

Plate.—77C; Figs. G.7, G.20.

187. GASTROCOCOS Morales, Repertorio Fisico-Natural de la Isla de Cuba 1:57. 1865. Type: *G. armentalis* Morales = **G. crispa** (Kunth) H. E. Moore (*Cocos crispa* Kunth).

Large, solitary, heavily armed, pleonanthic, monoecious palm. Stem erect, at maturity spindle-shaped, distinctly ventricose, bearing persistent leaves at first, eventually bare, ringed with narrow close leaf scars, gray, striate, densely armed, especially when young, with robust black spines in bands between the leaf scars, sometimes becoming smooth with age. Leaves large, numerous, pinnate, neatly abscising in mature trees; sheath becoming fibrous and splitting irregularly opposite the petiole, the whole densely armed with short to very long black spines, pointing in several directions; petiole ± absent in juveniles, a short petiole developed in adults, adaxially channeled, abaxially rounded or angled, with fibrous margins and sparse to abundant tomentum and spines abaxially, the abaxial midline often unarmed; rachis generally ± stiff, only slightly curving, sparsely armed abaxially with short or long spines; leaflets numerous, subregularly arranged in juveniles, in adults ± grouped in pairs and displayed in different planes, the proximal often very crowded, the distal farther apart, narrow, linear, ± acute or becoming briefly bifid in age, the margins smooth except at the base where armed with a few spines, glabrous, the adaxial surface bright green, the abaxial conspicuously glaucous, with short hairs, transverse veinlets obscure. Inflorescences interfoliar, becoming pendulous, apparently protandrous, branching to 1 order; peduncle elliptic in cross-section, densely spiny; prophyll tubular, 2-keeled, splitting longitudinally on the abaxial face, densely tomentose and spiny, persistent; peduncular bract woody, much longer than the prophyll, tubular at first, then splitting longitudinally on the abaxial face, densely tomentose, sparsely if at all spiny, persistent; rachis usually longer than the peduncle, sparsely spiny near the base, becoming unarmed distally, bearing spirally arranged, small, triangular bracts each subtending a straight or flexuous, slender rachilla; rachillae glabrous, with a short basal bare portion, then with rather distant, spirally arranged triads for ca. ⅓–½ the rachilla length, distally bearing more crowded, spirally arranged pairs of staminate flowers, except at the very tip where solitary; flower groups ± superficial, not sunken within pits, each subtended by a low triangular bract. Staminate flower ± symmetrical; calyx cupular, briefly 3-lobed; petals 3, about 5 times as long as the calyx, very briefly connate at the base, valvate, narrowly boat-shaped; stamens 6, filaments short, slender, free, erect, anthers linear, dorsifixed near the base, erect, latrorse; pollen subtriangular, trichotomosulcate or rarely tetrachotomosulcate, with coarsely reticulate, tectate exine; pistillode very short, deeply trifid. Pistillate flower much larger than the staminate; calyx cupular, short, with 3 low triangular lobes; petals much longer than the calyx, triangular, valvate, connate in the basal ca. ⅓; staminodes almost as long as the petals, connate for ca. ¾ their length into a membranous tube tipped with 6 triangular points, at the base adnate to the corolla, distally free; gynoecium ovoid, trilocular, triovulate, stigmas 3, fleshy, reflexed, ovule orthotropous, attached laterally. Fruit ± globose, 1-seeded, stigmatic remains apical; epicarp smooth, mesocarp fleshy with flat fibers, easily separated from the endocarp, endocarp thick, pitted, with 3 pores slightly above the equator. Seed rather irregular, basally attached, hilum circular,

←

186.—**Acrocomia. a,** portion of rachilla near apex with solitary staminate flowers ×3; **b,** intermediate portion of rachilla with paired staminate flowers ×6; **c,** portion of rachilla, staminate flowers removed ×6; **d,** staminate bud ×6; **e,** staminate bud in vertical section ×6; **f,** staminate sepal ×12; **g,** staminate bud, sepals removed ×6; **h,** staminate petal, interior view ×6; **i,** stamen in 3 views ×12; **j,** pistillode ×12; **k,** triad at base of rachilla ×3; **l,** triad, flowers removed ×3; **m,** pistillate bud ×3; **n,** pistillate flower in vertical section ×6; **o,** pistillate sepal, interior view ×6; **p,** pistillate petal, interior view ×6; **q,** staminodes, expanded ×6; **r,** gynoecium and staminodes ×6; **s,** stigmas ×12; **t,** ovary in cross-section ×6; **u,** fruit ×1; **v,** fruit in vertical section ×1; **w,** fruit in cross-section ×1; **x, y, z, aa,** endocarp in 4 views ×1½; **bb, cc, dd, ee,** seed in 4 views ×1½. *Acrocomia* sp.: **a–t,** *O. F. Cook s.n.*; *A. vinifera:* **u–ee,** *Coto Fernandez s.n.*

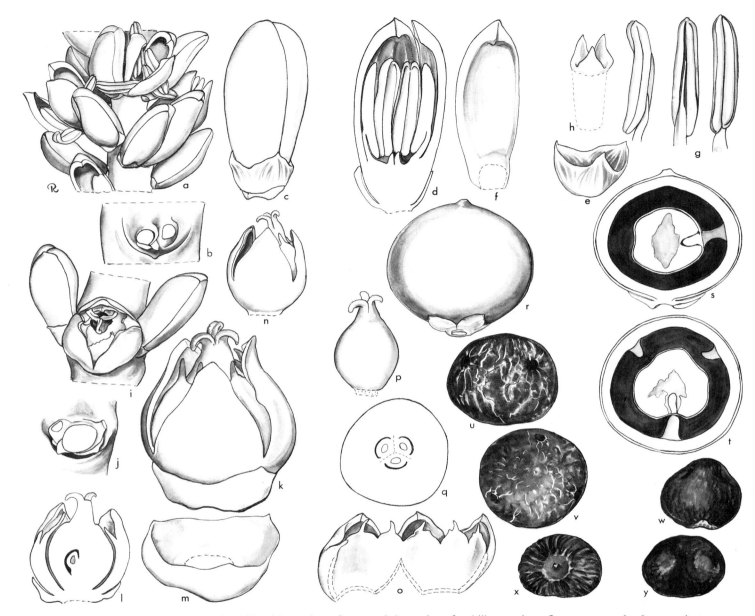

187.—**Gastrococos. a,** portion of rachilla with staminate flowers ×3; **b,** portion of rachilla, staminate flowers removed ×6; **c,** staminate bud ×6; **d,** staminate bud in vertical section ×6; **e,** staminate calyx ×6; **f,** staminate petal, interior view ×4; **g,** stamen in 3 views ×6; **h,** pistillode ×12; **i,** basal portion of rachilla with triad ×3; **j,** triad, flowers removed ×3; **k,** pistillate flower ×6; **l,** pistillate flower in vertical section ×3; **m,** pistillate calyx ×6; **n,** pistillate flower, calyx removed ×3; **o,** pistillate corolla and staminodes, expanded, interior view ×3; **p,** gynoecium ×3; **q,** ovary in cross-section ×6; **r,** fruit ×1½; **s,** fruit in vertical section ×1½; **t,** fruit in cross-section ×1½; **u, v,** endocarp in 2 views ×1½; **w, x, y,** seed in 3 views ×1½. *Gastrococos crispa:* **a-q,** *Read 821;* **r-y,** *Walsingham s.n.*

raphe branches anastomosing, endosperm homogeneous, hollow; embryo lateral, opposite an endocarp pore. Germination not recorded, eophyll simple, ovate. *n* = 15 (as *Acrocomia crispa,* Read 1966).

Anatomy. —Not studied.
Distribution. —Monotypic, endemic to Cuba.

Ecology. —Confined to calcareous soils throughout the island.
Fossil Record. —Not known.
Common Names and Uses. —Belly palm. A spectacular, if spiny, ornamental; in Cuba the leaflets are used for making brooms and for rope fiber. The

fruits are edible, containing an appreciable quantity of oil.

Notes.—*Gastrococos* is perhaps most closely related to *Acrocomia,* but differs in connation of sepals in both staminate and pistillate flowers, and of petals in the pistillate flowers. The genus is geographically isolated.

Taxonomic Account.—Moore (1967b).

Plate.—*77D.*

188. AIPHANES Willdenow, Memoires de l'Académie Royale des Sciences (Berlin) Berlin 1804:32. 1807. Type: **A. aculeata** Willdenow.

Marara Karsten, Linnea 28:389. 1857. Lectotype: *M. erinacea* Karsten (see H. E. Moore 1963c). (=*Aiphanes erinacea* (Karsten) H. A. Wendland).

Curima O. F. Cook, Bulletin of the Torrey Botanical Club 28:561. 1901. Type: *C. calophylla* O. F. Cook (=*Aiphanes acanthophylla* (Martius) Burret).

Tilmia O. F. Cook, Bulletin of the Torrey Botanical Club 28:565. 1901. Lectotype: *T. caryotifolia* (Kunth) O. F. Cook (*Martinezia caryotifolia* Kunth) (see H. E. Moore 1963c). (=*Aiphanes caryotifolia* (Kunth) H. A. Wendland).

Martinezia of many authors (non *Martinezia* Ruiz & Pavon 1794 = *Prestoea*).

Small to moderate, solitary, spiny, pleonanthic, monoecious palms. Stem often very short, the plant then ± acaulescent, or erect, becoming bare, conspicuously ringed with leaf scars and usually bearing horizontal rows or rings of robust black spines. Leaves few to numerous, pinnate or entire bifid, neatly abscising; sheaths tubular at first, soon disintegrating into a weft of fibers and broad shreds, usually densely spiny and/or tomentose, distally prolonged into a tubular, tattering ligule; petiole short to long, adaxially channeled in proximal part, flattened or angled distally, abaxially rounded or angled, usually variously golden-yellow to black-spiny and sometimes also tomentose, the spines themselves often bearing caducous tomentum; rachis (or axis of entire leaf) adaxially ± angled, abaxially rounded, often variously spiny and/or tomentose or glabrous; blade where undivided, with a shallow to deep apical notch, the margins praemorse, the main ribs unarmed or spiny on abaxial and/or adaxial surfaces, leaflets, where blade divided, narrow lanceolate to broad rhomboid, regularly arranged or grouped, held in one plane or twisted into several planes, proximal margins entire, the apical praemorse, shallowly or deeply lobed, variously tomentose or bristly or glabrous, variously armed with short to long spines along veins on one or both surfaces and along margins, transverse veinlets obscure. Inflorescences solitary, interfoliar, spicate (rarely) or branching to 1 order only, very rarely to 2, apparently protandrous; peduncle elongate curved to pendulous, ± elliptic to circular in cross-section, unarmed or sparsely to fiercely armed with spicules and spines, glabrous or tomentose; prophyll usually lanceolate, ± beaked, flattened, 2-keeled, tubular,

enclosing the inflorescence in bud, splitting longitudinally and tattering apically, but persistent, variously glabrous or tomentose, unarmed or spiny; peduncular bract inserted near the prophyll, much longer, ± terete, sometimes beaked, unarmed or variously spiny, persistent; rachis (where inflorescence branched) shorter than the peduncle, proximally often armed, distally usually unarmed, often scaly or tomentose, bearing spirally arranged, evenly spaced rachillae each subtended by a small triangular bract; rachillae slender, usually elongate, often spreading, straight or flexuous, with a short to long, basal bare portion, the whole glabrous or more usually scaly or tomentose, flowers borne spirally in triads proximally, distally the rachillae bearing solitary or paired staminate flowers, rarely the rachillae bearing staminate flowers only, very rarely flowers borne in tetrads of 2 pistillate and 2 staminate (according to Read 1979), flower groups superficial or sunken in pits, the rachilla bracts forming the lower lips of the pits; floral bracteoles minute. Staminate flowers usually small, sessile or with a brief stalk; sepals 3, distinct, or connate and spreading in a 3-lobed ring, triangular, membranous; petals 3, distinct or minutely connate basally, valvate, triangular, rather fleshy, much longer than the calyx, ± ovate to triangular, adaxially with impressions of the stamens; stamens 6, filaments short, fleshy, wider and minutely connate basally and/or briefly epipetalous, anthers orbicular, ± rectangular, or linear, medifixed, versatile, latrorse; pollen elliptic, monosulcate or rarely trichotomosulcate, with finely reticulate or foveolate, rarely echinate, tectate exine; pistillode minute, conical or trifid. Pistillate flowers larger than the staminate, sessile; sepals 3, distinct, broad, imbricate; petals 3, exceeding the sepals, fleshy, connate in the basal ca. ½, apically with 3, triangular, valvate lobes; staminodial ring 6-toothed, adnate to the corolla tube; gynoecium ovoid, trilocular, triovulate, stigmas 3, becoming reflexed at anthesis, ovules ?orthotropous, laterally attached. Fruit 1-seeded, ± globose, brilliant red at maturity, stigmatic remains small, apical; epicarp smooth, mesocarp thick, fleshy, fibrous, endocarp thick, very hard and woody, usually uneven, with 3, usually equatorially placed pores, surrounded by radiating fibers. Seed irregularly globose, basally attached, endosperm homogeneous with a central cavity; embryo lateral, opposite one of the pores. Germination adjacent-ligular; eophyll very shallowly to deeply bifid with praemorse tips, frequently densely spiny. $n = 15$ (*A. erosa, A. caryotifolia,* Read 1966). $n = 16$ (*A. caryotifolia* as *Martinezia caryotifolia,* Eichhorn 1957, Sharma and Sarkar 1957, Satô 1946—also reported $n = 32$ for this species). $n = 18$ (*A. erosa* as *Martinezia erosa,* Gassner 1941).

Anatomy.—Leaf (Tomlinson 1961).

Distribution.—About 38 species, a few in the West Indies, the rest in northern South America, especially diverse in Colombia.

Ecology.—Found in a variety of habitats in the undergrowth of tropical rain forest at low elevations to montane forest.

Common Names and Uses.—Ruffle palm, coyure

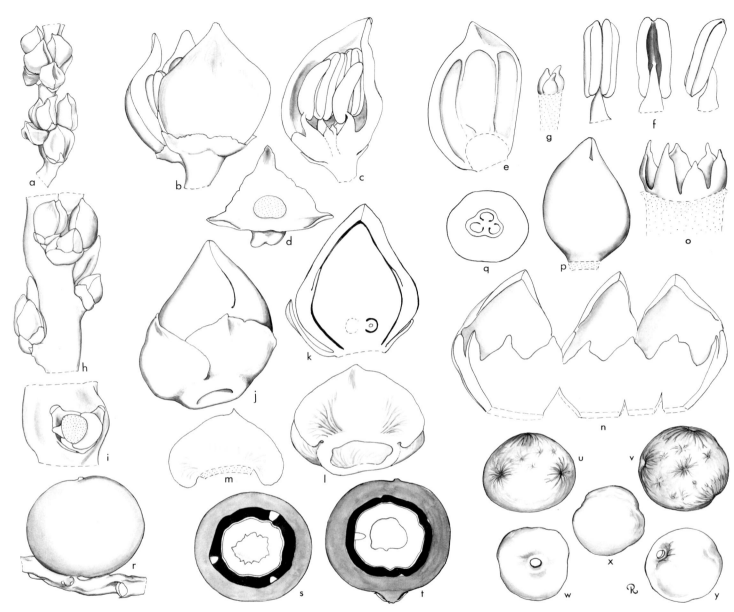

188.—**Aiphanes. a,** apical portion of rachilla with paired staminate flowers ×3; **b,** staminate flower ×12; **c,** staminate flower in vertical section ×12; **d,** staminate calyx ×12; **e,** staminate petal, interior view ×12; **f,** stamen in 3 views ×12; **g,** pistillode ×12; **h,** portion of rachilla with triads ×3; **i,** triad, flowers removed to show bracteoles ×6; **j,** pistillate flower ×12; **k,** pistillate flower in vertical section ×12; **l,** pistillate calyx, exterior view ×12; **m,** pistillate sepal, interior view ×12; **n,** pistillate corolla and staminodes, interior view, expanded ×12; **o,** staminodes ×12; **p,** gynoecium ×12; **q,** ovary in cross-section ×12; **r,** fruit ×1½; **s,** fruit in cross-section ×1½; **t,** fruit in vertical section ×1½; **u, v,** endocarp in 2 views ×1½; **w, x, y,** seed in 3 views ×1½. *Aiphanes caryotifolia:* **a-q,** *Read 905;* **r-y,** *Moore s.n.*

(*A. acanthophylla*). Fruits of *A. caryotifolia* are eaten; many species are very decorative.

Notes.—*Aiphanes* is unlikely to be confused with any other genus. The only other member of the Bactridinae with praemorse leaflets is *Bactris caryoti-* *folia* which however, has a very different inflorescence with connate sepals in flowers of both sexes. *Aiphanes* is a remarkable, diverse genus, much in need of a modern appraisal.

Taxonomic Accounts.—The last synopsis of the

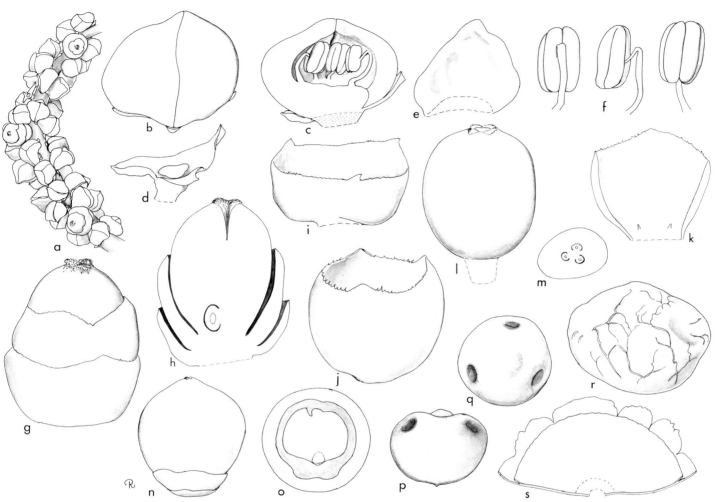

189.—**Bactris. a,** portion of rachilla ×1½; **b,** staminate bud ×9; **c,** staminate bud in vertical section ×9; **d,** staminate calyx ×9; **e,** staminate petal, interior view ×9; **f,** stamen in 3 views ×18; **g,** pistillate flower ×6; **h,** pistillate flower in vertical section ×6; **i,** pistillate calyx ×6; **j,** pistillate corolla ×6; **k,** portion of corolla of pistillate flower showing staminodes ×6; **l,** gynoecium ×6; **m,** ovary in cross-section ×6; **n,** fruit ×1½; **o,** fruit in cross-section ×1½; **p, q,** endocarp in 2 views ×1½; **r,** seed ×3; **s,** portion of pistillate corolla, interior view, showing staminodial cupule ×2¼. *Bactris setulosa*: **a-r,** *Moore et al. 9837*; *B. major*: **s,** *Bailey & Bailey s.n.*

genus is Burret (1932b). See Galeano-Garces and Bernal-Gonzalez (1983).

    Plates.—78A, B; Figs. G.4, G.15, G.23.

189. **BACTRIS** N. J. Jacquin ex Scopoli, Introductio ad Historiam Naturalem 70. 1777. Lectotype: *B. minor* N. J. Jacquin (illegitimate name) = **B. guineensis** (Linnaeus) H. E. Moore (*Cocos guineensis* Linnaeus) (see Karsten 1857).

Guilielma Martius, Palmarum Familia 21. 1824. Type: *G. speciosa* Martius (illegitimate name) (*G. gasipaes* (Kunth) L. H. Bailey (*Bactris gasipaes* Kunth)).

Augustinea Karsten, Linnaea 28:395. 1857 (Non Saint-Hilaire & Naudin 1844). Type: *A. major* (Jacquin) Karsten (*Bactris major* N. J. Jacquin).

Pyrenoglyphis Karsten, Linnaea 28:607. 1857 ("1856"). Type: *P. major* (N. J. Jacquin) Karsten (*Bactris major* N. J. Jacquin) (substitute name for *Augustinea* Karsten 1856, non Saint-Hilaire & Naudin 1844).

Amylocarpus Barbosa Rodrigues, Contributions du Jardin Botanique de Rio de Janeiro 3:69. 1902 (Non Currey 1859). Lectotype: *A. simplicifrons* (Martius) Barbosa Rodrigues (*Bactris simplicifrons* Martius) (see H. E. Moore 1963c).

Yuyba (Barbosa Rodrigues) L. H. Bailey, Gentes Herbarum 7:416. 1947. Type: *Y. simplicifrons*

(Martius) L. H. Bailey (*Bactris simplicifrons* Martius (substitute name for *Amylocarpus* Barbosa Rodrigues 1902, non Currey 1858).

Amylocarpus section *Yuyba* Barbosa Rodrigues, Contributions du Jardin Botanique de Rio de Janeiro 3:69. 1902.

Diminutive to large, solitary or clustered, unarmed (rarely) to very spiny, pleonanthic, monoecious palms. Stem subterranean and very short, to erect, very slender to moderate, with short to long internodes and, eventually, with conspicuous nodal scars, often scaly, frequently armed with short to long spines. Leaves pinnate or entire bifid, marcescent or neatly deciduous; sheaths usually splitting opposite the petiole, the margins smooth or becoming fibrous, unarmed to densely spiny, glabrous, scaly, hairy or bristly, a ligulelike projection sometimes also present; petiole very short to long, adaxially channeled, flat, or angled, abaxially rounded, variously unarmed to spiny; rachis usually longer than the petiole, adaxially angled except near base where channeled or not, abaxially rounded to flattened, variously armed or unarmed; blade where undivided with smooth or spiny margins, numerous ribs and an apical V-shaped notch, leaflets 1–several-fold, regularly arranged or irregularly grouped, often held in different planes within the groups, linear, lanceolate, or sigmoid, the tips very rarely praemorse (*B. caryotifolia*), acute or acuminate in a long drip tip, more rarely bifid or irregularly lobed, sometimes the abaxial surface covered in chalky-white indumentum, sometimes spiny along midrib on abaxial surface, the margins often bristly, blade surfaces sometimes softly hairy, midrib prominent adaxially, transverse veinlets conspicuous or obscure. Inflorescences interfoliar, or mostly becoming infrafoliar, solitary, spicate (rarely) or branching to 1 order, protogynous; peduncle usually relatively short, sometimes elongate, ± curved, oval in cross-section, armed or unarmed; prophyll short, tubular, 2-keeled, tightly sheathing, often concealed within the leaf sheath, usually membranous, unarmed, splitting along the abaxial face; peduncular bract inserted near the base of the peduncle, usually persistent, much longer than the prophyll, enclosing the rachillae in bud, coriaceous to woody, tightly sheathing the peduncle, tubular, later splitting longitudinally in distal region and often expanding and becoming boat-shaped or cowllike, usually bearing indumentum, often bearing spines on the outer face, inner face smooth, sometimes conspicuously cream-colored; rachis usually shorter than the peduncle, bearing spirally arranged, rather stiff, ± glabrous, densely hairy or bristly rachillae, each subtended by an inconspicuous triangular bract; rachillae bearing spirally arranged, usually rather crowded, small triangular rachilla bracts subtending flower groups, flowers borne in triads ± throughout the rachillae, or triads scattered among paired or solitary staminate flowers ± throughout the rachillae, or triads borne in proximal ca. ½ and solitary or paired staminate flowers distally; floral bracteoles minute. Staminate flowers often somewhat asymmetrical, sessile, or rarely borne on slender, unequal pedicels; calyx cupular or spreading, very short, shallowly trilobed; petals 3, fleshy, asymmetrically triangular, distally valvate, connate basally to ca. ½ their length and adnate basally to a fleshy floral axis; stamens usually 6, rarely 5–7 or 12, filaments slender, inflexed at the apex nearly from the middle in bud, sometimes curved, anthers usually dorsifixed, short to elongate, ± versatile, latrorse; pollen elliptic, subtriangular, or circular, monosulcate or trichotomosulcate, with verrucate, foveolate-fossulate or finely reticulate, tectate exine; pistillode absent. Pistillate flowers scarcely larger than the staminate; calyx annular, somewhat flattened or urn-shaped, truncate or very shallowly 3-lobed, sometimes hairy, scaly or spinulose; corolla much longer than the calyx or ± the same length, urn-shaped, truncate or very shallowly 3-lobed, variously hairy or spiny or glabrous; staminodes absent or forming a membranous ring, not adnate to the corolla; gynoecium columnar to ovoid, sometimes spiny or hairy, trilocular, triovulate, stigmas 3, very short, ovules laterally attached, orthotropous. Fruit usually 1-seeded, very small to large, ovoid, obpyriform, oblate, or top-shaped, yellow, red, green, brown, purple, or black; epicarp smooth, spiny, or hairy, mesocarp thin to very thick, fleshy, juicy or starchy with sparse or abundant fibers, endocarp thick, bony, with 3 pores at or above the equator, sometimes with fibers radiating from the pores. Seed irregularly globular, basally attached, hilum circular, raphe branches sparsely anastomosing (?always) endosperm homogeneous, with or without a central hollow; embryo next to one of the endocarp pores. Germination adjacent-ligular; eophyll bifid, often spiny, bristly or hairy. $2n = 28$ (*B. gasipaes*, Sharma 1970), $n = 15$ (*B. gasipaes*, *B.* sp., Read 1966). $n = 14$ (*B. caribaea*, *B. major*, Sarkar 1970).

Anatomy.—Leaf morphology (Clement and Urpi 1983), anatomy (Tomlinson 1961), flower (Uhl and Moore 1971, 1977a).

Distribution.—There are 239 recognized species distributed from Mexico and the West Indies south to Paraguay, with the greatest diversity in Brazil.

Ecology.—It is not surprising that there are species of *Bactris* adapted to a very wide range of habitats in the lowlands and uplands, but the genus appears to be absent from montane forest. There are species confined to the undergrowth of tropical rain forest, others adapted to the landward fringe of mangrove, to white sand savannahs, and to freshwater swamp forest. Pollination in *Bactris* is by beetles as discussed by Essig (1971a) and Beach (1984).

Fossil Record.—Leaves referred to *Bactrites* cannot safely be attributed to the extant genus; fossil vegetative parts, especially spines, can bear some resemblance to *Bactris* but there should be caution in equating them.

Common Names and Uses.—Peach palm, Pejibaye, Chonta, Pupunha, (*B. gasipaes*). Economically, the most important species is *B. gasipaes* (*Guilielma gasipaes*), which is widely cultivated and not known in the truly wild state (Mora-Urpi 1983). It produces thick mesocarp flesh, edible and tasty after cooking, and is sufficiently rich in nutrients and vitamins to be an important constituent of the diet of rural people. The "cabbage" of the same species is edible and good. See also Guerrero and Clement (1982) for references on *B. gasipaes*. Other species have edible fruits and some have been used as a source of walking sticks, and for thatch and fiber.

Notes. — This diverse and large genus is greatly in need of a modern critical revision. The genus is distinguished by staminate flowers in triads or dispersed among the triads on the rachillae and by pistillate flowers with united petals.

Taxonomic Accounts. — Burret (1933c, 1934a).

Plates. — 29B, 78C, D; Figs. G.4, G.19.

190. DESMONCUS Martius, Palmarum Familia 20. 1824 (conserved name, but conservation superfluous). Type: **D. polyacanthos** Martius.

Atitara O. Kuntze, Revisio Generum Plantarum 2: 726. 1891. Type: *A. polyacantha* (Martius) O. Kuntze (*Desmoncus polyacanthos* Martius).

Slender, clustering (?always), spiny, pleonanthic, monoecious climbing palms. Stem covered with leaf sheaths, eventually becoming bare, with long internodes and conspicuous nodal scars, the first stem slender, not usually reaching a great height before being replaced by more robust sucker shoots (?always). Leaves pinnate, marcescent; sheath tubular, tightly sheathing, elongate, often tomentose and densely armed with spines in the distal exposed areas or glabrous and/or unarmed; ocrea well developed, armed or unarmed like the sheath, entire or disintegrating into a fibrous network; petiole very short to elongate, adaxially channeled, abaxially angled, usually with reflexed, bulbous-based spines; rachis elongate, usually curved, usually armed with swollen-based, reflexed spines, apically extended into a long cirrus armed with spines and pairs of small to robust, reflexed acanthophylls, acanthophylls absent on juvenile leaves, very rarely absent on adults; leaflets usually ovate, acuminate, often much narrowed at the base into a brief stalk, rather distant, ± regularly arranged or grouped, thin to coriaceous, with a conspicuous midrib and several more slender lateral veins, in one unnamed taxon from Colombia (Dransfield et al. *4861*) the main rib extended into a long flexuous tendril, margins smooth or armed with short spines, the main rib sometimes bearing spines, indumentum sometimes present in bands and along veins, transverse veinlets sometimes conspicuous. Inflorescences interfoliar, emerging through the leaf sheath mouths, branching to 1 order, becoming ± pendulous, apparently protandrous; peduncle elongate, slender, semicircular in cross-section; prophyll inserted some distance above the base of the peduncle, thinly coriaceous, 2-keeled, tubular, splitting longitudinally on the abaxial face and tattering, only partially exserted, persistent; peduncular bract 1, longer than and inserted far above the prophyll, thick, coriaceous to subwoody, tubular, enclosing the rachillae in bud, later splitting longitudinally, ± persistent, variously unarmed or spiny, adaxially smooth, often pale-cream at anthesis, tomentose or ± glabrous abaxially; rachis shorter than the peduncle, bearing few to numerous, ± spirally arranged, flexuous, slender, short to elongate, often somewhat zig-zag rachillae, each subtended by a minute, triangular bract; rachillae very few to numerous, bearing rather distant, spiral, or subdistichous triads except in the distal ca. ⅓–⅕ where bearing paired or solitary staminate flowers, each flower group subtended by an inconspicuous triangular bract; bracteoles minute. Staminate flowers somewhat asymmetrical; calyx cupular, short, ± membranous with 3, low or acuminate, triangular lobes; petals 3, distinct, ± fleshy, ovate-lanceolate, much exceeding the calyx, acute or acuminate; stamens 6–9, filaments irregularly adnate to the petals, the free portion very short or moderate, very slender at the tip, anthers ± rectangular, basifixed, sagittate at the base, latrorse; pollen elliptic, monosulcate, with foveolate-fossulate, tectate exine; pistillode minute, conical, or absent. Pistillate flowers ± globular or ovoid, usually smaller than or equalling the staminate; calyx cupular or tubular, sometimes ± flattened, ± membranous, very briefly trilobed; corolla much exceeding the calyx, tubular, ± membranous, shallowly trilobed or truncate, sometimes minutely ciliate along the margins; staminodes 6, minute, toothlike, epipetalous; gynoecium ovoid or columnar, trilocular, triovulate, only slightly exceeding the corolla, stigmas 3, fleshy, reflexed, ovule laterally attached, ?orthotropus. Fruit 1-seeded, ± ovoid or spherical, bright red, deep purple, or black, with apical stigmatic remains; epicarp smooth, mesocarp thin, fleshy, endocarp stony with 3 pores slightly distal to the equator. Seed ovoid, with 3 surface hollows, basally attached, hilum basal, circular, raphe branches densely anastomosing, endosperm homogeneous; embryo lateral. Germination adjacent-ligular; eophyll bifid with rather broad, acute segments or pinnate (2 pairs of leaflets in *D. costaricensis*). Cytology not studied.

Anatomy. — Leaf (Tomlinson 1961).

Distribution. — Sixty-one species have been described but there are probably far fewer. *Desmoncus* is distributed from Mexico southwards to Brazil and Bolivia, and is absent from the West Indies except for Trinidad.

Ecology. — Most species are palms of the lowlands, often found in open areas, swamps, on riverbanks, and more rarely in the undergrowth of tropical rain forest.

Common Names and Uses. — For common names see Glassman (1972). Locally *Desmoncus* species may provide cane for cordage, basket frames, or rarely for inexpensive furniture; they are not, however, utilized to the same extent as the Asiatic rattans.

Notes. — The genus represents the New World counterpart of the Asiatic and African calamoid rattans. The parallel development of grapnel acantho-

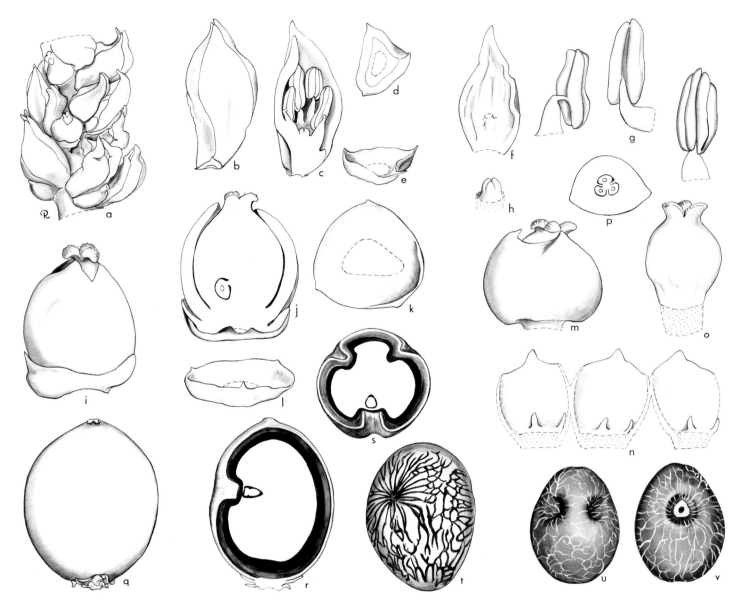

190.—**Desmoncus. a,** portion of rachilla with triads ×3; **b,** staminate bud ×6; **c,** staminate bud in vertical section ×6; **d, e,** staminate calyx in 2 views ×12; **f,** staminate petal, interior view ×6; **g,** stamen in 3 views ×12; **h,** pistillode ×12; **i,** pistillate flower ×12; **j,** pistillate flower in vertical section ×12; **k, l,** pistillate calyx in 2 views ×12; **m,** pistillate flower, calyx removed ×12; **n,** pistillate corolla and staminodes, interior view, expanded ×12; **o,** gynoecium ×12; **p,** ovary in cross-section ×12; **q,** fruit ×3; **r,** fruit in vertical section ×3; **s,** fruit in cross-section ×3; **t,** endocarp ×3; **u, v,** seed in 2 views ×3. *Desmoncus* sp.: **a–p,** *Moore & Parthasarathy 9471;* **q–v,** *C. J. Miller s.n.*

phylls on the cirrus of *Desmoncus* and of the cala-moid genera, *Eremospatha, Oncocalamus* and *Laccosperma* is noteworthy.

Taxonomic Account.—Taxonomy of this genus is in disarray because of the uncritical description of so-called new species in the past, and the perhaps excessive "lumping" of taxa in Surinam. A critical

revision is greatly needed. Work has been under-taken by de Medeiros Costa.

Plate.—29A; Fig. G.6.

191. **ASTROCARYUM** G. F. W. Meyer, Primitiae Florae Essequeboensis 265. 1818 (conserved name). Type: **A. aculeatum** G. F. W. Meyer.

Avoira Giseke, Praelectiones in Ordines Naturales Plantarum 38, 53. 1792 (name rejected in favor of *Astrocaryum*). Lectotype: *A. vulgaris* Giseke (see O. F. Cook, Journal Washington Academy Sciences 30:299. 1940) (=*Astrocaryum* sp.).

Hexopetion Burret, Notizblatt des Botanischen Gartens und Museums zu Berlin-Dahlem 12:156. 1934. Type: *H. mexicanum* (Liebmann ex Martius) Burret (*Astrocaryum mexicanum* Liebmann ex Martius).

Toxophoenix H. W. Schott in von Schreibers, Nachrichten von den Kaiserlichen Oesterreichischen Naturforschern in Brasilien 2 (Anhang):12. 1822. Type: *T. aculeatissima* H. W. Schott (=*Astrocaryum aculeatissimum* (Schott) Burret).

Moderate to robust, solitary or clustered, sometimes acaulescent, spiny, pleonanthic, monoecious palms. Stem very short to tall, often slender, obscured by leaf bases, or becoming bare and conspicuously ringed with leaf scars, often armed with fierce spines pointing in several directions, sometimes losing spines with age. Leaves few to numerous, regularly or irregularly pinnate, neatly abscissing or marcescent; sheath splitting opposite the petiole, usually fiercely armed with large and small spines, and frequently bearing abundant indumentum; petiole very short to long, adaxially channeled near the base, distally ± flattened or angled, abaxially rounded, bearing abundant spines of varying length and dense indumentum; rachis usually much longer than the petiole, adaxially ± angled, abaxially rounded, usually densely armed and tomentose like the petiole; leaflets numerous, single-fold, (or rarely few and composed of many folds), regularly arranged or grouped, and usually fanned within the groups, the whole leaf then appearing plumose, sometimes ± secondarily plicate, linear, acute, usually dark green and shiny adaxially, abaxially almost always with abundant white indumentum, the leaflet margins often conspicuously armed with short spines or bristles; transverse veinlets conspicuous or obscure. Inflorescences solitary, interfoliar, erect at first, becoming pendulous, ?protandrous, branching to 1 order; peduncle usually elongate, ± circular in cross-section, often heavily armed with spines, sometimes with spines confined only to the area just below the bract insertion, the surface frequently densely covered in indumentum; prophyll ± membranous, tubular, 2-keeled, unarmed (?always), ± included within the leaf sheath, soon tattering; peduncular bract much exceeding the prophyll, tubular, beaked, enclosing the rachillae in bud, splitting longitudinally along the abaxial face, arched over the rachillae, persistent or eroding, usually densely tomentose and heavily armed with spines, rarely unarmed; rachis shorter than the peduncle (often very much so) often armed as the peduncle, bearing numerous spirally arranged, crowded rachillae, each subtended by a narrow triangular bract; rachillae complex, elongate, with or without an armed or unarmed basal bare portion above which bearing a single triad or 2–5 distant triads, with or without a

slender bare portion distal to the triads, distal to which the rachillae appearing cylindrical, catkinlike and bearing densely packed staminate flowers in pairs or singly, immersed in pits; rachilla bracts ± acute, forming lower lip of pits, floral bracteoles very small, sometimes partially connate with rachilla bract; after anthesis, staminate portions of the rachillae eroding away, in those species with solitary triads, the fruit then borne in a close-packed "spike" or head, in those with several triads the fruit more loosely arranged. Staminate flowers small, ± symmetrical; sepals 3, very small, ± triangular, ?sometimes basally connate; petals 3, much exceeding the sepals, valvate, boat-shaped, connate basally and adnate to the receptacle; stamens 3 (rarely, Bernal-Gonzalez, pers. comm.) 6 (–12 fide Wessels Boer 1965), filaments epipetalous, short, inflexed in bud, anthers ± rectangular or linear, dorsifixed, versatile, latrorse; pollen elliptic, subtriangular or circular, monosulcate, sometimes very short, or trichotomosulcate, with finely reticulate, tectate exine; pistillode present and trifid or absent. Pistillate flower very much larger than the staminate; calyx urn-shaped or cup-shaped, truncate or shallowly 3-lobed, sometimes bearing numerous short spicules, usually densely tomentose; corolla not, briefly, or considerably exceeding, and similar to the calyx, or composed of 3 imbricate triangular lobes, connate basally; staminodes 6, epipetalous near the base of the corolla, connate into a low membranous ring or tooth-like; gynoecium varied in shape, trilocular, triovulate, the 3 large fleshy erect, or headlike, reflexed stigmas borne on a beak, protruding through the mouth of the corolla tube, sometimes bearing short spines and/or tomentum, ovule ?orthotropous, laterally attached. Fruit 1 (–2) seeded with apical stigmatic remains, beaked, spherical, top-shaped, prismatic, or ovoid, often brightly colored, brown, yellowish or orange-red, calyx and corolla persistent, enlarged and irregularly splitting; epicarp spiny or unarmed, tomentose or glabrous, mesocarp relatively thin, fleshy or dry and starchy, and fibrous, sometimes with the epicarp irregularly splitting and spreading to expose the endocarp, endocarp thick, stony, with numerous flattened, black longitudinal fibers on the surface, conspicuously radiating from the 3 subterminal pores. Seed irregularly globular, basally attached, hilum circular, raphe branches anastomosing, endosperm homogeneous, usually hollow; embryo subapical, opposite one of the endocarp pores. Germination adjacent-ligular; eophyll bifid, usually bristly. $n = 15$ (*A. mexicanum*, Read 1966).

Anatomy.—Leaf (Tomlinson 1961).

Distribution.—About 47 described species distributed from Mexico southwards to Brazil and Bolivia; absent from the West Indies except Trinidad.

Ecology.—Ecologically the genus is very varied; some species are undergrowth palms of primary lowland forest; other are light demanding and occur in secondary forest or forest margins (e.g. riverbanks). *A. vulgare* in Surinam is particularly frequent in white sand savannah. Most species seem to be confined to the lowlands.

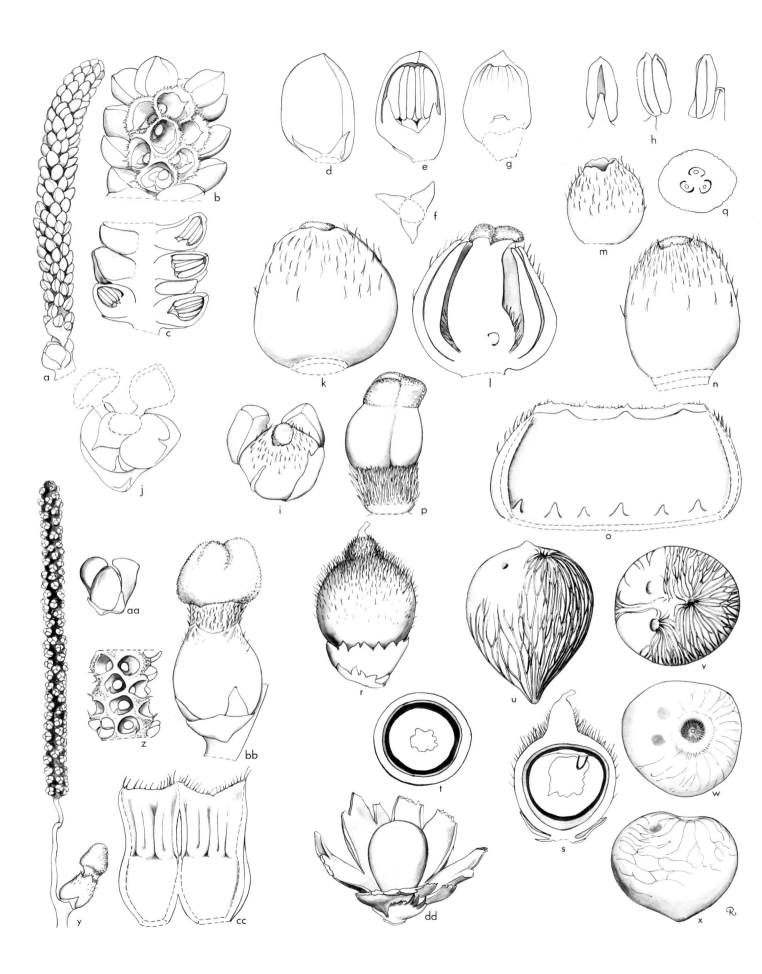

Fossil Record. — Fossils described as *Astrocaryopsis* from the Cenomanian of France (Fliche 1896) were said to be fruit of a cocoid palm, but their identity even at the family level, is uncertain.

Common Names and Use. — Tucumã. For common names see Pesce (1941). For local uses see Glassman (1972) and Balick (1985). The epidermis and hypodermis of the sword leaf of *A. vulgare* provides an important fiber used by Amerindians for manufacturing mats, hats, hammocks, fishing lines and nets. The mesocarp of some species is eaten by humans or fed to cattle. The kernel of *A. vulgare* produces a fine oil, excellent for eating or soap making. Fruits of *A. murumuru* and *A. aculeatum* have also been used as a source of oil, and the "cabbage" of many species is utilized.

Notes. — The specialized catkinlike staminate rachillae and the connation of petals in the pistillate flowers to form a tube or urnlike structure make this the most specialized member of the Bactridinae. It displays a wide range of form and would be an excellent subject for monographic study.

Taxonomic Account. — The latest synopsis of the genus is that of Burret (1934b).

Plate. — *79A, B; Figs. G.12, G.20, G.21.*

GEONOMEAE Drude in Martius, Flora Brasiliensis 3(2):275. 1881. Type: **Geonoma.**

Diminutive to large, acaulescent to erect, unarmed; leaves reduplicately pinnate or pinnately ribbed; crownshaft absent; inflorescences spicate or branched to 3 orders, peduncular bracts usually 1, sometimes 2 or more, rarely absent; flowers always in triads sunken in pits; petals of the pistillate flower connate basally in a soft tube; gynoecium tri- or uniovulate, style usually slender and elongate; fruit 1-seeded, stigmatic remains basal; endosperm homogeneous.

The six genera of this tribe are restricted to the New World (Map 51). Their habit ranges from subcanopy trees in *Welfia* and *Calyptronoma* to medium and small understory palms. The genus *Geonoma* is structurally the most specialized as well as

Map 51. — **Distribution of Geonomeae.**

the largest with more than 75 species distributed from Mexico to Brazil and Bolivia; *Calyptronoma* occurs in the Greater Antilles; *Welfia* in Central America and Colombia, and the other three genera in Central and South America. The genera show specializations in flower structure, such as connate sepals and petals, elongate floral receptacles, and styles. These characters are highly advanced in the family and are perhaps related to the enclosure of the flowers in pits. Five genera are triovulate but the sixth, *Geonomoa*, is pseudomonomerous. Correlations of floral anatomy with floral morphology can be recognized (Uhl and Moore 1977a). Several

←

191. — **Astrocaryum. a,** rachilla with basal pistillate flower and staminate flowers ×1; **b,** portion of axis with staminate flowers ×3; **c,** staminate portion of rachilla in vertical section ×3; **d,** staminate bud ×6; **e,** staminate bud in vertical section ×6; **f,** staminate sepals, basal view ×6; **g,** staminate petal, interior view ×6; **h,** stamen in 3 views ×6; **i,** pistillate flower and staminate buds ×3; **j,** triad, flowers removed to show bracteoles ×3; **k,** pistillate flower ×6; **l,** pistillate flower in vertical section ×6; **m,** pistillate calyx ×3; **n,** pistillate corolla ×6; **o,** pistillate corolla with staminodes, expanded, interior view ×6; **p,** gynoecium ×6; **q,** ovary in cross-section ×6; **r,** fruit ×1; **s,** fruit in vertical section ×1; **t,** fruit in cross-section ×1; **u, v,** endocarp in 2 views ×1½; **w, x,** seed in 2 views ×3; **y,** rachilla ×1; **z,** portion of staminate axis to show pits ×3; **aa,** staminate flower ×6; **bb,** pistillate flower ×3; **cc,** pistillate corolla with adnate staminodial cupule, interior view ×3; **dd,** fruit, dehisced ×1. *Astrocaryum mexicanum: a-q, Read 902; r-x, Moore 6021; A. murumuru:* **y-cc,** *Moore 9551; A. munbaca:* **dd,** *Moore 9523.*

similarities, such as triads of flowers in pits, and spicate inflorescences, occur in the subtribe Linospadicineae (Areceae) but these seem to be parallels.

Key to the Genera of the Geonomeae

1 Moderate to large tree palms; leaves regularly pinnate 2
1 Acaulescent or small (rarely moderate) understory palms; leaves undivided and bifid or variously divided, rarely evenly pinnate 3
2 Leaflets broadly lanceolate, lacking a distinct midrib; inflorescence stout, peduncle short, rachis very short bearing a few (ca. 8) long pendulous rachillae; stamens numerous 36 (–42); petals of pistillate flower connate for ⅔ their length, tips valvate, glumaceous; staminodes ca. 15, awl-shaped where free. Central America, Colombia .. 193. **Welfia**
2 Leaflets narrowly lanceolate, midrib and two pairs of lateral ribs evident abaxially; inflorescence moderate, peduncle long, rachis short bearing many (ca. 20 or more) ± clustered rachillae, stamens six; petals of pistillate flower connate in a tube, opening by a circumscissle cap; staminodes connate forming a fleshy tube enclosing the style and stigma. Greater Antilles .... 194. **Calyptronoma**
3 Bracts covering floral pits not "locked" into the rachilla distally but upper margins rounded, truncate, or split, lateral margins adnate to the rachilla beside the floral pits; anthers terminal on the end of the connective, inflexed in bud, thecae spread apart or parallel; ovary unilocular at anthesis. Central and South America. ...... 197. **Geonoma**
3 Bracts covering the floral pits overlapping laterally or immersed in the rachilla; anthers sagittate or thecae terminal on a bifid connective; ovary trilocular at anthesis 4
4 Stem short to moderate, leaves ± irregularly divided into several-fold leaflets; petioles long, slender; bracts covering the floral pits overlapping laterally, densely tomentose; filaments of stamens and staminodes united in a short tube but free and awl-shaped distally. Central and northern South America. .... 192. **Pholidostachys**
4 Stem usually very short or lacking, leaves bifid or with usually unequal, several-fold leaflets; petioles short, bracts covering the floral pits not overlapping laterally, glabrous or lightly hairy, not densely tomentose; filaments of stamens and staminodes various 5
5 Leaves almost always bifid; peduncular bract(s) inserted near the base of the peduncle, bracts covering the floral pits "locked" in bud by a distinct rounded upper lip; thecae separated on a bifid connective; staminodes free and fleshy distally. Central and northern South America .... 196. **Asterogyne**
5 Leaves irregularly divided; peduncular bract inserted distally on the peduncle just below the flowers, floral pits

without definite upper lip; anthers sagittate; staminodes united in a tube, constricted at the middle, rounded and very briefly 6-lobed distally. Central and northern South America. .... 195. **Calyptrogyne**

192. **PHOLIDOSTACHYS** H. A. Wendland ex J. D. Hooker in Bentham & J. D. Hooker, General Plantarum 3:915. 1883. Lectotype: **P. pulchra** H. A. Wendland ex Burret (see Burret 1930a).
Calyptrogyne H. A. Wendland subgenus *Pholidostachys* (H. A. Wendland) Wessels Boer, Verhandelingen der Koninklijke Nederlandsche Akademie van Wetenschappen, Afdeeling Natuurkunde, Tweede Reeks 58(1):73. 1968.

Small to moderate, solitary, unarmed, pleonanthic, monoecious palms. Stems slender, erect, closely ringed with leaf scars. Leaves pinnate, marcescent; sheath tubular at first, later splitting opposite the petiole, not forming a crownshaft, thin, coriaceous, margins fibrous, lightly hairy adaxially, with dense reddish-brown tomentum abaxially; petiole long, very slender, adaxially shallowly to deeply grooved, abaxially narrowly ridged, V-shaped in cross section, ± tomentose, becoming glabrous; rachis similar to the petiole; blade short, leaflets broadly lanceolate, tapering to a point, median leaflets much longer than the proximal or distal, all leaflets several-fold, folds narrow, midribs ca. 4–5, elevated adaxially, interfold ribs conspicuous abaxially, blade adaxially lightly tomentose near the base, abaxially sparsely covered in scales and a dense layer of wax, transverse veinlets inconspicuous. Inflorescence solitary, protandrous, erect, becoming pendulous and infrafoliar, spicate or digitately or paniculately branched to 1(–3) orders; peduncle short, rounded or ± flattened; prophyll short, tubular, adaxially flat and 2-keeled, keels toothed, inserted near the base of the peduncle, splitting abaxially at the tip, irregularly covered in dark reddish tomentum; peduncular bract tubular with a short solid tip, much longer (3 or more times) than the prophyll, inserted well above the prophyll, splitting adaxially near the tip, caducous or marcescent, thinly covered in dark red tomentum; other peduncular bracts several, small, spirally inserted, the lowest often shortly tubular, the others open, stiff, pointed; rachis lacking, very short, or elongate, bearing spirally inserted, short, stiff, irregular bracts each subtending a rachilla; rachillae bearing obovate bracts, alternating in 5–11 closely appressed rows, ± immersed in the axis, basally tomentose, margins thin, sometimes

→

192.—**Pholidostachys. a,** portion of spike in bud to show overlapping margins of bracts ×3; **b,** portion of spike at staminate anthesis ×4½; **c,** portion of spike at pistillate anthesis ×3; **d,** portion of spike in vertical section to show insertion of flowers in pits ×6; **e,** staminate flower ×6; **f,** staminate flower in vertical section ×6; **g,** staminate sepal ×6; **h,** staminate flower, sepals removed ×6; **i,** staminate petal, interior view ×6; **j,** androecium, perianth removed ×6; **k,** anther and top of filaments in 3 views ×9; **l,** pistillode ×9; **m,** pistillate flower ×6; **n,** pistillate flower in vertical section ×6; **o,** pistillate sepal ×6; **p,** pistillate flower, sepals removed ×6; **q,** perianth and staminodes expanded, interior view ×6; **r,** gynoecium ×6; **s,** ovary in cross-section ×12; **t,** fruit ×2¼; **u,** fruit in vertical section ×2¼; **v,** fruit in cross-section ×2¼; **w,** fruit, outer layer removed to show fibers ×3; **x, y,** endocarp in 2 views ×3; **z, aa, bb,** seed in 3 views ×3. *Pholidostachys pulchra*: **a–s,** *Hartshorn s.n.*; **t–bb,** *Moore & Parthasarathy 9410.*

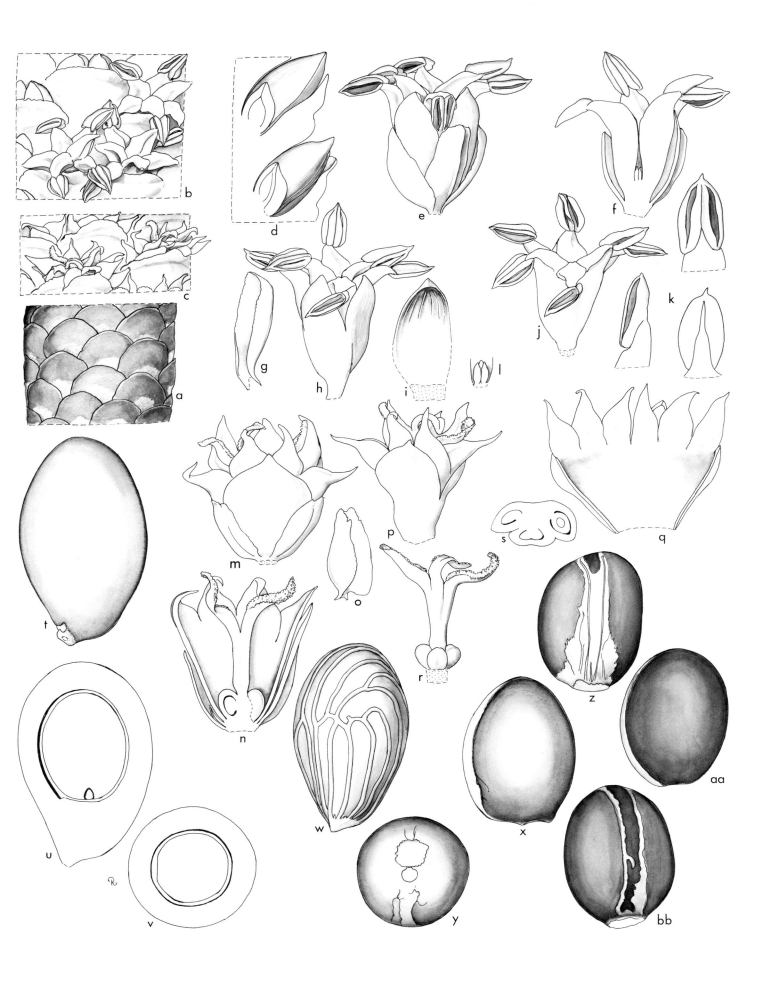

overlapping the margins of bracts of adjacent rows, each bract subtending a triad of flowers enclosed in a pit, floral bracteoles 3, narrow, keeled, chaffy, sepallike. Staminate flowers only about ½ exserted from the pit at anthesis; sepals 3, imbricate basally, keeled, chaffy, truncate or rounded to subacute and often toothed at the apex; petals 3, ovate with pointed tips, connate ca. ½ their length, valvate, briefly adnate to the receptacle basally, tips chaffy; stamens 6, filaments fleshy, connate for ⅔ their length in a thick tanniniferous tube, free parts angled-awlshaped, anthers sagittate, medifixed, erect in bud, exserted and spreading at anthesis, introrse, connectives with pointed tips; pollen elliptic, sometimes irregularly so, monosulcate, with vermiculate, tectate exine; pistillodes 3, minute, pointed. Pistillate flowers with only free parts of staminodes and stigmas exserted from the pit at anthesis; sepals 3, distinct, narrow unequal, imbricate basally, truncate or rounded to subacute, often toothed apically, keeled, chaffy; petals 3, fleshy and connate to about ⅓ to ½ their length basally (or perhaps sometimes less), with valvate, ± chaffy, free tips; staminodes 6–8, fleshy, connate in a tube ⅔ their length, adnate to the corolla for a short distance basally, the free portions angled, awlshaped, exserted and spreading at anthesis; gynoecium trilocular, triovulate, with a central elongate style terminating in 3 exserted, spreading, slender stigmas, ovules anatropous, only one maturing. Fruit moderate, obovoid, purple when ripe with basal remains of abortive carpels and stigmas; epicarp smooth, mesocarp with outer tannin layer, fleshy-granulate, with thick, curved and anastomosing, included fibers, endocarp tough, whitish, thinner over the hilum, with a small operculum over the embryo. Seed ellipsoidal, rapheal lines arched from the rounded hilum over the apex to the base, endosperm homogeneous, sometimes with a central hollow; embryo basal. Germination adjacent-ligular; eophyll bifid. Cytology not studied.

Anatomy.—For leaf of *P. pulchra* see Tomlinson (1961), for further information on leaf and stem anatomy see Wessels Boer (1968).

Distribution.—Three or more species from Costa Rica to Peru.

Ecology.—All species are found in the understory of tropical rain forest.

Common Names and Uses.—Common names not recorded. Would be attractive as ornamentals.

Notes.—*Pholidostachys* differs from other Geonomeae mainly in the androecium of six stamens with filaments united in a tube basally and free and awl-shaped distally. The short to moderate stem, long petioles, and often irregularly divided leaves give it a distinctive appearance in the forest.

Taxonomic Account.—Wessels Boer (1968).

Plate.—79C.

193. **WELFIA** H. A. Wendland, Gartenflora 18:242. 1869. Type: **W. regia** H. A. Wendland ex André.

Moderate, solitary, unarmed, pleonanthic, monoecious palms. Stem erect, leaf scars conspicuous, wide, rather distant, upper trunk orange to brown. Leaves large, marcescent, regularly pinnate, ± erect and arching at the tip in a feather-duster crown; sheath soon splitting opposite the petiole, not forming a crownshaft, abaxially thick, somewhat ridged, densely tomentose, margins disintegrating into large fibers; petiole short, deeply channeled adaxially, rounded abaxially, densely tomentose; rachis much longer than the petiole, adaxially flattened, laterally channeled, abaxially rounded; leaflets subopposite to almost alternate, broadly lanceolate, pendulous, single-fold, glabrous and darker adaxially, pale but with a dense layer of tomentum abaxially, midrib not evident, ca. 8–several, nearly equal, rather large veins more conspicuous abaxially, transverse veinlets not evident. Inflorescences interfoliar and erect in bud, becoming intrafoliar and pendulous, branched to 1(–2) orders, protandrous; peduncle short, very stout, recurved; prophyll tubular, flat, wide, woody, deeply grooved abaxially, tomentose, margins with wide flat keels, often notched; complete peduncular bracts 1, like the prophyll but shorter and thinner, leathery, subsequent peduncular bracts several, short, stiff, rounded, spirally inserted above the peduncular bract; rachis short, about as long as the peduncle, bearing spirally arranged, small, rounded or pointed, ovate bracts subtending rachillae; rachillae stout, bearing 8 rows of partly sunken, stiff ovate bracts each subtending a triad of flowers borne in a pit formed by the fused bases of the bracts. Staminate flowers sessile, borne to the outside of the pistillate flower within the pit; sepals 3, chaffy, briefly united basally to the floral receptacle, narrow, keeled, overlapping distally in bud; petals 3, elongate, connate and joined with the floral receptacle for ca. ⅓ their length, free lobes ± boat-shaped, valvate, chaffy; stamens 36 (27–42) in antesepalous and antepetalous groups (see Uhl and Moore 1980), filaments short, broad, connective with a pointed tip, anthers linear-sagittate, basifixed, introrse; pollen elliptic, slightly irregular, relatively large, monosulcate, with scabrate, tectate exine; pistillode consisting of 3 small tubercles

→

193.—**Welfia. a,** portion of rachilla in bud with pits closed by bracts ×1½; **b,** portion of rachilla in vertical section showing pits ×2; **c,** portion of rachilla with staminate flowers ×1½; **d,** staminate flower in abaxial view ×3; **e,** staminate flower in adaxial view ×2; **f,** staminate sepal ×3; **g,** staminate flower, sepals removed ×3; **h,** staminate flower, sepals removed, in vertical section ×3; **i,** staminate petal, interior view ×3; **j,** stamen in 3 views ×6; **k,** portion of rachilla with pistillate flower ×3; **l, m,** pistillate flower in abaxial and adaxial views ×3; **n,** pistillate flower in vertical section ×3; **o,** pistillate sepal, interior view ×3; **p,** pistillate flower, sepals removed ×3; **q,** pistillate petal, interior view ×3; **r,** staminodial tube and staminodes, expanded, interior view ×3; **s,** gynoecium ×3; **t,** ovary in cross-section ×6; **u,** portion of rachilla with fruit ×1; **v,** fruit ×1½; **w,** fruit in vertical section ×1½; **x,** fruit in cross-section ×1½; **y,** seed in 3 views ×1½. *Welfia georgii:* **a–b** and **k–y,** *Moore & Anderson 10183;* **c–j,** *Moore & Parthasarathy 9412* and *Tomlinson s.n.*

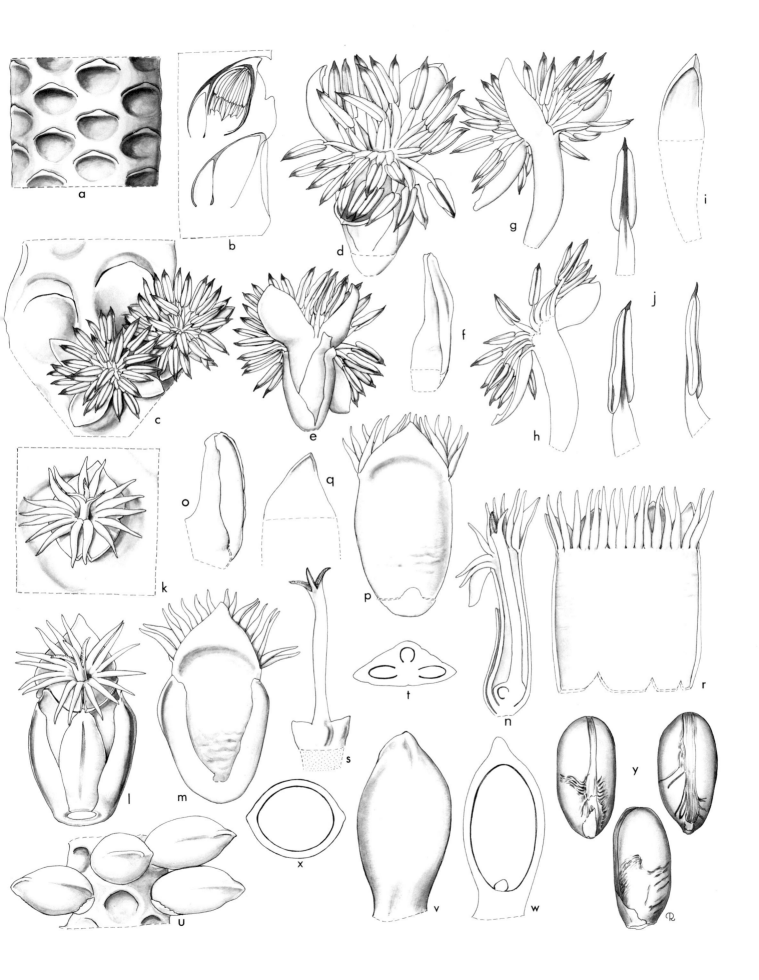

or lacking. Pistillate flower rounded, pointed in bud; sepals 3, distinct, narrow, overlapping, keeled, chaffy; petals 3, connate in a tube for ⅔ their length or more, distinct lobes triangular, valvate, chaffy; staminodes numerous (15–16), adnate to the corolla tube for ⅔ their length, free and awl-shaped or linear-triangular above; gynoecium trilocular, triovulate, 3-angled with the adaxial side longer, style long, cylindrical, stigmas 3, recurved, ovule axile at the center of the locule, hemianatropous. Fruit almond-shaped, slightly compressed dorsiventrally, laterally ridged, with a short apical point, dull purple, stigmatic remains and abortive carpels basal; epicarp smooth, ± shiny, mesocarp with slender parallel fibers, endocarp thin, crustaceous. Seed purple, ellipsoidal, rounded apically, covered in a white, sweet-tasting mucilagelike coating when ripe, hilum lateral at the base, raphe ± encircling the seed with short basal and apical branches, endosperm homogeneous; embryo eccentric at the base. Germination adjacent-ligular, eophyll bifid. Cytology unknown.

Anatomy.—Study of stamen development has shown that after sepal and petal origin, the floral apex expands in lobes opposite the sepals, and stamens arise in arcs of ca. 6 opposite each sepal and petal (Uhl and Moore 1980). The leaf has a 2-layered hypodermis, a distinct palisade layer, and numerous fibers (Tomlinson 1961, Wessels Boer 1968).

Distribution.—Two species, one in Honduras to west Colombia and the second in the Andes of eastern Colombia.

Ecology.—*W. regia* is found in dense forests usually between 1000 and 2000 m on slopes of the Andes; it is not found below 650 m. *W. georgii*, however, in contrast occurs near sea level.

Common Names and Uses.—Not recorded.

Notes.—These large subcanopy trees with feather duster crowns and leaves with large, several-ribbed pinnae are distinctive. The numerous (about 42) stamens with filaments united in a tube basally but free and fleshy distally are diagnostic in the tribe.

Taxonomic Account.—Wessels Boer (1968).

Plate.—*79D.*

194. CALYPTRONOMA Grisebach, Flora of the British West Indian Islands 518. 1864. Type: *C.*

swartzii Grisebach (illegitimate name) (= **Calyptronoma occidentalis** (Swartz) H. E. Moore (*Elaeis occidentalis* Swartz)).

Cocops O. F. Cook, Bulletin of the Torrey Botanical Club 28:568. 1901. Type: *C. rivalis* O. F. Cook (=*Calyptronoma rivalis* (Cook) L. H. Bailey).

Calyptrogyne subgenus *Calyptronoma* (Grisebach) Wessels Boer, Verhandelingen der Koninklijke Nederlandsche Akademie van Wetenschappen, Afdeeling Natuurkunde, Tweede Reeks 58(1):63. 1968.

Moderate, solitary, unarmed, pleonanthic, monoecious palms. Stem stout, erect, becoming bare, irregularly ringed with leaf scars. Leaves pinnate, erect or ± horizontal, arching, marcescent; sheath becoming open opposite the petiole, not forming a crownshaft, expanded and thicker basally, margins fibrous, both surfaces covered with waxy, caducous tomentum, thinner adaxially; petiole relatively short, deeply grooved adaxially, rounded abaxially; rachis adaxially grooved near the base, flat and laterally channeled distally; leaflets narrow, lanceolate, wider at the middle, tapering to a pointed tip, single-fold, adaxial surface lightly waxy, abaxial surface with thin waxy tomentum and scales along the midrib, midrib and 2 pairs of lateral ribs more evident abaxially, transverse veinlets not evident. Inflorescences solitary, interfoliar, becoming infrafoliar, erect at first, pendulous later, branched to 1 (–4) orders, protandrous; peduncle stout, elongate, elliptic in cross-section; prophyll tubular, dorsiventrally flattened, with 2, rather wide, lateral keels, pointed, splitting apically and ventrally, woody, lightly waxy, tomentose, inserted at the base of the peduncle; peduncular bract tubular, pointed, stiff, thinner than the prophyll, lightly waxy and tomentose, inserted about halfway along the peduncle, often shed before the prophyll, leaving a ruffled scar, subsequent peduncular bracts few, short, spirally inserted; rachis ca. ⅔ as long as the peduncle; rachis bracts short, wide and irregularly notched to pointed, ovate distally; lower branches with a short bare portion, then branched 1(–2) times into rachillae; rachillae moderate, rather short and crowded, bearing rows of partly sunken, short, rounded bracts, each subtending a triad of flowers borne in a pit; floral bracteoles 3, the first bracteole narrow-elongate, the second short, wide, truncate, the third short, pointed. Staminate flowers lateral and outside of the pistillate flower in the pit; sepals 3, distinct, unequal, long, narrow, ±

→

194.—**Calyptronoma. a,** portion of rachilla in bud, flowers not emergent ×3; **b,** portion of rachilla with staminate flowers and buds ×4; **c,** cross-section of rachilla ×3; **d,** staminate bud ×6; **e,** staminate flower at anthesis ×6; **f,** staminate bud in vertical section ×6; **g,** staminate sepals in 2 views ×12; **h,** staminate flower, sepals removed ×12; **i,** staminate corolla, interior view, expanded ×12; **j,** androecium ×6; **k,** anther in 3 views ×12; **l,** pistillode ×24; **m,** portion of rachilla at pistillate anthesis ×3; **n,** pistillate flower at anthesis, sepals bent downward, calyptra pushed open by distal portion of staminodial tube ×6; **o,** pistillate flower at anthesis, calyptra fallen ×6; **p, q,** pistillate flower at anthesis, calyptra and distal portion of staminodial tube fallen ×6; **r,** pistillate sepal in 2 views ×6; **s,** pistillate corolla, calyptra partially split off ×6; **t,** staminodial tube ×6; **u,** gynoecium ×6; **v,** ovary ×6; **w,** ovary in cross-section ×12; **x,** ovary in vertical section in ventral plane of **w** ×12; **y,** fruit ×3; **z,** fruit in vertical section ×3; **aa,** fruit in cross-section ×3; **bb,** endocarp in 3 views ×3; **cc,** seed in 2 views ×3. *Calyptronoma occidentalis:* **a-l** and **y-cc,** *Read 1610;* **m-x,** *Read 1693.*

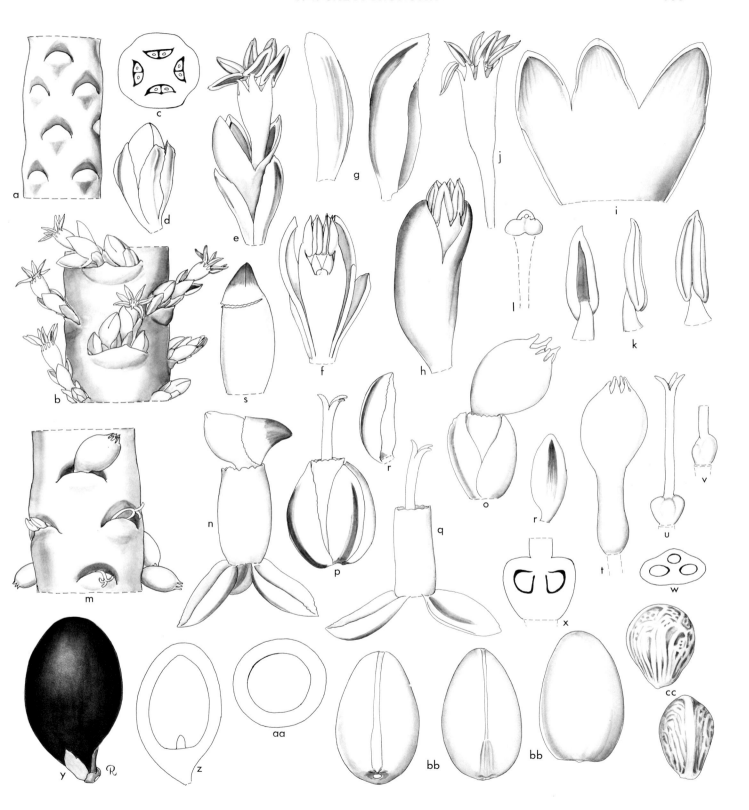

keeled, rounded or pointed distally, imbricate basally, chaffy; petals 3, adnate basally to the receptacle, connate for 2/3 their lengths in a tube, tips valvate; stamens 6, filaments fleshy, connate and adnate to the receptacle for 2/3 their length, the receptacle elongating at anthesis, forming a stalklike base to the androecium, the androecium hence far-exserted distally, the filaments terete, anthers sagittate, dorsifixed near the base, introrse, versatile and horizontal at anthesis, connective tanniniferous; pollen elliptic, subelliptic, or dilated at one end and subtriangular, monosulcate, the sulcus sometimes short, or trichotomosulcate, with scabrate or vermiculate, tectate exine; pistillode 3-lobed with minute tips or lacking. Pistillate flowers asymmetrically triangular in bud; sepals 3, distinct, imbricate, narrow, briefly keeled, pointed, margins irregular; petals 3, connate in a tube with short valvate apices, upper 1/4 shed as a circumscissile cap (calyptra); staminodes completely connate, urn-shaped, inflated above the corolla tube at anthesis, white, membranous, exserted, pushing off the corolla cap, the apex briefly 6-toothed; gynoecium trilocular, triovulate, ± 3-angled, adaxial side longest, style long, cylindrical, stigmatic lobes 3, short, linear, ovule large, anatropous. Fruit ovoid, 1-seeded, stigmatic remains basal; epicarp smooth, granular when dry, mesocarp fleshy with stout fibers anastomosing distally, one large fiber conspicuous, endocarp thin, colorless, tough, with a circular operculum over the embryo. Seed globose-ellipsoidal, raphe unbranched, encircling the seed, hilum short, basal, endosperm homogeneous; embryo basal. Germination adjacent-ligular; eophyll bifid. $n = 14$ (*C. occidentalis, C. rivalis,* Johnson 1985, Read 1966).

Anatomy.—See Wessels Boer (1968) and Tomlinson (1961) for leaf anatomy of *C. occidentalis.* Hypodermis is well developed, mesophyll has an indistinct palisade. Floral anatomy has not been investigated.

Distribution.—Three species in the Greater Antilles.

Ecology.—In swamps near the ocean and beside streams and in wet places in the mountains.

Common Names and Uses.—Manac palm, long thatch. The leaves resemble those of the coconut but have shorter leaflets which have been much used for thatch.

Notes.—*Calyptronoma* is most closely related to *Calyptrogyne.* It is morphologically an unusual and striking genus because of its large size and pistillate flower with a dehiscent petal cap and staminodial body. Studies of pollination should be interesting.

Taxonomic Account.—Wessels Boer (1968).

Plate.—*80A.*

195. CALYPTROGYNE H. A. Wendland, Botanische Zeitung 17:72. 1859. Lectotype: *C. spicigera* (Koch) H. A. Wendland (*Geonoma spicigera* Koch) (see H. E. Moore, 1963c) (=**C. ghiesbregh-**

tiana (Linden & H. A. Wendland) H. A. Wendland) (*Geonoma ghiesbreghtiana* Linden & H. A. Wendland).

Small, solitary, unarmed, pleonanthic, monoecious palms. Stem often subterranean or short and erect, leaf scars indistinct or clearly defined, internodes sometimes rusty-brown tomentose. Leaves few, about 10, pinnate, usually irregular, or bifid and pinnately veined, marcescent; sheath splitting opposite the petiole, densely covered in dark caducous tomentum, margins with large fibers; petiole slender, rather short, evenly concave adaxially, angled abaxially, sparsely tomentose; rachis angled adaxially, flattened abaxially; leaflets irregular in width, distant, 1–several-fold, tapering to pointed tips, lightly waxy-tomentose and with small scales on both surfaces, larger scales abaxially along midrib, midrib and 1–2 pairs of veins prominent abaxially, transverse veinlets usually not evident. Inflorescence interfoliar, slender, spicate, rarely branched to 1 order, erect peduncle very long, slender; prophyll tubular, rather thin, pointed, with two flat, narrow lateral keels, papery to coriaceous, striate, lightly scaly, splitting distally, inserted near the base of the peduncle; peduncular bract terete, pointed, striate, lightly scaly, membranous, splitting distally, inserted near or a short distance below the floral pits, often caducous leaving a ruffled scar; rachis very short, bearing 1–2 small empty bracts, short or long, often much larger in diameter than the peduncle, glabrous or densely brown tomentose; rachillae bearing alternate rows (7–11) of closely appressed, marginally thin, glabrous or tomentose, ovate bracts, each subtending a triad of flowers borne in a pit, floral bracteoles unequal, somewhat keeled, thin, membranous, tips pointed. Staminate flower slightly asymmetrical; sepals 3, free, elongate, unequal, imbricate at base or throughout in bud, narrow, tips irregular, somewhat truncate, sometimes tomentose; petals 3, asymmetrical, united in a soft tube for ca. 1/2 their length, free lobes unequal, valvate, chaffy; stamens 6, filaments fleshy, united and adnate to the receptacle forming a solid stalk, free lobes thick, awl-shaped, recurved at anthesis, anthers sagittate, dorsifixed near the base, decurved with bases uppermost at anthesis, introrse; pollen elliptic, sometimes dilated at one end, or circular, monosulcate, with finely reticulate or vermiculate, tectate exine; pistillode minute, deltoid. Pistillate flower asymmetrical, adaxial side curved to conform to the pit wall; sepals 3, free, unequal, imbricate, two lateral ones keeled, abaxial one smaller, flattened; petals united in a tube, very briefly free and valvate distally, tube striate, distal 1/3 shed as a cap (calyptra), lower part of tube remaining in the pit; staminodes united in a tube, constricted near the middle, very briefly 6-lobed distally, upper part shed to reveal the stigmas; gynoecium trilocular, triovulate, asymmetrically 3-lobed, style triangular in cross-section, elongate, ending in 3 linear stigmas, reflexed at anthesis, ovule anatropous, basally attached. Fruit obovoid, 1-seeded, purple or black when ripe, stigmatic residue and abortive carpels basal; epicarp smooth, mesocarp fleshy with inner layer of large anastomosing fibers, the largest median and completely encircling, endocarp ± transparent, tough. Seed ellipsoidal, basally attached, hilum short, raphe encircling, unbranched, endosperm ho-

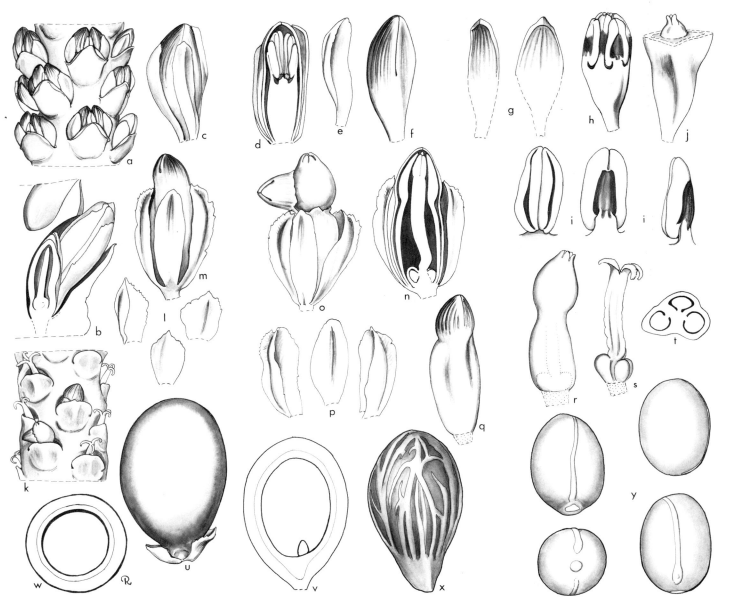

195.—**Calyptrogyne. a,** portion of axis with staminate buds ×3; **b,** portion of axis with staminate buds in vertical section to show orientation in pit, pistillate bud in section ×6; **c,** staminate bud ×6; **d,** staminate bud in vertical section ×6; **e,** staminate sepal ×6; **f,** staminate bud, sepals removed ×6; **g,** staminate petal in 2 views ×6; **h,** androecium ×6; **i,** stamen in 3 views ×12; **j,** androecium, stamens removed to show pistillode ×12; **k,** portion of axis at pistillate anthesis with flowers in 3 stages of expansion ×3; **l,** bracteoles ×6; **m,** pistillate bud ×6; **n,** pistillate bud in vertical section ×6; **o,** pistillate flower at anthesis, calyptrate corolla apex at left, expanded staminodial tube in center ×6; **p,** pistillate sepals ×6; **q,** pistillate corolla in bud ×6; **r,** staminodial tube at anthesis ×6; **s,** gynoecium ×6; **t,** ovary in cross-section ×12; **u,** fruit ×3; **v,** fruit in vertical section ×3; **w,** fruit in cross-section ×3; **x,** endocarp ×4; **y,** seed in 4 views ×3. *Calyptrogyne sarapiquensis*: **a–t,** *Moore & Parthasarathy 9405*; *C. ghiesbreghtiana*: **u–y,** *Moore 6785.*

mogeneous; embryo eccentrically basal. Germination adjacent-ligular; eophyll bifid. Cytology not studied.

Anatomy.—The leaf (Tomlinson 1961, Wessels Boer 1968) is characterized by hypodermis lacking or incomplete, palisade lacking, and fibers few.

Distribution.—About five species from Mexico and Guatemala to Colombia.

Ecology.—Understory palms of tropical rain forests. Abundant in swamps and along stream margins, some species at elevations below 700 m only,

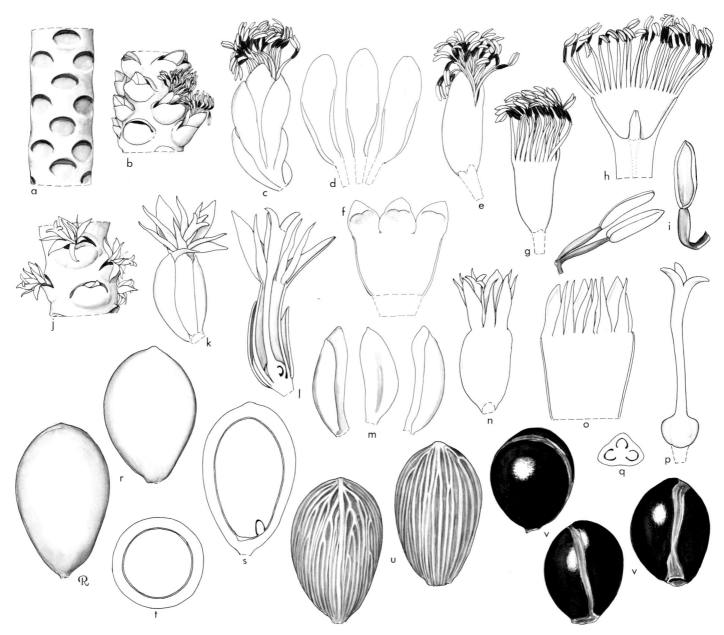

196.—**Asterogyne. a,** rachilla in early bud ×1½; **b,** rachilla with staminate flowers in late bud and at early anthesis ×1½; **c,** staminate flower ×4; **d,** staminate sepals ×4; **e,** staminate flower, sepals removed ×4; **f,** staminate corolla, expanded ×4; **g,** androecium ×4; **h,** androecium, expanded to show pistillode ×4; **i,** stamens, much enlarged; **j,** rachilla with pistillate flowers at anthesis ×3; **k,** pistillate flower ×6; **l,** pistillate flower in vertical section ×6; **m,** pistillate sepals ×6; **n,** pistillate flower, sepals removed ×6; **o,** pistillate corolla and staminodes, interior view, expanded ×6; **p,** gynoecium ×8; **q,** ovary in cross-section ×8; **r,** fruit in 2 views ×3; **s,** fruit in vertical section ×3; **t,** fruit in cross-section ×3; **u,** endocarp in 2 views ×3; **v,** seed in 3 views ×3. *Asterogyne spicata:* all from *Moore 9601.*

other species from 700–2200 m. Bats have been observed pollinating the flowers in Costa Rica (Beach, pers. comm.).

Common Names and Use. — Common names unknown. Desirable as ornamentals.

Notes. — *Calyptrogyne* is immediately distinguished from other understory geonomoid palms by the insertion of the peduncular bract at the apex of the peduncle. Flower structure, especially the unusual staminodes, and the insertion of the peduncular bract well above the prophyll are very similar to *Calyptronoma*. However, in habit and leaf structure the two genera are different.

Taxonomic Account. —Wessels Boer (1968).

Plate. —*80B.*

196. ASTEROGYNE H. A. Wendland ex J. D. Hooker in Bentham & J. D. Hooker, Genera Plantarum 3:914. 1883. Lectotype: **A. martiana** (H. A. Wendland) H. A. Wendland ex Hemsley (*Geonoma martiana* H. A. Wendland) (see Hemsley in Godman & Salvin 1885).

Aristeyera H. E. Moore, Journal of the Arnold Arboretum 47:3. 1966. Type: *A. spicata* H. E. Moore (=*Asterogyne spicata* (H. E. Moore) Wessels Boer).

Small, solitary, or rarely clustered, unarmed, pleonanthic, monoecious palms. Stem short, erect, sometimes prostrate for a time, rather closely ringed with inconspicuous, narrow, oblique leaf scars. Leaves erect, almost always undivided, bifid, sometimes becoming split irregularly, marcescent; sheath short, tubular, eventually splitting opposite the petiole, margins with a few stiff fibers, covered with dull, reddish-brown scales; petiole short, slender, flat and glabrous adaxially; rounded, with dark brown scales, often becoming brown-dotted abaxially, blade wedge-shaped, pinnately ribbed, distinctly plicate, thin but rather tough, deep green adaxially, silvery green abaxially, glabrous adaxially, small membranous scales and trichomes along large ribs abaxially, transverse veinlets not evident, large close ribs more evident abaxially, alternating with bands of small veins on both surfaces. Inflorescences solitary, ± erect, becoming ± curved in fruit, interfoliar, spicate or subdigitately branched to 1 order, protandrous; peduncle long, slender, covered with dark brown, caducous tomentum; prophyll tubular, pointed, thin, papery, with 2, very narrow, lateral keels, covered with dark red, caducous tomentum; peduncular bracts 1 or 2, tubular, like the prophyll but longer; rachis very short, bearing short, ovate, pointed bracts, the first 2 (or more) empty, others subtending rachillae; rachillae 1 or few (2–8), about equal in length, bearing sunken ovate bracts, each subtending a triad of flowers borne in a pit, pits with distinct upper "lips" which lock the bract over the developing flowers, rachillae ending in long, slender pointed tips, densely scaly; floral bracteoles 3, the outer bracteole shallow, the middle 2-keeled, the inner acute. Staminate flowers exserted at anthesis, borne laterally and outside the pistillate flower; sepals 3, briefly connate where adnate basally to the receptacle, free above, narrow, elongate, keeled, acute or emarginate apically; petals 3, about as long as the sepals, basally adnate to the receptacle, connate in a tube for about ⅔ their length, free and valvate above; stamens 6–ca. 24, filaments connate and adnate basally to the receptacle forming a solid stalklike base, united in a tube for an equal distance, distally free, erect, terete and tapering, connective bifid, tanniniferous, bearing separated thecae, inflexed in bud, ± erect at anthesis, introrse; pollen elliptic, monosulcate, with vermiculate or reticulate, tectate exine; pistillode shallow, irregularly

3-lobed. Pistillate flowers slightly asymmetrical; sepals 3, distinct, chaffy, imbricate in bud; petals 3, connate for about ⅔ their length in a soft tube, valvate and chaffy distally; staminodes ca. 15, connate basally and adnate to the petal tube, free, somewhat fleshy, angled or terete distally, tips dark like the connectives; gynoecium trilocular, triovulate, 3-lobed, style elongate, grooved, ending in 3 triangular, stigmatic lobes, probably recurved at anthesis, ovule hemianatropous, pendulous, attached in the top of the locule, only 1 normally maturing. Fruit ellipsoidal-ovoid, 1-seeded, dorsiventrally compressed, slightly keeled apically, abortive carpels and stigmatic remains basal; epicarp smooth, mesocarp fleshy to dry, with an inner layer of closely appressed, longitudinal fibers, endocarp thin, crustaceous, shiny. Seed ellipsoidal to obovoid, slightly compressed laterally, hilum small, basal, raphe encircling the seed, somewhat impressed, unbranched to furcate or with a few parallel branches, endosperm homogeneous; embryo eccentrically basal. Germination adjacent-ligular; eophyll bifid. Cytology not studied.

Anatomy. —See Tomlinson (1961, 1966) for leaf anatomy and Uhl (1966) for anatomy of flowers and structure of flower clusters and rachillae.

Distribution. —Three species in Central America and northern South America.

Ecology. —Found only in wet forest, often at low elevations ca. 200–400 m or less, sometimes on well drained slopes.

Common Names and Uses. —For local names see Glassman (1972). *Asterogyne* is a fine ornamental and is also used for thatch. The fruit of *A. spicata* is edible.

Notes. —Species of *Asterogyne* are elegant small palms distinguished by bifid leaves and by floral pits with covering bracts "locked" in bud by a distinct rounded lip. The separation of anther thecae on a bifid connective is distinctive.

Taxonomic Accounts. —Wessels Boer (1968), Henderson and Steyermark (1986).

Plates. —*30B; 80C; Figs. G.19, G.20.*

197. GEONOMA Willdenow, Species Plantarum 4(1): 174, 593. 1805. Lectotype: **G. simplicifrons** Willdenow (see H. E. Moore 1963c).

Vouay Aublet, Histoire des Plantes de la Guiane Française 2 (Appendix):99. 1775. Type not designated.

Gynestum Poiteau, Memoires du Museum d'Histoire Naturelle 9:387. 1822. Lectotype: *G. maximum* Poiteau (see H. E. Moore 1963c) (=*Geonoma maxima* (Poiteau) Kunth).

Kalbreyera Burret, Botanische Jahrbücher für Systematik 63:142. 1930. Type: *K. triandra* Burret (=*Geonoma triandra* (Burret) Wessels Boer).

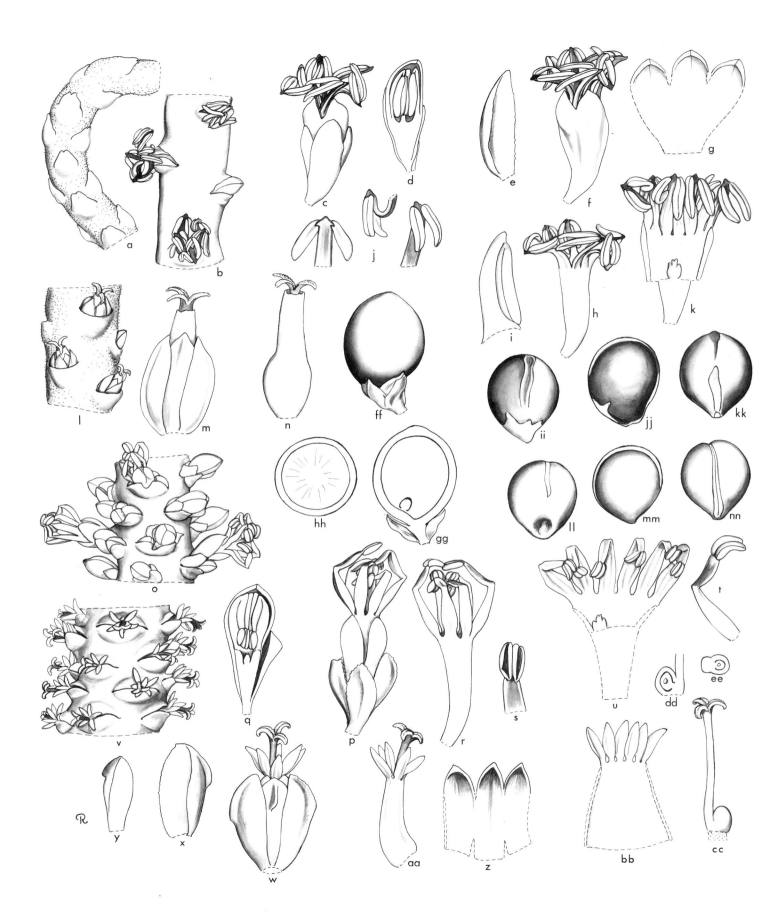

Taenianthera Burret, Botanische Jahrbücher für Systematik 63:267. 1930. Type: *T. macrostachys* (Martius) Burret (=*Genoma macrostachys* Martius).

Small to moderate, solitary or clustered, unarmed, pleonanthic, monoecious palms. Stem very short, subterranean, erect, or creeping, slender, sometimes tall, enclosed by thin leaf sheaths, becoming bare, usually cane-like, ringed with close or distant, conspicuous or inconspicuous leaf scars. Leaves pinnate, regularly or irregularly divided, or entire, and bifid; sheath short, splitting opposite the petiole, margins fibrous, glabrous or variously tomentose; petiole short to long, slightly grooved or flattened adaxially, rounded abaxially, glabrous or tomentose; blade bifid, or with 2 or 3 pairs of leaflets, or irregularly divided, or nearly evenly pinnate, thin and papery or somewhat leathery, usually glabrous adaxially, glabrous, tomentose or with scales abaxially, especially along the main ribs, uniseriate hairs present or absent, midribs of single folds conspicuous, transverse veinlets not evident. Inflorescences solitary, interfoliar or infrafoliar, spicate, forked, or branched to 3 (–4) orders, protandrous where known; peduncle very short to very long, glabrous or tomentose; prophyll tubular, short to long, pointed, very briefly 2-keeled laterally, membranous or leathery, glabrous or variously tomentose; peduncular bracts (0–) 1 (1–2), short or long, deciduous or persistent, like the prophyll; rachillae straight or folded and twisted in bud, short to moderate, bearing rounded, truncate, or distally split, ± raised bracts, laterally adnate to the branch, decussate, spiral, or whorled and in definite rows, bracts closely appressed and the rachillae larger than the peduncle in diameter, or bracts more distant and the rachillae narrow, each bract subtending a triad of flowers sunken in a pit, pits without upper lip or upper lip distinct, glabrous or hairy, pit cavity glabrous or variously hairy; floral bracteoles 3, irregular, small, membranous. Staminate flowers about ½ exserted from the pit; sepals 3, distinct, chaffy, narrow, elongate, tips rounded, keeled or not; petals 3, connate for ⅔ their length, tips distinct, valvate; stamens (3) 6, (rarely more), filaments united with receptacle in a stalklike base, connate in a tube above the base, free, narrow, flat, long or short distally, inflexed near the tip in bud, anthers borne at tips of the filaments, connective divided, thecae elongate, free and divaricate, or short and united, introrse; pollen elliptic, slightly irregular, monosulcate, with scabrate, finely reticulate, or fossulate,

tectate exine; pistillode small, round, 3-lobed. Pistillate flowers sunken in the pit with only the tips of the floral organs exserted; sepals 3, united basally and adnate to the receptacle, often keeled, free and imbricate distally; petals 3, connate in a soft tube, briefly adnate to receptacle basally, ending in 3, valvate, chaffy, spreading lobes; staminodes united in a tube, truncate, 6-toothed or 6-lobed, lobes, if present, spreading at anthesis, tubes basally adnate to the receptacle, and sometimes also the corolla tube; gynoecium tricarpellate but 2 carpels vestigial at anthesis, unilocular, uniovulate, ovule anatropous, style tubular, lateral to basal, elongate, ending in 3 linear stigmas, recurved at anthesis. Fruit ± globose, sometimes somewhat pointed, green, brown, or purple-black, 1 seeded, stigmatic remains basal, the rachillae often becoming brightly colored; epicarp thin, smooth, mesocarp thin, with narrow longitudinal fibers, endocarp thin, crustaceous to membranous. Seed ± globose, hilum short, basal, raphe encircling the seed, endosperm homogeneous; embryo erect basal. Germination adjacent-ligular; eophyll bifid. $n = 14$ (*G. camana*, Read 1966). $n = 16$ (*G. gracilis, G. pinnatifrons* as *G. vaga*, Sarkar 1970).

Anatomy.—See Tomlinson (1961) for leaf, Uhl and Moore (1971) for floral anatomy, and Wessels Boer (1968) for anatomy of leaf and fruit. In leaves of the species studied, the epidermal cells often contain chloroplasts, a colorless hypodermis and a palisade layer are lacking, and fibers are infrequent.

Distribution.—Seventy-five or more species ranging from Mexico to Brazil and Bolivia.

Ecology.—All species are understory rain forest palms, occurring at low to high elevations.

Common Names and Uses.—For local names see Glassman (1972). Many species are desirable ornamentals; some are also used for thatch. Young "cabbage" is sometimes eaten (*G. interrupta*).

Notes.—The reduction of two locules in the gynoecium make this, the largest genus in the tribe, immediately distinct from the other genera. The lack of an upper lip which closes the pit is also characteristic.

Taxonomic Account.—Wessels Boer (1968).

Plate.—80D; Figs. G.13, G.19, G.20.

←

197.—**Geonoma. a,** portion of rachilla in bud ×3; **b,** portion of rachilla at staminate anthesis ×3; **c,** staminate flower ×6; **d,** staminate bud in vertical section ×6; **e,** staminate sepal ×6; **f,** staminate flower, sepals removed ×6; **g,** staminate corolla, expanded ×6; **h,** androecium ×6; **i,** stamen in bud ×12; **j,** stamen in 3 views ×6; **k,** androecium, expanded to show pistillode ×6; **l,** portion of rachilla at pistillate anthesis ×6; **m,** pistillate flower ×12; **n,** staminodial tube and styles ×12; **o,** portion of rachilla at staminate anthesis ×3; **p,** staminate flower ×6; **q,** staminate bud in vertical section ×6; **r,** androecium ×6; **s,** anther locules ×6; **t,** stamen in side view ×6; **u,** androecium, expanded to show pistillode ×6; **v,** portion of rachilla at pistillate anthesis ×3; **w,** pistillate flower ×6; **x,** pistillate sepal ×6; **y,** pistillate petal ×6; **z,** pistillate corolla, interior view, expanded ×6; **aa,** androecium, style, and stigmas ×6; **bb,** androecium, expanded, interior view ×6; **cc,** gynoecium ×6; **dd,** gynoecium in vertical section ×6; **ee,** gynoecium in cross-section ×6; **ff,** fruit ×3; **gg,** fruit in vertical section ×3; **hh,** fruit in cross-section ×3; **ii, jj, kk,** endocarp in 3 views ×3; **ll, mm, nn,** seed in 3 views ×3. *Geonoma interrupta*: **a–k** and **ff–nn,** *Moore & Parthasarathy 9441*; *G. oxycarpa*: **l–n,** *Moore 6523*; *G. acaulis*: **o–ee,** *Moore et al. 8502*.

VI PHYTELEPHANTOIDEAE

PHYTELEPHANTOIDEAE Drude in Engler & Prantl, Natürlichen Pflanzenfamilien 2, 3:28, 86. 1887 ('*Phytelephantinae*'). Type: **Phytelephas.**

Moderate to rather large, acaulescent or erect; unarmed; pleonanthic, dioecious; leaves pinnate, reduplicate; inflorescences markedly dimorphic; prophyll rather short, usually obscured by the leaf sheath; peduncular bract 1; staminate inflorescence spikelike or racemose, pistillate inflorescence headlike; flowers multiparted, the staminate in monopodial clusters, the pistillate solitary, crowded; staminate flowers with much reduced perianth and very numerous stamens; pistillate flower with large, elongate, fleshy sepals and petals, gynoecium of 5–10 connate carpels, styles long; stigmas elongate; fruits 5–10 seeded, borne in a congested headlike cluster, stigmatic remains apical; mesocarp cracking to form irregular, fibrous, pyramidal warts; pyrenes smooth, hard, thin, enclosing individual seeds; endosperm very hard, homogeneous.

Map 52.—**Distribution of Phytelephantoideae.**

The three genera that make up this subfamily (the phytelephantoid major group of Moore 1973a) add an extraordinary dimension to inflorescence and flower structure in the Palmae. The genera occur in South America and Panama (Map 52) and their distribution coincides rather well with three refuges postulated by Haffer (1969) as areas where birds and plants of rain forests may have persisted during Pleistocene climatic changes (Moore 1973b). However, Prance (1982) has pointed out that these genera were probably isolated earlier during Andean uplift in the Miocene. The flower clusters are condensed monopodial units rather than cincinni (Uhl and Dransfield 1984). Flowers are multiparted and show a tetramerous pattern in early stages. Stamen numbers are very large, approaching 1000 in *Palandra,* the highest number known in the family. Development of stamens is centrifugal (Uhl and Moore 1977a). The chromosome number is 16.

The unusual inflorescence, flower, and fruit structure of these palms led some early workers to regard them as belonging to Cyclanthaceae and Pandanaceae (e.g. Kunth 1841, Wendland 1854). However, the pinnate leaf and uniovulate carpels clearly place them in the Palmae. The superficial resemblance of the fruiting heads to those of *Nypa* led to the placement of the two genera in the same group (Drude 1887, Martius 1849). The resemblance is superficial as the head of *Nypa* is composed of fruits from the single carpels of tricarpellate flowers, while heads of Phytelephantoideae are fruits from syncarpous, multicarpellate gynoecia.

Key to the Genera of the Phytelephantoideae

1 Staminate inflorescence a spike with sessile flowers; stamens ca. 36–250, filaments and anthers erect; fruits 4–10-seeded, seldom with 6 seeds. Amazon Basin, Colombia, Venezuela, and Panama . . . . 199. **Phytelephas**
1 Staminate inflorescence racemose, flowers borne on short stalks or branches, stamens more than 250, usually 500 or more. Fruits with six or several seeds 2

→

198.—**Palandra. a,** staminate flower cluster with four flowers ×¾; **b,** staminate flower cluster, cut to show base of one flower on right ×1; **c,** stamen in 3 views ×6; **d,** pistillate flower ×¾; **e,** outer four bracts surrounding pistillate flower *in situ,* and dissected ×1; **f,** bracteole of pistillate flower ×1; **g,** pistillate sepals ×1; **h,** pistillate petals ×1; **i,** gynoecium and staminodes ×1; **j,** base of gynoecium, some staminodes removed ×4½; **k,** ovary in vertical section ×4½; **l,** ovary in cross-section ×4½; **m,** fruit ×½; **n,** fruit, some epicarp and mesocarp removed to show separate endocarps ×½; **o,** single endocarp in 2 views ×1; **p,** endocarp in vertical section ×1; **q,** seed in 3 views ×¾. *Palandra aequatorialis*: all from *Moore 10210.*

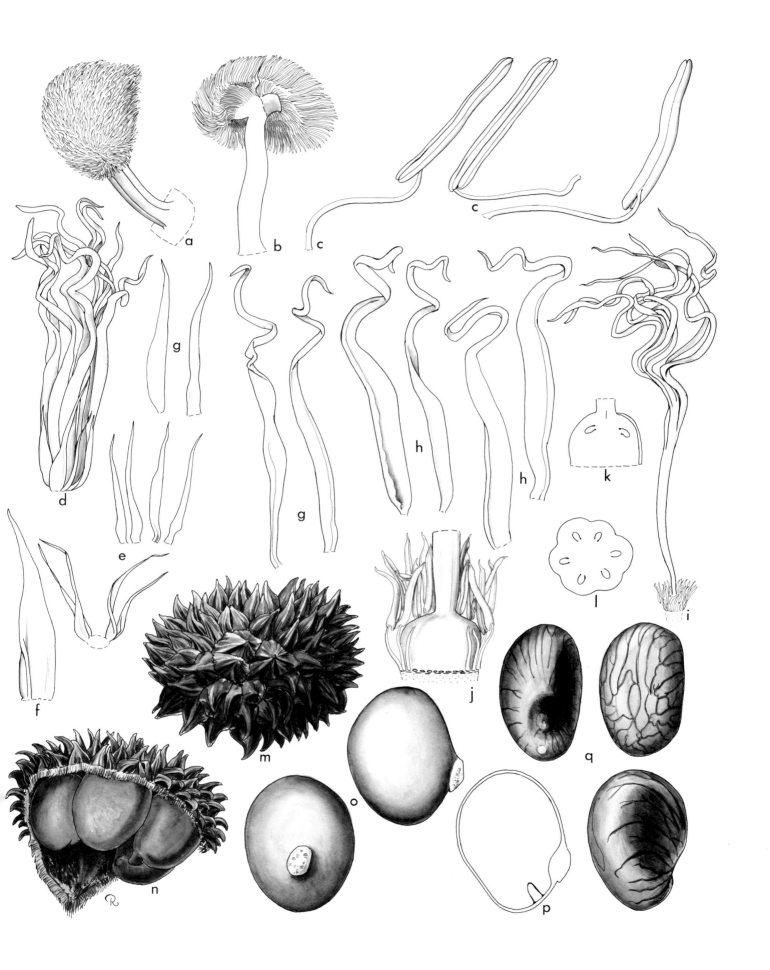

2 Staminate flowers in groups of four on a grooved stalk formed by the united pedicels, receptacles flattened, stamens ca. 1000, filaments flexible, slender, anthers elongate; corky projections on fruits numerous, small; fruits usually 6-seeded. Ecuador .... 198. **Palandra**
2 Staminate flowers borne singly but crowded on the ends of short branches; receptacles angled, stamens ca. 500, filaments short or lacking, anthers rounded or slightly elongate; corky projections on fruits few, large, fruits several seeded. Colombia .... 200. **Ammandra**

Vegetative Key to the Genera of the Phytelephantoideae

1 Leaflets mostly in groups of 2–5, in two planes ....
.... 198. **Palandra**
1 Leaflets regularly arranged 2
2 Petiole long and cylindrical above the sheath; leaflets regularly arranged with a median and one pair of submarginal ribs prominent abaxially, grooved between submarginal ribs and margins .... 200. **Ammandra**
2 Petiole short, rounded abaxially, shallowly channeled adaxially; leaflets regularly arranged with only a large central rib prominent adaxially .... 199. **Phytelephas**

198. **Palandra** O. F. Cook, Journal of the Washington Academy of Sciences 17:228. 1927. Type: **P. aequatorialis** (Spruce) O. F. Cook (*Phytelephas aequatorialis* Spruce).

Moderate, solitary, unarmed, pleonanthic, dioecious palm. Stem erect, robust, often covered with leaf bases, bracts, and old inflorescences, when bare, rough with deep, triangular, leaf scars. Leaves pinnate, large, erect, marcescent; sheath inconspicuous, splitting, fibrous along the margins, glabrous; petiole short, channeled and slightly convex adaxially, rounded abaxially; rachis adaxially angled, abaxially rounded to flattened; leaflets irregularly inserted in 2 planes, often in groups of 2–5, single-fold, long, pointed, thin, dull green, adaxially shining, transverse veinlets not evident. Staminate and pistillate inflorescenses dissimilar, solitary, interfoliar; staminate inflorescence elongate, spicate; peduncle short, dorsiventrally flattened; prophyll tubular, short, dorsiventrally compressed, 2-keeled laterally, broadly pointed, splitting apically; complete peduncular bracts 1, similar to the prophyll but longer and narrower, splitting abaxially, followed by several incomplete peduncular bracts, the first 2 lateral, subopposite, relatively large, others (4–5) small, shallow, pointed, bracts subtending flower clusters triangular, low, barely discernible at maturity, borne in curved rows, flower clusters consisting of 4 flowers on an elongate, grooved stalk formed by their united pedicels. Staminate flowers ±

symmetrical; sepals ca. 4, very small; petals 4(–5) very small, united with the sepals in a shallow cupule surrounding the stamens; stamens over 900, filaments long, flexible, variously curved, slender, terete, anthers elongate, unequal, basifixed, apiculate, latrorse; pollen elliptic, monosulcate, with finely reticulate, tectate exine; pistillodes small, follicular, sometimes evident in young stages. Pistillate inflorescence unbranched, headlike; peduncle moderate, laterally compressed; prophyll and peduncular bract as in the staminate, subsequent peduncular bracts larger and more numerous, pointed, overlapping, sheathing the peduncle and lower flowers, flowers spirally arranged, appearing sessile, each actually on a short branch (Uhl and Dransfield 1984), subtended by an elongate triangular bract and bearing 2–4 smaller bracts below the perianth parts. Pistillate flowers asymmetrical; sepals ca. 4, irregular, rather long, pointed; petals ca. 4, very long, narrow, variously folded and wrinkled; staminodes numerous, like the stamens of staminate flowers but smaller and less regular; gynoecium of 6 carpels, united laterally, ovarian part short, rounded, style long, cylindrical, stigmas elongate, conduplicately folded, bearing stigmatoid tissue along the extensive margins, each carpel bearing a single, apparently anatropous ovule. Fruits borne in a large head, each fruit rounded, several-seeded (–6), covered in numerous, small, pointed, woody warts; epicarp woody, mesocarp fibrous, endocarp surrounding each seed, ± kidney-shaped, shelllike, with round, knoblike attachment. Seed ± kidney-shaped, hilum circular, raphe with many ascending and anastomosing branches, endosperm homogeneous, white, very hard (vegetable ivory); embryo basal near the hilum. Germination remote-ligular; eophyll pinnate. Cytology unknown.

Anatomy.—Studies of development have shown that the numerous stamens develop centrifugally and that the flower clusters are monopodial unlike those of other subfamilies (Uhl and Moore 1977b, Uhl and Dransfield 1984).

Distribution.—A single species occurring in Ecuador and perhaps northward over the Colombian border.

Ecology.—Found in rain forest in the Guayaquilan plain and up the Andean valleys to an elevation of 1600 m.

Common Names and Uses.—Ivory palm, tagua. Provides vegetable ivory.

Notes.—Distinguished from *Phytelephas* and *Ammandra* by its clustered leaflets, and distinctive flower clusters with united pedicels, and also by the

---

→

199.—**Phytelephas. a,** portion of staminate spike × 3; **b,** staminate flower × 3; **c,** staminate flower in vertical section × 3; **d,** stamen × 6; **e,** two pistillate flowers × ½; **f, g,** bracts, floral bracteole, sepals, and petals of pistillate flower (separate organs not distinguishable at maturity) × ½; **h,** gynoecium and staminodes × ½; **i,** gynoecium and staminodes × 1; **j,** staminode × 1½; **k,** ovary in vertical section × 1½; **l,** ovary in cross-section × 1½; **m,** fruiting axis, fruits removed × ½; **n,** fruit × ½; **o,** single endocarp × ½; **p,** endocarp and seed in vertical section × ½; **q,** seed × ½. *Phytelephas macrocarpa*: **a–l,** *Moore s.n.*; **m–q,** *Moore et al. 8480.*

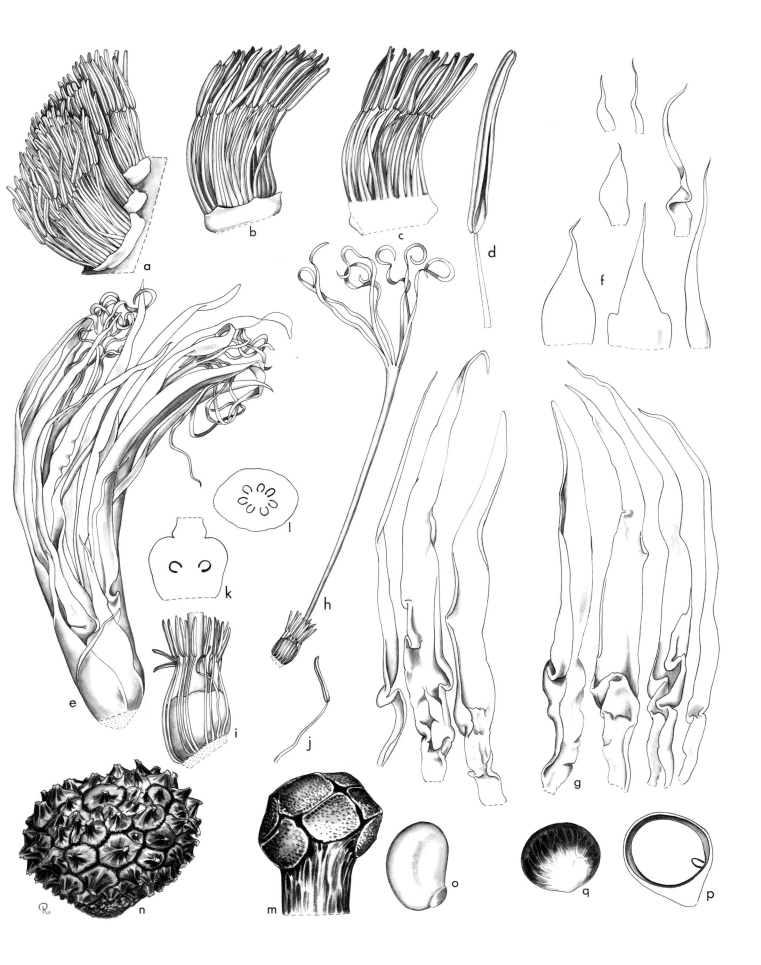

largest number of stamens in the family, over 900 per flower.

Taxonomic Account. — Cook (1927).

Plates. — *30A; 81A.*

199. PHYTELEPHAS Ruiz & Pavon, Systema Vegetabilium. 299. 1798. Lectotype: **P. macrocarpa** Ruiz & Pavon (see O. F. Cook 1927).

Elephantusia Willdenow, Species Plantarum. 4(2): 890, 1156. 1806. Type: *E. macrocarpa* (Ruiz & Pavon) Willdenow (*Phytelephas macrocarpa* Ruiz & Pavon).

Yarina O. F. Cook, Journal of the Washington Academy of Sciences 17:223. 1927. Type: *Y. microcarpa* (Ruiz & Pavon) O. F. Cook (*Phytelephas microcarpa* Ruiz & Pavon).

Moderate, solitary or clustered, unarmed, pleonanthic, dioecious palms. Stem robust or rarely rather slender, erect or procumbent, internodes short, covered with a mass of fibers and petiole bases, when bare marked by spiral, triangular, often pitted leaf scars. Leaves numerous or rarely few, erect, arching, evenly pinnate, marcescent; sheath tubular, sometimes with a large ligule opposite the petiole, becoming fibrous; petiole short, lacking, or rarely elongate, shallowly channeled adaxially, rounded abaxially, margins rounded or sharp; rachis adaxially rounded or angled, abaxially rounded to flat, with grayish brown scales abaxially; leaflets regularly arranged in one plane, subopposite, single-fold, pointed, often pinched in at the base, usually smaller basally and distally, glossy dark green adaxially, paler and duller beneath; tomentose abaxially along a conspicuous midrib, transverse veinlets conspicuous. Inflorescences interfoliar, staminate and pistillate dissimilar; staminate unbranched; peduncle short; prophyll short, tubular, 2-keeled laterally, broadly pointed, splitting apically; complete peduncular bracts 1, like the prophyll but longer, splitting abaxially, persistent above the inflorescence, subsequent peduncular bracts several (4–5), incomplete, spirally inserted below the flowers. Staminate flowers sessile, in groups of 4, usually lacking a subtending bract; perianth a low cupule with 3–8 points, not separable into sepals and petals at maturity (but see Uhl and Moore 1977b); stamens 36–250(–400?), filaments erect, awl-shaped, anthers elongate, latrorse; pollen elliptic, often with one end dilated, monosulcate or trichotomosulcate, with tectate, reticulate exine; pistillode lacking. Pistillate inflorescence headlike; peduncle short, dorsiventrally flattened; prophyll and first peduncular bract as in the staminate, subsequent peduncular bracts numerous, larger than in the staminate, sometimes in series, elongate, pointed, ± covering the flowers. Pistillate flowers each subtended by a pointed bract, spirally arranged, closely appressed; sepals 3 or more, triangular, ± elongate; petals 7–10, long, narrow, variously folded and wrinkled; staminodes numerous, 35 or more, like the stamens but irregular in size; gynoecium of 4–10 united carpels, ovarian part short, rounded, stigma long, narrow, cylindrical, styles as many as the carpels, long, narrow, conduplicately folded with stigmatoid tissue along the margins, ovules 1 per carpel, hemianatropous or anatropous. Fruit borne in large headlike clusters, individual fruits ± rounded, 4–10-seeded, covered with large, woody, pointed warts, stylar remains terminal; epicarp woody, mesocarp fibrous, endocarp surrounding each seed bony or shelllike, bifacial adaxially with round basal projection, rounded abaxially. Seed ± kidney-shaped, basally or laterally attached, hilum round, median to basal, raphe branches numerous, laterally ascending and anastomosing; endosperm homogeneous, hard (vegetable ivory), embryo basal or lateral. Germination remote-ligular; eophyll pinnate. $n = 16$ (*P.* sp., Read 1966); $n = 12$ (*P. macrocarpa*, Sarkar 1970); $n = 18$ (*P. macrocarpa*, Eichhorn 1957).

Anatomy. — Vegetative (Tomlinson 1961); floral (Moore and Uhl 1973, Uhl and Moore 1977b, Uhl and Dransfield 1984).

Distribution. — Twelve or fewer species with a bicentric distribution; six species occurring in the Amazonian Basin in Bolivia, Ecuador, and Peru, and an equal number along the northwest coast of Colombia and into Venezuela and Panama.

Ecology. — Strictly confined to rain forest usually under large trees along streams and on wet hillsides.

Fossil Record. — Fruit reported from the Tertiary of Ecuador (Brown 1956b). Fossil stem material from West Indies is questionable (Kaul 1943).

Common Names and Uses. — Ivory palms, tagua, yarina. Leaves are used for thatch; immature pericarp and endosperm are edible; mature endosperm is hard and used as vegetable ivory for carvings.

Notes. — The three genera of this subfamily are separated largely on characters of the staminate flowers. *Phytelephas* is distinguished from *Palandra* by sessile staminate flowers and by up to about 250 rather than over 900 stamens, and from *Ammandra* by sessile flowers and flat rather than club-shaped receptacles in staminate flowers.

Taxonomic Account. — Cook (1927).

Plates. — *30C; 81C.*

→

200. — **Ammandra. a,** staminate rachilla × 1½; **b,** staminate flower × 3; **c,** stamen in 3 views × 9; **d,** pistillate flower in 2 views × ¾; **e,** pistillate bract × ¾; **f,** pistillate sepals × ¾; **g,** pistillate petals × ¾; **h,** gynoecium and staminodes × ¾; **i,** base of gynoecium and staminodes × 1½; **j,** staminode in 3 views × 6; **k,** stigma × 1½; **l,** ovary in vertical section × 1½; **m,** ovary in cross-section × 3; **n,** fruit in 2 views × ½; **o,** endocarp in 2 views × ¾; **p,** endocarp in vertical section × ¾; **q,** seed in 3 views × ¾. *Ammandra decasperma*: all from *Moore & Parthasarathy 9456.*

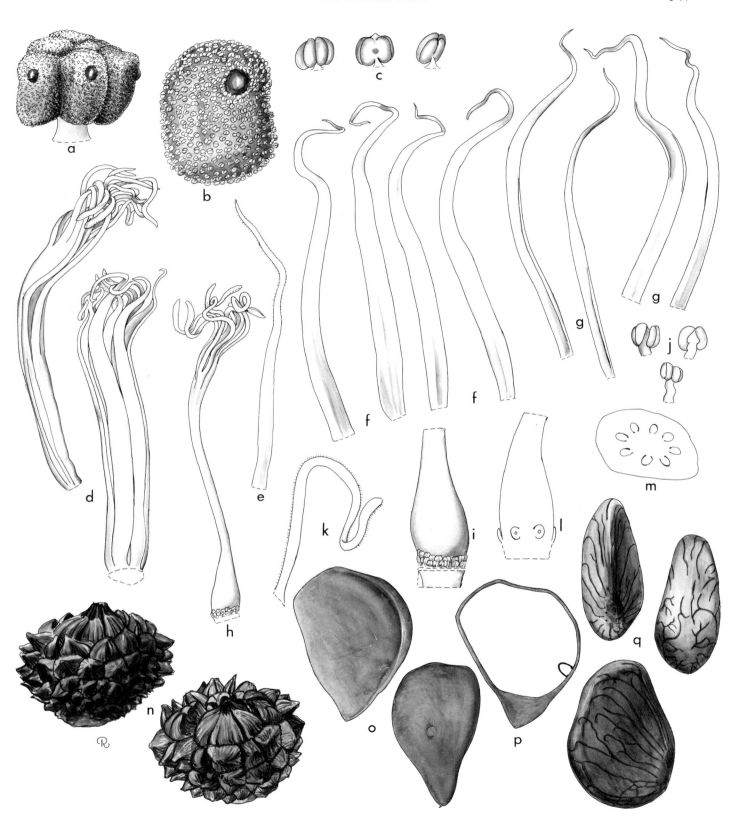

200. **AMMANDRA** O. F. Cook, Journal of the Washington Academy of Sciences 17:220. 1927. Type: **A. decasperma** O. F. Cook.

Solitary, stemless or short-trunked, unarmed, pleonanthic, dioecious palms. Stem extremely short, internodes short, obscured by a loose network of long, slender, straight, sheath fibers. Leaf pinnate; sheath soon disintegrating into a mass of long straight fibers resembling horse hair; petiole erect, long, slender, grooved adaxially at the base, becoming cylindrical distally; rachis adaxially angled, abaxially rounded to flattened; leaflets very regular except for the lowermost which may be irregular, stiffly horizontal, the lowest very narrow, the middle lanceolate, the terminal very short, shiny dark green, a midrib and a pair of marginal veins prominent abaxially, the submarginal veins forming a prominent ridge with a resulting outer groove along the leaflet margins, transverse veinlets not evident. Staminate and pistillate inflorescences dissimilar; staminate short, racemose, recurved at anthesis, branched to 1 order; peduncle moderate, rounded, glabrous; prophyll tubular, short, shallowly 2-keeled, rounded to a shallow point, splitting apically; complete peduncular bracts 1, similar to the propyll but longer, other peduncular bracts few (5 according to Cook), large or small and shallow; rachis slightly longer than the peduncle, bearing spirally arranged, short, terete branches, each subtended by a small pointed bract; first-order branches each bearing ca. 6(–9), crowded, staminate flowers, subtending bracts small, pointed, membranous or not evident. Staminate flowers with a short terete stalk; perianth consisting of a low membranous rim or absent; floral receptacle chunky with several flat sides all bearing irregularly to somewhat spirally arranged stamens, filaments very short, appressed, or briefly elongate, anthers short, rounded or ± elongate, basifixed, latrorse; pollen elliptic, monoporate, with reticulate, tectate exine; pistillode terminal, conical, whitish, irregular in position. Pistillate inflorescence headlike, unbranched; prophyll tubular, short, 2-keeled laterally, flattened, pointed, splitting along one side; peduncular bracts several, the first complete, tubular, rounded, with a short pointed tip, splitting apically on one side, the second and third bracts incomplete, short, united basally to form a tube, distal parts distinct, triangular, fourth to sixth bracts also united basally into a shorter tube with distinct, tapering tips, seventh and eight bracts united basally on one side, open on the other side. Pistillate flowers spirally arranged, closely appressed, each subtended by a bract; sepals ± 4, narrow, elongate; petals ± 4, like the sepals but longer and somewhat wider, variously wrinkled; staminodes apparently absent; gynoecium consisting of ca. 8 carpels, connate laterally, ovarian part terete, tapering into an elongate, cylindrical style and ca. 8 curly, elongate stigmas, conduplicately folded, bearing stigmatoid tissue along the margins. Fruits borne in large headlike clusters of 3–6, clusters smaller than those of *Phytelephas*, each fruit rounded, covered in large, pointed warts, stylar remains terminal, forming a large beak; epicarp with short, close fibers, mesocarp fibers fine, endocarp shelllike with adherent fibers enclosing each seed. Seed ± kidney-shaped, hilum basal, raphe fibers parallel, ascending, with short branches forming grooves in the endosperm, endosperm homogeneous, very hard; embryo lateral near the base. Germination remote-ligular; eophyll pinnate. Cytology not studied.

Anatomy. —Not studied.

Distribution. —One species known from the western coastal regions of Colombia and a recently discovered second species from eastern Colombia (see Balslev and Henderson in press).

Ecology. —Undergrowth palms in deep forests where rainfall is heavy and nearly continuous throughout the year. Many beetles emerged from inflorescences of *A. decasperma* collected by Cook.

Common Names and Uses. —Ivory palms, cabecita. Used for vegetable ivory and thatch.

Notes. —For diagnostic characters see notes under *Phytelephas.*

Taxonomic Accounts. —Cook (1927). Balslev and Henderson (in press).

Plates. —30D; 81B, D; Fig. G.20.

GENERIC NAMES OF DUBIOUS APPLICATION

The following generic names have been validly published but their application is in doubt because the original descriptions are too meager and type specimens have not been found.

CHAMAETHRINAX H. A. Wendland ex R. Pfister, Beiträge zur vergleichenden Anatomie der Sabaleenblätter 51. 1892. Type: **C. hookeriana** H. A. Wendland ex R. Pfister.

MICRONOMA H. A. Wendland ex J. D. Hooker, in Bentham & J. D. Hooker, Genera Plantarum 3: 882. 1883. Type: not designated.

PARIPON Voigt, Sylloge Plantarum Novarum 2:51. 1828. Type: **P. palmiri** Voigt.

POROTHRINAX H. A. Wendland ex Grisebach, Catalogus Plantarum Cubensium 221. 1866. Type: **P. pumilio** (Loddiges ex J. A. & J. H. Schultes) H. A. Wendland ex Grisebach (*Thrinax pumilio* Loddiges ex J. A. & J. H. Schultes) (name of uncertain application).

ROEBELIA Engel, Linnaea 33:680. 1865. Type: **R. solitaria** Engel.

ADDITIONAL GENERIC NAMES OF NO FORMAL STANDING

The following names, listed by Burret and Potztal (1956) as genera, were never validly published at the rank of genus, or are clearly printer's errors when published.

ANACLASMUS Griffith (published as a section of *Areca* including species now referable to *Nenga* and *Pinanga*)

ANOOSPERMA Kunze (typographical error = *Oncosperma*)

ARAUCASIA Bentham & J. D. Hooker (typographical error for *Arausiaca* = *Orania*)

BLUMEA Zippelius ex Miquel (= *Arenga*)

CALYCODON H. A. Wendland (= *Hyospathe*)

DRYPSIS Duchartre (typographical error = *Dypsis*)

DIPLORIPHIS Drude (published as a section of *Mauritia* including species now referable to *Mauritiella*)

JATITARA Marcgraf (= *Desmoncus*)

ONISCOPHORA H. A. Wendland ex Burret (? = *Chrysalidocarpus*)

OPSICOCOS H. A. Wendland (? = *Actinorhytis*)

Geographical Listing of Genera

Arabia
Borassus
Hyphaene
Livistona
Nannorrhops
Phoenix
Argentina
Acrocomia
Allagoptera
Butia
Copernicia
Euterpe
Syagrus
Trithrinax
Australia (See also **Lord Howe Island**)
Archontophoenix
Arenga
Calamus
Carpentaria
Caryota
Cocos
Corypha
Gronophyllum
Gulubia
Hydriastele
Laccospadix
Licuala
Linospadix
Livistona
Normanbya
Nypa
Oraniopsis
Ptychosperma
Wodyetia
Bolivia
Acrocomia
Aiphanes
Astrocaryum
Bactris
Ceroxylon
Chamaedorea
Chelyocarpus
Copernicia
Desmoncus
Dictyocaryum
Euterpe
Geonoma
Iriartea
Mauritia
Oenocarpus
Orbignya
Parajubaea
Scheelea
Socratea
Syagrus
Trithrinax
Borneo
Areca
Arenga

Borassodendron
Calamus
Caryota
Ceratolobus
Corypha
Cyrtostachys
Daemonorops
Eleiodoxa
Eugeissona
Iguanura
Johannesteijsmannia
Korthalsia
Licuala
Livistona
Nenga
Nypa
Oncosperma
Orania
Pholidocarpus
Pinanga
Plectocomia
Plectocomiopsis
Pogonotium
Retispatha
Salacca
Brazil
Acrocomia
Aiphanes
Attalea
Allagoptera
Astrocaryum
Bactris
Barcella
Butia
Chelyocarpus
Copernicia
Desmoncus
Elaeis
Euterpe
Geonoma
Hyospathe
Iriartea
Iriartella
Itaya
Jessenia
Leopoldinia
Lepidocaryum
Lytocaryum
Manicaria
Mauritia
Mauritiella
Maximiliana
Oenocarpus
Orbignya
Pholidostachys
Phytelephas
Polyandrococos
Prestoea
Raphia
Scheelea

Socratea
Syagrus
Trithrinax
Burma
Areca
Arenga
Borassus
Calamus
Caryota
Corypha
Daemonorops
Korthalsia
Licuala
Livistona
Myrialepis
Nypa
Oncosperma
Phoenix
Pinanga
Plectocomia
Salacca
Trachycarpus
Wallichia
Central America
Acoelorraphe
Acrocomia
Aiphanes
Asterogyne
Astrocaryum
Attalea
Bactris
Brahea
Calyptrogyne
Chamaedorea
Colpothrinax
Cryosophila
Desmoncus
Elaeis
Euterpe
Gaussia
Geonoma
Hyospathe
Iriartea
Manicaria
Neonicholsonia
Oenocarpus
Orbignya
Pholidostachys
Phytelephas
Prestoea
Pseudophoenix
Raphia
Reinhardtia
Roystonea
Sabal
Scheelea
Schippia
Socratea
Synechanthus
Welfia

Chile (See also **Juan Fernandez Islands**)
Jubaea
China
Arenga
Calamus
Caryota
Chuniophoenix
Corypha
Daemonorops
Guihaia
Licuala
Livistona
Nypa
Phoenix
Pinanga
Plectocomia
Rhapis
Salacca
Trachycarpus
Wallichia
Colombia
Acrocomia
Aiphanes
Ammandra
Asterogyne
Astrocaryum
Attalea
Bactris
Catoblastus
Ceroxylon
Chamaedorea
Chelyocarpus
Cryosophila
Desmoncus
Dictyocaryum
Elaeis
Euterpe
Geonoma
Iriartea
Iriartella
Hyospathe
Jessenia
Leopoldinia
Lepidocaryum
Manicaria
Mauritia
Mauritiella
Maximiliana
Oenocarpus
Orbignya
Pholidostachys
Phytelephas
Prestoea
Raphia
Reinhardtia
Sabal
Scheelea
Socratea
Syagrus

Synechanthus
Welfia
Wettinia
Continental USA
Acoelorraphe
Coccothrinax
Pseudophoenix
Rhapidophyllum
Roystonea
Sabal
Serenoa
Thrinax
Washingtonia
Ecuador
Aiphanes
Ammandra
Astrocaryum
Attalea
Bactris
Catoblastus
Ceroxylon
Chamaedorea
Chelyocarpus
Desmoncus
Dictyocaryum
Elaeis
Euterpe
Geonoma
Hyospathe
Iriartea
Jessenia
Manicaria
Mauritia
Mauritiella
Maximilliana
Oenocarpus
Palandra
Parajubaea
Pholidostachys
Phytelephas
Prestoea
Scheelea
Socratea
Syagrus
Synechanthus
Welfia
Wettinia
Europe, N. Africa, Egypt, Asia Minor
Chamaerops
Hyphaene
Medemia
Phoenix
Fiji and Samoa
Alsmithia
Balaka
Calamus
Clinostigma
Cyphosperma
Goniocladus
Metroxylon

Neoveitchia
Physokentia
Pritchardia
Veitchia
Greater Antilles (Cuba, Hispaniola, Jamaica, Puerto Rico)
Acoelorraphe
Acrocomia
Attalea
Bactris
Calyptronoma
Coccothrinax
Colpothrinax
Copernicia
Gastrococos
Gaussia
Geonoma
Prestoea
Pseudophoenix
Roystonea
Sabal
Scheelea
Thrinax
Zombia
Guianas
Acrocomia
Astrocaryum
Attalea
Bactris
Desmoncus
Dictyocaryum
Elaeis
Euterpe
Geonoma
Hyospathe
Iriartea
Iriartella
Lepidocaryum
Manicaria
Mauritia
Mauritiella
Maximiliana
Oenocarpus
Prestoea
Roystonea
Scheelea
Socratea
Syagrus
Hawaii
Pritchardia
India, including Andamans and Nicobars
Areca
Arenga
Bentinckia
Borassus
Calamus
Caryota
Corypha
Daemonorops
Hyphaene

Korthalsia
Licuala
Livistona
Nannorrhops
Nypa
Phoenix
Pinanga
Plectocomia
Rhopaloblaste
Trachycarpus
Wallichia
Indochina
Areca
Arenga
Borassus
Calamus
Caryota
Corypha
Chuniophoenix
Daemonorops
Guihaia
Korthalsia
Licuala
Livistona
Myrialepis
Nenga
Nypa
Oncosperma
Phoenix
Pinanga
Plectocomia
Rhapis
Salacca
Trachycarpus
Wallichia
Iran, Afghanistan, Pakistan
Hyphaene
Nannorrhops
Phoenix
Java
Areca
Arenga
Borassus
Calamus
Caryota
Ceratolobus
Corypha
Daemonorops
Korthalsia
Licuala
Livistona
Nenga
Nypa
Oncosperma
Orania
Pinanga
Plectocomia
Salacca
Juan Fernandez Islands
Juania
Lesser Antilles
Acrocomia

Aiphanes
Coccothrinax
Desmoncus
Euterpe
Geonoma
Prestoea
Pseudophoenix
Roystonea
Sabal
Syagrus
Thrinax
Lesser Sunda Islands
Borassus
Calamus
Caryota
Corypha
Licuala
Nypa
Lord Howe Island
Hedyscepe
Howea
Lepidorrhachis
Madagascar and Comores Islands
Beccariophoenix
Bismarckia
Borassus
Chrysalidocarpus
Dypsis
Elaeis
Halmoorea
Hyphaene
Louvelia
Marojejya
Masoala
Neodypsis
Neophloga
Orania
Phoenix
Phloga
Raphia
Ravenea
Vonitra
Malaya
Areca
Arenga
Borassodendron
Calamus
Calospatha
Caryota
Ceratolobus
Corypha
Cyrtostachys
Daemonorops
Eleiodoxa
Eugeissona
Iguanura
Johannesteijsmannia
Korthalsia
Licuala
Livistona
Maxburretia

Myrialepis
Nenga
Nypa
Oncosperma
Orania
Phoenix
Pholidocarpus
Pinanga
Plectocomia
Plectocomiopsis
Pogonotium
Rhopaloblaste
Salacca
Marquesas
Pelagodoxa
Mascarenes
Acanthophoenix
Dictyosperma
Hyophorbe
Latania
Tectiphiala
Mexico
Acoelorraphe
Acrocomia
Asterogyne
Astrocaryum
Bactris
Brahea
Calyptrogyne
Chamaedorea
Coccothrinax
Cryosophila
Desmoncus
Gaussia
Geonoma
Orbignya
Pseudophoenix
Reinhardtia
Roystonea
Sabal
Scheelea
Synechanthus
Thrinax
Washingtonia
Micronesia
Clinostigma
Gulubia
Heterospathe
Livistona
Metroxylon
Nypa
Pinanga
Ptychosperma
Moluccas
Areca
Arenga
Borassus
Calamus
Calyptrocalyx
Caryota
Corypha
Daemonorops
Drymophloeus

Gronophyllum
Gulubia
Heterospathe
Licuala
Livistona
Metroxylon
Nypa
Oncosperma
Orania
Pholidocarpus
Pigafetta
Pinanga
Ptychosperma
Rhopaloblaste
Siphokentia
New Caledonia
Actinokentia
Alloschmidia
Basselinia
Brongniartikentia
Burretiokentia
Campecarpus
Chambeyronia
Clinosperma
Cyphokentia
Cyphophoenix
Cyphosperma
Kentiopsis
Lavoixia
Mackeea
Moratia
Pritchardiopsis
Veillonia
New Guinea and the Bismarck
  Archipelago
Actinorhytis
Areca
Arenga
Borassus
Brassiophoenix
Calamus
Calyptrocalyx
Caryota
Clinostigma
Corypha
Cyrtostachys
Daemonorops
Drymophloeus
Gronophyllum
Gulubia
Heterospathe
Hydriastele
Korthalsia
Licuala
Linospadix
Livistona
Metroxylon
Nypa
Orania
Physokentia
Pigafetta
Pinanga
Ptychococcus

Ptychosperma
Rhopaloblaste
Sommieria
New Hebrides
Calamus
Carpoxylon
Clinostigma
Gulubia
Licuala
Metroxylon
Physokentia
Veitchia
New Zealand
Rhopalostylis
Paraguay
Acrocomia
Allagoptera
Attalea
Bactris
Butia
Copernicia
Geonoma
Scheelea
Syagrus
Trithrinax
Peru
Aiphanes
Astrocaryum
Attalea
Bactris
Calyptrogyne
Catoblastus
Ceroxylon
Chamaedorea
Chelyocarpus
Desmoncus
Dictyocaryum
Elaeis
Euterpe
Geonoma
Hyospathe
Iriartea
Iriartella
Itaya
Jessenia
Lepidocaryum
Mauritia
Mauritiella
Maximiliana
Oenocarpus
Orbignya
Pholidostachys
Phytelephas
Prestoea
Scheelea
Socratea
Syagrus
Wendlandiella
Wettinia
Philippines
Areca
Arenga
Calamus

Caryota
Cocos
Corypha
Daemonorops
Heterospathe
Korthalsia
Licuala
Livistona
Nypa
Oncosperma
Orania
Phoenix
Pinanga
Plectocomia
Salacca
Veitchia
Ryukyu Islands
Arenga
Livistona
Nypa
Phoenix
Satakentia
Seychelles
Deckenia
Lodoicea
Nephrosperma
Phoenicophorium
Roscheria
Verschaffeltia
Solomon Islands
Actinorhytis
Areca
Calamus
Caryota
Clinostigma
Cyrtostachys
Drymophloeus
Gulubia
Heterospathe
Licuala
Livistona
Metroxylon
Nypa
Physokentia
Ptychosperma
Rhopaloblaste
Southern Africa
Borassus
Hyphaene
Jubaeopsis
Phoenix
Raphia
Sri Lanka (Ceylon)
Areca
Borassus
Calamus
Caryota
Corypha
Loxococcus
Oncosperma
Phoenix

Sulawesi (Celebes)
Areca
Arenga
Borassus
Calamus
Caryota
Corypha
Daemonorops
Gronophyllum
Korthalsia
Licuala
Livistona
Nypa
Oncosperma
Orania
Pholidocarpus
Pigafetta
Pinanga

Sumatra
Areca
Arenga
Calamus
Caryota
Ceratolobus
Corypha
Cyrtostachys
Daemonorops
Eleiodoxa
Iguanura
Johannesteijsmannia
Korthalsia
Licuala
Livistona
Myrialepis

Nenga
Nypa
Oncosperma
Orania
Phoenix
Pholidocarpus
Pinanga
Plectocomia
Plectocomiopsis
Rhapis
Salacca

Thailand
Areca
Arenga
Borassodendron
Borassus
Calamus
Caryota
Ceratolobus
Corypha
Cyrtostachys
Daemonorops
Eleiodoxa
Eugeissona
Iguanura
Johannesteijsmannia
Kerriodoxa
Korthalsia
Licuala
Livistona
Maxburretia
Myrialepis
Nenga

Nypa
Oncosperma
Orania
Phoenix
Pinanga
Plectocomia
Plectocomiopsis
Rhapis
Salacca
Trachycarpus
Wallichia

Tropical East Africa
Borassus
Elaeis
Eremospatha
Hyphaene
Laccosperma
Livistona
Medemia
Phoenix
Raphia

Tropical West Africa
Borassus
Elaeis
Eremospatha
Hyphaene
Laccosperma
Oncocalamus
Phoenix
Podococcus
Raphia
Sclerosperma

Uruguay
Butia

Syagrus
Trithrinax

Venezuela, Trinidad, and Tobago
Aiphanes
Asterogyne
Astrocaryum
Attalea
Bactris
Catoblastus
Coccothrinax
Copernicia
Desmoncus
Elaeis
Euterpe
Geonoma
Hyospathe
Iriartea
Jessenia
Leopoldinia
Manicaria
Mauritia
Mauritiella
Maximiliana
Oenocarpus
Orbignya
Prestoea
Raphia
Sabal
Scheelea
Socratea
Syagrus

GLOSSARY

Abaxial—the side of an organ that faces away from the axis which bears it, e.g. the under surface of a leaf, the lower surface of the petiole, or the outer surface of a tubular bract (Figs. G.1, G.10, G.11, G.19).

Abcission—separation, often by a distinct layer.

Acanthophyll—a spine, often large, derived from a leaflet (Fig. G.7).

Acaulescent—lacking a visible stem (Fig. G.2).

Acervulus—a group of flowers borne in a line (Fig. G.18).

Acropetal—toward the apex.

Acuminate—tapering to a point (Fig. G.16).

Acute—distinctly and sharply pointed but not drawn out (Figs. G.15, G.16).

Adaxial—the side of an organ toward the axis which bears it; e.g. the upper side of a leaf, the upper surface of a petiole, or the inner surface of a tubular bract (Figs. G.1, G.10, G.11, G.19).

Adjacent-ligular—in germination, the new shoot developing next to the seed and enclosed by a ligule (Fig. G.24).

Adnate—attached to, usually of one kind of organ to another kind, as bract to axis (Figs. G.17, G.18).

Anastomose—to unite, usually forming a network (Fig. G.23).

Anatropous—an ovule bent parallel to its stalk so that the micropyle is adjacent to the hilum (Fig. G.20).

Androecium—collective term for the stamens (Fig. G.18).

Anther—the part of a stamen which contains the pollen, usually 2-chambered (Figs. G.18, G.19).

Anthesis—time of fertilization of a flower, i.e. shedding of pollen or receptivity of stigma.

Apiculate—bearing a short, sharp but not stiff point (Fig. G.19).

Apocarpous—with free carpels (Fig. G.20).

Aril—an outgrowth of the stalk of the ovule, sometimes resembling a third integument (G.20).

Armed—bearing some form of spines (Figs. G.4, G.5, G.6, G.7).

Arundinaceous—reedlike, usually having a hollow stem like some grasses. Not used in this book but sometimes applied to palms (Fig. G.4).

Auricle—an earlike lobe (Fig. G.6).

Axillary—borne in an axil which is the angle between the stem and the leaf or another organ which arises from the stem, such as a bract.

Basifixed—attached by the base (Fig. G.19, G.20).

Basipetal—developing from the apex toward the base.

Bicarinate—having two keels (Fig. G.17).

Bifid—divided in two, usually equal parts (Figs. G.8, G.10, G.16).

Bijugate—used for a pinnate leaf with 2 pairs of leaflets (Fig. G.13).

Bipinnate—doubly pinnate (the leaf of *Caryota*) (Figs. G.8, G.14).

Bract—modified leaf associated with the inflorescence (Fig. G.17).

Bracteole—a small bract borne on a flower stalk, often present even when the flower is essentially sessile (Fig. G.18).

Caducous—dropping off early or gradually.

Caespitose—clustered (Fig. G.2).

Calyx—the outermost or lowermost whorl of floral organs, the sepals (Figs. G.18, G.19, G.20).

Campo rupestre—rocky grassland (in South America).

Campylotropous—an ovule curved with the micropyle close to the hilum and the embryo sac also curved (Fig. G.20).

Capitate—headlike (see *Nypa*, G.17).

Carpel—the single unit of the gynoecium (Figs. G.20, G.21).

Catkinlike—used to describe a cylindrical rachilla resulting when flowers are densely crowded (Fig. G.17).

Chartaceous—paperlike, thin and stiff.

Ciliate—bearing a fringe of hairs (Fig. G.18).

Cincinnus—a flower cluster wherein each successive flower arises in the axil of a bracteole borne on the stalk of the previous flower (Figs. G.18, I.6).

Cirrate—bearing a cirrus.

Cirrus—a climbing organ, structurally a whiplike extension of the leaf rachis, armed with reflexed spines and/or acanthophylls, cf. flagellum (Figs. G.2, G.6).

Clustered—with several stems (Fig. G.2).

Connate—united, used when organs of the same kind are joined, as sepals connate; see "tubular calyx" (Fig. G.20).

Connective—the part of a stamen that connects the anthers, usually distinct from the filament (Fig. G.19).

Coriaceous—leathery.

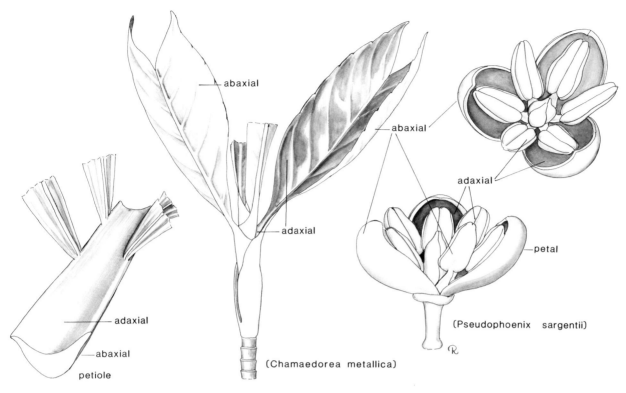

abaxial

abaxial

adaxial

adaxial

petal

(Pseudophoenix sargentii)

adaxial

abaxial

petiole

adaxial

(Chamaedorea metallica)

G.1—Adaxial and Abaxial.

Corolla—the second whorl of flower organs, the petals, inside or above the calyx (Figs. G.19, G.20).

Cortex—the ground tissue between the vascular cylinder and the epidermis.

Costa—a rib, when single, the midrib or vein (Fig. G.8).

Costapalmate—shaped like the palm of a hand and having a short midrib or costa (Figs. G.8, G.10).

Crenulate—shallowly scalloped or bearing rounded teeth (Fig. G.20).

Crown—the cluster of leaves borne at the tip of the stem (Fig. G.2).

Crownshaft—a conspicuous cylinder formed by tubular leaf sheaths at the top of the stem (Fig. G.5).

Cupule—a small cuplike structure (Figs. G.19, G.20).

Deciduous—shed periodically, falling.

Decumbent—reclining, but with the apex or tip ascending (Fig. G.2).

Deltoid—shaped like an equilateral triangle.

Dentate—toothed (Fig. G.20).

Determinate—bearing a terminal organ, as in an inflorescence when a branch ends in a flower bud.

Dichotomous (stem)—equally forking (Fig. G.2).

Didymous—of anthers where the connective is almost absent (Fig. G.19).

Digitate—like fingers (Fig. G.17).

Dimorphic—with two different forms (Fig. G.18).

Dioecious—when staminate and pistillate flowers are borne on different plants.

Distal—farthest from the place of attachment.

Distant—widely separated.

Distichous—arranged in two ranks (Figs. G.13, G.17).

Divaricate—spread widely (Fig. G.19).

Dorsifixed—attached by the abaxial (usually outer) side (Fig. G.19).

Dyad—a pair (Fig. G.18).

Elliptic—oblong with regularly rounded ends (Fig. G.19).

Emarginate—with a notch cut out, often at the apex (Figs. G.15, G.16).

Embryo—the rudimentary plant present in a seed (Figs. G.22, G.23).

Endocarp—the innermost layer of the fruit wall (Figs. G.22, G.23).

Endosperm—in palms the nutritive body of a seed (Figs. G.22, G.23).

Entire (leaf)—undivided (Fig. G.8).

Eophyll—in a seedling the first leaf having a blade (Fig. G.24).

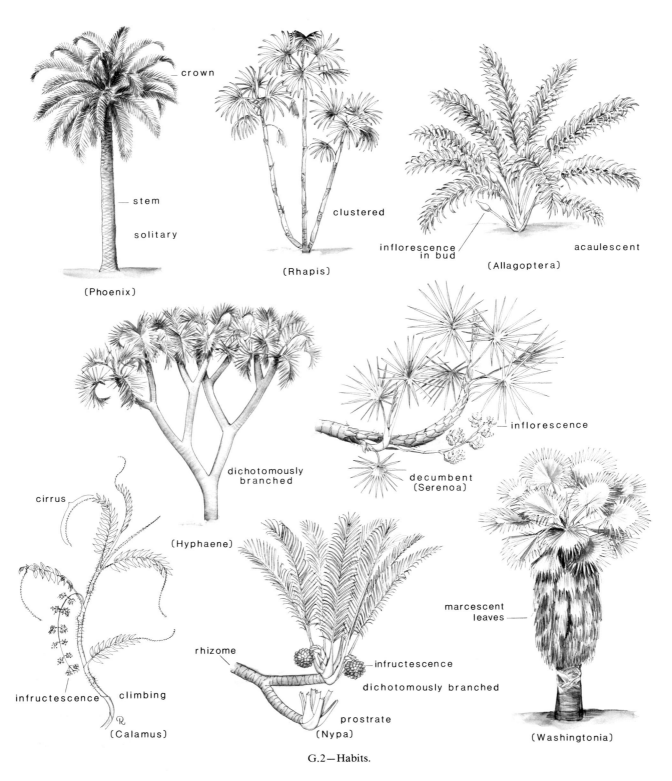

crown

stem

solitary

(Phoenix)

clustered

(Rhapis)

inflorescence
in bud

acaulescent

(Allagoptera)

cirrus

dichotomously
branched

inflorescence

decumbent
(Serenoa)

(Hyphaene)

infructescence

climbing

(Calamus)

rhizome

infructescence

dichotomously branched

prostrate
(Nypa)

marcescent
leaves

(Washingtonia)

G.2—Habits.

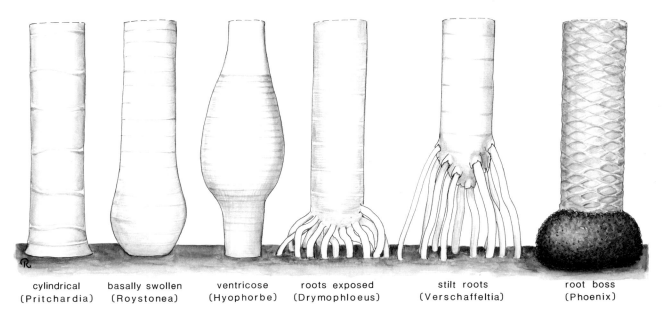

cylindrical (Pritchardia) basally swollen (Roystonea) ventricose (Hyophorbe) roots exposed (Drymophloeus) stilt roots (Verschaffeltia) root boss (Phoenix)

G.3—Stem Bases and Roots.

Epicarp—the outermost layer of the fruit wall (Fig. G.22).

Epipetalous—united with, often appearing to be borne on, the petals (Fig. G.19).

Exine—the outer coat of a pollen grain.

Extrorse—of anthers, opening abaxially, away from the center of the flower (Fig. G.19).

Fenestrate—with holes or openings, sometimes like windows (Fig. G.13, *Reinhardtia*).

Fibrous—composed of or including fibers (G.5).

Filament—of a stamen, the stalk which bears the anther (Figs. G.18, G.19).

Filamentous—threadlike (Fig. G.16).

Flabellate—fan-shaped or wedge-shaped, sometimes pleated (Fig. G.15).

Flagellum—a whiplike climbing organ derived from an inflorescence, bearing reflexed spines, cf. "cirrus" (Fig. G.6).

Floccous—bearing soft, uneven hairs or scales (G.7).

Funiculus—the stalk of an ovule (Fig. G.20).

Gamo—as a prefix, united or fused (see sepals and petals, Calamoideae).

Gibbous—more convex on one side than another, as a not quite full moon (G.20).

Glabrous—smooth, lacking hairs, scales or other indument (see *Arenga*, G.21).

Glaucous—covered with a bluish gray or greenish bloom.

Glomerule—a knoblike cluster of flowers (see *Livistona*).

Grapnel—a small anchor or hook with three or more flukes (Fig. G.6, see *Calamus* flagellum).

Graywackes—poorly sorted sandstone containing clay.

Gynoecium—the ovule bearing organ of the flower, composed of 1–several carpels and divisible into an ovary, a style, and one or several stigmas (Figs. G.18, G.20).

Hapaxanthic—describing shoots flowering then dying, cf. "pleonanthic" (Fig. I.4).

Hastula—a flap of tissue borne at the insertion of the blade on the petiole on the upper, lower, or both leaf surfaces (Fig. G.11).

Hemianatropous—an ovule turned so that the micopyle is at right angles to its stalk (funiculus) (Fig. G.20).

Hermaphrodite—flowers having both stamens and gynoecium (Fig. G.18).

Hilum—the scar left on the seed where it was attached (Fig. G.23).

Homogeneous—uniform, the same throughout (Fig. G.23).

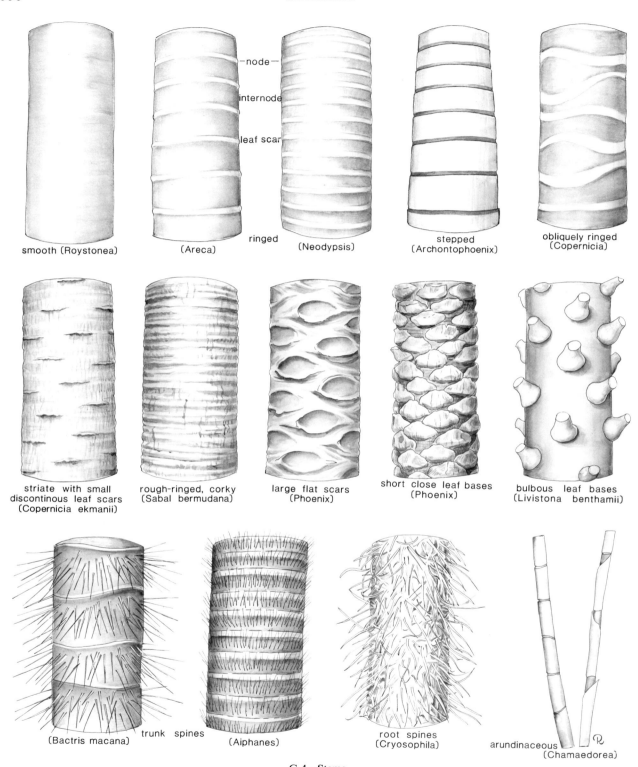

smooth (Roystonea)

(Areca)

node

internode

leaf scar

ringed

(Neodypsis)

stepped
(Archontophoenix)

obliquely ringed
(Copernicia)

striate with small
discontinous leaf scars
(Copernicia ekmanii)

rough-ringed, corky
(Sabal bermudana)

large flat scars
(Phoenix)

short close leaf bases
(Phoenix)

bulbous leaf bases
(Livistona benthamii)

(Bactris macana)   trunk spines

(Aiphanes)

root spines
(Cryosophila)

arundinaceous
(Chamaedorea)

G.4—Stems.

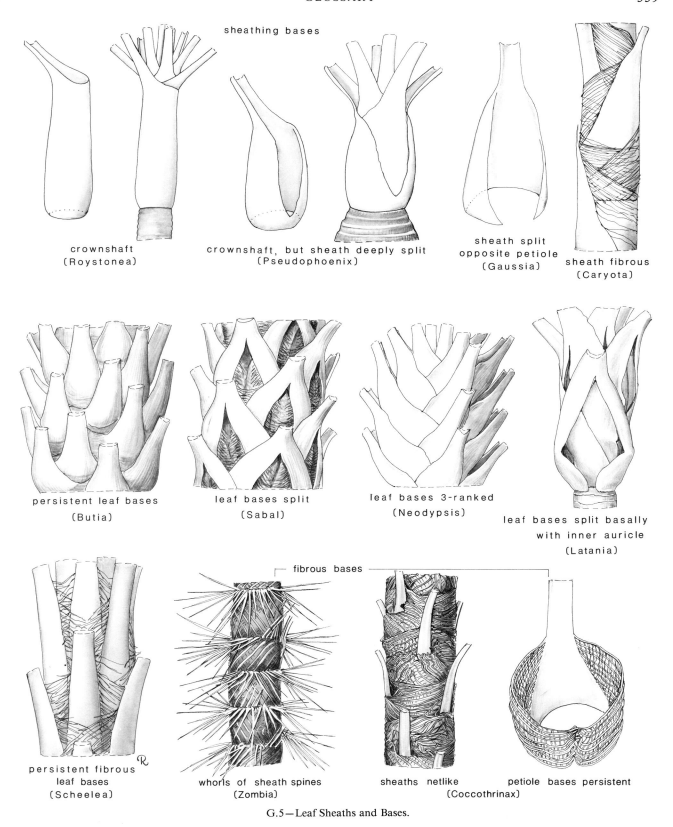

sheathing bases

crownshaft
(Roystonea)

crownshaft, but sheath deeply split
(Pseudophoenix)

sheath split
opposite petiole
(Gaussia)

sheath fibrous
(Caryota)

persistent leaf bases
(Butia)

leaf bases split
(Sabal)

leaf bases 3-ranked
(Neodypsis)

leaf bases split basally
with inner auricle
(Latania)

persistent fibrous
leaf bases
(Scheelea)

fibrous bases

whorls of sheath spines
(Zombia)

sheaths netlike
(Coccothrinax)

petiole bases persistent

G.5—Leaf Sheaths and Bases.

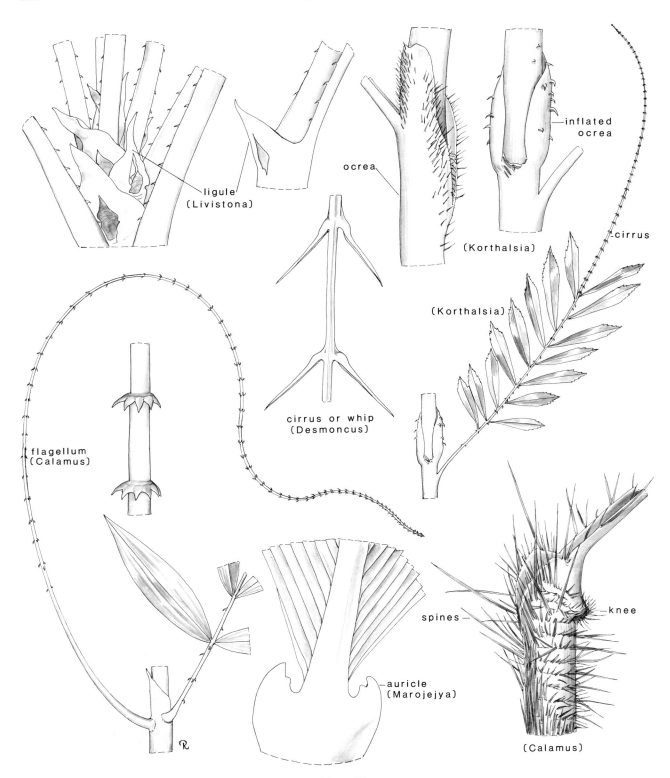

G.6—Special Leaf Structures.

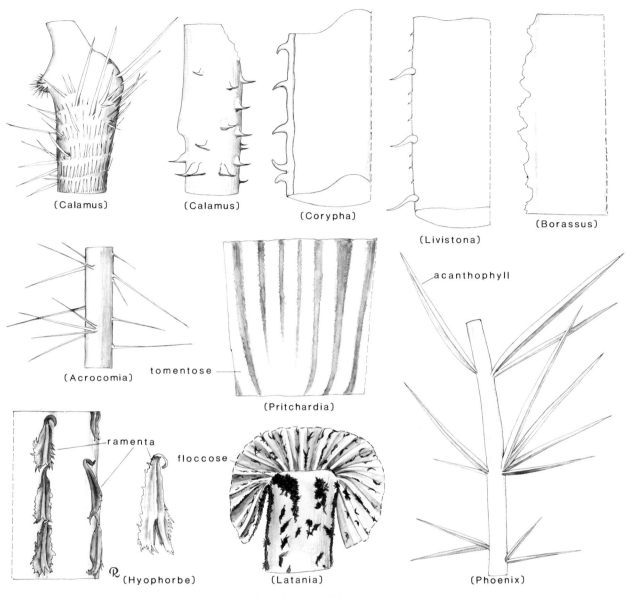

G.7—Spines and Pubescence.

Imbricate—overlapping, cf. "valvate" (Figs. G.19, G.20, G.21).

Imparipinnate—unevenly pinnate, bearing a terminal leaflet (Fig. G.13).

Indeterminate—not bearing a terminal flower or other organ.

Indument—any covering as hairs or scales (Fig. G.7).

Induplicate—V-shaped in cross section, trough-shaped (Figs. G.9, G.12).

Inflexed—bent or curved inward toward the center (Fig. G.19).

Inflorescence—the branch that bears the flowers, including all its bracts and branches (Figs. G.2, I.4, I.5).

Infrafoliar—borne below the leaves (Fig. I.4).

Infructescence—as inflorescence but in fruit (Fig. G.2).

Integument—a covering or envelope enclosing the ovule (Fig. G.20).

Interfoliar—borne among the leaves.

Internode—the space or part of a stem between the attachments of two leaves (G.4).

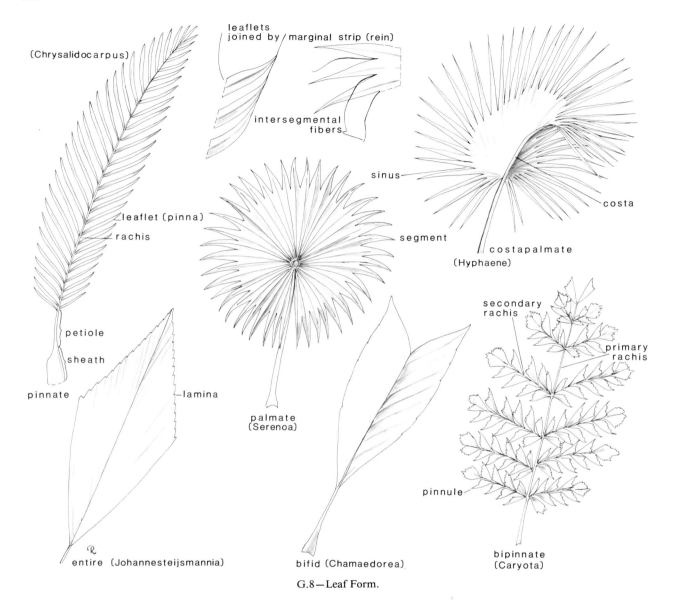

G.8—Leaf Form.

Intersegmental fibers—fibers resulting from disintegration of the ribs between the segments of palmate leaves (Fig. G.8).

Introrse—of anthers, opening toward the center of the flower (Fig. G.19).

Keeled—bearing a ridge, like the keel of a boat (G.20).

Kerangas—heath forest (in Borneo).

Knee—a swelling on the leaf sheath at the base of the petiole, present in most rattans (Fig. G.6).

Lamina—blade (Figs. G.8, G.10).

Lanceolate—narrow, tapering at both ends, the basal end often broader (Fig. G.15).

Latrorse—of anthers, opening lateral to the filament (Fig. G.19).

Leaflets—as used in this book, divisions of pinnate leaves.

Ligule—a distal projection of the leaf sheath (Figs. G.6, G.24).

Linear—several times longer than wide, usually narrow (Fig. G.15).

Locule—the cavity in which the ovule is borne (Fig. G.20).

Marcescent—withering before being shed (Fig. G.2).

Medifixed—attached at the middle.

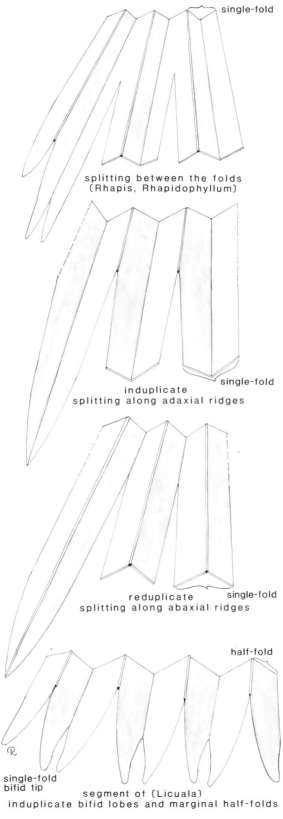

single-fold

splitting between the folds
(Rhapis, Rhapidophyllum)

induplicate
splitting along adaxial ridges

single-fold

reduplicate   single-fold
splitting along abaxial ridges

half-fold

single-fold
bifid tip

segment of (Licuala)
induplicate bifid lobes and marginal half-folds

G.9—Leaf Division.

PALMATE LEAVES

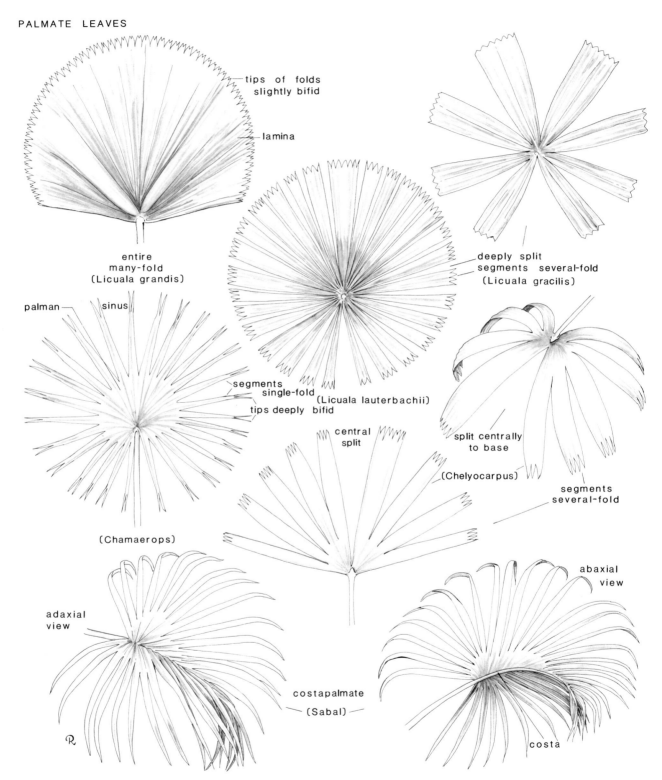

tips of folds
slightly bifid

lamina

entire
many-fold
(Licuala grandis)

deeply split
segments several-fold
(Licuala gracilis)

palman   sinus

segments
single-fold   (Licuala lauterbachii)
tips deeply bifid

central
split

split centrally
to base

(Chelyocarpus)

segments
several-fold

(Chamaerops)

adaxial
view

abaxial
view

costapalmate

(Sabal)

costa

G.10—Palmate Leaves.

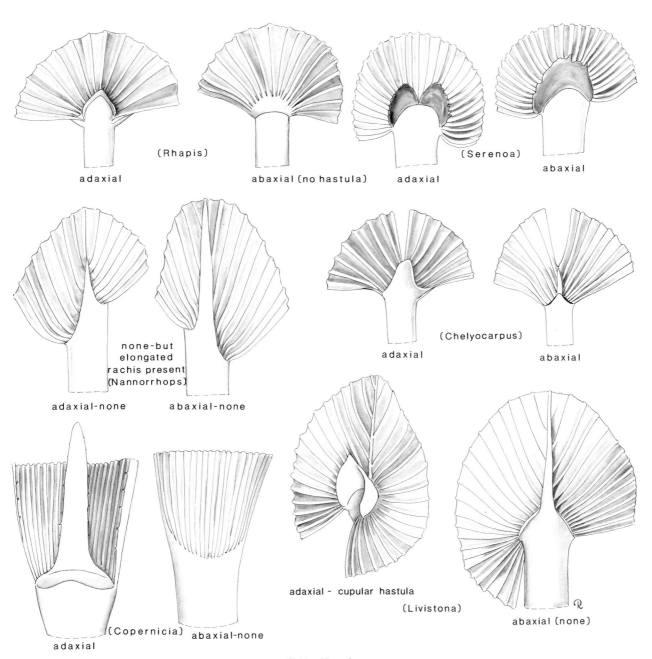

adaxial

(Rhapis)

abaxial (no hastula)   adaxial   (Serenoa)

abaxial

none-but
elongated
rachis present
(Nannorrhops)

(Chelyocarpus)

adaxial-none   abaxial-none   adaxial   abaxial

adaxial - cupular hastula

(Livistona)

(Copernicia)   abaxial-none

adaxial   abaxial (none)

G.11—Hastulas.

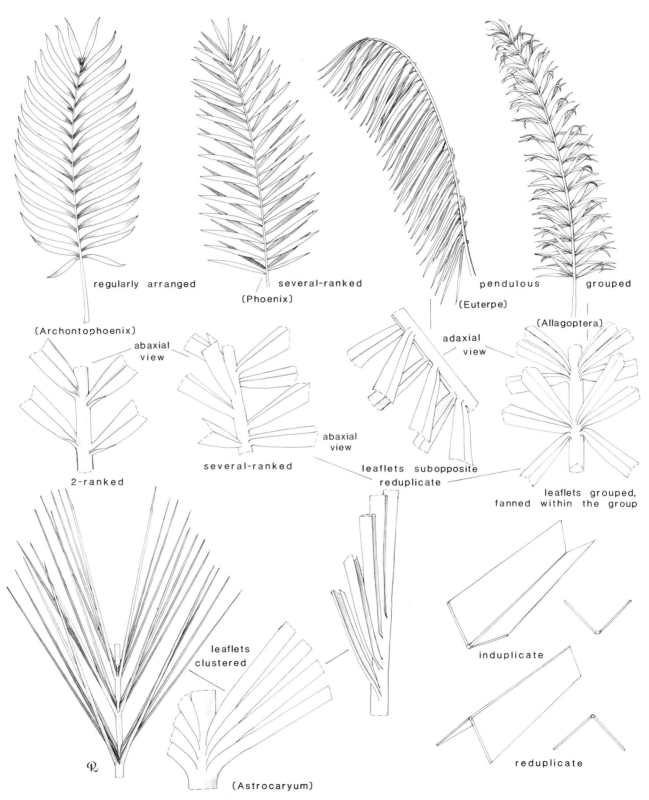

regularly arranged

several-ranked

(Phoenix)

pendulous   grouped

(Euterpe)

(Archontophoenix)

(Allagoptera)

abaxial
view

adaxial
view

2-ranked

several-ranked

abaxial
view

leaflets subopposite
reduplicate

leaflets grouped,
fanned within the group

leaflets
clustered

induplicate

reduplicate

(Astrocaryum)

G.12—Pinnate Leaves.

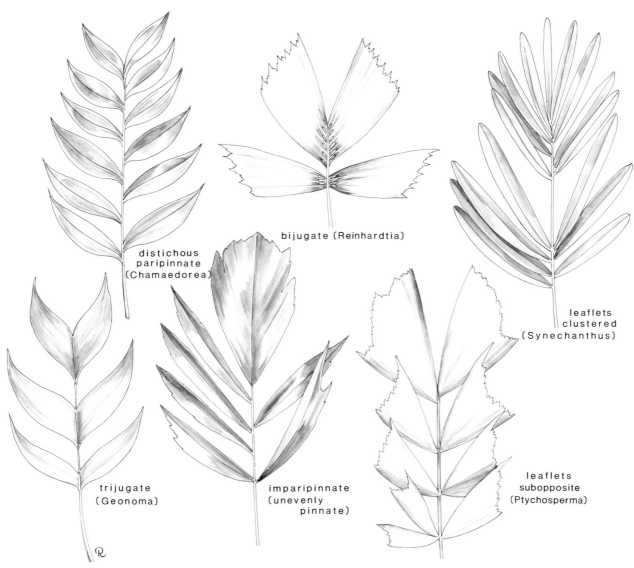

distichous
paripinnate
(Chamaedorea)

bijugate (Reinhardtia)

leaflets
clustered
(Synechanthus)

trijugate
(Geonoma)

imparipinnate
(unevenly
pinnate)

leaflets
subopposite
(Ptychosperma)

G.13—Some Pinnate Leaf Forms.

Meristem—the growing region of a plant, a special area of undifferentiated cells wherein new cells and organs are developed.

Mesocarp—the middle layer of the fruit wall (Fig. G.22).

Micropyle—an aperture through the integuments of the ovule (Fig. G.20).

Moderate—medium or intermediate in size.

Monocarpic—fruiting once, then dying completely.

Monoecious—describing a plant bearing both staminate and pistillate flowers (Fig. G.17).

Monomerous—formed of a single member.

Monopodial—with a single main axis.

Node—the area of a stem where a leaf is attached (G.4).

Oblate—± spherical but flattened at the poles (*Arenga,* G.21).

Obovoid—egg-shaped, broader distally (Fig. G.21, G.23).

Obpyriform—pear-shaped but attached at the broad end (Fig. G.21).

Ocrea—an extension of the leaf sheath beyond the petiole insertion (Fig. G.6).

Ontogeny—the development of an individual through its various stages.

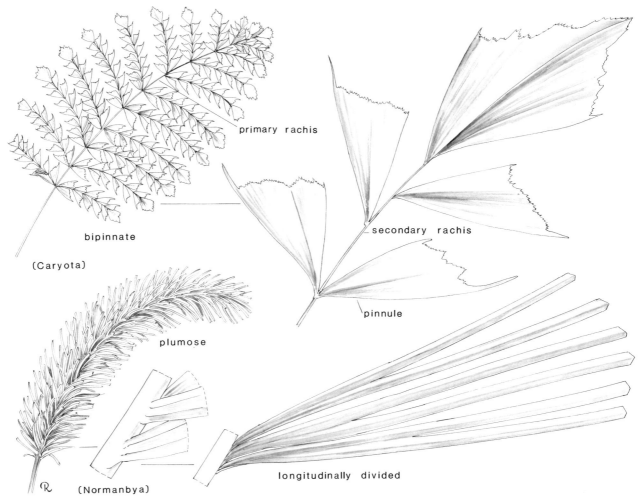

primary rachis

bipinnate

(Caryota)

secondary rachis

pinnule

plumose

longitudinally divided

(Normanbya)

G.14—Bipinnate Leaves.

Operculum—a lid or cover (Fig. G.23).

Order (and its extensions, first, etc.)—a sequence, as of branching: a first order branch branches to produce a second order branch, etc. (Figs. I.5, G.17).

Orthotropous—an erect ovule with the micropyle distal and hilum basal (Fig. G.20).

Ovary—the ovule-bearing part of the gynoecium (Fig. G.18).

Ovoid—egg-shaped (Fig. G.21).

Ovule—the young or developing seed (Figs. G.18, G.20).

Palman—the undivided central part of a palmate leaf (Fig. G.10).

Palmate—shaped like the palm of the hand, all ribs or leaflets arising from a central area (Figs. G.8, G.10).

Papillose—bearing nipplelike projections.

Paripinnate—evenly pinnate, lacking a terminal leaflet (Fig. G.13).

Pedicel—a floral stalk (Figs. G.18, G.19).

Peduncle—the lower unbranched part of an inflorescence (Figs. G.17, I.4, I.5).

Peduncular bracts—empty bracts on main inflorescence axis between prophyll and the first rachis bract (Figs. G.17, I.4, I.5).

Peltate—round, shieldlike, attached in the center.

Perianth—the sepals and the petals together (Fig. G.21).

Petal—one unit of the inner floral envelope or corolla (Figs. G.1, G.18–G.20).

Petiole—the stalk of a leaf (Figs. G.1, G.5, G.8).

Pinna(ae)—a leaflet (leaflets) of a pinnate leaf (Fig. G.8).

Pinnate—featherlike, lateral ribs or leaflets arising from a central axis (Figs. G.8, G.12, G.13).

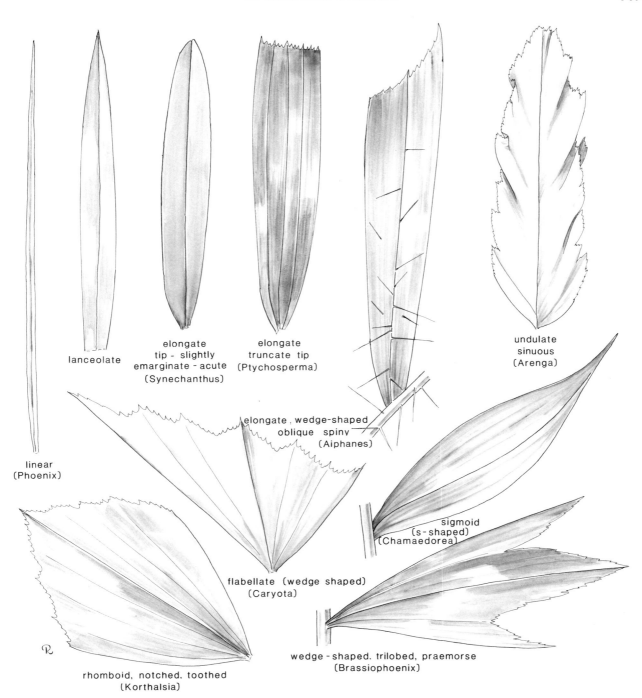

linear
(Phoenix)

lanceolate

elongate
tip - slightly
emarginate - acute
(Synechanthus)

elongate
truncate tip
(Ptychosperma)

undulate
sinuous
(Arenga)

elongate, wedge-shaped
oblique spiny
(Aiphanes)

sigmoid
(s - shaped)
(Chamaedorea)

flabellate (wedge shaped)
(Caryota)

rhomboid, notched, toothed
(Korthalsia)

wedge - shaped, trilobed, praemorse
(Brassiophoenix)

G.15—Leaflet Shapes.

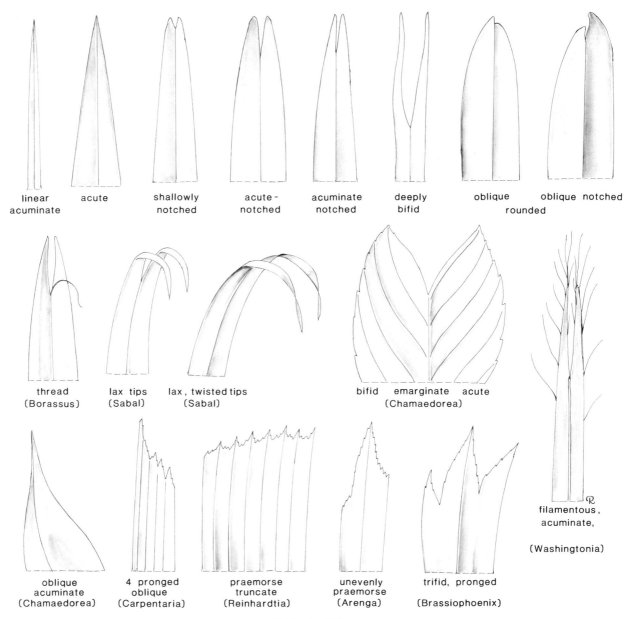

linear acuminate   acute   shallowly notched   acute-notched   acuminate notched   deeply bifid   oblique rounded   oblique notched

thread (Borassus)   lax tips (Sabal)   lax, twisted tips (Sabal)   bifid   emarginate   acute (Chamaedorea)   filamentous, acuminate, (Washingtonia)

oblique acuminate (Chamaedorea)   4 pronged oblique (Carpentaria)   praemorse truncate (Reinhardtia)   unevenly praemorse (Arenga)   trifid, pronged (Brassiophoenix)

G.16—Leaf Tips.

Pinnule—the leaflet of a bipinnate leaf (Figs. G.8, G.14).

Pistillate—bearing a pistil (gynoecium), the ovule-bearing organ of the flower (Figs. G.18, G.20).

Pistillode—a sterile gynoecium (Fig. G.19).

Pit—a cavity formed by united bracts, enclosing flowers (Fig. G.18).

Pith—the parenchymatous or often spongy center of a stem.

Pleonanthic—describing shoots flowering continuously, not dying after flowering, cf. "hapaxanthic" (Fig. I.4).

Plicate—pleated (G.9).

Plumose—softly feathered (Fig. G.14).

Pneumatophores—"breathing" roots.

Podsol—a zoned soil with a layer of humus overlying an acidic, highly leached layer, and a basal layer with iron deposition.

Polygamo-dioecious—bearing hermaphrodite and either male or female flowers.

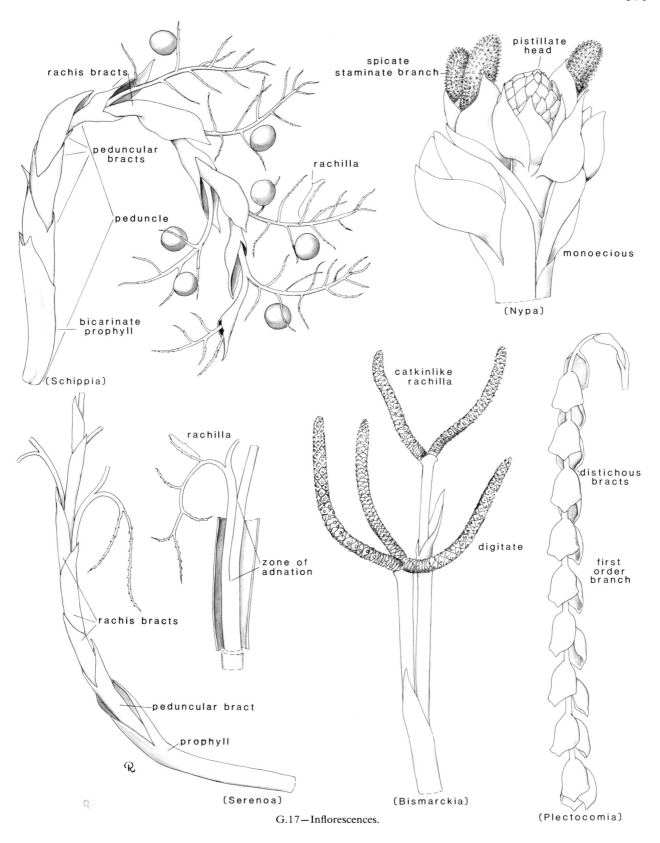

G.17—Inflorescences.

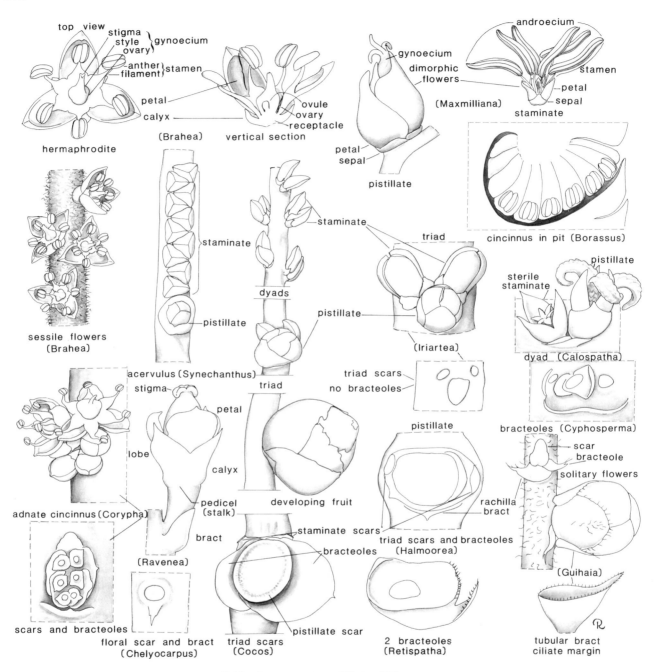

G.18—Arrangements and Parts of Flowers.

Poricidal—opening by pores (Fig. G.19).

Praemorse—jaggedly toothed, as if bitten (Fig. G.15, G.16).

Prophyll—the first bract borne on the inflorescence, usually 2-keeled (Figs. G.17, I.4, I.5).

Prostrate—lying flat (Fig. G.2).

Protandrous—of flowers or inflorescences, pollen shed before the stigma is receptive.

Protogynous—of flowers or inflorescences, the stigma receptive before the pollen is shed.

Proximal—nearest to the attachment, basal.

Pseudomonomerous—appearing to be of one member but actually of several, as a gynoecium with one fertile carpel and one locule but parts of two other carpels present (Fig. G.20).

Punctiform—dotlike (G.20, *Acrocomia*).

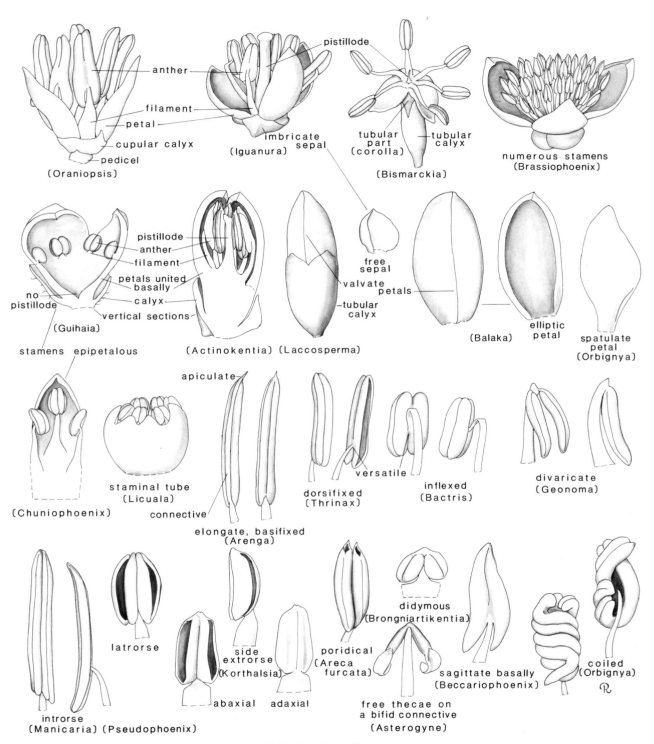

G.19—Staminate Flowers.

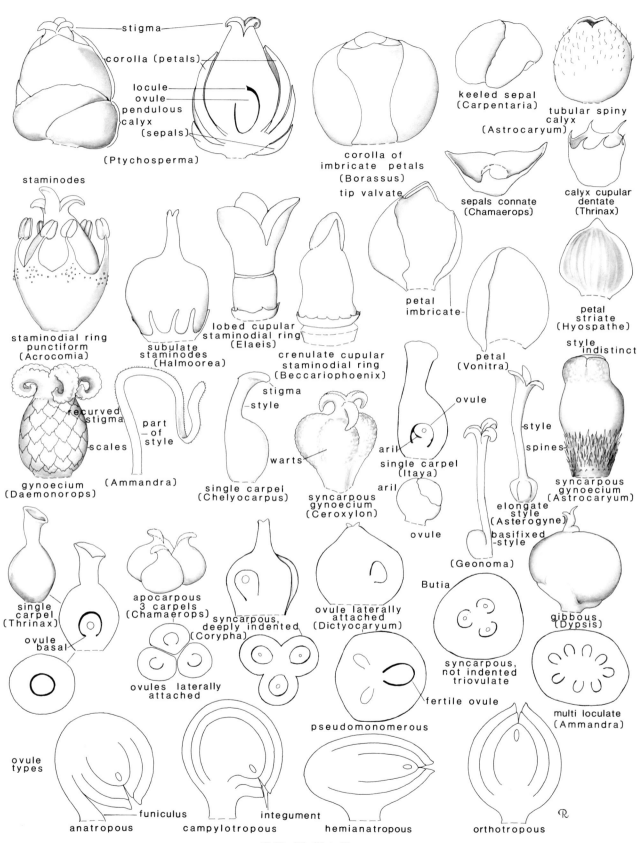

G.20—Pistillate Flowers.

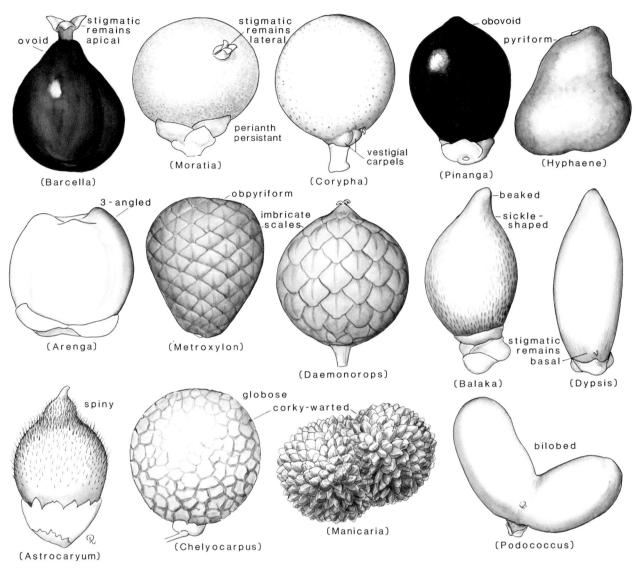

G.21—Fruits.

Pyrene—a seedlike body formed by a hard, often sculptured layer of endocarp which surrounds the seed (see "Borasseae" and accompanying generic drawings).

Pyriform—pear-shaped (Fig. G.21).

Rachilla—the branch that bears the flowers (Fig. G.17).

Rachis—the axis of a leaf beyond the petiole (Fig. G.14), or the axis of an inflorescence beyond the first branches, i.e. beyond the peduncle (Figs. G.17, I.5).

Rachis bracts—bracts subtending first-order branches of the inflorescence (Figs. I.5, G.17).

Radicle—the first root formed by the embryo (Fig. G.24).

Ramenta—rather thin scales with ragged edges, often large and irregular in shape (Fig. G.7).

Rank—a row, usually a vertical one (Fig. G.12).

Raphe—a ridge or depression on the seed, usually the source of fibrovascular branches (Fig. G.23).

Raphides—bundles of needle-shaped crystals of calcium oxalate.

Receptacle—the central axis of a flower to which the organs—sepals, petals, stamens, carpels—are attached.

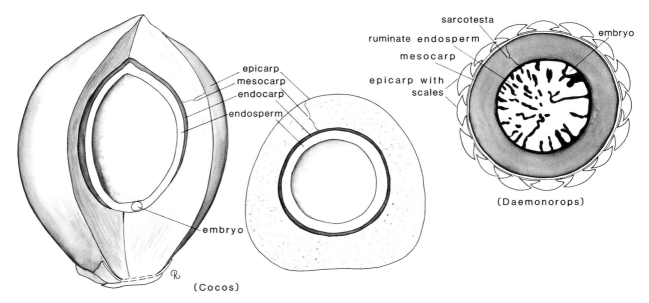

G.22—Fruit Structure.

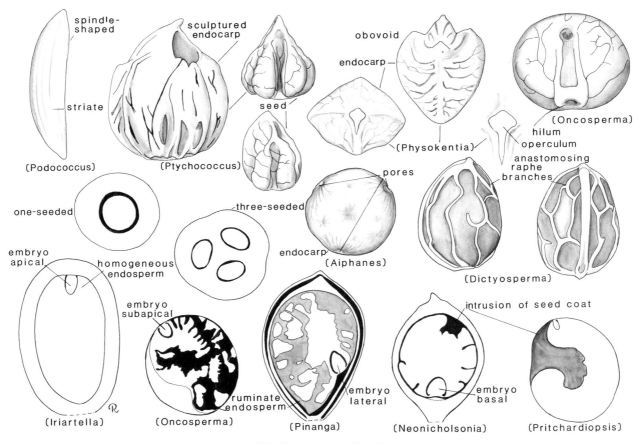

G.23—Endocarps and Seeds.

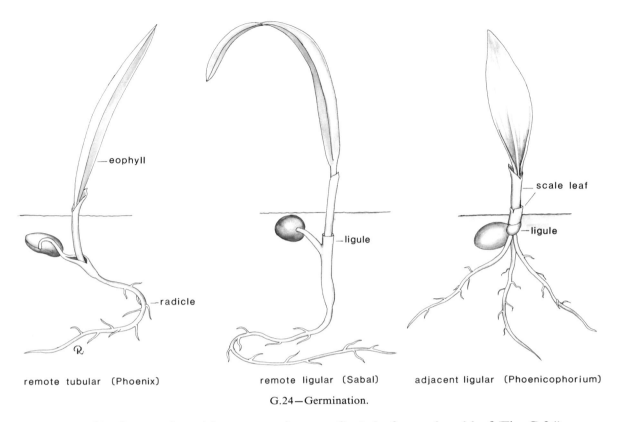

remote tubular (Phoenix)   remote ligular (Sabal)   adjacent ligular (Phoenicophorium)

G.24—Germination.

Reduplicate—of leaflets ∧-shaped in cross section (Figs. G.9, G.12).

Rein—in palms a narrow marginal strip which is shed when the compound leaf unfolds (Fig. G.8).

Remote-ligular—in germination, the young plant connected to the seed by a long tubular cotyledonary petiole, bearing a ligule (Fig. G.24).

Remote-tubular—in germination, the young plant connected to the seed by a long tubular cotyledonary petiole, lacking a ligule (Fig. G.24).

Rheophyte—a plant adapted to growing in or on the banks of fast-flowing rivers, leaflets of rheophytic palms usually very narrow, often lanceolate.

Rhizome—underground stem (Fig. G.2).

Root boss—a rounded basal protuberance from which lateral roots emerge (Fig. G.4).

Root spines—spines developed from short roots (Fig. G.4).

Rugose—wrinkled.

Ruminate—darkly streaked due to infolding of the seed coats (Figs. G.22, G.23).

Sagittate—enlarged at the base into two acute, straight lobes like the barbed head of an arrow (G.19, *Beccariophoenix*).

Sarcotesta—a fleshy layer developed (in palms) from the outer seed coat (Fig. G.22).

Scale leaf—a reduced leaf (Fig. G.24).

Segment—the division of a palmate or costapalmate leaf (Figs. G.8, G.10).

Sepal—a single part of the outermost whorl of floral organs, the calyx (Figs. G.19, G.20).

Seral—a temporary or developing vegetation type.

Sessile—lacking a stalk (G.18, *Guihaia*).

Sheath—the lowest part, or the base of the leaf which is always tubular at first but often splits during or after maturity (Figs. G.5, G.8).

Sigmoid—S-shaped (Fig. G.15).

Sinuous—wavy (Fig. G.15).

Solitary—single stemmed, not clustering (G.2).

Spadix—in palms, the whole inflorescence. Not used in this book because of ambiguities with other families.

Spathe—a large sheathing bract usually either the prophyll or peduncular bract. Not used in this book because of its ambiguity within palms.

Spatulate—shaped like a small spatula, oblong with an extended basal part (Fig. G.19).

Spicate—spikelike, the inflorescence unbranched, the flowers apparently borne directly on the axis (Fig. G.17).

Spicule—a very slender brittle, needlelike spine.

Spinules—very small spines.

Spur—a short, often curved and tapered projection (see *Kerriodoxa*).

Stamen—the male organ of a flower; a stalk or filament bearing an anther containing pollen (Figs. G.18, G.19).

Staminate—bearing stamens, the pollen bearing organs of a flower (Fig. G.18, G.20).

Staminode—a vestigial stamen often greatly modified in form (Fig. G.20).

Stem—the main axis (Figs. G.2, G.3, G.4).

Stigma—the pollen receptor on the gynoecium, usually distal (Figs. G.18, G.20, G.21).

Stilt roots—oblique, lateral roots, often large as in *Socratea* (Fig. G.3), also called prop roots.

Striate—lined (Figs. G.4, G.20, G.23).

Style—the often attenuate part of a carpel or gynoecium between the ovary and the stigma (Figs. G.18, G.20).

Sub—as a prefix, meaning nearly or almost, e.g. subopposite—nearly opposite (Fig. G.13).

Subulate—awl-shaped (Fig. G.20).

Sulcate—grooved or furrowed (G.23, *Podococcus* fruit).

Sympodial—a stem made of superposed branches, lacking a single main axis (see Fig. I.6 for sympodial flower clusters).

Syncarpous—with united carpels (Fig. G.20).

Terete—circular in cross section, usually cylindrical.

Testa—the outer coat of the seed.

Thecae—the locules of an anther (Fig. G.19).

Tomentose—densely covered with short hairs, scales, wool, or down.

Triad—a special group of 2 lateral staminate and a central pistillate flower, structurally a short cincinnus (Figs. G.18, I.6).

Trijugate—bearing 3 pairs of leaflets (Fig. G.13).

Trilocular—having 3 chambers, each usually bearing an ovule or seed (Figs. G.20, G.23).

Triovulate—gynoecium with 3 ovules, one in the locule of each carpel (Fig. G.20).

Truncate—as though cut off nearly straight across (Fig. G.15).

Tubercles—short stout, persistent floral stalks, appearing as small humps in coryphoid palms.

Undulate—waved (Fig. G.15).

Unilocular—with a single cavity (Fig. G.20).

Uniovulate—with a single ovule (Fig. G.20).

Valvate—meeting exactly without overlapping, cf. "imbricate" (Figs. G.19, G.20).

Ventricose—swollen (Fig. G.3).

Versatile—of anthers, attached near the center and movable on the filament (Fig. G.19).

Whip—a climbing organ in some Calamoideae, general term for cirrus and flagellum (Fig. G.6).

Pollen terms

Adapted from Kremp (1965), as used by Thanikaimoni (1971) but with some modification.

annulosulcate: with an encircling sulcus.

areolate: with small circular or polygonal areas separated by grooves, forming a network.

baculate: bearing baculae or rodlike excrescences.

clavate: bearing club-shaped excrescences (Figs. I.7C, I.8G, I.9H).

diporate: with two rounded apertures (Fig. I.8C).

disulcate: with two sulci (Fig. I.7D, E).

echinate: bearing spinelike excrescences.

exine: the outer, resistant layer of the pollen wall.

fossulate: with scattered elongate depressions.

foveate: with small round depressions.

foveolate: provided with small pits.

gemmate: bearing excrescences with basal constrictions.

intectate: single walled (of pollen grains) (Fig. I.7C).

meridionosulcate: with an encircling sulcus (Figs. I.7G, I.8B, I.9E).

monoporate: with a single rounded aperture (Fig. I.7C, H).

monosulcate: with one sulcus (Figs. I.7F, J, M, I.8A, D, E, G, I.9A–D, F, H).

perforate: pierced with holes (Fig. I.8B–D).

pontoperculate: monosulcate but with an operculum, the extremities of which merge with the surrounding exine (Fig. I.8F).

punctate: minutely dotted.

reticulate: consisting of a network enclosing small, often ± irregular spaces (Figs. I.7B, I.9A).

rugulate: irregularly sculptured with elongate elements (Fig. I.7E).

scabrate: flecked with minute projections (Fig. I.8H).

scrobiculate: marked by minute pits or depressions.

sulcus: furrowlike aperture of a pollen grain.

supratectal: referring to emergences on pollen grains borne on the outer wall of the exine (Fig. I.8B).

tectate: two-walled (of pollen grains) (Fig. I.7A).

tetrachotomosulcate: with a four-slit aperture.

trichotomosulcate: with a three-slit aperture (Figs. I.7K, I.9G).

triporate: with three rounded apertures (Fig. I.7L).

urceolate: bearing urnlike emergences (Fig. I.9D).

vermiculate: bearing grooves like wormtracks.

verrucate: bearing broad, rather large, isodiametric excrescences (Fig. I.8A).

LITERATURE CITED

ACHILLI, J. 1913. Contribution à l'étude anatomique des Dypsidées de Madagascar. Ann. Inst. Bot.-Géol. Colon. Marseille, sér. 3, 1:99–147.

AINSLIE, J. R. 1926. The physiography of Southern Nigeria and its effect on the forest flora of the country. Oxford Forest. Mem. 5:1–36.

ALLEN, P. H. 1953. Two new fan palms from Central America. Ceiba 3:173–178.

———. 1956. The Rain Forests of Golfo Dulce. Univ. of Florida Press, Gainesville.

———. 1965. Rain forest palms of Golfo Dulce. Principes 9(2): 48–62.

AMBWANI, K. 1981. *Palmoxylon arviensis* sp. nov. from the Deccan Intertrappean beds of Nawargaon, Wardha District, Maharashtra. Palaeobotanist 27:132–137.

ANDERSON, A. B. 1985. Productivity of a forest-dominant palm (*Orbignya phalerata* Mart.) in Brazil. Abstracts, Association for Tropical Biology Meetings, 1985:38.

——— AND M. J. BALICK. Taxonomy of the babassu palm complex (*Orbignya* spp.: Palmae). Syst. Bot. (in press).

———, W. I. OVERAL, AND A. HENDERSON. Pollination ecology of a forest-dominant palm (*Orbignya phalerata* Mart.) in northern Brazil. Biotropica (in press).

ANDERSON, R. AND S. MORI. 1967. A preliminary investigation of *Raphia* palm swamps, Puerto Viejo, Costa Rica. Turrialba 17:221–224.

ANDERSON, T. 1869. An enumeration of the palms of Sikkim. J. Linn. Soc., Bot. 11(49):4–14.

ARGUIJO, M. H. 1979. *Palmoxylon bororoense,* n. sp. de la formación Cerro Bororó (Paleoceno), Provincia de Chubut, Republica Argentina. Physis 38:87–96.

ARYAVAND, A. 1977. *In* IOPB Chromosome number reports LVII. Taxon 26(4):443–452.

AUDLEY-CHARLES, M. G. (in press). Dispersal of Gondwanaland: relevance to evolution of the angiosperms. Proceedings of Symposium on Wallace's Line, ICSEB III.

———, A. M. HARLEY, AND A. G. SMITH. 1981. Continental movements in the Mesozoic and Cenozoic. Pages 9–23 *in* T. C. Whitmore (ed.). Wallace's Line and Plate Tectonics. Oxford Univ. Press, London.

AXELROD, D. I. 1950. Evolution of desert vegetation. Publ. Carnegie Inst. Washington 590:215–306.

BAILEY, L. H. 1933. Certain palms of Panama. Gentes Herb. 3(2):33–116.

———. 1934. American palmettoes. Gentes Herb. 3(6):274–339.

———. 1935a. The royal palms—preliminary survey. Gentes Herb. 3(7):343–387.

———. 1935b. The king palms of Australia—*Archontophoenix.* Gentes Herb. 3(8):389–409.

———. 1935c. Certain ptychosperma palms of horticulturists. Gentes Herb. 3(8):410–437.

———. 1936. *Washingtonia.* Gentes Herb. 4(2):53–82.

———. 1937a. *Erythea*—the Hesper Palms. Gentes Herb. 4(3): 85–118.

———. 1937b. Notes on *Brahea.* Gentes Herb. 4(3):119–125.

———. 1939a. *Howea* in cultivation—the Sentry Palms. Gentes Herb. 4(6):188–198.

———. 1939b. New Haitian genus of palms. Gentes Herb. 4(7): 239–246.

———. 1940a. The problem of *Colpothrinax.* Gentes Herb. 4(10):357–360.

———. 1940b. *Acoelorraphe* vs. *Paurotis*—Silver-saw palm. Gentes Herb. 4(10):361–365.

———. 1940c. The generic name *Corozo.* Gentes Herb. 4(10): 373–374.

———. 1941. *Acrocomia*—preliminary paper. Gentes Herb. 4(12):421–476.

———. 1942. Palms of the Seychelles Islands. Gentes Herb. 6(1):3–48.

———. 1944. Revision of the American palmettoes. Gentes Herb. 6(7):367–459.

——— AND H. E. MOORE, JR. 1949. Palms uncertain and new. Gentes Herb. 8(2):93–205.

BAKER, R. F. 1980. An inventory of palms in Hawaii. Principes 24(2):55–64.

BALICK, M. J. 1980. The biology and economics of the *Oenocarpus–Jessenia* (Palmae) complex. Ph.D. Thesis. Harvard University, Cambridge, MA.

———. 1981. *Mauritiella* (Palmae) reconsidered. Brittonia 33(3): 459–460.

———. 1985. The indigenous palm flora of "Las Gaviotas," Colombia, including observations on local names and uses. Bot. Mus. Leaflets, Harvard Univ. 30(3):1–34.

———. 1986. Systematics and economic botany of the *Oenocarpus-Jessenia* (Palmae) complex. Advances in Economic Botany 3:1–140.

——— AND S. N. GERSHOFF. 1981. Nutritional evaluation of the *Jessenia batua* palm: source of high quality protein and oil from tropical America. Econ. Bot. 35:261–271.

BALICK, M. J., C. U. B. PINHEIRO, AND A. B. ANDERSON. 1987a. Hybridization in the babassu palm complex. I. *Orbignya phalerata* × *O. eichleri.* Amer. J. Bot. 74:1013–1032.

———, A. B. ANDERSON, AND J. T. DE MEDEIROS-COSTA. 1987b. Hybridization in the babassu palm complex. II. *Attalea compta* Mart. × *Orbignya oleifera* Burret. Brittonia 39(1): 26–36.

BALL, O. M. 1931. A contribution to the paleobotany of the Eocene of Texas. Bull. Agr. Mech. Coll. Texas, ser. 4, 2(5): 1–173.

BALSLEV, H. AND A. HENDERSON. 1987. The identity of *Ynesa colenda* O. F. Cook (Palmae). Brittonia 39(1):1–6.

——— AND A. HENDERSON. A new *Ammandra* (Palmae) from Ecuador. Syst. Bot. (in press).

BARBOSA RODRIGUES, J. 1903. Sertum Palmarum Brasiliensium. 2 vols. Veuve Monnom, Brussels.

BARRY, D., JR. 1962. The possibility of mycorrhizae in palms. Principes 6(3):87–90.

BARTLETT, H. H. 1935. Various Palmae. Corypheae of Central America and Mexico. Publ. Carnegie Inst. Wash. 461:27–41.

BEACH, J. H. 1984. The reproductive biology of the Peach or "Pejibaye" Palm (*Bactris gasipaes*) and a wild congener (*B. porschiana*) in the Atlantic lowlands of Costa Rica. Principes 28(3):107–119.

BEAL, J. M. 1937. Cytological studies in the genus *Phoenix.* Bot. Gaz. 99:400–407.

BECCARI, O. 1877. Le specie di palme raccolte alla Nuova Guinea da O. Beccari e dal medesimo adesso descritte, con note sulle specie dei paesi circonvicini. Malesia 1:9–102.

————. 1885. Reliquiae Schefferianae. Illustrazione di alcune palme viventi nel Giardino Botanico di Buitenzorg. Ann. Jard. Bot. Buitenzorg 2:77–171.

————. 1886. Nuovi studi sulle palme asiatiche. Malesia 3:58–149.

————. 1890. Rivista monografica delle specie del genere *Phoenix* Linn. Malesia 3:345–416.

————. 1908. Asiatic palms—Lepidocaryeae. Part I. The species of *Calamus*. Ann. Roy. Bot. Gard. (Calcutta) 11:1–518.

————. 1910a. Studio monografico del genere *Raphia*. Webbia 3:37–130.

————. 1910b. Contributo alla conoscenza delle "Lepidocaryeae" affricane. Webbia 3:247–294.

————. 1911. Asiatic palms—Lepidocaryeae. Part II. The species of *Daemonorops*. Ann. Roy. Bot. Gard. (Calcutta) 12(1):1–237.

————. 1912. The palms indigenous to Cuba I. Pom. Coll. J. Econ. Bot. 2(2):253–276.

————. 1913a. Contributi alla conoscenza delle palme. Webbia 4:143–240.

————. 1913b. Asiatic palms—Lepidocaryeae. Supplement to Part I. The species of *Calamus*. Ann. Roy. Bot. Gard. (Calcutta) 11(App.):1–142.

————. 1914a. Palme del Madagascar. Istituto Micrografico Italiano, Firenze, 59 pp.

————. 1914b. Contributo alla conoscenza della palma a olio (*Elaeis guineensis*). Agric. Colon. 8(1):5–37, 108–118, 201–212, 255–270.

————. 1916. Il genera *Cocos* Linn. e le palme affine. Agric. Colon, 10(2):435–471, 489–532, 585–623.

————. 1918. Asiatic palms—Lepidocaryeae. Part III. Ann. Roy. Bot. Gard. (Calcutta) 12(2):1–231.

————. 1920. Le Palme della Nuova Caledonia. M. Ricci, Firenze. Preprinted from Webbia 5:71–146. 1921.

————. 1924. Palme della Tribù Borasseae (*ed*. U. Martelli). G. Passeri, Firenze.

————. 1931. Asiatic palms—Corypheae (*ed*. U. Martelli). Ann. Roy. Bot. Gard. (Calcutta) 13:1–356.

———— AND R. G. PICHI-SERMOLLI. 1955. Subfamiliae Arecoidearum palmae gerontogeae tribuum et generum conspectus. Webbia 11:1–187.

———— AND J. F. ROCK. 1921. A monographic study of the genus *Pritchardia*. Mem. Bernice Pauahi Bishop Mus. 8(1):1–77.

BERNAL-GONZALEZ, R. AND A. HENDERSON. 1986. A new species of *Socratea* (Palmae) from Colombia with notes on the genus. Brittonia 38:55–59.

BERRY, E. W. 1911. Contributions to the Mesozoic flora of the Atlantic Coastal Plain VII. Bull. Torrey Bot. Club 38:399–424.

————. 1914. Fruits of a date palm in the Tertiary deposits of eastern Texas. Amer. J. Sci. 187:403–406.

————. 1916. Lower Eocene floras of southeastern North America. U.S. Geol. Surv. Profess. Paper 91:1–481.

————. 1921a. A palm nut from the Miocene of the Canal Zone. Proc. U.S. Natl. Mus. 59:21–22.

————. 1921b. Tertiary fossil plants from Venezuela. Proc. U.S. Natl. Mus. 59:553–579.

————. 1926. *Cocos* and *Phymatocaryon* in the Pliocene of New Zealand. Amer. J. Sci. 212:181–184.

————. 1929. A palm nut of *Attalea* from the Upper Eocene of Florida. J. Wash. Acad. Sci. 19:252–255.

————. 1937. *Gyrocarpus* and other fossil plants from the Cumarebo field in Venezuela. J. Wash. Acad. Sci. 27:501–506.

BOMHARD, M. L. 1937. The wax palms. Annual Rep. Board of Regents Smithsonian Inst. 1936:303–324.

BORHIDI, A. AND O. MUÑIZ. 1985. Adiciones al catálogo de las palmas de Cuba. Acta Botanica Hungarica 31(1-4):225–230.

BOSCH, E. 1947. Blutenmorphologische und zytologische Untersuchungen an Palmen. Ber. Schweiz. Bot. Ges. 57:37–100.

BOUILLENNE, R. 1930. Un voyage botanique dans le bas-Amazone. Arch. Inst. Bot. Univ. Liège 8:1–185.

BOULOS, L. 1968. The discovery of *Medemia* palm in the Nubian Desert of Egypt. Bot. Not. 121:117–120.

BOUREAU, E. AND U. PRAKASH. 1968. Sur un pétiole fossile de palmier de Tiemassas (Sénégal) et sur son mode d'acroissement diamétral. Palaeobotanist 17(3):247–253.

BOYD, L. 1932. Monocotylous seedlings: morphological studies in the post-seminal development of the embryo. Trans. and Proc. Bot. Soc. Edinburgh 31:1–224.

BROWN, K. E. 1976. Ecological studies of the Cabbage Palm, *Sabal palmetto*. Principes 20(1):3–10.

BROWN, R. W. 1956a. Palmlike plants from the Dolores Formation (Triassic) Southwestern Colorado. U.S. Geol. Surv. Profess. Paper 274H:205–209.

————. 1956b. Ivory-nut palm from late Tertiary of Ecuador. Science 123:1131–1132.

BROWN, W. H. AND E. D. MERRILL. 1919. Philippine palms and palm products. Bull. Bur. Forest. Philipp. Islands, No. 18. Manila.

BUCKLEY, R. AND H. HARRIES. 1984. Self-sown wild-type coconuts from Australia. Biotropica 16(2):148–151.

BULLOCK, S. 1980. Demography of an undergrowth palm in littoral Cameroon. Biotropica 12:247–255.

BURKILL, I. H. 1966. A Dictionary of the Economic Products of the Malay Peninsula. 2nd Ed., Vol. II. Ministry of Agriculture and Cooperatives, Kuala Lumpur, Malaysia.

BURRET, M. 1927. Eine neue Palmengattung von den Molukken. Notizbl. Bot. Gart. Berlin-Dahlem 10:198–201.

————. 1928a. Beitrage zur Kenntnis der Palmen von Malesia, Papua und der Sudsee. Repert. Spec. Nov. Regni Veg. 24:253–296.

————. 1928b. Die Palmengattung *Manicara* Gaertn. Notizbl. Bot. Gart. Berlin-Dahlem 10:389–394.

————. 1929a. Die Gattung *Ceroxylon* Humb. et Bonpl. Notizbl. Bot. Gart. Berlin-Dahlem 10:841–854.

————. 1929b. Die Gattung *Euterpe* Gaertn. Bot. Jahrb. Syst. 63:49–76.

————. 1929c. Die Gattung *Hyospathe* Mart. Notizbl. Bot. Gart. Berlin-Dahlem 10:854–859.

————. 1930a. Geonomae americanae. Bot. Jahrb. Syst. 63:123–270.

————. 1930b. Iriarteae. Notizbl. Bot. Gard. Berlin-Dahlem 10:918–942.

————. 1932a. Die Palmengattungen *Kajewskia* Guillaumin und *Carpoxylon* H. Wendl. et Drude von der Insel Aneityum (Neu-Hebriden). Notizbl. Bot. Gart. Berlin-Dahlem 11:38.

————. 1932b. Die Palmengattungen *Martinezia* und *Aiphanes*. Notizbl. Bot. Gart. Berlin-Dahlem 11:557–577.

————. 1933a. *Chamaedorea* Willd. und verwandte Palmengattungen. Notizbl. Bot. Gart. Berlin-Dahlem 11:724–768.

————. 1933b. *Schippia*, eine neue Palmengattung aus Brit. Honduras. Notizbl. Bot. Gart. Berlin-Dahlem 11:867–869.

————. 1933c. *Bactris* und verwandte Palmengattungen. Repert. Spec. Nov. Regni Veg. 34:167–184.

————. 1934a. *Bactris* und verwandte Palmengattungen. Repert. Spec. Nov. Regni Veg. 34:186–253.

————. 1934b. Die Palmengattung *Astrocaryum* G. F. W. Meyer. Repert. Spec. Nov. Regni Veg. 35:114–158.

————. 1935a. Neue Palmen aus Neuguinea II. Notizbl. Bot. Gart. Berlin-Dahlem 12:309–348.

————. 1935b. New Palms from Fiji. Occas. Pap. Bernice Pauahi Bishop Mus. 11(4):1–14.

————. 1936a. Die Palmengattung *Gronophyllum* Scheff. Notizbl. Bot. Gart. Berlin-Dahlem 13:200–205.

————. 1936b. Die Palmengattungen *Nengella* Becc. und *Leptophoenix* Becc. Notizbl. Bot. Gart. Berlin-Dahlem 13:312–317.

————. 1937a. Die Palmengattungen *Hydriastele* Wendl. et Drude und *Adelonenga* Becc. Notizbl. Bot. Gart. Berlin-Dahlem 13:482–487.

————. 1937b. Palmae chinenses. Notizbl. Bot. Gart. Berlin-Dahlem 13:582–606.

————. 1940. Palmen und Tiliaceen von der Sudsee aus der Sammlung des Bernice P. Bishop Museums, Honolulu, Hawaii. Notizbl. Bot. Gart. Berlin-Dahlem 15:85–96.

————. 1941. Die Palmengattung *Tessmanniodoxa* gen. nov. Notizbl. Bot. Gart. Berlin-Dahlem 15:336–338.

————. 1942. Neue Palmen aus der Gruppe der Lepidocaryoideae. Notizbl. Bot. Gart. Berlin-Dahlem 15:728–755.

———— AND E. POTZTAL. 1956. Systematische Übersicht über die Palmen (Fortsetzung). Willdenowia 1:350–385.

BURTT, B. D. 1929. A record of fruits and seeds dispersed by mammals and birds from the Singida District of Tanganyika Territory. J. Ecol. 18:351–355.

BŮŽEK, C. 1977. Date-palm seeds from the Lower Miocene of Central Europe. Věstn. Ústředního Ústavu Geol. 52:159–168.

CARDENAS, M. 1970. Palm forests of the Bolivian High Andes. Principes 14(2):50–54.

CHANDLER, M. E. J. 1961–64. The Lower Tertiary Floras of Southern England. 4 vols. Brit. Mus. (Nat. Hist.), London.

————. 1978. Supplement to the Lower Tertiary Floras of Southern England. Part 5. Tertiary Research Special Paper #4. The Tertiary Research Group, London.

CHAZDON, R. 1986. Physiological and morphological basis of shade tolerance in rain forest understory palms. Principes 30(3):92–99.

CHEADLE, V. I. 1943. Vessel specialization in the late metaxylem of the various organs in the Monocotyledoneae. Amer. J. Bot. 30:484–490.

————. 1944. Specialization of vessels within the xylem of each organ in the Monocotyledoneae. Amer. J. Bot. 31:81–92.

————. 1948. Observations on the phloem in the Monocotyledoneae. II. Additional data on the occurrence and phylogenetic specialization in structure of the sieve tubes in the metaphloem. Amer. J. Bot. 35:129–131.

———— AND N. B. WHITFORD. 1941. Observations on the phloem in the Monocotyledoneae. I. The occurrence and phylogenetic specialization in structure of the sieve tubes in the metaphloem. Amer. J. Bot. 28:623–627.

CHENNAVEERAIAH, M. S. 1981. The palms. Palaeobotanist 27(3):314–331.

CHILD, R. 1974. Coconuts. 2nd Ed. Longmans, Green and Co., Ltd., London.

CLEMENT, C. R. AND J. M. URPI. 1983. Leaf morphology of the Pejibaye palm (*Bactris gasipaes* H.B.K.) Rev. Biol. Trop. 31(1):103–112.

CONWENTZ, H. 1886. Die Flora des Bernsteins 2. Danzig, Germany.

COOK, O. F. 1915a. A new genus of palms allied to *Archontophoenix*. J. Wash. Acad. Sci. 5:116–122.

————. 1915b. *Glaucothea*, a new genus of palms from Lower California. J. Wash. Acad. Sci. 5:236–241.

————. 1926. A new genus of palms based on *Kentia forsteriana*. J. Wash. Acad. Sci. 16:392–397.

————. 1927. New genera and species of ivory palms from Colombia, Ecuador and Peru. J. Wash. Acad. Sci. 17:218–230.

———— AND C. B. DOYLE. 1913. Three new genera of stilt palms (Iriarteaceae) from Colombia with a synoptical review of the family. Contr. U.S. Natl. Herb. 16:225–238.

CORNER, E. J. H. 1966. The Natural History of Palms. Weidenfeld and Nicolson, London.

CORNETT, J. W. 1985a. Germination of *Washingtonia filifera* seeds eaten by coyotes. Principes 29(1):19.

————. 1985b. Reading the fan palms. Natural History: 94(10):64–73.

COUPER, R. A. 1952. The spore and pollen flora of the *Cocos*-bearing beds, Mangonui, North Auckland. Trans. Roy. Soc. New Zealand, Bot. 79:340–348.

CRANWELL, L. M., H. J. CARRINGTON, AND I. G. SPEDEN. 1960. Lower Tertiary microfossils from McMurdo Sound, Antarctica. Nature 186:700–702.

CRONQUIST, A. 1981. An Integrated System of Classification of Flowering Plants. Columbia Univ. Press, New York.

CZECZOTT, O. H. AND K. JUCHNIEWICZ. 1980. Palmae (II). Flora Kopalna Turowa Kolo Bogatyni II(5):23–29. Prace Muzeum Ziemi z. 33, Warszawa.

DAGHLIAN, C. P. 1978. Coryphoid palms from the Lower and Middle Eocene of southeastern North America. Palaeontographica Abt. B 166:44–82.

————. 1981. A review of the fossil record of monocotyledons. Bot. Rev. 47:517–555.

DAHLGREN, B. E. AND S. F. GLASSMAN. 1961. A revision of the genus *Copernicia* 1. South American species. Gentes Herb. 9(1):3–40.

———— AND ————. 1963. A revision of the genus *Copernicia* 2. West Indian species. Gentes Herb. 9(2):43–232.

DAHLGREN, R. M. T. AND H. T. CLIFFORD. 1982. The Monocotyledons: A Comparative Study. Academic Press, New York.

————, ————, AND P. F. YEO. 1985. The Families of the Monocotyledons. Springer Verlag, Berlin.

DAMIANI, A. 1929. Recherches anatomiques sur les feuilles de *Vonitra* et le piassava de Madagascar. Ann. Inst. Bot.-Géol. Colon. Marseille, sér. 4, 7(2):5–28.

DAMMER, U. 1905. Zwei neue Amerikanische Palmen. Bot. Jahrb. Syst. 36, Beibl. 80:31–32.

DELPINO, F. 1870. Ulteriori osservazioni e considerazioni sulla dicogamia nel regno vegetale. Atti. Soc. Ital. Sci. Nat. 13:167–205.

DE MASON, P., K. W. STOLTE, AND B. TISSERAT. 1982. Floral development in *Phoenix dactylifera*. Can. J. Bot. 60(8):1437–1446.

DENGLER, N. R., R. E. DENGLER, AND D. R. KAPLAN. 1982. The mechanism of plication inception in palm leaves: histogenetic observations on the pinnate leaf of *Chrysalidocarpus lutescens*. Can. J. Bot. 60:2976–2998.

DE STEVEN, D. 1986. Comparative demography of a clonal palm (*Oenocarpus panamanus*). Principes 30(3):100–104.

—— AND F. E. PUTZ. 1985. Mortality rates of some rain forest palms in Panama. Principes 29(4):162–165.

—— AND ——. (in press). Vegetative and reproductive phenologies of a palm assemblage in Panama. Biotropica.

DIETZ, R. S. AND J. C. HOLDEN. 1970. The breakup of Pangaea. Sci. Amer. 223(4):30–41.

DRANSFIELD, J. 1970. Studies in the Malayan palms *Eugeissona* and *Johannesteijsmannia*. Ph.D. Thesis. University of Cambridge.

——. 1972a. The genus *Borassodendron* (Palmae) in Malesia. Reinwardtia 8:351–363.

——. 1972b. The genus *Johannesteijsmannia* H. E. Moore Jr. Gard. Bull., Singapore 26:63–83.

——. 1973. Notes on the palm flora of central Sumatra. Reinwardtia 8:519–531.

——. 1974. Notes on *Caryota no* Becc. and other Malesian *Caryota* species. Principes 18(3):87–93.

——. 1976a. Terminal flowering in *Daemonorops*. Principes 20(1):29–32.

——. 1976b. A note on the habitat of *Pigafetta filaris* in North Celebes. Principes 20(2):48.

——. 1978a. The genus *Maxburretia* (Palmae). Gentes Herb. 11(4):187–199.

——. 1978b. Growth forms of rain forest palms. Pages 247–268 *in* P. B. Tomlinson and M. H. Zimmermann (*eds.*). Tropical Trees as Living Systems. Cambridge University Press, New York.

——. 1979a. A Manual of the Rattans of the Malay Peninsula. Malaysian Forest Records No. 29. Forest Dept., Kuala Lumpur, Malaysia.

——. 1979b. A monograph of the genus *Ceratolobus* (Palmae). Kew Bull. 34:1–33.

——. 1979c. *Retispatha*, a new Bornean rattan genus (Palmae: Lepidocaryoideae). Kew Bull. 34:529–536.

——. 1980a. *Pogonotium* (Palmae: Lepidocaryoideae), a new genus related to *Daemonorops*. Kew Bull. 34:761–768.

——. 1980b. Systematic notes on *Pinanga* (Palmae) in Borneo. Kew Bull. 34:769–788.

——. 1981a. A synopsis of *Korthalsia* (Palmae-Lepidocaryoideae). Kew Bull. 36:163–194.

——. 1981b. Palms and Wallace's Line. Pages 43–56 *in* T. C. Whitmore (*ed.*). Wallace's Line and Plate Tectonics. Oxford University Press, London.

——. 1981c. A house in Thailand. Principes 25(1):36–38.

——. 1982a. A day on the Klingkang Range. Principes 26(1):19–33.

——. 1982b. *Clinostigma* in New Ireland. Principes 26(2):73–76.

——. 1982c. A reassessment of the genera *Plectocomiopsis*, *Myrialepis* and *Bejaudia* (Palmae: Lepidocaryoideae). Kew Bull. 37:237–254.

——. 1982d. Nomenclatural notes on *Laccosperma* and *Ancistrophyllum*. (Palmae: Lepidocaryoideae). Kew Bull. 37:455–457.

——. 1982e. *Pinanga cleistantha*, a new species with hidden flowers. Principes 26(3):126–129.

——. 1982f. *Pogonotium moorei*, a new species from Sarawak. Principes 26(4):174–177.

——. 1983. *Kerriodoxa*, a new coryphoid palm genus from Thailand. Principes 27(1):3–11.

——. 1984a. The Rattans of Sabah. Sabah Forest Records No. 13. Forest Department, Sabah.

——. 1984b. The palm flora of Gunung Mulu National Park. Pages 41–75 *in* A. C. Jermy (*ed.*). Studies on the Flora of Gunung Mulu National Park, Sarawak. Forest Department, Kuching, Sarawak.

——. 1984c. The genus *Areca* (Palmae: Arecoideae) in Borneo. Kew. Bull. 39:1–22.

——. 1986. Palmae. Flora of Tropical East Africa. A. A. Balkema, Rotterdam.

——, I. K. FERGUSON, AND N. W. UHL. 1987. The coryphoid palms: patterns of variation and evolution. Ann. Missouri Bot. Gard. (in press).

——, J. R. FLENLEY, S. M. KING, D. D. HARKNESS, AND S. RAPU. 1984. A recently extinct palm from Easter Island. Nature 312(5596):750–752.

——, A. K. IRVINE, AND N. W. UHL. 1985a. *Oraniopsis appendiculata*, a previously misunderstood Queensland palm. Principes 29(2):56–63.

——, S. K. LEE, AND F. N. WEI. 1985b. *Guihaia*, a new coryphoid genus from China and Vietnam. Principes 29(1):3–12.

—— AND J. P. MOGEA. 1984. The flowering behaviour of Arenga (Palmae: Caryotoideae). Bot. J. Linn. Soc. 88:1–10.

—— AND H. E. MOORE, JR. 1982. The Martian Correlation—two editions of Martius' Historia Naturalis Palmarum compared. Kew Bull. 37:91–110.

—— AND N. W. UHL. 1983a. The transfer of *Livistona kingiana* (Palmae) to *Pholidocarpus*. Kew Bull. 38:197–198.

—— AND N. W. UHL. 1983b. *Wissmannia* (Palmae) reduced to *Livistona*. Kew Bull. 38:199–200.

—— AND N. W. UHL. 1984a. A magnificent new palm from Madagascar. Principes 28(4):151–154.

—— AND N. W. UHL. 1984b. *Halmoorea*, a new genus from Madagascar, with notes on *Sindroa* and *Orania*. Principes 28(4):163–167.

—— AND N. W. UHL. 1986. An outline of a classification of palms. Principes 30(1):3–11.

DRUDE, O. 1882. Palmae. Pages 253–583 *in* K. F. P. v. Martius. Flora Brasiliensis 3(2).

——. 1887. Palmae. Pages 1–93 *in* A. Engler and K. Prantl. Die Natürlichen Pflanzenfamilien 2(3).

DUGAND, A. 1961. Palms of Colombia. Principes 5(4):135–144.

——. 1974. Letter to the editor. Principes 18(2):59.

EAMES, A. J. 1961. Morphology of the Angiosperms. McGraw Hill, New York.

EICHHORN, A. 1953. Étude caryologique des Palmiers. I. Rév. Cyt. et. Biol. Vég. 14:13–30.

——. 1957. Nouvelle contribution à l'étude caryoligique des Palmiers. Rév. Cyt. et Biol. Vég. 18(2):139–151.

EITEN, G. 1972. The cerrado vegetation of Brazil. Bot. Rev. 38:201–341.

ELIAS DE PAULA, J. 1975. Anatomia de *Euterpe oleracea* Mart. Acta Amazonica 5(3):265–278.

ENGELHARDT, H. 1891. Uber Tertiärpflanzen von Chile. Abh. Senckenberg Naturforsch. Gesellsch. 16:629–692.

ESSIG, F. B. 1970. New chromosome counts in *Chamaedorea* (Palmae). Principes 14(4):136–137.

——. 1971a. Observations on pollination in *Bactris*. Principes 15(1):20–24, 35.

————. 1971b. New chromosome counts. Principes 15(4):126.

————. 1973. Pollination in some New Guinea palms. Principes 17(3):75–83.

————. 1975a. *Brassiophoenix schumannii* (Palmae). Principes 19(3):100–103.

————. 1975b. A systematic study of the genus *Ptychosperma* (Palmae). Ph.D. Thesis, Cornell University.

————. 1977a. A preliminary analysis of the palm flora of New Guinea and the Bismarck Archipelago. Papua New Guinea Botany Bulletin No. 9.

————. 1977b. A systematic histological study of palm fruits. I. The *Ptychosperma* alliance. Syst. Bot. 2:151–168.

————. 1978. A revision of the genus *Ptychosperma*. Allertonia 1:415–478.

————. 1980. The genus *Orania* in New Guinea. Lyonia 1(5): 211–233.

————. 1982. A synopsis of the genus *Gulubia*. Principes 26(4): 159–173.

———— AND B. E. YOUNG. 1979. A systematic histological study of palm fruits. II. The *Areca* alliance. Syst. Bot. 4:16–28.

———— AND B. E. YOUNG. 1985. A reconsideration of *Gronophyllum* and *Nengella* (Arecoideae). Principes 29(3):129–137.

FERGUSON, I. K. 1987. Observations on the variation in pollen morphology of Palmae and its significance. Can. J. Bot. 64: 3079–3090.

————, J. DRANSFIELD, F. C. PAGE, AND G. THANIKAIMONI. 1983. Notes on the pollen morphology of *Pinanga* with special reference to *P. aristata* and *P. pilosa* (Palmae: Arecoideae). Grana 22: 65–72.

FERNANDO, E. S. 1983. A revision of the genus *Nenga*. Principes 27(2):55–70.

FISHER, J. B. 1973. Unusual branch development in the palm, *Chrysalidocarpus*. J. Linn. Soc., Bot. 66:83–95.

————. 1974. Axillary and dichotomous branching in the palm *Chamaedorea*. Amer. J. Bot. 61:1046–1056.

————. 1985. Palmae (Arecaceae). *In* A. H. Halevy (*ed.*). CRC Handbook of Flowering. Vol. 1:337–354. CRC Press, Boca Raton, Florida.

———— AND J. DRANSFIELD. 1977. Comparative morphology and development of inflorescence adnation in rattan palms. J. Linn. Soc., Bot. 75:119–140.

———— AND J. P. MOGEA. 1980. Intrapetiolar inflorescence buds in *Salacca* (Palmae): development and significance. J. Linn. Soc., Bot. 81:47–59.

———— AND H. E. MOORE, JR. 1977. Multiple inflorescences in palms (Arecaceae): their development and significance. Bot. Jahrb. Syst. 98:573–611.

———— AND P. B. TOMLINSON. 1973. Branch and inflorescence production in saw palmetto (*Serenoa repens*). Principes 17(1): 10–19.

FLICHE, P. 1896. Études sur la flore fossile de l'Argonne Albien-Cenomanien. Bull. Soc. Sci. Nancy, sér. 2, 14:114–306.

FOX, J. J. 1977. Harvest of the Palm; Ecological Change in Eastern Indonesia. Harvard Univ. Press, Cambridge, Massachusetts.

FREDERIKSEN, N. O., V. D. WIGGINS, I. K. FERGUSON, J. DRANSFIELD, AND C. M. AGER. 1985. Distribution, paleoecology, paleoclimatology and botanical affinity of the Eocene pollen genus *Diporoconia* n. gen. Palynology 9:37–60.

FRENCH, J. C., K. CLANCY, AND P. B. TOMLINSON. 1983. Vascular patterns in stems of the Cyclanthaceae. Amer. J. Bot. 70(9):1386–1400.

FURLEY, P. A. 1975. The significance of the Cohune palm *Orbignya cohune* (Mart.) Dahlgren on the nature and in the development of the soil profile. Biotropica 7:32–36.

FURTADO, C. X. 1933. The limits of *Areca* L. and its sections. Repert. Spec. Nov. Regni Veg. 33:217–239.

————. 1934. Palmae Malesicae. Repert. Spec. Nov. Regni Veg. 35:18–25.

————. 1940. Palmae Malesicae VIII—The genus *Licuala* in the Malay Peninsula. Gard. Bull. Straits Settlem. 11:31–73.

————. 1949. Palmae Malesicae X. The Malayan species of *Salacca*. Gard. Bull. Singapore 12:378–403.

————. 1953. The genus *Daemonorops* in Malaya. Gard. Bull. Singapore 14:49–147.

GALEANO-GARCES, G. 1986. Two new species of Palmae from Colombia. Brittonia 38:60–64.

———— AND R. BERNAL-GONZALEZ. 1982. Two new species of *Ceroxylon* from Colombia. Principes 26(4):178–181.

———— AND ————. 1983. Novedades de las Palmas de Colombia. Caldasia XIII(65):693–699.

GAMBLE, J. S. 1935. Flora of the Presidency of Madras. Botanical Survey of India, Calcutta 3:1085–1086.

GASSNER, G. G. 1941. Über Bau der männlichen Blüten und Pollenentwicklung einiger Palmen der Unterfamilie der Ceroxylinae. Beih. Bot. Centralbl. 61A:237–276.

GILLETT, G. W. 1971. *Pelagodoxa* in the Marquesas Islands. Principes 15(2):45–48.

GINIEIS, C. 1960. Structure de la feuille d'un Palmier-liane: l'*Ancistrophyllum secundiflorum* Wendl. Bulletin de l'I.F.A.N.T XXII ser. A, No 3:730–742.

GISEKE, P. D. 1792. Palmae. Pages 21–122 *in* C. Linnaeus. Praelectiones in Ordines Naturales. B. G. Hoffmann, Hamburg.

GLASSMAN, S. F. 1972. A revision of B. E. Dahlgren's index of American palms. Phanerogamarum Monographiae, Tomus VI. Cramer, Germany.

————. 1977a. Preliminary taxonomic studies in the palm genus *Attalea* H.B.K. Fieldiana, Bot. 38:31–61.

————. 1977b. Preliminary taxonomic studies in the palm genus *Orbignya* Mart. Phytologia 36:89–115.

————. 1977c. Preliminary taxonomic studies in the palm genus *Scheelea* Karsten. Phytologia 37(3):219–250.

————. 1978. Preliminary taxonomic studies in the palm genus *Maximiliana* Mart. Phytologia 38:161–172.

————. 1979. Re-evaluation of the genus *Butia* with a description of a new species. Principes 23(2):65–79.

————. 1987. Revisions of the palm genus *Syagrus* Mart. and other selected genera in the *Cocos* alliance. Illinois Biological Monographs 56:1–230.

————, J. B. HARBORNE, J. ROBERTSON, AND P. J. HOLLOWAY. 1981. Chemotaxonomic studies of selected cocosoid palms. Principes 25(2):54–62.

GRANVILLE, J.-J. DE. 1974. Aperçu sur la structure des pneumatophores de deux especes des sols hydromorphes en Guyane: *Mauritia flexuosa* L. et *Euterpe oleracea* Mart. (Palmae). Generlisation au système respiratoire racinaire d'autres palmiers. Cahiers O.R.S.T.O.M. Séries Biologie 23:3–22.

————. 1977. Notes biologiques sur quelques palmiers guyanais. Cahiers O.R.S.T.O.M. Séries Biologie 12(4):347–353.

————. 1978. Recherches sur la Flore et la Vegetation Guyanaises. Thesis, Université des Sciences et Techniques du Languedoc, Montpellier.

GREGOR, H. J. 1980. Zum vorkommen fossiler Palmenreste im Jungtertiär Europas unter besonderer Berücksichtigung der Ablagerungen der Oberen Süsswasser-Molasse Süd-Deutschlands. Ber. Bayer. Bot. Ges. 51:135–144.

———. 1982. Palmae. In Die Jungtertiären Floren Süddeutschlands. Ferdinand Enke Verlag, Stuttgart.

GRIFFITH, W. 1844. The palms of British East India. Calcutta J. Nat. Hist. 5:1–103, 311–355.

———. 1845. The palms of British East India. Calcutta J. Nat. Hist. 5:445–491.

GRUEZO, W. M. AND H. C. HARRIES. 1984. Self-sown, wild-type coconuts in the Philippines. Biotropica 16:140–147.

GUERRERO, A. M. A. DE AND C. R. CLEMENT. 1982. Bibliografía sobre Pejibaye (Bactris gasipaes). Centro Agronómico Tropical de Investigación y Enseñanza unidad de Recursos Genéticos CATIE/GT2. Turrialba, Costa Rica.

HAFFER, J. 1969. Speciation in Amazonian forest birds. Science 165:131–137.

HALLÉ, F. 1977. The longest leaf in palms? Principes 21(1):18.

———, R. A. A. OLDEMAN, AND P. B. TOMLINSON. 1978. Tropical Trees and Forests: An Architectural Analysis. Springer Verlag, Berlin.

HARBORNE, J. B., C. A. WILLIAMS, J. GREENHAM, AND P. MOYNA. 1974. Distribution of charged flavones and caffeylshikimic acid in Palmae. Phytochemistry 13:1557–1559.

HARRIES, H. C. 1978. The evolution, dissemination and classification of Cocos nucifera L. Bot. Rev. 44:265–319.

HARTLEY, C. W. S. 1977. The Oil Palm, 2nd ed. Longmans, London.

HAY, A. J. M. 1984. 3. Palmae. Pages 195–318 in R. J. Johns and A. J. Hay (eds.). A Guide to the Monocotyledons of Papua New Guinea. Dept. of Forestry, P.N.G. University of Technology, P.O. Private Bag, Lae, Papua New Guinea.

HEKEL, H. 1972. Pollen and spore assemblages from Queensland Tertiary Sediments. Publ. Geol. Surv. Qld. 355 (Palaeont. Pap. 30):1–33.

HEMSLEY, U. B. 1885. Godman and Salvin. Biologia Centrali-Americana. Botany 4:276.

HENDERSON, A. 1984. Observations on pollination of Cryosophila albida (Palmae). Principes 28(3):120–126.

———. 1985. Pollination of Socratea exorrhiza and Iriartea ventricosa. Principes 29(2):64–71.

———. 1986a. A review of pollination studies in the Palmae. Bot. Rev. 52(3):221–259.

———. 1986b. A new Prestoea from Panama. Brittonia 38:266–268.

———. 1986c. Barcella odora. Principes 30(2):74–76.

——— AND J. STEYERMARK. 1986. New palms from Venezuela. Brittonia 38(4):309–313.

HENDERSON, R. 1947. Palms of the Carrizo country. Desert Mag. 10(6):19–22.

HERNGREEN, G. F. W. 1975. Palynology of Middle and Upper Cretaceous strata in Brazil. Meded. Rijks. Geol. Dienst. N. S. 26:39–116.

HICKEY, L. J. AND J. A. DOYLE. 1977. Early Cretaceous fossil evidence for angiosperm evolution. Bot. Rev. 43:3–104.

HILGEMAN, R. H. 1954. The differentiation, development and anatomy of the axillary bud, inflorescence and offshoot in the date palm. Date Grower's Inst. Rep. 31:6–10.

HNATIUK, R. J. 1977. Population structure of Livistona eastonii Gardn., Mitchell Plateau, Western Australia. Austral. J. Ecol. 2:461–466.

HODEL, D. 1980. Notes on Pritchardia in Hawaii. Principes 24(2):65–81.

———. 1982. In search of Carpoxylon. Principes 26(1):34–41.

HODGE, W. H. 1965. Palm cabbage. Principes 9(4):124–131.

HOEKEN-KLINKENBERG, P. M. J. VAN 1964. A palynological investigation of some Upper-Cretaceous sediments in Nigeria. Pollen et Spores 6:209–231.

HOGAN, K. P. 1986. Plant architecture and population ecology in the palms Socratea durissima and Scheelea zonensis on Barro Colorado Island, Panama. Principes 30(3):105–107.

HOLBROOK, N. M., F. E. PUTZ, AND P. CHAI. 1985. Above ground branching of the stilt-rooted palm, Eugeissona minor. Principes 29(3):142–146.

HOLLAWAY, J. D. 1979. A Survey of the Lepidoptera, Biogeography and Ecology of New Caledonia. W. Junk, The Hague.

HOLTTUM, R. E. 1955. Growth-habits of monocotyledons—variations on a theme. Phytomorphology 5:399–413.

HOOKER, J. D. 1883. Palmae. Pages 870–948 in G. Bentham and J. D. Hooker. Genera Plantarum 3. L. Reeve and Co., London.

HOUSE, A. P. N. 1984. The ecology of Oncosperma horridum on Siberut Island, Indonesia. Principes 28(2):85–89.

HSU, P. S. AND S. F. HUANG. 1985. Index to plant chromosome numbers reported in Chinese literature. Invest. Studum Naturae 5:1–116.

HUMBERT, H. 1955. Palms. In Une merveille de la nature à Madagascar: première exploration botanique du Massif du Marojejy et de ses satellites. Mém. Inst. Sci. Madagascar, Sér. B, Biol. Veg. 6:1–210.

IMCHANITZKAJA, N. 1985. Arecaceae Seu Palmae. Leningrad Branch Soviet Science Press. NAUKA.

INTERNATIONAL CODE OF BOTANICAL NOMENCLATURE. 1983. E. G. Voss et al. (eds.). W. Junk, The Hague.

IRVINE, A. 1983. Wodyetia, a new arecoid genus from Australia. Principes 27(4):158–167.

JANAKI AMMAL, E. K. 1945. Pages 316–319 in C. D. Darlington and E. K. Janaki Ammal. Chromosome Atlas of Cultivated Plants. George Allen and Unwin Ltd., London.

JANOS, D. P. 1977. Vesicular-arbuscular mycorrhizae affect the growth of Bactris gasipaes. Principes 21(1):12–18.

JANZEN, D. H. 1971. The fate of Scheelea rostrata fruits beneath the parent tree: predispersal attack by bruchids. Principes 15(3):89–101.

JARDINÉ, S. AND L. MAGLOIRE. 1965. Palynologie et stratigraphie du Crétacé des bassins du Sénégal et de Côte d'Ivoire. Mém. Bur Recherches Géol. Minieres 32:187–245.

JARZEN, D. M. 1978. Some Maestrichtian palynomorphs and their phytogeographical and paleoecological implications. Palynology 2:29–38.

JOHNSON, D. V. 1977. Recent Malaysian studies on the oil palm. Principes 21(2):82–84.

———. 1983a. A bibliography of graduate theses on the date and other Phoenix spp. Date Palm J. 2(2):257–267.

———. 1983b. A bibliography of major works on the oil palm. Oil Palm News 27:4–6.

———. 1983c. Multi-purpose palms in agroforestry: a classification and assessment. Int. Tree Crops J. 2:217–244.

———. 1984. Additional graduate theses on the date palm and other Phoenix spp. Date Palm J. 3(2):437.

————. 1985. Present and potential economic uses of palms in arid and semi-arid areas. *In* "Plants for arid lands." Royal Bot. Gard. Kew.

JOHNSON, M. A. T. 1979. The chromosomes of *Ceratolobus* (Palmae). Kew Bull. 34(1):35–36.

————. 1985. New chromosome counts in the Palmae. Kew Bull. 40(1):109–114.

JUMELLE, H. AND H. PERRIER DE LA BÂTHIE. 1945. Palmiers. 30. *In* H. Humbert (*ed.*). Flore de Madagascar et des Comores. Tananarive.

KAEMPFER, E. 1712. Amoenitatum Exoticarum. Lemgo, Lippe.

KAHN, F. AND A. DE CASTRO. 1985. The palm community in a forest of central Amazonia, Brazil. Biotropica 17(3):210–216.

KAPLAN, D. R., N. G. DENGLER, AND R. E. DENGLER. 1982a. The mechanism of plication inception in palm leaves; problem and developmental morphology. Can. J. Bot. 60:2939–2975.

————, ————, AND ————. 1982b. The mechanism of plication inception in palm leaves: histogenetic observations on the palmate leaf of *Rhapis excelsa*. Can. J. Bot. 60:2999–3016.

KARSTEN, H. 1857. Typification of *Bactris*. Linnaea 28:607.

KAUL, K. N. 1943. A palm stem from the Miocene of Antigua, W. I.—*Phytelephas sewardii*, sp. nov. Proc. Linn. Soc. London 155:3–4.

————. 1945. A fossil palm stem from South Africa (*Palmoxylon du Toitii*), sp. nov. Proc. Linn. Soc. London 156:197–198.

————. 1951. A palm fruit from Kapurdi (Jodhpur, Rajasthan Desert), *Cocos sahnii* sp. nov. Curr. Sci. 20:138.

KEPLER, C. B. 1970. Appendix A: The Puerto Rican parrot. Pages E 186–E 188 *in* H. T. Odum (*ed.*). A Tropical Rain Forest. Div. Tech. Info., U.S. Atomic Energy Comm., Oak Ridge, Tenn.

KIEW, R. 1972. The natural history of *Iguanura geonomaeformis* Martius: a Malayan undergrowth palmlet. Principes 16(1):3–10.

————. 1976. The genus *Iguanura* Bl. (Palmae). Gard. Bull. Singapore 28(2):191–226.

————. 1979. New species and records of *Iguanura* (Palmae) from Sarawak and Thailand. Kew Bull. 34(1):143–145.

KIMNACH, M. 1977. The species of *Trachycarpus*. Principes 21(4):155–160.

KLOTZ, L. H. 1978a. Form of the perforation plates in the wide vessels of metaxylem in palms. J. Arnold Arbor. 59(2):105–128.

————. 1978b. The number of wide vessels in petiolar vascular bundles of palms: an anatomical feature of systematic significance. Principes 22(2):64–69.

————. 1978c. Observations on diameters of vessels in palms. Principes 22(3):99–106.

KOCH, B. E. AND W. L. FRIEDRICH. 1972. Stereoskopische Rontgenaufnahmen von fossilen Fruchten. Bull. Geol. Soc. Denmark 21:358–367.

KREMP, G. O. W. 1965. Morphologyie. Encyclopedia of Palynology. Univ. of Arizona Press, Tucson.

KUNTH, C. S. 1826. Recherches sur les plantes trouvées dans les tombeaux egyptiens par M. Passalacqua. Ann. Sci. Nat. 8:418–423.

————. 1841. Enumeratio Plantarum Vol. 3. Stuttgart and Tubingen.

LAKHANPAL, R. N. 1970. Tertiary floras of India and their bearing on the historical geology of the region. Taxon 19:675–694.

————, U. PRAKASH, AND K. AMBWANI. 1979. Two petrified palm woods from the Deccan Intertrappean beds of Mandla District, Madhya Pradesh. Paleobotanist 26:119–129.

LAMOTTE, R. S. 1952. Catalogue of the Cenozoic plants of North America through 1950. Mem. Geol. Soc. Amer. 51:1–381.

LECK, C. F. 1969. Palmae: hic et ubique. Principes 13(2):80.

LEON, H. 1939. Contribucion al estudio de las palmas de Cuba. III. Género *Coccothrinax*. Mém. Soc. Cub. Hist. Nat. "Felipe Poey" 13:107–156.

————. 1946. Palmaceas. *In* Flora de Cuba I. Cultural, S. A., La Habana.

LEPESME, P. 1947. Les Insectes des Palmiers. Paul Lechevalier, Editeur, Paris.

LINNAEUS, C. 1753. Species Plantarum. 2 vols. Stockholm.

LLERAS, E. 1985. *Acrocomia*, um gênero com grande potencial. Noticiário 1:3–5. EMBRAPA/CENARGEN, Brasilia.

LOUVEL, M. 1931. Atlas des Plantes Ornamentales et Curieuses de Madagascar. Gouvernement Général de Madagascar.

LUCAS, G. L. I. AND H. SYNGE. 1978. The I.U.C.N. Plant Red Data Book. I.U.C.N., Morges, Switzerland.

MACBRIDE, J. F. 1960. Flora of Peru. Field Mus. Nat. Hist., Bot. Series 13:321–418.

MACHIN, J. 1971. Plant microfossils from Tertiary deposits of the Isle of Wight. New Phytol. 70:851–872.

MADULID, D. A. 1981. A monograph of *Plectocomia* (Palmae: Lepidocaryoideae). Kalikasan 10:1–94.

MAGNANO, S. M. DE. 1973. *Trithrinax campestris* (Palmae): inflorescencia y flor con especial referencia al gineceo. Kurtziana 7:137–152.

MAHABALE, T. S. AND N. N. UDWADIA. 1960. Studies on palms: Part IV—Anatomy of palm roots. Proc. Natl. Inst. Sci. India, Pt. B, Biol. Sci. 26:73–104.

MAI, P. H. AND H. WALTHER. 1978. Die Floren der Haselbacher Serie in Weisselster-Becken (Bezirk Leipzig, D.D.R.). Abh. des Staatl. Mus. für Mineral und Geol. Dresden 28:1–200.

MANN, G. AND H. A. WENDLAND. 1864. On the palms of western tropical Africa. Trans. Linn. Soc. London 24(15):421–439.

MANOKARAN, N. 1984. Biological and ecological considerations pertinent to the silviculture of rattans. Pages 95–105 *in* N. Manokaran and K. M. Wong (*eds.*). Proceedings of the Rattan Seminar, 2nd–4th October 1984, Kuala Lumpur, Malaysia. The Rattan Information Centre, Forest Research Institute, Kepong, Malaysia.

MARKLEY, K. S. 1955. Caranday—a source of palm wax. Econ. Bot. 9:39–52.

MARTELLI, U. 1932. *Pelagodoxa henryana* Becc., palma della Isole Marquesas. Nuovo Giorn. Bot. Ital. n.s. 39:243–250.

MARTIUS, C. F. P. VON. 1823–1850. Historia Naturalis Palmarum. 3 vols. Munich.

————. 1824. Palmarum Familia Ejusque Genera. Lindauer, Munich.

MAURY, C. J. 1930. O Cretaceo da Parahyba do Norte. As floras do Cretaceo Superior da America do Sul. Monogr. Serv. Geol. Mus. Brasil 8:1–305.

MCKAMEY, L. 1983. Secret of the Orient: Dwarf *Rhapis excelsa*. Grunwald Printing Co., Corpus Christi, Texas.

MEDEIROS-COSTA, J. T. DE AND S. PANIZZA. 1983. Palms of the

Cerrado vegetation formation of Sao Paulo State, Brazil. Principes 27(3):118–125.

MÉDUS, J. 1975. Palynologie des sédiments Tertiaires du Sénégal Méridional. Pollen et Spores 17:545–601.

MENDIS, N. M., I. K. FERGUSON AND J. DRANSFIELD. 1987. The pollen morphology of the subtribe Oncospermatinae (Palmae: Arecoideae: Areceae). Kew Bull. 42:47–63.

MENENDEZ, C. A. 1969. Die fossilen Floren Südamerikas. Monogr. Biol. 19:519–561.

MEYERS, R. L., M. DUVALL, AND R. KIESTER. 1985. The ecology of *Raphia taedigera* in Costa Rican palm swamps. Abstracts, Association for Tropical Biology Meetings, 1985:39.

MILLER, R. H. 1964. The versatile sugar palm. Principes 8(4):115–147.

MOGEA, J. P. 1978. Pollination in *Salacca edulis*. Principes 22(2):56–63.

———. 1980. The flabellate-leaved species of *Salacca* (Palmae). Reinwardtia 9(4):461–479.

———. 1981. Notes on *Salacca wallichiana*. Principes 25(3):120–123.

MONTEILLET, J. AND J. R. LAPPARTIENT. 1981. Fruits et graines du Crétace superieur des carrières de Paki (Sénégal). Rev. Palaeobot. Palynol. 34:331–344.

MOORE, H. E., JR. 1951. Critical studies. 7. *Neonicholsonia* vs. *Woodsonia*. Gentes Herb. 8(3):239–243.

———. 1953. Exotic palms in the Western world. Gentes Herb. 8(4):295–315.

———. 1957a. Synopses of various genera of Arecoideae. 21. *Veitchia*. Gentes Herb. 8(7):483–536.

———. 1957b. Synopses of various genera of Arecoideae. 22. *Neoveitchia*. Gentes Herb. 8(7):537–540.

———. 1957c. Synopses of various genera of Arecoideae. 23. *Reinhardtia*. Gentes Herb. 8(7):541–576.

———. 1960. A new subfamily of palms—the Caryotoideae. Principes 4(3):102–117.

———. 1962a. *Allagoptera* and *Diplothemium*. Principes 6(1):37–39.

———. 1962b. The genera of Steck's "De Sagu" (1957) and comments on *Sagus* Steck. Taxon 11:164–166.

———. 1963a. Two new palms from Peru. Principes 7(3):107–115.

———. 1963b. The typification and species of *Palma* Miller (1754). Gentes Herb. 9(3):235–244.

———. 1963c. The types and lectotypes of some palm genera. Gentes Herb. 9(3):245–274.

———. 1963d. *Iriartella* H. Wendland emended. Gentes Herb. 9(3):275–285.

———. 1965a. *Ptychococcus lepidotus*—a new species from New Guinea. Principes 9(1):10–13.

———. 1966. Palm hunting around the world. V. New Guinea to the New Hebrides. Principes 10(2, 3):64–85.

———. 1967a. A lectotype for *Polyandrococos*. Principes 11(3):77.

———. 1967b. The genus *Gastrococos* (Palmae-Cocoideae). Principes 11(4):114–121.

———. 1969a. *Satakentia*—a new genus of Palmae-Arecoideae. Principes 13(1):3–12.

———. 1969b. New palms from the Pacific, II. Principes 13(2):67–76.

———. 1969c. New palms from the Pacific, III. Principes 13(3):99–108.

———. 1969d. A synopsis of the genus *Physokentia* (Palmae-Arecoideae). Principes 13(4):120–136.

———. 1969e. Three new palms from Venezuela. Principes 13(4):137–140.

———. 1969f. The genus *Juania* (Palmae-Arecoideae). Gentes Herb. 10(4):385–393.

———. 1970. The genus *Rhopaloblaste* (Palmae). Principes 14(3):75–92.

———. 1971a. The genus *Synechanthus* (Palmae). Principes 15(1):10–19.

———. 1971b. Additions and corrections to "An annotated checklist of cultivated palms." Principes 15(3):102–106.

———. 1972. *Chelyocarpus* and its allies *Cryosophila* and *Itaya* (Palmae). Principes 16(3):67–88.

———. 1973a. The major groups of palms and their distribution. Gentes Herb. 11(2):27–141.

———. 1973b. Palms in the tropical forest ecosystems of Africa and South America. Pages 63–88 *in* B. J. Meggers, E. S. Ayensu, and W. D. Duckworth (*eds.*). Tropical Forest Ecosystems in Africa and South America: A Comparative Review. Smithsonian Institution Press, Washington, D.C.

———. 1977. Endangerment at the specific and generic levels in palms. Pages 267–282 *in* G. T. Prance and T. S. Elias (*eds.*). Extinction is Forever: The Status of Threatened and Endangered Plants of the Americas. New York Botanical Garden, Bronx.

———. 1978a. The genus *Hyophorbe* (Palmae). Gentes Herb. 11(4):212–245.

———. 1978b. *Tectiphiala*, a new genus of Palmae from Mauritius. Gentes Herb. 11(4):284–290.

———. 1979. Arecaceae. Pages 392–438 *in* A. C. Smith. Flora Vitiensis Nova 1. Pacific Tropical Garden, Lawaii, Kauai, Hawaii.

———. 1980a. Palmae. Pages 1–6 *in* K. H. Rechinger. Flora Iranica 146. Akademische Druck, Austria.

———. 1980b. Four new species of Palmae from South America. Gentes Herb. 12(1):30–38.

———. 1982. A new species of *Wettinia* (Palmae) from Ecuador. Principes 26(1):42–43.

——— AND A. B. ANDERSON. 1976. *Ceroxylon alpinum* and *Ceroxylon quindiuense* (Palmae). Gentes Herb. 11(3):168–185.

——— AND J. DRANSFIELD. 1978. A new species of *Wettinia* and notes on the genus. Notes Roy. Bot. Gard. Edinburgh 36:259–267.

——— AND ———. 1979. The typification of Linnean palms. Taxon 28(1, 2/3):59–70.

——— AND F. R. FOSBERG. 1956. The palms of Micronesia and the Bonin Islands. Gentes Herb. 8(6):423–478.

——— AND L. J. GUÉHO. 1980. *Acanthophoenix* and *Dictyosperma* (Palmae) in the Mascarene Islands. Gentes Herb. 12(1):1–16.

——— AND L. J. GUÉHO. 1984. Flore des Mascareignes. 189. Palmiers: 1–34.

——— AND W. MEIJER. 1965. A new species of *Arenga* from Borneo. Principes 9(3):100–103.

———, R. H. PHILLIPS, AND S. VODONAIVALU. 1982. Additions to the palms of Fiji. Principes 26(3):122–125.

——— AND N. W. UHL. 1973. The monocotyledons: their evolution and comparative biology. VI. Palms and the origin and evolution of monocotyledons. Qu rt. Rev. Biol. 48:414–436.

——— AND N. W. UHL. 1982. Major trends of evolution in palms. Bot. Rev. 48(1):1–69.

———— AND N. W. UHL. 1984. The indigenous palms of New Caledonia. Allertonia 3(5):313–402.

MOORE, L. B. AND E. EDGAR. 1970. The flora of New Zealand. Vol. 2. A. R. Shearer, Wellington, New Zealand.

MORA-URPI, J. 1983. El Pejibaye (*Bactris gasipaes* H.B.K.): origen, biología floral y manejo agronómico. Palmeras Poco Utilizadas de America Tropical: Informe de la Reunión de Consulta Organizada por FAO y Catie: 118–160. Turrialba, Costa Rica.

MOREAU, R. E. 1966. The Bird Faunas of Africa and its Islands. Academic Press, New York.

MORROW, L. O. 1965. Floral morphology and anatomy of certain Coryphoideae (Palmae). Ph.D. Thesis, Cornell University.

MULLER, J. 1964. Palynological contributions to the history of Tertiary vegetation in N. W. Borneo. Page 271 *in* Abstracts Xth Int. Bot. Congress, Edinburgh.

————. 1968. Palynology of the Pedawan and Plateau sandstone formations (Cretaceous-Eocene) in Sarawak, Malaysia. Micropalaeontology 14:1–37.

————. 1970. Palynological evidence on early differentiation of angiosperms. Biol. Rev. 45:417–450.

————. 1972. Palynological evidence for change in geomorphology, climate and vegetation in the Mio-Pliocene of Malesia. Pages 6–16 *in* Trans. II Aberdeen-Hull Symp. Malesian Ecol. Univ. Hull, Dept. Geograph. Miscell. Series no. 13.

————. 1979. Reflections on fossil palm pollen. IV Int. Palynol. Conf. Lucknow (1976–77) 1:568–578.

————. 1981. Fossil pollen records of extant angiosperms. Bot. Rev. 47:1–142.

————. 1984. Significance of fossil pollen for angiosperm history. Ann. Missouri Bot. Gard. 71:419–443.

MUÑIZ, O. AND A. BORHIDI. 1982. Catálogo de las palmas de Cuba. Acta Bot. Hungarica 28:309–345.

MURRAY, S. G. 1971. The Developmental Anatomy of Certain Palm Fruits. Ph.D. Thesis, Cornell University.

————. 1973. The formation of endocarp in palm fruits. Principes 17(3):91–102.

MYERS, R. L., M. DUVAL, AND R. KIESTER. 1985. The ecology of *Raphia taedigera* in Costa Rican palm swamps. Abstracts, Association for Tropical Biology meetings, 1985:39.

OLAH, L. VAN. 1954. The cytology of *Corypha umbraculifera* L. Part 1. Meiosis. Ann. Bogor. 1(3):201–222.

ONO, M. AND Y. MASUDA. 1981. Chromosome numbers of some endemic species of the Bonin Islands II. Ogasawara Res. 4:1–24.

OOI, P. A. C. 1982. The oil palm pollinating weevil. Nature Malaysiana 8(2):12–15.

OTEDOH, M. 1977. The African origin of *Raphia taedigera*— Palmae. Nigerian Field 42(1):11–16.

————. 1982. A revision of the genus *Raphia* Beauv. (Palmae). J. Nigerian Inst. Oil Palm Research 6(22):145–189.

OYAMA, T. AND H. MATSUO. 1964. Notes on palmaean leaf from Oarai flora (Upper Cretaceous), Oarai Machi, Ibaraki Prefecture, Japan. Trans. Proc. Palaeontol. Soc. Japan. N. S. 55:241–246.

PARATHASARATHY, M. V. 1968. Observations on metaphloem in the vegetative parts of palms. Amer. J. Bot. 55:1140–1168.

————. 1974. Ultrastructure of phloem in palms. III. Mature phloem. Protoplasma 79:265–315.

———— AND L. H. KLOTZ. 1976. Palm "wood." I. Anatomical aspects. Wood Science Tech. 10:215–229.

———— AND P. B. TOMLINSON. 1967. Anatomical features of metaphloem in stems of *Sabal, Cocos* and two other palms. Amer. J. Bot. 54(9):1143–1151.

PERISAMY, K. 1966. Morphological and ontogenetic studies in palms. II. Growth pattern of the leaves of *Cocos nucifera* and *Borassus flabellifer* after initiation of plications. Austral. J. Bot. 13:225–234.

————. 1967. Morphological and ontogenetic studies in palms. III. Growth patterns of the leaves *Caryota* and *Phoenix* after the initiation of plications. Phytomorphology 16:474–490.

PESCE, C. 1941. Oil palms and other oil seeds of the Amazon. Translated by D. V. Johnson, 1985. Reference Publ. Inc., Algonac, Michigan.

PIJL, L. VAN DER 1969. Principles of Dispersal in Higher Plants. Springer-Verlag, New York.

PIÑERO, D. AND J. SARUKHÁN. 1982. Reproductive behaviour and its individual variability in a tropical palm, *Astrocaryum mexicanum*. J. Ecology. 70:461–472.

————, ————, AND M. MARTINEZ-RAMOS. 1984. A population model of *Astrocaryum mexicanum* and a sensitivity analysis of its finite rate of increase. J. Ecology 72:977–991.

————, M. MARTÍNEZ-RAMOS, A. MENDOZA, E. ALVAREZ-BUYLLA AND J. SARUKHÁN. 1986. Demographic studies in *Astrocaryum mexicanum* and their use in understanding community dynamics. Principes 30(3):108–116.

PINGITORE, E. J. 1978. Revision de las especies del genero *Trithrinax*. Revista Inst. Munic. Bot. 4:95–109.

PINHEIRO, C. U. B. AND M. J. BALICK. 1987. Brazilian palms. Notes on their uses and vernacular names compiled and translated from Pio Correa's "Dicionário das Plantas (Uteis do Brasil e das Exóticas Cultivadas.") with updated nomenclature and added illustrations. Contr. from N.Y. Bot. Gard. (in press).

PLOTKIN, M. J. AND M. J. BALICK. 1984. Medicinal uses of South American palms. J. Ethnopharmacology 10:157–179.

POTZTAL, E. 1964. Reihe Principes. *In* H. Melchior (*ed.*). A. Engler's Syllabus der Pflanzenfamilien. ed. 12, 2:579–588. Gebrüder Borntraeger, Berlin.

PRAKASH, U. AND K. AMBWANI. 1980. A petrified *Livistona*-like palm stem, *Palmoxylon livistonoides* sp. nov. from the Deccan Intertrappean beds of India. Palaeobotanist 26(3):297–306.

PRANCE, G. T. 1982. A review of the phytogeographic evidences for Pleistocene climatic changes in the Neotropics. Ann. Missouri Bot. Gard. 69:594–624.

PROFIZI, J. P. 1985. *Raphia hookeri*: a survey of some aspects of the growth of a useful swamp lepidocaryoid palm in Benin (West Africa). Principes 29(3):108–114.

PUTZ, F. E. 1979. Biology and human use of *Leopoldinia piassaba*. Principes 23(4):149–156.

————. 1983. Developmental morphology of *Desmoncus isthmius*, a climbing colonial, cocosoid palm. Principes 27(1):38–42.

PYYKKÖ, M. 1985. Anatomy of the stem and petiole of *Raphia hookeri* (Palmae). Ann. Bot. Fennici 22:129–138.

QUERO, H. J. 1980. *Coccothrinax readii*, a new species from the peninsula of Yucatan, Mexico. Principes 24(3):118–124.

————. 1981. *Pseudophoenix sargentii* in the Yucutan Peninsula, Mexico. Principes 25(2):63–72.

———— AND R. W. READ. 1986. A revision of the palm genus *Gaussia*. Syst. Bot. 11(1):145–154.

RADERMACHER, A. 1925. Die Gametophyten von *Nipa fruticans* und *Actinophloeus macarthurii* Becc. Msc. sowie ein

Versuch die Systematik der Angiospermen durch die haploide generation zu ergänzen. Ann. Jard. Bot. Buitenzorg 35: 1–54.

RAICH, JAMES W. 1983. Understory palms as nutrient traps: a hypothesis. Brenesia 21:119–129.

RANGASAMY, S. R. S. AND P. DEVASAHAYAM. 1971. Cytology and sex determination in Palmyrah Palm (*Borassus flabellifer* Linn.). La Cellule 69(2):129–133.

RAO, A. R. AND V. ACHUTHAN. 1973. A review of fossil palm remains from India. Palaeobotanist 20(2):190–202.

RAUWERDINK, J. B. 1986. An essay on *Metroxylon*, the sago palm. Principes 30(4):165–180.

RAVEN, P. H. AND D. I. AXELROD. 1974. Angiosperm biogeography and past continental movements. Ann. Missouri Bot. Gard. 61:539–673.

READ, R. W. 1963. Palm chromosomes. Principes 7(3):85–88.

———. 1964. Palm chromosome studies facilitated by pollen culture on a colchicine-lactose medium. Stain Technol. 39(2): 99–106.

———. 1965a. Palm chromosomes by air mail. Principes 9(1): 4–10.

———. 1965b. Chromosome numbers in the Coryphoideae. Cytologia 30(4):385–391.

———. 1966. New chromosome counts in the Palmae. Principes 10(2, 3):55–61.

———. 1968. A study of *Pseudophoenix* (Palmae). Gentes Herb. 10(2):169–213.

———. 1969a. *Colpothrinax cookii*— a new species from Central America. Principes 13(1):13–22.

———. 1969b. Some notes on *Pseudophoenix* and a key to the species. Principes 13(2):77–79.

———. 1975. The genus *Thrinax* (Palmae: Coryphoideae). Smithsonian Contr. Bot. 19:1–98.

———. 1979. Palmae. Pages 320–368 *in* R. A. Howard (*ed.*). Flora of the Lesser Antilles 3. Arnold Arboretum, Harvard Univ.

———. 1980. Notes on Palmae, I. Phytologia 46(5):285–287.

——— AND L. J. HICKEY. 1972. A revised classification of fossil palm and palmlike leaves. Taxon 21:129–137.

——— AND H. E. MOORE, JR. 1967. More chromosome counts by mail. Principes 11(3):77.

———, T. A. ZANONI, AND M. MEJÍA. 1987. *Reinhardtia paiewonskiana* (Palmae): a new species for the West Indies. Brittonia 39(1):20–25.

REID, E. AND M. E. J. CHANDLER. 1933. The London Clay Flora. Brit. Mus. (Nat. Hist.), London.

RHEEDE TOT DRAKENSTEIN, H. VAN 1678–1693. Hortus Indicus Malabaricus. 12 vols. J. v. Someren and J. v. Dyck, Amsterdam.

RICH, P. M. 1986. Mechanical architecture of arborescent rain forest palms. Principes 30(3):117–131.

———. 1987. Mechanical structure of the stem of arborescent palms. Bot. Gaz. 148(1):42–50.

RICHARDS, P. W. 1952. The Tropical Rainforest. Cambridge Univ. Press, Cambridge.

RIDD, M. F. 1971. Southest Asia as part of Gondwanaland. Nature 234:531–533.

ROBERTSON, B. L. 1976a. Embryology of *Jubaeopsis caffra* Becc.: 1. Microsporangium, microsporogenesis and microgametogenesis. J. S. African Bot. 42(2):97–108.

———. 1976b. Embryology of *Jubaeopsis caffra* Becc.: 2. Megasporangium, megasporogenesis and megagametogenesis. J. S. Afr. Bot. 42(2):173–184.

———. 1977a. Morphology and development of the fruit and seed of *Jubaeopsis caffra* Becc. Principes 21(1):23–30.

———. 1977b. Aspects of the morphology of *Jubaeopsis caffra* Becc. Principes 21(4):169–175.

ROMERO, E. J. 1968. *Palmoxylon patagonicum* n. sp. del Terciaro Inferior de la Provincia de Chubut, Argentino. Ameghiniana 5:417–432.

RUMPHIUS, G. E. 1741–1755. Herbarium Amboinense. 6 vols. J. Burmann, Meinard Uytwerf, Amsterdam.

RUSSELL, T. A. 1965. The *Raphia* palms of West Africa. Kew Bull. 19:173–196.

SAAKOV, S. G. 1954. Palms and Their Culture in the USSR. Acad. Sci. USSR, Moscow and Leningrad.

SARKAR, A. K., N. DATTA, R. MALLICK AND U. CHATTERJEE. 1978. *In* IOPB Chromosome number reports LIX. Taxon 27(1):53–61.

SARKAR, S. K. 1958. Chromosome studies in palms. Proc. 45th Indian Sci. Congr. Assoc. 3:296–297.

———. 1970. Palmales. *In* Research Bull. Univ. of Calcutta, Dept. of Botany, Cytogenetics Lab. 2:22–23.

SARUKHÁN, J. 1978. Studies on the demography of tropical trees. Pages 163–184 *in* P. B. Tomlinson and M. H. Zimmermann (*eds.*). Tropical Trees as Living Systems. Cambridge University Press, New York.

———, D. PIÑERO, AND M. MARTÍNEZ-RAMOS. 1985. Plant demography: a community level interpretation. *In:* J. White (*ed.*). Studies on Plant Demography: a Festschrift for John Harper. Academic Press Inc., London.

SATAKE, T. 1962. A new system of the classification of Palmae. Hikobia 3:112–133.

SATÔ, D. 1946. Karyotype alteration and phylogeny, VI. Karyotype analysis in Palmae. Cytologia 14:174–186.

SAVAGE, A. J. P. AND P. S. ASHTON. 1983. The population structure of the double coconut and some other Seychelles palms. Biotropica 15:15–25.

SCHEFFER, R. H. C. C. 1873. Sur quelques palmiers du groupe des Arecinees. Natuurk. Tijdschr. Ned.-Indie 32:149–193.

———. 1876. Sur quelques palmiers du groupe des Arecinees. Deuxieme partie. Ann. Jard. Bot. Buitenzorg 1:103–164.

SCHMID, R. 1970. Notes on the reproductive biology of *Asterogyne martiana* (Palmae). II. Pollination by Syrphid flies. Principes 14(2):39–49.

SCOTT, R. A., P. L. WILLIAMS, L. C. CRAIG, E. S. BARGHOORN, L. J. HICKEY, AND H. D. MACGINITIE. 1972. "Pre-Cretaceous" angiosperms from Utah; evidence for Tertiary age of the palm woods. Amer. J. Bot. 59(9):886–896.

SHARMA, A. K. 1970. The Research Bulletin. Annual Report, Cytogenetics Laboratory, Department of Botany, University of Calcutta, Vol. 2, 1967–1968.

——— AND S. K. SARKAR. 1957. Cytology of different species of palms and its bearing on the solution of the problems of phylogeny and speciation. Genetica 28:361–488.

SHETE, R. H. AND A. R. KULKARNI. 1980. *Palmocaulon hyphaeneoides* sp. nov. from Deccan Intertrappean beds of Wardha District, Maharashtra, India. Palaeontographica Abt. B. 172:15–17.

SHUEY, A. G. AND R. P. WUNDERLIN. 1977. The needle palm: *Rhapidophyllum hystrix*. Principes 21(2):47–59.

SINOTÔ, Y. 1929. Chromosome studies in some dioecious plants, with special reference to the allosomes. Cytologia 1:109–186.

SMALL, I. K. 1923. The needle palm *Rhapidophyllum hystrix*. J. New York Bot. Gard. 24:105–114.

SOLEREDER, H. AND F. J. MEYER. 1928. Palmae. Pages 1–85 *in*

Systematische Anatomie der Monocotyledonen III. Gebrü-der Borntraeger, Berlin.

SOWUNMI, M. A. 1972. Pollen morphology of the Palmae and its bearing on taxonomy. Rev. Palaeobot. Palynol. 13:1–80.

SPERRY, J. S. 1985. Xylem embolism in the palm *Rhapis excelsa*. IAWA Bull. n.s. 6:283–292.

SPRUCE, R. 1871. Palmae Amazonicae. J. Linn. Soc. Bot. 11(50-51):65–183.

STAFF, I. A. AND J. T. WATERHOUSE. 1981. The biology of arborescent monocotyledons, with special reference to Australian species. Pages 216–257 *in* A. J. McComb and J. S. Pate (*eds.*). The Biology of Australian Plants. Univ. of Western Australia Press, Nedlands, WA.

STANDLEY, P. C. AND J. A. STEYERMARK. 1958. Flora of Guatemala. Fieldiana: Botany 24:217–253.

STEENIS, C. G. G. J. VAN. 1981. Rheophytes of the World: An Account of the Flood-Resistant Flowering Plants and Ferns and the Theory of Autonomous Evolution. Sijthoff and Noordhoff, Alphen aan den Rijn.

SYED, R. A. 1979. Studies on oil palm (*Elaeis guineensis*) pollination by insects. Bull. Entomol. Res. 69(2):213–224.

TANG, C. Z. AND T. L. WU. 1977. A new species of *Chuniophoenix* (Palmae) from Hainan. Acta Phytotax. Sin. 15(2):111–112.

THANIKAIMONI, G. 1971. Les palmiers: palynologie et systématique. Inst. Français de Pondichéry, Trav. Sec. Sci. Tech. 11:1–286.

———, C. CARATINI, B. S. VENKATACHALA, C. G. K. RAMANUJAM, AND R. K. KAR. 1984. Selected Tertiary angiosperm pollens from India and their relationship with African Tertiary pollens. Inst. Français de Pondichéry, Trav. Sec. Sci. Tech. 19.

THORNE, R. F. 1983. Proposed new realignments in the angiosperms. Nord. J. Bot. 3:85–117.

TIDWELL, W. D., S. R. RUSHFORTH, J. L. REVEAL, AND H. BEHUNIN. 1970. *Palmoxylon simperi* and *Palmoxylon pristina*: two pre-Cretaceous angiosperms from Utah. Science 168(3933):835–840.

TOLEDO, J. F. 1952. Notas sôbre o gênero *Acanthococos* Barb. Rodr. Arq. Bot. Estado São Paulo 3:3–5.

TOMLINSON, P. B. 1960a. Seedling leaves in palms and their morphological significance. J. Arnold Arbor. 41:414–428.

———. 1960b. Anatomy of the Caryotoideae. Principes 4(3):118–119.

———. 1961. Palmae. *In* C. R. Metcalfe (*ed.*). Anatomy of the Monocotyledons II. Clarendon Press, Oxford.

———. 1964. The vascular skeleton of coconut leaf base. Phytomorphology 14(2):218–230.

———. 1966. Notes on the vegetative anatomy of *Aristeyera spicata* (Palmae). J. Arnold. Arbor. 47:23–29.

———. 1967. Dichotomous branching in *Allagoptera*? Principes 11(2):72.

———. 1969. The anatomy of the vegetative organs of *Juania australis* (Palmae). Gentes Herb. 10(4):412–424.

———. 1971a. Flowering in *Metroxylon* (the sago palm). Principes 15(2):49–62.

———. 1971b. The shoot apex and its dichotomous branching in the *Nypa* palm. Ann. Bot. (London) 35:865–879.

———. 1979. Systematics and ecology of the Palmae. Ann. Rev. Ecol. Syst. 10:85–107.

———. 1984. Development of the stem conducting tissues in monocotyledons. Pages 1–51 *in* R. A. White and W. C.

Dickison (*eds.*). Contemporary Problems in Plant Anatomy. Academic Press, New York.

——— AND H. E. MOORE, JR. 1966. Dichotomous branching in palms. Principes 10(1):21–29.

——— AND ———. 1968. Inflorescence in *Nannorrhops ritchiana* (Palmae). J. Arnold Arbor. 49:16–34.

——— AND P. K. SODERHOLM. 1975. The flowering and fruiting of *Corypha elata* in South Florida. Principes 19(3):83–99.

——— AND M. H. ZIMMERMANN. 1968. Anatomy of the palm *Rhapis excelsa*, V. Inflorescence. J. Arnold Arbor. 49:291–306.

TRACEY, J. G. AND L. J. WEBB. 1975. Key to the vegetation of the humid tropical region of North Queensland. Vegetation maps at 1:100,000. Topographic Survey R631 Series, CSIRO, Melbourne.

TRAIL, J. W. H. 1877. Descriptions of new species of palms collected in the valley of the Amazon in north Brazil in 1874. J. Bot. 15:75–81.

TRALAU, H. 1964. The genus *Nypa* van Wurmb. Kongl. Svenska Vetenskapsakad. Handl. ser. 4, 10(1):1–29.

TULEY, P. 1965. The inflorescence of Nigerian lepidocaryoid palms. Principes 9(3):93–98.

UHL, N. W. 1966. Morphology and anatomy of the inflorescence axis and flowers of a new palm, *Aristeyera spicata*. J. Arnold Arbor. 47:9–22.

———. 1969a. Anatomy and ontogeny of the cincinni and flowers in *Nannorrhops ritchiana* (Palmae). J. Arnold Arbor. 50:411–431.

———. 1969b. Floral anatomy of *Juania, Ravenea,* and *Ceroxylon* (Palmae-Arecoideae). Gentes Herb. 10:394–411.

———. 1972a. Inflorescence and flower structure in *Nypa fruticans* (Palmae). Amer. J. Bot. 59:729–743.

———. 1972b. Floral anatomy of *Chelyocarpus, Cryosophila,* and *Itaya* (Palmae). Principes 16(3):89–100.

———. 1972c. Leaf anatomy in the *Chelyocarpus* alliance. Principes 16(3):101–110.

———. 1976a. Developmental studies in *Ptychosperma* (Palmae). I. The inflorescence and the flower cluster. Amer. J. Bot. 63:82–96.

———. 1976b. Developmental studies in *Ptychosperma* (Palmae). II. The staminate and pistillate flowers. Amer. J. Bot. 63:97–109.

———. 1978a. Floral anatomy of *Maxburretia* (Palmae). Gentes Herb. 11(4):200–211.

———. 1978b. Floral anatomy of the five species of *Hyophorbe* (Palmae). Gentes Herb. 11(4):246–267.

———. 1978c. Leaf anatomy in the species of *Hyophorbe* (Palmae). Gentes Herb. 11(4):268–283.

——— AND J. DRANSFIELD. 1984. Development of the inflorescence, androecium, and gynoecium with reference to palms. Pages 397–449 *in* R. A. White and W. C. Dickison (*eds.*). Contemporary Problems in Plant Anatomy. Academic Press, New York.

——— AND J. MARTENS. (In prep.). Systematic leaf anatomy of New Caledonian palms. Allertonia.

——— AND H. E. MOORE, JR. 1971. The palm gynoecium. Amer. J. Bot. 58:945–992.

——— AND ———. 1973. The protection of pollen and ovules in palms. Principes 17(4):111–149.

——— AND ———. 1975. Observations on the structure of the palm androecium. Abstracts. XII International Botanical Congress, Leningrad, p. 238.

———— AND ————. 1977a. Correlations of inflorescence, flower structure, and floral anatomy with pollination in some palms. Biotropica 9:170–190.

———— AND ————. 1977b. Centrifugal stamen initiation in phytelephantoid palms. Amer. J. Bot. 64:1152–1161.

———— AND ————. 1978. The structure of the acervulus, the flower cluster of chamaedoreoid palms. Amer. J. Bot. 65(2): 197–204.

———— AND ————. 1980. Androecial development in six polyandrous genera representing five major groups of palms. Ann. Bot. (London) ser. 2, 45:57–75.

————, L. O. MORROW, AND H. E. MOORE, JR. 1969. Anatomy of the palm *Rhapis excelsa*, VII. Flowers. J. Arnold Arbor. 50:138–152.

VALEN, L. VAN 1975. Life, death, and energy of a tree. Biotropica 7:259–269.

VANDERMEER, J. H., J. STOUT, AND S. RISCH. 1979. Seed dispersal of a common Costa Rican rainforest palm (*Welfia georgii*). Trop. Ecol. 20:17–26.

VAUGHAN, J. G. 1960. Structure of *Acrocomia* fruit. Nature 188(4744):81.

VENKATASUBBAN, K. R. 1945. Cytological studies in Palmae. Pt. I. Chromosome numbers in a few species of palms of British India and Ceylon. Proc. Indian Acad. Sci. Sect. B, 22:193–207.

VILMORIN, P. L. F. L. DE. 1895. Blumengärtnerei. Berlin.

VOGL, R. J. AND L. T. MCHARGUE. 1966. Vegetation of California fan palm oases on the San Andreas fault. Ecology 47: 532–540.

WALKER, J. W. AND A. G. WALKER. 1984. Ultrastructure of lower Cretaceous angiosperm pollen and the origin and early evolution of flowering plants. Ann. Missouri Bot. Gard. 71: 464–521.

———— AND ————. 1986. Ultrastructure of early Cretaceous angiosperm pollen and its evolutionary implications. *In* S. Blackmore and I. K. Ferguson (*eds.*). Pollen and Spores; Form and Function. Academic Press, New York.

WALLACE, A. R. 1853. The Palm Trees of the Amazon and Their Uses. John van Voorst, London.

WATERHOUSE, J. T. AND C. J. QUINN. 1978. Growth patterns in the stem of the palm *Archontophoenix cunninghamiana*. Bot. J. Linn. Soc. 77:73–93.

WENDLAND, H. A. 1854. Palmae. Pages 1–42 *in* Index Palmarum, Cyclanthearum, Pandanearum, Cycadearum, quae in hortis europaeis coluntur synonymis gravioribus interpositis. Hannover.

———— AND O. DRUDE. 1875. Palmae Australasicae. Linnaea 39:153–238.

WESSELS BOER, J. G. 1965. The Indigenous Palms of Suriname. Pp. 1–172. E. J. Brill, Leiden.

————. 1968. The geonomoid palms. Verh. Kon. Ned. Akad. Wetensch., Afd. Natuurk., Tweede Reeks 58(1):1–202.

WHITMORE, T. C. 1975. Tropical Rain Forests of the Far East. Clarendon Press, Oxford.

WHITTEN, A. J. 1980. *Arenga* fruit as food for gibbons. Principes 24(4):143–146.

————, S. J. DAMANIK, J. ANWAR, AND N. HISYAM. 1984. The Ecology of Sumatra. Gadjah Mada University Press, Yogyakarta, Indonesia.

WILBERT, J. 1980a. The Temiche cap. Principes 24(3):105–109.

————. 1980b. The palm-leaf sail of the Warao Indians. Principes 24(4):162–169.

WILLIAMS, C. A., J. B. HARBORNE, AND H. T. CLIFFORD. 1973. Negatively charged flavones and tricin as chemosystematic markers in the Palmae. Phytochemistry 12:2417–2430.

————, ————, AND S. F. GLASSMAN. 1983. Flavonoids as taxonomic markers in some cocosoid palms. Pl. Syst. Evol. 142:157–169.

YEATEN, R. I. 1979. Intraspecific competition in a population of the stilt palm *Socratea durissima* (Oerst.) Wendl. on Barro Colorado Island, Panama. Biotropica 11(2):155–158.

ZEVEN, A. C. 1967. The semi-wild oil palm and its industry in Africa. Agricultural Research Reports 689. Centre for Agricultural Publications and Documentation, Wageningen, The Netherlands.

ZIMMERMANN, M. H. AND P. B. TOMLINSON. 1965. Anatomy of the palm *Rhapis excelsa*, I. Mature vegetative axis. J. Arnold Arbor. 46:160–178.

———— AND ————. 1974. Vascular patterns in palm stems: variations of the *Rhapis* principle. J. Arnold Arbor. 55:402–424.

INDEX OF SCIENTIFIC NAMES

SUBJECT INDEX

FINDING LIST OF GENERIC NAMES